D1159690

Book Two

Modern Algebra

A Logical Approach

INCLUDING TRIGONOMETRY

By

HELEN R. PEARSON

Lecturer at Purdue University
INDIANAPOLIS, INDIANA

and

FRANK B. ALLEN

Chairman, Department of Mathematics
Lyons Township High School and Junior College
LA GRANGE, ILLINOIS

GINN AND COMPANY

© COPYRIGHT, 1966, BY GINN AND COMPANY

ALL RIGHTS RESERVED

Home Office: Boston, Massachusetts 02117

Library of Congress Catalog Card No.: 64–4164

Preface

This text provides a two or three semester course for above-average and average students who have completed a year of algebra. It offers a strong course which should prove both challenging and satisfying to these students.

The text is directed toward three goals—(1) giving students thorough understanding of the structure of algebra and the nature of proof; (2) helping students to develop those manipulative skills that will enable them to perform algebraic operations with competence; and (3) helping students to develop the power to think logically and creatively.

A distinguishing feature of the text is its emphasis upon deductive reasoning and proof. In Chapter 2, the nature of deductive reasoning is explained, and various forms of proof are discussed. Thereafter, from the simplest of beginnings, an algebra of real numbers is developed as a system of logical thought. Proofs for the more important statements are given, and students are encouraged to justify their own mathematical statements by logical argument. Although proof is an essential part of the course, each new theorem is explained, either before or after it is presented, and is accompanied by one or more examples. Thus students with a lower level of mathematical maturity can, without studying all the proofs, follow the development of the text in full assurance that reasons for the principles they are learning do exist. Each bit of theory is followed by exercises designed to develop understanding of the topic under discussion and to relate it to other topics.

The text is carefully constructed and is complete. Painstaking attention has been given to clarity and precision of language. Definitions are well stated and are adhered to meticulously in succeeding developments. A spiral development of topics ties each new topic to topics studied previously and leads the student to deeper and deeper understanding of important ideas. Exercises are plentiful and are designed to do more than merely provide repetitive practice. They develop and reinforce ideas, encourage thought, and stimulate originality.

The book is a modern text in every sense of the word. It is a product reflecting the authors' own teaching experiences and the conclusions of the authors gained from participation in and careful analysis of the present-day cooperative programs to improve mathematics instruction. The spirit, the subject-matter, and the symbolism are up-to-date.

The text contains those time-tested features desired by most teachers. At the end of each chapter there is a list of Essentials that should have been learned from study of the chapter, a list of algebraic terms whose meaning and spelling should have been mastered, a Chapter Review, and a Chapter Test. The book also contains four Cumulative Reviews and four Cumulative Tests.

Individual differences are provided for by the organization of the text and by a wide variety of exercises. As has been stated, the text is so organized that students with a lower level of mathematical maturity can follow the development of the various topics without studying the proof of every theorem. Exercises range from those designed to reinforce the simplest basic concepts to those truly challenging to the top students. The easier exercises are grouped together and designated as A Exercises, and the more difficult are designated as B Exercises.

The authors take this opportunity to acknowledge the assistance of Mr. Darwin Newton and the fine editorial staff of Ginn and Company. They likewise wish to thank Dr. Walter Fleming for his careful reading of parts of the manuscript and for his many helpful suggestions.

Helen R. Pearson
Frank B. Allen

Contents

13 Systems Involving Quadratic Sentences 687

14 Sequences, Series, and Binomial Theorem 720

NOTE TO TEACHERS. An annotated edition and other aids are available with this text.

List of Symbols

C	Set of counting numbers
W	Set of whole numbers
Q	Set of rational real numbers
I	Set of integers
R	Set of real numbers
Z	Set of complex numbers
$A \subseteq B$	A is a subset of B. ($A \nsubseteq B$ A is not a subset of B.)
$A \subset B$	A is a proper subset of B.
$\emptyset$	The empty set, or null set
U	The universal set
$A \cap B$	The intersection of set A and set B
$A \cup B$	The union of set A and set B
A'	The complement of set A
$A \smallsmile B$	Set of elements that belong to A but not to B, or $A \cap B'$
$x \in A$	x is an element of set A. ($x \notin A$ x is not an element of set A.)
$A = \{a, b, c, \cdots\}$	A is the set of elements a, b, c, and so on.
$A = \{a, b, c, \cdots, n\}$	A is the set of elements a, b, c, and so on, to and including, n.
$\{x \mid \ \}$	Set-builder notation
$=$	Is equal to ($\neq$ Is not equal to)
$<$	Is less than ($\nless$ Is not less than)
$>$	Is greater than ($\ngtr$ Is not greater than)
$\leq$	Is less than or equal to ($\nleq$ Is not less than or equal to)
$\geq$	Is greater than or equal to ($\ngeq$ Is not greater than or equal to)
$\approx$	Is approximately equal to
$\{\}, [\,], (\,), \text{---}$	Symbols of grouping
$p \ or \ q$	Disjunction of p and q
$p \ and \ q$	Conjunction of p and q
$p \longrightarrow q$	If p, then q.
$p \longleftrightarrow q$	p is equivalent to q.
$\sim p$	Contradiction of p, read "not p"
$|r|$	Absolute value of r
$\overleftrightarrow{AB}$	Line AB
$\overline{AB}$	Line segment AB
$\overrightarrow{AB}$	Ray AB
$|AB|$	Measure of line segment AB
AB	Directed distance from A to B
$\overrightarrow{AB}$	Vector AB
$A \times B$	Cartesian product of set A and set B
$f(x)$	Function notation
$\displaystyle\sum_{k=1}^{n}$	Summation notation

x

Language of Algebra — Sets, Expressions, and Sentences

Sets

During recent years the language of sets has become an important part of the language of mathematics. As you study the language of sets, you will see how it helps us to give clear expression to many mathematical ideas.

A *set* is a collection of objects. We use the word "object" in a very broad sense to mean any person, idea, or thing. The individual objects in the set are called *members* or *elements* of the set and are said to belong to the set. We use a capital letter to name a set and we use the symbol ϵ for the phrase "is a member of" or "is an element of." Thus $x \epsilon S$ expresses the thought "x is a member of S." We write $a, b \epsilon R$ to indicate that $a \epsilon R$ and $b \epsilon R$; $a, b, c \epsilon R$ to indicate that $a \epsilon R$ and $b \epsilon R$ and $c \epsilon R$; and so on. To indicate that the object represented by t is not a member of the set W, we write $t \notin W$. The symbol ϵ may also be read "belongs to" and the symbol $\notin$, "does not belong to."

When we have made clear which objects belong to a set and which do not, we have *defined* the set. To define the set whose elements are the numbers 1, 2, 3, 4, 5, we may write "B is the set whose elements are 1, 2, 3, 4, 5." We may express this idea more briefly by writing $B = \{1, 2, 3, 4, 5\}$. Listing the members of a set between braces in this way is often referred to as the *roster method* of defining a set.

In general when we say that S is the set of elements satisfying given conditions, we mean that S contains all elements which satisfy these conditions and <u>no</u> others. For example when we say "S is the set of counting numbers less than 8," we mean that S contains all the elements 1, 2, 3, 4, 5, 6, and 7 and no others.

A set may also be defined by stating a *rule* or a *condition* which enables us to determine whether or not a given object is a member of the set. Thus, the set $B = \{1, 2, 3, 4, 5\}$ may also be defined by the rule method as *the set of the first five counting numbers*. In this case the description "the set of the first five counting numbers" states the conditions under which a number belongs or does not belong to the set. We know that $3 \epsilon B$ and $5 \epsilon B$ are true statements while $\pi \epsilon B$ and $0 \epsilon B$ are false statements.

We must, of course, recognize that the symbols 1, 2, 3, 4, 5 are not numbers. They are numerals. A *numeral* is a symbol which names a number. Sometimes, when no confusion can arise, we refer to 1, 2, 3, 4, 5, and $\frac{7}{3}$, -21.6, $\sqrt{3}$, and other such numerals as numbers even though we know that they are only symbols which name numbers.

Equal Sets

Equal sets are sets that have exactly the same members. It is important to observe that the order in which the elements of a set are listed does not matter. Thus if $K = \{a, e, i, o, u\}$ and $V = (i, u, a, o, e\}$, then K and V are equal sets and we can write $K = V$. When we write the symbol $=$ between two symbols we mean that the two symbols are names for the same object.

Number of Elements in a Set

If x represents the number of elements in a set, then we know that x represents a whole number. Consider the sets:

$K = \{25\}$

$D = \{$Christopher Columbus, Harry Truman, the Rosetta stone, Mother's Day$\}$

$E = \{$the Statue of Liberty, the Empire State Building, the prime meridian, Hannibal$\}$

$M = $ the set of people who live in Kalamazoo, Michigan

$B = $ the set of even prime numbers greater than 2

$C = \{1, 2, 3, \cdots\} = $ the set of counting (or natural) numbers

$W = \{0, 1, 2, 3, \cdots\} = $ the set of whole numbers

$I = \{\cdots, -2, -1, 0, 1, 2, \cdots\} = $ the set of integers

It is easy to count the number of elements in sets K, D, and E. It would require a great deal of time and energy to complete the task of counting all of the elements in set M, but it could be done.

Set B is remarkable in that it contains no elements. It is, nevertheless, a set. A set having no elements is called the *empty set* or the *null set* and is designated by the symbol $\emptyset$. Note that we do not use braces when we write the symbol to designate the empty set. Writing $\{\emptyset\}$ designates not the empty set, but rather the set whose only member is the empty set. Observe, too, that $\emptyset$ is not the same as $\{0\}$. The set represented by $\{0\}$ is not empty because it has the one member 0.

If the members of one set can be paired with the members of another set in such a way that each member of each set is paired with exactly one member of the other set, we say that the two sets can be put in *one-to-one corre-spondence*. For example, $\{1, 2, 3\}$ and $\{a, b, c\}$ can be put in one-to-one correspondence by pairing 1 with a, 2 with b, and 3 with c. There are, of course, other ways to do this.

Two non empty sets are said to be *equivalent* if their members can be put in one-to-one correspondence. Sets D and E above are equivalent sets.

We say that a set is *finite* if it is the null set or if the elements of the set can be counted with the counting coming to an end. All other sets are called *infinite* sets. There is no end to the process of counting the elements in an infinite set. Sets K, D, E, M, and B are finite sets. Sets C, W, and I are infinite sets.

A set is said to be *countable* if it is a finite set or if it is equivalent to set C. A set that is equivalent to set C is said to be countably infinite. For example, set I is countably infinite because it is equivalent to set C. The fact that set I is equivalent to set C is shown by the matching plan displayed below. This matching shows that corresponding to each element of one set there is exactly one element of the other set.

$$
\begin{array}{ccccccccc}
1 & 2 & 3 & 4 & 5 & 6 & 7 & 8 & \cdots \\
\updownarrow & \updownarrow & \updownarrow & \updownarrow & \updownarrow & \updownarrow & \updownarrow & \updownarrow & \cdots \\
0 & 1 & -1 & 2 & -2 & 3 & -3 & 4 & \cdots
\end{array}
$$

Is set W countably infinite? Can you think of other sets that are countably infinite? Do you think that there are some infinite sets that are not countable?

Notice that in the sets C and I shown above we used the symbol $\cdots$ to indicate "and so on." Thus when we write $\{2, 4, 6, \cdots\}$, we mean the set of all even counting numbers, not just the first three. $\{2, 4, 6, \cdots, 24\}$ means the set consisting of 2, 4, 6, and so on to, and including, 24. When the three dots precede the indicated members of the set as in $\{\cdots, -3, -2, -1\}$, we mean that the members continue to the left in the same pattern without end.

1. In each of the following insert either the symbol ϵ or the symbol $\notin$ to form a true statement if $B = \{1, 4, 9, 16, \cdots, 100\}$.

   a. 1 _?_ B **c.** 36 _?_ B **e.** $\frac{1}{2}$ _?_ B

   b. 16 _?_ B **d.** 51 _?_ B **f.** -14 _?_ B

2. Use the roster method to define each of the following sets.

   a. The set of subjects you are studying this semester

   b. The set of counting numbers less than 10

   c. The set of counting numbers greater than 500

   d. The set of whole numbers

   e. The set of whole numbers that, multiplied by three, produce 100

3. Use the rule method to define each of the sets indicated below.

   a. $\{2, 4, 6, 8, 10\}$ **c.** $\{3, 6, 9, 12, 15, \cdots\}$

   b. $\{1^2, 2^2, 3^2, \cdots, 5^2\}$ **d.** $\{\frac{0}{4}, \frac{1}{4}, \frac{2}{4}, \frac{3}{4}, \cdots, \frac{12}{4}\}$

   e. $\{$George Washington, John Adams, Thomas Jefferson$\}$

4. In which of the following pairs are the two sets equal, in which are they equivalent but not equal, and in which are they neither equal nor equivalent?

   a. $D = \{1, 2, 3, 4\}$ $B = \{4, 3, 2, 1\}$

   b. $M = \{1, 2, 3, 4\}$ $L = \{5, 6, 7, 8\}$

   c. $F = \{2, 4, 6\}$ $E = \{1, 3, 5, 7, 9\}$

   d. $G = \{$red, white, blue$\}$ $H = \{8, 9, 10\}$

   e. $L = \{0\}$ $K = \emptyset$

   f. $T =$ the set of multiples of 3 which are greater than 6 and less than 15
   $S = \{6, 9, 12\}$

5. In which of the following pairs of sets are the two sets equal, and in which are they equivalent but not equal?

   a. $\{-4, -3, -2, -1\}$, $\{-5, -1, -3, -2\}$

   b. $\{1, 5, 9\}$, $\{9, 1, 5\}$

   c. $\{2, 4, 6, 8, 10\}$, $\{10, 8, 6, 4, 2\}$

   d. $\{1, 2, 3, 4, 5\}$, $\{\frac{1}{1}, \frac{1}{2}, \frac{1}{3}, \frac{1}{4}, \frac{1}{5}\}$

6. Indicate which of the following sets are finite and which are infinite.

   a. The set of all people who live in Oregon

   b. The set of all students in your school

   c. $\{1, 4, 9, 16, 25, \cdots\}$

d. The set of numbers which can be represented by $\frac{a}{b}$ where $a \in W$, $b \in C$, and a is less than b

e. The set of all whole numbers

f. The set of counting numbers less than 1 (Zero is not a counting number.)

g. The set of fractions with whole number numerators less than 3 and with the denominator 5

h. The set of two-digit positive integers less than 100 whose digits are alike

Subsets

If every element of set S is also an element of set B, then set S is a *subset* of set B; that is, set S is included in set B. For example, your algebra class is a subset of the set of all the people in the world who are studying algebra. Similarly, the set of pages of this chapter is a subset of the set of all pages in this book.

To write "set S is a subset of set B" or "set S is included in set B" we write $S \subseteq B$. If set S is included in set B, then, of course, set B includes set S. To write "set B includes set S," we write $B \supseteq S$.

According to our definition of subset, any set is a subset of itself. Thus $B \subseteq B$ because any element of set B is an element of set B.

If $S = B$, then $S \subseteq B$ and $B \subseteq S$.
If $S \subseteq B$ and $B \subseteq S$, then $S = B$.

Let us now consider the statement

If $S \subseteq B$ and $B \subseteq D$, then $S \subseteq D$.

The diagram at the right shows the meaning of this statement. Let the circular regions labeled S, B, and D contain points representing all the members of sets S, B, and D, respectively. To illustrate the statement $S \subseteq B$, we may place region S entirely within region B, and to illustrate the statement $B \subseteq D$, we may place region B entirely within region D. (It is understood, of course, that if $S \subseteq B$, region S may entirely fill the space of region B and that if $B \subseteq D$, region B may entirely fill the space of region D.) Since any point within region S is also within region B and any point within region B is also

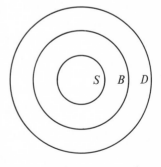

within region D, the diagram makes it obvious that any point within region S is also within region D. In other words, the statement "If $S \subseteq B$ and

$B \subseteq D$, then $S \subseteq D$" is true. Note that the reasoning above can be extended to involve four sets and give us the statement:

$$\text{If } S \subseteq B,\ B \subseteq D,\ \text{and } D \subseteq E,\ \text{then } S \subseteq E.$$

Similar statements can be made to apply to five or more sets in which each set is a subset of its successor.

If every element of set S is also an element of set B and there is at least one element of set B which is not in set S, we say that set S is a *proper subset* of set B. To write "set S is a proper subset of set B" or "set S is properly included in set B," we write $S \subset B$. Of course, if set S is properly included in set B, then set B properly includes set S, and we write $B \supset S$. We see that if either of the statements $S \subset B$ or $B \supset S$ is true, the other is true, and if either is false, the other is false. Two statements that are related in this way are said to be *equivalent statements*. The symbol $\longleftrightarrow$ written between two statements means that they are equivalent. Thus we may write

$$S \subset B \longleftrightarrow B \supset S.$$

If set S is a proper subset of set B, then set B is said to be a *superset* of set S.

The Empty Set

Suppose that six of your school's track athletes qualify for the state track finals in six different events. If E represents the set of qualifiers and S represents the set of those among the qualifiers who win their events in the state track meet, then $S \subseteq E$. Note that we cannot be sure that $S \subset E$ because in the happy event that all of your six qualifiers win, S is not a proper subset of E. If none of your qualifiers win, $S = \emptyset$. Since the null set is considered a subset of every set, it follows that $\emptyset \subset E$.

The reasoning which leads us to accept the null set as a subset of E or of any other set is as follows: If $\emptyset \nsubseteq E$, then $\emptyset$ must contain a member which is not a member of E. This is impossible because $\emptyset$ contains no members. Hence $\emptyset \nsubseteq E$ is false. If $\emptyset \nsubseteq E$ is false, then $\emptyset \subseteq E$ must be true. In reaching this conclusion we have used a type of reasoning known as *indirect proof*. Indirect proof will be further considered on page 82.

Variables

If a merchant who operates a sporting goods store has 22 footballs in stock and if he makes a profit of 2 dollars on each football he sells, we can say that his profit, expressed in dollars, on the sale of x footballs is $2x$.

In this case, x holds a place for any of the numerals 1, 2, 3, $\cdots$, 22. For example, if the merchant sells 10 footballs, $x = 10$ and $2x = 20$. When we use a letter in this way we call it a variable. A *variable* is a symbol that holds a place for the name of any element in a given nonempty set. In this course variables usually will be used to hold the place for the names of numbers. We call the given set the *replacement set* or *domain* of the variable. Any member of the replacement set is called a *value* of the variable. When we say $\{1, 2, 3, \cdots, 22\}$ is the replacement set, or domain of the variable x in the preceding example, we mean that the numbers represented by 1, 2, 3, $\cdots$, 22 are values x may have.

If the replacement set of a variable contains one and only one member, the variable is called a *constant*. Since numerical·expressions name specific numbers, they are also called constants.

 EXERCISES

1. Write eight possible subsets of B if $B = \{1, 2, 3\}$.

2. Given $S = \{1, 2, 3, 4, 5, 6, 7, 8, 9\}$, use set notation to indicate each of the following subsets of S.

   a. The set of odd numbers in S

   b. The set of perfect square integers in S

   c. The set of elements in S that are greater than 9

   d. The set of counting numbers in S

   e. The set of elements in S that are 1 greater than twice another element of S

   f. The elements in S less than 5

3. If $D = \{1, 3, 5, 7, 9\}$, $E = \{1, 2, 3\}$, and $F = \{7, 9\}$, which of the following statements are true?

   a. $F \subseteq D$ **c.** $E \nsubseteq D$ **e.** $\emptyset \subset E$

   b. $F \subset D$ **d.** $D \subseteq D$ **f.** $D \supset F$

4. Complete each of the following to form a true statement.

   a. If $R \subseteq S$ and $S \subseteq R$, then _____.

   b. If $M \subset S$ and $S \subset T$, then _____.

   c. If $K = L$ and $L \subset M$, then _____.

   d. If $P \subseteq Q$, $Q \subseteq R$, and $R \subseteq S$, then _____.

5. Using the roster method, indicate the elements belonging to E when $D = \{2, 4, 6\}$, $E \subset D$, $6 \notin E$, and $\{2\} \subset E$.

6. If x is a variable whose replacement set is $\{1, 3, 5, 7\}$, what numbers can be represented by each of the following?

a. $3\,x$ c. $2\,x+3$ e. $4\,x^2$

b. $x+1$ d. x^2 f. $2\,x-1$

7. If the domain of the variable y is $\{\frac{1}{4}, \frac{2}{4}, \frac{3}{4}\}$, what set of numbers can be represented by each of the following?

a. $4\,y$ c. y^3 e. $2\,y+3$

b. $2+y$ d. $\frac{1}{3}\,y$ f. $3\,y^2$

8. Which of the following statements are true and which false?

a. The null set is a subset of every set.

b. Any set is a subset of itself.

c. Every set has a subset that is a proper subset of itself.

d. The set of counting numbers is a subset of the set of whole numbers.

e. The set of counting numbers is equivalent to the set of whole numbers.

f. $\{0\} = \emptyset$

g. $\{3\} \subset \{3\}$

h. $\emptyset \subseteq \{0\}$

i. $\emptyset \subset \{1\}$

9. If $A \subseteq \emptyset$, then $A = \emptyset$. Explain.

10. Show that a set having two elements has 2^2 subsets and that a set having three elements has 2^3 subsets. Does a set having 4 elements have 2^4 elements? Do you think that a set having n elements has 2^n subsets?

Universal Set

If, in a certain discussion, all of the sets under consideration are subsets of a given set, we may designate the given set as the *universal set* or the *universe*, for that discussion. For example, if all of the sets we are discussing at a particular time are subsets of the set of integers $I = \{\cdots, -2, -1, 0, 1, 2, \cdots\}$, then I can be chosen as the universal set for that discussion. In another discussion the universal set might be the set of whole numbers, the set of counting numbers, the set of adults who live in Cook County, Illinois, or the set of baseball teams in the major leagues. In a discussion it is usually helpful to describe the universal set from which the elements of all of the sets under discussion are to be chosen. We often denote the universal set by U. For example, if we are considering subsets of the set of integers, we may write $U = \{\cdots, -2, -1, 0, 1, 2, \cdots\}$.

Venn Diagrams

We sometimes use Venn diagrams to picture relationships between sets. Let M denote the set of all people who live in Missouri and let U denote the set of all people who live in the United States. 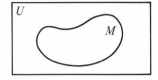 The figure at the right is a Venn diagram showing that the set of all people who live in Missouri is a subset of the set of all people who live in the United States. We think of the rectangle as a line enclosing a set of points which represent the members of set U and of the closed curve within the rectangle as a line enclosing a set of points which represent the members of set M. Since the curve is entirely inside the rectangle, set M is pictured as a subset of set U.

The following Venn diagrams picture various relationships between non-empty sets D and B.

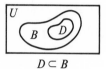

$$D \subset B$$

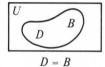

$$D = B$$

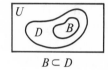

$$B \subset D$$

D and B have one or more
elements in common

D and B have no
elements in common

Two or more sets that have no elements in common are called *disjoint* sets or *mutually exclusive* sets. Two such sets are pictured in the last diagram above.

Operations with Sets

If we are given two numbers, we can perform certain operations with them to obtain another number. For example, we can add the numbers 5 and 2 and thereby obtain the number 7. The number produced may even be one of the original numbers as it is when we add 5 and 0 to obtain 5. Similarly, if we are given two sets, we can perform certain operations with them to produce another set. This may be a different set or it may be one of the original sets. Three very important operations are: (1) finding the intersection of two given sets, (2) finding the union of two given sets, and (3) finding the complement of a set with respect to a given universal set.

The *intersection* of two sets X and Y is the set of elements that belong to both X and Y. This set is designated by the symbol $X \cap Y$ which is read "X cap Y," "X intersection Y," or "the intersection of X and Y." Suppose that $X = \{-7, -5, -2\frac{1}{2}, -1\frac{1}{3}, 0, 4, 15\}$ and that $Y = \{-11, -5, -2\frac{1}{2}, -2, 1, 7, 15, 21\}$. Since the elements -5, $-2\frac{1}{2}$, and 15 are the only ones that belong to both X and Y, we know that $X \cap Y = \{-5, -2\frac{1}{2}, 15\}$. In the diagram labeled $X \cap Y$ the region within the closed curve labeled X contains a set of points representing the members of set X and the region within the closed curve labeled Y contains a set of points representing the members

$X \cap Y$ $X \cap Y = \emptyset$

of Y. The shaded portion of the figure contains all of the points and only the points common to both regions and consequently represents $X \cap Y$. The diagram labeled $X \cap Y = \emptyset$ indicates two sets, X and Y, that are disjoint, that is, two sets whose intersection is the null set. The two diagrams at the right illustrate the statement $Y \subseteq X$. The shaded portion in each figure contains all the points and only those points representing elements common to both sets and consequently represents $X \cap Y$. We see that when $Y \subseteq X, X \cap Y = Y$.

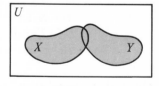

$X \cap Y = Y$

The *union* of two sets X and Y is the set of elements that belong to X, to Y, or to both X and Y. This set is designated by the symbol $X \cup Y$ which is read "X cup Y," "X union Y," or "the union of X and Y." If $X = \{-7, -5, -2\frac{1}{2}, -1\frac{1}{3}, 0, 4, 15\}$ and $Y = \{-11, -5, -2\frac{1}{2}, -2, 1, 7, 15, 21\}$, we have $X \cup Y = \{-11, -7, -5, -2\frac{1}{2}, -2, -1\frac{1}{3}, 0, 1, 4, 7, 15, 21\}$. In the diagram at the right the set $X \cup Y$ is represented by the shaded area.

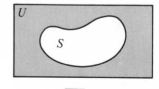

$X \cup Y$

If S is any subset of a universal set U, the set of elements of U which are not members of S is called the *complement* of S and is denoted by S'. In the diagram at the right S' is represented by the shaded area. The two sets S and S' are said to be *complementary to each other with respect to the universe U*.

S'

Let us consider some examples which illustrate these ideas.

Example 1. Draw Venn diagrams to show $D \cup E = E$ when $D \subseteq E$.

Solution. If D is a subset of E, then any element of D is also an element of E. The possible relationships between D and E are shown by the two diagrams at the right. The shaded area in each diagram represents $D \cup E$. We see that when $D \subseteq E$, $D \cup E = E$.

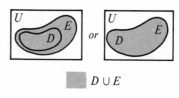

$D \cup E$

Example 2. Is the following statement of equivalence true?

$$D \cup E = E \longleftrightarrow D \subset E$$

Solution. When $D = E$, the statement $D \cup E = E$ is true and the statement $D \subset E$ is false. Hence these statements are not equivalent.

Example 3. Suppose that we are interested in the part of the complement of set M that is contained in set N for sets M and N shown in the diagram. This is the set $N \cap M'$. The shaded area in the figure represents $N \cap M'$. Is $N \cap M'$ a subset of $N \cup M$? of N?

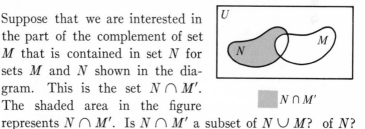

$N \cap M'$

Example 4. Draw Venn diagrams to illustrate the statement $D \cap E' = \emptyset$.

Solution. If $D \cap E' = \emptyset$, regions D and E' have no points in common. There are two relationships between D and E for which the statement $D \cap E' = \emptyset$ is true. These are shown in the diagrams.

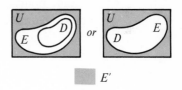

E'

Operations Involving Three or More Sets

The intersection of sets is a binary operation, that is, an operation involving exactly two sets. For this reason we must explain what we mean by the intersection of three or more sets. We state the following definitions:

If X, Y, Z, and T are sets,

$$X \cap Y \cap Z = (X \cap Y) \cap Z$$
$$X \cap Y \cap Z \cap T = (X \cap Y \cap Z) \cap T$$

To find the intersection of more than four sets we continue in this pattern.

Since the union of sets is also a binary operation, we define the union of three or more sets as follows:

If X, Y, Z, and T are sets,

$$X \cup Y \cup Z = (X \cup Y) \cup Z$$
$$X \cup Y \cup Z \cup T = (X \cup Y \cup Z) \cup T$$

To find the union of more than four sets we continue in this pattern.

Observe that in the statements above we have used the parentheses, ( ), to say "do this operation first." Thus $(X \cap Y) \cap Z$ means "first find the set that is the intersection of sets X and Y; then find the intersection of that set and set Z."

Example 1.   For sets X, Y, and Z represented by the regions within closed curves in the diagram, indicate $(X \cap Y) \cap Z$.

Solution.   In the diagram the area representing set $X \cap Y$ is shaded with vertical lines and the area representing set Z with horizontal lines. Thus, the set $(X \cap Y) \cap Z$ is represented by the crosshatched portion of the figure.

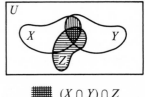

$(X \cap Y) \cap Z$

Example 2.   Let the universe U be the set of all people. In the diagram, points within circular region H represent the set of all of Harry's friends, points within circular region B represent the set of all of Ben's friends, and points within circular region E represent the set of all of Eleanor's friends. What set of people is represented by the shaded portion of the diagram?

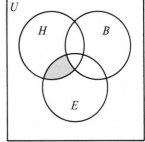

Solution.   The shaded portion of the diagram represents all of the people who are friends of Harry and of Eleanor but not of Ben.

Example 3.   Draw a Venn diagram to illustrate the statement: If $D \subset E$ and $E \cap F = \emptyset$, then $D \cap F = \emptyset$.

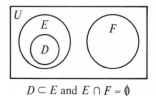

$D \subset E$ and $E \cap F = \emptyset$

Solution.   If $D \subset E$, every element of D is also an element of E and there is at least one element of E which is not an element of D. If $E \cap F = \emptyset$, E and F have no common elements. The diagram at the right shows the only possible relationship among sets D, E, and F for which $D \subset E$ and $E \cap F = \emptyset$. We see that $D \cap F = \emptyset$.

 EXERCISES

1. For each of the following, copy the diagram given and use shading in a way similar to that of Example 2 to indicate the following sets.

   a. All people who are friends of Harry and Eleanor

   b. All people who are friends of Harry, Ben, and Eleanor

   c. All people who are not friends of Ben

   d. All people who are friends of Eleanor but not of Ben

2. Using Venn diagrams, show all of the possible relationships between the universal set U and three of its nonempty, proper subsets X, Y, and Z if $X \neq Z$, $Y \neq Z$, and $X \subset Y$.

3. Sets B and D are related as shown in the diagram. Draw a Venn diagram and use appropriate shading to illustrate each of the following.

   a. $B \cap D'$ **g.** $(B')'$

   b. $B' \cap B'$ **h.** $(B')' \cup (D')'$

   c. $B' \cup D$ **i.** $B' \cap D'$

   d. $B' \cup D'$ **j.** $(B' \cup D')'$

   e. $(B \cup D)'$ **k.** $(B')' \cap (D')'$

   f. $(B \cap D)'$ **l.** $(B \cup D')'$

4. X is a proper subset of the universe U.

   a. $(X \cap X') \cap U = \_?\_$

   b. $(X' \cap X) \cup (X \cup X') = \_?\_$

5. Draw a Venn diagram to illustrate $X \cup X'$ as a subset of the universe U. What set is this?

6. If $U = \{-3, -2, -1, 0, 1, 2, 3, 4, 5\}$, $X = \{-3, -2, -1, 0\}$, $Y = \{-1, 0, 1, 2, 3\}$, and $Z = \{0, 5\}$, define each of the following sets by the roster method.

   a. $X \cap Y$ **d.** $X \cup Y$ **g.** $(X \cup Y) \cap Z$

   b. $(X \cap Y)'$ **e.** $(X \cup Y)'$ **h.** $(X \cap Y) \cup Z$

   c. $X' \cup Y'$ **f.** $X' \cap Y'$ **i.** $(X \cap Y) \cup (X \cap Z)$

7. In the Venn diagram at the right, the shaded area represents $(D \cap F) \cap E'$ and also $D \cap (F \cap E')$. If D, E, and F are related as in this diagram, draw a Venn diagram for each of the following.

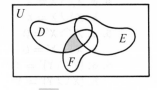

$(D \cap F) \cap E'$

a. $(D \cap E) \cap F$ d. $D \cup (E \cup F)$

b. $D \cap (E \cap F)$ e. $(D \cap E) \cap F'$

c. $(D \cup E) \cup F$ f. $(D' \cap E) \cup (D \cap E')$

8. If D, E, and F are nonempty proper subsets of the universal set U, $D \neq E$, $D \neq F$, and $E \subset F$, decide which of the following statements are true by shading the appropriate areas in Venn diagrams. For each statement consider all possible relationships among the sets involved.

a. $(D' \cup E)' = D \cap E'$ c. $(D \cap E)' = D' \cap E'$

b. $(D \cup E)' = D' \cup E'$ d. $(D \cup E) \cap F = (D \cap E) \cup F$

9. If the sets considered in a particular discussion are all subsets of the universal set U and U is the set of prime numbers, which of the following are not subsets of U? (A prime number is a positive integer greater than 1 which is non-factorable.)

a. $\{7\}$ b. $\{3, 5, 7, 11, 13\}$ c. $\{15, 17, 21\}$ d. $\{31, 33\}$

10. The set of counting numbers could be chosen as the universal set for which of the following?

a. $\{1, 2, 3 \cdots, 100\}$, $\{3, 5, 7, 9\}$, and $\{2, 4, 6, \cdots, 500\}$

b. $\{1, 3, 9, 27\}$, $\{-4, -3, -2, -1\}$, and $\{2, 4, 6, 8, \cdots\}$

c. $\{0, 1, 2, 3, \cdots\}$ and $\{1, 3, 5, 7, 9\}$

d. $\emptyset$, $\{1\}$, and $\{2, 3\}$

e. $\{0\}$, $\{1\}$, and $\{2, 3\}$

Properties of Operations with Sets

On the basis of your experience in drawing Venn diagrams you will no doubt agree with each of the following statements. These statements are the properties of operations with sets.

1. a. $X \cap Y = Y \cap X$ Commutative property of intersection

    b. $X \cup Y = Y \cup X$ Commutative property of union

2. a. $(X \cap Y) \cap Z = X \cap (Y \cap Z)$ Associative property of intersection

    b. $(X \cup Y) \cup Z = X \cup (Y \cup Z)$ Associative property of union

3. a. $X \cap (Y \cup Z) =$ Distributive property of intersection
        $(X \cap Y) \cup (X \cap Z)$ over union

    b. $X \cup (Y \cap Z) =$ Distributive property of union over
        $(X \cup Y) \cap (X \cup Z)$ intersection

4. a. $X \cap X = X$
  b. $X \cup X = X$
5. a. $X \cap X' = \emptyset$
  b. $X \cup X' = U$
6. a. $(X \cap Y)' = X' \cup Y'$ (These are known as De Morgan's laws.)
  b. $(X \cup Y)' = X' \cap Y'$
7. $(X')' = X$
8. a. $U' = \emptyset$
  b. $\emptyset' = U$
9. a. $U \cap X = X$
  b. $U \cup X = U$
10. a. $\emptyset \cap X = \emptyset$
  b. $\emptyset \cup X = X$

Example.   Find $\{1, 2, 3, 4\} \cap \{3, 4, 5\} \cap \{2, 4, 6, 8\}$ in two ways.

Solution.   By the definition of the intersection of three sets we know that
$\{1, 2, 3, 4\} \cap \{3, 4, 5\} \cap \{2, 4, 6, 8\} = (\{1, 2, 3, 4\} \cap \{3, 4, 5\}) \cap \{2, 4, 6, 8\} = \{3, 4\} \cap \{2, 4, 6, 8\} = \{4\}.$
By the associative property of intersection we know that $(\{1, 2, 3, 4\} \cap \{3, 4, 5\}) \cap \{2, 4, 5, 6\} = \{1, 2, 3, 4\} \cap (\{3, 4, 5\} \cap \{2, 4, 6, 8\}) = \{1, 2, 3, 4\} \cap \{4\} = \{4\}.$

ORAL EXERCISE

1. Express in words each of the properties of operations with sets.

 EXERCISES

1. Suppose that we are to find $X \cup Y \cup Z$. Suppose, too, that it is easier for us to do so using $Y \cup X \cup Z$ rather than the given expression. Which of the properties of operations with sets assures us that interchanging the X and Y will not affect the result?

2. If $M = \{1, 2, 3, 4, 5\}$, $Q = \{2, 4, 6, 8\}$, and $P = \{9\}$, find each of the following in two ways without changing the order in which the sets appear.

  a. $M \cap Q \cap P$ **b.** $M \cup Q \cup P$

3. If $B = \{1, 3, 5, 7\}$, $D = \{2, 4, 6, 8\}$, and $E = \{1, 2, 3, 4\}$, use either of the two possible procedures (not including the commutative properties) to find:

  a. $B \cap D \cap E$ **b.** $B \cup D \cup E$

4. If $D = \{-3, -2, -1\}$, $B = \{1, 2, 3\}$, and $C = \{0\}$, find:

  a. $D \cup B \cup C$ **b.** $D \cap B \cap C$

5. If $W = \{1, 5, 10, 15, 20\}$, $V = \{1, 3, 6, 9\}$, $T = \{1, 2, 4, 6, 8\}$, and $F = \{1, 4, 16, 20\}$, find:

a. $W \cup V \cup T \cup F$

b. $W \cap V \cap T \cap F$

6. a. Given that $G = \{5, 6, 7, 8\}$, $D = \{6, 8, 10\}$, and $E = \{1, 2, 3, 4, 5\}$, verify that the distributive property of intersection over union is true for sets D, G, and E.

b. For the sets of part **a**, verify that the distributive property of union over intersection is true.

7. If $B = \{1, 2, 3, 4, 5, 6, 7, 8\}$, list the members of each of the following sets.

a. $B \cup B$ **b.** $B \cap B$

8. If $U = \{1, 2, 3, \cdots\}$ and $D = \{1, 3, 5, \cdots\}$, find each of the following sets.

a. $D \cap D'$ **b.** $D \cup D'$

9. a. Given that $U = \{0, 1, 2, 3, 4, 5, 6, 7, 8, 9\}$, $B = \{1, 2, 3, 4\}$, and $D = \{3, 5, 7\}$, verify that the first of De Morgan's laws is true for sets U, B, and D.

b. For the same sets, verify that the second of De Morgan's laws is true.

10. Given that X and Y are nonempty proper subsets of U:

a. Draw Venn diagrams to illustrate all possible sets indicated by the left member of De Morgan's first law.

b. Draw Venn diagrams to illustrate all possible sets indicated by the right member of De Morgan's first law.

c. How do the Venn diagrams show that the law is true for sets X and Y as described?

11. Given that $U = \{1, 2, 3, 4, 5, 6, 7, 8, 9\}$ and $E = \{4, 5, 6, 7\}$:

a. Find E'.   **c.** What is true of the sets E and $(E')'$?

b. Find $(E')'$.   **d.** Your answer for part **c** is an application of which of the properties of operations with sets?

12. If $U = \{1, 2, 3, 4, 5, 6, 7, 8, 9\}$ and $B = \{2, 4, 6\}$ indicate each of the following sets.

a. U' **c.** $U \cap B$ **e.** $\emptyset \cap B$

b. $\emptyset'$ **d.** $U \cup B$ **f.** $\emptyset \cup B$

Subsets of the Real Numbers

We use R to denote the set of real numbers. These are the numbers that you studied in your first course in algebra. In this course we have mentioned the following subsets of R:

C, the set of counting numbers, is $\{1, 2, 3, \cdots\}$

W, the set of whole numbers, is $\{0, 1, 2, 3, \cdots\}$

I, the set of integers, is $\{\cdots, -2, -1, 0, 1, 2, \cdots\}$

An important subset of R that we have not yet considered in this course is Q, the set of *rational numbers*. The statement "A number is a rational number" means that the number can be expressed as the quotient of two integers provided that the divisor is not zero. Thus,

$$x \in Q \longleftrightarrow x = \frac{i_1}{i_2}; \quad i_1, i_2 \in I \text{ and } i_2 \neq 0.$$

The following are names of rational numbers: $\dfrac{4}{3}, \dfrac{-7}{6}, \dfrac{5}{-2}, \dfrac{28}{-1}, \dfrac{55}{1}, \dfrac{0}{21}.$

Since you are already familiar with the statement $-\dfrac{a}{b} = \dfrac{-a}{b} = \dfrac{a}{-b}$, you

know that $-\dfrac{7}{6} = \dfrac{-7}{6} = \dfrac{7}{-6}.$ You know, therefore, that $-\dfrac{7}{6}$ is a name

for a rational number. Since any integer i can be expressed in the form $\dfrac{i}{1}$,

it is evident that all integers are rational numbers. Thus I is a proper subset of Q. A study of the rosters of $C, W,$ and I reveals that W is a proper subset of I and that C is a proper subset of W. Thus in the language of sets, $C \subset W \subset I \subset Q.$

You are no doubt aware that there are some real numbers that are not rational. A well-known example is the square root of 2. Later (Chapter 3)

we shall show that $\sqrt{2} \in R$ and that it cannot be expressed in the form $\dfrac{i_1}{i_2}$

where i_1 and i_2 are integers and $i_2 \neq 0$. Any real number that is not rational is said to be an *irrational* number. Because the set of irrational numbers is the complement of set Q with respect to the universe R, we denote the set by Q'. Using set language to summarize, we may say:

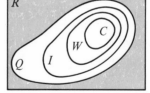

$$Q \cup Q' = R$$
$$Q' \neq \emptyset$$
$$Q \cap Q' = \emptyset$$

$\blacksquare \ Q'$

The diagram at the right pictures the observations we have made thus far in this section.

If we use the symbol $W \frown C$ to denote the set of elements which belong to W but not to C, we see that the set $W \frown C$ has only the one element, zero. Thus $W \frown C = \{0\}$. Note that $W \frown C$ can also be written $W \cap C'$.

The Number Line

A number line provides a convenient geometrical interpretation of the real numbers. To construct a number line we choose any point on a horizontal line and label it with the numeral 0. We refer to this point as the *origin*. Next we choose a second point to the right of the origin and label it with the numeral 1. We refer to this point as the *unit point*. Using the distance between the origin and the unit point as a unit of measure, we locate other points to the right of the unit point and to the left of the origin so that they, with the origin and unit point, form a set of equally spaced points along the line. We think of this set of points as continuing without end even though we can show only a few of the points. Now we label the successive points to the right of the unit point with the numerals 2, 3, 4, $\cdots$ and the successive points to the left of the origin with the numerals -1, $-2, -3, \cdots$ as shown below. Note that we place a small arrowhead at each end of the portion of the number line we have drawn to indicate that the line extends without end.

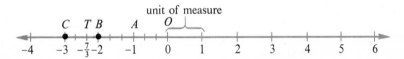

Having located points corresponding to the integers, we can now locate points corresponding to other rational numbers which are not also integers. To locate the point corresponding to $-\frac{7}{3}$ we divide the segments between O and A, A and B, and B and C (see the number line above) each into three equal parts. The first of these points of division to the left of B (marked T in the diagram) corresponds to the rational number $-\frac{7}{3}$. In a similar way points corresponding to other rational numbers can be located. The number line also contains points which correspond to the irrational numbers.

When we consider all of these points (those corresponding to the rational numbers and those corresponding to the irrational numbers), we have exactly one point corresponding to each real number. Moreover, each point in the number line corresponds to exactly one real number. We express these thoughts by saying that we have established a one-to-one correspondence between the set of real numbers and the set of points in the number line. Thus if S is the set of points in the number line and R the set of real numbers, S is equivalent to R. The real number associated with a point in the number line is called the *coordinate* of the point and the point is called the *graph* of the number. Thus the point labeled T in the number line above is the graph of the number $-\frac{7}{3}$ and the number $-\frac{7}{3}$ is the coordinate of the point labeled T.

The *graph of a given set of numbers* is the set of points whose coordinates are the members of the given set of numbers. The process of indicating points whose coordinates are the members of a given set of numbers is called *drawing the graph of the set*, or more briefly, *graphing the set*.

We observe that the graph of the set of positive real numbers P is the part of the number line to the right of the origin. The graph of the set of negative real numbers N is the part of the number line to the left of the origin. The graph of the union of these two sets with the origin comprise the entire number line so that we can write

$$P \cup \{0\} \cup N = R.$$

Numbers whose graphs are located on opposite sides of the origin and at the same distance from it are called *opposites* or *additive inverses* of each other. Thus, -6 and 6 are opposites of each other. The symbol $-a$ is read "the opposite of a" or "the additive inverse of a." If a is positive, the additive inverse of a is negative. Thus, if $a = 7$, $-a = -7$. If a is negative, the additive inverse of a is positive. Thus, if $a = -7$, then $-a = -(-7) = 7$. For any real number a, $-(-a) = a$. Moreover, 0 is its own opposite. Why?

Example 1. Draw the graph of the set of real numbers greater than -2 and less than 5.

Solution. Since every point in the number line corresponds to a real number and every real number corresponds to a point in the number line, we indicate the required set by drawing a solid black line from the point corresponding to -2 and extending to the point corresponding to 5 as shown below. To show that the numbers -2 and 5 are not in the set being graphed, we draw circles around the points corresponding to them. This indicates that these points are not part of the graph.

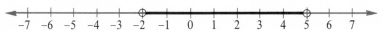

Example 2. Draw the graph of the set of rational numbers containing 3 and all rational numbers greater than 3.

Solution. Since the points corresponding to the rational numbers do not completely fill the number line, we draw a wavy line rather than a solid black one. Since the number 3 is included in the set whose graph is being drawn, we use a solid dot for the graph of 3. We indicate that the graph extends to the right without end by drawing an arrowhead at the end of the portion we draw as shown below.

Ⓐ **EXERCISES**

1. On your paper, copy the portion of the number line shown below. Then above each point indicated on the graph write c if the point corresponds to a counting number, w if it corresponds to a whole number, q if it corresponds to a rational number, s if it corresponds to an irrational number, and r if it corresponds to a real number. Be sure to leave plenty of space because some points will be labeled more than once.

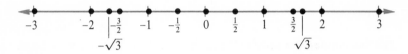

2. **a.** List the positive numbers whose graphs are indicated in the number line of Ex. 1.

   b. List the negative numbers whose graphs are indicated in that number line.

   c. List the numbers which are neither positive nor negative and which are indicated in that number line.

3. What is the additive inverse of each of the following numbers?

   a. -2 **b.** $-\sqrt{5}$ **c.** 3   **d.** 14.3   **e.** $-\pi$ **f.** 0   **g.** a **h.** $-b$

4. If x represents a real number, what is the additive inverse of x when:

   a. $x = 4$ **b.** $x = -3$ **c.** $x = 1\frac{1}{3}$ **d.** $x = 0$

5. The graph below is the graph of the set of integers less than 3. (Notice the "etc." which indicates that the graph extends to the left without end.)

   For which of the integers whose graphs are shown is the graph of the opposite also shown?

6. Draw the graph of each of the following sets of numbers.

   a. The set of integers greater than -4

   b. $\{-\frac{3}{2}, -\frac{1}{2}, 0, \frac{1}{2}, \frac{3}{2}\}$

   c. The set of rational numbers from $-\frac{3}{2}$ to $\frac{3}{2}$ and including $-\frac{3}{2}$ and $\frac{3}{2}$

   d. The set of real numbers greater than -3 and less than $\frac{7}{2}$

   e. The set of real numbers less than 6

   f. The set of even counting numbers

   g. The set of whole numbers which are the values of $\frac{1}{2}x$ when $x \in \{0, 1, 2, 3, 4, 5\}$

   h. The set of counting numbers which $x + 3$ can represent when $x \in \{1, 2, 3, 4, 5, 6, 7\}$

Properties of Equality

The sentence $a = b$ says that a and b name the same number. Such a sentence is called an *equation*. Let us review the properties of equality.

▶ **The Reflexive Property of Equality:** If a represents a real number, then $a = a$.

This property is applied when we accept such statements as $-17 = -17$, $\pi = \pi$, and $7^3 = 7^3$.

The Substitution Property of Equality: If a and b represent the same real number (that is, $a = b$) the truth or falsity of any statement in which the number is referred to by the name a is not changed if the name b is used instead.

Thus, if $a = b$, then $a > 7 \longleftrightarrow b > 7$. (Recall that $>$ means "is greater than.")

The Symmetric Property of Equality: If $a, b \in R$ and $a = b$, then $b = a$.

For example, if $3 + 6 = 9$, then $9 = 3 + 6$.

The Transitive Property of Equality: If $a, b, c \in R$, $a = b$, and $b = c$, then $a = c$.

For example, if $x = 3 + 5$ and $3 + 5 = 8$, then $x = 8$.

The Addition Property of Equality: If $a, b, c, d \in R$, $a = b$, and $c = d$, then $a + c = b + d$.

For example, if $x = 2$ and $y = 7$, then $x + y = 2 + 7$.

The Multiplication Property of Equality: If $a, b, c, d \in R$, $a = b$, and $c = d$ then $ac = bd$.

For example, if $x = 2$ and $y = 7$, then $xy = 2(7)$.

In some of the examples above, we introduced variables. Since a variable holds the place for the name of a number, these properties remain valid when variables are used.

Operations with Real Numbers

The operations of addition and multiplication are defined for real numbers in such a way that the real numbers have the following properties:

▷ If $a, b, c \in R$,

1. $a + b$ is a real number.	Closure property of addition (To each pair of real numbers there corresponds a real number called their sum.)
2. ab is a real number.	Closure property for multiplication (To each pair of real numbers there corresponds a real number called their product.)
3. $a + b = b + a$.	Commutative property of addition
4. $ab = ba$.	Commutative property of multiplication
5. $(a + b) + c = a + (b + c)$.	Associative property of addition
6. $(ab)c = a(bc)$.	Associative property of multiplication
7. There is a unique real number 0 such that $a + 0 = a$.	Addition property of zero (This property states the existence of an additive identity.)
8. There is a unique real number 1, $1 \neq 0$, such that $a \cdot 1 = a$.	Multiplication property of one (This property states the existence of a multiplicative identity.)
9. For each a there is an additive inverse $-a$ in R such that $a + (-a) = 0$.	Existence of the additive inverse
10. For each a, $a \neq 0$, there is a multiplicative inverse $\frac{1}{a}$ in R such that $a\left(\frac{1}{a}\right) = 1$.	Existence of the multiplicative inverse
11. $a(b + c) = ab + ac$.	Distributive property

The above eleven properties are listed here for reference because they provide a basis for understanding the operations with real numbers. Note that Properties 9 and 10 include the following definitions:

> If the sum of two numbers is 0, then each is the additive inverse of the other.

> If the product of two numbers is 1, then each is the multiplicative inverse of the other.

You will recall that multiplication and addition are binary operations and that each addition produces a unique sum and each multiplication produces a unique product.

Any set that has at least two elements with two operations defined so that the preceding eleven properties hold true is called a field. Thus we see that the set of real numbers with the operations of addition and multiplication defined so that the preceding eleven properties hold true, is a number field.

Absolute Value

In order to review the rules for adding and multiplying real numbers, we should first define what is meant by the *absolute value* of a number. We use the symbol $|x|$ for "the absolute value of x." You recall that $|3| = 3$, $|0| = 0$, $|-3| = 3$. We state the following definition: If r is a real number which is positive or zero, then $|r| = r$; if r is a negative real number, then $|r| = -r$. This definition tells us that for any non-negative a,

$$|x| = a \longleftrightarrow x = a \quad \text{or} \quad x = -a.$$

Addition of Real Numbers

Now that we have defined the absolute value of a number we can easily review the procedure for adding real numbers. *Note.* If two numbers are both positive or both negative, we say that they have the same sign. If one number is positive and the other is negative, we say that they have unlike signs.

The rules for adding real numbers are:

Rule 1. The sum of zero and any real number is the latter number.

Examples. $7 + 0 = 7$, $0 + (-6) = -6$
In general $a + 0 = 0 + a = a$. (Commutative property of addition and addition property of zero)

Rule 2. The sum of two nonzero real numbers having the same sign is a real number having that sign and having for its absolute value the sum of the absolute values of the given numbers.

Examples. $7 + 3 = |7| + |3| = 7 + 3 = 10$
$(-5) + (-13) = -(|-5| + |-13|) = -(5 + 13) = -18$
In general, if $a > 0$ and $b > 0$, then $a + b = |a| + |b|$ and if $a < 0$ and $b < 0$, then $a + b = -(|a| + |b|)$.

Rule 3. The sum of a positive real number and a negative real number having equal absolute values is zero, since each is the additive inverse of the other.

Example. $(-3.5) + (3.5) = 0$

Rule 4. The sum of a positive real number and a negative real number having unequal absolute values is positive if the positive number has the greater absolute value and negative if the negative number has the greater absolute value. The absolute value of the sum is obtained by subtracting the smaller absolute value from the larger absolute value.

Examples. $11 + (-5) = |11| - |-5| = 6$
In general, if $a > 0$, $b < 0$, and $|a| > |b|$, then $a + b = |a| - |b|$

$7 + (-13) = -(|-13| - |7|) = -(13 - 7) = -6$
In general, if $a > 0$, $b < 0$, and $|b| > |a|$, then $a + b = -(|b| - |a|)$.

We know that the addition of real numbers is a binary operation (an operation involving only two numbers at a time). For this reason we define what we mean by the sum of three or more real numbers:

If $a, b, c, d \in R$,
$$a + b + c = (a + b) + c$$
$$a + b + c + d = (a + b + c) + d.$$

To find the sum of more than four real numbers, we continue in this pattern.

Subtraction of Real Numbers

From our understanding of addition we are able to define subtraction for the real numbers. For example, we know that $12 - 8 = 4$ means $12 = 4 + 8$. In general, if a and b are two real numbers, we define $a - b$ to be a real number c such that $c + b = a$. Thus we have the following *definition of subtraction* of the real numbers.

If $a, b, c \in R$, then $a - b = c$ means $c + b = a$.

Since $a - b = c$, we may substitute $a - b$ for c in $c + b = a$. This gives us $(a - b) + b = a$. This statement says that adding b undoes the effect of subtracting b. Since $c + b = a$, we may substitute $c + b$ for a in $a - b = c$. This gives us $(c + b) - b = c$. This statement says that subtracting b undoes the effect of adding b. Two operations such that each undoes the other are said to be *inverse operations*. *Addition and subtraction are inverse operations*.

Now let us show that $a - b = a + (-b)$, that is, that subtraction of b from a can be replaced by the addition of the additive inverse of b to a.

We have seen that $(a - b) + b = a$. From this it follows that

$$(a - b) + b + (- b) = a + (- b) \quad \text{Addition property of equality}$$
$$(a - b) + [b + (- b)] = a + (- b) \quad \text{Associative property of addition}$$
$$(a - b) + 0 = a + (- b) \quad \text{Definition of Additive Inverse}$$
$$a - b = a + (- b) \quad \text{Addition property of zero}$$

Observe the dual use of the minus sign in the expression $7 - (- 3)$. The $-$ immediately after the 7 indicates the operation of subtraction. The $- 3$ in parentheses is read "the opposite of 3," "the additive inverse of 3," or "negative 3." In this case the symbol $-$ is part of the name of the number. In some books $7 - (- 3)$ is written $7 - (^-3)$ to emphasize the dual nature of the symbol $-$. However, it becomes inconvenient to use the raised minus sign, and consequently it will not be used in this text.

When we have a series of additions and subtractions like $6 - 3 - 2 + 4 - 13$, we treat it as $6 + (- 3) + (- 2) + 4 + (- 13)$. Expressions such as $6 - 3 - 2 + 4 - 13$, $- 5 - a - b$, and $x + y + z$ are called *algebraic sums*.

ORAL EXERCISES

1. What thought is stated by the closure property of addition?

2. Why is it unnecessary to state the closure, commutative, and associative properties for the subtraction of two real numbers?

3. Explain the meaning of "additive identity" and "additive inverse."

4. Which property states that every real number has an opposite?

 EXERCISES

1. Which of the two numbers $- 7$ and 3 has the greater absolute value?

2. Find the absolute value of each of the following numbers.

   a. 4   **c.** $- 9$ **e.** $- 95$ **g.** 7432
   b. $- \frac{1}{2}$ **d.** 0   **f.** 14×10 **h.** $10 + 12$

3. Is the absolute value of a positive or negative when a is a positive real number? when a is a negative real number?

4. Indicate which of the following statements are true. Each variable represents a real number.

   a. The absolute value of a is always positive or zero.

   b. If n is a negative number, then $| n |$ is greater than n.

   c. If p is a positive number, then $| p | = p$.

   d. If $| x | = 4$, then $x = 4$ or $x = - 4$.

   e. The absolute value of a real number is never less than the number.

5. Find each of the following.

    a. $|5|+|-2|$ **c.** $|4|+|0|$ **e.** $|-6|+|-1|$

    b. $|-3|+|3|$ **d.** $|0|+|-3|$ **f.** $|7|+|7|$

6. Find each of the following.

    a. $4+(-3)$ **e.** $14+(-22)$ **i.** $12+10+(-1)$

    b. $-19+1$ **f.** $-16+(-16)$ **j.** $-18+6+(-5)+2$

    c. $15+(-15)$ **g.** $2+(-5)+7$ **k.** $-17+5+4+2$

    d. $-9+(-5)$ **h.** $-4+(-2)+(-3)$ **l.** $21+(-3)+6+(-4)$

7. Find each of the following.

    a. $7-2$ **c.** $-8-3$ **e.** $4-11$ **g.** $8\frac{1}{3}-(-2\frac{2}{3})$

    b. $7-(-2)$ **d.** $-1-15$ **f.** $6-12\frac{1}{2}$ **h.** $-4.8-(-3.2)$

8. State the property which is illustrated by each of the following statements.

    a. $4+0=4$ **d.** $6+4=4+6$

    b. $\sqrt{2}+(-\sqrt{2})=0$ **e.** $9+(-9)=0$

    c. $3+(-2)=-2+3$ **f.** $3+[6+(-1)]=(3+6)+(-1)$

Multiplication of Real Numbers

In your first course in algebra you used the following rules for the multiplication of real numbers.

    Rule 1. If $a=0$ or $b=0$ then $ab=0$.

    Rule 2. If a and b are both positive or both negative, $ab=|a|\cdot|b|$.

    Rule 3. If one of the numbers a and b is positive and the other negative, $ab=-(|a|\cdot|b|)$.

These rules form a definition of multiplication for real numbers.

Examples. $(-3)\times5=-(|-3|\cdot|5|)=-(3\times5)=-15$ Rule 3

           $(-4)\times(-11)=|-4|\cdot|-11|=4\times11=44$ Rule 2

Since the multiplication of real numbers is also a binary operation, we define what we mean by the product of three or more real numbers:

If $a, b, c, d \in R$,

$$abc=(ab)c$$
$$abcd=(abc)d.$$

To find the product of more than four numbers, we continue in the same pattern.

Each of the numbers a, b, c, and d is called a <u>factor</u> of the product $abcd$.

Example. $(-3) \times (-5) \times (-11) = [(-3) \times (-5)] \times (-11) =$
$$15 \times (-11) = -165.$$

In the example above -165 is the product of the factors -3, -5, and -11, and $(-3) \times (-5) \times (-11)$ is the *indicated product* of these factors. Observe that the product of an odd number of negative factors is a negative number.

Division of Real Numbers

From our understanding of the multiplication of real numbers, we are able to define division for the real numbers in terms of multiplication. For example, we know that $12 \div 3 = 4$ means $4 \times 3 = 12$. In general, if a and b $(b \neq 0)$ are real numbers, we define $\dfrac{a}{b}$ or $a \div b$ to be a real number that we may represent by c such that $c \cdot b = a$. Thus we have the following definition of division of the real numbers:

If $a, b, c \in R$ and $b \neq 0$, then $\dfrac{a}{b} = c$ means $c \cdot b = a$.

Since $\dfrac{a}{b} = c$ we may substitute $\dfrac{a}{b}$ for c in $c \cdot b = a$ and obtain $\left(\dfrac{a}{b}\right) b = a$. This tells us that if we first divide a by b and then multiply the quotient by b, the result is a; in other words, it tells us that multiplying by b undoes the effect of dividing by b. Since $c \cdot b = a$, we may substitute $c(b)$ for a in $\dfrac{a}{b} = c$. This gives us the statement $\dfrac{c(b)}{b} = c$ and tells us that if c is first multiplied by b and then divided by b the result is c. Thus we see that dividing by b undoes the effect of multiplying by b. *Multiplication and division are inverse operations.*

Let us return to the statement $\left(\dfrac{a}{b}\right) b = a$. If we multiply both members of this equation by $\dfrac{1}{b}$ (the multiplicative inverse of b), we have $\left(\dfrac{a}{b}\right) b \cdot \dfrac{1}{b} = a \cdot \dfrac{1}{b}$, and by using the associative property of multiplication, we obtain $\dfrac{a}{b}\left(b \cdot \dfrac{1}{b}\right) = a \cdot \dfrac{1}{b}$. By the definition of multiplicative inverse, $b \cdot \dfrac{1}{b} = 1$. Consequently, we have $\dfrac{a}{b} \cdot 1 = a \cdot \dfrac{1}{b}$. By the multiplication property of 1, $\dfrac{a}{b} \cdot 1 = \dfrac{a}{b}$; hence $\dfrac{a}{b} = a \cdot \dfrac{1}{b}$. This statement tells us that all divisions can be converted into multiplications by applying the rule: To divide a by b when $b \neq 0$, multiply a by the multiplicative inverse of b.

Since 1 is a positive number and since $b \cdot \dfrac{1}{b} = 1$, we see that b and $\dfrac{1}{b}$ must have the same sign. Thus $\dfrac{a}{b}$ is positive if a and b have like signs because in this case a and $\dfrac{1}{b}$ have like signs and the product of two numbers having like signs is positive. Similarly, $\dfrac{a}{b}$ is negative if a and b have unlike signs.

Consider the quotient $\dfrac{0}{b}$ where $b \neq 0$. Let $\dfrac{0}{b} = c$. Then $0 = bc$ by the definition of division. It can be shown that if the product of two real numbers is zero, at least one of them must be zero. Since $bc = 0$ and $b \neq 0$, it follows that $c = 0$. Thus no matter what nonzero number is represented by b, $\dfrac{0}{b} = 0$.

Reviewing the preceding discussion we state the following rules for dividing real numbers a and b.

Rule 1. If a and b are both positive or both negative, their quotient $\dfrac{a}{b} = \dfrac{|a|}{|b|}$.

Example. $\dfrac{-12}{-2} = \dfrac{|-12|}{|-2|} = \dfrac{12}{2} = 6$

Rule 2. If one of the numbers a and b is positive and the other negative, the quotient is negative. $\dfrac{a}{b} = -\dfrac{|a|}{|b|}$.

Example. $\dfrac{-10}{5} = -\dfrac{|-10|}{|5|} = -\dfrac{10}{5} = -2$

Rule 3. Division by zero is not defined.

Rule 4. If a is zero and b is not zero, the quotient $\dfrac{a}{b}$ is zero.

Example. $\dfrac{0}{-3} = 0$.

ORAL EXERCISES

1. What is the meaning of the closure property of the multiplication of real numbers?

2. Why is it unnecessary to state the closure, commutative, and associative properties of the division of real numbers?

3. Explain the meaning of "multiplicative identity" and of "multiplicative inverse."

4. Which property states that for the real number 3 there exists the real number $\frac{1}{3}$, for the real number -2 there exists the real number $\frac{1}{-2}$, and so on?

Ⓐ EXERCISES

1. Using the rules for the multiplication of real numbers, find the following:

   a. $3 \times (-1)$ **e.** $2(\frac{1}{2})$ **i.** $(-1)^3$

   b. $-4(-3)$ **f.** $\frac{1}{11} \cdot 11$ **j.** $(\frac{1}{2})(-\frac{2}{3})(-\frac{1}{4})(4)$

   c. $(-\frac{1}{2}) \cdot (-\frac{1}{3})$ **g.** $4(5)(6)$ **k.** $12 \cdot 3 \cdot (-2)$

   d. $45 \cdot 0$ **h.** $-2 \cdot 6 \cdot (-5)$ **l.** $(-2)(-2)(-4)(-5)$

2. Using the rules for the division of real numbers, find the following:

   a. $\dfrac{-12}{2}$ **c.** $\dfrac{-12}{-4}$ **e.** $\dfrac{0}{21}$ **g.** $\dfrac{-10}{-1}$

   b. $\dfrac{15}{-3}$ **d.** $\dfrac{16}{-16}$ **f.** $\dfrac{-2.4}{2}$ **h.** $\dfrac{-1.2}{-.2}$

3. If $a = -3$, $b = -2$, and $c = 0$, find the integer represented by each of the following.

   a. ab **c.** $6(-a)$ **e.** $(-a)(b)$ **g.** $7\,abc$

   b. $-4\,ab$ **d.** $-3\,bc$ **f.** $-(ab)$ **h.** a^2b^2

4. Find the number represented by each of the following.

   a. $3(-5+2)$ **e.** $9 - 3 + 4(-7)$

   b. $(-8)[-3+(-2)]$ **f.** $(12-15)(-3)$

   c. $\frac{1}{2}[-4-(-2)]$ **g.** $(-14-3)+(-1)$

   d. $-4 + 6[3+(-1)]$ **h.** $5 + (-2-4) - 6$

5. If $a = -1$, $b = 3$, and $c = 2$, find the number represented by each of the following.

   a. $\dfrac{ab}{c}$ **c.** $7 - a$ **f.** $a^2 + b^2$

                   d. $b(7-c)$ **g.** $bc(6\,a+c)$

   b. $\dfrac{b+c}{a}$ **e.** $\dfrac{4(5\,a - 3\,b)}{c}$ **h.** $\dfrac{12\,b - 3\,c}{bc}$

6. a. What restriction must be placed on a if $\dfrac{1}{a}$ is to represent a real number?

   b. What restriction must be placed on a if $\dfrac{1}{a-7}$ is to represent a real number?

7. State the property which justifies each of the following statements.

a. $5 \cdot \frac{1}{5} = 1$

e. $\frac{1}{4} \cdot \frac{1}{\frac{1}{4}} = 1$

b. $6 \cdot 0 = 0$

f. $[4 \cdot (-2)] \cdot (-1) = 4 \cdot [(-2) \cdot (-1)]$

c. $0 \cdot 0 = 0$

g. $\frac{1}{a+b}(a+b) = 1; \ a+b \neq 0$

d. $(-9) \cdot 1 = -9$

h. $4(-3) = (-3)4$

8. Which of the following are always true statements when a, b, and c are real numbers?

a. $a - b$ is a real number.

f. If a is a real number, $-a$ is a real number.

b. $\frac{a}{b}$ is a real number.

g. $a(b+c) = ab + ac$

c. $(ab)c = a(bc)$

h. $a + (-a) = 0$

d. $a\left(\frac{1}{a}\right) = 1$

i. $\frac{1}{c}\left(\frac{1}{a} + \frac{1}{b}\right)$ represents a real number.

e. $(a+6)\dfrac{1}{a+6} = 1$

j. $a - b = a + (-b)$

9. According to the distributive property, a multiplication may be distributed over the sum of two real numbers. Explain why it may be assumed that a multiplication may be distributed over the sum of more than two numbers as stated in $a(b+c+d+\cdots) = ab + ac + ad + \cdots$.

Example.   Use the distributive property to find $(m+3)(m-4)$ when m is a real number.

Solution.   We see that $m - 4 = m + (-4)$. Hence $(m+3)(m-4)$ can be written in the form $(m+3)[m+(-4)]$. Since m and 3 are real numbers, by the closure property of the addition of real numbers, $m+3$ is a real number. Hence, $(m+3)[m+(-4)]$ has the form $a(b+c)$. Since $a(b+c) = ab + ac$, we can write: $(m+3)[m+(-4)]$ $= (m+3)(m) + (m+3)(-4) = m^2 + 3\ m + m(-4) + 3(-4) = m^2$ $+ 3\ m + (-4)m + (-12) = m^2 + 3\ m - 4\ m - 12 = m^2 - m - 12$. Can you give a property of the real numbers or a definition to justify each of the steps of this solution?

10. Use the distributive property to find:

a. $6(4+x)$

e. $(a-7)(a-1)$

i. $(a+b+2)(a+2\ b+3)$

b. $-3(-2+y)$

f. $(a+2)(a+b+c)$

j. $(a^2+1)(a+2)$

c. $(a+2)(a+5)$

g. $(3\ a-1)(a+4)$

d. $(a-3)(a+6)$

h. $(2\ a-5)(3\ a+2)$

Cartesian Products

Consider the two pairs $(a, 1)$ and $(1, a)$. Obviously, the members of the two pairs appear in different orders. When the order in which the members of a pair appear is established, we call such a pair an *ordered pair*.

Consider the two sets $A = \{a, b, c\}$ and $B = \{1, 2\}$. If we construct the set of all possible ordered pairs in which an element of A is the first member of the pair and an element of B is the second member of the pair, we have a set called the *Cartesian product* of A and B. We denote this set by $A \times B$, read "A cross B." Thus $A \times B = \{(a, 1), (a, 2), (b, 1), (b, 2), (c, 1), (c, 2)\}$. Note that $A \times B \neq B \times A$. However, $A \times B$ is equivalent to $B \times A$. A nonempty subset of $A \times B$ is called a *relation* in $A \times B$. Thus, if $M = \{(b, 1), (b, 2), (c, 2)\}$, M is a relation in $A \times B$. We define relation as follows: A relation is a set of ordered pairs. Thus, if A and B are any two sets, then every nonempty subset of $A \times B$ is a relation in $A \times B$.

The set of first members of the ordered pairs in a relation is called the *domain* of the relation and the set of second members of the ordered pairs in a relation is called the *range* of the relation. Thus the relation $\{(1, 3), (2, 6), (3, 9), (4, 12)\}$ has $\{1, 2, 3, 4\}$ as its domain and $\{3, 6, 9, 12\}$ as its range. The relation $\{(-1, 4), (-2, 4), (-3, 4), (-4, 4)\}$ has $\{-1, -2, -3, -4\}$ as its domain and $\{4\}$ as its range.

If $D = \{1, 2, 3\}$, then $D \times D = \{(1, 1), (1, 2), (1, 3), (2, 1), (2, 2), (2, 3), (3, 1), (3, 2), (3, 3)\}$. If I is the set of all integers, $I \times I$ has infinitely many elements. Although we cannot list all of these, we can determine if a given ordered pair does or does not belong to $I \times I$. For example, we know that $(100, 201) \in I \times I$ because both 100 and 201 are integers and we know that $(\frac{1}{2}, 1) \notin I \times I$ because $\frac{1}{2}$ is not an integer. Thus it is possible to determine whether or not a particular set is a relation in $I \times I$. The set $R \times R$, where R is the set of real numbers, contains every ordered pair of two real numbers.

Given the sets $A = \{1, 2, 3\}$, $B = \{4, 5\}$, and $D = \{6, 7\}$, we can construct a set $A \times B \times D$ in which the first member of each ordered triple is from A, the second member from B, and the third member from D. Thus the Cartesian product $A \times B \times D = \{(1, 4, 6), (1, 4, 7), (1, 5, 6), (1, 5, 7), (2, 4, 6), (2, 4, 7), (2, 5, 6), (2, 5, 7), (3, 4, 6), (3, 4, 7), (3, 5, 6), (3, 5, 7)\}$. Note that our definition of a relation does not apply to the Cartesian product $R \times R \times R$ or any subsets of $R \times R \times R$.

Graphs of Cartesian Products

If $M = \{-1, -2, -3\}$ and $N = \{3, 4, 5, 6\}$, then $M \times N = \{(-1, 3), (-1, 4), (-1, 5), (-1, 6), (-2, 3), (-2, 4), (-2, 5), (-2, 6), (-3, 3), (-3, 4), (-3, 5), (-3, 6)\}$. In using variables to hold places for the elements of a Cartesian product it is customary to let x represent the elements of the set furnishing the first member of each ordered pair and to let y represent the elements of the set furnishing the second member of the pair. Thus if $(x, y) \in M \times N$, it is understood that $x \in M$ and $y \in N$.

To draw the graph of $M \times N$, we construct two number lines perpendicular to each other and having the same origin as shown at the right. Note that the vertical number line is so placed that the graphs of the positive numbers are above the horizontal number line. We place X beside the horizontal line to indicate that this line is to contain the graphs of the values of x. We call this line the *x-axis*. We place Y beside the vertical number line to indicate that this line is to contain the graphs of the values of y. We call this line the *y-axis*.

To locate a point corresponding to the ordered pair $(-1, 3)$, we locate the point corresponding to -1 on the x-axis and draw a vertical line through the point. Next we locate the point corresponding to 3 on the y-axis and draw a horizontal line through this point. The intersection of these two lines is said to be a graph of the ordered pair $(-1, 3)$. Proceeding in this way, we locate the graph of each of the ordered pairs in $M \times N$. The complete set of dots in the figure at the left is the graph of $M \times N$.

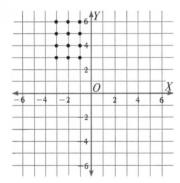   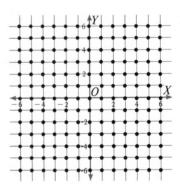

The figure at the right shows part of the graph of $I \times I$ where I is the set of integers. Since $I \times I$ is an infinite set, its entire graph cannot possibly be drawn. It must be understood that this array of dots extends to all parts of the plane. When you are asked to draw the graph of an infinite set of points, draw sufficient points to give a good indication of the nature of the graph.

In the figure at the right some of the points in the graph of *I* X *I* have been marked with black dots. The points form a subset of the complete set of points which is the graph of *I* X *I*. The set of coordinates of the points marked in black, that is, {(1, 1), (1, 2), (1, 3), (2, 1), (2, 2), (2, 3)}, is a relation in *I* X *I*. The set of black dots is a graph of this relation.

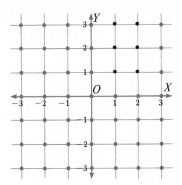

Since the set *R* X *R* consists of all ordered pairs of real numbers, the graph of *R* X *R* consists of the entire plane. Every point in the plane will represent an ordered pair of real numbers and every ordered pair of real numbers will be represented by a point in the plane.

Example 1.   **a.** Draw the graph of the relation consisting of all ordered pairs in *I* X *I* such that the second member of each is the opposite of its first member. Show the graph of the relation as a subset of the graph of *I* X *I*.

b. Draw the graph of the relation consisting of all ordered pairs in *R* X *R* such that the second member of each is the opposite of its first member. Show the graph of the relation as a subset of the graph of *R* X *R*.

Solution.   **a.** First we use red dots to indicate the graph of *I* X *I*. Since the relation is a subset of *I* X *I*, it will consist of ordered pairs of integers.

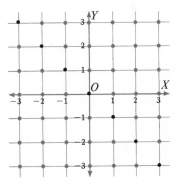

Each integer will be the first member of an ordered pair in the relation; in other words, the domain of the relation is {· · ·, − 3, − 2, − 1, 0, 1, 2, 3, · · ·}. Since the second member of each ordered pair is the opposite of the first member of the pair, the relation is {· · ·, (− 3, 3), (− 2, 2), (− 1, 1), (0, 0), (1, − 1), (2, − 2), (3, − 3), · · ·}. To draw the graph of this relation, we place black dots at the points in the graph of *I* X *I* corresponding to ordered pairs in the relation. Obviously, we cannot show all of these points but we can show enough of them to make the graph meaningful.

b. The graph of $R \times R$ consists of the entire plane. Since the relation is a subset of $R \times R$, it will consist of ordered pairs of real numbers. Each real number will be a first member of an ordered pair in the relation. We cannot list all of these ordered pairs, but we know that it consists of such ordered pairs as $(-\frac{5}{2}, \frac{5}{2})$, $(-2, 2)$, $(\frac{2}{3}, -\frac{2}{3})$, $(\sqrt{3}, -\sqrt{3})$, and $(4, -4)$. To draw the graph of the relation we locate a few of these points and draw a line joining them. The points in the line are the points of the graph of the required relation.

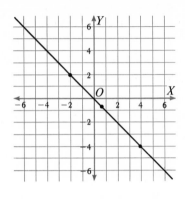

Example 2.   Draw the graph of $I \times R$ where I is the set of integers and R is the set of real numbers. In this graph indicate the subset of points for which $x \in \{1, 2, 3\}$ and y is a real number less than 4 and greater than 1.

Solution.   Since the first member of each ordered pair in $I \times R$ is an element of I and the second member of each ordered pair is an element of R, the graph of $I \times R$ will consist of the vertical red lines shown at the right. The portions of these lines drawn in black indicate the graph of the subset of $I \times R$ which consists of the set of ordered pairs each of which has 1, 2, or 3 as its first member and a real number greater than 1 and less than 4 as its second member.

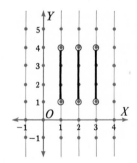

                                            Ⓐ EXERCISES

1. By listing its elements within braces, indicate each of the Cartesian products described below.

   a. $A \times B$ if $A = \{1, 2, 3\}$ and $B = \{5, 6\}$

   b. $G \times G$ if $G = \{1, 2, 3\}$

   c. $M \times N$ if $M = \{1, 2, 3, 4, 5\}$ and $N = \{-2, -3\}$

   d. $S \times S$ if $S = \{-2, -1, 0, 1, 2\}$

   e. $E \times F \times G$ if $E = \{1, 2\}$, $F = \{3, 4, 5\}$, and $G = \{6\}$.

2. Draw the graphs of the Cartesian products in parts **a**, **b**, **c**, and **d** of Ex. 1.

3. Draw the graph of $\{(1, 1,), (2, 2), (3, 3), (4, 4)\}$.

4. Draw the graph of $\{(-1, 2), (-1, 3), (-1, 4), (-2, 2), (-2, 3)\}$.

5. Draw the graph of the relation which consists of all ordered pairs in $I \times I$ for which the second member of each ordered pair is twice the first.

6. Draw the graph of the relation which consists of all ordered pairs in $R \times R$ for which the second member of each ordered pair is twice the first.

7. Draw the graph of the relation which consists of all ordered pairs (x, y) whose first member is a real number and whose second member is 4.

8. Draw the graph of the relation which consists of all the ordered pairs (x, y) whose first member is 2 and whose second member is a real number less than 3.

Numerical Expressions

We have noted that a numeral is a symbol which names a number. A *numerical expression* is a numeral or an arrangement of numerals and symbols of operation $(+, -, \times, \text{etc})$ which names a number. Thus $5 + 1, 3 \times 2$, $\dfrac{-18}{-3}$, and $\sqrt{36}$ are a few of the numerical expressions which name the number whose *common name* is 6.

Below we list a few numerical expressions and their more common names.

Numerical expression	Common name	Numerical expression	Common name
$7 + 31$	38	3^5	243
$7 - 18.9$	-11.9	$\sqrt{5 + 11}$	4
$(2.9)(-3.2)$	-9.28	$\dfrac{7^2}{3}$	$\dfrac{49}{3}$
$(3 + 7)5$	50	$\dfrac{-13}{5^2 - 2^2}$	$\dfrac{-13}{21}$
$\dfrac{-48.3}{16.1}$	-3	$\sqrt[3]{343}$	7

As we proceed we shall have more to say about common names.

When we write an equality sign $(=)$ between two numerical expressions, we are saying that they name the same number. Thus, since $\dfrac{\sqrt{36}}{2}$ and $\dfrac{1-4}{5-6}$ both name the number whose common name is 3, we may write:

$$\frac{\sqrt{36}}{2} = \frac{1-4}{5-6}$$

Similarly, we may write: $\qquad -\dfrac{7}{6} = \dfrac{(-2)^3 - 6}{5 + 7}$

Evaluating Numerical Expressions

The *value* of a numerical expression is the number which it represents. The process of finding a common name for the value of a numerical expression is called *evaluating the expression*. We shall often refer to this common name as the value of the expression. Thus when we say that 49 is the value of the expression $\dfrac{5^3 - 3^3}{5 - 3}$, we mean that 49 is the common name for the number represented by this expression.

We shall accept as common names for numerical expressions which represent rational numbers the numerals $\cdots, -3, -2, -1, 0, 1, 2, 3, \cdots$ and fractions of the form $\dfrac{a}{b}$ when a and b are elements of the set of numerals $\{\cdots, -3, -2, -1, 0, 1, 2, 3, \cdots\}$ and $b \neq 0$. Furthermore a and b represent integers which have no common integral factors other than 1 and -1.

To evaluate numerical expressons such as $4 \times 2 + 5$, we must make decisions about which operation to perform first. If we perform the multiplication first, we obtain $4 \times 2 + 5 = 8 + 5 = 13$; but if we perform the addition first, we obtain $4 \times 2 + 5 = 4 \times 7 = 28$. To take care of such situations we agree to the following rules:

> When more than one of the operations addition, subtraction, multiplication, and division appear in an expression and when there are no symbols of grouping, we shall first perform the multiplications and divisions in the order in which they appear from left to right and then the additions and subtractions in the order in which they appear.

> If there are indicated operations enclosed within parentheses or other symbols of grouping, we shall perform these operations first. When grouping symbols occur within grouping symbols, we perform the operations within the innermost grouping symbols first, then the operations within the next innermost grouping symbols, etc.

Other than parentheses, the symbols of grouping most commonly used are brackets, [ ], and the vinculum, ——.

Example 1.   Evaluate $6 + (3 + 2)$.

Solution. $6 + (3 + 2) = 6 + 5 = 11$.

Example 2.   Evaluate $4 \times \overline{9 + 3} + 2$.

Solution. $4 \times \overline{9 + 3} + 2 = 4 \times 12 + 2 = 48 + 2 = 50$.

> *Note.* The serial use of equal signs is justified by the transitive property of equality.

Example 3. Evaluate $\sqrt{9+7}$.

Solution. $\sqrt{9+7} = \sqrt{16} = 4$. *Note.* The symbol $\sqrt{}$ consists of the radical sign, $\sqrt{}$, and the vinculum, —. The radical sign indicates that a non-negative square root is to be found; the vinculum indicates the numerical expression whose square root is to be found.

Example 4. Evaluate $5(7^2 + 21)$.

Solution 1. By the rules for order of operations above:
$5(7^2 + 21) = 5(49 + 21) = 5(70) = 350$.

Solution 2. By the distributive property:
$5(7^2 + 21) = 5(7^2) + 5(21) = 5(49) + 5(21) = 245 + 105 = 350$.

Example 5. Evaluate $\dfrac{21 - 3}{3 \times 2}$

Solution. $\dfrac{21 - 3}{3 \times 2} = \dfrac{(21 - 3)}{(3 \times 2)} = \dfrac{18}{6} = 3$. *Note.* The horizontal bar which separates the numerator from the denominator also serves as a grouping symbol.

Ⓐ EXERCISES

1. Evaluate each of the following numerical expressions.

a. $3(17 + 4)$

b. $\dfrac{3(5^2)}{8 + 7}$

c. $\frac{1}{3}(24 - 3)$

d. $\frac{1}{5}(6 + 9) + 4(1 - 8)$

e. $6(-10 - 2) + (-2)(11 - 8)$

f. $\dfrac{3 \times 6 - 2}{5 - 3}$

g. $\frac{4}{3}(6 - 8 - 4)$

h. $1.5 \times 3 - 6.0$

i. $\dfrac{1 + \frac{2}{3}}{3 + 2}$

j. $\sqrt{50 - 1}$

2. Which of the following statements are true and which are false?

a. $\dfrac{7 + 5 + 1}{13} = 1$

b. $\dfrac{7 - 7}{14} = 0$

c. $\dfrac{8 - 11}{\frac{1}{3}} = 3^2$

d. $\dfrac{1}{9 + 3}(9 + 2 + 1) = \dfrac{11 + 3}{2(7)}$

e. $14 - 3 \times 2 = 22$

f. $8 \times \frac{12}{3} = 32$

g. $\dfrac{22}{3 \times 4 - 1} = \dfrac{22}{9}$

h. $4 + [-3 + 5(2 + 4)] = 31$

i. $(4 \cdot 2 - 3) - (2 - 6 \cdot 3) = 21$

j. $4(-5) - \frac{1}{2}(16) = 12$

Algebraic Expressions

If one or more of the numerals in a numerical expression is replaced with variables, the result is an *open expression*. An *algebraic expression* is either a numerical expression or an open expression. For convenience we shall often refer to algebraic expressions simply as *expressions*.

The column on the left below contains numerical expressions; the column on the right contains open expressions. Each open expression was obtained by replacing one or more numerals of the corresponding numerical expression with variables.

Numerical Expressions	Open expressions
-17	t
$4 \cdot 11$	$4x$
5^3	x^3
$-4(11-23)$	$x(11-y)$
$\dfrac{17}{5+31}$	$\dfrac{y}{x+31}$

Note. If the replacement set of a variable is not specified, it will be assumed that the replacement set is the set of real numbers.

The process of finding a common name for the numerical expression obtained by replacing each variable in an open expression with a member of its replacement set is called *evaluating* the open expression.

Comparison Symbols

The symbol for equality ($=$) is one of several comparison symbols whose meaning you must understand in order to use the language of mathematics effectively. Some comparison symbols are listed below. Each symbol is followed by an equivalent verbal phrase and by a sentence showing how the symbol is used.

Comparison Symbol	Verbal Phrase	Sentence
1. $=$	is equal to	$7(-3)+11 = -10$
2. $>$	is greater than	$-7 > -23.5$
3. $<$	is less than	$-5 < 3$
4. $\neq$	is not equal to	$2+3 \neq 6$
5. $\not>$	is not greater than	$11 \not> 5+6$
6. $\not<$	is not less than	$|-5| \not< 3$
7. $\geq$	is greater than or equal to	$|x| \geq x; \ x \in R$
8. $\lessgtr$	is less than or greater than	$\dfrac{1}{x} \lessgtr 0; \ x \in R$

Comparison Symbol	Verbal Phrase	Sentence
9. $\leq$	is less than or equal to	$2\,xy \leq x^2 + y^2;\ x, y \in R$
10. $\nleq$	is not less than or equal to	$-7 \nleq -23$
11. $\nlessgtr$	is not less than or greater than	$7(-3) + 11 \nlessgtr -10$
12. $\ngeq$	is not greater than or equal to	$-5 \ngeq 3$

Algebraic Sentences

The result of writing a comparison symbol between two algebraic expressions is an *algebraic sentence*. The entire expression to the left of the comparison symbol is called the *left member* of the algebraic sentence and the entire expression to the right of the comparison symbol is called the *right member* of the algebraic sentence. In the sentence $4\,x + 3\,y - 13 > 17\,z$, the expression $4\,x + 3\,y - 13$ is the left member and $17\,z$ the right member.

If both members of an algebraic sentence are numerical expressions, the sentence is called a *numerical sentence*. The first six and the last three of the twelve sentences listed are numerical sentences. If either or both members of an algebraic sentence are open expressions, the sentence is called an *open algebraic sentence* or, when no confusion can result, an *open sentence*. The seventh, eighth, and ninth sentences above are open algebraic sentences.

If an open algebraic sentence contains one and only one variable, the *replacement set for the sentence* consists of all of the members of the replacement set of the variable for which the open sentence becomes a numerical sentence. If the open sentence becomes a numerical sentence for every value of the variable, the replacement set for the open sentence is the same as the replacement set for its variable. This is the case for each of the following open algebraic sentences.

$$7\,x = 343;\ x \in C; \quad x < 9;\ x \in I; \quad 5\,x = 3\,x + 2\,x;\ x \in R$$

If there are some values of the variable in an open algebraic sentence in one variable for which the open sentence does not become a numerical sentence, these values of the variable must be excluded from the replacement set of the open sentence. In this situation the replacement set of the open sentence is a proper subset of the replacement set for its variable. This is the case for the open sentence $\frac{1}{x} > x;\ x \in I$. The replacement set for this sentence contains all of the integers except 0. We see that 0 is not included because if we write 0 for x, we obtain $\frac{1}{0} > 0$. This is not a numerical sentence because $\dfrac{1}{0}$ is not a numerical expression. (*Remember.* A numerical sentence consists of a comparison symbol written between two numerical expressions.) If we let K represent the replacement set for this open sentence, then $K = I \smallfrown \{0\}$.

If an open algebraic sentence contains two variables, x and y, whose replacement sets are respectively A and B, the replacement set for the sentence contains all members of $A \times B$ for which the open sentence becomes a numerical sentence. A similar statement applies to sentences with three or more variables.

If an open algebraic sentence becomes a numerical sentence for every member of the Cartesian product of the replacement sets of its individual variables, then this Cartesian product is the replacement set for the sentence. This is the case for each of the following open sentences.

Sentence	Replacement set for sentence
$x + y > 5; \quad x, y \in I$	$I \times I$
$y < x^2; \quad x \in Q, y \in R$	$Q \times R$
$x^2 + 2x = y; \quad x, y \in R$	$R \times R$
$x^2 + y^2 = z^2; \quad x, y, z \in C$	$C \times C \times C$

If the Cartesian product of the replacement sets for the individual variables of a given open numerical sentence contains members for which the open sentence does not become a numerical sentence, these members must be excluded from the replacement set for the sentence. In this case the replacement set for the open sentence is a proper subset of the Cartesian product of the replacement sets for the individual variables. For example, the replacement set K for the open sentence $\dfrac{4}{x+1} \le y$; when $x, y \in R$ is the set consisting of all ordered pairs of real numbers except those whose first member is -1. Thus $(5, 2) \in K$ but $(-1, 5) \notin K$.

The ordered pair $(-1, 5)$ is not in the replacement set of the sentence because when we substitute -1 for x and 5 for y, we obtain $\dfrac{4}{-1+1} \le 5$. This is not a numerical sentence because $\dfrac{4}{-1+1}$, that is, $\dfrac{4}{0}$ is not a numerical expression.

We have defined the replacement set for an open algebraic sentence in such a way that an open algebraic sentence becomes a numerical sentence for every member of its replacement set.

EXERCISES

1. Which of the following sentences are numerical and which are open?

a. $\dfrac{4+3}{2} = \dfrac{7}{2}$ b. $\dfrac{9+a}{4} = 15$; $a \,\epsilon\, R$

c. $x^2 + x + 1 = 13$; $x \,\epsilon\, C$

d. $3(-2) + (-8)(-6) > 40$

2. After each of the following sentences the replacement set for each variable is indicated. Indicate the replacement set for each sentence.

a. $6\,a = -94$; $a \,\epsilon\, I$

b. $\dfrac{4}{x} = 15$; $x \,\epsilon\, C$

c. $\dfrac{10}{x} < 5$; $x \,\epsilon\, R$

d. $x^2 + y^2 = 16$; $x,\, y \,\epsilon\, C$

e. $\dfrac{1}{x} + \dfrac{1}{y} = 5$; $x \,\epsilon\, R,\, y \,\epsilon\, C$

f. $y = x^2 + 3$; $x \,\epsilon\, Q,\, y \,\epsilon\, R$

3. Which of the entries on the right are members of the replacement set for the corresponding open sentence on their left?

a. $7\,x = 28$; $x \,\epsilon\, C$ $2,\ 4,\ \frac{1}{2},\ 100$

b. $\dfrac{3}{x} = 4$; $x \,\epsilon\, Q$ $1,\ 2,\ \frac{1}{4},\ -6$

c. $(x+7)(x-1) > 2$; $x \,\epsilon\, R$ $-7,\ 1,\ \sqrt{5},\ 0$

d. $\dfrac{1}{x+7} = \dfrac{1}{9}$; $x \,\epsilon\, R$ $-7,\ 7,\ 0,\ \frac{2}{3}$

e. $x + y = 5$; $x,\, y \,\epsilon\, R$ $(-3, 8),\ (2, 3),\ (0, 1)$

f. $\dfrac{x}{x+y} = 12$; $x,\, y \,\epsilon\, R$ $(-2, 2),\ (3, -3),\ (0, 2)$

Simple and Compound Sentences

The comparison symbols $>$, $=$, $<$, $\not>$, $\neq$, and $\not<$ are called *simple comparison symbols* because when one of these is written between two algebraic expressions, the resulting algebraic sentence has a verbal translation which is a simple sentence. Such an algebraic sentence is called a *simple algebraic sentence*. For example, the sentence $3 + 2 = 5$ formed by writing $=$ between the two algebraic expressions $3 + 2$ and 5 is a simple algebraic sentence because it is an algebraic sentence that may be translated as the simple verbal sentence "The sum of 3 and 2 is equal to 5."

If we join two or more simple algebraic sentences with a conjunction such as *and* or *or*, the resulting sentence is a *compound algebraic sentence*. Each of the simple sentences in a compound sentence is called a *clause* of the compound sentence. Thus, if we join the two simple algebraic sentences $2 + 3 = 5$ and $4 < 9$ with the conjunction *and*, we have the compound algebraic sentence $2 + 3 = 5$ *and* $4 < 9$. Each of the comparison symbols $\geq, \lessgtr, \leq, \ngtr, \nless$, and $\nleq$ is called a *compound comparison symbol* because when one of these is written between two simple algebraic expressions, the result is a compound algebraic sentence.

If the idea expressed by a sentence (either simple or compound) is true, we say that the sentence is true; if the idea expressed is false, we say that the sentence is false. Thus, the sentence $4 > 11$ is false because the idea it expresses is false, and the sentence $3 \cdot 6 = 18$ is true because the idea it expresses is true.

Statements

If we can determine that a sentence is either true or false, we call it a *statement*. Such sentences as "Tie your shoe" and "Is the door open?" are not statements because they cannot be classified as either true or false. According to this definition, any numerical sentence is a statement. Numerical sentences are sometimes called *closed statements* because they do not contain variables.

If we replace the variables in an open sentence with specific names and can determine whether the resulting sentence is either true or false, we call the open sentence an *open statement*. The open sentence $x + y = 10$ is an open statement because when the variables x and y in the open sentence are replaced by any members in their respective replacement sets, the resulting statement is either a true or a false closed statement.

Not all open sentences are open statements. For example, the open sentence "Multiply 7 by x" is not an open statement because when x is replaced by a specific name, the resulting sentence cannot be classified as either true or false.

Solution Set for an Open Algebraic Sentence

Any member of the replacement set of an open algebraic sentence for which the sentence becomes a true numerical sentence (when the substitutions are made) is a *solution* of the open algebraic sentence. For example, -19 is a solution of the open sentence $2x + 7 = -31$; $x \, \epsilon \, R$ because $2(-19) + 7 = -31$. Similarly, $(5, 8)$ is a solution for the open sentence $x + y = 13$; $x \, \epsilon \, I$, $y \, \epsilon \, I$ because $(5, 8) \, \epsilon \, I \times I$ and the numerical sentence $5 + 8 = 13$ is true.

The set of all the solutions for a given open algebraic sentence is the solution set or truth set for the sentence. It follows that the solution set of an open algebraic sentence is a subset of the replacement set of the sentence.

1. Indicate which of the following sentences are simple sentences and which are compound sentences.

a. $2 + 3 = 5$ c. $x^2 = 16$ *and* $x < 5$ e. $4 \lessgtr x$ g. $x > 2$ *or* $x < -3$

b. $2x + 4 = x + 1$ d. $9 \not> 3$ f. $x \geq 12$ h. $x \not< 5$ *and* $x \not> 7$

2. Indicate which of the following numerical sentences are true and which are false.

a. $4^2 < 18$ c. $2 \neq 2$ e. $\dfrac{8+6}{5+2} > 1$ f. $3 \times 5 + 4 \neq 27$

b. $5 \not> 6$ d. $4 \not\lessgtr 4$

3. Which of the following sentences are statements?

a. Go to apartment 21.   d. $5 \times 4 = 18$ g. $x + y = 6$; $x, y \in C$

b. Multiply 5 by 4.   e. $x > 2$; $x \in R$ h. $4x + 1 = 12$; $x \in I$

c. $5 \times 4 = 20$ f. $x + 5 = 12$; $x \in C$

4. Name all of the solutions for the statement $x < 5$; $x \in \{1, 2, 3, 4, 5, 6, 7, 8, 9\}$.

5. Use the roster method to define the solution set of the statement $x > 3$; $x \in \{1, 2, 3, 4, 5, 6\}$.

Example. Indicate the truth set of each of the following:

    a. $|x| = -7$; $x \in C$ b. $|2x - 1| = 5$; $x \in R$

Solutions.   a. By definition, $|x|$ is non-negative. Thus the solution set of $|x| = -7$ is $\emptyset$.

            b. By definition, $|2x - 1| = 5 \longleftrightarrow 2x - 1 = 5$ *or* $2x - 1 = -5$. Thus the solution set is $\{-2, 3\}$.

6. Indicate the truth set for each of the following statements.

a. $x - 7 = 12$; $x \in R$ e. $4x + 2x < -6x$; $x \in R$

b. $2x = 5$; $x \in I$ f. $(x - 2)(x - 3) = 0$; $x \in R$

c. $x \not< 15$; $x \in C$ g. $2x(x - 4) = 0$; $x \in I$

d. $|x| = -8$; $x \in R$ h. $(x - 1)(x + 2)(x - 3) = 0$; $x \in C$

Equations

As we have indicated previously, an *equation* is an algebraic sentence whose comparison symbol is the sign of equality. If both members of the equation are numerical expressions, the equation, like any numerical sentence, is a statement. The equation may be true or it may be false. For example, the first equation below is true and the second is false.

$$3 + (-13) = -10 \qquad\qquad \tfrac{1}{7} + \tfrac{1}{4} = \tfrac{2}{11}$$

If either member of an equation is an open algebraic expression, or if both members are open algebraic expressions, the equation is an open statement of equality.

The replacement set E for each of the open statements of equality below is shown in the column at the right.

1. $3x = 42; \quad x \in C$ $E = C$

2. $3x = 41; \quad x \in C$ $E = C$

3. $x^2 = 9; \quad x \in I$ $E = I$

4. $x = x + 1; \quad x \in R$ $E = R$

5. $x^2 - 1 = (x + 1)(x - 1); \quad x \in R$ $E = R$

6. $7x = 5x + 2x; \quad x \in R$ $E = R$

7. $\dfrac{x^2 - 1}{x - 1} = x + 1; \quad x \in R$ $E = R \smallsmile \{1\}$

8. $\dfrac{4x}{5x} = \dfrac{4}{5}; \quad x \in R$ $E = R \smallsmile \{0\}$

9. $x + 3y = 21; \quad (x, y) \in I \times I$ $E = I \times I$

10. $x^3 + y^3 = z^3; \quad (x, y, z) \in C \times C \times C$ $E = C \times C \times C$

11. $x + y = y + x; \quad (x, y) \in R \times R$ $E = R \times R$

12. $x^3 + y^3 = (x + y)(x^2 - xy + y^2);$
           $(x, y) \in R \times R$ $E = R \times R$

13. $\dfrac{4(x - y)}{5(x - y)} = \dfrac{4}{5}; \quad (x, y) \in C \times C$ $E = C \times C \smallsmile$
                                            $\{(1, 1), (2, 2), (3, 3), \cdots\}$

We now make the following observations about the truth sets for these equations. We shall use T to denote the truth set for each equation.

—Equation 1 has one solution, 14. The equation is false for all other members of its replacement set. Thus, $T \subset E$.

—Equation 2 has no solution for $x \in C$. $T = \emptyset$ and $T \subset E$. The same equation would have one solution for $x \in Q$, namely $\dfrac{41}{3}$.

—Equation 3 has two solutions, 3 and -3. $T = \{3, -3\}$ and $T \subset E$.

—Equation 4 is remarkable in that it has no solution for any replacement set that might be assigned to it. $T = \emptyset$ and $T \subset E$.

—Equation 9 has infinitely many solutions. Some of these are $(0, 7)$, $(6, 5)$, $(33, -4)$, There are also many elements of the replacement set for this equation which makes the equation false. Some of these are $(-2, -7)$, $(0, 0)$, $(-4, -13)$. Therefore $T \subset E$.

—No solution has ever been found for equation 10 although many persons have tried, some even using high-speed computers. This, of course, does not prove that $T = \emptyset$. Any solutions which exist must be in $C \times C \times C$. Therefore $T \subset E$.

For each of the equations 1, 2, 3, 4, 9, and 10, the truth set is a proper subset of the replacement set. $(T \subset E)$. These open statements of equality are called *conditional equations*. The truth set of each of the equations 5, 6, 7, 8, 11, 12, and 13 is equal to the replacement set for that equation. In each case $T = E$. These open statements of equality are called *identities*. We adopt the following definitions:

> An open statement of equality whose truth set is a proper subset of its replacement set is a conditional equation.
>
> An open statement of equality whose truth set is equal to its replacement set is called an identity.

The members of an identity are said to be *identically equal*. Thus two algebraic expressions are identically equal if they are the members of an identity. When we wish to assert that two open algebraic expressions are identically equal, we sometimes use the symbol $\equiv$ instead of the symbol of equality, $=$. Thus the sentence $|x| \equiv \sqrt{x^2}$ is read "The absolute value of x is identically equal to the principal square root of x^2."

We state the following method for determining when two algebraic expressions are identically equal.

> Two algebraic expressions are identically equal if and only if each can be transformed into the other or into a third algebraic expression by using the rules for operating with real numbers (pages 21–22), the properties of equality (page 21), and accepted definitions.

For example, $x^2 + 5x + 6 \equiv (x + 3)(x + 2)$ because we can use the rules for operating with real numbers and the properties of equality to transform either member into the other member. Again we see that $x + x + 3 + 4 \equiv 5x - 3x + 13 - 6$ because it is easy to transform each member into the expression $2x + 7$.

Example 1.   Show that $x^2 y^2 \equiv (xy)^2$.

Solution. $x^2 y^2 \equiv x \cdot x \cdot y \cdot y \equiv xy \cdot xy \equiv (xy)^2$

Example 2.   Show that $\dfrac{x^2}{y^2} \equiv \left(\dfrac{x}{y}\right)^2$.

Solution. $\dfrac{x^2}{y^2} \equiv \dfrac{x \cdot x}{y \cdot y} \equiv \dfrac{x}{y} \cdot \dfrac{x}{y} \equiv \left(\dfrac{x}{y}\right)^2$

1. If T represents the truth set for each of the following equations and E represents the replacement set for the equation, indicate E, T, and the relationship between E and T for each equation. The responses for the first three equations have been indicated to serve as a guide.

	E	T	Relationship between T and E
a. $3x = 12$; $x \in I$	I	$\{4\}$	$T \subset E$
b. $\dfrac{1}{x} = 5$; $x \in R$	$R \sim \{0\}$	$\{\frac{1}{5}\}$	$T \subset E$
c. $3x + x = 4x$; $x \in C$	C	C	$T = E$
d. $4x = 28$; $x \in C$	_?_	_?_	_?_
e. $\dfrac{7x}{8x} = \dfrac{7}{8}$; $x \in C$	_?_	_?_	_?_
f. $\dfrac{7x}{8x} = \dfrac{7}{8}$; $x \in R$	_?_	_?_	_?_
g. $12x = x(10 + 2)$; $x \in R$	_?_	_?_	_?_
h. $(x - 2)(x - 3) = x^2 - 5x + 6$; $x \in I$	_?_	_?_	_?_
i. $x + y = 10$; $x, y \in C$	_?_	_?_	_?_
j. $xy = 7x$; $x, y \in C$	_?_	_?_	_?_

2. Indicate which of the equations in parts **a–j** of Ex. 1 are conditional equations and which are identities.

3. Indicate which of the following are conditional equations and which are identities.

   a. $x + 7 - 3 = x + 4$; $x \in C$

   b. $x + 9 = 11$; $x \in I$

   c. $4x = 19$; $x \in C$

   d. $3x + 4x = 7$; $x \in R$

   e. $x^2 - y^2 = (x - y)$; $x, y \in R$

   f. $x^2 - 5x = -6$; $x \in R$

   g. $\dfrac{x}{7} + \dfrac{2x}{3} = \dfrac{-85}{21}$; $x \in R$

   h. $x(-3 + x) = x^2 - 4x + x$; $x \in R$

   i. $\dfrac{-1}{x} = 24$; $x \in R$

   j. $\dfrac{3 - 5x}{x} = \dfrac{3 - 2x}{x}$; $x \in R$

Order Properties

Each comparison symbol denotes an order relationship for real numbers. This relationship is a binary relationship because it relates two real numbers. For example, the sentence $4 < 7$ relates the two numbers 4 and 7. It states that the number 4 is less than the number 7.

The order relationship between two real numbers a and b determines the order in which their respective graphs, A and B, appear in the number line We can write three sets of equivalent statements as follows:

1. $(a < b) \longleftrightarrow A$ is to the left of $B \longleftrightarrow B$ is to the right of $A \longleftrightarrow (b > a)$.

2. $(a = b) \longleftrightarrow A$ and B are the same point $\longleftrightarrow (b = a)$.

3. $(a > b) \longleftrightarrow A$ is to the right of $B \longleftrightarrow B$ is to the left of $A \longleftrightarrow (b < a)$.

The order relationships have the following properties. Later, we shall prove some of these properties.

▶ **Comparison property:** If $a, b \in R$, then exactly one of the following statements is true: $a < b$, $a = b$, or $a > b$.

Transitive property of inequality: If $a, b, c \in R$, $a > b$, and $b > c$, then $a > c$.

Addition property of inequality: If $a, b, c \in R$ and $a > b$, then $a + c > b + c$.

Multiplication property of inequality:
  a. If $a, b, c \in R$, $a > b$, and $c > 0$, then $ac > bc$.
  b. If $a, b, c \in R$, $a > b$, $c < 0$, then $ac < bc$.

We sometimes refer to these properties as the *order properties*.

If a and b are two real numbers such that $a > b$, then $b < a$, and if $a \not> b$, then $b \not< a$. In other words, it is true that $a > b \longleftrightarrow b < a$. Thus we see that each of the order properties will have exactly the same meaning if the sentence $a > b$ is replaced by the sentence $b < a$.

1. Replace each of the following question marks with one of the simple comparison symbols to form a true statement.

    According to the comparison property, if a, b, $c \in R$, exactly one of the statements $a < b$, $a = b$, or $a > b$ is true. It follows that

    a. If $a \nless b$ and $a \neq b$, then a _?_ b

    b. If $a \ngtr b$ and $a \neq b$, then a _?_ b

    c. If $a \nless b$ and $a \ngtr b$, then a _?_ b

    d. If $a < b$, then a _?_ b and a _?_ b

    e. If $a = b$, then a _?_ b and a _?_ b

    f. If $a > b$, then a _?_ b and a _?_ b

    g. If $a \nless b$, then either a _?_ b or a _?_ b

    h. If $a \neq b$, then either a _?_ b or a _?_ b

    i. If $a \ngtr b$, then either a _?_ b or a _?_ b

    j. If either $a < b$ or $a = b$, then a _?_ b

    k. If either $a = b$ or $a > b$, then a _?_ b

    l. If either $a < b$ or $a > b$, then a _?_ b

2. Replace each question mark below with one of the symbols $>$, $<$, or $=$ to make a true sentence when a and b represent real numbers.

    a. If $a > b$, then $a + 3$ _?_ $b + 3$.

    b. If $a > b$, then $a + (-1)$ _?_ $b + (-1)$.

    c. If $a < b$, then $4 a$ _?_ $4 b$.

    d. If $a > b$, then $-2 a$ _?_ $-2 b$.

    e. If $a < -3$, then $-4 a$ _?_ 12.

    f. If $8 > -1$ and $a > 0$, then $8 a$ _?_ $-1(a)$.

    g. If $a > -2$ and $-2 > b$, then a _?_ b.

    h. If $-2 > -5$ and $-5 > b$, then -2 _?_ b.

3. In each of the following cases arrange the three numbers in order from least to greatest.

    a. $9, -15, 2$ **c.** $14, 40, -40$ **e.** $-1, -6, -15$

    b. $-4, -47, -73$ **d.** $-15, 0, -21$ **f.** $-6, 0, -5$

4. Match each verbal sentence on the left with the algebraic sentence on the right that expresses the same thought. In each case a is a real number.

    a. a is a positive number.   (1) $a = 0$

    b. a is a negative number.   (2) $a > 0$

    c. a is neither positive nor negative.   (3) $a < 0$

Representing Truth Sets of Open Sentences

The open sentence $x < 7$ when $x \in C$ has the truth set $\{1, 2, 3, 4, 5, 6\}$. The sentence is false for the other elements $7, 8, 9, \cdots$ in C. In other words, the sentence sorts the elements of its replacement set into two subsets— the subset of elements for which the sentence is true, and the subset of elements for which the sentence is false. This example illustrates the following important fact: Any open sentence acts as a *sorter* for the elements of its replacement set. The two sets formed are complements of each other with respect to the replacement set; that is, the union of the two sets is the replacement set.

We indicated the truth set of $x < 7$ when $x \in C$ by writing $\{1, 2, 3, 4, 5, 6\}$. We might also have indicated this set by writing $\{x$ such that $x < 7$ and $x \in C\}$. We read this as "the set of all x such that x is less than 7 and x represents a natural number." In place of words "such that" we might have drawn a vertical bar, $|$. Thus we would have indicated the truth set by writing $\{x \mid x < 7; \ x \in C\}$. Had we been certain that everyone concerned understood that the replacement set is C, we might have written merely $\{x \mid x < 7\}$. We call the symbol $\{x \mid \quad \}$ a *set builder*.

 A EXERCISES

1. If $U = \{-3, -2, -1, 0, 1, 2, 3\}$ and $x \in U$, use the roster method to indicate (1) the subsets of elements in U for which each of the following statements is true and (2) the subset of elements in U for which the statement is false.

    a. $x > -2$

    b. $x + 5 < 7$

    c. $x + 1 = 5$

    d. $(x - 1)(x + 3) = 0$

    e. $|x| = 2$

    f. $x + 3x = 4x$

    g. $4x = 10$

    h. $x^2 = 9$

    i. $3x + 4x = 16 - x$

    j. $\dfrac{1}{x} = -\dfrac{1}{2}$

    k. $\dfrac{1}{x + 2} = -1$

    l. $\dfrac{1}{x + 5} > \dfrac{1}{7}$

2. Use the set-builder notation to indicate the truth set for each of the following sentences.

    a. $x > 3; \ x \in C$

    b. $x + 1 = 16; \ x \in I$

    c. $2x = 11; \ x \in R$

    d. $5x + 3 = 17; \ x \in R$

    e. $3x - 8x = 18; \ x \in R$

    f. $4x + 2x = 21 - x; \ x \in C$

    g. $-8x < -5; \ x \in R$

    h. $3x - 5x > -2; \ x \in R$

Before you leave this chapter make sure that you

1. Can define a set by the roster method and by the rule method. (Pages 1–2.)

2. Know the meaning of "equal sets," "infinite set," "finite set," "equivalent sets," and "empty set." (Pages 2–3.)

3. Know the meaning of "subset" and "proper subset" and can use the correct symbols to indicate "is a subset of" and "is a proper subset of." (Pages 5–6.)

4. Know the meaning of "variable" and can use one properly. (Page 7.)

5. Know the meaning of "universal set" and can perform operations involving this set. (Page 8.)

6. Can draw and interpret Venn diagrams. (Page 9.)

7. Can find the intersection of two sets, the union of two sets, and the complement of a given set with respect to a universal set. (Pages 10–11.)

8. Understand the basic properties of the operations with sets. (Pages 14–15.)

9. Can identify and relate the various subsets of the set of real numbers. (Pages 16–17.)

10. Can draw and use a number line. (Pages 18–19.)

11. Understand and can use the properties of equality. (Page 21.)

12. Understand and can use the basic properties of addition and multiplication of the real numbers. (Page 22.)

13. Know the rules for adding, subtracting, multiplying, and dividing real numbers. (Pages 23–28.)

14. Can find the Cartesian product of two or more sets and can use variables to represent the elements of this set. (Page 31.)

15. Know the meaning of "relation" and can draw the graph of a relation as a subset of the graph of a Cartesian product. (Pages 31–34.)

16. Know the meaning of "numerical expression," "open expression," and "algebraic expression." (Pages 35–38.)

17. Know the meaning of "algebraic sentences," "open algebraic sentences," and "replacement set for an open algebraic sentence." (Pages 39–40.)

18. Understand the meanings of the comparison symbols and can correctly identify as simple or compound the sentences formed when one of them joins two algebraic expressions. (Pages 38–39, 41–42.)

19. Know when a sentence is a statement. (Page 42.)

20. Can determine when two expressions are identically equal. (Page 45.)

21. Understand and can use the order properties. (Page 47.)

22. Can use the set-builder notation to denote the truth set of an algebraic sentence. (Page 49.)

23. Can spell and use the following words and phrases properly:

absolute value (Page 23.) integer (Page 2.)
algebraic expression (Page 38.) intersection (Page 10.)
Cartesian product (Page 31.) numeral (Page 2.)
comparison symbol (Page 38.) numerical expression (Page 35.)
complement (Page 10.) operation (Pages 9, 12.)
compound sentence (Page 41.) property (Pages 14, 21.)
coordinate (Page 18.) rational number (Page 17.)
disjoint sets (Page 9.) relation (Page 31.)
domain (Page 7.) replacement set (Page 7.)
element (Page 1.) roster method (Page 1.)
equivalent sets (Page 3.) reflexive property (Page 21.)
evaluate (Page 36.) solution (Page 42.)
finite set (Page 3.) substitution property (Page 21.)
graph (Page 18.) symmetric property (Page 21.)
identity (Page 45.) transitive property (Page 21.)
indicated product (Page 27.) union (Page 10.)
infinite set (Page 3.) Venn diagram (Page 9.)

CHAPTER REVIEW

1. a. Use the roster method to define the set of counting numbers less than or equal to 10.

b. Use the rule method to define $\{2, 4, 6, 8, 10, 12\}$.

2. Given the following sets: $A = \{1, 2, 3, \cdots\}$, $B = \{2, 4, 6, 8\}$, $D = \{27\}$, $F = \{\frac{1}{1}, \frac{1}{2}, \frac{1}{3}, \cdots\}$, $G = \{-3, -2, -1, 0\}$, $H = \{\cdots, -3, -2, -1, 0\}$, $\emptyset$, set C, and set R

a. List the given sets which are finite sets.

b. List the given sets which are infinite sets.

c. List the pairs of sets that are equal.

d. List the pairs of sets that are equivalent.

3. Write a verbal sentence expressing the thought of each of the following sentences.

a. $A \subset B$ **c.** $A \subset B \longleftrightarrow B \supset A$ **e.** $x \in A$

b. $A \subseteq B$ **d.** $A \not\subset B$ **f.** $x \notin A$

4. Replace each question mark below with a word or symbol to form a true statement about the Venn diagram above it.

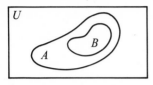

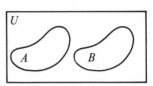

a. B _?_ A; B _?_ U

b. A and B are _?_

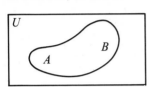

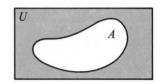

c. A _?_ B

d. The shaded area is _?_

5. If C is the universal set for $A = \{1, 2, 3, 4, 5, 6\}$, $B = \{4, 5, 6, 7, 8\}$, and $D = \{8, 9\}$, find each of the following sets.

   a. $A \cup B$ **d.** $A \cap D$ **g.** $(A \cup B)'$

   b. $(A \cup B) \cup D$ **e.** $(A \cap B) \cap D$ **h.** $A' \cup B'$

   c. $A \cap B$ **f.** A' **i.** $[(A \cup B) \cup D]'$

6. **a.** Name one number that is a whole number but not a counting number. Are there others?

   b. Name one rational number that is not an integer. Are there others?

   c. Can you name an integer that is not a rational number?

7. Draw a number line and in it locate:

   a. The graph of 3

   b. The graph of the additive inverse of 3

   c. The graph of the sum of 3 and its additive inverse

8. Draw the graph of each of the following sets.

   a. $\{x \mid x > 5;\ x \in R\}$

   b. The truth set of $x \le -2$ when $x \in R$

   c. C, the set of counting numbers

   d. N, the set of negative real numbers

9. What property of the real numbers assures us that if a and b are real numbers, then $a + b$ is a real number?

10. What property of the real numbers assures us that if a, b, and c are real numbers, then $(ab)c = a(bc)$?

11. Perform each of the following indicated operations.

a. $6 + (-2)$

b. $-9 - 4$

c. $(-3)(-2)$

d. $(-5)(2)(-3)$

e. $18 - 6 + 4 + 10$

f. $\dfrac{-18}{-2}$

g. $8 - (-3)$

h. $3 + (5 - 1) - 10$

i. $-8(4 + 2 - 3)$

j. $(-2\frac{1}{2})(-\frac{1}{5})$

k. $(-2)(-3)(-5)(-1)$

l. $\dfrac{-5 - 3 + 14}{-2}$

12. What restrictions, if any, must be placed on the variable in each of the following expressions if the expression is to represent a real number?

a. $\dfrac{1}{x}$

b. $\dfrac{4}{x+3}$

c. $x + 5$

d. $\dfrac{x}{12}$

13. Perform each of the following operations.

a. $|-2| + |3|$

b. $6|-5|$

c. $|4| \cdot |-4|$

d. $|-2| \cdot |-3|$

14. Find the solution set for each of the following sentences when x represents a real number.

a. $|x| = 2$

b. $|x| = -4$

c. $|x + 1| = 3$

d. $|3 - x| = 4$

15. If $A = \{1, 2, 3\}$ and $B = \{4, 5\}$, list within braces the members of $A \times B$.

16. If $(x, y) \in A \times B$, when $A \times B$ is defined as in Ex. 15, list within braces the values that x may represent. List within braces those that y may represent.

17. Graph the relation which consists of all ordered pairs in $C \times C$ for which the first member of each ordered pair is twice the second.

18. Indicate which of the words *numerical, open,* or *algebraic* can be used to describe each of the following expressions if the variables represent real numbers.

a. 14

b. $3(14 + 2)$

c. $4x$

d. $x^2 + y^2$

e. 0

f. $\dfrac{x + y + z}{2}$

19. Evaluate each of the following expressions.

a. $\dfrac{4 \times 5 - 2}{2}$

b. $2(6)^2 - 10$

c. $\frac{1}{3}(18 - 6)$

d. $4(-10 - 3) - 2(11 + 1)$

20. In which of the following pairs are the two expressions identically equal? Each variable represents a real number.

a. $\sqrt{25}, 5$

b. $2x + 3x, 5x$

c. $x + 3, 4$

d. $\dfrac{5x}{6x}, \dfrac{5}{6}$

e. $4x + 2y - y, 4x + y$

f. $\dfrac{x^2 + x}{x}, x + 1$

g. $x^2 + 4x, x(x + 4)$

h. $1 + \dfrac{4}{x+1}, x + 5$

21. Indicate whether *numerical* or *open algebraic* is appropriate for each of the following sentences.

    a. $x^2 = 5$ **b.** $2 + 3 = 5$ **c.** $x + 3 = 5$ **d.** $x^2 - y^2 = (x - y)(x + y)$

22. Indicate the replacement set for each of the following sentences.

    a. $3\,x = 18;\ x \in C$ **c.** $x - y = 10;\ x,\ y \in R$

    b. $\dfrac{3}{x} = 18;\ x \in R$ **d.** $\dfrac{7}{x + 1} = \dfrac{1}{y};\ x,\ y \in R$

23. Which of the following sentences are compound and which are simple?

    a. $x + 1 = 5$ *and* $x = 4$ **c.** $8 < 14$

    b. $x \geq 18$ **d.** $2 < 5$ *or* $5 < 7$

24. Which of the following sentences are statements?

    a. Add 6 to 14.   **c.** $9 < 1$

    b. $x + 14 = 20;\ x \in C$ **d.** $x + y \not< 17;\ x,\ y \in R$

25. Indicate the truth set for each of the following sentences.

    a. $x < 4;\ x \in \{1, 2, 3, 4, 5\}$ **f.** $\dfrac{3}{x + 2} = \dfrac{1}{x - 2};\ x \in R$

    b. $x + 5 = 17;\ x \in Q$

                                     g. $2\,x(x - 1) = 0;\ x \in R$

    c. $(x + 1)(x - 3) = 0;\ x \in R$

    d. $x \not> 7;\ x \in C$ **h.** $1 + \dfrac{x}{x - 4} = 5;\ x \in R$

    e. $\dfrac{1}{x} = 5;\ x \in R$

26. Which of the following equations are identities and which are conditional equations? $x \in R$

    a. $3\,x + 5\,x = 8\,x$ **c.** $\dfrac{3\,x}{7\,x} = \dfrac{3}{7}$ **d.** $10\,x = x(8 + 2)$

    b. $4\,x = 36$

27. If a, b, $c \in R$, which of the following statements are true and which are false?

    a. If $a > b$, then $a + 4 > b + 4$.

    b. If $a > b$, then $-3\,a > -3\,b$.

    c. If $a > -3$ and $-3 > -10$, then $a > -10$.

    d. If $a \not> b$, then $a < b$ or $a = b$.

    e. If $a < b$, then $a \not> b$ and $a \neq b$.

    f. If $a < b$, then $5\,a < 5\,b$.

28. Use the set-builder notation to indicate the truth set of each of the following statements.

    a. $x > 4;\ x \in R$ **b.** $x + 5 = 7;\ x \in C$ **c.** $x^2 + y^2 = 25;\ x,\ y \in R$

Indicate which of the following sets fit the descriptions stated in Ex. 1-4.

$B = \{2, 4, 6\}$, $C = \{1, 2, 3, \cdots\}$, $D = \{1, 3, 5\}$, and $E = \{5, 1, 3\}$.

1. The infinite sets   **3.** Two sets that are equal

2. The finite sets   **4.** Two sets that are equivalent

For sets B, C, D, and E defined above, which of the following statements are true?

5. $D \subseteq C$ **6.** $C \not\supseteq B$ **7.** $D \subseteq E$ **8.** $\emptyset \subset C$

If $A = \{3, 5, 7, 9\}$, $B = \{1, 2, 3, 4\}$, and $D = \{4, 5, 6\}$, use the roster method to define each of the sets described in Ex. 9–12.

9. $A \cup B$ **10.** $A \cap B$ **11.** $A \cap D$ **12.** $A \cup D$

If $U = \{-3, -2, -1, 0, 1, 2, 3\}$, $B = \{1, 2, 3\}$, and $D = \{-1, -2, -3\}$, list within braces the members of the sets indicated in Ex. 13–15.

13. B' **14.** $(B')'$ **15.** $(B \cap D)'$

Draw the graph of each of the sets described in Ex. 16 and 17.

16. $\{1, 2, 3, \cdots\}$ **17.** The set of real numbers greater than -2 and less than 3

Given $U = \{-6, -5, -\frac{9}{2}, -4, -\frac{1}{2}, 0, 1, \frac{3}{2}, \sqrt{3}, 3, 5\}$, indicate each of the sets described in Ex. 18–21.

18. The negative numbers in U **20.** The integers in U

19. The rational numbers in U **21.** The real numbers in U

For Ex. 22–25 write the name of the property which is illustrated by the statement appearing in the exercise.

22. $a + b = b + a$ **23.** $a(b + c) = ab + ac$ **24.** $(ab)c = a(bc)$ **25.** $a + 0 = a$

26. If $A = \{1, 2\}$ and $B = \{3, 4\}$, list within braces the members of the set $A \times B$.

27. Evaluate $-4(-18 - 3)$.   **28.** Evaluate $\frac{1}{3}(-15) - 4(\frac{3}{4})$.

In Ex. 29–31 which of the pairs of expressions are identically equal? In each case, $x \in R$.

29. 18×3, 54 **30.** $4x + 2$, 10 **31.** $\frac{4x}{5x}$, $\frac{4}{5}$

In Ex. 32–35 indicate the solution set for the sentence.

32. $x > 5$; $x \in R$

34. $\frac{x^2 - 1}{x + 1} = x + 1$; $x \in R$

33. $x \neq 3$; $x \in \{1, 2, 3, 4\}$

35. $x = 18$; $x \in R$

In Ex. 36–38 indicate whether each equation is a conditional equation or an identity. $x \in R$.

36. $4x = 24$ **37.** $2x + 3x = 5x$ **38.** $(x + 2)(x - 3) = x^2 - x - 6$

In Ex. 39–42, a, b, and c represent real numbers. In each of these exercises replace the question mark by a comparison symbol to make a true statement.

39. If $a \not> b$, then a _?_ b or a _?_ b.

40. If $a > b$, then $-3a$ _?_ $-3b$.

41. If $a > b$ and $b > c$, then a _?_ c.

42. If $a < b$, then $a + (-4)$ _?_ $b + (-4)$.

43. Use the set-builder notation to indicate the truth set of $x > -2$; $x \in R$

If $x \in A$, $A = \{1, 2, 3, 4, 5, 6, 7\}$, and A is the universal set, answer the questions indicated in Ex. 44–47.

44. What is the solution set for $x < 4$?

45. What is the subset of A for which the sentence of Ex. 44 is false?

46. How are the subsets of A indicated in Ex. 44 and 45 related?

47. What is the solution set for $3x + 2x = 5x$?

2

Language
of Algebra — Logic

Truth Values, Equivalent Statements

The particular label "true" or "false" which we assign to a given statement is the *truth value* of the statement. Two statements are *equivalent* if they have the same truth value· that is, they are equivalent if when either is true the other is true and when either is false the other is false; otherwise they are not equivalent. We shall continue to use the symbol ⟷ to mean "is equivalent to." For example, if s and t are two statements, then the statement $s \longleftrightarrow t$ represents "statement s is equivalent to statement t."

The truth table at the right summarizes the thought of the preceding paragraph. In the table, T written under s means that statement s is true, F written under s means that statement s is false, and so on. Line 1 of the table says that the statement $s \longleftrightarrow t$ is true when statements s and t are both true. Line 4

s	t	$s \longleftrightarrow t$
T	T	T
T	F	F
F	T	F
F	F	T

says that the statement $s \longleftrightarrow t$ is true when the statements s and t are both false. Lines 2 and 3 say that the statement $s \longleftrightarrow t$ is false when the statement s is true and the statement t is false, and that the statement $s \longleftrightarrow t$ is false when the statement s is false and the statement t is true. If we examine the four entries in the column headed $s \longleftrightarrow t$ we see that the statement $s \longleftrightarrow t$ is true only when statements s and t are both true or both false.

Now let us consider *equivalent open statements*. To represent an open statement we shall use a symbol such as s_x in which the subscript x indicates the variable in the statement. Two open statements are equivalent if and only if they have the same replacement set and the same truth set. If s_x and t_x are two open statements in one variable x, the statement $s_x \longleftrightarrow t_x$ means "the open statement s_x is equivalent to the open statement t_x." To indicate the solution set of s_x we may write $\{x \mid s_x; \ x \, \epsilon \, D\}$, and to indicate the solution set of t_x we may write $\{x \mid t_x; \; x \in D\}$. Thus to say that s_x and t_x are equivalent if and only if they have the same truth set we may write:

$$(s_x \longleftrightarrow t_x) \longleftrightarrow (\{x \mid s_x; \; x \in D\} = \{x \mid t_x; \; x \in D\}).$$

On the basis of the preceding discussion we draw the following conclusions regarding equivalent statements (open and closed).

1. Any statement is equivalent to itself. $s \longleftrightarrow s$

2. s is equivalent to t if and only if t is equivalent to s. $(s \longleftrightarrow t) \longleftrightarrow (t \longleftrightarrow s)$.

3. If each of two statements is equivalent to the same statement, then the two statements are equivalent to each other. If $s \longleftrightarrow t$ and $t \longleftrightarrow v$, then $s \longleftrightarrow v$.

4. If we substitute one of two equivalent statements for the other in any third statement, we obtain an equivalent statement.

Example 1.   Show that $(x > 6) \longleftrightarrow (2x + 1 > 13)$ when $x \in A$ and $A = \{1, 2, 3, 4, 5, 6, 7, 8, 9, 10\}$.

Solution. $\{x \mid x > 6; \; x \in A\} = \{7, 8, 9, 10\}$. $\{x \mid 2x + 1 > 13; \; x \in A\} = \{7, 8, 9, 10\}$. Since $x > 6$ and $2x + 1 > 13$ have the same truth set, $(x > 6) \longleftrightarrow (2x + 1 > 13)$.

Example 2.   Show that $(\mid x \mid = 5, \; x \in R) \longleftrightarrow (x^2 = 25, \; x \in R)$.

Solution. $\{x \mid \mid x \mid = 5, \; x \in R\} = \{-5, 5\}$.
$\{x \mid x^2 = 25, \; x \in R\} = \{-5, 5\}$.
Since $(\mid x \mid = 5, \; x \in R)$ and $(x^2 = 25, \; x \in R)$ have the same truth set, $(\mid x \mid = 5, \; x \in R) \longleftrightarrow (x^2 = 25; \; x \in R)$.

Note that the two equations $\mid x \mid = 5$ and $x^2 = 25$ would still have been equivalent had the domain of x been the set of counting numbers. Why?

Ⓐ EXERCISES

1. The statement $2 + 3 = 5$ is true. The statement $3 - 1 = 2$ is true. Is it true that $2 + 3 = 5 \longleftrightarrow 3 - 1 = 2$?

2. The statement $4 \times 8 = 12$ is false. The statement $8^2 = 16$ is false. Is it true that $4 \times 8 = 12 \longleftrightarrow 8^2 = 16$?

3. The statement $2 + 1 = 3$ is true and the statement $4 \times 5 = 9$ is false. Is it true that $2 + 1 = 3 \longleftrightarrow 4 \times 5 = 9$?

4. The statement $4 \times 3 = 12$ is true and the statement "St. Louis is in Missouri" is true. Is it true that $4 \times 3 = 12 \longleftrightarrow$ St. Louis is in Missouri?

5. The statement $5^2 = 25$ is true. If statement s is equivalent to the statement $5^2 = 25$, is statement s true?

6. The statement $3 \times 1 = 1$ is false. If statement t is equivalent to $3 \times 1 = 1$, is statement t true or false?

7. We know that statement s_x is equivalent to statement t_x and we know that statement s_a is true. Is statement t_a true or false?

8. The open statement "$x + 2 = 8$; $x \in C$" has the solution set $\{6\}$. The statement "$2x = 12$; $x \in C$" has the solution set $\{6\}$. Is it true that $(x + 2)$; $x \in C = 8 \longleftrightarrow (2x = 12$; $x \in C)$?

9. The open statement "$x > 3$; $x \in \{1, 2, 3, 4, 5\}$" has the solution set $\{4, 5\}$. The open statement "$(x - 4)(x - 5) = 0$; $x \in \{1, 2, 3, 4, 5\}$" has the solution set $\{4, 5\}$. Is it true that $[x > 3$; $x \in \{1, 2, 3, 4, 5\}] \longleftrightarrow [(x - 4)(x - 5) = 0$; $x \in \{1, 2, 3, 4, 5\}]$?

10. The open statement "$|x| = 3$; $x \in I$" has the solution set $\{-3, 3\}$. The open statement "$(x + 3)(x - 3) = 0$; $x \in I$" has the solution set $\{-3, 3\}$. Is it true that $[|x| = 3$; $x \in I] \longleftrightarrow [(x + 3)(x - 3) = 0$; $x \in I]$?

11. Which of the following statements are true and which are false?

a. $-5 + 2 = 7 \longleftrightarrow \sqrt{4} = 2$

b. $\frac{99}{3} + 11 = 44 \longleftrightarrow -4 \cdot 11 = 44$

c. $\dfrac{18 + 5}{2} + \dfrac{3}{2} = \dfrac{13}{2} \longleftrightarrow 4 > 1$

d. $5 < 2 \times 3 \longleftrightarrow \frac{12}{4} + 1 = 5$

e. $1 + 1 = 3 \longleftrightarrow 3 + 3 = 9$

12. Which of the following statements are true and which are false?

a. $\frac{1}{2}x = 12$; $x \in C \longleftrightarrow x + 5 = 29$; $x \in C$

b. $x = 4$; $x \in C \longleftrightarrow (x - 4)(x + 4) = 0$; $x \in C$

c. $\dfrac{1}{x} = \dfrac{1}{10}$; $x \in C \longleftrightarrow x > 9$; $x \in C$

d. $x^2 = 36$; $x \in R \longleftrightarrow x^2 - 12x + 36 = 0$; $x \in R$

Conjunction

Compound sentences with the connective *and* are called *conjunctive sentences*. We define conjunction as follows: If $a, b, c, \cdots$ are simple statements, the sentence "*a and b and c and* $\cdots$" is the *conjunction* of $a, b, c, \cdots$. The simple statements $a, b, c, \cdots$ are called the *clauses* of the conjunctive sentence.

The truth table at the right is the truth table for the conjunction of two simple statements a and b. As shown by the table, a conjunctive sentence having two clauses is true if both of its clauses are true; otherwise, it is false. In general, a conjunctive sentence is true if all of its clauses are true; otherwise, it is false. Since

a	b	a and b
T	T	T
T	F	F
F	T	F
F	F	F

this ruling makes a conjunctive sentence either true or false in all cases, we can say that a conjunctive sentence is a statement.

Conjunctive statements are often somewhat disguised. For example, the statement "Today is Friday the 29th of February" has the equivalent conjunctive form "Today is Friday and today is the 29th of February." This statement is true only on those rare occasions when both of its clauses are true. The statement "Harry, Tom, and Jim are juniors" is equivalent to the conjunctive statement "Harry is a junior, and Tom is a junior, and Jim is a junior." When is this statement true?

In this text we are primarily concerned with conjunctive statements whose clauses are open algebraic statements. Such conjunctive statements are called *open conjunctive algebraic statements*, or when no confusion can result, *open conjunctive statements*.

Let us consider the truth set of the open conjunctive statement $x < 6$ *and* $x > 3$ when $x \in C$. We have said that an open conjunctive statement is true if and only if both of its clauses are true. Accordingly, when $x \in C$, the conjunctive statement $x < 6$ *and* $x > 3$ is true if and only if both the clause $x < 6$ is true and the clause $x > 3$ is true. The clause $x < 6$ has the truth set $\{1, 2, 3, 4, 5\}$ and the clause $x > 3$ has the truth set $\{4, 5, 6, \cdots\}$. Since each clause is true for those values of x and only those values which are members of its own truth set, the conjunctive statement is true for those values of x and only those values common to the truth sets of both of its clauses, namely 4 and 5. As you already learned, the set of elements common to two sets is the intersection of the two sets. Thus, the truth set of the statement $x < 6$ *and* $x > 3$ when $x \in C$ is $\{4, 5\}$, the intersection of the truth sets of its clauses. Similar reasoning applies in the case of an open conjunctive statement having three or more clauses. In general we say: The *truth set of an open conjunctive statement* is the intersection of the truth sets of its clauses.

We express this definition about an open conjunctive statement having two clauses in one variable as follows:

$$\{x \mid s_x \wedge t_x\} = \{x \mid s_x\} \cap \{x \mid t_x\}$$

Notice that in this sentence we used the symbol $\wedge$ for the word *and*. This is a common practice. Notice, too, that we did not state the domain of the variable x. This does not mean that we are not considering the domain; it merely means that we are assuming that the domain is known and can be omitted to simplify the statement. We also assume that the variable in both clauses has the same domain. For an open conjunctive statement with three clauses we have the true statement

$$\{x \mid s_x \wedge t_x \wedge w_x\} = \{x \mid s_x\} \cap \{x \mid t_x\} \cap \{x \mid w_x\}.$$

If you study the truth table below, you will see that the columns with the statements $(a \land b) \land d$, $a \land (b \land d)$, and $a \land b \land d$ as headings have the same entries; in other words, when one of these statements is true, the others are true, and when one is false the others are false. This tells us that if a, b, and c are statements, $(a \land b \land d) \longleftrightarrow (a \land b) \land d \longleftrightarrow a \land (b \land d)$. Do you agree that we can describe equivalent statements as statements having the same truth table?

a	b	d	$a \land b$	$(a \land b) \land d$	$b \land d$	$a \land (b \land d)$	$a \land b \land d$
T	T	T	T	T	T	T	T
T	T	F	T	F	F	F	F
T	F	T	F	F	F	F	F
F	T	T	F	F	T	F	F
F	F	T	F	F	F	F	F
F	T	F	F	F	F	F	F
T	F	F	F	F	F	F	F
F	F	F	F	F	F	F	F

Let A represent the truth set of statement a, let B represent the truth set of statement b, and let D represent the truth set of statement d. By definition (see page 11) $A \cap B \cap D = (A \cap B) \cap D$. By the associative property of the intersection of sets, $(A \cap B) \cap D = A \cap (B \cap D)$. It follows, as you have already discovered, that

$$A \cap B \cap D = (A \cap B) \cap D = A \cap (B \cap D).$$

Note the similarity between this statement and the statement proved by the truth table above, namely: If a, b, and d are three statements, then

$$a \land b \land d \longleftrightarrow (a \land b) \land d \longleftrightarrow a \land (b \land d).$$

Example 1.   Show that $\{x \mid (x > -3 \land x < -5); \ x \in R\} = \emptyset$.

Solution.   It is obvious that no real number can be simultaneously less than -5 and greater than -3. Nevertheless, a graph helps us to interpret the solution. The graph of $\{x \mid x > -3; \ x \in R\}$ is shown in the number line below as the black segment extending to the right from the graph of -3. The graph of $\{x \mid x < -5; \ x \in R\}$ is shown

in the same number line as the black segment extending to the left from the graph of -5. Since the two segments have no points in common, we know that the two truth sets have no elements in common; in other words, the intersection of the two sets is $\emptyset$.

Example 2.   Construct the graph of $\{x \mid (x > -3 \wedge x < 4); \; x \in R\}$.

Solution.   The graph of the solution set for $x > -3$ is shown as the black segment extending to the right from the graph of -3 in the line below.

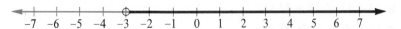

The graph of the solution set for $x < 4$ is shown as the black segment extending to the left from the graph of 4 in the number line below.

The graph of $\{x \mid x > -3 \wedge x < 4); \; x \in R\}$ is the intersection of the sets of points in these two graphs; in other words, it consists of the set of points common to the two graphs. This set of points is shown as the black segment extending from the graph of -3 to the graph of 4 in the number line below.

(A)   **EXERCISES**

1. The statement $4 + 1 = 5$ is true. The statement $4^2 = 16$ is true. Is the conjunctive statement $4 + 1 = 5$ *and* $4^2 = 16$ true or false?

2. The statement $-5 - 3 = 8$ is false. The statement $(-3)(-2) = 6$ is true. Is the conjunctive statement $-5 - 3 = 8$ *and* $(-3)(-2) = 6$ true or false?

3. The statement $-5 - 3 = 8$ is false. The statement $-2(3 + 2) = 10$ is false. Is the conjunctive statement $-5 - 3 = 8$ *and* $-2(3 + 2) = 10$ true or false?

4. The statement $6 + (-2) = 4$ is true. Let s be a statement. If the conjunctive statement "$6 + (-2) = 4$ *and* s" is true, is the statement s true or false?

5. The statement $6 + (-2) = 4$ is true. Let t be a statement. If the conjunctive statement "$6 + (-2) = 4$ *and* t" is false, is statement t true or false?

6. The statement $-3 + 9 = -12$ is false. Let a be a statement. If the statement "$-3 + 9 = -12$ *and* a" is false, can statement a be identified as true or false? Explain.

7. For each of the following pairs of statements, write a conjunctive statement having the two statements as its clauses.

a. $3 + 1 = 4$ **b.** $5 + (-8) = 13$ **c.** $-4 - 3 = 7$ **d.** $2 < 7$
   $9 \times 4 = 36$ $9 + 1 = 10$ $-5 - 8 = 13$ $3 > 9$

8. Indicate which of the conjunctive statements you wrote in Ex. 7 are true and which are false.

9. Which of the following statements are true and which are false?

   a. $3^2 = 9$ *and* $14 > 12$ *and* $9 < 12$

   b. $18 + 11 < 18 + 12$ *and* $- 3 > 3$ *and* $4^2 = 16$

   c. $(2 \neq 2) \wedge (4 \not> 1) \wedge (2 < 0) \wedge (1^2 = 2)$

10. Find the solution set for each of the following open conjunctive statements.

    a. $(x > 1$ *and* $x < 5)$; $x \in \{1, 2, 3, 4, 5\}$ **d.** $(x < 9 \wedge x > - 2)$; $x \in C$

    b. $(2x = 16$ *and* $x + 4 = 18)$; $x \in R$ **e.** $(x > 8 \wedge x < 4)$; $x \in R$

    c. $(2x = 16 \wedge x + 4 = 18)$; $x \in R$ **f.** $(x > 2$ *and* $x > 7)$; $x \in R$

11. Make a graph to indicate the truth set of each of the following open conjunctive statements. In each case $x \in R$.

    a. $x < 7$ *and* $x > 2$ **d.** $x < 8$ *and* $x < 4$ *and* $x = 2$

    b. $x > 5$ *and* $x > 3$ **e.** $x + 9 \neq 15 \wedge x > 1$

    c. $x < 12$ *and* $x = 10$ **f.** $x + 3 = - 2 \wedge 2x < 6$

12. Which of the following statements are true and which are false?

    a. $\{x \mid (x = 4$ *and* $x + 6 = 10)$; $x \in R\} = \{4\}$

    b. $\{x \mid (x > 2$ *and* $x < 5)$; $x \in R\} = \{x \mid 2 < x < 5$; $x \in R\}$

    c. $\{x \mid (x < 8 \wedge x < 5 \wedge x < 2)$; $x \in R\} = \{x \mid x < 5$; $x \in R\}$

    d. $\{x \mid (x < 0 \wedge x > 5 \wedge x > 1)$; $x \in R\} = \emptyset$

Disjunction

Compound sentences with the connective *or* are called *disjunctive sentences*. We define disjunction as follows: If $a, b, c, \cdots$ are simple statements, the sentence "*a or b or c or* $\cdots$" is the *disjunction* of $a, b, c, \cdots$.

The truth table at the right is the truth table for the disjunction of two simple statements a and b. As shown by the table, a disjunctive sentence having two clauses is false if both of its clauses are false; otherwise it is true. In general, a disjunctive sentence is false if all of its clauses are false; otherwise, it is true. Since this ruling makes a disjunctive sentence either true or false

a	b	$a\ or\ b$
T	T	T
T	F	T
F	T	T
F	F	F

in all possible cases, we can say that a disjunctive sentence is a statement.

In this text we are primarily concerned with disjunctive statements whose clauses are open algebraic statements. Such disjunctive statements are called *open disjunctive algebraic statements,* or when no confusion can result, simply *open disjunctive statements.*

Let us consider the truth set of the open disjunctive statement $x < 3$ *or* $x > 7$ when $x \in C$. We have said that an open disjunctive statement is true if and only if one or both of its clauses are true. Accordingly, when $x \in C$, the open disjunctive statement $x < 3$ *or* $x > 7$ is true if and only if $x < 3$ is true, or $x > 7$ is true, or both of these statements are true. The statement $x < 3$ has the truth set $\{1, 2\}$. The statement $x > 7$ has the truth set $\{8, 9, 10, \cdots\}$. Since each clause is true for those values of x and only those values which are elements of its own truth set, the disjunctive sentence is true for those values of x and only those values in the truth sets of either or both of its clauses, namely, the elements 1, 2, 8, 9, 10 and the counting numbers greater than 10. By definition, the set of elements that belong to either or both of two sets is the union of the sets. Thus the truth set of $x < 3$ *or* $x > 7$ when $x \in C$ is $\{1, 2\} \cup \{8, 9, 10, \cdots\}$. Similar reasoning can be used in the cases of a disjunctive statement having more than two clauses. In general we say: The *truth set of an open disjunctive statement* is the union of the truth sets of its clauses.

We express this idea in set-language form for an open disjunctive statement having two clauses in one variable as follows:

$$\{x \mid s_x \vee t_x\} = \{x \mid s_x\} \cup \{x \mid t_x\}.$$

Notice that in this sentence we used the symbol $\vee$ for the word *or*. This is a common practice. Notice, too, that we did not state the domain of x. This does not mean that the domain is unimportant; it merely means that we are assuming that the domain is known and can be omitted to simplify the statement. Also, we assume that the variable in both clauses has the same domain. For an open disjunctive statement with three clauses we have the true statement

$$\{x \mid s_x \vee t_x \vee w_x\} = \{x \mid s_x\} \cup \{x \mid t_x\} \cup \{x \mid w_x\}.$$

By means of a truth table for disjunction, similar to that for conjunction on page 61, we can show that if a, b, and d are statements,

$$a \vee b \vee d \longleftrightarrow (a \vee b) \vee d \longleftrightarrow a \vee (b \vee d).$$

If we let A represent the truth set of statement a, B the truth set of statement b, and D the truth set of statement d, we have by the definition of the union of sets: $A \cup B \cup D = (A \cup B) \cup D$. By the associative property of the union of sets we have $(A \cup B) \cup D = A \cup (B \cup D)$. It follows that

$$A \cup B \cup D = (A \cup B) \cup D = A \cup (B \cup D).$$

Notice the similarity between this statement and the statement for clauses a, b, and d earlier in this paragraph.

Example. Draw a graph of the open statement $x \not< 4$ when $x \in R$.

Solution. By the comparison property, one and only one of the statements $x < 4$, $x = 4$, or $x > 4$ can be true. Since it is given that $x \not< 4$, it must be true that $x = 4$ or that $x > 4$. We write this as the disjunctive statement $x \geq 4$. In the number line below, the graph of the truth set of $x = 4$ when $x \in R$ is shown by the single dot labeled 4, and the graph of $x > 4$ when $x \in R$ is shown as the black segment extending to the right from the graph of 4 but not including it. Since the truth set of a disjunctive statement is the union of the truth sets of its clauses, when $x \in R$ the graph of the truth set of $x \geq 4$, and consequently of $x \not< 4$, consists of the graph of 4 and all points to the right of 4 in the number line.

Since the comparison property states that one and only one of the three statements $x < 4$, $x = 4$, or $x > 4$ is true, it is obvious that $x = 4$ and $x > 4$ cannot both be true. This, however, does not mean that the statement $x \geq 4$ cannot be used. Since it is not possible for both clauses of the disjunctive statement $x > 4$ *or* $x = 4$ to be true at the same time, we interpret $x \geq 4$ to be true when either $x > 4$ is true and $x = 4$ is false, or $x > 4$ is false and $x = 4$ is true, and to be false when $x > 4$ is false and $x = 4$ is false.

 EXERCISES

1. Form a disjunction of the statements in each of the following sets of statements.

a. $-2 - 3 = -5$
$-3 + 1 = -2$

b. $4^2 = 8$
$5 < 7$

c. $3 < 9$
$4 > 5$

d. $|-2| + |5| = 7$
$|-3| - |6| = -9$

e. $2(6 + 5) = 2(6) + 2(5)$
$4(3) + 4(-7) = 4(3 + 7)$
$5 - 3 + 6 = 8$

2. Indicate which of the disjunctive statements you wrote in Ex. 1 are true and which are false.

3. Let s and t be two simple statements.

a. If the statement $s \lor t$ is false and the statement s is false, does it follow that t is false?

b. If $s \lor t$ is true and s is true, does it follow that t is true?

4. Replace the question mark below with either $=$ or $\neq$ to make the following a false disjunctive statement: $2(3) \neq 6$ *or* $5 + 1 \neq 6$ *or* $5 \_?\_ 6$.

5. Find the truth set for each of the following open statements.

a. $(x > 2$ *or* $x < 5)$; $x \in C$

b. $(x < 3 \lor x = 4)$; $x \in R$

c. $(x < 4 \lor x > 5)$; $x \in \{1, 2, 3, 4, 5, 6\}$

d. $x \not> -5$; $x \in I$

e. $(x < 4$ *or* $x > 4)$; $x \in I$

f. $(x = 0 \lor x < -2)$; $x \in I$

6. Draw the graph of the truth set for each of the following open statements. Unless otherwise specified, $x \in R$.

a. $x > 3$ *or* $x < -3$

b. $x < 7$ *or* $x < 2$

c. $x = 2$ *or* $x > 2$

d. $x \leq 4$

e. $x \not\leq -5$

f. $x > -3 \lor x < 5$

g. $(x < 2 \lor x < 7)$; $x \in C$

h. $(x < 5 \lor x < 2)$; $x \in I$

i. $x < 2 \lor x = 4$

j. $x \not< 3$

7. a. Copy and complete the following truth table.

b. What do you find true of the entries for the columns headed $(a \lor b) \lor d$, $a \lor (b \lor d)$, and $a \lor b \lor d$?

a	b	d	$a \lor b$	$(a \lor b) \lor d$	$b \lor d$	$a \lor (b \lor d)$	$a \lor b \lor d$
T	T	T					
T	T	F					
T	F	T					
T	F	F					
F	T	T					
F	T	F					
F	F	T					
F	F	F					

Conditional Sentences—Implications

We have considered sentences formed by joining statements with the connective *and* and sentences formed by joining statements with the connective *or*. Now we consider sentences formed by joining two statements with the words *if-then*. For example, given the two statements

$$p: \text{ I am a homeowner}$$
$$q: \text{ I am a taxpayer}$$

we can form the complex sentence: "*If* I am a homeowner, *then* I am a taxpayer." Notice that this statement has the form: If p, *then* q. To write "*If* p, *then* q" we often write $p \longrightarrow q$.

When p and q are statements, a sentence of the form "If p, then q" is called a *conditional sentence* or a *conditional*. The statements p and q are the *terms* of the conditional. The statement p is called the *hypothesis* of the conditional and the statement q is called the *conclusion* of the conditional. Observe that the word *if* is not part of the hypothesis and that the word *then* is not part of the conclusion. "If" and "then" are merely connectives that join the hypothesis and conclusion. In the conditional "If I am a homeowner, then I am a taxpayer" the hypothesis is "I am a homeowner" and the conclusion is "I am a taxpayer."

The conditional sentence *if p, then q* is a statement if we can find a rule by which we can always determine whether the sentence is true or false. Since we want our rule to be as consistent as possible with common usage, let us consider the sentence "If I am a homeowner, then I am a taxpayer." This sentence asserts that I cannot be a homeowner without being a taxpayer. We see that

1. If I am a homeowner and also a taxpayer, this conditional should be labeled *true*.
2. If I am a homeowner and I am not a taxpayer, then the conditional should be labeled *false*.

One might argue that if I am not a homeowner, then the conditional sentence does not apply in my case. However, in order for a conditional sentence to be a statement, we must be able to assign it a truth value for even the cases when the hypothesis is false. Since we cannot rely entirely upon plausible arguments, we shall adopt the following definition: The sentence *If p, then q* is false when p is true and q is false; otherwise, it is true.

By using this definition we can always determine that a given conditional is either true or false. Thus we can say that a conditional sentence is a statement. The truth table at the right is a truth table for a conditional statement.

a	b	$a \longrightarrow b$
T	T	T
T	F	F
F	T	T
F	F	T

In mathematics the conditional statement *If p, then q* is often replaced by *p implies q*. For this reason a conditional statement is also called an *implication*. Thus each of the statements *If p, then q* and $p \longrightarrow q$ is equivalent to the implication *p implies q* whose hypothesis is p and whose conclusion is q. We may write

$$\text{If } x > 3, \text{ then } x^2 > 9$$
$$x > 3 \longrightarrow x^2 > 9$$
$$x > 3 \text{ implies } x^2 > 9$$

with the assurance that the three statements all have the same meaning. In our study of if-then statements we shall usually use the word *implication* instead of the word *conditional*.

The implication "If I am a homeowner, then I am a taxpayer" is a special case of the more general implication "If x is a homeowner, then x is a taxpayer." In the latter case, the replacement set for x could be the universal set of all people. The statement now has the form: $p_x \longrightarrow q_x$. When we say "$p_x \longrightarrow q_x$ *is true*," we mean that $p_x \longrightarrow q_x$ *is a true implication for all values in the replacement set of* x. The statement $p_x \longrightarrow q_x$ is true if and only if $\{x \mid p_x;\ x \in U\} \subseteq \{x \mid q_x;\ x \in U\}$. This is shown in the Venn diagram at the right. In the diagram $P = \{x \mid p_x;\ x \in U\}$ and $Q = \{x \mid q_x;\ x \in U\}$. We can state this result more generally by saying: If P is the truth set for the open statement p, and Q is the truth set for the open statement q, then $(p \longrightarrow q) \longleftrightarrow (P \subseteq Q)$.

Variation in Stating an Implication

In making an if-then statement we frequently omit the word *then*. For example, to say, "If I live in Euphoria, then I live in Luxuria," we may say, "If I live in Euphoria, I live in Luxuria."

The if-clause of an implication need not be the first clause. For example, instead of saying, "If $x > 2$, then $x^2 > 4$," we may say, "$x^2 > 4$ if $x > 2$." We may also say, "$x^2 > 4$ provided $x > 2$."

The following are several verbal statements which can be regarded as meaning *If p, then q*.

p implies q	p only if q
q if p	p is a sufficient condition for q
q provided p	q is a necessary condition for p

We may state an implication without using either or both of the words *if* and *then*. Sometimes such implications are so disguised that it is difficult to recognize them as implications. In the column at the left below are examples of implications that are somewhat disguised. In the column at the right, each implication is expressed in an equivalent if-then form.

All clams are mollusks.	If x is a clam, then x is a mollusk.
Only logicians are mathematicians.	If x is a mathematician, then x is a logician.
I shall break par only if I score 3 or less on the last hole.	If I break par, then I shall have scored 3 or less on the last hole.
When I lose sleep, I get tired.	If I lose sleep, then I get tired.
No fish is a fowl.	If x is a fish, then x is not a fowl.
I shall get a letter in football provided I stay eligible.	If I stay eligible, then I shall get a letter in football.

Ⓐ **EXERCISES**

1. State the hypothesis of each of the following conditional statements. State the conclusion of each.

   a. If our team wins tomorrow, then it will receive the regional trophy.

   b. Fred will furnish the wieners if we have the cook-out.

   c. If both members of the equation $2x = 16$ are divided by 2, the resulting equation is $x = 8$.

   d. If a, b, and c represent real numbers and $a > b$, then $a + c > b + c$.

2. Write each of the following statements in if-then form.

   a. No freshmen are invited.

   b. All sentences that are equations contain an equal sign.

   c. Any rational number can be written in the form $\frac{a}{b}$ where a and b are integers and $b \neq 0$.

   d. When a fraction has its denominator greater than its numerator, it is called a proper fraction.

3. Write $s \longrightarrow t$ in two other ways.

4. If s and t are two statements, in which of the following will $s \longrightarrow t$ be true?

   a. s is true and t is true.   **c.** s is true and t is false.

   b. s is false and t is true.   **d.** s is false and t is false.

5. Which of the following implications should be labeled "true" and which "false"?

   a. If $2 \times 2 = 4$, then apples grow on apple trees.

   b. $4 + 1 = 5 \longrightarrow$ New York is on the Pacific coast.

   c. If $4 < 9$, then $9 > 4$.   **f.** If $3 + 2 = 6$, then $4 > 7$.

   d. $\frac{20}{5} = 4 \longrightarrow 20 = 4 \times 5$.   **g.** If $3^2 = 6$, then $2 + 3 = 5$.

   e. If $9 - 4 = 5$, then $9 = 5 + 4$.   **h.** If $2 + 3 = 5$, then $3^2 = 6$.

6. When x represents a counting number, the implication "$(x - 2)(x - 3) = 0 \longrightarrow 2x < 20$" is true.

   a. $\{x \mid (x - 2)(x - 3) = 0\} = \_?\_$. (Indicate the set.)

   b. $\{x \mid 2x < 20\} = \_?\_$ (Indicate the set.)

   c. Is it true or false that $\{x \mid (x - 2)(x - 3) = 0\} \subseteq \{x \mid 2x < 20\}$?

7. When x represents a counting number, the implication "$x + 4 = 9 \longrightarrow x < 7$" is a true statement.

   a. $\{x \mid x + 4 = 9\} = \_?\_$.   **b.** $\{x \mid x < 7\} = \_?\_$.

   c. Is it true or false that $\{x \mid x + 4 = 9\} \subseteq \{x \mid x < 7\}$?

8. When x represents a counting number, the implication "$x + 4 = 11 \longrightarrow x = 7$" is true.

   a. What is the truth set of $x + 4 = 11$?

   b. What is the truth set of $x = 7$?

   c. Is it true or false that the truth set of $x + 4 = 11$ is a subset of the truth set of $x = 7$?

9. When x represents a real number, the sentence "$|x| = 3 \longrightarrow x > 4$" is false.

   a. The truth set of $|x| = 3 =$ _?_.

   b. The truth set of $x > 4 =$ _?_.

   c. Is it true or false that the truth set of $|x| = 3$ is a subset of the truth set of $x > 4$?

10. Consider the implication: $|x| = 4 \longrightarrow x < 10$. $x \epsilon I$.

   a. $\{x \,|\, |x| = 4\} =$ _?_.

   b. $\{x \,|\, x < 10\} =$ _?_.

   c. Replace the question mark with the proper symbol $\subseteq$ or $\nsubseteq$.

$$\{x \,|\, |x| = 4\} \ \_?\_ \ \{x \,|\, x < 10\}.$$

   d. Is the implication "$|x| = 4 \longrightarrow x < 10$" true or false?

11. Consider the conditional statement $x < 7 \longrightarrow 4 + x = 13$. $x \epsilon I$.

   a. $\{x \,|\, x < 7\} =$ _?_.

   b. $\{x \,|\, 4 + x = 13\} =$ _?_.

   c. Replace the question mark with the proper symbol $\subseteq$ or $\nsubseteq$.

$$\{x \,|\, x < 7\} \ \_?\_ \ \{x \,|\, 4 + x = 13\}.$$

   d. Is the original implication true or false?

12. Determine which of the following implications are true and which are false when x represents a real number.

   a. If $x + 3 = 8$, then $x < 4$.   **c.** $7 - x = 12 \longrightarrow x = 5$.

   b. If $2x = 16$, then $3x = 25$.   **d.** $9x = 36 \longrightarrow x < 5$.

Contradictions

   We have frequently used symbols which convey the idea of contradiction. For example, we have used $\neq$ for *is not equal to*, $\not>$ for *is not greater than*, and $\nsubseteq$ for *is not a subset of*. Consider the relationships between the two statements in each of the following pairs.

$$\begin{array}{cc} a = b & a \neq b \\ a > b & a \not> b \\ A \subseteq B & A \nsubseteq B \end{array}$$

Each of these pairs is a pair of contradictory statements. Two statements are *contradictory* if they have "opposite" truth values;   that is, they are contradictory if when either is true the other is false;   otherwise they are not contradictory. Two open algebraic statements having the same replacement set are said to be contradictory if their truth sets are complements of each other with respect to that set.

Example 1.   In the column of statements at the right, statement (3) is a contradiction of statement (a) because if (a) is true, then (3) is false, and if (a) is false, then (3) is true.

    (a) Harry is a junior.
    (1) Harry is a senior.
    (2) Harry is a freshman.
    (3) Harry is not a junior.
    (4) "Harry is a junior" is false.

Similarly, statements (4) and (a) are contradictory.

It would be a mistake to say that (a) and (1) are contradictory statements because it is possible for both to be false at the same time. For example, if Harry is really a sophomore, both (a) and (1) are false. Thus, even though (a) and (1) cannot both be true, they can both be false. We say that such statements are *contrary* rather than contradictory. Statements (a) and (2) are also contrary.

Example 2.   Let us compare the truth sets of the open statements
"$|x| < 3$; $x \epsilon R$" and "$|x| \nless 3$; $x \epsilon R$" by means of a graph.

Solution.   The graph of the truth set of $|x| < 3$ consists of all points in the number line which are between the graphs of -3 and 3 as shown.

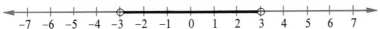

Since $|x| \nless 3$ is equivalent to $|x| \geq 3$, the graph of the truth set of $|x| \geq 3$ (and the graph of the truth set of $|x| \nless 3$) consists of the graph of 3, all points in the number line to the right of the graph of 3, the graph of -3, and all points to the left of -3 as shown below.

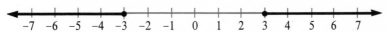

Now we see that the graph of the truth set of $|x| < 3$ is the complement of the graph of the truth set of $|x| \nless 3$ with respect to R. Since the graphs of the two sentences have no point in common, there is no value of x for which both statements are true. Since the two graphs combine to fill the line completely, there is no value of x for which both statements are false. Consequently, we know that $|x| < 3$ and $|x| \nless 3$ are contradictory.

Two statements which are contradictions of the same statement are equivalent as shown by the table at the right. This table shows that each of the statements b and c is a contradiction of statement a. Since statements b and c have the same truth values, they are equivalent—each is true when and only when the other is true and is false when and only when the other is false.

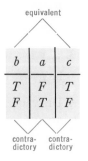

We designate a contradiction of statement a by $\sim a$, a contradiction of b by $\sim b$, and so on. We read $\sim a$ as "a contradiction of a" or as "not a." A study of the table at the right reveals that a contradiction of a contradiction of a statement is equivalent to the statement itself. Thus, $\sim(\sim a) \longleftrightarrow a$. What statement is equivalent to $\sim[\sim(\sim a)]$?

Example 3. Use a truth table to show that $(a \longleftrightarrow b) \longleftrightarrow (\sim a \longleftrightarrow \sim b)$.

Solution. In the truth table at the right, the column headed $a \longleftrightarrow b$ is the same as the column headed $\sim a \longleftrightarrow \sim b$. Therefore, the two statements are equivalent.

$\sim a$	a	b	$\sim b$	$a \longleftrightarrow b$	$\sim a \longleftrightarrow \sim b$
F	T	T	F	T	T
F	T	F	T	F	F
T	F	T	F	F	F
T	F	F	T	T	T

same truth table

When two statements have like columns in a truth table which displays all possible combinations of truth values for the component statements involved, we say that the two statements "have the same truth table" and are, therefore, equivalent.

Among the contradictions of statement a there is one that has a special form and name. This contradiction is called the *negation* of a. It is written in one and only one way, namely, *a is false*. Thus, while the statement $x < 3$ has many contradictions, for example, $3x \not< 9$, $x + 1 \not< 4$, $x \geq 3$, $x \not< 3$, $x < 3$ is false, only the last of these ($x < 3$ is false) is the negation of $x < 3$.

Ⓐ EXERCISES

1. In which of the following pairs are the two statements contradictory?

a. $3 \times 4 = 12$
$2(-8) = -16$

b. $4 + 1 = 5$
$4 + 1 = 7$

c. $8(2) + 3 = 19$
$4 + 5 = 9$

d. $|-3| + 3 = 6$
$2 \cdot |-3| + 2(3) = 12$

2. a. Write the simplest statement that expresses the same thought as
$$\sim (x+1=3).$$

b. Write the simplest statement that expresses the same thought as
$$\sim [\sim (x+3=3)].$$

3. a. Write the negation of $x-5=2$.

b. Write the negation of $\sim (x-5=2)$.

4. Draw a graph to show that the two statements in each of the following pairs are (or are not) contradictory. State your conclusion and give a reason for it.

a. $x>3$	d. $\mid x\mid=5$	g. $x\geq 2$
$x<3$	$x\neq 5$	$x<2$
b. $x+1=7$	e. $x\not> 1$	h. $\mid x\mid=3$
$x\neq 6$	$x\leq 1$	$x\not\leqslant 3$
c. $x>6$	f. $2x=8$	i. $x\leq 4$
$x<4$	$x\not\leqslant 4$	$x>4$

5. If the statement s_x has the truth set $\{1, 2, 3\}$, what is the truth set of any contradiction of s_x when $x\,\epsilon\,\{-3,-2,-1,0,1,2,3\}$?

6. If $\{x\mid x>4;\ x\,\epsilon\,R\}$ is the truth set of statement s_x, what is the truth set of the negation of s_x?

7. In which of the following cases is s_x a contradiction of t_x?

a. $\{x\mid s_x;\ x\,\epsilon\,C\}=\{5,6,7,\cdots\}$ **c.** $\{x\mid s_x;\ x\,\epsilon\,R\}=R\!\smile\!\{0\}$
$\{x\mid t_x;\ x\,\epsilon\,C\}=\{1,2,3,4\}$ $\{x\mid t_x;\ x\,\epsilon\,R\}=\{0\}$

b. $\{x\mid s_x;\ x\,\epsilon\,W\}=\{1,2,3,\cdots\}$ **d.** $\{x\mid s_x;\ x\,\epsilon\,R\}=R\!\smile\!\{1\}$
$\{x\mid t_x;\ x\,\epsilon\,W\}=\{0,1,2,3,\ldots\}$ $\{x\mid t_x;\ x\,\epsilon\,R\}=R$

8. In a Venn diagram illustrate S, the truth set of statement s_x, and T, the truth set of the negation of s_x when the universe is U and $S\subset U$.

9. Construct a truth table for: $s\wedge\sim s$.

10. Complete the following table to obtain the truth values of $(s\vee\sim t)\wedge r$.

s	t	r	$\sim t$	$s\vee\sim t$	$(s\vee\sim t)\wedge r$
T	T	T			
T	T	F			
T	F	T			
T	F	F			
F	T	T			
F	T	F			
F	F	T			
F	F	F			

Contradicting Conjunctions, Disjunctions, and Implications

The following truth table clearly indicates that

$$\sim (a \wedge b) \longleftrightarrow \sim a \vee \sim b \quad \text{(columns 6 and 7)}$$
$$\sim (a \vee b) \longleftrightarrow \sim a \wedge \sim b \quad \text{(columns 9 and 10)}$$

a	b	$\sim a$	$\sim b$	$a \wedge b$	$\sim (a \wedge b)$	$\sim a \vee \sim b$	$a \vee b$	$\sim (a \vee b)$	$\sim a \wedge \sim b$
T	T	F	F	T	F	F	T	F	F
T	F	F	T	F	T	T	T	F	F
F	T	T	F	F	T	T	T	F	F
F	F	T	T	F	T	T	F	T	T

same truth table   same truth table

Example 1. A contradiction of the conjunctive statement "Jim owns a car and Harry plays football" is "Jim does not own a car or Harry does not play football."

Example 2. A contradiction of the disjunctive statement "$x > 3$ *or* $x = 3$" is "$x \not> 3$ *and* $x \neq 3$."

A study of the following truth table reveals that

$$(p \longrightarrow q) \longleftrightarrow (\sim p \vee q). \quad \text{(Last two columns)}$$

p	q	$\sim p$	$p \longrightarrow q$	$\sim p \vee q$
T	T	F	T	T
T	F	F	F	F
F	T	T	T	T
F	F	T	T	T

same truth table

In this truth table, the fact that $p \longrightarrow q$ is false when p is true and q is false (line 2) suggests that $\sim (p \longrightarrow q) \longleftrightarrow p \wedge \sim q$. This equivalence can be easily verified by a truth table.

Example 3. Write a contradiction of the statement, "If Mr. Matley is a propertyowner, then he is a taxpayer."

Solution. Let p represent the hypothesis, "Mr. Matley is a propertyowner," and let q represent the conclusion, "he is a taxpayer." Since a contradiction of *If p, then q* is $p \wedge \sim q$, the contradiction we are seeking is: Mr. Matley is a propertyowner and he is not a taxpayer.

1. Write a contradiction of each of the following statements.

  a. $x = 4$ *or* $x = 5$ **c.** $x > 5$ *and* $x = 5$ **e.** $x > 5$ *or* $x < 5$

  b. $x < 3 \lor x > 3$ **d.** $x \neq 6 \land x < 6$ **f.** $x \neq 2$ *and* $x \neq 4$

  g. I shall wear my raincoat or I shall take an umbrella.

2. Write a contradiction of each of the following implications.

  a. If $x + 4 = 5$, then $x = 1$.   **b.** $x^2 = 36 \longrightarrow x = 6$.

  c. If x is an even number, then x is divisible by 2.

  d. If John does not study, he will fail.

  e. x is a natural number implies that x is a real number.

  f. If $a > b$, then a is a positive number.

3. Make a truth table to show that $\sim (p \longrightarrow q) \longleftrightarrow (p \land \sim q)$.

More about Implication and Equivalence

In the examples we have considered thus far, the statements p and q in the implication *If p, then q* have been simple statements. We call such an implication a *simple implication*. By rearranging, contradicting, or rearranging and contradicting the hypothesis and conclusion of a given simple implication, we can obtain three other implications. These are shown below along with the name we give to each.

Given implication	*If p, then q*	$p \longrightarrow q$
Converse	*If q, then p*	$q \longrightarrow p$
Inverse	*If $\sim p$, then $\sim q$*	$\sim p \longrightarrow \sim q$
Contrapositive	*If $\sim q$, then $\sim p$*	$\sim q \longrightarrow \sim p$

The following truth table has a column devoted to each of these implications.

p	q	$p \longrightarrow q$	$q \longrightarrow p$	$\sim p$	$\sim q$	$\sim p \longrightarrow \sim q$	$\sim q \longrightarrow \sim p$
T	T	T	T	F	F	T	T
T	F	F	T	F	T	T	F
F	T	T	F	T	F	F	T
F	F	T	T	T	T	T	T

converse ⟷ inverse

given implication ⟷ contrapositive

From this table we see that the contrapositive of a simple implication is equivalent to the implication.

$$(p \longrightarrow q) \longleftrightarrow (\sim q \longrightarrow \sim p)$$

The table also shows that the inverse of a simple implication is equivalent to the converse of the implication.

It is important to note that a simple implication is not necessarily equivalent to its converse. For example, the implication $x > 5 \longrightarrow x^2 > 25$ is true for all real numbers x. However, its converse $x^2 > 25 \longrightarrow x > 5$ is false for some real numbers x. For example, it is false for $x = -7$ because for this value of x, the hypothesis $x^2 > 25$ is true and the conclusion $x > 5$ is false. We know that an implication with a true hypothesis and a false conclusion is a false implication. Since the truth sets for the statements $(x > 5 \longrightarrow x^2 > 25)$ and $(x^2 > 25 \longrightarrow x > 5)$ are not equal, we conclude that these statements are not equivalent.

The paragraph above shows that it is often easy to prove that a general statement is false. The statement $x^2 > 25 \longrightarrow x > 5$ is a general statement. It could be written: For all real numbers, $x^2 > 25 \longrightarrow x > 5$. We have found, however, that there is at least one value of x (that is, -7) for which the statement $x^2 > 25 \longrightarrow x > 5$ is false. Therefore, the assertion that the statement is true for all real numbers is false. This illustrates a very important fact:

Any exception will destroy the truth of a general statement.

Any such exception is called a *counterexample*. In the case just discussed -7 is a counterexample.

Having noted that an implication $p \longrightarrow q$ and its converse $q \longrightarrow p$ are not equivalent, let us investigate the relation that exists between two statements p and q for which both $p \longrightarrow q$ and $q \longrightarrow p$ are true. We recall that if P and Q are the truth sets for p_x and q_x respectively and $p_x \longrightarrow q_x$ is true for all values in the replacement set of x, then $(p_x \longrightarrow q_x) \longleftrightarrow (P \subseteq Q)$ [see diagram (a)] and if $q_x \longrightarrow p_x$ is true for all values in

(a)   **(b)**

the replacement set of x, then $(q_x \longrightarrow p_x) \longleftrightarrow (Q \subseteq P)$ [see diagram (b)]. $P \subseteq Q$ means that every member of P is a member of Q and $Q \subseteq P$ means that every member of Q is a member of P. If both of these statements are true, then every member of either set is a member of the other. Thus, P and Q have the same members and are equal. But if $P = Q$, then $p_x \longleftrightarrow q_x$ is true because statements with the same truth set are equivalent. This suggests that $p \longleftrightarrow q$ is true if and only if the conjunctive statement $(p \longrightarrow q)$ *and* $(q \longrightarrow p)$ is true. In other words, it suggests that two statements are equivalent if and only if it is true that each implies the other. The following truth table shows that $(p \longleftrightarrow q) \longleftrightarrow [(p \longrightarrow q) \wedge (q \longrightarrow p)]$ is true.

p	q	$p \longleftrightarrow q$	$p \longrightarrow q$	$q \longrightarrow p$	$[(p \longrightarrow q) \wedge (q \longrightarrow p)]$
T	T	T	T	T	T
T	F	F	F	T	F
F	T	F	T	F	F
F	F	T	T	T	T

same truth table

We may state $p \longrightarrow q$, $q \longrightarrow p$, and $p \longleftrightarrow q$ by using the words "if" and "only if," as shown by the chart below.

$p \longrightarrow q$	If p, then q $(q, \text{if } p)$ p only if q
$q \longrightarrow p$	If q, then p $(p, \text{if } q)$ q only if p
$p \longleftrightarrow q$	If p, then q *and* if q then p p if and only if q

Sometimes we use the symbol "iff" for the phrase "if and only if."

A **EXERCISES**

1. The statement p: "$2x < 8$; $x \in C$" has the truth set $P = \{1, 2, 3\}$. The statement q: "$3x < 12$; $x \in C$" has the truth set $Q = \{1, 2, 3\}$. Which of the following statements are true?

   a. $P \subseteq Q$ **b.** $Q \subseteq P$ **c.** $P = Q$ **d.** $p \longrightarrow q$ **e.** $q \longrightarrow p$ **f.** $p \longleftrightarrow q$

2. The statement p: "$(x - 2)(x - 3) = 0$; $x \in C$" has the truth set $P = \{2, 3\}$, and the statement q: "$x < 5$; $x \in C$" has the truth set $Q = \{1, 2, 3, 4\}$. Which of the following statements are true?

   a. $P \subseteq Q$ **b.** $Q \subseteq P$ **c.** $P = Q$ **d.** $p \longrightarrow q$ **e.** $q \longrightarrow p$ **f.** $p \longleftrightarrow q$

3. **a.** The implication shown on line 1 of the table below is true as shown by the relationship of the truth sets of its clauses. Complete the table by writing the converse, the inverse, and the contrapositive of the implication and indicating the relationship of the truth sets of the clauses of each statement.

Statement		Relationship of truth sets of its clauses
Given	$(3x > 15 \longrightarrow x > 1)$; $x \in C$	$\{6, 7, 8, \cdots\} \subseteq \{2, 3, 4, 5, 6, \cdots\}$
Converse	_ _?_ _	_ _?_ _
Inverse	_ _?_ _	_ _?_ _
Contrapositive	_ _?_ _	_ _?_ _

b. Which of the implications that you wrote in part **a** is true?

   c. What does the relationship of the truth sets of the clauses of the converse and of the inverse tell you about these statements?

   d. What does the relationship of the truth sets of the clauses of the given implication and of the clauses of the contrapositive tell you about these statements?

4. In which of the following situations can you say that the two implications are equivalent?

   a. $s \longrightarrow t$ and $t \longrightarrow s$ **d.** $s \longrightarrow t$ and $\sim t \longrightarrow \sim s$

   b. $s \longrightarrow \sim t$ and $\sim t \longrightarrow s$ **e.** $\sim s \longrightarrow \sim t$ and $\sim t \longrightarrow \sim s$

   c. $t \longrightarrow s$ and $\sim t \longrightarrow \sim s$ **f.** $\sim s \longrightarrow \sim t$ and $t \longrightarrow s$

5. Write each of the following in three other ways.

   a. s only if t **c.** m if n

   b. s iff t **d.** $m \longleftrightarrow n$

6. Write the contrapositive of each of the following statements.

   a. If x is an even number, then x is a multiple of 2.

   b. If $n > 0$, then n is a positive number.

   c. $(-2x > 6 \longrightarrow x < -3)$; $x \in R$

   d. $(x + 7 = 15$ only if $x < 9)$; $x \in C$

7. Write the converse of each of the statements of Ex. 6.

8. a. Which of the contrapositives that you wrote in Ex. 6 are true?

   b. Which of the converses that you wrote in Ex. 7 are true?

9. State each of the following using the words "if and only if" or, if you prefer, "iff."

   a. x is a positive number $\longleftrightarrow x > 0$.

   b. $(x + 3 = 5 \longleftrightarrow x = 2)$ when $x \in R$.

   c. The statement $3x = 18$ when $x \in R$ is equivalent to the statement $2x = 12$ when $x \in R$.

10. Which of the following can be written in the form $p \longrightarrow q$ and which in the form $p \longleftrightarrow q$?

   a. $x > 3$ only if $x > 0$.

   b. A triangle is a right triangle if and only if it contains a right angle.

   c. I can come if I can get the car.

   d. John gets good grades only if he attends school regularly.

   e. If it rains, the game will be postponed.

   f. If $a < 0$, then a is a negative number.

Implications with Conjunctive Hypotheses

Often the hypothesis of an implication is a conjunctive statement. For example, when we first considered equal sets we considered the statement: If $A \subseteq B$ and $B \subseteq A$, then $B = A$. Observe that in this case the hypothesis is the compound sentence, $A \subseteq B$ *and* $B \subseteq A$. The implication "If $A \subseteq B$ and $B \subseteq A$, then $A = B$," can be written in the following form:

$$\left. \begin{array}{c} A \subseteq B \\ B \subseteq A \end{array} \right\} \longrightarrow A = B$$

When we write an implication in this form, we shall mean $[(A \subseteq B)$ *and* $(B \subseteq A)] \longrightarrow (A = B)$. Note that we do not write the "and." It is understood when this form is used.

The implication $(a \wedge b \wedge c) \longrightarrow x$, or $\left. \begin{array}{c} a \\ b \\ c \end{array} \right\} \longrightarrow x$, has a converse which

is written $x \longrightarrow (a \wedge b \wedge c)$, or $x \longrightarrow \left\{ \begin{array}{c} a \\ b \cdot \\ c \end{array} \right.$ We shall seldom, if ever, be

interested in this converse, which might be described as the *complete converse*. We shall often, however, use forms known as partial converses. The implication $(a \wedge b \wedge c) \longrightarrow x$ has the partial converses $(x \wedge b \wedge c) \longrightarrow a$, $(a \wedge x \wedge c) \longrightarrow b$, and $(a \wedge b \wedge x) \longrightarrow c$. The component statements $a, b, c, \cdots$ of a conjunctive hypothesis are often called premises. If the conclusion of an implication is a simple statement and if the hypothesis of the implication contains n premises each of which is a simple statement, then any one of the n implications obtained by interchanging one of the premises with the conclusion is a *partial converse* of the implication. Hereafter, we shall drop the words partial and complete and refer to both partial and complete converses as converses.

Let us now consider the contrapositives of the implication $(a \wedge b \wedge c) \longrightarrow x$. This implication has a *complete contrapositive* which is written as $\sim x \longrightarrow \sim (a \wedge b \wedge c)$. We shall have little use for this form. We shall, however, find the following partial contrapositives very useful:

$$\left. \begin{array}{c} \sim x \\ b \\ c \end{array} \right\} \longrightarrow \sim a \qquad \left. \begin{array}{c} a \\ \sim x \\ c \end{array} \right\} \longrightarrow \sim b \qquad \left. \begin{array}{c} a \\ b \\ \sim x \end{array} \right\} \longrightarrow \sim c$$

If the conclusion of an implication is a simple statement and if the hypothesis of the implication contains n premises each of which is a simple statement, then any one of the n implications obtained by interchanging a contradiction of one of the premises with a contradiction of the conclusion is a *partial contrapositive* of the implication. Hereafter, we shall make no distinction between complete and partial contrapositives. We shall refer to both as contrapositives. It is important to note that each of the contrapositives of an implication is equivalent to the original implication and to the others.

Implications which can be proved and which are important in the development of mathematics are called *theorems*.

 EXERCISES

1. Write all of the converses of each of the following implications.

    a. If a is a whole number and $a \neq 0$, then a is a natural number.

    b. $(x = 0 \ and \ y = 1) \longrightarrow xy = 0$.

    c. If $3x + 1 = 10$ and x is a natural number, then $x = 3$.

    d. If a is an integer and b is a nonzero integer, then $\dfrac{a}{b}$ represents a real number.

    e. $\dfrac{1}{x}$ represents a real number if $x \in R$ and $x \neq 0$.

2. Write all of the contrapositives of each of the implications in Ex. 1.

3. Write a verbal translation of each of the following implications. The capital letters denote sets and the small letters denote real numbers.

    a. $(A \subset B \land B \cap C = \emptyset) \longrightarrow A \cap C = \emptyset$ **d.** $(a < b \land b < c) \longrightarrow a < c$

    b. $(a = b \land c = d) \longrightarrow a + c = b + d$ **e.** $(a < b \land c > 0) \longrightarrow ac < bc$

    c. $(a = b \land c = d) \longrightarrow ac = bd$ **f.** $(a < b \land c < 0) \longrightarrow ac > bc$

4. Show by a truth table that each of the following statements is true.

    a. $[(a \land b) \longrightarrow c] \longleftrightarrow [\sim c \longrightarrow \sim (a \land b)]$

    b. $[(a \land b) \longrightarrow c] \longleftrightarrow [(\sim c \land b) \longrightarrow \sim a]$

    c. $[(a \land b) \longrightarrow c] \longleftrightarrow [(a \land \sim c) \longrightarrow \sim b]$

Tautologies

A *tautology* is a compound statement which is true regardless of the truth or falsity of its component statements.

We use truth tables to show that certain compound statements are tautologies. For example, the compound statement $a \lor \sim a$ is a tautology because whether the statement a is true or false the statement $a \lor \sim a$ is true. This is shown by the fact that both entries in the column headed $a \lor \sim a$ are T's.

a	$\sim a$	$a \lor \sim a$
T	F	T
F	T	T

As another example of a tautology let us consider the statement $[p \land (p \longrightarrow q)] \longrightarrow q$. The following truth table shows us that regardless of the truth or falsity of p, q, and $p \longrightarrow q$, every entry under $[p \land (p \longrightarrow q)] \longrightarrow q$ is T.

p	q	$p \longrightarrow q$	$p \land (p \longrightarrow q)$	$[p \land (p \longrightarrow q)] \longrightarrow q$
T	T	T	T	T
T	F	F	F	T
F	T	T	F	T
F	F	T	F	T

This tautology is important enough to deserve a special name. It is called a *syllogism*. Statement p is called the *minor premise* of the syllogism; statement $p \longrightarrow q$ is called the *major premise*, and statement q is called the *conclusion*. If we accept statement p and statement $p \longrightarrow q$ in this tautology, we conclude or infer that we must accept q; in other words, if we accept the truth of the premises of a syllogism, we must accept the truth of its conclusion.

As a third example of a tautology consider the statement $[(p \longrightarrow q) \land (q \longrightarrow r)] \longrightarrow (p \longrightarrow r)$. It is called the *transitive property of implication*. We sometimes write this as $\left. \begin{array}{l} p \longrightarrow q \\ q \longrightarrow r \end{array} \right\} \longrightarrow (p \longrightarrow r)$

p	q	r	$p \longrightarrow q$	$q \longrightarrow r$	$p \longrightarrow r$	$(p \longrightarrow q \land q \longrightarrow r)$	$(p \longrightarrow q \land q \longrightarrow r) \longrightarrow (p \longrightarrow r)$
T	T	T	T	T	T	T	T
T	T	F	T	F	F	F	T
T	F	T	F	T	T	F	T
T	F	F	F	T	F	F	T
F	T	T	T	T	T	T	T
F	T	F	T	F	T	F	T
F	F	T	T	T	T	T	T
F	F	F	T	T	T	T	T

The transitive property of implication is, of course, readily extended to three, four, or any finite number of implications. For three implications we have $[(p \longrightarrow q) \land (q \longrightarrow r) \land (r \longrightarrow s)] \longrightarrow (p \longrightarrow s)$. If we accept the truth of $p \longrightarrow q$, $q \longrightarrow r$, and $r \longrightarrow s$, we must accept the truth of $p \longrightarrow s$. We observe that each implication after the first has the conclusion of the preceding implication for its hypothesis. The conjunction of the implications in such a series is called a *deductive sequence*. This deductive sequence can be written more compactly as $p \longrightarrow q \longrightarrow r \longrightarrow s$. Thus we may write $[(p \longrightarrow q) \wedge (q \longrightarrow r) \wedge (r \longrightarrow s)] \longrightarrow (p \longrightarrow s)$ as $(p \longrightarrow q \longrightarrow r \longrightarrow s) \longrightarrow (p \longrightarrow s)$.

Using the conjunction of the statement p and the deductive sequence $(p \longrightarrow q \longrightarrow r \longrightarrow s)$ as the hypothesis, we can form the tautology $[p \wedge (p \longrightarrow q \longrightarrow r \longrightarrow s)] \longrightarrow s$. The truth table to show that this statement is a tautology requires 16 lines.

As a fifth example of a tautology let us consider the statement $[\sim t \wedge (\sim q \longrightarrow t)] \longrightarrow q$. The following truth table shows that this statement is also a tautology.

q	t	$\sim q$	$\sim t$	$\sim q \longrightarrow t$	$\sim t \wedge (\sim q \longrightarrow t)$	$[\sim t \wedge (\sim q \longrightarrow t)] \longrightarrow q$
T	T	F	F	T	F	T
T	F	F	T	T	T	T
F	T	T	F	T	F	T
F	F	T	T	F	F	T

This tautology is a pattern we use for indirect proof. It says, in effect, that if a contradiction of a statement q implies a false statement, then the statement q is true.

Example 1. Show that $a \longleftrightarrow a$ is a tautology.

Solution. This is proved by the truth table shown at the right.

a	$a \longleftrightarrow a$
T	T
F	T

Example 2. Show that $a \longrightarrow (a \vee b)$ is a tautology.

Solution. This is shown by the truth table at the right.

a	b	$a \vee b$	$a \longrightarrow (a \vee b)$
T	T	T	T
T	F	T	T
F	T	T	T
F	F	F	T

Argument and Proof

Let us consider how tautologies are related to argument and proof.

An *argument* is an assertion that a certain statement called the conclusion of the argument is true when certain other statements called the premises are true. Let us consider two arguments.

Linda argues as follows concerning the pupils in her high school.

(1) Harold sits in Section II in the school assembly.

(2) If a pupil is a sophomore, then he sits in Section II in the assembly.

(3) Therefore Harold is a sophomore.

Linda's argument is not valid. We can accept her premises (1) and (2) and still not accept her conclusion (3). For example, Section II may provide seats for juniors as well as sophomores, in which case even though Harold is in Section II and all sophomores sit in Section II, Harold may still be a junior. If we let b represent the statement "Harold sits in Section II in the school assembly" and $a \longrightarrow b$ represent the statement "If a pupil is a sophomore, then he sits in Section II," Linda's argument takes the form $[b \wedge (a \longrightarrow b)] \longrightarrow a$. A truth table will show that this implication is not a tautology. We know that the truth of the conclusion of an implication does not guarantee the truth of the hypothesis.

Let us now consider another argument. John, a pupil in school X, argues as follows:

(1) I live more than a mile and a half from school X.

(2) If a pupil lives more than a mile and a half from school X and in that school district, he is entitled to ride the school bus.

(3) I am entitled to ride the school bus.

John's argument is *valid*. If we agree with his premises as stated in (1) and (2), then we cannot deny his conclusion (3). If we let p represent the statement "I live more than a mile and a half from school," let $p \longrightarrow q$ represent the statement "If a pupil lives more than a mile and a half from school, he is entitled to ride the school bus," and let q represent the statement "I am entitled to ride the school bus," John's argument takes the form $[p \wedge (p \longrightarrow q)] \longrightarrow q$ which is a syllogism. Since we have shown that the statement $[p \wedge (p \longrightarrow q)] \longrightarrow q$ is a tautology, John's argument is valid according to the following definition of *valid argument*: An argument is valid if the implication which has the premise(s) of the argument for its hypothesis and the conclusion of the argument for its conclusion is a tautology.

When we say that John's argument is valid, we do not mean that we must agree with his conclusion. There is still the question of the truth of the premises. For example, a careful check may show that John does not actually live more than a mile and a half from school, or it may be that there is really no ruling that a pupil who lives more than a mile and a half from school is entitled to ride the school bus. These are statements of fact whose truth value can be determined. If, however, we accept the premises p and $p \longrightarrow q$, we must accept the conclusion q and agree that John has proved his conclusion, according to the following definition of proof: A *proof* is a valid argument having true premises.

Each of the following tautologies becomes a proof of its conclusion if we know that each statement in its hypothesis is true.

$$[p \wedge (p \longrightarrow q)] \longrightarrow q$$
$$[(p \longrightarrow q) \wedge (q \longrightarrow r)] \longrightarrow (p \longrightarrow r)$$
$$[\sim t \wedge (\sim q \longrightarrow t)] \longrightarrow q$$
$$[p \wedge (p \longrightarrow q \longrightarrow r \longrightarrow s)] \longrightarrow s$$

Example.   Show that "If $\sim a$ and $a \vee b$, then b" is a valid argument.

Solution.   We must show that the implication $[\sim a \wedge (a \vee b)] \longrightarrow b$ is a tautology. This is easily done by means of the truth table below.

a	b	$\sim a$	$a \vee b$	$\sim a \wedge (a \vee b)$	$[\sim a \wedge (a \vee b)] \longrightarrow b$
T	T	F	T	F	T
T	F	F	T	F	T
F	T	T	T	T	T
F	F	T	F	F	T

Thus if we know that a is false and that $a \vee b$ is true, we have a proof of b.

Ⓐ **EXERCISES**

1. Show that each of the following is a tautology.

   a. $[\sim b \wedge (a \longrightarrow b)] \longrightarrow \sim a$ **d.** $a \longrightarrow (a \vee b)$

   b. $[\sim a \wedge (\sim a \longrightarrow b)] \longrightarrow b$ **e.** $\sim a \longrightarrow (a \longrightarrow b)$

   c. $(a \wedge b) \longrightarrow a$ **f.** $\sim a \longrightarrow \sim (a \wedge b)$

2. Which of the statements in Ex. 1 are valid arguments?

3. **a.** Show that $(a \longrightarrow b) \longrightarrow (\sim a \vee b)$ is a tautology.

   b. Show that $(\sim a \vee b) \longrightarrow (a \longrightarrow b)$ is a tautology.

   c. Show that $(a \longrightarrow b) \longleftrightarrow (\sim a \vee b)$ is a tautology.

   d. Are the results you have found for parts **a**, **b**, and **c** consistent with the statement "If $p \longrightarrow q$ and $q \longrightarrow p$, then $p \longleftrightarrow q$"?

4. Show that each of the following is a tautology.

   a. $(a \longrightarrow b) \longleftrightarrow (\sim b \longrightarrow \sim a)$

   b. $a \wedge (b \vee c) \longleftrightarrow [(a \wedge b) \vee (a \wedge c)]$

   c. $(a \longrightarrow b) \longleftrightarrow \sim (a \wedge \sim b)$

5. Which of the following are valid arguments?

a. $(a \wedge b) \longrightarrow (a \vee b)$ **c.** $(a \wedge b) \vee c \longrightarrow a \wedge (b \vee c)$

b. $(a \vee b) \longrightarrow (a \wedge b)$ **d.** $(a \longrightarrow b) \longrightarrow [(a \wedge c) \longrightarrow (b \wedge c)]$

Statements Used in Proof

The statements used for reasons in a proof may be assumptions, definitions, or previously proved statements.

Assumptions are statements which are accepted as true without proof. Examples of assumptions are "If a, $b \in R$, then $a + b = b + a$" and "The set of counting numbers is closed under addition."

In developing algebra we assume that certain statements are true and use these in constructing valid arguments which prove new statements. These statements, in turn, can be used in constructing still other proofs, and so on. Among the statements we have assumed true are the properties of real numbers and the properties of equality.

When we state a *definition* we seek to give an exact description of a set of objects (persons, ideas, things). This set, which may contain only one object, is the *subject* of the definition. In order to be useful, a definition must be broad enough to include all objects that belong to that set and, at the same time, detailed enough to exclude any that do not belong to the set. When we define a particular object, we seek to place it in the smallest possible class to which it belongs and then to distinguish it from other members of that class. Thus, in defining a prime number we first classify it as "a positive integer which is greater than one," and then we distinguish it from other members in that class by adding the phrase "and which is not factorable."

A good definition is always reversible when expressed in the if-then form. Thus if we designate the statement "A numeral is a symbol which names a number" as a definition, we are saying that the set of numerals is the same as the set of symbols that name numbers, and we know that *both* of the following if-then statements are true:

If an object is a numeral, *then* it is a symbol that names a number.
If an object is a symbol that names a number, *then* it is a numeral.

It is evident that when we write our first definition in any subject we must use words that have not been defined. We gradually gain an under-standing of these undefined terms from the way in which they are used. Thus our definitions must rest upon undefined terms just as our logical system must rest upon certain assumptions.

Arrangements of Proofs

Let us consider the following array of implications.

$$
\left.\begin{array}{l} a \\ b \end{array}\right\} \longrightarrow c \\
\left.\begin{array}{l} d \\ e \end{array}\right\} \longrightarrow f \quad \Big\} \longrightarrow q
$$

This array contains three distinct implications, $(a \wedge b) \longrightarrow c$, $(d \wedge e) \longrightarrow f$, and $(c \wedge f) \longrightarrow q$.

It can be shown by a 128-line truth table that $[(a \wedge b \wedge d \wedge e) \wedge [(a \wedge b) \longrightarrow c] \wedge [(d \wedge e) \longrightarrow f] \wedge [(c \wedge f) \longrightarrow q]] \longrightarrow q$ is a tautology. Hence, if the implications $(a \wedge b) \longrightarrow c$, $(d \wedge e) \longrightarrow f$, and $(c \wedge f) \longrightarrow q$ are known to be true (as they would be if they were previously proved theorems) and if a, b, d, and e are true, we have a valid argument with true premises that is a proof of the statement q.

It can also be shown by a 128-line truth table that $[[(a \wedge b) \longrightarrow c] \wedge [(d \wedge e) \longrightarrow f] \wedge [(c \wedge f) \longrightarrow q]] \longrightarrow [(a \wedge b \wedge c \wedge d) \longrightarrow q]$ is a tautology. Then when the implications in the array

$$
\left.\begin{array}{l} a \\ b \end{array}\right\} \longrightarrow c \\
\left.\begin{array}{l} d \\ e \end{array}\right\} \longrightarrow f \quad \Big\} \longrightarrow q
$$

are accepted as true, we have a proof of the implication $(a \wedge b \wedge d \wedge e) \longrightarrow q$ because we have a valid argument with true premises.

While the consideration of a truth table is a reliable procedure for checking the validity of an argument, it is hardly feasible to use this procedure when 128 lines are required. If an argument involves n statements (for example, the seven statements, a, b, c, d, e, f, and q above), a truth table involving 2^n lines is required (thus 2^7, or 128, in the above argument). In practice we shall not construct truth tables for each proof. You will be asked to accept the validity of an argument on the basis of its form, that is, the way the proof is arranged. We shall construct a proof by (1) giving a reason for each statement in order to establish the truth of the statement, and by (2) arranging our work in such a way that it is clear that each conclusion is implied by previously established statements.

If the conclusion of our implication is a statement of equivalence such as $x \longleftrightarrow y$, then the implication has the form $(a \wedge b) \longrightarrow (x \longleftrightarrow y)$. This implication can be proved by proving the two implications $(a \wedge b \wedge x) \longrightarrow y$ and $(a \wedge b \wedge y) \longrightarrow x$. This follows from the fact that

$$\left[\begin{Bmatrix} a \\ b \\ x \end{Bmatrix} \longrightarrow y \wedge \begin{Bmatrix} a \\ b \\ y \end{Bmatrix} \longrightarrow x \right] \longrightarrow \left[\begin{Bmatrix} a \\ b \end{Bmatrix} \longrightarrow (x \longleftrightarrow y) \right]$$

is a tautology, as can be shown by means of a 16-line truth table. Thus if the two implications $(a \wedge b \wedge x) \longrightarrow y$ and $(a \wedge b \wedge y) \longrightarrow x$ are accepted as true, we have a proof of the implication $(a \wedge b) \longrightarrow (x \longleftrightarrow y)$ because this implication is the conclusion of a valid argument having true premises.

There are three principal ways to arrange a proof so that others can follow our reasoning. There are flow diagrams, ledger arrangements, and paragraph arrangements (sometimes called essay-type arrangements). Each is illustrated below for the proof of statement q. We are assuming that a, b, d, and e are given as true and that $(a \wedge b) \longrightarrow c$, $(d \wedge e) \longrightarrow f$, and $(c \wedge f) \longrightarrow q$ are previously proved theorems.

In the flow-diagram proof we simply put a number above each statement in an array of implications and then supply a supporting reason. By numbering the reason to correspond to the number inserted in the flow diagram, we indicate which reason supports a particular statement. Thus

$$
\begin{array}{l}
(1) \\
\left. \begin{array}{l} a \\ (2) \\ b \end{array} \right\} \begin{array}{l} (3) \\ \longrightarrow c \end{array} \\[4pt]
\hspace{3em} \left. \begin{array}{l} (7) \\ \longrightarrow q \end{array} \right. \\[4pt]
\left. \begin{array}{l} (4) \\ d \\ (5) \\ e \end{array} \right\} \begin{array}{l} (6) \\ \longrightarrow f \end{array}
\end{array}
$$

(1) Given, (2) Given, (3) Theorem: $(a \wedge b) \longrightarrow c$, (4) Given, (5) Given, (6) Theorem: $(d \wedge e) \longrightarrow f$, (7) Theorem: $(c \wedge f) \longrightarrow q$

In the ledger-type proof we arrange our work as follows:

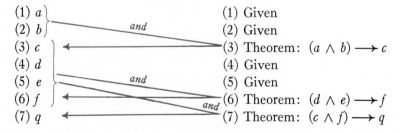

(1) a	(1) Given
(2) b	(2) Given
(3) c	(3) Theorem: $(a \wedge b) \longrightarrow c$
(4) d	(4) Given
(5) e	(5) Given
(6) f	(6) Theorem: $(d \wedge e) \longrightarrow f$
(7) q	(7) Theorem: $(c \wedge f) \longrightarrow q$

The lines, arrows, and braces printed in red show that the development of a ledger proof is basically the same as that of a flow-diagram proof.

An essay-type proof can be presented as follows:

Since we know that a and b are true, by the theorem $(a \wedge b) \longrightarrow c$ we know that c is true. Since we know that d and e are true, by the theorem $(d \wedge e) \longrightarrow f$ we know that f is true. Since we have proved c and f true, by the theorem $(c \wedge f) \longrightarrow q$ we know that q is true and our proof is complete.

Many of the proofs that you will encounter in more advanced courses in mathematics will be of the essay type. These have the advantage of being compact, but they are more difficult to follow because they often show only the principal ideas in the proof. Often some of the reasons and even some of the more obvious statements or steps are omitted. Your best preparation for understanding and writing essay-type proofs is to study the structure of flow-diagram and ledger-form proofs. We shall not try to prove every statement we make in this book since that would be both tedious and time-consuming. We shall, however, prove many statements in order to give you a better understanding of the nature of proof and to help you see the logical structure of algebra.

Some Theorems from Your First Course in Algebra

Below we list a few of the theorems that you used in your first course in algebra. Later some of the proofs of these theorems will be reviewed and other theorems both new and old added to the list.

 Theorem 1–2. If $a \in R$ and $a \neq 0$, then a has only one multiplicative inverse.

Corollary to Theorem 1–2. If $a \in R$ and $a \neq 0$, then the multiplicative inverse of the multiplicative inverse of a is a.

Theorem 2–2. If $a \in R$, then $a \cdot 0 = 0$.

Theorem 3–2. If $a, b \in R$ and $ab = 0$, then $a = 0$ or $b = 0$.

Theorem 4–2. If $a, b \in R$ and $b \neq 0$, then $\dfrac{a}{b} = \dfrac{1}{b} \cdot a$.

Theorem 5–2. If $a, b \in R$ and $ab \neq 0$, then $\dfrac{1}{a} \cdot \dfrac{1}{b} = \dfrac{1}{ab}$.

Theorem 6–2. If $a, b, c, d \in R$ and $bd \neq 0$, then $\dfrac{a}{b} \cdot \dfrac{c}{d} = \dfrac{ac}{bd}$.

Theorem 7–2. If $a, b, c \in R$ and $bc \neq 0$, then $\dfrac{a}{b} = \dfrac{ac}{bc}$.

Theorem 8–2. If $a \in R$, then a has only one additive inverse.

Corollary 1 to Theorem 8–2. If $a \in R$, then $-(-a) = a$.

Corollary 2 to Theorem 8–2. $-0 = 0$.

Theorem 9–2. If $a, b \in R$, then $a - b = a + (-b)$.

Theorem 10–2. If $a \in R$, then $(-1)a = -a$.

Theorem 11–2. If $a, b \in R$, then $(-a)b = -(ab)$.

Theorem 12–2. If $a, b \in R$, then $(-a)(-b) = ab$.

Theorem 13–2. If $a, b, c \in R$, then $a - (b + c) = a - b - c$.

Theorem 14–2. If $a, b, c \in R$, then $a(b - c) = ab - ac$.

Theorem 15–2. If $a, b, c, d \in R$, then $(a - b)(c - d) = ab - bc - ad + bd$.

Theorem 16–2. If $a, b \in R$, then $-(a - b) = b - a$.

Theorem 17–2. If $a, b \in R$ and $b \neq 0$, then $\dfrac{-a}{b} = \dfrac{a}{-b} = -\dfrac{a}{b}$.

Theorem 18–2. If $a, b \in R$ and $b \neq 0$, then $\dfrac{-a}{-b} = \dfrac{a}{b}$.

Theorem 19–2. If $a, b, c \in R$ and $b \neq 0$, then $\dfrac{a}{b} + \dfrac{c}{b} = \dfrac{a + c}{b}$.

Theorem 20–2. If $a, b, c, d \in R$ and $bd \neq 0$, then $\dfrac{a}{b} + \dfrac{c}{d} = \dfrac{ad + bc}{bd}$.

Theorem 21–2. If $a, b, c, d \in R$ and $bd \neq 0$, then $\dfrac{a}{b} = \dfrac{c}{d} \longleftrightarrow ad = bc$.

Theorem 22–2. If $a, b, c, d \in R$ and $bcd \neq 0$, then $\dfrac{\frac{a}{b}}{\frac{c}{d}} = \dfrac{ad}{bc}$.

In Examples 1–3 we shall prove the first three theorems mentioned above. In the exercises you are asked to prove or complete the proofs of others.

Example 1. Prove Theorem 1–2: If $a \in R$ and $a \neq 0$, then a has only one multiplicative inverse.

Proof. This theorem will be proved if we can show that if a has two multiplicative inverses, they are equal.

1. $a \in R$ and $a \neq 0$ 1. Given

2. Let us assume that $\dfrac{1}{a}$ and x are   2. Assumption

   multiplicative inverses of a.

3. $a \cdot x = 1$ 3. Definition of multiplicative inverse

4. $\dfrac{1}{a}(ax) = \dfrac{1}{a} \cdot 1$ 4. Multiplication property of equality

5. $\left(\dfrac{1}{a} \cdot a\right)x = \dfrac{1}{a} \cdot 1$ 5. Associative property of multiplication

6. $1 \cdot x = \dfrac{1}{a} \cdot 1$ 6. Definition of multiplicative inverse

7. $x = \dfrac{1}{a}$ 7. Multiplication property of 1

Example 2.   Prove Theorem 2–2: If $a \in R$, then $a \cdot 0 = 0$.

Proof.

$$
\begin{array}{l}
\overset{(1)}{1 \in R} \overset{(2)}{\longrightarrow} 1 + 0 = 1 \\
\quad\quad\quad\quad \overset{(3)}{} \\
\quad\quad\quad\quad a \in R
\end{array}
\Bigg\}
\overset{(4)}{\longrightarrow} a(1 + 0) = a \cdot 1 \overset{(5)}{\longrightarrow} a \cdot 1 + a \cdot 0 = a \cdot 1
$$

$$
\overset{(6)}{\longrightarrow} a + a \cdot 0 = a \overset{(7)}{\longrightarrow} a \cdot 0 = 0
$$

$$\therefore\; a \in R \longrightarrow a \cdot 0 = 0$$

Reasons: (1) There is a unique real number 1 such that $a \cdot 1 = a = 1 \cdot a$, (2) Addition property of zero, (3) Given, (4) Multiplication property of equality, (5) Distributive property, (6) Multiplication property of one, (7) There is a unique number 0 such that $a + 0 = a$. (Thus, $a \cdot 0$ must be another name for 0.)

We can write the concluding statement ($a \in R \longrightarrow a \cdot 0 = 0$) of the proof in the preceding example because our proof is a valid argument, and having accepted the hypotheses as true, we have proved the conclusion true. Thus we have a proof of our theorem. We shall not always make a concluding statement when giving a proof since all of the arguments we use can be shown to be valid arguments.

Example 3.   Prove Theorem 3–2: If $a, b \in R$ and $ab = 0$, then $a = 0$ or $b = 0$.

Solution.   The following argument is partly in essay form. It conveys the general idea of the proof but omits some of the details.

There are two possibilities for a—either $a = 0$ or $a \neq 0$. (See the tautology $a \vee \sim a$ on page 80.) If $a = 0$, the theorem is proved because if $a = 0$ it is certainly true that $a = 0$ or $b = 0$. (In Example 2, page 82, we showed that $a \longrightarrow (a \vee b)$ is a tautology.)

If $a \neq 0$, then a has a multiplicative inverse $\dfrac{1}{a}$. Why? In this case we reason as follows:

$$
\overset{(1)}{0} = \frac{1}{a} \cdot 0 \overset{(2)}{\longrightarrow} 0 = \frac{1}{a}(ab) \overset{(3)}{\longrightarrow} 0 = \left(\frac{1}{a} \cdot a\right)b \overset{(4)}{\longrightarrow} 0 = 1 \cdot b \overset{(5)}{\longrightarrow} 0 = b.
$$

The reasons are: (1) Th. 2–2, (2) Substitution property of equality —we know that $ab = 0$, (3) Associative property of multiplication, (4) Definition of multiplicative inverse, (5) Multiplication property of one.

Thus if $a \neq 0$, then $b = 0$. Therefore, at least one of the numbers a or b is 0. This means that the disjunction $a = 0 \vee b = 0$ is true and our proof is complete.

Note that we may also write a proof such as

$$\overset{(1)}{0=\frac{1}{a}}\cdot 0 \overset{(2)}{\longrightarrow} 0 = \frac{1}{a}(ab) \overset{(3)}{\longrightarrow} 0 = \left(\frac{1}{a}\cdot a\right)b \overset{(4)}{\longrightarrow} 0 = 1\cdot b \overset{(5)}{\longrightarrow} 0 = b$$

in a more compact form as follows:

$$\overset{(1)}{0=\frac{1}{a}}\cdot 0 \overset{(2)}{=} \frac{1}{a}(ab) \overset{(3)}{=} \left(\frac{1}{a}\cdot a\right)b \overset{(4)}{=} 1\cdot b \overset{(5)}{=} b.$$

The reasons are the same in both forms of this proof.

 A EXERCISES

1. Below we have written some of the statements and some of the reasons for these statements. You are to replace each "Why?" with the correct reason.

a. Proof of Theorem 4–2: If $a, b \in R$ and $b \neq 0$, then $\dfrac{a}{b} = \dfrac{1}{b}\cdot a$.

$$\overset{(1)}{a, b \in R \text{ and } b \neq 0} \longrightarrow \overset{(2)}{\frac{a}{b} \text{ is a real number}} \overset{(3)}{\longrightarrow} b\cdot\frac{a}{b} = a \longrightarrow$$

$$\overset{(4)}{\longrightarrow} \frac{1}{b}\left(b\cdot\frac{a}{b}\right) = \frac{1}{b}(a) \overset{(5)}{\longrightarrow} \left(\frac{1}{b}\cdot b\right)\frac{a}{b} = \frac{1}{b}(a) \overset{(6)}{\longrightarrow} 1\cdot\frac{a}{b} = \frac{1}{b}\cdot a \overset{(7)}{\longrightarrow} \frac{a}{b} = \frac{1}{b}\cdot a.$$

The reasons are: (1) Why? (2) Why? (3) Why? (4) Why? (5) Why? (6) Why? (7) Why?

b. Proof of Theorem 5–2. If $a, b \in R$ and $ab \neq 0$, then $\dfrac{1}{a}\cdot\dfrac{1}{b} = \dfrac{1}{ab}$.

1. a is a nonzero real number
   b is a nonzero real number

   1. Why?

2. a has a multiplicative inverse $\dfrac{1}{a}$ such that $a\cdot\dfrac{1}{a} = 1$ and b has a multiplicative inverse $\dfrac{1}{b}$ such that $b\cdot\dfrac{1}{b} = 1$

   2. Existence of multiplicative inverse

3. $\left(a\cdot\dfrac{1}{a}\right)\left(b\cdot\dfrac{1}{b}\right) = 1\cdot 1$

   3. Why?

4. $(a\cdot b)\left(\dfrac{1}{a}\cdot\dfrac{1}{b}\right) = 1$

   4. Commutative and associative properties of the multiplication of real numbers and the multiplicative property of 1

5. ab is a nonzero real number   5. Why?

6. ab has a multiplicative inverse   6. Why?

$\dfrac{1}{ab}$ such that $ab \cdot \dfrac{1}{ab} = 1$

7. From steps 4, 6 we conclude   7. Why?

$\dfrac{1}{a} \cdot \dfrac{1}{b} = \dfrac{1}{ab}$

c. Proof of Theorem 6–2: If a, b, c, $d \, \epsilon \, R$ and $bd \neq 0$, then $\dfrac{a}{b} \cdot \dfrac{c}{d} = \dfrac{ac}{bd}$.

$$\overset{(1)}{} \quad \overset{(2)}{} \quad \overset{(3)}{} \quad \overset{(4)}{}$$

$$\frac{a}{b} \cdot \frac{c}{d} = \left(a \cdot \frac{1}{b}\right)\left(c \cdot \frac{1}{d}\right) = ac\left(\frac{1}{b} \cdot \frac{1}{d}\right) = ac\left(\frac{1}{bd}\right) = \frac{ac}{bd}$$

The reasons are: (1) Why? (2) Why? (3) Why? (4) Why?

d. Proof of Theorem 7–2: If a, b, $c \, \epsilon \, R$ and $bc \neq 0$, then $\dfrac{a}{b} = \dfrac{ac}{bc}$.

1. If in Theorem 6–2 we write c for d, we have   1. Why?

$\dfrac{a}{b} \cdot \dfrac{c}{c} = \dfrac{ac}{bc}$.

2. $\dfrac{a}{b}\left(c \cdot \dfrac{1}{c}\right) = \dfrac{ac}{bc}$ 2. Why?

3. $\dfrac{a}{b} \cdot 1 = \dfrac{ac}{bc}$ 3. Why?

4. $\dfrac{a}{b} = \dfrac{ac}{bc}$ 4. Why?

e. Proof of Theorem 8–2: If $a \, \epsilon \, R$, then a has only one additive inverse.

1. $a \, \epsilon \, R$ 1. Why?

2. a has an additive inverse $- a$ such that   2. Why?
    $a + (- a) = 0$

3. Let k be an additive inverse of a 3. Assumption

4. $a + k = 0$ 4. Definition of additive inverse

5. $a + k = a + (- a)$ 5. Why?

6. $(- a) + (a + k) = - a + [a + (- a)]$ 6. Why?

7. $(- a + a) + k = (- a + a) + (- a)$ 7. Why?

8. $0 + k = 0 + (- a)$ 8. Why?

9. $k = - a$ 9. Why?

2. Complete each of the following proofs.

a. Proof of Theorem 9–2: If a, $b \, \epsilon \, R$, then $a - b = a + (- b)$.

1. a and b are real numbers   1. Given

2. $(a - b) + b = a$ 2. Why?

3. $[(a - b) + b] + (- b) = a + (- b)$ 3. Why?

4.   4. Why?

5.   5. Why?

6.   6. Why?

b. Proof of Theorem 10–2: If $a \epsilon R$, then $(-1)a = -a$.

$\overset{(1)}{} \quad \overset{(2)}{} \qquad \overset{(3)}{} \qquad\qquad\qquad\qquad\qquad \overset{(4)}{}$
$a \epsilon R \longrightarrow a = a \longrightarrow (-1)a + a = (-1)a + 1 \cdot a \longrightarrow (-1)a + a = a(-1+1)$

$\overset{(5)}{} \qquad\qquad\qquad \overset{(6)}{} \qquad\qquad\qquad \overset{(7)}{}$
$\longrightarrow (-1)a + a = a \cdot 0 \longrightarrow (-1)a + a = 0 \longrightarrow (-1)a = -a.$ Reasons:
(1) Why? (2) Why? (3) Addition property of equality, multiplication property of one, substitution property of equality, (4) Why? (5) Why? (6) Why? (7) Why?

c. Proof of Theorem 11–2; If $a, b \epsilon R$, then $(-a)b = -(ab)$.

$\qquad\quad \overset{(1)}{} \qquad\qquad \overset{(2)}{}$
$(-a)b = [(-1)a]b =$
Reasons: (1) Why? (2) Why? ...

3. Prove each of the theorems indicated below.

a. Theorem 12–2	**e.** Theorem 16–2	**i.** Theorem 20–2
b. Theorem 13–2	**f.** Theorem 17–2	**j.** Theorem 21–2
c. Theorem 14–2	**g.** Theorem 18–2	**k.** Theorem 22–2
d. Theorem 15–2	**h.** Theorem 19–2	

More about Equivalent Open Statements

To indicate the truth set of the equation $5(2z + 7) = -15$ we may write: $\{z \mid 5(2z + 7) = -15\}$. This, however, does not list the numbers that belong to the truth set. To determine these numbers we solve the equation. *Solving an equation* is the process whereby we convert a given equation into an equivalent equation which is so simple that we can determine its truth set by inspection. Since equivalent equations have the same truth set, the truth set of this derived equation is also the truth set of the given equation. Let us analyze the process of solving the equation $5(2z + 7) = -15$. When the domain of the variables in an equation or inequality is not stated, we assume that it is the set of real numbers. We make this assumption in the following solution.

By the distributive property we know that when $z \epsilon R$, $5(2z + 7) = 10z + 35$ and by the substitution property of equality we know that one of two equal expressions may be substituted for the other without changing the truth or falsity of the equation. Thus, we know that

$$5(2z + 7) = -15 \longleftrightarrow 10z + 35 = -15.$$

We can also show that

$$10z + 35 = -15 \longleftrightarrow 10z = -50$$

and that $\qquad\qquad\qquad 10z = -50 \longleftrightarrow z = -5.$

Since statements that are equivalent to the same statement are equivalent to each other, we have:

$$5(2z+7) = -15 \longleftrightarrow 10z + 35 = -15 \longleftrightarrow 10z = -50 \longleftrightarrow z = -5$$

We know that equivalent equations have the same truth sets. Using set-builder notation, we write:

$$\{z \mid 5(2z+7) = -15\} = \{z \mid z = -5\} = \{-5\}$$

Example 1. Find the solution set for the equation $\dfrac{x-2}{7} + 2 = \dfrac{44-3x}{14}$.

Solution. Since the domain of x is not stated, we assume that x is a real number.

$$\overset{(1)}{\dfrac{x-2}{7} + 2 = \dfrac{44-3x}{14}} \longleftrightarrow \overset{(2)}{14\left(\dfrac{x-2}{7} + 2\right) = 14\left(\dfrac{44-3x}{14}\right)} \longleftrightarrow \overset{(3)}{2x}$$

$$\overset{(4)}{-4 + 28 = 44 - 3x} \longleftrightarrow 2x + 24 = 44 - 3x \overset{(5)}{\longleftrightarrow} 5x = 20 \overset{(6)}{\longleftrightarrow}$$
$$x = 4.$$

The reasons are: (1) Given, (2) Multiplication property of equality, (3) Distributive property and rules for operating with real numbers, (4) Addition fact, (5) Addition property of equality, (6) Multiplication property of equality.

Check.
$$\dfrac{4-2}{7} + 2 \overset{?}{=} \dfrac{44 - 3(4)}{14}$$

$$\tfrac{2}{7} + 2 \overset{?}{=} \tfrac{16}{7}$$

$$\tfrac{16}{7} \overset{\checkmark}{=} \tfrac{16}{7}$$

(*Note.* The question mark over the equal sign indicates that we are asking, "Is it true that the left member names the same number as the right member?" The check mark over the equal sign indicates that we have found that the right and left members do name the same number.)

The solution set for $\dfrac{x-2}{7} + 2 = \dfrac{44-3x}{14}$ is $\{4\}$.

Example 2. Solve the following inequality and graph its solution set: $(2x+1)(3x-1) \geq 0$.

Solution. $(2x+1)(3x-1) \geq 0 \longleftrightarrow [(2x+1)(3x-1) > 0]$ *or* $[(2x+1)(3x+1) = 0] \longleftrightarrow [(2x+1 > 0 \text{ and } 3x-1 > 0) \text{ or } (2x+1 < 0 \text{ and } 3x-1 < 0) \text{ or } (2x+1 = 0 \text{ or } 3x-1 = 0)] \longleftrightarrow [(2x > -1 \text{ and } 3x > 1) \text{ or } (2x < -1 \text{ and } 3x < 1) \text{ or } (2x = -1) \text{ or } (3x = 1)] \longleftrightarrow [(x > -\frac{1}{2} \text{ and } x > \frac{1}{3}) \text{ or } (x < -\frac{1}{2} \text{ and } x < \frac{1}{3}) \text{ or } (x = -\frac{1}{2}) \text{ or } (x = \frac{1}{3})].$
$\{x \mid [(x > -\frac{1}{2} \text{ and } x > \frac{1}{3}) \text{ or } (x < -\frac{1}{2} \text{ and } x < \frac{1}{3}) \text{ or } (x = -\frac{1}{2}) \text{ or }$

$(x = \frac{1}{3})]\} = \{x \mid x > -\frac{1}{2} \text{ and } x > \frac{1}{3}\} \cup \{x \mid x < -\frac{1}{2} \text{ and } x < \frac{1}{3}\}$
$\cup \{x \mid x = -\frac{1}{2}\} \cup \{x \mid x = \frac{1}{3}\} = \{x \mid x > \frac{1}{3}\} \cup \{x \mid x < -\frac{1}{2}\}$
$\cup \{x \mid x = -\frac{1}{2}\} \cup \{x \mid x = \frac{1}{3}\} = \{x \mid x \geq \frac{1}{3}\} \cup \{x \mid x \leq -\frac{1}{2}\}.$
The graph is shown by the black portion of the line below.

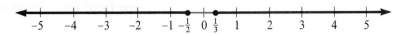

Example 3. Find the solution set for $\left|\dfrac{1}{x}\right| \geq 3$ and draw its graph.

Solution. $\left|\dfrac{1}{x}\right| \geq 3 \longleftrightarrow \dfrac{1}{x} \geq 3 \text{ or } \dfrac{1}{x} \leq -3.$

We know that $x \neq 0$; consequently we know that $x > 0$ or $x < 0$.

If $\dfrac{1}{x} \geq 3$, we seek the value of x among the positive numbers. Thus

$\dfrac{1}{x} \geq 3 \text{ and } x > 0 \longleftrightarrow 1 \geq 3\,x \text{ and } x > 0 \longleftrightarrow \frac{1}{3} \geq x \text{ and } x > 0.$

If $\dfrac{1}{x} \leq -3$, we seek the values of x among the negative numbers.

Thus $\dfrac{1}{x} \leq -3 \text{ and } x < 0 \longleftrightarrow 1 \geq -3\,x \text{ and } x < 0 \longleftrightarrow -\frac{1}{3} \leq x$

and $x < 0$. Therefore $\left\{x \mid \left|\dfrac{1}{x}\right| \geq 3\right\} = \{x \mid 0 < x \leq \frac{1}{3} \text{ or } -\frac{1}{3} \leq x$

$< 0\} = \{x \mid -\frac{1}{3} \leq x \leq \frac{1}{3} \text{ and } x \neq 0\}.$ *Note.* The conjunctive
statement $-\frac{1}{3} \leq x \text{ and } x < 0$ can be written in the more compact
form $-\frac{1}{3} \leq x < 0$. The graph is shown by the black portion of the
number line below.

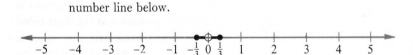

Example 4. Find the solution set for $\left|\dfrac{3\,x - 2}{4}\right| \leq 1.$

Solution. $\left|\dfrac{3\,x - 2}{4}\right| \leq 1$ and from the definition of absolute value $\left|\dfrac{3\,x - 2}{4}\right|$

$\geq 0.$ Thus $\left|\dfrac{3\,x - 2}{4}\right| \geq 0 \text{ and } \left|\dfrac{3\,x - 2}{4}\right| \leq 1 \longleftrightarrow 0 \leq \left|\dfrac{3\,x - 2}{4}\right| \leq 1$

$\longleftrightarrow 0 \leq \dfrac{3\,x - 2}{4} \leq 1 \text{ or } -1 \leq \dfrac{3\,x - 2}{4} \leq 0 \longleftrightarrow 0 \leq 3\,x - 2 \leq 4$

$\text{or} -4 \leq 3\,x - 2 \leq 0 \longleftrightarrow 2 \leq 3\,x \leq 6 \text{ or } -2 \leq 3\,x \leq 2 \longleftrightarrow \frac{2}{3} \leq$
$x \leq 2 \text{ or } -\frac{2}{3} \leq x \leq \frac{2}{3} \longleftrightarrow -\frac{2}{3} \leq x \leq 2.$ $\therefore$ the solution set is
$\{x \mid -\frac{2}{3} \leq x \leq 2\}.$ The graph is shown by the black portion of
the line below.

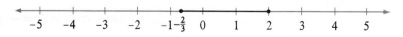

Example 5. On the average Bob can check the cultures in the laboratory in 55 minutes. If it usually takes Jim 65 minutes to do the same work, approximately how long will it take the boys to check the cultures if they work together?

Solution. Since Bob can do the work in 55 minutes, he can do $\frac{1}{55}$ of the work each minute. Similarly, Jim can do $\frac{1}{65}$ of the work each minute. If we let n represent the number of minutes needed by the boys to complete the work when they work together, then $\dfrac{n}{55}$ represents the portion of the work Bob can do in n minutes and $\dfrac{n}{65}$ represents the portion of the work Jim can do in n minutes. Thus,

$$\frac{n}{55} + \frac{n}{65} = 1 \longleftrightarrow 3575\left(\frac{n}{55} + \frac{n}{65}\right) = 3575 \cdot 1 \longleftrightarrow 65\,n + 55\,n = 3575$$
$$\longleftrightarrow 120\,n = 3575 \longleftrightarrow n = 29\tfrac{19}{24}.$$

It requires approximately 30 minutes for the boys to complete the work when they work together.

 EXERCISES

1. Solve each of the following equations, assuming that no denominator is 0.

   a. $\dfrac{6\,x}{14} - \dfrac{20}{7} = x$

   b. $\dfrac{1}{x} + \dfrac{7}{x} = -12$

   c. $\dfrac{-x}{2} + \dfrac{2\,x}{3} = \dfrac{x}{3} - 2$

   d. $5\,t - 12 - 4(t + 7) = 4\,t - 1$

   e. $x - (1 - 6\,x) = x + 4 - (4 - 7\,x)$

   f. $\dfrac{1}{x} = \dfrac{7}{20} - \dfrac{3}{4\,x}$

   g. $\dfrac{y+6}{3} - \dfrac{3-4\,y}{5} = \dfrac{8\,y}{5}$

   h. $.2\,x + .03\,x + 5 = 4.77$

   i. $r + \dfrac{3\,r-9}{2} = \dfrac{4\,r}{11} + 19$

   j. $\tfrac{1}{4}\,t + \tfrac{2}{3}\,t - \tfrac{33}{4} = 0$

2. Find the truth set for each of the following inequalities. Draw the graph of each truth set. No denominator is zero.

   a. $4\,x + 5\,x + 1 > 28$

   b. $\dfrac{r}{4} + 5 \le \dfrac{r}{3} - r$

   c. $4\,m + 7 \le m + 5$

   d. $7\,x - 3 \le 4\,x + 6$

   e. $\tfrac{1}{2}\,y + 10 \ge 15$

   f. $6\,x - 9\,x \ge 18$

   g. $\dfrac{1}{x} + \dfrac{3}{x} < -12$

   h. $6\,x - 9\,x + 9 \ge -3$

   i. $-4(x - 5) + 2 > 3\,x + 1$

   j. $\dfrac{x}{5} - \dfrac{3\,x}{10} \le -1$

   k. $\dfrac{y}{3} - \dfrac{2\,y}{9} \ge -2$

3. Find the solution set for each of the following sentences and graph the solution set in the number line.

a. $|x| = 5$

b. $|3x| = 12$

c. $\left|\dfrac{x}{5}\right| = 10$

d. $|y+4| \geq 6$

e. $\left|\dfrac{y+2}{3}\right| = 5$

f. $\left|\dfrac{y+5}{3}\right| < 1$

g. $\left|\dfrac{1}{x}\right| \geq 4$

h. $\left|\dfrac{1}{x}\right| \leq 6$

i. $|4x+5| < 25$

j. $\left|\dfrac{2x+1}{3}\right| \leq 1$

k. $\left|\dfrac{5x}{6}+2\right| \geq 7$

l. $\left|1-\dfrac{3x}{5}\right| \leq 4$

4. If the sum of a certain real number and 6 is divided by 4, the quotient is the the same as the quotient obtained when 2 is subtracted from the same real number and the result is divided by 2. What is the number or numbers?

5. For what real number or numbers is it true that when $\frac{4}{5}$ of the number is subtracted from $\frac{2}{5}$ of the number, the result is 4?

6. The length of the base of a rectangle is 4 feet longer than twice the width. If the perimeter of the rectangle is 50 feet, what are the length and the width?

7. Bob could build a pier at the lake in 40 hours. If he hired a skilled workman, the two of them could do it in 15 hours. How long would it take the workman to build the pier alone?

8. A collection of nickels, dimes, and quarters is worth $4.95. If the number of dimes in the collection is $\frac{3}{7}$ of the number of nickels and the number of quarters is $\frac{4}{7}$ of the number of nickels, how many of each kind of coin are there in the collection?

9. Mr. Jones deposited $5500 in the bank, part at $3\frac{1}{2}\%$ and part at 4%. If the amount deposited at $3\frac{1}{2}\%$ earned $5 more interest than the amount deposited at 4%, how much was deposited at each rate?

ESSENTIALS

Before you leave this chapter make sure that you

1. Understand the truth table for equivalent statements. (Page 57.)

2. Understand the four conclusions concerning equivalent statements and can use them. (Page 58.)

3. Know when a conjunctive statement is true and when it is false. (Page 59.)

4. Understand the relationship between the truth set of a conjunctive open statement and the truth sets of its clauses. (Page 60.)

5. Can draw the graph of the truth set of an open conjunctive statement. (Pages 61–62.)

6. Know when a disjunctive statement is true and when it is false. (Page 63.)

7. Understand the relationship between the truth set of an open disjunctive statement and the truth sets of its clauses. (Page 64.)

8. Can draw the graph of the truth set of an open disjunctive statement. (Page 65.)

9. Can recognize a conditional statement and can properly identify its hypothesis and its conclusion. (Pages 66–68.)

10. Know when a conditional statement is true and when it is false. (Page 67.)

11. Understand the relationship between the replacement set of an open conditional sentence and the replacement sets of its hypothesis and its conclusion. (Page 68.)

12. Understand the meaning of "open contradictory statements." (Page 71.)

13. Understand how the truth sets of open contradictory statements are related. (Page 71.)

14. Can write the contradiction of a conjunction and the contradiction of a disjunction. (Page 74.)

15. Know the relationship between $p \longrightarrow q$ and $(\sim p \vee q)$, and between $\sim (p \longrightarrow q)$ and $(p \wedge \sim q)$. (Page 74.)

16. Can form the converse, the inverse, and the contrapositive of a simple implication and can recognize the relationships among these statements. (Page 75.)

17. Can form the converses and contrapositives of implications with conjunctive hypotheses. (Page 79.)

18. Know the meaning of "tautology" and can use a truth table to determine whether a particular statement is a tautology. (Pages 80–81.)

19. Know the meaning of "syllogism." (Page 81.)

20. Understand the relationships among tautologies, arguments, and proof. (Pages 82–83.)

21. Understand why we need assumptions and definitions. (Page 85.)

22. Can write a proof in each of the ways discussed in this chapter. (Pages 86–88.)

23. Have reviewed and can prove the theorems from your first course in algebra mentioned in this chapter. (Pages 88–89.)

24. Can find the truth sets of simple, conjunctive, and disjunctive open statements. (Pages 93–95.)

25. Know the meaning of the following words and phrases and can spell
them.

argument (Page 82.)   disjunction (Page 63.)
assumption (Page 85.)   equivalent statements (Page 57.)
conclusion (Page 67.)   hypothesis (Page 67.)
conditional sentence (Page 66.)   implication (Page 67.)
conjunction (Page 59.)   major premise (Page 81.)
contradiction (Page 70.)   minor premise (Page 81.)
contrapositive (Page 75.)   proof (Page 84.)
contrary statement (Page 71.)   tautology (Page 80.)
counterexample (Page 76.)   truth value (Page 57.)
deductive sequence (Page 81.)   valid argument (Page 83.)

CHAPTER REVIEW

1. What do we mean by the truth value of a statement?

2. What are equivalent statements?

3. If a and b are two equivalent open statements, what is known about their
truth sets?

4. If a and b are two contradictory open statements, what is known about their
truth sets?

5. If m and n are two open statements joined by the connective *and*, how are the
truth sets of m and n related to the truth set of the open statement m *and* n?

6. If m and n are two statements joined by the connective *or*, how are the truth
sets of m and n related to the truth set of the open statement m *or* n?

7. Which of the following statements are true and which are false?

    a. $2 < 7 \longleftrightarrow 3 + 1 = 4$ **b.** $4^2 = 8 \longleftrightarrow 9 - 1 = 10$

    c. $x < 5; \ x \in C \longleftrightarrow (x - 3)(x - 4) = 0; \ x \in C$

    d. $x^2 = 16; \ x \in R \longleftrightarrow 4x = 16; \ x \in R$

8. Indicate the solution set for each of the following statements.

    a. $\dfrac{x + 4}{2} + 5 = 3x - 8$ *and* $2(x + 3) - (1 - x) = 4x$

    b. $\dfrac{1}{x} + \dfrac{2}{x} = 18 \wedge x = 6$

    c. $x - 1 \geq 2 \wedge 3x + 1 > 10$

    d. $y^2 = 49 \wedge 4y + 1 < 29$

9. Graph the truth set of each of the compound open statements in Ex. 8.

10. **a.** Write the disjunction of the two statements $18 + 2 > 10$ and $6 \not> 5$.
    b. Is the statement you have written true or false?

11. Find the truth set of each of the following disjunctive statements.
    a. $4(x + 1) - (2x + 3) = 3x - 2$ or $-3x < 12$
    b. $\dfrac{2t + 4}{5} > t \vee 3(t + 1) > 2$
    c. $|2y + 1| = 7 \vee 3y + 1 > 10$
    d. $2(y + 4) - (7 - y) = 13$ or $2(y - 1) < 6$

12. Graph the truth set of each compound sentence in Ex. 11.

13. If m and n are two statements, which of the following words or phrases are appropriate to use in referring to the statement $m \longrightarrow n$?
    a. conditional sentence   **c.** if-then sentence
    b. implication   **d.** conjunction

14. If m and n are two closed statements, under which of the following conditions will the statement $m \longrightarrow n$ be true?
    a. m and n are both true   **c.** m is true and n false
    b. m and n are both false   **d.** m is false and n true

15. If m and n are two open statements having the truth sets M and N respectively, and $m \longrightarrow n$ is true, which of the following is true?
    a. $M \subseteq N$ **b.** $M \subset N$ **c.** $M = N$ **d.** $N \subset M$ **e.** $N \subseteq M$ **f.** $M \neq N$

16. In which of the following implications is the truth set of the hypothesis a subset of the truth set of the conclusion?
    a. $x + 4 = 10 \longrightarrow x = 6$
    b. $x + 17 > 5 \longrightarrow x^2 = 144$
    c. If $x^2 = 9$, then $x \geq -3$
    d. If $\dfrac{x + 2}{3} + 5 = x + 1$, then $x \geq 7$
    e. If $x \geq 7$, then $\dfrac{x + 2}{3} + 5 = x + 1$

17. Which of the implications of Ex. 16 are true?

18. State each of the following in if-then form.
    a. All mountain climbers are brave.
    b. No careless driver is a good insurance risk.
    c. Only seniors will be admitted.
    d. I can come only if I can get the car.

19. a. State the negation of $x > 4$.

    b. State two other contradictions of $x > 4$.

20. Draw the graph of the truth set of the negation of $x > -2$.

21. If statement s_x has the truth set $\{1, 4, 9\}$, draw the graph of the truth set of any contradiction of s_x if $x \in \{1, 2, 3, 4, 5, 6, 7, 8, 9\}$.

22. Write a contradiction of each of the following compound statements.

    a. $x = 3$ or $x = 6$ **d.** $x \not> 7 \wedge x < 3$

    b. $x < 7$ or $x > 3$ **e.** $x < 5 \vee x \ne 9$

    c. $x > -2$ and $x < 6$ **f.** $x \ne 2 \vee x = 8$

23. Write a contradiction of each of the following implications.

    a. $x = 2 \longrightarrow x < 3$

    b. If x is a whole number, then x is a counting number.

    c. "a is a positive number" implies that $a < 0$.

24. Given the implication "If $10\,x = 90$, then $x < 10$," write

    a. The converse of the implication

    b. The inverse of the implication

    c. The contrapositive of the implication

25. Using the results of Ex. 24, complete each of the following:

    a. The converse of the implication is equivalent to _?_.

    b. The inverse of the implication is equivalent to _?_.

    c. The contrapositive of the implication is equivalent to _?_.

26. Write each of the following in three other ways.

    a. $r \longrightarrow s$ **b.** m iff n **c.** If p, then q **d.** $d \longleftrightarrow e$

27. Write all of the converses of $(r \wedge s \wedge t) \longrightarrow w$

28. Write all of the contrapositives of $(r \wedge s \wedge t) \longrightarrow w$

29. Show that $[p \vee (q \wedge r) \longleftrightarrow (p \vee q) \wedge (p \vee r)]$ is a tautology.

30. Show that $[(a \longrightarrow b) \wedge (\sim c \longrightarrow \sim b)] \longrightarrow (\sim c \longrightarrow \sim a)$ is a valid argument.

31. Find the solution set for each of the following open sentences.

    a. $\dfrac{2\,x+9}{3} + \dfrac{4\,x-1}{5} = x$ **d.** $|1-4\,x| = 2$

    b. $\dfrac{-2\,x+4}{5} \le 2$ **e.** $\left|\dfrac{1}{x}\right| > 6$

    c. $2(x-1) + 3(2\,x+8) + x = 4$ **f.** $x \not> 4$ *and* $x+7 = 11$

1. a. Write the open statement which is the conjunction of the open statement $3(x-2)+2(6-2x)=x$ and the open statement $|1-x|=2$.

   b. What is the truth set of the open statement you have written?

2. a. Write the open statement which is the disjunction of the two open statements $\dfrac{3x+1}{2} > 8$ and $1-6x > -5$.

   b. What is the truth set of the open statement you have written?

3. a. Complete: If $a \longrightarrow b$ and $b \longrightarrow a$ is true, then _____.

   b. If A is the truth set of statement a and B is the truth set of statement b in part **a**, what is the relationship of A to B?

4. Copy and complete the following truth table.

a	b	$a \vee b$	$\sim a$	$(a \vee b) \wedge \sim a$	$[(a \vee b) \wedge \sim a] \longrightarrow b$
T	T				
T	F				
F	T				
F	F				

5. Show that $[(r \longleftrightarrow s) \wedge r] \longrightarrow s$ is a valid argument.

6. Prove that if a and b are real numbers and $a = -b$, then $-a = b$.

Find the truth set for each of the following statements.

7. $4(x+3)-(x-5)=2(1-x)$

8. $\dfrac{6+x}{2}+\dfrac{x}{3} \geq x+2$

9. $|x+2|=5$

10. $(x-3)(x+2) \geq 0$

The Real Numbers

The Real Numbers Form a Number Field

On page 22 we stated eleven properties satisfied by the real numbers with the operations of addition and multiplication defined. You will recall that any set of numbers, with at least two elements, for which these properties are true is called a *number field*. The properties are called the *field properties*. If, in addition to the field properties, the order properties (see page 47) are also true for a particular set of numbers, the set is called an *ordered number field*. Since the order properties are true for the real numbers, the set of real numbers is an ordered number field.

Properties of Equality

On page 21 we stated six properties of equality. It is noteworthy that the last four of these (the symmetric property, the transitive property, the addition property, and the multiplication property) can be proved by the use of the first two (the reflexive property and the substitution property). These proofs will be developed in the exercises at the end of this section.

We shall now develop a theorem closely related to the addition property of equality which, you will recall, is "If a, b, c, $d \in R$, $a = b$ and $c = d$, then $a + c = b + d$." Since in this property $c = d$, we may write c for d to obtain: (1) $a = b \longrightarrow a + c = b + c$. The converse (2) $a + c = b + c \longrightarrow a = b$ is readily proved as follows:

Statements	Reasons
1. $a + c = b + c$	1. Given
2. c has the additive inverse $- c$	2. Existence of additive inverse
3. $- c = - c$	3. Reflexive property of equality
4. $(a + c) + (- c) = (b + c) + (- c)$	4. Addition property of equality
5. $a + [c + (- c)] = b + [c + (- c)]$	5. Associative property of addition
6. $a + 0 = b + 0$	6. Definition of additive inverse
7. $a = b$	7. Addition property of zero

Since both statements (1) and (2) are true, we know that the conjunctive statement

$$\left.\begin{array}{l} a, b, c \in R \\ a = b \end{array}\right\} \longrightarrow a + c = b + c \quad \text{and} \quad \left.\begin{array}{l} a, b, c \in R \\ a + c = b + c \end{array}\right\} \longrightarrow a = b$$

is true. We may write this statement more compactly as:

 Theorem 1–3. If $a, b, c \in R$, then $a = b \longleftrightarrow a + c = b + c$.

You will recall that the multiplication property of equality is "If $a, b, c, d \in R$, $a = b$, and $c = d$, then $ac = bd$."

Since in the statement of the multiplication property of equality $a, b, c,$ and d represent any real numbers, we may let $a = c$ and $b = d$. This gives us the statement: If $a, b \in R$ and $a = b$, then $a^2 = b^2$. This statement is a special case of a more general statement:

 Theorem 2–3: If $a, b \in R$, $a = b$, and $n \in C$, then $a^n = b^n$.

Ⓐ EXERCISES

1. Provide the reasons for the following proof of the symmetric property of equality:
   If $a, b \in R$ and $a = b$, then $b = a$.

Statements	Reasons
1. $a = b$	1. Why?
2. $b = b$	2. Why?
3. $b = a$	3. Why?

2. Provide the reasons for the following proof of the transitive property of equality:
   If $a, b, c \in R$, $a = b$, and $b = c$, then $a = c$.

Statements	Reasons
1. $a = b$	1. Why?
2. $b = c$	2. Why?
3. $a = c$	3. Why?

3. The transitive property of equality has two interesting converses:

   (1) If $a, b, c \in R$, $a = c$, and $b = c$, then $a = b$.
   (2) If $a, b, c \in R$, $a = b$ and $a = c$, then $b = c$.

   Why are these statements true?

4. Is each of the following statements true?

   (1) If $a, b, c \in R$, $a \neq c$ and $b = c$, then $a \neq b$.
   (2) If $a, b, c \in R$, $a = b$ and $a \neq c$, then $b \neq c$.

   Explain.

5. Provide the reasons for the following proof of the addition property of equality.
If a, b, c, $d \in R$, $a = b$ and $c = d$, then $a + c = b + d$.

Statements	Reasons
1. $a + c = a + c$	1. Why?
2. $a = b$ and $c = d$	2. Why?
3. $a + c = b + d$	3. Why?

6. Provide the reasons for the following proof of the multiplication property of equality.
If a, b, c, $d \in R$, $a = b$ and $c = d$, then $ac = bd$.

Statements	Reasons
1. $ac = ac$	1. Why?
2. $a = b$ and $c = d$	2. Why?
3. $ac = bd$	3. Why?

7. Since in the multiplication property of equality $c = d$ we may write c for d to obtain: If a, b, $c \in R$ and $a = b$, then $ac = bc$. A converse of the preceding implication is "If a, b, $c \in R$ and $ac = bc$, then $a = b$." Give a counterexample to show that this converse is not always true.

8. Is the following implication true? "If a, b, c, $d \in R$, $a = b$, and $ac \neq bd$, then $c \neq d$." Explain.

9. A converse of the multiplication property of equality is "If a, b, c, $d \in R$ and $ac = bd$, then $a = b$ and $c = d$." Is this converse true? Explain.

Closure

If the result of performing a certain operation on any element of a set S or on any two elements of a set S is always an element of S, we say that S is *closed with respect to that operation* or *closed under that operation*. Let us study set R and some of its subsets, C, I, and Q, to see which are closed with respect to the operations of addition, subtraction, multiplication, division, involution (raising to a power), and evolution (extracting a root).

We know that addition and subtraction are inverse operations. Similarly we know that multiplication and division are inverse operations provided that division by zero is barred. Moreover, our experience tells us that under certain circumstances the process of raising a number to the nth power and the process of extracting the nth root of a number are inverse operations. (For the present we consider only those roots and powers for which $n \in C$.) Thus, if we extract the cube root of 8 and then cube the resulting number, we obtain 8; $(\sqrt[3]{8})^3 = 8$. Similarly, if we cube 8 and then extract the cube root of the resulting number, we again obtain 8; $\sqrt[3]{8^3} = 8$. In this case, extracting the cube root and cubing are inverse operations.

In the table at the right we have indicated that a given set is closed with respect to a specified operation by means of a check ($\checkmark$) and that it is not closed with respect to a certain operation by means of an asterisk (*). The letters in the column at the left indicate the set, and the letters in the row at the top indicate addition, multiplication, involution, subtraction, division, and

	A	M	Iv	S	D	Ev
C	$\checkmark$	$\checkmark$	$\checkmark$	*	*	*
I	$\checkmark$	$\checkmark$	$\checkmark$	$\checkmark$	*	*
Q	$\checkmark$	$\checkmark$	$\checkmark$	$\checkmark$	*	*
R	$\checkmark$	$\checkmark$	$\checkmark$	$\checkmark$	*	*

evolution, respectively. For example, the check mark to the right of C and below A means that set C is closed with respect to addition, the * to the far right of C and under Ev indicates that set C is not closed under the operation of evolution. We make the following observations about a few of the entries in the table.

The counting numbers under evolution. The counting numbers are not closed under extraction of roots. For example, $\sqrt{5}$ is not a counting number because there is no counting number whose square is 5.

The rational numbers under division. We know that $0 \in Q$ and that division by 0 is barred in our algebra. (Such expressions as $\frac{4}{0}$, $\frac{1}{0}$, and $\frac{0}{0}$ are not numbers; in fact, they are meaningless.) Therefore, we cannot say that the quotient of any two rational numbers is a rational number; in other words, we cannot say that the set of rational numbers is closed under the operation of division. However, if $a, b \in Q$ and $b \neq 0$, we can be sure that $\frac{a}{b}$ is a rational number.

The rational numbers under evolution. While the square roots of some rational numbers are rational (for example, $\sqrt{\frac{4}{9}} = \frac{2}{3}$) there are some rational numbers whose square roots are not rational. In a later section we shall show that $\sqrt{2}$ is not a rational number. Assuming that this is true, we say that Q is not closed under evolution.

The real numbers under evolution. In a later section we present an argument designed to show that there is a real positive number whose square is 2, that is, that $\sqrt{2} \in R$. When we say $\sqrt[3]{-7} \in R$, we are saying that there is a real number whose cube is -7. Similarly, we can say that $\sqrt{3} \in R$ and $\sqrt[5]{-31} \in R$. However, $\sqrt{-4} \notin R$ because there is no real number whose square is -4. In Chapter 11 we shall discuss a set of numbers, the complex numbers, which has set R as one of its subsets and which contains such numbers as $\sqrt{-4}$.

Example. Show that $\frac{a}{b} \in Q$ when $a, b \in Q$ and $b \neq 0$.

Solution. Since $a \in Q$, $a = \dfrac{c}{d}$ where $c, d \in I$ and $d \neq 0$. Since $b \in Q$ and $b \neq 0$,

$b = \dfrac{e}{f}$ where $e, f \in I$, $e \neq 0$, and $f \neq 0$. Therefore $\dfrac{a}{b} = \dfrac{c}{d} = \dfrac{\frac{c}{d}(df)}{\frac{e}{f}(df)} =$

$\dfrac{\left(\frac{c}{d} \cdot d\right)f}{\left(\frac{e}{f} \cdot f\right)d} = \dfrac{cf}{de}$. Since $c \in I$ and $f \in I$, we know that $cf \in I$ because the

set of integers is closed under multiplication. By the same reasoning $de \in I$. Moreover $de \neq 0$ because the product of two non-zero real numbers is a nonzero real number (contrapositive of Th. 1–3). Since $\dfrac{cf}{de}$ has the form $\dfrac{a}{b}$ where a and b represent integers and $b \neq 0$, we know that $\dfrac{cf}{de}$ represents a rational number.

Would the result of division involving any two nonzero integers be an integer? Would the result of division involving any two nonzero real numbers be a real number?

 EXERCISES

1. Which of the following are real numbers?

    a. $\sqrt{1}$ d. $\sqrt{a^2}$; $a \in R$ g. $\sqrt{\frac{2}{3}}$

    b. $\sqrt{10}$ e. $\sqrt{a}$; $a \in R$ h. $\sqrt{-\frac{1}{2}}$

    c. $\sqrt{-5}$ f. $\sqrt{0}$ i. $\sqrt{(-a)^2}$; $a \in R, a > 0$

2. Which of the following are true statements?

    a. $a \in R$ and $b \in R \longrightarrow ab \in R$ e. $a \in C \wedge b \in C \longrightarrow (a-b) \in C$

    b. $a \in Q$ and $b \in Q \longrightarrow (a+b) \in Q$ f. $b \in R \longrightarrow \sqrt{b} \in R$

    c. $a \in Q \wedge b \in Q \longrightarrow \dfrac{a}{b} \in Q$ g. $d \in Q \longrightarrow d^2 \in Q$

    d. $a \in C \longrightarrow \sqrt{a} \in C$ h. $a \in C \wedge b \in Q \longrightarrow (a+b) \in C$

3. a. If $a \in I$ and $b \in Q$, then $ab \in Q$. Explain.

    b. If $a \in I$ and $b \in C$, then it is not necessarily true that $a+b \notin C$. Explain.

    c. If $a \in I, b \in I$, and $b \neq 0$, then it is not necessarily true that $\dfrac{a}{b} \in I$, but it is true that $\dfrac{a}{b} \in R$. Explain.

    d. If $a \in C$ and $b \in C$, is it true that $\dfrac{a}{b} \in C$?

4. a. We know that 3 and 4 are integers. Show that if a represents an integer, then $3(a + 4)$ is an integer.

b. If a represents an integer, which of the following statements are always true?

$$\frac{a + 4}{3} \in I, \qquad \frac{3 + 4}{a} \in I, \qquad a(3 + 4) \in I$$

5. Show that if a and b represent rational numbers, then $\dfrac{a + 2b}{3}$ is a rational number.

6. Write a proof for each of the following implications that you determine to be true.

a. $(a \in C \wedge b \in C) \longrightarrow \dfrac{1}{a + b} \in C$

b. $(a \in I \wedge b \in C) \longrightarrow ab \in I$

c. $(a \in I \wedge b \in I) \longrightarrow \dfrac{a}{b} \in I$

d. $(a \in Q \wedge b \in C) \longrightarrow a + b \in Q$

The Field Properties and Subsets of R

In the preceding section we said that R, the set of real numbers, is closed under addition, subtraction, and multiplication, but not under division. In other sections we have pointed out that all of the field properties are true for the set of real numbers. These properties are also true for Q, the subset of rational numbers in R. Thus, both R and its subset Q are number fields. We sometimes emphasize that Q (as a field) is a subset of R (as a field) by saying that Q is a subfield of R. A *subfield* of a given field is a field whose elements are elements of the given field and whose operations are the operations of the field.

It is not true that all subsets of R are subfields of R. For example, since there is no multiplicative inverse in I, the subset of integers in R, set I is not a field. Similarly, since C, the subset of counting numbers in R, has no additive identity, additive inverse, and no multiplicative inverse, set C is not a field.

Density

Q has another property not shared by C and I. This is the property of density. This property is stated as follows:

> ▶ **Property of Density:** If a and b are rational numbers such that $a \neq b$, then there is a rational number c such that $a < c < b$ or $b < c < a$.

It follows that between any two rational numbers there are infinitely many rational numbers. This property of rational numbers is often expressed by saying that the rational numbers are *dense*. The property of density is, of course, shared by the real numbers.

The Order Properties and Subsets of R

In Chapter 1 (see page 47), we stated some of the order properties which hold for C, I, and W. It is important to note that two order properties which have not been stated previously are required for later work. One of these is:

▶ **The Archimedean Property:** If a and b are positive real numbers such that $a < b$, there is a counting number n such that $na > b$.

The other is:

▶ **The Well-Ordering Property:** If each nonempty subset of a given set contains a least member, the given set is a well-ordered set.

Any nonempty finite set of integers is well-ordered. Also, set W has this property, as does any nonempty subset of W. For example, $\{8, 9, 10, \cdots\}$ is a nonempty subset of W which has a least member. The well-ordering property is not valid for I, Q, or R. For example, $\{\cdots, -7, -6, -5\}$ is a nonempty subset of I which has no least member.

ORAL EXERCISES

1. **a.** What is a field?
   b. Is the set of counting numbers a field? Explain your answer.
   c. Is the set of rational numbers a field? Explain your answer.

2. **a.** State the definition of "density" for the rational numbers.
   b. Can we state a definition of density for the counting numbers? Explain.
   c. Do the real numbers possess the property of density? Explain.

3. **a.** We know that $2 < 5$. Name one counting number n such that $2n > 5$.
   b. What property of the counting numbers is illustrated by your answer to part **a**?
   c. We know that $0 < 5$. Can you name an integer n such that $0n > 5$? Does the property that you named in part **b** hold for set I? for set Q? for set R?

4. Which of the following subsets of R are well-ordered sets?
   a. $\emptyset$ **c.** $\{2, 4, 6, \cdots\}$ **e.** $\{x \mid x \geq 5; \ x \in R\}$
   b. $\{1, 2, 3\}$ **d.** $\{x \mid x < 5; \ x \in R\}$

Ⓐ EXERCISES

1. State the field property which justifies each of the following equalities.

   a. $\frac{1}{2} + 0 = \frac{1}{2}$ d. $\frac{3}{2} + (-\frac{3}{2}) = 0$ g. $\sqrt{5} + (-\sqrt{5}) = 0$

   b. $(-4) \cdot 1 = -4$ e. $5 \cdot \frac{1}{5} = 1$ h. $(\sqrt[3]{5} \cdot \sqrt{2})\sqrt{3} = \sqrt[3]{5}(\sqrt{2} \cdot \sqrt{3})$

   c. $(4 \cdot \frac{1}{3})9 = 4(\frac{1}{3} \cdot 9)$ f. $\frac{1}{6} \cdot \frac{1}{\frac{1}{6}} = 1$ i. $8 + (7 + 0) = 8 + 7$

2. In each of the following give the reasons. Note that each reason is a field property.

   a. $a \cdot 1 + b \cdot 1 \overset{(1)}{=} (a + b) \cdot 1 \overset{(2)}{=} a + b; \ a, b \in R$
      (1) Why? (2) Why?

   b. $0 + 1 \cdot (x + y) \overset{(1)}{=} 1 \cdot (x + y) \overset{(2)}{=} x + y; \ x, y \in I$
      (1) Why? (2) Why?

   c. $(a + b) + a \overset{(1)}{=} (b + a) + a \overset{(2)}{=} b + (a + a) \overset{(3)}{=} b + (a \cdot 1 + a \cdot 1)$
      $\overset{(4)}{=} b + (1 + 1)a = b + 2a; \ a, b \in R$
      (1) Why? (2) Why? (3) Why? (4) Why?

3. Give the reasons that justify each numbered step in the proof of the following statement: If $a, b \in R$, then $-b + (a + b) = a$.

   $a, b \in R \overset{(1)}{\longrightarrow} (-b \in R \wedge a + b \in R) \overset{(2)}{\longrightarrow} -b + (a + b) = -b + (b + a) \overset{(3)}{\nrightarrow}$
   $\overset{(3)}{\nrightarrow} -b + (a + b) = (-b + b) + a \overset{(4)}{\longrightarrow} -b + (a + b) = 0 + a \overset{(5)}{\nrightarrow}$
   $\overset{(5)}{\nrightarrow} -b + (a + b) = a. \ \therefore (a, b \in R) \overset{(6)}{\longrightarrow} -b + (a + b) = a.$

4. State the field property which justifies each of steps (1), (2), and (3).

   $(x + 2)(x + 3) \overset{(1)}{=} (x + 2)x + (x + 2)3 \overset{(2)}{=} x^2 + 2x + 3x + 6 \overset{(3)}{=} x^2 + (2 + 3)x + 6 = x^2 + 5x + 6.$
   (1) Why? (2) Why? (3) Why?

Decimal Representation of Real Numbers

We can use the long division algorithm to convert any rational number (at least approximately) into a decimal expansion having the form $a_0 + .a_1a_2a_3 \cdots a_n$ where a_0 is a whole number and $a_1, a_2, a_3, \cdots$ are the base-ten *digits* (that is, 0, 1, 2, 3, 4, 5, 6, 7, 8, 9). We say that a_1 is the digit in the first place (after the decimal point), a_2 is the digit in the second place, $\cdots$, a_n is the digit in the nth place.

Some rational numbers have terminating decimal expansions. For example,

$$\tfrac{1}{2} = 0.5 \qquad \tfrac{1}{4} = 0.25 \qquad \tfrac{1}{5} = 0.2 \qquad \tfrac{1}{20} = 0.05$$

while others have decimal expansions where certain digits or blocks of digits repeat endlessly. For example,

$$\tfrac{1}{3} = 0.3333 \cdots \qquad \tfrac{1}{7} = 0.142857142857 \cdots \qquad \tfrac{1}{11} = 0.0999 \cdots$$

We indicate the blocks of repeating digits by using dots above the digits which repeat. Thus,

$$\tfrac{1}{3} = 0.\dot{3} \qquad \tfrac{1}{7} = 0.\dot{1}4285\dot{7} \qquad \tfrac{1}{11} = 0.0\dot{9}$$

We can regard terminating decimal expressions as those in which the repeating blocks consist of only zeros. These can also be regarded as repeating decimals in which the block of repeating digits consists of the single digit 0.

Let us try to convert the rational number $\tfrac{5}{17}$ into a repeating decimal. Our work is shown at the right. As we proceed, we continue to get different remainders. When a certain remainder occurs a second time after all of the nonzero digits have been brought down, the decimal expression in the quotient repeats from this place. In our division thus far we have encountered the following numbers as remainders: 16, 7, 2, 3, 13. We see that we cannot continue to get different remainders endlessly because each remainder must be a nonnegative integer less than 17 and there are only 17 of these, 0, 1, 2, $\cdots$, 16. In other words, there will come a time when the digits in the quotient will begin to repeat.

```
          .29411
    17)5.00000
      3 4
      1 60
      1 53
         70
         68
         20
         17
         30
         17
        130
```

In general, our divisor is a counting number n. The set of possible remainders is $\{0, 1, 2, 3, \cdots, n-1\}$ which has n members. If we continue our division process until we have brought down more than n zeros, we shall have a set of more than n remainders. Such a set must contain at least one repetition. Since any such repeated remainder will have a zero brought down behind it, there will result a repetition of a block of digits in the quotient which will repeat thereafter. On the basis of this reasoning we state the following theorem.

▶ **Theorem 3–3.** If $x \in Q$, then x can be expressed as a repeating decimal.

We have observed that the number of digits, which is at least one, in the repeating block never exceeds the divisor n. Indeed, the number of digits in the repeating block cannot exceed $n - 1$ because if any remainder is zero, the quotient consists only of zeros to the right of this place. Thus if our divisor is 17, the greatest number of digits in the repeating block is 16 digits. The repeating decimal expression for $\frac{5}{17}$ has a repeating block of 16 digits, that is, $.\overset{...}{2}941176470588235$.

Now we inquire about the converse of Theorem 3–3. Is it true that each repeating decimal expression represents a rational number? To help us answer this question let us consider three examples.

Example 1. Let $c = 0.\overset{...}{4}4\overset{...}{1}$. Then $10^3c = 441.\overset{...}{4}4\overset{...}{1} = 441 + .\overset{...}{4}4\overset{...}{1} = 441 + c$ and $(10^3 - 1)c = 441$. Therefore $c = \frac{441}{999} = \frac{49}{111}$.

Example 2. Let $d = 26.5137\overset{...}{4}4\overset{...}{1}$. Then $10^4d = 265137.\overset{...}{4}4\overset{...}{1} = 265137 + \frac{49}{111}$. $d = \frac{1}{10000}(265137 + \frac{49}{111})$. Clearly $d \in Q$.

Example 3. Let $b = -26.5137\overset{...}{4}4\overset{...}{1}$. Then $b = (-1)26.5137\overset{...}{4}4\overset{...}{1}$. By Example 2, $26.5137\overset{...}{4}41 = \frac{1}{1000}(265137 + \frac{49}{111})$. Therefore $-26.5137\overset{...}{4}4\overset{...}{1} = -\frac{1}{1000}(265137 + \frac{49}{111})$.

These examples lead to the following theorem:

▶ **Theorem 4–3.** If x has a repeating decimal expression, then $x \in Q$.

There are decimal expressions which are not repeating decimals. Consider, for example, the decimal expression, 0.10100100010000100000100000001 ... formed by using only the digits 0 and 1. Notice that after the first 1 there is one zero, after the next there are two, after the next there are three, and so on. This decimal expression does not repeat. We can produce any number of such decimal expressions.

Assuming that each such nonrepeating decimal names a real number, the set of real numbers is the union of two disjoint sets of numbers—those named by the repeating decimals and those named by the nonrepeating decimals. We know that the latter set is not empty because we have just seen that nonrepeating decimals can be formed. Theorems 3–3 and 4–3 tell us that the subset of numbers named by the repeating decimals is the set Q of rational numbers. The contrapositives of these theorems are:

Contrapositive of Theorem 3–3: If x has a nonrepeating decimal expression, then $x \notin Q$.

Contrapositive of Theorem 4–3: If $x \notin Q$, then x has a nonrepeating decimal expression.

Thus, we see that these theorems also tell us that a number is irrational if and only if it can be represented by a nonrepeating decimal.

EXERCISES

1. Without actually finding their decimal expressions, tell which of the following numbers will have repeating decimal expressions.

   a. $\frac{1}{4}$

   b. -5

   c. $\frac{3}{7}$

   d. $\frac{\sqrt{6}}{5}$

   e. $-\dfrac{\sqrt{16}}{3}$

   f. $\sqrt{17}$

   g. $\sqrt{-3}$

   h. 0

2. Express each of the following which represents a rational number as the quotient of two integers:

   a. $1.\dot{1}\dot{2}$ b. $0.04004\ldots$ c. $0.\dot{3}2\dot{1}$ d. 5.666 e. $356.24\dot{2}\dot{4}$ f. 14.27

3. Use Theorem 4–3 to show that $5\frac{1}{7}$ is a rational number.

4. Show that the terminating decimal 4.83215 is a rational number.

5. Show that $0.\dot{1}4285\dot{7}$ can be expressed as the quotient of two integers.

Order among the Real Numbers

The four order properties stated below have been mentioned previously.

▶ For real numbers a, b, and c:

   Trichotomy (Comparison): Exactly one of the following is true: $a < b$, $a = b$, $a > b$.

   Addition: $a > b \longrightarrow a + c > b + c$.

   Transitivity: $(a > b$ and $b > c) \longrightarrow a > c$.

   Multiplication: (1) $(a > b$ and $c > 0) \longrightarrow ac > bc$.   (2) $(a > b$ and $c < 0) \longrightarrow ac < bc$.

In this section we draw some important inferences from these properties. These inferences are suggested by our experience with order on the number line. However, we do not rely on the number line in proving them, nor do we depend upon our previously stated rules for adding and multiplying real numbers. We shall continue to use the properties of equality and those field properties which apply.

First we define *positive* and *negative* real numbers in accordance with the ideas we acquired from our study of the number line. This definition is: If $a \in R$, then a is a positive number if and only if $a > 0$, and a is a negative number if and only if $a < 0$. Thus, by the transitive property, any positive number is greater than any negative number.

Our experience leads us to believe that the following theorem is true. Now we are ready to prove the theorem.

▶ **Theorem 5–3.** If a, $b \in R$, then $a > b \longleftrightarrow a - b > 0$ and $a < b \longleftrightarrow a - b < 0$.

Proof of Theorem 5–3: If $a, b \in R$, $a > b \longleftrightarrow a - b > 0$ and $a < b \longleftrightarrow a - b < 0$.

Proof: $a > b \longleftrightarrow a - b > 0$.

For the left-to-right proof we have: $a \overset{(1)}{>} b \overset{(2)}{\longrightarrow} [a + (-b) \overset{(3)}{>} b + (-b)] \overset{(3)}{\not\longrightarrow}$

$\overset{(3)}{\not\longrightarrow} (a - b > 0)$.

Reasons: (1) Given, (2) Addition property of inequality, (3) Theorem 9–2 and definition of additive inverse.

For the right-to-left proof we have: $a - b \overset{(1)}{>} 0 \overset{(2)}{\longrightarrow} (a - b) + b \overset{(3)}{>} 0 + b \overset{(3)}{\not\longrightarrow}$

$\overset{(3)}{\not\longrightarrow} a + [(-b) + b] \overset{(4)}{>} 0 + b \overset{(5)}{\longrightarrow} a + 0 > 0 + b \longrightarrow a > b$.

Reasons: (1) Given, (2) Addition property of inequality, (3) Theorem 9–2 and associative property of addition, (4) Definition of additive inverse, (5) Addition property of zero. Since we have proved that $(a > b) \longrightarrow (a - b > 0)$ and that $(a - b > 0) \longrightarrow (a > b)$, we know that $(a > b) \longleftrightarrow (a - b > 0)$. This follows because two statements are equivalent if it is true that each implies the other. With the proof that $(a < b) \longleftrightarrow (a - b < 0)$, which is left as an exercise, the proof of Theorem 5–3 is complete.

Now according to our definition of positive and negative numbers, we can say

$(a - b) > 0 \longleftrightarrow (a - b)$ is positive

and $(a - b) < 0 \longleftrightarrow (a - b)$ is negative.

From these statements and the statements proved in Theorem 5–3 we have

$a > b \longleftrightarrow (a - b) > 0 \longleftrightarrow (a - b)$ is positive

and $a < b \longleftrightarrow (a - b) < 0 \longleftrightarrow (a - b)$ is negative.

Since $a = b + (a - b)$, we see that $a = b + p$ (where p is a positive number) if and only if $a > b$.

Since $a = b + (a - b)$, we see that $a = b + n$ (where n is a negative number) if and only if $a < b$.

The statements in Theorem 5–3 are true for all real numbers. If we let $a = 0$ in each part of the theorem, we obtain:

$0 > b \longleftrightarrow -b > 0$

and $0 < b \longleftrightarrow -b < 0$

Thus we have proved the following:

Corollary to Theorem 5–3: A real number is negative if and only if its opposite is positive, and a real number is positive if and only if its opposite is negative.

We now prove a theorem which helps us to verify some of our rules for adding real numbers.

▷ **Theorem 6–3.** If $a, b, c, d \in R$, $a > b$, and $c > d$, then $a + c > b + d$.

Proof of Theorem 6–3: If $a, b, c, d \in R$, $a > b$, and $c > d$, then $a + c > b + d$.

$$\left.\begin{array}{c} \overset{(1)}{a > b} \overset{(2)}{\longrightarrow} a + c > b + c \\ \overset{(3)}{c > d} \overset{(4)}{\longrightarrow} b + c > b + d \end{array}\right\} \overset{(5)}{\longrightarrow} a + c > b + d$$

Reasons: (1) Given, (2) Addition property of inequality, (3) Given, (4) Addition property of inequality, (5) Transitive property of inequality.

If $b = 0$ and $d = 0$, Theorem 6–3 tells us that $(a > 0$ *and* $c > 0) \longrightarrow$ $(a + c > 0 + 0) \longrightarrow (a + c > 0)$. If $a = 0$ and $c = 0$, Theorem 6–3 tells us that $(0 > b$ *and* $0 > d) \longrightarrow (0 + 0 > b + d) \longrightarrow (0 > b + d)$. Thus we have the following:

Corollary to Theorem 6–3: The sum of two positive real numbers is positive and the sum of two negative real numbers is negative.

This result is not particularly startling because it only confirms our intuitive ideas. However, it is important that we were able to derive it from the order properties without any use of numerical examples or the number line.

Now let us see if we can prove

▷ **Theorem 7–3.** If $a, b \in R$, then $a > b \longleftrightarrow -a < -b$ and $a < b$ $\longleftrightarrow -a > -b$.

Proof of Theorem 7–3: If $a, b \in R$, $a > b \longleftrightarrow -a < -b$ and $a < b \longleftrightarrow -a > -b$.

First we show that $a > b \longrightarrow -a < -b$ as follows:

$$\overset{(1)}{a > b} \overset{(2)}{\longrightarrow} a + [(-a) + (-b)] > b + [(-a) + (-b)] \overset{(3)}{\longrightarrow} [a + (-a)] + (-b)$$

$$\overset{(4)}{> [b + (-b)] + (-a)} \longrightarrow 0 + (-b) > 0 + (-a) \overset{(5)}{\longrightarrow} -b > -a \overset{(6)}{\nrightarrow}$$

$$\overset{(6)}{\nrightarrow} -a < -b.$$ The reasons are left to you.

Similarly we prove that $-a < -b \longrightarrow a > b$. The proof is left to you. Together these deductive sequences establish that (i) $a > b \longleftrightarrow -a < -b$. Now we establish that $a < b \longleftrightarrow -a > -b$. We do this by interchanging a and b in (i). Thus, $b > a \longleftrightarrow -b < -a$. This statement is equivalent to the statement (ii) $a < b \longleftrightarrow -a > -b$. Reasons are left to you. Statements (i) and (ii) establish the theorem.

A positive real number is said to have a *positive sign* and a negative real number is said to have a *negative sign*. Two real numbers are said to have like signs if and only if they are both positive or both negative. Two real numbers are said to have opposite or unlike signs if and only if one is positive and the other negative.

Let us try to confirm our rules for multiplying real numbers. We must show that the product of two numbers having like signs is positive and the product of two numbers having opposite signs is negative.

We begin with the statement (1) of the multiplication property of order: If $a, b, c \in R$, $a > b$, and $c > 0$, then $ac > bc$. If we let $b = 0$, we have:

$$\overset{(1)}{a, c \in R}, \land a > 0 \land c > 0 \overset{(2)}{\longrightarrow} ac > 0 \cdot c \overset{(3)}{\longrightarrow} ac > 0 \qquad (i)$$

Reasons: (1) Given, (2) Multiplication property of inequality, (3) Multiplication property of zero. Observe that the above sequence proves that the product of two positive numbers is positive.

If $a < 0$ and $c < 0$, we reason as follows:

$$\left.\begin{array}{c}\overset{(1)}{a \in R} \land \overset{(2)}{a < 0 \longrightarrow -a > 0} \\ \overset{(3)}{c \in R} \land \overset{(4)}{c < 0 \longrightarrow -c > 0}\end{array}\right\} \overset{(5)}{\longrightarrow} (-a)(-c) > 0 \overset{(6)}{\longrightarrow} ac > 0 \qquad (ii)$$

Reasons: (1) Given, (2) Corollary to Theorem 5–3, (3) Given, (4) Corollary to Theorem 5–3, (5) Statement (1) proved above, (6) Theorem 12–2. Together statements (i) and (ii) tell us

(a) If two real numbers have like signs, their product is positive.

Next we use statement (*ii*) of the multiplication property of inequality: If $a, b, c \in R$, $a > b$, and $c < 0 \longrightarrow ac > bc$. If we let $b = 0$, this statement becomes:

If $a, c \in R$, $a > 0$, and $c < 0 \longrightarrow ac < 0 \cdot c \longrightarrow ac < 0$ \qquad (*iii*)

Statement (*iii*) tells us

(b) If two real numbers have unlike signs, their product is negative.

We must realize that in the reasoning above we were dealing with nonzero real numbers. For nonzero numbers the statements, "Their product is positive" and "Their product is negative" are contradictory statements because the product of nonzero numbers cannot be zero (contrapositive of Theorem 3–2) and the trichotomy property allows only two other possibilities. Also, two nonzero numbers either have like signs or they have opposite signs. Therefore, the contrapositives of the two statements (a) and (b) above are:

(a') If the product of two real numbers is negative, then they have unlike signs.

(b') If the product of two real numbers is positive, then they have like signs.

We summarize statements (a), (b), (a'), and (b') in

▷ **Theorem 8–3.** If $a, b \in R$, then $(ab > 0 \longleftrightarrow a$ and b have like signs) and $(ab < 0 \longleftrightarrow a$ and b have opposite signs).

This theorem has the following important corollaries:

Corollary 1. (1) If $a \in R$, then $a^2 \geq 0$.
(2) If $a \in R$ and $a \neq 0$, then $a^2 > 0$.

Corollary 2. $1 > 0$ and $-1 < 0$

Corollary 3. If $a \in R$ and $a \neq 0$, then a and $\dfrac{1}{a}$ have like signs.

We conclude our discussion of order among the real numbers by stating the following important theorems. The proofs of these will be considered in the examples and exercises at the end of this section.

▷ **Theorem 9–3.** If $a, b, c \in R$ and $a > 0$, then $b > c \longleftrightarrow ab > ac$.

Theorem 10–3. If $a, b, c \in R$ and $a < 0$, then $b > c \longleftrightarrow ab < ac$.

Theorem 11–3. If $a, b \in R$, $a > b$, and $ab > 0$ then $\dfrac{1}{a} < \dfrac{1}{b}$.

Theorem 12–3. If $a, b, c, d \in R$, $a > b > 0$, and $c > d > 0 \longrightarrow ac > bd$.

Corollary to Theorem 12–3. If $a, b \in R$, $a > b > 0$, then $a^2 > b^2$.

Theorem 13–3. If $a, b \in R$, $a > 0$, $b > 0$, then $a > b \longleftrightarrow a^2 > b^2$.

Theorem 14–3. If $a, b \in R$, $a > 0$, $b > 0$, then $a^2 = b^2 \longleftrightarrow a = b$.

The properties and theorems above can be extended to the $\geq$ relation. Each of the following can be verified. To avoid making a special comment in each of the theorems, we assume that $a, b, c, d \in R$.

▷ **Theorem 15–3.** $a \geq b \longrightarrow a + c \geq b + c$

Theorem 16–3. $(a \geq b \wedge b > c) \longrightarrow a > c$

Theorem 17–3. $(a \geq b \wedge b \geq c) \longrightarrow a \geq c$

Theorem 18–3. $(a \geq b \wedge c > 0) \longrightarrow ac \geq bc$

Theorem 19–3. $(a \geq b \wedge c > d) \longrightarrow a + c > b + d$

Theorem 20–3. $(a \geq b \wedge c \geq d) \longrightarrow a + c \geq b + d$

Theorem 21–3. $(a \geq b \wedge c < 0) \longrightarrow ac \leq bc$

Theorem 22–3. If $a > 0$, then $b \geq c \longleftrightarrow ab \geq ac$.

Theorem 23–3. If $a < 0$, then $b \geq c \longleftrightarrow ab \leq ac$.

Theorem 24–3. $(a > b > 0 \text{ and } c \geq d > 0) \longrightarrow ac > bd$

Theorem 25–3. $(a \geq b \geq 0 \text{ and } c \geq d \geq 0) \longrightarrow ac \geq bd$

Theorem 26–3. If $a > 0$ and $b \geq 0$, then $a \geq b \longleftrightarrow a^2 \geq b^2$.

Theorem 27–3. If $a \geq 0$ and $b \geq 0$, then $a^2 = b^2 \longleftrightarrow a = b$.

Example 1. Solve $\dfrac{1-x}{x+4} < 0$; $x \in R$.

It follows from Theorem 4–2, Corollary 3 to Theorem 8–3, and Theorem 8–3 that $\left(\dfrac{a}{b} < 0\right) \longleftrightarrow$ (a and b have opposite signs).

Therefore, $\dfrac{1-x}{x+4} < 0 \longleftrightarrow$ ($1 - x$ and $x + 4$ have opposite signs)

$\longleftrightarrow [(1 - x > 0) \wedge (x + 4 < 0)] \vee [(1 - x < 0) \wedge (x + 4 > 0)]$

Therefore $\left\{x \,\middle|\, \dfrac{1-x}{x+4} < 0\right\} = S \cup T$ where

$$S = \{x \mid (1 - x > 0) \wedge (x + 4 < 0)\} \text{ and}$$
$$T = \{x \mid (1 - x < 0) \wedge (x + 4 > 0)\}.$$

Now $S = \{x \mid x < 1\} \cap \{x \mid x < -4\} = \{x \mid x < -4\}$

and $T = \{x \mid x > 1\} \cap \{x \mid x > -4\} = \{x \mid x > 1\}$.

Therefore, $\left\{x \,\middle|\, \dfrac{1-x}{x+4} < 0\right\} = \{x \mid x < -4\} \cup \{x \mid x > 1\}$. The graph of the solution set is shown below.

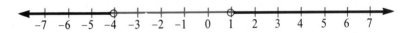

Example 2. Prove: If $x, y \in R$, $x > y \longrightarrow a - x < a - y$.

Proof.
$$\overset{(1)}{x > y} \overset{(2)}{\longrightarrow} -x < -y \overset{(3)}{\longrightarrow} (-x) + a < (-y) + a \overset{(4)}{\longrightarrow} a + (-x)$$
$$\overset{(5)}{< a + (-y)} \longrightarrow a - x < a - y.$$

Reasons: (1) Given, (2) Multiplication property of inequality, (3) Addition property of inequality, (4) Commutative property of addition, (5) Theorem 9–2.

Example 3. Find the truth set for $\dfrac{1}{x+3} < \dfrac{2}{x-2}$ when $x \in R$.

Solution. From the statement of this inequality, we know that $x + 3 \neq 0$ and $x - 2 \neq 0$. We also know that $x + 3 \neq 0 \wedge x - 2 \neq 0 \longleftrightarrow$

$x \lessgtr -3 \wedge x \lessgtr 2 \longleftrightarrow (x < -3 \vee x > -3) \wedge (x < 2 \vee x > 2)$

$\longleftrightarrow (x > -3 \wedge x < 2) \vee (x > -3 \wedge x > 2) \vee (x < -3 \wedge$

$x < 2) \vee (x < -3 \wedge x > 2) \longleftrightarrow x < -3 \vee (x > -3 \wedge x < 2) \vee$

$x > 2$. Note that the solution set of $x < -3 \wedge x > 2$ is $\emptyset$. Thus to find the solution, we consider the following cases:

(1) $\dfrac{1}{x+3} < \dfrac{2}{x-2} \wedge (x > -3 \wedge x > 2)$

(2) $\dfrac{1}{x+3} < \dfrac{2}{x-2} \wedge (x > -3 \wedge x < 2)$

(3) $\dfrac{1}{x+3} < \dfrac{2}{x-2} \wedge (x < -3 \wedge x < 2)$

(1) $\dfrac{1}{x+3} < \dfrac{2}{x-2} \wedge (x > 2 \wedge x > -3) \longleftrightarrow x-2 < 2x+6 \wedge$
$x > 2 \wedge x > -3 \longleftrightarrow x > -8 \wedge x > 2 \wedge x > -3$

Therefore, $\left\{ x \mid \dfrac{1}{x+3} < \dfrac{2}{x-2} \wedge x > 2 \wedge x > -3 \right\} = \{x \mid x > 2\}$.

(2) $\dfrac{1}{x+3} < \dfrac{2}{x-2} \wedge (x > -3 \wedge x < 2) \longleftrightarrow x-2 > 2x+6 \wedge$
$x > -3 \wedge x < 2 \longleftrightarrow x < -8 \wedge x > -3 \wedge x < 2$

Therefore, $\left\{ x \mid \dfrac{1}{x+3} < \dfrac{2}{x-2} \wedge x > -3 \wedge x < 2 \right\} = \emptyset$.

(3) $\dfrac{1}{x+3} < \dfrac{2}{x-2} \wedge (x < -3 \wedge x < 2) \longleftrightarrow x-2 < 2x+6 \wedge$
$x < -3 \wedge x < 2 \longleftrightarrow x > -8 \wedge x < -3 \wedge x < 2$

Therefore, $\left\{ x \mid \dfrac{1}{x+3} < \dfrac{2}{x-2} \wedge x < -3 \wedge x < 2 \right\} =$
$\{x \mid -8 < x < -3\}$.

Thus, the solution set is $\left\{ x \mid \dfrac{1}{x+3} < \dfrac{2}{x-2}; \ x \in R \right\} = \{x \mid x > 2\}$
$\cup \{x \mid -8 < x \wedge x < -3\} = \{x \mid (x > 2) \ or \ (-8 < x < -3) \}$

Example 4. For what values of x is $x^2 + 2x - 15 \geq 0$ true when $x \in R$?

Solution. Since $x^2 + 2x - 15 = (x+5)(x-3)$, we see that this expression is positive when $x > 3$ (for then both factors are positive) or when $x < -5$ (for then both factors are negative). Moreover this expression is zero when $x = -5$ or $x = 3$. Accordingly $\{x \mid x^2 + 2x - 15 \geq 0\} = \{x \mid x \leq -5\} \cup \{x \mid x \geq 3\}$. A more detailed analysis is shown below.

$\{x \mid x^2 + 2x - 15 \geq 0\} = \{x \mid (x+5)(x-3) \geq 0\} = \{x \mid (x+5)(x-3) > 0 \ or \ (x+5)(x-3) = 0\} = \{x \mid (x+5 > 0 \ and \ x-3 > 0)$
$or \ (x+5 < 0 \ and \ x-3 < 0) \ or \ (x+5 = 0 \ or \ x-3 = 0)\} =$
$\{x \mid (x > -5 \ and \ x > 3) \ or \ (x < -5 \ and \ x < 3) \ or \ (x = -5 \ or$
$x = 3)\} = \{x \mid x > -5 \ and \ x > 3\} \cup \{x \mid x < -5 \ and \ x < 3\} \cup$
$\{x \mid x = -5 \ or \ x = 3\} = (\{x \mid x > -5\} \cap \{x \mid x > 3\}) \cup (\{x \mid x$
$< -5\} \cap \{x \mid x < 3\}) \cup (\{x \mid x = -5\} \cup \{x \mid x = 3\}) = \{x \mid x$
$> 3\} \cup \{x \mid x < -5\} \cup \{x \mid x = -5\} \cup \{x \mid x = 3\} = \{x \mid x \geq 3\}$
$\cup \{x \mid x \leq -5\}$.

Observe that to simplify the writing we did not state $x \in R$ in each set; however, we think of the phrase as being there. The graph of the solution set of $x^2 + 2x - 15 \geq 0$ is shown below.

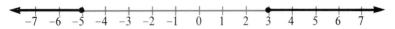

Example 5. Prove Theorem 10–3: If $a, b, c \in R$ and $a < 0$, then $b > c \longleftrightarrow ab < ac$.

Solution. Note that the proof of this theorem has the form $[(x \wedge y \longrightarrow z) \wedge (x \wedge z \longrightarrow y)] \longrightarrow [x \longrightarrow (y \longleftrightarrow z)]$ (see page 86). Observe that $(a < 0 \wedge b > c) \longrightarrow ab < ac$ is the second multiplication property of inequality. However, we can prove (i) $(a < 0 \wedge b > c) \longrightarrow ab < ac$ by means of the first multiplication property of inequality and other theorems now available as follows:

$$
\begin{array}{l}
\overset{(1)}{a < 0} \overset{(2)}{\longrightarrow} -a > 0 \Big\} \overset{(4)}{} \overset{(5)}{} \overset{(6)}{} \\
 \overset{(3)}{} \Big\} \longrightarrow (-a)b > (-a)c \longrightarrow -ab > -ac \longrightarrow \\
 b > c \\
\overset{(6)}{} \\
\longrightarrow ab < ac.
\end{array}
$$

Reasons: (1) Given, (2) Corollary to Theorem 5–3, (3) Given, (4) First multiplication property of inequality, (5) Theorem 11–2, (6) Theorem 7–3.

Note. The fact that the second multiplication property of inequality can be proved indicates that we have not attempted to keep the number of assumptions to a minimum.

(ii) $(a < 0 \wedge ab < ac) \longleftrightarrow b > c$ is proved as follows:

$$
\begin{array}{l}
\overset{(1)}{a < 0} \overset{(2)}{\longrightarrow} \frac{1}{a} < 0 \Big\} \overset{(4)}{} \overset{(5)}{} \overset{(6)}{} \\
 \overset{(3)}{} \Big\} \longrightarrow \frac{1}{a}(ab) > \frac{1}{a}(ac) \longrightarrow \left(\frac{1}{a} \cdot a\right)b > \left(\frac{1}{a} \cdot a\right)c \longrightarrow \\
 ab < ac \\
\overset{(6)}{} \\
\longrightarrow b > c
\end{array}
$$

Reasons: (1) Given, (2) Corollary 3 to Theorem 8–3, (3) Given, (4) (i) above, (5) Associative property of multiplication, (6) Definition of multiplicative inverse and multiplication property of 1. Therefore $(a, b, c \in R \wedge a < 0) \longrightarrow b > c \longleftrightarrow ab < ac.$

A EXERCISES

1. For which numbers is each of the following true if x represents a real number?

a. $(x + 6)(x - 3) \geq 0$

b. $(x - 3)(x + 3) \geq 7$

c. $(3x + 2)(2x - 5) < 0$

d. $(2x - 3)(x - 3) \geq 0$

e. $(5x - 1)(3x - 2) < 0$

f. $(x + 3)(x + 1) > 0$

2. Solve each of the following assuming that each variable represents a real number. (Remember that algebraic expressions cannot have zero denominators.)

a. $\dfrac{4-x}{2+x} < 0$

b. $\dfrac{2x}{5-x} > 0$

c. $\dfrac{5}{2m+8} + \dfrac{4}{3m+12} > 0$

d. $\dfrac{6}{r+3} + \dfrac{r}{r+3} \le -1$

e. $\dfrac{1}{x+2} < \dfrac{6}{x-3}$

f. $\dfrac{5}{x+7} + 3 \ge \dfrac{8}{x+7}$

3. Replace each question mark with one of the symbols $<, >, \ge, \le$ to form a true statement. Each variable represents a real number.

a. $x \ge a \wedge a > 2 \longrightarrow x \; \_?\_ \; 2$

b. $x \ge a \wedge a \ge 3 \longrightarrow x \; \_?\_ \; 3$

c. $x > 3 \wedge a < 0 \longrightarrow ax \; \_?\_ \; 3a$

d. $x \ge 2 \wedge 4 > d \longrightarrow x+4 \; \_?\_ \; 2+d$

e. $a \ge 5 \wedge 5 \ge b \longrightarrow a \; \_?\_ \; b$

f. $x > 0 \wedge r \ge s \longrightarrow xr \; \_?\_ \; xs$

B **EXERCISES**

4. Solve:

a. $\left(\dfrac{1}{x+1} - 1\right)\left(\dfrac{1}{x-1} + 1\right) > 0$

b. $\dfrac{x}{x^2-9} + \dfrac{5}{x+3} < 0$

c. $\dfrac{x}{x-2} + \dfrac{5}{x+4} \ge 0$

d. $\dfrac{9}{y} + \dfrac{3}{y+1} \le 0$

5. Provide the reasons for the proof of the following statement which is the second part of Theorem 5–3:

If $a, b \in R$, then $a < b \longleftrightarrow a - b < 0$.

For the left-to-right proof we have:

$$\overset{(1)}{a < b} \overset{(2)}{\longrightarrow} b > a \overset{(3)}{\longrightarrow} b+(-b) > a+(-b) \overset{(4)}{\longrightarrow} 0 > a-b \overset{(5)}{\longrightarrow} a-b < 0$$

For the right-to-left proof we have:

$$\overset{(1)}{a-b < 0} \longrightarrow \overset{(2)}{0 > a-b} \longrightarrow \overset{(3)}{0+b > (a-b)+b} \longrightarrow \overset{(4)}{0+b > a+}$$
$$\overset{(5)}{[(-b)+b]} \longrightarrow 0+b > a+0 \overset{(6)}{\longrightarrow} b > a \overset{(7)}{\longrightarrow} a < b.$$

6. Prove each of the following theorems.

a. Theorem 9–3

b. Theorem 11–3

c. Theorem 12–3

d. Theorem 13–3

e. Theorem 14–3

7. Prove: If $a, b \in R$ and $a \ne b$, then $a^2 + b^2 > 2ab$. (*Hint.* $(a-b)^2 > 0$. Why?)

8. Prove: If $a, b \in R$, then $a^2 + b^2 \ge 2ab$.

9. Prove: If $a \in R$, $a > 0$, and $a \neq 1$, then $a + \dfrac{1}{a} > 2$. (*Hint.* $(a-1)^2 > 0$. Why?)

10. Prove: The sum of any positive real number and its reciprocal is equal to or greater than 2.

11. Prove: If $a, b \in R$, $a > 0$, $b > 0$, and $a \neq b$, then $\dfrac{a}{b} + \dfrac{b}{a} > 2$.

Computation with Irrational Numbers

In this section we review and extend our knowledge of the rules for computing with real numbers. First we shall consider non-negative roots of equations such as $x^2 = a$ when a is a non-negative real number. We make the following assumption and then later prove that the assumption is correct: If $a \in A$ (A is the set of non-negative real numbers), there exists an x in A such that $x^2 = a$. Theorem 27–3 tells us that x is unique; for in $y \in A$ and $y^2 = a$, then $x^2 = y^2$ and hence $x = y$. Hence, our assumption and Theorem 27–3 combine to establish the conclusion that there is one and only one x in A such that x^2 is equal to a given number a. We call the unique positive root the principal square root of a and designate it by the symbol $\sqrt{a}$. Thus, we have established

▶ **Theorem 28–3.** If a is a non-negative real number, then there is a unique non-negative real number $\sqrt{a}$ such that $(\sqrt{a})^2 = a$.

To simplify expressions involving indicated nth roots of numbers that are not nth powers of any rational number, we must know how to find the products and quotients involving such radicals as $\sqrt{7}$, $\sqrt[3]{11}$, $\sqrt[5]{-31}$. For radical expressions involving square roots we have

▶ **Theorem 29–3.** (1) If a is a non-negative real number and b is a non-negative real number, then $\sqrt{a}\sqrt{b} = \sqrt{ab}$.

(2) If a is a non-negative real number and b is a positive real number, then

$$\frac{\sqrt{a}}{\sqrt{b}} = \sqrt{\frac{a}{b}}.$$

Proof of Theorem 29–3 (1): If a is a non-negative real number and b is a non-negative real number, then $\sqrt{a}\sqrt{b} = \sqrt{ab}$.

1. $a \geq 0$ and $b \geq 0$	1. Given
2. There is a unique non-negative real number $\sqrt{a}$ such that $(\sqrt{a})^2 = a$ and there is a unique real number $\sqrt{b}$ such that $(\sqrt{b})^2 = b$	2. Theorem 28–3
3. $(\sqrt{a})^2(\sqrt{b})^2 = ab$	3. Multiplication property of equality

4. $(\sqrt{a})^2(\sqrt{b})^2 = (\sqrt{a}\sqrt{b})^2$

5. $(\sqrt{a}\sqrt{b})^2 = ab$

6. $\sqrt{a}\sqrt{b}$ is a non-negative real number and ab is a non-negative real number

7. There is a non-negative real number $\sqrt{ab}$ such that $(\sqrt{ab})^2 = ab$

8. $(\sqrt{ab})^2 = (\sqrt{a}\sqrt{b})^2$

9. $\sqrt{ab} = \sqrt{a}\sqrt{b}$

4. $x^2y^2 \equiv (xy)^2$

5. Transitive property of equality

6. The product of two non-negative real numbers is a non-negative real number.

7. Theorem 28–3

8. Transitive property of equality

9. Theorem 27–3.

Proof of Theorem 29–3 (2): This proof follows the same pattern as the proof of (1). We leave it to you as an exercise.

We know that $\sqrt{a}$ represents a real number if and only if a is a non-negative real number. Such symbols as $\sqrt{-4}$ and $\sqrt{-23}$ do not represent real numbers. We know that -4 has no real square root because there is no real number x such that $x^2 = -4$. In Chapter 11 we consider "the square root of a" for the case in which a is negative. For the present we want the symbol $\sqrt[n]{a}$ to represent a real number whose nth power is a. $\sqrt[4]{-16}$ and $\sqrt{-43}$ do not represent real numbers although $\sqrt[3]{-27}$ and $\sqrt[5]{-32}$ represent negative real numbers.

We state the following generalizations:

1. When n is an even counting number and a is a real number:
   a. If a is negative, then a has no real nth root.
   b. If a is positive, then a has exactly two real nth roots. The positive root is indicated by $\sqrt[n]{a}$ and the negative root by $-\sqrt[n]{a}$. The positive root is referred to as the principal nth root.
   c. If a is 0, then a has exactly one nth root, 0.
2. When n is an odd counting number and a is a real number:
   a. Whether a is positive or negative, a has exactly one real nth root which we denote by $\sqrt[n]{a}$. If a is negative, then $\sqrt[n]{a}$ is negative. If a is positive, then $\sqrt[n]{a}$ is positive.
   b. If a is 0, then a has exactly one nth root, 0.

In Chapter 11 we study set Z, a superset of R (a set of which R is a proper subset), in which we can find for each number except 0 two square roots, three cube roots, four fourth roots, and so on.

We are now ready to interpret the following generalization of Theorem 29–3 which we present without proof.

▶ **Theorem 30–3.** (1) If $\sqrt[n]{a} \in R$, $\sqrt[n]{b} \in R$, and $n \in C$, then $\sqrt[n]{a}\sqrt[n]{b} = \sqrt[n]{ab}$.

(2) If $\sqrt[n]{a} \in R$, $\sqrt[n]{b} \in R$, $n \in C$, and $b \neq 0$, then $\dfrac{\sqrt[n]{a}}{\sqrt[n]{b}} = \sqrt[n]{\dfrac{a}{b}}$.

This theorem is applied in performing computations with irrational numbers. The following are examples:

1. $\sqrt{10}\sqrt{2} = \sqrt{20} = \sqrt{4 \cdot 5} = \sqrt{4}\sqrt{5} = 2\sqrt{5}$

2. $\sqrt{108} = \sqrt{36 \cdot 3} = \sqrt{36}\sqrt{3} = 6\sqrt{3}$

3. $\sqrt[3]{-40} = \sqrt[3]{(-8) \cdot 5} = \sqrt[3]{-8}\sqrt[3]{5} = -2\sqrt[3]{5}$

4. $\sqrt[3]{108} - 7\sqrt[3]{4} = \sqrt[3]{27 \cdot 4} - 7\sqrt[3]{4} = \sqrt[3]{27}\sqrt[3]{4} - 7\sqrt[3]{4} = 3\sqrt[3]{4} - 7\sqrt[3]{4} =$
$$- 4\sqrt[3]{4}$$

5. $\dfrac{\sqrt{11}}{\sqrt{3}} = \dfrac{\sqrt{11}}{\sqrt{3}} \cdot \dfrac{\sqrt{3}}{\sqrt{3}} = \dfrac{\sqrt{33}}{\sqrt{3^2}} = \dfrac{\sqrt{33}}{3}.$ If it is desired to find the decimal approximation of $\dfrac{\sqrt{11}}{\sqrt{3}}$, it is easily done by using the $\dfrac{\sqrt{33}}{3}$ form. Thus $\dfrac{\sqrt{33}}{3} \approx \dfrac{5.7446}{3} \approx 1.91.$ Had we used the original form $\dfrac{\sqrt{11}}{\sqrt{3}}$, we would have had to perform the laborious division $\dfrac{3.3166}{1.7321}.$ Note the use of $\approx$ to mean "is approximately equal to."

6. To find $\sqrt[3]{\dfrac{-37}{4}}$ to the nearest hundredth, we might proceed in either of of the following ways:

Method 1.

$$\sqrt[3]{\dfrac{-37}{4}} = \sqrt[3]{\dfrac{-37}{4} \cdot \dfrac{2}{2}} = \sqrt[3]{\dfrac{-74}{8}} = \dfrac{\sqrt[3]{-74}}{\sqrt[3]{8}} = \dfrac{\sqrt[3]{-74}}{2} = \dfrac{-\sqrt[3]{74}}{2} \approx \dfrac{-4.198}{2}$$

Method 2.

$$\sqrt[3]{\dfrac{-37}{4}} = \dfrac{\sqrt[3]{-37}}{\sqrt[3]{4}} = \dfrac{\sqrt[3]{-37} \cdot \sqrt[3]{2}}{\sqrt[3]{4} \cdot \sqrt[3]{2}} = \dfrac{\sqrt[3]{-74}}{\sqrt[3]{8}} = \dfrac{-\sqrt[3]{74}}{2} \approx \dfrac{-4.198}{2}$$

Note. When we ask that a real number of the form $\sqrt[n]{\dfrac{a}{b}}$ or $\dfrac{\sqrt[n]{a}}{\sqrt[n]{b}}$; $n \in C$, $n \geq 2$, and $a, b \in I$ be expressed with a rational denominator, we mean that it should be expressed in an identically equal form $\dfrac{\sqrt[n]{c}}{d}$ when $c, d \in I$ and $d \neq 0$. Thus $\sqrt[3]{\dfrac{-37}{4}}$ is expressed with a rational denominator when it is written in the form $\dfrac{\sqrt[3]{-74}}{2}$ or $\dfrac{-\sqrt[3]{74}}{2}.$

7. Express with a rational denominator: $\dfrac{4}{\sqrt{3} - 2\sqrt{7}}.$ In order to obtain an identically equal fraction whose denominator is rational, we first multiply both numerator and denominator by $\sqrt{3} + 2\sqrt{7}$ (that is, multiply

both numerator and denominator by the expression that differs from the denominator only in that the sign of the second term is changed).

$$\frac{4}{\sqrt{3}-2\sqrt{7}} = \frac{4(\sqrt{3}+2\sqrt{7})}{(\sqrt{3}-2\sqrt{7})(\sqrt{3}+2\sqrt{7})} = \frac{4\sqrt{3}+8\sqrt{7}}{3-28} = \frac{4\sqrt{3}+8\sqrt{7}}{-25}$$

The process of expressing a fraction which has one or more radical expressions in its denominator as an identically equal fraction whose denominator is free of radicals is called *rationalizing the denominator*. There are situations in which it is desirable to *rationalize the numerator*. The following example shows how a numerator may be rationalized.

8. Rationalize the numerator of $\dfrac{\sqrt{x+1}-\sqrt{x-1}}{\sqrt{x+1}+\sqrt{x-1}}$. We multiply both the numerator and the denominator by $\sqrt{x+1}+\sqrt{x-1}$ (that is, by the expression which is like the *numerator* except for the sign between the two radicals). We have:

$$\begin{aligned}
\frac{\sqrt{x+1}-\sqrt{x-1}}{\sqrt{x+1}+\sqrt{x-1}} &= \frac{(\sqrt{x+1}-\sqrt{x-1})(\sqrt{x+1}+\sqrt{x-1})}{(\sqrt{x+1}+\sqrt{x-1})(\sqrt{x+1}+\sqrt{x-1})} \\
&= \frac{(x+1)-(x-1)}{(x+1)+2\sqrt{x^2-1}+(x-1)} \\
&= \frac{2}{2x+2\sqrt{x^2-1}} \\
&= \frac{1}{x+\sqrt{x^2-1}}.
\end{aligned}$$

Note that in Example 8 we assumed that $x > 1$. In all cases in which variables appear under radical signs it will be assumed that their domains are restricted to values for which the radical expressions name real numbers.

Simplified Form of a Radical

The radical expression $\sqrt[n]{a}$ when $n \geq 2$ and $n \in C$ is in simplest form if a is an integer which does not have the nth power of any integer other than 1 or -1 as a factor.

Example.   Express in simplest form a. $\sqrt{72}$, b. $\sqrt[3]{-54}$, c. $-\sqrt{12}\sqrt{6}$

Solution.   a. $\sqrt{72} = \sqrt{36}\sqrt{2} = 6\sqrt{2}$
  b. $\sqrt[3]{-54} = \sqrt[3]{-27}\sqrt[3]{2} = -3\sqrt[3]{2}$
  c. $-\sqrt{12}\sqrt{6} = -\sqrt{72} = -\sqrt{36}\sqrt{2} = -6\sqrt{2}$

1. Express each of the following in simplest form.

a. $\sqrt{18}$ c. $\sqrt[3]{250}$ e. $\sqrt[4]{16}$ g. $-5\sqrt{675}$

b. $2\sqrt{192}$ d. $\sqrt[3]{-512}$ f. $\sqrt[4]{1250}$ h. $-\sqrt[3]{-128}$

2. Express each in its simplest form.

a. $\sqrt{14}\sqrt{2}$ d. $3\sqrt[3]{-108}\sqrt[3]{16}$ g. $-\sqrt{125}\sqrt{18}$

b. $\sqrt[3]{16}\sqrt[3]{16}$ e. $\sqrt[3]{128}(-\sqrt[3]{250})$ h. $(-\sqrt{147})(-\sqrt{3})$

c. $\sqrt{108}\cdot\sqrt{48}$ f. $\sqrt{288}\cdot 2\sqrt{2}$ i. $\sqrt{5}\cdot\sqrt{6}\cdot\sqrt{7}$

3. Express each of the following so that no radical signs appear in the denominator. Each variable is a positive number.

a. $\dfrac{6\sqrt{13}}{\sqrt{3}}$

b. $\dfrac{\sqrt[3]{40}}{\sqrt[3]{5}}$

c. $\sqrt{\tfrac{18}{5}}$

d. $\sqrt{\tfrac{12}{7}}$

e. $\dfrac{3}{1-\sqrt{5}}$

f. $\dfrac{5}{\sqrt{3}+2\sqrt{7}}$

g. $\dfrac{7+\sqrt{2}}{7-\sqrt{2}}$

h. $\dfrac{5-\sqrt{3}}{2-\sqrt{3}}$

i. $\dfrac{x}{\sqrt{x}+\sqrt{y}}$

j. $\dfrac{2}{\sqrt{x+2}-\sqrt{x-2}}$

k. $\dfrac{\sqrt{x+1}}{\sqrt{x+1}+\sqrt{x-1}}$

l. $\dfrac{\sqrt{a+b}-\sqrt{a-b}}{\sqrt{a+b}+\sqrt{a-b}}$

4. Rationalize each numerator. Each variable is a positive number.

a. $\dfrac{\sqrt{3}}{2}$

b. $\dfrac{\sqrt{5}+1}{3}$

c. $\dfrac{4+\sqrt{6}}{1-\sqrt{6}}$

d. $\dfrac{\sqrt[3]{-16}}{\sqrt[3]{2}+1}$

e. $\dfrac{\sqrt{x+3}-\sqrt{x-4}}{\sqrt{x+3}+\sqrt{x-4}}$

f. $\dfrac{\sqrt{x}+\sqrt{x-y}}{\sqrt{x+y}-\sqrt{x}}$

5. Express each of the following in simplest form, assuming that each variable represents a positive number.

a. $\dfrac{\sqrt{125\,y}}{\sqrt{7\,y^2}}$

b. $\sqrt{\dfrac{7}{8}}\cdot\sqrt{\dfrac{3\,x}{14}}$

c. $\dfrac{\sqrt{5\,m}}{\sqrt{3\,m^2}}\cdot\dfrac{\sqrt{5}}{\sqrt{10\,m}}$

d. $\sqrt{\tfrac{4}{5}-\tfrac{1}{6}}$

e. $\sqrt{(\tfrac{2}{3}+\tfrac{3}{2})12}$

f. $\sqrt{x-3+\dfrac{1}{x}}$

Closure in Q, Q′, and R

We have said that $a \,\epsilon\, Q$ if and only if a can be expressed in the form $\dfrac{c}{d}$ where $c,\ d \,\epsilon\, I$ and $d \neq 0$. We have observed that $R = Q \cup Q'$ and that $Q \cap Q' = \emptyset$. We have been assuming that Q is closed with respect to addition and multiplication. Since $x - y = x + (-y)$ and since $(-y) \in Q$ if $y \in Q$, it follows that Q is closed with respect to subtraction. Since $\dfrac{x}{y}$ does not name a rational number (or even a real number) when y is the rational number 0, it follows that Q is not closed with respect to division. We have proved earlier that division in Q always produces a rational number when division by 0 is excluded. Now we shall prove that Q is closed with respect to addition and subtraction.

 Theorem 31–3. (1) If $a \in Q$ and $b \in Q$, then $(a + b) \in Q$.

(2) If $a \in Q$ and $b \in Q$, then $(a - b) \in Q$.

Proof of Theorem 31–3. (1). If $a \in Q$ and $b \in Q$, then $(a + b) \in Q$.

1. $a \in Q$ and $b \in Q$	1. Given
2. $a = \dfrac{c}{d}$ where $c, d \in I$ and $d \neq 0$ $b = \dfrac{e}{f}$ where $e, f \in I$ and $f \neq 0$	2. Definition of a rational number
3. $a + b = \dfrac{c}{d} + \dfrac{e}{f}$	3. Addition property of equality
4. $\dfrac{c}{d} + \dfrac{e}{f} = \dfrac{cf + de}{df}$	4. Theorem 20–2
5. $a + b = \dfrac{cf + de}{df}$	5. Transitive property of equality
6. $(cf + de) \in I$ $df \in I$	6. I is closed with respect to addition and multiplication.
7. $df \neq 0$	7. Contrapositive of Theorem 3–2
8. $a + b \in Q$	8. Definition of rational numbers

Proof of Theorem 31–3. (2). If $a \in Q$ and $b \in Q$, then $(a - b) \in Q$.

The proof of this part of Theorem 31–3 follows closely from the first part as implied above.

 Theorem 32–3. (1) If $a \in Q$ and $b \in Q$, then $ab \in Q$.

(2) If $a \in Q$, $b \in Q$, and $b \neq 0$, then $\dfrac{a}{b} \in Q$.

The proof of part (2) of this theorem was given in the example on pages 106–107. The proof of Part (1) is left to you as an exercise.

Now that we know that Q is closed with respect to addition, subtraction, and multiplication, but not with respect to division, let us consider whether the same is true of Q'. What is true of $x + y$ and of xy when $x, y \in Q'$?

Let us first consider what is true of $x + y$ and of xy when $x \in Q$ and $y \in Q'$. If $\sqrt{3} + 4 = t$, then $\sqrt{3} = t + (-4)$. We know that t is either rational or irrational. In other words, the statements (*i*) "t is rational" and (*ii*) "t is irrational" are contradictory statements. If we can show that (*i*) is false we must conclude that (*ii*) is true. If (*i*) is true, then $\sqrt{3}$ is a rational number because the sum of two rational numbers is a rational number. However, we know that $\sqrt{3}$ is not rational. Therefore, we reject the idea that t is rational because it implies a false conclusion. Since (*i*) is false, its contradiction (*ii*) "t is irrational" is true. This discussion suggests the following theorem:

▷ **Theorem 33–3.** If $x \in Q'$ and $y \in Q$, then $(x + y) \in Q'$.

Let us now consider the product of an irrational number and a nonzero rational number. What can we say, for example, about $\frac{7}{5}\sqrt{3}$? Let $\frac{7}{5}\sqrt{3} = t$. Then $\sqrt{3} = t \cdot \frac{5}{7}$. An argument similar to the one in the preceding paragraph, but involving Theorem 32–3 (1) "If $a \in Q$ and $b \in Q$, then $ab \in Q$," will show that t is an irrational number. This suggests the following theorem:

▷ **Theorem 34–3.** If $x \in Q'$, $y \in Q$, and $y \neq 0$, then $xy \in Q'$.

Consider the contrapositive of Theorem 34–3 which is obtained by interchanging the contradiction of the conclusion with the contradiction of the first statement in the hypothesis: If $xy \in Q$, $y \in Q$, and $y \neq 0$, then $x \in Q$. Clearly this is Theorem 32–3, (2) with xy written for a and y for b. Hence, a proof of Theorem 32–3, (2) also establishes Theorem 34–3.

Similar considerations enable us to show that "If $x \in Q'$ and $y \in Q$, then $\frac{x}{y} \in Q'$" and "If $x \in Q'$ and $y \in Q$, then $x - y \in Q'$" are contrapositives of true theorems and therefore are true.

We now return to our question about the sum and product of two irrational numbers. We rely upon a counterexample to disprove the idea that the sum of two irrational numbers is necessarily irrational. Observe that $7 - \sqrt{2}$ and $7 + \sqrt{2}$ are irrational numbers with the rational sum 14. We must also reject the idea that the product of two irrational numbers is always irrational. Observe that the product of $\sqrt{3}\sqrt{12}$ is the rational number 6, yet each of the factors $\sqrt{3}$ and $\sqrt{12}$ is irrational. Also, the irrational factors $7 - \sqrt{2}$ and $7 + \sqrt{2}$ have the rational product 47. Of course the sum of two irrational numbers may be irrational as in the case of $3\sqrt{7}$ and $4\sqrt{7}$. Also, the product of two irrational numbers may be irrational as in the case of $\sqrt{3}$ and $\sqrt{5}$. We conclude that the sum or product of two irrational numbers may be either rational or irrational.

1. Fill each blank with either the phrase "$\epsilon\,Q$" or the phrase "$\epsilon\,Q'$" to form a true statement.

   a. $5\,\epsilon\,Q$ and $\sqrt{3}\,\epsilon\,Q'$. $5\sqrt{3}$ _?_.

   b. $\sqrt{72}\,\epsilon\,Q'$ and $\sqrt{2}\,\epsilon\,Q'$. $\sqrt{72}\sqrt{2}$ _?_.

   c. $\sqrt{72}\,\epsilon\,Q'$ and $\sqrt{3}\,\epsilon\,Q'$. $\sqrt{72}\sqrt{3}$ _?_.

   d. $\sqrt{5}\,\epsilon\,Q'$ and $\sqrt{6}\,\epsilon\,Q'$. $(\sqrt{5}+\sqrt{6})$ _?_.

   e. $\sqrt{4}\,\epsilon\,Q$ and $3\,\epsilon\,Q$. $(\sqrt{4}+3)$ _?_.

   f. $\sqrt{11}\,\epsilon\,Q'$ and $5\,\epsilon\,Q$. $(\sqrt{11}-5)$ _?_.

   g. $\sqrt{12}\,\epsilon\,Q'$ and $\sqrt{4}\,\epsilon\,Q$. $\dfrac{\sqrt{12}}{\sqrt{4}}$ _?_.

   h. $\sqrt{32}\,\epsilon\,Q'$ and $\sqrt{2}\,\epsilon\,Q'$. $\dfrac{\sqrt{32}}{\sqrt{2}}$ _?_.

   i. $\sqrt{81}\,\epsilon\,Q$ and $\sqrt{27}\,\epsilon\,Q'$. $\dfrac{3}{\sqrt{3}}$ _?_.

   j. $\sqrt{216}\,\epsilon\,Q'$ and $54\,\epsilon\,Q'$. $\dfrac{\sqrt{216}}{\sqrt{54}}$ _?_.

2. Complete each sentence correctly by filling the blank with one of the phrases "is always a rational number," "is always an irrational number," or "is sometimes a rational number and sometimes an irrational number."

   a. The sum of two rational numbers _?_.

   b. The sum of two irrational numbers _?_.

   c. The sum of a rational number and an irrational number _?_.

   d. The product of two rational numbers _?_.

   e. The product of two irrational numbers _?_.

   f. The product of a rational number and an irrational number _?_.

   g. The difference of two rational numbers _?_.

   h. The difference of two irrational numbers _?_.

   i. The difference of a rational number and an irrational number _?_.

   j. The quotient of two rational numbers when the denominator is not zero _?_.

   k. The quotient of an irrational number by a nonzero irrational _?_.

   l. The quotient of a rational number by a nonzero irrational number _?_.

   m. The quotient of an irrational number by a nonzero rational number _?_.

3. Prove: If $a\,\epsilon\,Q$ and $b\,\epsilon\,Q$, then $ab\,\epsilon\,Q$.

Statements Involving Absolute Value

The expressions $|x|$ and $\sqrt{x^2}$ are identically equal. Let us consider the reason for this. The identity $\sqrt{x^2} = |x|$ is a direct consequence of the definitions we have stated for these expressions. We recall that

$$|x| \text{ is } x \text{ when } x \geq 0 \text{ and } -x \text{ when } x < 0. \tag{a}$$

Since $\sqrt{x^2}$ is the non-negative real number whose square is x^2, we see that

$$\sqrt{x^2} = x \text{ when } x \geq 0 \text{ and } -x \text{ when } x < 0. \tag{b}$$

Thus, statements (a) and (b) establish the following theorem:

▷ **Theorem 35–3.** If $x \in R$, then $\sqrt{x^2} = |x|$.

This theorem has several important consequences. We know, of course, that $|5| = |-5|, |11| = |-11|$, and in general that $|x| = |-x|$. Theorem 35–3 helps us to show that this is true. According to this theorem, $|x| = \sqrt{x^2}$ and $|-x| = \sqrt{(-x)^2}$. Moreover, we know that $x^2 = (-x)^2$. Therefore, $\sqrt{x^2} = \sqrt{(-x)^2}$, and it follows that $|x| = |-x|$. Thus we have:

▷ **Theorem 36–3.** If $x \in R$, then $|x| = |-x|$.

Consider the unary operations on real numbers—taking the absolute value and squaring. Let us look at a numerical example in which we compare the square of the absolute value of a number with the absolute value of the square of the number. Let our given real number be -7.

$$|-7| = 7, \text{ therefore } |-7|^2 = 7^2 = 49$$
$$(-7)^2 = 49, \text{ therefore } |(-7)^2| = |49| = 49$$

Also, if our given number is 6, we have $|6|^2 = |6^2| = 36$. We conjecture that $|x|^2 = |x^2|$ and we state this conjecture as the following theorem:

▷ **Theorem 37–3.** If $x \in R$, then $|x|^2 = |x^2| = x^2$.

Proof of Theorem 37–3: If $x \in R$, then $|x|^2 = |x^2| = x^2$.

$$\begin{array}{c}
\overset{(1)}{} \quad \overset{(2)}{} \qquad \overset{(3)}{} \\
x \in R \longrightarrow x^2 \geq 0 \longrightarrow |x^2| = x^2 \\
\overset{(4)}{} \quad \overset{(5)}{} \qquad \overset{(6)}{} \\
x \in R \longrightarrow |x| = \sqrt{x^2} \longrightarrow |x|^2 = x^2
\end{array} \left.\begin{array}{c} \\ \end{array}\right\} \overset{(7)}{\longrightarrow} |x|^2 = |x^2| = x^2$$

Reasons:
(1) Given, (2) Theorem 8–3, Cor. 1, (3) Definition of absolute value, (4) Given, (5) Theorem 35–3, (6) Theorem 2–3, (7) Transitive property of equality.

The following statements about real numbers x and y are useful in the proofs of some of the theorems which we encounter later in this section.

$(i)\ |x| \geq 0$ $(ii)\ |x| \geq -|x|$ $(iii)\ |x| + |y| \geq 0$

The proofs of these statements will be considered in the exercises.

We know that a real number cannot be greater than its absolute value and we know that it cannot be less than the negative of its absolute value. Thus, the conjunctive statement (iv) $x \leq |x|$ *and* $x \geq -|x|$ is true for all real values of x. For example, $7 \leq |7|$ and $7 \geq -|7|$; $-5 \leq |-5|$ and $-5 \geq -|-5|$.

We see that (iv) has the form $x \leq a$ *and* $x \geq b$. This statement is equivalent to $b \leq x \leq a$. That is, (v) $(x \leq a$ *and* $x \geq b) \longleftrightarrow (b \leq x \leq a)$. Therefore, $(x \leq |x|$ *and* $x \geq -|x|) \longleftrightarrow (-|x| \leq x \leq |x|)$. These considerations lead us to state the following theorem:

▶ **Theorem 38–3.** If $x \in R$, then $-|x| \leq x \leq |x|$.

In the following examples we compare the absolute value of the product of two real numbers with the product of their absolute values.

$|(-7)(-3)| = |21| = 21$ $|(5)(-11)| = |-55| = 55$
$|-7| \cdot |-3| = 7 \cdot 3 = 21$ $|5| \cdot |-11| = 5 \cdot 11 = 55$
Thus   Thus
$|(-7)(-3)| = |-7| \cdot |-3|.$ $|(5)(-11)| = |5| \cdot |-11|.$

We generalize these results in the following theorem:

▶ **Theorem 39–3.** If $x, y \in R$, then $|x| \cdot |y| = |xy|$.

Proof of Theorem 39–3: If $x, y \in R$, then $|x| \cdot |y| = |xy|$.

$$|x| \cdot |y| \overset{(1)}{=} \sqrt{x^2}\sqrt{y^2} \overset{(2)}{=} \sqrt{x^2 y^2} \overset{(3)}{=} \sqrt{(xy)^2} \overset{(4)}{=} |xy|$$

The reasons are left to you.

Now we shall consider some other statements involving absolute value. Under what circumstances can we say that $|x| \leq |y|$? Is it sufficient to know that $x \leq y$? Let us test this conjecture by letting $x = 7$ and $y = 13$. Is it true that $|7| \leq |13|$? We see that it is. Suppose that $x = -7$ and $y = 13$. Is it true that $|-7| \leq |13|$? Again the answer is "Yes." Now let us test the conjecture by letting $x = -17$ and $y = -5$. Is it true that $|-17| \leq |-5|$? The answer is "No." Since $-17 < -5$ but $|-17| > |-5|$, this example destroys our theory that the larger number has the larger absolute value. Since the squares of real numbers, like the absolute values of real numbers, are non-negative, perhaps we can compare two real numbers by comparing their squares. Perhaps the number with the larger square has the larger absolute value. The fact that $(-17)^2 > (-5)^2$ supports this theory. After you have tried other numerical examples perhaps you will agree that the following theorem is true.

▷   **Theorem 40–3.** If x, $y \in R$, then $x^2 \leq y^2 \longrightarrow |x| \leq |y|$.

Before we can prove this theorem we should first note that the following statements about real numbers are true: (*vi*) If $ab \leq 0$ and $a > 0$, then $b \leq 0$, and (*vii*) If $x \neq 0$, then $|x| + |y| > 0$. The proofs of (*vi*) and (*vii*) are left to you as exercises.

Proof of Theorem 40–3: If x, $y \in P$, $x^2 \leq y^2 \longrightarrow |x| \leq |y|$.

If $x = 0$, the theorem is obviously true. Therefore, let us assume that $x \neq 0$.

$$\overset{(1)}{x^2} \leq \overset{(2)}{y^2} \longrightarrow \overset{(3)}{|x|^2 \leq |y|^2} \longrightarrow \overset{(4)}{|x|^2 - |y|^2 \leq 0} \nrightarrow$$

$$\overset{(4)}{\nrightarrow} (|x| + |y|)(|x| - |y|) \leq 0 \Big\} \overset{(7)}{\longrightarrow} |x| - |y| \leq 0 \overset{(8)}{\longrightarrow} |x| \leq |y|$$
$$\overset{(5)}{x \neq 0} \overset{(6)}{\longrightarrow} |x| + |y| > 0 \Big\}$$

Reasons:
(1) Given, (2) Theorem 37–3, (3) Theorem 5–3, addition property of equality, Theorem 9–2, and definition of additive inverse, (4) Factoring (distributive property), (5) Given, (6) (*vii*), (7) (*vi*), (8) Addition property of inequality.

Note. If $x = 0$, then $x^2 \leq y^2 \longrightarrow |x| \leq |y|$, and if $x \neq 0$, then $x^2 \leq y^2 \longrightarrow |x| \leq |y|$. Now either $x = 0$ or $x \neq 0$. Therefore, under all possible circumstances, this theorem is true.

Since $|x|$ represents the measure of the distance between a point in the number line whose coordinate is x and the origin, it seems reasonable to suppose that the statement "$|x| < a$" is equivalent to the statement "The measure of the distance between the point X whose coordinate is x and the origin is less than a."

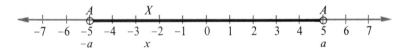

Thus if $a = 5$, X must be in the interval between A and A' as shown above. This means that $x > -5$ and $x < 5$; that is, $-5 < x < 5$. This leads us to state the following theorem:

▷   **Theorem 41–3.** If x, $a \in R$ and $a > 0$, then $|x| < a \longleftrightarrow -a < x < a$.

The following true statement about real numbers will be needed in proving Theorem 41–3. (*viii*) If $a > 0$, then $(x - a)(x + a) < 0 \longleftrightarrow x - a < 0$ *and* $x + a > 0$.

The proof of this statement is left to you as an exercise.

Proof of Theorem 41–3: If x, $a \in R$ and $a > 0$, $|x| < a \longleftrightarrow -a < x < a$.

$$\overset{(1)}{0 \leq} |x| \overset{(2)}{< a \longleftrightarrow} \underset{(16)}{|x|^2} \overset{(3)}{< a^2 \longleftrightarrow} \underset{(15)}{x^2} \overset{(4)}{< a^2 \longleftrightarrow} \underset{(14)}{x^2} \overset{(5)}{- a^2 < 0 \longleftrightarrow} \underset{(13)}{(x - a)(x + a)}$$

$$\overset{(6)}{< 0 \longleftrightarrow} \underset{(12)}{(x - a < 0 \text{ and } x + a > 0)} \overset{(7)}{\longleftrightarrow} \underset{(11)}{(x < a \text{ and } x > -a)} \overset{(8)}{\longleftrightarrow} \underset{(10)}{-a} < x < a.$$

Reasons:
(Left-to-right) (1) Given and definition of absolute value, (2) Corollary to Theorem 12–3, (3) Theorem 37–3, (4) Theorem 5–3, (5) Factoring (distributive property), (6) (*viii*) We use the left-to-right part, (7) Addition property of inequality, (8) (*v*) You may supply the reasons 9–16 from right-to-left.

When $a \geq 0$, we have $|x| = a \longleftrightarrow (x = a \text{ or } x = -a)$. This statement may be combined with Theorem 41–3 to prove the following:

Corollary to Theorem 41–3. If x, $a \in R$ and $a \geq 0$, then $|x| \leq a \longleftrightarrow -a \leq x \leq a$.

Example 1. Express the following inequality without using absolute value signs: $|2x - 5| \leq 7$.

Solution. $|2x - 5| \leq 7 \longleftrightarrow -7 \leq (2x - 5) \leq 7 \longleftrightarrow -2 \leq 2x \leq 12 \longleftrightarrow -1 \leq x \leq 6$.

Example 2. Show that $c < z < d \longleftrightarrow \left| z - \dfrac{c+d}{2} \right| < \dfrac{d-c}{2}$.

Solution. The proof is easily obtained by applying Theorem 41–3:

$$|x| < a \longleftrightarrow -a < x < a$$

Now letting $x = z - \dfrac{c+d}{2}$ and $a = \dfrac{d-c}{2}$ and substituting these values in the statement of Theorem 41–3 we have:

$$\left| z - \frac{c+d}{2} \right| < \frac{d-c}{2} \longleftrightarrow -\frac{d-c}{2} < z - \frac{c+d}{2} < \frac{d-c}{2} \longleftrightarrow -(d-c)$$
$$< 2z - (c+d) < d - c \longleftrightarrow -(d-c) + (c+d) < 2z < (d-c) + (c+d) \longleftrightarrow$$
$$2c < 2z < 2d \longleftrightarrow c < z < d.$$

Let us consider whether or not the sum of the absolute values of two real numbers is equal to the absolute value of their sum. It is easy to see that $|x|+|y|$ does not equal $|x+y|$ when $x=7$ and $y=-3$. We have $|7|+|-3|>|7+(-3)|$. Indeed when x and y represent any two real numbers having opposite signs $|x|+|y| \neq |x+y|$. This leads us to state the following theorem:

 Theorem 42–3. If $x, y \in R$, then $|x+y| \leq |x|+|y|$.

Proof of Theorem 42–3. If $x, y \in R$, then $|x+y| \leq |x|+|y|$.

First we observe that in the trivial case where $x=y=0$ the theorem is true.

1. If x and y are not both zero, then $|x|+|y|>0$.
2. $-|x| \leq x \leq |x|$ and $-|y| \leq y \leq |y|$
3. $-|x|+(-|y|) \leq x+y \leq |x|+|y|$
4. $-(|x|+|y|) \leq x+y \leq |x|+|y|$
5. $|x+y| \leq |x|+|y|$

1. (*vii*) p. 132
2. Theorem 38–3
3. Theorem 20–3
4. Distributive property
5. Corollary to Theorem 41–3

Theorem 42–3 is very important in mathematics. It is called the *triangle inequality*. If, in the theorem, we replace x by $x-y$, we readily obtain

Corollary to Theorem 42–3. If $x, y \in R$, then $|x|-|y| \leq |x-y|$.

Example 3. Replace each of the following with an equivalent single inequality involving absolute value: (a) $-5 \leq x \leq 7$, (b) $7 < 3 - 2x < 23$.

Solutions. (a) $-5 \leq x \leq 7 \leftrightarrow -6 \leq x-1 \leq 6 \leftrightarrow |x-1| \leq 6$
(b) $7 < 3 - 2x < 23 \leftrightarrow -7 > 2x-3 > -23 \leftrightarrow -4 > 2x > -20 \leftrightarrow -2 > x > -10 \leftrightarrow 4 > x+6 > -4 \leftrightarrow |x+6| < 4$. In the last step by letting $a=4$ and $-a=-4$ we applied Theorem 41–3 as we did in Example 2.

Example 4. Prove that $|x-y| \geq -(|x|-|y|)$.

Proof.
1. $|y-x| \geq |y|-|x|$
2. $|y-x| = |-(x-y)|$
3. $|-(x-y)| = |x-y|$
4. $|y-x| = |x-y|$

1. Corollary to Theorem 42–3. (Since the corollary is true of all x and y, it is true when x and y are interchanged.)
2. Distributive property and commutative property of addition
3. Theorem 36–3
4. Transitive property of equality

5. $|y| - |x| = -(|x| - |y|)$ **5.** Distributive property and commutative property of addition

6. $|x - y| \geq -(|x| - |y|)$ **6.** Substitution property of equality

Ⓐ EXERCISES

1. Assuming that $x, y \in R$, write a simpler name for each of the following numbers.

a. $\sqrt{4\,x^2}$

b. $\dfrac{\sqrt{32\,x^3}}{\sqrt{2\,x}};\ x > 0$

c. $\sqrt{\dfrac{x^2}{y^2}} \cdot \sqrt{\dfrac{y^2}{x^4}};\ xy \neq 0$

d. $\sqrt{16\,x^2} + 3\sqrt{x^2}$

e. $\sqrt{3\,x} \cdot \sqrt{7\,x};\ x > 0$

f. $\sqrt{44\,y^2} + \sqrt{99\,y^2} - \sqrt{11\,y^2}$

2. Which of the following statements are true and which are false? Assume that each variable represents a real number.

a. $12 + \sqrt{x^2} = 12 + |x|$

b. $|5 - b| \geq 5 - |b|$

c. $|(4)(-3)| = 12$

d. $|5|^2 = 25$

e. $|-5|^2 = 25$

f. $9\,x^2 \leq 16\,y^2 \longrightarrow 3\,|x| \leq 4\,|y|$

g. $|a| + |b| = |a + b|$

h. $|x| \leq 9 \longleftrightarrow -9 < x < 9$

i. $x^2 \leq 5^2 \longleftrightarrow |x| \leq 5$

j. $|r - s| = |r| + |-s|$

3. For each of the following numbers write a name that does not involve an absolute value symbol.

a. $|0 - 7|$

b. $|2 - 3| \cdot |-4|$

c. $-|4^2| \cdot |-3|$

d. $|12 - 17| + |5^2|$

e. $|3| + |-5|$

f. $|4 - 0| \cdot |0|$

g. $\dfrac{|16 + 4|}{|-2|}$

h. $\dfrac{-|3 + 2| \cdot |5 + 4|}{-|2^3|}$

4. Find the solution set for each of the following sentences.

a. $|x - 3| > 4$

b. $|2\,x - 4| < 8$

c. $|x + 1| \leq 5$

d. $\sqrt{(x - 1)^2} = 5$

e. $\left|\dfrac{1}{x}\right| \geq 2$

f. $\sqrt{x^2} \leq \tfrac{1}{9}$

g. $\left|\dfrac{2}{x}\right| < 6$

h. $|3\,x + 1| > 7$

i. $|\tfrac{1}{2}\,x| - 1 = -2$

Ⓑ EXERCISES

5. Prove: If $a, b \in R$, $(ab \leq 0 \text{ and } a > 0) \longrightarrow b \leq 0$.

6. Prove: If $x, a \in R$ and $a > 0$, $[(x - a)(x + a) < 0] \longrightarrow [x - a < 0 \text{ and } x + a > 0]$.

7. Explain how the statement $(i)\ |x| \geq 0$ is the direct consequence of the definition of the absolute value of a real number.

8. Supply reasons for the following ledger proof of the statement (ii) $|x| \geq -|x|$ when $x \in R$.

Statements	Reasons
1. $x \in R$	1. Why?
2. $|x| \geq 0$	2. Why?
3. $-|x| \leq 0$	3. Why?
4. $|x| \geq -|x|$	4. Why?

9. Supply the reasons indicated by the numbers (1)–(12) in the following essay proof of Theorem 38–3. If $x \in R$, $-|x| \leq x \leq |x|$.

Since $x \in R$, we must have $x \geq 0$ or $x < 0$. (1) Why?

If $x \geq 0$, then $|x| = x$. (2) Why? Hence, $|x| \geq x$. (3) Why? (See Example 2, page 82.) We know that $|x| \geq -|x|$. (4) Why? The conjunction of $|x| = x$ and $|x| \geq = -|x|$ establishes $x \geq -|x|$. (5) Why? The conjunction of $|x| \geq x$ and $x \geq -|x|$ is equivalent to $-|x| \leq x \leq |x|$. (6) Why?

If $x < 0$, then $|x| = -x$. (7) Why? Hence, $x = -|x|$. (8) Why? Now if $x = -|x|$, then $x \geq -|x|$. (9) Why? We know that $|x| \geq -|x|$. (10) Why? The conjunction of $x = -|x|$ and $|x| \geq -|x|$ establishes $|x| \geq x$. (11) Why? The conjunction of $x \geq -|x|$ and $|x| \geq x$ is equivalent to $-|x| \leq x \leq |x|$. (12) Why?

Now our proof is complete because if $x \in R$ we must have $x \geq 0$ or $x < 0$, and in either case our conclusion follows.

10. The preceding proof has the form $[p \wedge (p \longrightarrow a \vee b) \wedge (a \longrightarrow q) \wedge (b \longrightarrow q)] \longrightarrow q$. It can be shown by a 16-line truth table that this is a tautology. What statements in Exercise 9 are represented by the letters p, a, b, and q?

11. Supply reasons for the following proof of (iii) $|x| + |y| \geq 0$ when $x, y \in R$.

$$x, y \in R \xrightarrow{\text{(1)}} (|x| \geq 0 \wedge |y| \geq 0) \xrightarrow{\text{(2)}} |x| + |y| \geq 0.$$

12. Write a proof of statement (vii): $|x| + |y| > 0$ when $x, y \in R$ and $x \neq 0$. Give reasons for each step in your proof.

The Equation $x^2 = 2$ Has No Solution in Q

We have stated that there is no rational number whose square is 2. This is equivalent to saying that $\sqrt{2} \notin Q$. How do we know this? In order to answer this question we need to review and extend our knowledge of the integers.

If $a, b, c \in I$ and $ac = b$, then each of the integers a and c is a factor of the integer b.

Since $15 = (-5)(-3)$, -5 and -3 are factors of 15.

Since $13 = 1 \cdot 13$, 1 and 13 are factors of 13.

Since $0 = -43 \cdot 0$, -43 and 0 are factors of 0.

Another way to say "a is a factor of b" is to say "b is a multiple of a." Note that we are factoring over the integers. We do not accept $\frac{3}{4}$ and $\frac{32}{3}$ as factors of 8 even though their product is 8, because $\frac{3}{4}$ and $\frac{32}{3}$ are not integers.

An *even integer* is defined to be an integer which is a multiple of 2. Thus, if n is an even integer, then $n = 2\,k$ where k is an integer. An *odd integer* is an integer which is not even. We state the following theorem:

▶ **Theorem 43–3.** If t is an odd integer, then $t = 2\,n + 1$ where n is an integer.

The proof is left as an exercise.

Theorem 43–3 has a true converse which is also useful. Its proof is left to you as an exercise. The theorem and its converse give us the equivalence:

$$t \text{ is an odd integer} \longleftrightarrow t = 2\,n + 1; \; n \in I.$$

Copy and complete each of the following statements. You may want to try some numerical examples before you make your decision.

(1) The sum of two even integers is an _?_ integer.
(2) The sum of two odd integers is an _?_ integer.
(3) The sum of three odd integers is an _?_ integer.
(4) The product of two even integers is an _?_ integer.
(5) The product of an even integer and any integer is an _?_ integer.
(6) The product of two odd integers is an _?_ integer.
(7) The square of an even integer is an _?_ integer.
(8) The square of an odd integer is an _?_ integer.
(9) If the square of a given integer is an odd integer, then the given integer is an _?_ integer.
(10) If the square of a given integer is an even integer, then the given integer is an _?_ integer.

Statements (8) and (10) of this list deserve special consideration. Let us restate (8) as

▶ **Theorem 44–3.** If a is an odd integer, then a^2 is an odd integer.

The proof of the theorem is left to you as an exercise.
Let us restate (10) as

▶ **Theorem 45–3.** If a^2 is an even integer, then a is an even integer.

The proof of the theorem is left to you as an exercise. We now undertake to prove:

▶ **Theorem 46–3.** There is no rational number p such that $p^2 = 2$.

We may express this theorem in symbols by writing $\sim (p \in Q \wedge p^2 = 2)$.

Proof of Theorem 46–3: There is no rational number p such that $p^2 = 2$. First we shall show that the conjunction of $p \in Q$ and $p^2 = 2$ leads to a false statement.

(1)
$$p \in Q \longleftrightarrow p = \frac{a}{b}$$ where a and b are integers, $b \neq 0$, and a and b have no common factors other than 1 or -1.

(2)   (3)   (4)   (5)   (6)
$$p^2 = 2 \longrightarrow \left(\frac{a}{b}\right)^2 = 2 \longrightarrow \frac{a^2}{b^2} = 2 \longrightarrow a^2 = 2\,b^2 \longrightarrow a^2 \text{ is an even integer} \longrightarrow a$$

(7)   (8)   (9)   (10)
is an even integer $\longrightarrow a = 2\,k$ where $k \in I \longrightarrow a^2 = 4\,k^2 \longrightarrow 2\,b^2 = 4\,k^2 \longrightarrow b^2$

(11)   (12)   (13)
$= 2\,k^2 \longrightarrow b^2$ is an even integer $\longrightarrow b$ is an even integer $\longrightarrow b = 2\,l$ where $l \in I$.

Reasons:
(1) Definition of rational number, (2) Substitution property of equality, (3) Theorem 6–1, (4) Multiplication property of equality, (5) Definition of an even number, (6) Theorem 44–3, (7) Definition of an even integer, (8) Why? (9) Substitution property of equality $(2\,b^2 = a^2)$, (10) Why? (11) Definition of an even integer, (12) Theorem 44–3, (13) Definition of an even integer.

We have now proved that if $(p \in Q \wedge p^2 = 2)$ is true, then there are two integers a and b with the following properties:

(i) a and b have no common factors other than 1 or -1

(ii) a and b are both multiples of 2

That is, $(p \in Q \wedge p^2 = 2) \longrightarrow [(i) \wedge (ii)]$. However, ($i$) and ($ii$) are contrary statements and cannot both be true at the same time. Hence, their conjunction is false and $\sim [(i) \wedge (ii)]$ is true. Thus, we have the following tautology (see Ex. 1. a. page 84):

$$\left. \begin{array}{l} \sim [(i) \wedge (ii)]] \\ (p \in Q \wedge p^2 = 2) \longrightarrow [(i) \wedge (ii)]] \end{array} \right\} \longrightarrow \sim (p \in Q \wedge p^2 = 2)$$

whose premises are true, and our proof of $\sim (p \in Q \wedge p^2 = 2)$ is complete.

We have shown that the equation $x^2 = 2$ has no solution in Q. It can be shown that there are many other equations which have no solution in Q. For example, $x^2 = 3$ has no solution in Q. There are many points in the number line whose coordinates are not in Q. This is true for each of the points C and E in the drawing at the right. What can you

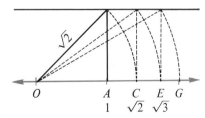

say about the coordinate of point G? Points C and E are the graphs of irrational numbers. Set R, which includes not only the rational numbers but also the irrational numbers, is far more useful to us than the set of rational numbers. Set R contains the solutions to many equations that have no solution in Q, and there is a one-to-one correspondence between the members of the set of real numbers and all of the points in a number line.

 EXERCISES

1. Prove Theorem 43–3: If t is an odd integer, then $t = 2n + 1$ when n is an integer. Hints: Show that $\frac{t}{2} \neq k$ when k is an integer, then show that $\frac{t}{2}$ is between two consecutive integers. Finally use multiplication to show that t is between two integers having one and only one integer between them.

2. Prove the converse of Theorem 43–3.

3. Prove Theorem 44–3: If a is an odd integer, then a^2 is an odd integer. *Hints.* Use Theorem 43–3 to state, $a = 2k + 1$. Square both members of this equation and use algebraic processes to complete the proof.

4. Prove Theorem 45–3: If a^2 is an even integer, then a is an even integer.

Completeness Property of Real Numbers

In this section we shall describe a fundamental property of the real numbers which is called the completeness property. It is this property which provides the logical foundation of the statement: If a is a non-negative real number, then there exists a non-negative real number x such that $x^2 = a$. Up to this time we have assumed that this statement is true.

In order to state the completeness property, we need two definitions:

> Let S be any nonempty set of real numbers and suppose that y is a real number such that the statement $x \leq y$ is true for every real number x in S. We call y an *upper bound* of S and we say that S is *bounded above.*

Example 1.   If $S = \{5, 6, 7, 8, 9, 10\}$, then 10 is an upper bound of S and so are 11, 43, 75, and $\sqrt{192}$. Indeed, any real number which is greater than or equal to 10 is an upper bound.

Example 2.   If S is the set of real numbers less than 12, then 12, 13, 26, and 45 are upper bounds of S.

Example 3.   If S is the set of positive numbers x such that $x^2 < 2$, then 2 is an upper bound. Why? Are there upper bounds that are smaller than 2?

It is interesting to note that R has no upper bound. This is indicated by the following indirect argument: Suppose that R does have an upper bound b. This means that every number in R is less than or equal to b. But $b + 1$ is in R because, by the closure property for addition, the sum of any two real numbers is a real number. Moreover, the statement $b + 1 \leq b$ is false because it is equivalent to the false statement $1 \leq 0$. Since the assumption that R has an upper bound has led to a contradiction, this assumption is false. Hence, its negation is true and we conclude that R does not have an upper bound.

The second definition we need is:

> Let S be a nonempty set of real numbers and let b be an upper bound of S. If no real number less than b is an upper bound of S, then b is called the *least upper bound* of S.

Example 1.   Zero is the least upper bound of the set N which contains all of the negative numbers. Observe that the least upper bound of N is not in N in this instance.

Example 2.   If S is the set of real numbers that are less than or equal to 5, then 5 is the least upper bound of S. In this instance the least upper bound of S is in S.

Example 3.   If S is the set of real numbers that are less than 5.4, then 5.4 is the least upper bound of S. This is another instance in which the least upper bound of a set is not in the set.

Example 4.   If S is the set of real numbers less than or equal to 100, then 100 is the least upper bound of S. This is another instance in which the least upper bound of the set is in the set.

We now state the completeness property of the real numbers:

▶ **Completeness Property of Real Numbers:** If S is a nonempty subset of R that has an upper bound in R, then it has a least upper bound in R.

The lower bound is defined as follows:

> Let S be any nonempty set of real numbers and suppose that b is a real number such that the statement $a \geq b$ is true for every real number a in S. We call b a *lower bound* of S and we say that S is *bounded below*.

It follows that:

> If S is a nonempty set of real numbers and b is a lower bound of S and if no real number greater than b is a lower bound of S, then b is called the *greatest lower bound* of S.

1. Which of the following sets have an upper bound? which a least upper bound?

   a. C

   b. R

   c. I

   d. Q

   e. the set of positive integers

   f. the set of negative real numbers

   g. the set of counting numbers less than 10

   h. the set of integers greater than -5

2. State the least upper bound (if one exists) for each of the following sets.

   a. $\{x \mid x \in C \text{ and } x > 7\}$

   b. $\{x \mid x \in C; \; x < 5\}$

   c. $\{x \mid x \in R; \; x \geq 7\}$

   d. $\{x \mid x \in R \text{ and } x < 0\}$

   e. the set of negative rational numbers

   f. $\{x \mid x \in R; \; x \leq 17\}$

   g. $\{x \mid x + 1 > 3 \text{ and } x \in I\}$

   h. $\{x \in C, \; x \geq 9 \text{ and } x \leq 22\}$

3. Which of the sets of Ex. 2 have a least upper bound (if one exists) within the set?

4. For each of the sets of Ex. 2, state greatest lower bound (is one exists).

5. Show that $\{x \mid |x| \leq 2; \; x \in R\}$ has a least upper bound and that it is 2.

The Completeness Property and $x^2 = a$.

The completeness property can be used to prove that if a is a non-negative real number, there exists a non-negative real number x such that $x^2 = a$. We outline the argument for $a = 2$. The arguments for other values of a such that $a \geq 0$ are similar.

Let S be the set of all positive real numbers whose squares are less than 2. This is a nonempty set because $1^2 < 2$, and S is *bounded above*. (3, for example, has its square larger than 2.) Therefore, by the completeness property, S has a least upper bound in R which we shall call x. Since x is an upper bound of a set of positive numbers, x is positive.

We want to show that $x^2 = 2$. The trichotomy property tells us that if x^2 and 2 are real numbers, one and only one of the following is true: $x^2 > 2$, $x^2 < 2$, or $x^2 = 2$. We sketch the argument which shows that the first two possibilities must be rejected.

If $x^2 > 2$, it can be shown (See Exercise 1 below) that there exists a positive real number t which is less than x but whose square is greater than 2. $(0 < t < x \text{ and } t^2 > 2)$. Since $t^2 > 2$, t is an upper bound of S and since $t < x$, it is an upper bound less than x. This contradicts the fact that x is the least upper bound of S and shows that $x^2 > 2$ cannot hold.

Suppose that $x^2 < 2$. It can be shown (See Exercise 2 below) that there exists a positive real number s such that $s > x$ and $s^2 < 2$. Since s is a positive real number whose square is less than 2, $s \in S$. Thus s is an element of S which is greater than x and we have a contradiction of the fact that x is the least upper bound of S. This shows that $x^2 < 2$ cannot hold.

Therefore by the trichotomy property of order, $x^2 = 2$. Thus, we have shown that there exists a positive real number x such that $x^2 = 2$. We denote the unique positive solution of $x^2 = 2$ by the symbol $\sqrt{2}$.

We generalize the above argument as follows: If $a \geq 0$, there exists a non-negative real number x such that $x^n = a$ when $n \in C$. This unique non-negative solution of $x^n = a$ is denoted by the symbol $\sqrt[n]{a}$.

Ⓐ **EXERCISES**

1. It is shown below that if $x^2 > 2$ and $x > 0$, there exists a positive number t which is less than x and whose square is greater than 2. You are to supply the reason or reasons for each of the steps.

Statements	Reasons
1. $x^2 > 2$ and $x > 0$.	1. Given
2. Let $t = x - \dfrac{x^2 - 2}{2x}$. Then $t < x$.	2. Why?
3. $t = x - \dfrac{x^2 - 2}{2x} = \dfrac{1}{2}\left(x + \dfrac{2}{x}\right)$	3. Why?
4. From (3), $t > 0$.	4. Why?
5. From (2), $t^2 = \left(x - \dfrac{x^2-2}{2x}\right)^2 = x^2 - (x^2-2) + \left(\dfrac{x^2-2}{2x}\right)^2 =$ $2 + \dfrac{(x^2-2)^2}{4x^2}$.	5. Why?
6. From (5), $t^2 > 2$.	6. Why?

Therefore, the number t such that $t = x - \dfrac{x^2 - 2}{2x}$ is a positive number which is less than x and whose square is greater than 2.

2. It is shown below that if $x^2 < 2$ and $x > 1$, there exists a positive number s which is greater than x and whose square is less than 2. You are to supply the reason or reasons for each of the steps.

1. $x^2 < 2$ and $x > 1$. (Given)

2. $\dfrac{2 - x^2}{3x}$ is a positive number. (Why?)

3. From (1), $1 < x^2$ (Why?), and hence $2 < 2x^2$. (Why?)

4. Since $1 < 2$, from (3) $1 < 2x^2$ (Why?), and hence $2 < 4x^2$. (Why?)

5. From (4) $2 - x^2 < 3x^2$ (Why?), and hence $\dfrac{2 - x^2}{3x} < x$. (Why?)

6. Let $b = \dfrac{1}{2}\left(\dfrac{2 - x^2}{3x}\right)$. Then $b < \dfrac{2 - x^2}{3x}$ (Why?), and $0 < b < x$. (Why?)

7. From (6), $3\,bx < 2 - x^2$. (Why?)
8. $(x + b)^2 = x^2 + b(2\,x + b)$. (Why?)
9. Since $b > 0$ and $b < x$ from (6), $(x + b)^2 < x^2 + b(2\,x + x)$ (Why?), and hence $(x + b)^2 < x^2 + 3\,bx$. (Why?)
10. From (7) and (9), $(x + b)^2 < x^2 + (2 - x^2)$ (Why?), and hence $(x + b)^2 < 2$. (Why?).
11. $x + b > x$ (Why?)

Therefore, the number s such that $s = x + \dfrac{1}{2}\left(\dfrac{2 - x^2}{3\,x}\right)$ is a positive number which is greater than x and whose square is less than 2.

3. If $a,\, b \,\epsilon\, R$ and $n \,\epsilon\, C$, show that $a^n - b^n = (a - b)$
$(a^{n-1} + a^{n-2}b + a^{n-3}b^2 + \cdots + a^2 b^{n-3} + ab^{n-2} + b^{n-1})$.
Hint. Form the product of the two factors in the right member.

4. Use the results of Ex. 3 to prove the following generalization of Theorem 14–3: If $a,\, b \,\epsilon\, R$, a and b have the same sign, and $n \,\epsilon\, C$, then $a^n = b^n \longleftrightarrow a = b$.

ESSENTIALS

Before you leave this chapter make sure that you

1. Know what we mean by a number field and by an ordered number field. (Page 103.)

2. Understand the symmetric, transitive, addition, and multiplication properties of equality. (Page 103.)

3. Understand the meaning of closure and know which of the sets C, I, Q, and R are closed under each of the operations: addition, subtraction, multiplication, division, involution, and evolution. (Pages 105–106.)

4. Know which of the field properties hold for each of the sets C, I, Q, and R. (Page 108.)

5. Understand the Archimedean and well-ordering properties. (Page 109.)

6. Understand the relationships existing between rational numbers and repeating decimal expressions. (Pages 110–112.)

7. Understand the order properties, can apply them properly, and understand the proofs related to order which are given in this chapter. (Pages 113–120.)

8. Understand the rules for computing with irrational numbers. This includes understanding the proofs related to irrational numbers given in this chapter. (Pages 122–125.)

9. Know whether or not the rational numbers and the irrational numbers are closed under the operations of addition, subtraction, multiplication, division, evolution, and involution. (Pages 127–128.)

10. Understand the statements involving absolute value discussed in this chapter. (Pages 130–135.)

11. Can show that $\sqrt{2} \notin Q$. (Page 138.)

12. Understand the completeness property of R and can use it in showing that a solution exists among the real numbers for $x^2 = a$. (Page 139–140.)

13. Can spell and use the following words and phrases correctly.

Archimedean property (Page 109.)	involution (Page 105.)
closure (Page 105.)	irrational (Page 112.)
completeness property (Page 140.)	least upper bound (Page 140.)
density (Page 108.)	lower bound (Page 140.)
evolution (Page 105.)	ordered number field (Page 103.)
field properties (Page 103.)	upper bound (Page 139.)
greatest lower bound (Page 140.)	well-ordering property (Page 109.)

CHAPTER REVIEW

1. Which of the following always name real numbers?

a. x; $x \in R$

b. $\sqrt{x}$; $x \in R$

c. xy; $x \in I, y \in I$

d. x^2; $x \in C$

e. $\dfrac{1}{x}$; $x \in C$

f. $\dfrac{2}{x}$; $x \in R$

g. $\dfrac{4}{x+y}$; $x, y \in R$

h. $\sqrt{x^2}$; $x \in R$

i. $\dfrac{x+y}{x^2}$; $x, y \in R$

2. State the field property which justifies each of the following statements.

a. $\frac{3}{4} + (\frac{1}{4} + 5) = (\frac{3}{4} + \frac{1}{4}) + 5$

b. $|5| + 0 = |5|$

c. $6 \cdot \frac{1}{6} = 1$

d. $\sqrt{5}(\sqrt{6} \cdot \sqrt{2}) = (\sqrt{5} \cdot \sqrt{6})\sqrt{2}$

e. $(-5) \cdot 1 = -5$

f. $6 + (-6) = 0$

g. $\sqrt{9} + |3| = |3| + \sqrt{9}$

h. $|-2| \cdot (|5| + |7|) = |-2| \cdot |5| + |-2| \cdot |7|$

3. Replace (1), (2), and (3) with the statement of the field property which justifies the step having that number.

$$\overset{(1)}{(a+x) + (-x)} = \overset{(2)}{a + [x + (-x)]} = \overset{(3)}{a + 0} = a$$

4. Replace (1), (2), and (3) with the statement of the field property which justifies the step having that number.

$$\overset{(1)}{a \cdot 1 + a \cdot 0} = \overset{(2)}{a(1 + 0)} = \overset{(3)}{a \cdot 1} = a$$

5. Express each of the following which represents a rational number as the quotient of two integers.

a. $1.\dot{2}\dot{1}$ **b.** $0.121121112 \cdots$ **c.** $0.41\dot{5}1\dot{5}$ **d.** 7.333 **e.** $142.\dot{3}\dot{7}$ **f.** 4.50

6. Which of the following numbers will have repeating decimal expressions?

a. $\sqrt{5}$ **b.** $\frac{1}{3}$ **c.** $\sqrt{-2}$ **d.** 471

7. Find the decimal expression for $\frac{9}{7}$.

8. Solve, assuming that $x \in R$.

a. $(x + 5)(x - 1) > 0$

   c. $\dfrac{3 + x}{1 - x} < 0$

b. $(x - 3)(x - 4) \leq 0$

   d. $1 \geq \dfrac{3}{x - 4}$

9. Graph the solution set of each statement in Ex. 8.

10. Replace each question mark with one of the symbols $>$, $<$, $\geq$, or $\leq$ to form a true statement. Each variable represents a real number.

a. $x \geq y \longrightarrow x + a \,\_?\_\, y + a$ **c.** $x \geq y \wedge c > 0 \longrightarrow xc \,\_?\_\, yc$

b. $x \geq y \wedge y > c \longrightarrow x \,\_?\_\, c$ **d.** $a < 0 \wedge x \geq y \longrightarrow ax \,\_?\_\, ay$

11. Prove: If $a, b, c \in R$, $a \neq b$, $a \neq c$, and $b \neq c$, then $a^2 + b^2 + c^2 > ab + ac + bc$.

12. Express in simplest form.

a. $\sqrt{180}$ **c.** $\sqrt[4]{625}$ **e.** $4\sqrt{18}$
b. $\sqrt[3]{27} \cdot \sqrt[3]{8}$ **d.** $-\sqrt{1024}$ **f.** $5\sqrt[3]{-64}$

13. Express in simplest form.

a. $\sqrt{192}\sqrt{3}$ **b.** $\sqrt[3]{-125}\sqrt[3]{27}$ **c.** $4\sqrt{15} \cdot 2\sqrt{3}$

14. Rationalize each denominator.

a. $\dfrac{\sqrt{108}}{\sqrt{5}}$ **b.** $\dfrac{3}{4 - \sqrt{5}}$ **c.** $\dfrac{\sqrt{x}}{\sqrt{x} + \sqrt{y}}$

15. Rationalize the numerator of $\dfrac{\sqrt{x} - \sqrt{y}}{\sqrt{x} + \sqrt{y}}$

16. Which of the following numbers are rational and which irrational?

a. $5\sqrt{36}$ **b.** $4\sqrt{18}$ **c.** $\sqrt{2} + \sqrt{3}$ **d.** $\frac{1}{5}\sqrt{15}$ **e.** $\dfrac{\sqrt{25}}{2}$ **f.** $4 + \sqrt{6}$

17. a. Is the sum of two irrational numbers always an irrational number?

b. Is the sum of a rational number and an irrational number a rational number or an irrational number?

c. Is the product of a rational number and an irrational number a rational number or an irrational number?

d. Is the product of two irrational numbers always an irrational number?

e. Is the product of two rational numbers a rational number or an irrational number?

18. Which of the following statements are true and which false?

a. $4 + \sqrt{x^2} = 4 + x$
c. $\sqrt{9\,x^2} = 3\,x$

b. $|-2| \cdot |5| = 10$
d. $x^2 \leq 6^2 \longleftrightarrow x \leq 6$

19. Solve each of the following, assuming that $x \in R$.

a. $|x + 1| > 7$

b. $\left|\dfrac{1}{x} + 3\right| = 2$

c. $\left|\dfrac{1}{x}\right| \geq 8$

d. $|3\,x + 5| \leq 11$

20. Write a simpler name for each of the following, assuming that each variable represents a real number.

a. $\sqrt{9\,y^2}$

c. $\sqrt{\dfrac{128\,x^3}{2\,x}}$; $x > 0$

e. $\sqrt{3\,x} \cdot \sqrt{5\,x}$; $x > 0$

b. $\sqrt{25\,x}$; $x > 0$

d. $\dfrac{\sqrt{14}}{\sqrt{7\,x^2}}$

f. $4\sqrt{5\,y^2} + \sqrt{16\,y^2}$

21. For each of the following write a name that does not involve a symbol for absolute value.

a. $|-4 + 7|$ **b.** $|8|^2$ **c.** $|-3| \cdot |(-5)^2|$ **d.** $\dfrac{|0 - 9|}{|3|}$

22. State the least upper bound of each of the following sets, if there is such a bound.

a. R

b. C

c. $\{x \mid x < 5; \ x \in R\}$

d. $\{x \mid x \geq 2; \ x \in R\}$

e. $\{x \mid x \leq 19; \ x \in R\}$

f. $\{x \mid x \geq 5 \text{ and } x \geq 2; \ x \in Q\}$

23. In which of the sets of Ex. 22 is the least upper bound within the set?

24. What is the name of the property which states that if S is a nonempty subset of R that has an upper bound in R, then it has a least upper bound in R?

1. State the field property which justifies each of the following statements.

a. $4 + (-4) = 0$

c. $7 \cdot \frac{1}{7} = 1$

b. $\sqrt{3}(\sqrt{5} + 2) = \sqrt{3} \cdot \sqrt{5} + \sqrt{3} \cdot 2$

d. $6(5 \cdot \frac{1}{6}) = (6 \cdot \frac{1}{6})5$

2. Which of the following represent rational numbers?

a. $1.3\dot{6}$

b. $0.\dot{1}7\dot{4}\dot{2}$

c. $0.323323332 \cdots$

d. 5

3. Solve: $(x - 7)(x + 5) \geq 0$

4. Solve: $\dfrac{5 + x}{1 - x} > 0$

5. Express in simplest form.

a. $\sqrt{320}$

b. $\sqrt[3]{-24}$

c. $\sqrt{12} \cdot \sqrt{72}$

d. $\dfrac{5\sqrt[4]{16}}{\sqrt[4]{81}}$

6. Rationalize the denominator: $\dfrac{2x}{\sqrt{x+1} + \sqrt{x-1}}$

7. Complete each of the following sentences by replacing each question mark with an expression that will make the sentence true.

a. $\sqrt{9\,x^2} = \_?\_$

c. $x^2 < 3^2 \longleftrightarrow \_?\_$

b. $9 - 11^2 \cdot 8(-2) = \_?\_$

d. $\dfrac{0 - 5}{-2} = \_?\_$

8. Solve: $3\,x + 1 \geq 0$

9. Prove: If $a, b, c \in R$, $(a > b) \longrightarrow (a - c > b - c)$

10. Which of the following sets have a least upper bound within the set?

a. $\{x \mid x \leq 6 \text{ or } x \geq 3;\ x \in R\}$

b. $\{x \mid x < 19 \text{ and } x > 2;\ x \in R\}$

c. $\{x \mid x - 1 \geq 4;\ x \in R\}$

4

Polynomials and Rational Expressions

Polynomials over the Real Numbers

In this chapter you will learn more about the set of polynomials, a very important subset of the set of algebraic expressions. We shall designate the set of polynomials by the letter P.

Each of the following is a special kind of polynomial known as a monomial:

$7, 7x, y, -ab, -13(-a)(b)(-c), 2(-2)(11), 0, 1, \frac{3}{4}xy, 2.4, -\sqrt{13}\,abc,$ $\frac{\sqrt[4]{11}}{\sqrt[5]{43}}x^2$. Each of these is a monomial over the real numbers. We define a

monomial over the real numbers as follows: Let N_R be the set of numerical expressions which name real numbers and do not involve addition or subtraction; let V be the set of variables $a, b, c, \cdots, x, y, \cdots$ and their opposites $-a, -b, -c, \cdots, -x, -y, \cdots$; and let $T = N_R \cup V$. Then any element of T or any expression which can be formed by using two or more elements of T and the operations of multiplication or division, provided that division by 0 and by expressions containing variables is barred, is a monomial over the real numbers. Note that this definition bars expressions such as $\frac{1}{x}$ from the set of monomials.

If $T = N_Q \cup V$ where N_Q is the set of numerical expressions which name rational numbers and do not involve addition or subtraction, the definition of the preceding paragraph is the definition of a *monomial over the rational numbers*. Thus the first ten monomials named above are monomials over the rational numbers. If $T = N_I \cup V$ where N_I is the set of numerical expressions which name integers and do not involve addition, subtraction, or division, the definition of the preceding paragraph is the definition of a *monomial over the integers*. The first eight monomials named above are monomials over the integers.

Each monomial has a *numerical coefficient*. The monomial 7 has the numerical coefficient 7, the monomial $7x$ has the numerical coefficient 7, the monomial y has the numerical coefficient 1, and the monomial $- ab$ has the numerical coefficient $- 1$.

We give the following definitions:

The *numerical coefficient* of a monomial which is a numerical expression is the numerical expression itself.

The *numerical coefficient* of a monomial which is an open expression is the numerical expression which the open expression becomes when each variable is replaced by 1.

Now we are ready to define a polynomial over the real numbers. We say: A *polynomial over the real numbers* is a monomial over the real numbers or the algebraic sum of two or more monomials over the real numbers. Similar definitions may be stated for polynomials over the rational numbers and polynomials over the integers.

Each monomial referred to in the definition of a polynomial over the real numbers is a *term* of the polynomial. The coefficients of the terms of a polynomial are referred to as the *coefficients of the polynomial*. According to our definition, a polynomial is a polynomial over a given set of numbers if each of its coefficients names a number in that set.

A polynomial which has two terms is called a *binomial*. Each of the following is a binomial: $3 x + 7 y$, $8 a - 9 b$, $a + 0$, $b + b$, $xyz - 1$, $7 + 13$, $14 - 2 ab$. Of course, the binomial $7 + 13$ could be written as the monomial 20, but when we write $7 + 13$ we write a binomial.

A polynomial which has three terms is called a *trinomial*. Each of the following is a trinomial: $a + b + 1$, $2 - 7 a^2 - 21 ab$, $x^2 + 2 xy + y^2$, $0 + a - b$. Polynomials which are the sum of more than three monomials do not have special names.

According to our definition $7(x + y)$ is not a monomial because it is not an element of T or an expression formed by using elements of T and just the operations of multiplication or division. Moreover, it is not the algebraic sum of two or more monomials. Since all polynomials are monomials or the algebraic sum of two or more monomials, we conclude that $7(x + y)$ is not a polynomial even though it is identically equal to the polynomial $7 x + 7 y$.

Expressions such as $7(x + y)$ or $8(3 x - c) - 4(x^2 + 13)$ are called polynomial expressions. We define a *polynomial expression* as follows: If P is the set of polynomials, then any member of P or any expression which can be formed by using two or more members of P and indicating the operations of addition or multiplication is a polynomial expression. Note that, as usual, the *or* is inclusive, that is, we may indicate addition only, multiplication only, or both addition and multiplication.

1. Which of the following monomials are monomials over the integers, which are monomials over the rational numbers, which are monomials over the irrational numbers, and which are monomials over the real numbers? (Note that more than one of these descriptions may apply to a given monomial.)

a. $\sqrt{3}\, y$

c. $\dfrac{9\,x^2}{14}$

e. -16

g. $5\,xyz$

b. $4(-5)(\tfrac{1}{3})$

d. $-\sqrt{15}\, a^4 b$

f. 3.999

h. $\sqrt{-8}\, ab$

2. State the numerical coefficient of each of the monomials in Ex. 1.

3. Which of the following are polynomials?

a. 14

d. $\tfrac{1}{2}\, abc$

g. $5\,xy + 15\,y + 45\,x + 27$

b. $x + 3\,y + 7$

e. $-18\,a + 4\,b + \sqrt{3}$

h. $-1(xy - x^2)$

c. $1 + 1 - 3 - 8$

f. $(\sqrt[3]{5}\, xy^5 z)(3 + y)$

i. $\sqrt{11} \cdot \sqrt{3} \cdot a^4 + \sqrt{5}$

4. Which of the polynomials of Ex. 3 are monomials, which are binomials, which are trinomials, and which are polynomials other than these?

5. Name the terms of the polynomial $\tfrac{1}{6}\, x^3 - \tfrac{1}{3}\, x^2 y + xy - 2\,y^2$.

6. Name the coefficients of the polynomial of Ex. 5.

7. Two terms of the polynomial of Ex. 5 have numerical coefficients which are integers. May we say that the polynomial is a polynomial over the integers? a polynomial over the rational numbers? a polynomial over the real numbers?

8. Evaluate each of the following polynomials when $a = \tfrac{1}{2}$, $b = -3$, and $c = \tfrac{2}{3}$.

a. $a^2 b$

b. $\tfrac{1}{2}\, a + \tfrac{1}{3}\, bc + 2$

c. $9\,bc^3 - 1$

d. $6\,a^2 b^3 (-\tfrac{1}{3}\, ac)$

9. Evaluate each of the following polynomials when $x = -2$, $y = 3$, and $z = 5$.

a. $x^3 - y^3$

c. $3\,x^2 + 4\,xy^2 + y^3$

b. $x^3 - \tfrac{2}{9}\, y^2 + z^2$

d. $x^3 + 3\,x^3 y^2 - 5\,x^2 y^3 + xy$

Whole Numbers as Exponents

Before we continue our study of polynomials, it is appropriate for us to review the laws which govern the use of whole numbers as exponents. You recall that if $b \in R$ and $n \in C$ the symbol b^n is another name for the product $\underbrace{b \cdot b \cdot b \cdots b}_{n \text{ factors}}$. The real number represented by b^n is called a *power* (in this case the nth power of b). The positive integer n is called the *exponent* and the real number b is called the *base* of the power b^n. A power with the exponent 2 is called the *square* of the base or the *second power* of the base. A power with exponent 3 is called the *cube* of the base or the *third power* of the base. A power with the exponent 4 is called the *fourth power* of the base.

You are familiar with the following laws for operating with powers:

1. $a^m \cdot a^n = a^{m+n}$; $a \in R$; and $m, n \in C$
2. $(a^m)^n = a^{mn} = (a^n)^m$; $a \in R$; and $m, n \in C$
3. $(ab)^n = a^n b^n$; $a, b \in R$; and $n \in C$

You recall that for all nonzero real numbers a the expression a^0 is defined as another name for 1. This choice is dictated by our desire to define a^0 in such a way that the laws stated above remain valid when $m, n \in W$. If $n = 0$ and $a \neq 0$ in the first law, we have

$$a^m \cdot a^0 = a^{m+0} \longrightarrow a^m \cdot a^0 = a^m.$$

We see that a^0 must be accepted as another name for 1 because in a field the multiplicative identity is unique (Field property 8). Note that 0^0 is not defined; that is, 0^0 is not a meaningful expression.

We accepted $a^0 = 1$ in order to make the first law true for whole number exponents. It can be readily shown that laws 2 and 3 are also true if we accept a^0 as another name for 1. Hence these laws are valid for whole number exponents except when both the base and the exponent are zero.

To define what it means to "simplify" an expression by means of these laws, we rule that:

(i) a^{m+n} is a simpler form than $a^m \cdot a^n$
(ii) a^{mn} is a simpler form than either $(a^m)^n$ or $(a^n)^m$
(iii) $a^n b^n$ is a simpler form than $(ab)^n$
(iv) 1 is a simpler form than a^0

Example 1. Simplify the expression $(a^3 b^5)^7$.

Solution. $(a^3 b^5)^7 = (a^3)^7 (b^5)^7 = a^{21} b^{35}$

Example 2. Simplify $(x^0)^{387}$; $x \neq 0$

Solution. $(x^0)^{387} = 1^{387} = 1$

We have been considering the laws for operating with powers in multiplication. You are also familiar with the following laws for operating with powers in division.

4a. $\dfrac{a^m}{a^n} = a^{m-n}$; $a \in R$; $a \neq 0$; $m, n \in W$; and $m > n$

b. $\dfrac{a^m}{a^n} = \dfrac{1}{a^{n-m}}$; $a \in R$; $a \neq 0$; $m, n \in W$; and $m < n$

c. $\dfrac{a^m}{a^n} = a^0 = 1$; $a \in R$; $a \neq 0$; $m, n \in W$; and $m = n$

5. $\left(\dfrac{a}{b}\right)^n = \dfrac{a^n}{b^n}$; $a, b \in R$; $n \in W$; $b \neq 0$; $a \neq 0$ when $n = 0$

To define what it means to "simplify" an expression by means of these laws, we rule that:

(v) If $m > n$, a^{m-n} is simpler than $\dfrac{a^m}{a^n}$.

(vi) If $m < n$, $\dfrac{1}{a^{n-m}}$ is simpler than $\dfrac{a^m}{a^n}$.

Example 3. Simplify $\dfrac{24\, x^8yz}{8\, x^2y^4z}$.

Solution. $\dfrac{24\, x^8yz}{8\, x^2y^4z} = \dfrac{3\, x^{8-2}z^0}{y^{4-1}} = \dfrac{3\, x^6}{y^3}$. The result $3\,\dfrac{x^6}{y^3}$ is also in simplified form.

 EXERCISES

1. Without simplifying the expression requested, write each of the following.

   a. The second power of x^3.   **c.** The cube of $-5\, rs$

   b. The square of the nth power of 51   **d.** The nth power of $18\, x^5y$

   e. The sum of the squares of $14\, xy$ and $-5\, x^2y$

   f. The sum of the second power of a^n and the cube of a^2y

   g. The product of the fourth power of a^2 and the third power of b^2

   h. The product of the 0th power of $(-11\, a)$ and the nth power of $(-3\, a)$

   i. The quotient of the fourth power of a^2 and the third power of a

   j. The quotient of 4 times the second power of x and 2 times the fourth power of x

2. Simplify each of the following expressions.

   a. $(a^2)^5$ **e.** $(-11\, x^2y^3)(-3\, x^4y^2)$ **i.** $(11\, ab)(-4)^2(a^2b)^3$

   b. $3\, x^2(x^5y)$ **f.** $a^8(-5\, a^2b)(b^2)^3$ **j.** $0\cdot(4\, a^3)^2 + 3\, a(2\, a^3)^2$

   c. $4^2 + (573)^0$ **g.** $3\, x^3y^6 + (4\, xy^2)^3$ **k.** $a^2b(a^3b^3 - 4\, a^2b + 5)$

   d. $\dfrac{(5\, a^2b)^3}{5}$ **h.** $\dfrac{16\, x^2y^3}{5\, x^2y}$ **l.** $\dfrac{1}{a^2b}(a^3b^2 + a^2b + b^3)$

3. Which of the expressions in Ex. 2 are polynomials?

4. Supply the reason for each step in the following proofs. In each case $a, b \in R$ and all exponents are counting numbers.

   $$\text{a. } \overset{(1)}{(ab)^n =} \underbrace{(ab)(ab)\cdots(ab)}_{n \text{ factors}} \overset{(2)}{\longrightarrow} (ab)^n = \underbrace{(a)(a)\cdots(a)}_{n \text{ factors}}\underbrace{(b)(b)\cdots(b)}_{n \text{ factors}} \overset{(3)}{\dashv}$$

   $\overset{(3)}{\mapsto} (ab)^n = a^nb^n$. Is this proof reversible?

b. $\overset{(1)}{a^x \cdot a^y \cdot a^z} = \overset{(2)}{(a^x a^y) a^z} = \overset{(3)}{a^{x+y} \cdot a^z} = \overset{(4)}{a^{(x+y)+z}} = a^{x+y+z}$

c. $\overset{(1)}{(b^m)^n} = \overset{(2)}{\underbrace{(b^m)(b^m) \cdots (b^m)}_{n \text{ factors}}} = \overset{\overbrace{\phantom{b^{m+m}}}^{n \text{ addends}}}{b^{m+m\cdots+m}} = b^{mn} = \overset{\overbrace{\phantom{b^{n+n}}}^{m \text{ addends}}}{b^{n+n\cdots+n}} = \overset{(4)}{\underbrace{(b^n)(b^n) \cdots (b^n)}_{m \text{ factors}}}$

$= (b^n)^m.$

5. a. Prove that Law 2, stated on page 151, is valid when $m = n = 0$ and $a \neq 0$.

b. Prove that Law 3 is valid when $n = 0$ and $ab \neq 0$.

Degree of a Polynomial

In order to determine the degree of a polynomial we must be able to determine the degree of a monomial. First we note that a monomial whose coefficient is zero is called a *zero monomial*; a monomial whose coefficient is not zero is called a *nonzero monomial*. The degree of a zero monomial is not defined. The *degree of a nonzero monomial* is determined by the following definition: If a nonzero monomial contains no variables, its degree is zero; if it contains one variable, its degree is the exponent of that variable; and if it contains two or more variables, its degree is the sum of the exponents of the variables. We observe that according to this definition, the degree of a nonzero monomial is a whole number. Examples are:

The degree of $3 x^7$ is 7. The degree of $\frac{23}{9}$ is 0.

The degree of $- 6 ab^4$ is $1 + 4 = 5$. The degree of $0 xy^2$ is not defined.

The degree of $17 x^a y^b z^c$ is $a + b + c$ when $a, b, c \in W$ and x, y, and z are nonzero real numbers.

The degree of $-\sqrt{15} x^0 y^0 z^0$ is $0 + 0 + 0$, or 0, when x, y, and z are nonzero real numbers.

The degree of $15 xy^2 (x^2 z)^3$ is $1 + 2 + 6 + 3$, or 12, when x, y, and z are nonzero real numbers.

If each coefficient of a polynomial is zero, the polynomial is called a *zero polynomial*. If at least one coefficient of a polynomial is not zero, the polynomial is called a *nonzero polynomial*. The degree of a zero polynomial is not defined. The degree of a nonzero polynomial is determined by the following definition: The *degree of a nonzero polynomial* is the degree of its nonzero term whose degree is equal to or greater than the degree of any of its other nonzero terms. For example,

The degree of $5 x^2 - 7 x + 8 y$ is 2.

The degree of $- 11 abcd + 11 + 7 a^2 b^2$ is 4.

The degree of $0\,x^4 + 18\,xy + 4\,x + 5\,y + 1$ is 2.
The degree of $0\,x^3 + 0\,ab$ is not defined.
The degree of $5\,x^2y + 7\,xy^4 - 13\,a^3xz^5$ is 9.

The degree of a polynomial *with respect to* or *in* a certain variable in the polynomial is the degree of the highest power of that variable which appears in a nonzero term of the polynomial. For example, the last polynomial above is of the second degree with respect to x, the third degree with respect to a, the fourth degree with respect to y, and the fifth degree with respect to z.

Since each zero polynomial having variables is equal to 0 for all values of its variables, we refer to every zero polynomial as *the* zero polynomial. Henceforth, when we speak of a polynomial, we shall mean a nonzero polynomial unless we specify otherwise.

Like Monomials

Let m_1 and m_2 be two nonzero monomials whose coefficients are respectively c_1 and c_2. Then m_1 and m_2 are *like monomials* if and only if $\frac{m_1}{m_2} = \frac{c_1}{c_2}$ is an identity. Thus $-7\,x^2yz^3$ and $5\,x^2yz^3$ are like monomial expressions because $\frac{-7\,x^2yz^3}{5\,x^2yz^3} = \frac{-7}{5}$ is an identity. On the other hand, $4\,ab^2$ and $-5\,a^2b$ are unlike terms because $\frac{4\,ab^2}{-5\,a^2b}$ is not identically equal to $\frac{4}{-5}$.
Why?

We observe that like monomials which involve variables must involve the same variables and each variable in one monomial must have the same exponent as the corresponding variable in the other monomial. It follows from the definition that nonzero numerical expressions which do not involve addition or subtraction are like monomials.

If two terms of a polynomial are like monomials, they are called *like terms*. In the simplest form of a polynomial each term is in simplest form and the members of each set of like terms are combined into one term by the use of the distributive property.

Example. Simplify each of the following: **a.** $(-3)a^2ba^3(b^3)^3(-8)$; **b.** $7\,xy + 11 - 9\,xy + 13$; **c.** $3\,x^2 + \sqrt{11}\,x^2$

Solutions. **a.** $(-3)a^2ba^3(b^3)^3(-8) = (-3)(-8)a^2 \cdot a^3 \cdot b \cdot (b^3)^3 = 24\,a^5b^{10}$

b. $7\,xy + 11 - 9\,xy + 13 = 7\,xy - 9\,xy + 11 + 13 = (7-9)xy + 24$
$= -2\,xy + 24$

c. $3\,x^2 + \sqrt{11}\,x^2 = (3 + \sqrt{11})x^2$

1. State the degree of each of the following. Each variable represents a nonzero real number unless specified otherwise.

a. 4

b. $-15\,x^2$

c. $0\,rs$

d. $\sqrt[5]{41}\,xy^3$

e. 1

f. $(147.6\,x^3)^2$

g. $5\,x^4(y^3z)^2$

h. $(3\,a^2)^4(2\,a)^3;\ a\,\epsilon\,C$

i. $8\,x^ay^b;\ a,\,b\,\epsilon\,C$

j. $(4\,x^a)^a;\ a\,\epsilon\,C$

k. $3\,x^ry^{2r};\ r\,\epsilon\,C$

l. $(4\,x^0y^3)^2;\ a\,\epsilon\,C$

2. State the degree of each of the following if each variable represents a nonzero real number.

a. $2+2+2$

b. $x+y$

c. $4\,a^2b+9\,ab$

d. $4\,a^3b+9\,ab$

e. $(3\,rs^2)^3+6\,r^2s^4$

f. $(4\,m^2n^3)^4+10\,m^5-(m^3)^5$

g. $7\,x^ay^b+2\,x^{2a}y^b;\ a,\,b\,\epsilon\,C$

h. $2\,x^a+4\,y^ab^{3a}+6^0;\ a\,\epsilon\,C$

3. In which of the following pairs are the monomials *like monomials*?

a. $3\,x,\ 5$

b. $14\,x^2y,\ 5\,x^2y$

c. $4\,xyz,\ 8\,xy^2z$

d. $-5\,abc,\ 25\,a^2b^2c^2$

e. $4(a^2)^3b^3(c^3)^2;\ 14\,a^6b^3c^6$

f. $9(x^a)^2y^4;\ a\,\epsilon\,W,\ (3\,y^2)^2x^{2a};\ a\,\epsilon\,W$

g. $(3\,y^3)^3(z^2)^5,\ 3\,y^6z^7$

h. $4,\ 1$

4. Simplify:

a. $4\,a^2+6\,b+(3\,a)^2+1$

b. $15+\sqrt{3}\,y+2+5\,y$

c. $18\,x^2yz+2\,xy^2z-3\,xyz^2$

d. $4\,a^2b^6c+(2\,ab^3)^2c-(abc)^2$

e. $14\,xy-3\,xy^2+2\,xy-7\,x^2y$

f. $\sqrt{5}\,x-\sqrt[3]{27}\,x+1$

g. $2\,a-11\,a+a^0+2$

h. $4\,x^2yz-8-3\,x^2y+5\,z+2$

5. A polynomial having one variable is called a polynomial in that variable. Thus $a_0x^n+a_1x^{n-1}+a_2x^{n-2}+\cdots+a_{n-1}x+a_n$ is called a polynomial in x provided $a_0,\,a_1,\,a_2,\,\cdots$ are numerical expressions which are not all zero, do not involve addition or subtraction, and $n\,\epsilon\,W$.

a. Write a polynomial in x that expresses the cubic inch measure of the volume of a cube the length of whose edge is one inch less than the length of the edge of another cube whose volume is x^3 cubic inches.

b. At the right is pictured a square piece of metal the length of whose side is 30 inches. If an x-inch square is cut from each corner of the piece of metal which is then folded so as to form a box, write a polynomial in x which represents the measure in cubic inches of the volume of the box.

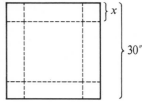

Operations with Polynomials

The domain of each variable in any polynomial is the set of real numbers unless otherwise specified. While $3 x^2 - 5 xy + 8 y^2$ is a polynomial over the integers (because its coefficients are integers), the domain of each of the variables x and y is the set of real numbers. The replacement set of the polynomial is therefore $R \times R$. Moreover, this polynomial names a real number for each member of its replacement set. A polynomial having n distinct variables has $R \times R \times R \times \cdots$ to n R's for its replacement set and such a polynomial names a real number for each member of its replacement set. We expect, therefore, that operations with polynomials will obey the laws that govern operations with real numbers.

Identically Equal Polynomials

Identically equal polynomials are polynomials that are identically equal algebraic expressions. That is, two polynomials are identically equal if and only if each can be transformed into the other or into a third polynomial using the rules for operating with real numbers, the properties of equality, and accepted definitions. Thus $2 x^2y + 5 xyz$ and $5 yzx + 2 yx^2$ are identically equal polynomials.

The following theorems are direct consequences of our definition of identically equal polynomials.

Theorem 1–4. Two monomials are identically equal if they are like monomials having the same numerical coefficient.

Theorem 2–4. Two polynomials, each in simplest form, are identically equal if for each monomial in either there is exactly one identically equal monomial in the other.

Theorem 3–4. Two polynomials are identically equal if they are identically equal to the same polynomial.

Example 1. Show that $p_1 \equiv p_2$ if $p_1 = 3 x + x + 4 x^2 + 5 x^2 + 7$ and $p_2 = 3 + 2 x + 2 x + x^2 + 8 x^2 + 4$.

Solution. We are to show that $3 x + x + 4 x^2 + 5 x^2 + 7 \equiv 3 + 2 x + 2 x + x^2 + 8 x^2 + 4$. First we transform p_1 by the rules for operating with real numbers as follows: $3 x + x + 4 x^2 + 5 x^2 + 7 = (3 + 1)x + (4 + 5)x^2 + 7 = 4 x + 9 x^2 + 7$. Now we similarly transform p_2 as follows: $3 + 2 x + 2 x + x^2 + 8 x^2 + 4 = 2 x + 2 x + x^2 + 8 x^2 + 3 + 4 = (2 + 2)x + (1 + 8)x^2 + 3 + 4 = 4 x + 9 x^2 + 7$. Therefore, $p_1 \equiv p_2$ by Theorem 3–4.

Example 2. Find a value for each of the coefficients a, b, c, and d so that $ax^3 + 11 x^2 - 19 x + b \equiv 5 x^3 + cx^2 + dx + 13$.

Solution. We see that if $a = 5, b = 13, c = 11$, and $d = -19$, the polynomials are identically equal by Theorem 2–4.

 A **EXERCISES**

1. In which of the following pairs are the two polynomials identically equal?

   a. $4x^2 + 6x + 7 + 2x^2 + x + 7; \quad 5x^2 + 7x + x^2 + 14$

   b. $6x^2 + 5x + 2x^2 + 1; \quad 8x^2 + 6x + 2 - x - 1$

   c. $x^3 + 5x^2 - 2x + 6 - x^2 + x - 10; \quad x^3 + 4x^2 - 3x - 4$

   d. $9x^2 + 6x^2 + x - 11 + 2x^2 - x; \quad 15x^2 - 8 + x^2 - 3 + x^2$

2. For what values of a, b, and c is it true that $7x^2 + bx + c \equiv ax^2 + 8x + 5$?

3. Find the numbers that must be represented by a, b, and c if $ar^2 - 5rs + bs^2 \equiv 4r^2 + crs + s^2$.

4. For what values of a, b, c, and d is $ax^4 + bx^3 - 11x^2 + dx + 1 \equiv x^4 + 6x^3 - cx^2 + 5x + 1$?

5. Study the polynomials below. If the two polynomials in each pair are members of an identity, replace the _?_ with $\equiv$. If they are not identically equal, replace _?_ with $=$ to form a conditional equation.

   a. $9x^2 + 4x + 2 \underline{\ ?\ } 7x^2 + 4x + 1 + 2x^2 + 1$

   b. $8x^2 + 5x + 3 \underline{\ ?\ } 8x^2 + 6x + 2$

   c. $2x^2 + 6xy + 5 \underline{\ ?\ } x^2 + 4xy + 1 + xy$

   d. $x^3 + 4x^2y + 5xy^2 + y^3 \underline{\ ?\ } x^2 + x + 4x^2y + 3xy^2 + y^3$

   e. $r^3 + 3rs + s^3 \underline{\ ?\ } 6r^3 + rs - s^3 - 3r^3 + 2rs + 4s^3$

6. Replace a, b, c, and d so that each of the following is a true statement.

   a. $5m^3 + bm^2 + 8m + d \equiv am^3 + 4m^2 + cm + 2$

   b. $6r^2 + brs + cs^2 \equiv ar^2 + 4rs + 3s^2 + rs$

Addition and Multiplication of Polynomials

We accept the following definitions for P, the set of polynomials:

a. If each of p_1 and p_2 is a polynomial, their sum is the algebraic expression $p_1 + p_2$.

b. If each of p_1 and p_2 is a polynomial, we shall use the notation $p_1 \cdot p_2$ to represent the *indicated product* of p_1 and p_2 and we shall use the notation p_1p_2 to represent the *product* of p_1 and p_2. Note that $p_1 \cdot p_2 \equiv p_1p_2$. When at least one of the polynomials p_1 and p_2 has two or more terms, the product p_1p_2 is the algebraic sum of all the products obtained by multiplying each term of p_1 by each term of p_2. This algebraic sum contains only one term if p_1 and p_2 are monomials.

c. If each of p_1, p_2, p_3, p_4, $\cdots$, p_n is a polynomial,

$p_1 + p_2 + p_3 = (p_1 + p_2) + p_3$

$p_1 + p_2 + p_3 + p_4 = (p_1 + p_2 + p_3) + p_4$

$p_1 + p_2 + p_3 + p_4 + \cdots + p_{n-1} + p_n$
$$= (p_1 + p_2 + p_3 + p_4 + \cdots + p_{n-1}) + p_n$$

d. If each of p_1, p_2, p_3, p_4, $\cdots$, p_n is a polynomial,

$p_1 p_2 p_3 = (p_1 p_2) p_3$

$p_1 p_2 p_3 p_4 = (p_1 p_2 p_3) p_4$

$p_1 p_2 p_3 p_4 \cdots p_{n-1} p_n = (p_1 p_2 p_3 p_4 \cdots p_{n-1}) p_n$

With these definitions established, it can be shown that if p_1, p_2, and p_3 represent any polynomials, each of the following statements is true.

1. $(p_1 + p_2) \in P$ (Closure property of addition)

2. $p_1 p_2 \in P$ (Closure property of multiplication)

3. $p_1 + p_2 = p_2 + p_1$ (Commutative property of addition)

4. $p_1 p_2 = p_2 p_1$ (Commutative property of multiplication)

5. $(p_1 + p_2) + p_3 = p_1 + (p_2 + p_3)$ (Associative property of addition)

6. $p_1(p_2 p_3) = (p_1 p_2) p_3$ (Associative property of multiplication)

7. There is a polynomial 0 such that $p_1 + 0 = 0 + p_1 = p_1$. (Addition property of the zero polynomial, that is, the additive identity)

8. There is a polynomial 1, $1 \neq 0$, such that $p_1 \cdot 1 = 1 \cdot p_1 = p_1$. (Multiplication property of the polynomial 1, that is, the multiplicative identity)

9. For each polynomial p_1 there is a unique additive inverse $- p_1$ such that $p_1 + (- p_1) = 0$. (Existence and definition of the additive inverse for a polynomial)

10. $p_1(p_2 + p_3) = p_1 p_2 + p_1 p_3$. (Distributive property)

We see that the set of polynomials with the operations of addition and multiplication is not a field since some nonzero elements in P do not have a multiplicative inverse.

Are all of the above properties true for the set of polynomial expressions?

Example 1. If p_1 and p_2 are polynomials, explain why the expression $p_1 + p_2$ is a polynomial.

Solution. Since p_1 is a polynomial it must, by definition, be composed of n monomial term(s) when $n \in C$. Similarly, p_2 must be composed of m monomial term(s) when $m \in C$. The expression $p_1 + p_2$ is therefore the algebraic sum of $(n + m)$ monomial terms and hence is a polynomial by definition.

Example 2. Write the sum of p_1 and p_2 and express this sum in simplest form if $p_1 = 3 x^2 - 11 y^2 + 31 xy$ and $p_2 = 13 xy - 21 y^2 + 5 z^3$.

Solution. The required sum is $(3\,x^2 - 11\,y^2 + 31\,xy) + (13\,xy - 21\,y^2 + 5\,z^3)$. The simplest form of this sum is obtained by using the distributive, commutative, and associative properties to combine like terms where possible. Thus, the simplest form of $p_1 + p_2$ is $3\,x^2 + (31 + 13)xy + (-11 - 21)y^2 + 5\,z^3 = 3\,x^2 + 44\,xy - 32\,y^2 + 5\,z^3$.

Example 3. Find the simplest form of the product of p_1 and p_2 when $p_1 = 3\,x^2 - 5\,x + 11$ and $p_2 = 4\,x - 5$.

Solution. $(3\,x^2 - 5\,x + 11)(4\,x - 5) = (3\,x^2 - 5\,x + 11)4\,x + (3\,x^2 - 5\,x + 11)(-5) = 4\,x(3\,x^2 - 5\,x + 11) + (-5)(3\,x^2 - 5\,x + 11)$
$= 12\,x^3 - 20\,x^2 + 44\,x - 15\,x^2 + 25\,x - 55$
$= 12\,x^3 + (-20 - 15)x^2 + (44 + 25)x - 55$
$= 12\,x^3 - 35\,x^2 + 69\,x - 55.$

Since both p_1 and p_2 are not monomials, the process of finding the polynomial $p_1 p_2$ involves converting the indicated product $p_1 \cdot p_2$ into an identically equal algebraic sum. This conversion requires repeated use of the commutative, associative, and distributive properties. Sometimes we facilitate this process by arranging our work as follows:

$$
\begin{array}{r}
3\,x^2 - 5\,x + 11 \\
4\,x - 5 \\
\hline
12\,x^2 - 20\,x^2 + 44\,x \\
-15\,x^2 + 25\,x - 55 \\
\hline
12\,x^3 - 35\,x^2 + 69\,x - 55
\end{array}
$$

Example 4. Express the polynomial identically equal to the indicated product $(4\,ab - 5\,b^2 + 3\,a^2)(7\,b^2 + 2\,a^2 - 15\,ab)$ in simplest form.

Solution. Our work is a little easier if we first arrange the terms in each factor in order of descending powers with respect to one of the variables: $(4\,ab - 5\,b^2 + 3\,a^2)(7\,b^2 + 2\,a^2 - 15\,ab) = (3\,a^2 + 4\,ab - 5\,b^2)(2\,a^2 - 15\,ab + 7\,b^2)$. The indicated multiplication can be performed as follows:

$$
\begin{array}{r}
3\,a^2 + 4\,ab - 5\,b^2 \\
2\,a^2 - 15\,ab + 7\,b^2 \\
\hline
6\,a^4 + 8\,a^3b - 10\,a^2b^2 \\
-45\,a^3b - 60\,a^2b^2 + 75\,ab^3 \\
21\,a^2b^2 + 28\,ab^3 - 35\,b^4 \\
\hline
6\,a^4 - 37\,a^3b - 49\,a^2b^2 + 103\,ab^3 - 35\,b^4
\end{array}
$$

Thus $(4\,ab - 5\,b^2 + 3\,a^2)(7\,b^2 + 2\,a^2 - 15\,ab) \equiv 6\,a^4 - 37\,a^3b - 49\,a^2b^2 + 103\,ab^3 - 35\,b^4$ and the polynomial in the right member of the identity is in simplest form.

Division of Polynomials

If p_1 and p_2 are polynomials, the expression $\dfrac{p_1}{p_2}$ is the indicated quotient

of p_1 and p_2. $\left(\text{The indicated quotient of } p_2 \text{ and } p_1 \text{ is } \dfrac{p_2}{p_1}\right)$. Now we know that

when p_1 and p_2 are the integers i_1 and i_2, respectively, there may or may not be an integer i_3 such that $i_1 = i_2 \cdot i_3$. For instance, there is no such

integer i_3 when $i_1 = 11$ and $i_2 = 3$. In this case $\dfrac{i_1}{i_2}$ does not name an integer.

Similarly, there may or may not exist a polynomial p_3 such that $p_1 = p_2 \cdot p_3$.

If there is no such polynomial p_3, then there is no polynomial equal to $\dfrac{p_1}{p_2}$.

Example 1.   Express each of the following expressions as a polynomial if possible.

a. $\dfrac{10\,x^2 - 29\,xy - 21\,y^2}{2\,x - 7\,y}$ c. $\dfrac{8\,y^3 + 22\,y^2 - 65\,y + 37}{4\,y - 3}$

b. $\dfrac{6\,x^3 + x^2 - 12\,x + 5}{2\,x - 1}$

Solution.   One procedure that may enable us to express each of these as a polynomial is known as the long division algorithm. This procedure is shown below.

$$
\begin{array}{r}
5x\ +\ 3y \\
2x - 7y\,\overline{)10\,x^2 - 29\,xy - 21\,y^2} \\
10\,x^2 - 35\,xy \\
\hline
6\,xy - 21\,y^2 \\
6\,xy - 21\,y^2 \\
\hline
\end{array}
$$

a.

Thus, $5\,x + 3\,y$ is a polynomial identically equal to

$$\dfrac{10\,x^2 - 29\,xy - 21\,y^2}{2\,x - 7\,y}.$$

$$
\begin{array}{r}
3\,x^2 + 2\,x\ -\ 5 \\
2x - 1\,\overline{)6\,x^3 +\ \ x^2 - 12\,x + 5} \\
6\,x^3 - 3\,x^2 \\
\hline
4\,x^2 - 12\,x + 5 \\
4\,x^2 -\ \ 2\,x \\
\hline
-\,10\,x + 5 \\
-\,10\,x + 5 \\
\hline
\end{array}
$$

b.

Thus, $3\,x^2 + 2\,x - 5$ is a polynomial identically equal to

$$\dfrac{6\,x^3 + x^2 - 12\,x + 5}{2\,x - 1}.$$

$$
\begin{array}{r}
2\,y^2 + 7\,y - 11 \\
\text{c. } 4\,y - 3\overline{)8\,y^3 + 22\,y^2 - 65\,y + 37} \\
\underline{8\,y^3 - 6\,y^2} \\
28\,y^2 - 65\,y + 37 \\
\underline{28\,y^2 - 21\,y} \\
-44\,y + 37 \\
\underline{-44\,y + 33} \\
4
\end{array}
$$

In this case $\dfrac{8\,y^3 + 22\,y^2 - 65\,y + 37}{4\,y - 3} \equiv 2\,y^2 + 7\,y - 11 + \dfrac{4}{4\,y - 3}$,

but $2\,y^2 + 7\,y - 11 + \dfrac{4}{4\,y - 3}$ is not a polynomial.

Observe that the remainder in this case is 4 and that the degree of the remainder is one less than the degree of the divisor.

The fact that the division process for the quotient of two polynomials each having one and the same variable can be continued until the degree of the remainder is less than the degree of the divisor reminds us of an analogous property for the division of integers. We know that the ordinary process of long division of one integer a by another b can be carried out until the remainder is smaller than the divisor. For example, if $a = 483$ and $b = 11$, we have the quotient 43 and the remainder, $r = 10$. $483 = 11 \cdot 43 + 10$. We may state this as a general theorem:

Theorem 4–4. If a is any integer and b is a positive integer, there are integers q and r such that $a = bq + r$, where $0 \le r < b$.

The proof of this theorem is considered in the exercises which follow.
For polynomials we have the following theorem:

Theorem 5–4. If p is any polynomial in x, and d is any nonzero polynomial in x, then there are polynomials q and r in x such that $p = qd + r$ where $r = 0$ or the degree of r is less than the degree of d.

 **EXERCISES**

1. **a.** Is $(a + b)(c + d)$ a polynomial?
   b. $(a + b)(c + d) \equiv ac + ad + bc + bd$. Is $ac + ad + bc + bd$ a polynomial?
   c. Can we always express the product of two polynomials as a polynomial?

2. **a.** Is $\dfrac{a + b}{c + d}$ a polynomial?
   b. Can we always express the quotient of two polynomials as a polynomial?

3. Is the sum of two polynomials a polynomial?

4. Is the difference of two polynomials a polynomial?

5. a. If $(3 m + 4 n - 5) + x = 0$, write the polynomial involving m and n which is represented by x.

b. What name do we apply to this polynomial?

c. State the property which indicates that the polynomial you have written is the only polynomial that can be represented by x.

6. a. If $(6 a^2 - 4 a - 3) + x \equiv 6 a^2 - 4 a - 3$, what polynomial involving a is represented by x?

b. How many such polynomials can be represented by x? Explain your answer.

7. If $(4 a + 1) \cdot x \equiv 4 a + 1$, what expression involving a is represented by x?

8. In some cases we write $(11 + 3 y) + [(- 11 - 3 y) + (5 y^2 + 7 y + 6)]$ in the form $[(11 + 3 y) + (- 11 - 3 y)] + (5 y^2 + 7 y + 6)$. State the property which defends our right to do this.

9. State the property which indicates that
$(a^2 + 2 a + 3)(a + 4) \equiv (a^2 + 2 a + 3)a + (a^2 + 2 a + 3)4$.

10. Express each of the following in simplest form.

a. $(9 rs + 6 ry + 5) + (3 rs + 7 ry - 4) + (12 rs + 14 ry + 10)$

b. $(6 xy + 7 - 2 xy - 8 + 4 xy + 10) + (5 - 8 xy)$

c. $(\frac{1}{2} a^2b^2 + \frac{1}{3} a^2b + \frac{2}{3} a) + (2 a^2b - \frac{1}{3} a) - (\frac{5}{2} a^2b^2 + \frac{1}{3} a^2b)$

d. $(6 m^3 + 4 m^2n - 3 mn^2 - 5 n^3) - (6 m^3 - 4 m^2n + 5 mn^2 + 4 n^3)$

e. $(6 a^2 + 3 a + 5)(3 a + 4 b)$ **h.** $(3 x^2 + 2 x + 1)(x^2 - 3 x + 5)$

f. $(7 m + 8 n - 2)(4 m - 2 n + 3)$ **i.** $(5 x + 3 y - 4)(6 x - 8 y + 1)$

g. $(4 a + 3 b)(x + 2 y + 4)$ **j.** $(2 - 3 x + 4 x^2)(3 x^2 + 2 x + 1)$

11. Express each of the following as a polynomial if possible.

a. $\dfrac{x^2 + 5 x - 14}{x - 2}$ **e.** $\dfrac{6 r^3 + 10 s^3 - 16 rs^2}{r - s}$

b. $\dfrac{2 x^2 + 9 xy - 5 y^2}{x + 5 y}$ **f.** $\dfrac{a^3 + 6 a^2 - 29 a - 42}{a^2 - 4 a - 21}$

c. $\dfrac{x^3 - 3 x^2 - 10 x + 24}{x^2 - 6 x + 8}$ **g.** $\dfrac{2 y^3 - 5 y^2 - 17 y + 20}{2 y + 5}$

d. $\dfrac{12 a^2 - 7 ab + 12 b^2}{3 a - 4 b}$ **h.** $\dfrac{2 x^2 + xy - x - 3 y^2 + 6 y - 8}{x - y + 2}$

12. Determine k so that the remainder is zero when $x^3 + 6 x^2 + 4 x + k$ is divided by $x + 3$.

13. Determine k so that $\dfrac{4 x^3 - 2 x^2 - kx + 2}{x - 1}$ can be expressed as a polynomial.

14. Determine k so that $(x-3)$ is a factor of $(x^3 + x^2 - 7x - k)$.

15. One factor of $2x^3 - 11x^2 + 3$ is known to be $2x+1$. Use division to find the other factor.

B **EXERCISE**

16. The following is a proof for Theorem 4–4: If a is any integer and b is a positive integer, there are integers q and r such that $a = bq + r$ where $0 \leq r < b$.

a. Study the statements given and supply the reasons indicated by each "Why?"

Proof: Any integer a is either a multiple of b, that is, $a = bq$, or a lies between two successive multiples of b, that is, $bq < a < b(q+1)$. In the first case, $a = bq + r$ with $r = 0$.

In the second case,

(i) $bq < a \longrightarrow a - bq > 0$. Why? Therefore $r > 0$. Why?

(ii) $a < b(q+1) \longrightarrow a < bq + b \longrightarrow a - bq < b$. Why? Therefore, $r < b$. Why?

Together, the first case and the two inequalities (i) and (ii) of the second case tell us that there are integers q and r such that $a = bq + r$ and $0 \leq r < b$.

b. Copy and complete the truth table to show that $[(a \vee b) \wedge (a \longrightarrow s) \wedge (b \longrightarrow t)] \longrightarrow (s \vee t)$ is a tautology and that the argument is valid.

a	b	s	t	$a \vee b$	$a \longrightarrow s$	$b \longrightarrow t$	$(a \vee b) \wedge (a \longrightarrow s) \wedge (b \longrightarrow t)$	$s \vee t$	$\begin{matrix}(a \vee b) \\ (a \longrightarrow s) \\ (b \longrightarrow t)\end{matrix} \longrightarrow s \vee t$
T	T	T	T						
T	T	T	F						
T	T	F	T						
T	T	F	F						
T	F	T	T						
T	F	T	F						
T	F	F	T						
T	F	F	F						
F	T	T	T						
F	T	T	F						
F	T	F	T						
F	T	F	F						
F	F	T	T						
F	F	T	F						
F	F	F	T						
F	F	F	F						

Factoring Integers

Before we consider the factoring of polynomials we should review the factoring of those simple polynomials that are integers. We remind you of the definition: The integer a is a *factor* of the integer b if and only if there is an integer c such that $ac = b$. We commented in the preceding chapter that since $(-5)(-3) = 15$, then -5 and -3 are factors of 15; since $1 \cdot 13 = 13$, then 1 and 13 are factors of 13; since $0 \cdot -43 = 0$, then -43 and 0 are factors of 0. We also commented that another way to say, "a is a factor of b," is to say, "b is a multiple of a." 15 is a multiple of -5, 13 is a multiple of 13, and so on.

A nonzero factor of the integer b is called a *divisor* of b. Thus, $1, -1, 2, -2, 7, -7, 14,$ and -14 are the divisors of 14. When we consider a statement such as $11 \cdot 0 = 0$, we observe that according to our definition 11 is a divisor of 0 but 0 is not. There are other ways to say "a is a divisor of b." Thus we may say "a divides b" or "b is divisible by a." For example, we may express the statement "-5 is a divisor of 35" by either of the statements "-5 divides 35" or "35 is divisible by -5."

If $ac = b$, when $a, b, c \, \epsilon \, I$ and neither a nor c is $-1, 0,$ or 1, then a and c are *proper factors* of b. Thus if a nonzero integer b has a factor other than 1, $-1, b,$ or $-b$, this factor is a proper factor of b. Note that 0 has no proper factors.

A *factorable integer* is an integer that has proper factors. Such an integer is also called a *composite integer*. A *nonfactorable integer* is one that does not have proper factors. A *prime number* is an integer which is greater than 1 and which is nonfactorable.

Example 1.　Is 13 a factor of -1547?

Solution.　We ask: Is there an integer c such that $13\,c = -1547$? Multiplying each member of this equation by $\frac{1}{13}$ we find $c = -119$. Since $-1547 = 13(-119)$ and since -119 is an integer, we see that 13 is a factor of -1547.

Example 2.　Is -23 a divisor of 437?

Solution.　Since $437 = (-23)(-19)$ we see that -23 is a nonzero factor of 437 and hence is a divisor of 437.

Example 3.　Are the statements "b is a multiple of a" and "a is a divisor of b" equivalent?

Solution.　Consider the statement $0 \cdot 11 = 0$. Since divisors are nonzero factors, 0 is not a divisor of 0. On the other hand we must accept the statement "0 is a factor of 0," and this is equivalent to the statement "0 is a multiple of 0." Thus when $a = 0$ and $b = 0$, the statement "b is a multiple of a" is true and the statement "a is a divisor of b" is false. Hence the statements are not equivalent.

Example 4.   Is 119 factorable?

Solution.   After some experimentation we find that $119 = 17 \times 7$. Since 119 is the product of two factors neither of which is 1 or -1, we conclude that 119 is factorable.

Example 5.   Is -17 a composite integer?

Solution.   Since -17 has no factors other than $1, -1, 17,$ and -17, it is not a composite integer.

Example 6.   Are the statements "b has factors" and "b is factorable" equivalent statements?

Solution.   We know that 5 has factors but no proper factors and hence is nonfactorable. Thus the given statements are not equivalent.

ORAL EXERCISES

1. When is a factor of a not a proper factor of a?

2. If an integer has factors, is it necessarily factorable?

3. What do we mean when we say that an integer is factorable?

4. Are all factors of an integer divisors of the integer?

 EXERCISES

1. Each of the following questions has the form "Is a a factor of b?" If the answer is "No," explain why it is "No." If the answer is "Yes," write b as the product of a and another factor.

   a. Is 13 a factor of 1885?

   b. Is 14 a factor of 1052?

   c. Is 0 a factor of 0?

   d. Is -18 a factor of 270?

   e. Is 21 a factor of 337?

   f. Is 4 a factor of 4?

2. The factors of 6 are $2, -2, 3, -3, 6, -6, 1,$ and -1. Which of these are proper factors of 6?

3. Write the factors of 30. Which of these factors are proper factors?

4. Write the factors of 31. Which of these factors are proper factors?

5. Is 11 factorable?

6. Read each of the following questions. If the answer is "Yes," write the quotient. If the answer is "No," explain why it is "No."

a. Is 253 divisible by 11?   **d.** Is 16 divisible by 5?

b. Does 5 divide 102?   **e.** Is 1 divisible by 1?

c. Is − 12 a divisor of 216?   **f.** Is 0 divisible by 0?

7. Which of the following numbers are factorable?   **a.** 15   **b.** 121   **c.** − 168   **d.** 1

8. Which of the integers in Ex. 7 are composite integers?

Complete Factorization of an Integer

An integer can be expressed as a product of integers in several ways. For example, $75 = 1 \times 75 = 5 \times 15 = (-25)(-3) = (-5)(5)(-3) = 3 \times 5 \times 5$. Any indicated product of integers which is equal to a given integer is called a *factored form* or a *factorization* of the given integer.

We adopt the following definition: The *complete factorization of a factorable positive integer* is the factored form of the integer in which each factor is a prime number. The *complete factorization of a factorable negative integer* is − 1 multiplied by the complete factorization of the opposite of the integer. For example, the complete factorization of 75 is $3 \times 5 \times 5$ and the complete factorization of − 75 is $(-1) \times 3 \times 5 \times 5$. The nonfactorable integers (0, 1, − 1, the prime numbers and their opposites) do not have complete factorizations although they do have factored forms.

It can be shown that any factorable positive integer has a *unique* complete factorization. The importance of this statement is indicated by the fact that it is known as the *Fundamental Theorem of Arithmetic*.

 EXERCISES

1. Find the complete factorization of each of the following integers.

a. 1890   **b.** 462   **c.** 180   **d.** − 286   **e.** 756   **f.** 40172   **g.** 273   **h.** − 1960

2. We may write 31 in the factored form 1×31. When we do this may we say that 31 has been factored completely? Explain.

3. Which of the following numbers can be factored completely?

a. 12   **b.** − 180   **c.** − 11   **d.** 165   **e.** 1428   **f.** 1   **g.** − 1   **h.** 10001

4. If $b \times c$ represents the complete factorization of a, what information can you state about b and c?

5. If $a, b, c, d, e \in I$, $b \times c$ is the complete factorization of a, and $d \times e$ is the complete factorization of a, how do you know that $[(b = d \text{ and } c = e) \text{ or } (b = e \text{ and } c = d)]$ is a true statement?

Greatest Common Factor

A *common factor* of two or more integers is an integer which is a factor of each of them.

The *greatest common factor* (GCF) of two or more integers is the greatest integer which is a factor of each of them.

One procedure for finding the greatest common factor of two or more integers is as follows:

(1) Find the complete factorization of each integer which is not a prime number or the opposite of a prime number. If a given integer is a prime number or the opposite of a prime, use a factorization of the absolute value of the given integer. Note that if 1 is one of the given integers, the GCF of the given integers is 1.

(2) Form the product of those prime numbers that are common to all of these factorizations—using each as a factor the least number of times that it appears as a factor in any of the factorizations.

Example 1. Find the GCF of 441, 1029, and 735.

Solution. The complete factorizations of the given numbers are as follows:

$$441 = 3 \times 3 \times 7 \times 7$$
$$1029 = 3 \times 7 \times 7 \times 7$$
$$735 = 3 \times 5 \times 7 \times 7$$

3 and 7 appear in all of these factorizations. The least number of times that 3 appears in any factorization is once, and the least number of times that 7 appears is twice. Consequently, the GCF is $3 \times 7 \times 7$ or 147.

Example 2. Find the GCF of $- 424$, 901, 53, and 477.

Solution. The complete factorization of $- 424$, 901, and 477 and the factored form of the prime number 53 are as follows:

$$- 424 = (- 1) \times 2 \times 2 \times 2 \times 53$$
$$901 = 53 \times 17$$
$$53 = 1 \times 53$$
$$477 = 3 \times 3 \times 53$$

53 appears in all of these factorizations. The least number of times that 53 appears in any factorization is once. Consequently, the greatest common factor (GCF) of $- 424$, 901, 53, and 477 is 53.

The greatest common factor of two or more integers is often called the *greatest common divisor* (GCD) of these integers. There is a method for finding the greatest common divisor which is interesting and which leads us to consider several important theorems. This method, known as *Euclid's algorithm*, is illustrated in the following problem of finding the greatest common divisor of 527 and 731.

$$
\begin{array}{r}
1 \\
527\overline{)731} \\
527 \quad 2 \\
\overline{204)527} \\
408 \quad 1 \\
\overline{119)204} \\
119 \quad 1 \\
\overline{85)119} \\
85 \quad 2 \\
\overline{34)85} \\
68 \quad 2 \\
\overline{17)34} \\
34 \\
\overline{0}
\end{array}
$$

We conclude that the greatest common factor of 527 and 731 is 17. Thus, the greatest common divisor of 527 and 731 is 17. In order to see the reason for this conclusion we present the results of these repeated divisions in the following array.

(1) $731 = 1 \times 527 + 204$ (4) $119 = 1 \times 85 + 34$
(2) $527 = 2 \times 204 + 119$ (5) $85 = 2 \times 34 + 17$
(3) $204 = 1 \times 119 + 85$ (6) $34 = 2 \times 17$

Step (6) tells us that 17 is a factor of 34. Since 17 is a factor of both 17 and 34 step (5) tells us that 17 is a factor of 85. Why? Since 17 is a factor of both 34 and 85 step (4) tells us that 17 is a factor of 119. Why? Continuing in this pattern we are led to the conclusion that 17 is a factor of 527 and 731.

This, however, proves only that 17 is a common factor of 731 and 527. We must now show that it is the greatest common factor. We know that the greatest common factor of two integers is the common factor which contains every other common factor as a factor. Now from (1) any common factor of 731 and 527 is a factor of 204. Why? From (2) any common factor of 527 and 204 is a factor of 119. Why? Continuing in this way we are led to the conclusion that any factor common to 731 and 527 is a factor of 17. Since 17 is the common factor of 731 and 527 which contains all factors common to 731 and 527, it must be the greatest common factor of these integers.

Each of the questions asked in the preceding discussion can be answered by the following theorem whose proof is left as an exercise.

▷ **Theorem 6–4.** If a is a factor of b and a is a factor of c, then a is a factor of $b + c$ when a, b, $c \in I$.

We can use Euclid's algorithm to express 17 as the sum of two integral multiples of our two given numbers 731 and 527. This means that there exist integers x and y such that $17 = 731\, x + 527\, y$. Moreover, we can use Euclid's algorithm in reverse to find these integers as follows: From line (5) we have (i) $17 = 85 - 2 \times 34$. From line (4) we have (ii) $34 = 119 - 85$. Substituting for 34 from (ii) in (i), we obtain $17 = 85 - 2(119 - 85)$ or (iii) $17 = 3 \cdot 85 - 2 \cdot 119$. Now we repeat this operation. Solving (3) for 85 and substituting in (iii), we obtain (iv) $17 = 3 \cdot 204 - 5 \cdot 119$. Solving (2) for 119 and substituting in (iv), we have (v) $17 = 13 \cdot 204 - 5 \cdot 527$. Finally solving (1) for 204 and substituting in (v), we have (vi) $17 = 13 \cdot 731 - 18 \cdot 527$. Thus, $x = 13$ and $y = -18$, and it can be readily verified that (vi) is true.

Since this process can be applied to express the GCD of any two integers a and b as the sum of two multiples of these integers, we state the following theorem which is important in number theory as well as in later courses in algebra.

▷ **Theorem 7–4.** If a and b are integers and $ab \neq 0$, there exist integers x and y such that the greatest common divisor of a and b is $ax + by$.

Two integers are *relatively prime* if their greatest common divisor is 1. Using this definition we have the following:

Corollary to Theorem 7–4. If a and b are relatively prime integers, there exist integers x and y such that $ax + by = 1$.

Since any two distinct prime numbers are relatively prime, the above corollary is a true statement when the word "relatively" is replaced by "distinct" in the statement. How do we know that two distinct prime numbers are relatively prime?

Example. The integers 17 and 13 are prime and therefore relatively prime. Find x and y such that $17\, x + 13\, y = 1$.

Solution. $17 = 13 + 4$ and $13 = 3 \cdot 4 + 1$. Therefore, $1 = 13 - 3(17 - 13) = 4 \cdot 13 - 3 \cdot 17$. We see that $x = -3$ and $y = 4$.

Suppose that b divides ac but is relatively prime to a. What can we conclude? Consideration of this question leads us to the following theorem which is easily proved by means of the corollary just stated.

Theorem 8–4. If a, b, $c \in I$ and b divides ac but is relatively prime to a, then b divides c.

Proof of Theorem 8–4. If a, b, $c \in I$ such that b divides ac but is relatively prime to a, then b divides c.

1. a is relatively prime to b	1. Given
2. $ax + by = 1$; $x, y \in I$	2. Why?
3. $acx + bcy = c$	3. Why?
4. b divides ac	4. Given
5. $ac = kb$; $k \in I$	5. Why?
6. $kbx + bcy = c$	6. Why?
7. $b(kx + cy) = c$	7. Why?
8. $(kx + cy) \in I$	8. Why?
9. b, $c \in I$	9. Why?
10. b divides c	10. Why?

Least Common Multiple

A *common multiple* of two or more given integers is an integer which is a multiple of each of them. Thus 45 is a common multiple of 5, -3, 9, and -15. This set of integers has many other common multiples, among them -90, 135, and 225. The product of two or more integers always is a common multiple of them. For example, since $5 \times (-3) \times 9 \times (-15) = 2025$, then 2025 is one of the common multiples of 5, -3, 9, and -15.

The *least common multiple* (LCM) of two or more integers is the smallest positive integer which is a multiple of each of them. To find the least common multiple of two or more composite integers.

(1) Find the complete factorization of each integer or of its absolute value if it is negative.

(2) Form the product of those prime numbers which appear in these factorizations—using each as a factor the greatest number of times that it appears as a factor in any of the factorizations.

Example. Find the LCM of 315, 525, 55, and 2205.

Solution. The complete factorizations are shown below.

$$315 = 3^2 \times 5 \times 7 \qquad 2205 = 3^2 \times 5 \times 7^2$$
$$525 = 3 \times 5^2 \times 7 \qquad 55 = 5 \times 11$$

The prime numbers that appear in these factorizations are 3, 5, 7, 11. The product obtained by using each as a factor the greatest number of times that it appears in any factorization is $3^2 \times 5^2 \times 7^2 \times 11$ or 121,275. The required LCM is 121,275.

In the example we note that the factor 7 of 315 must be a factor of 121,275. The reason is that 7 is a factor of 7^2 and 7^2 is a factor of 121,275. This observation suggests the following simple but important theorem.

▶ **Theorem 9–4.** If a, b, $c \in I$, a is a factor of b, and b is a factor of c, then a is a factor of c.

Ⓐ **EXERCISES**

1. Find the greatest common factor of the integers in each of the following sets.

   a. 15, 18, 21

   b. 56, 63, 77

   c. 175, 210, 1025

   d. 648, 225, 270, 576

   e. 375, $-$ 15, $-$ 75, 60

   f. 108, 36, 648, $-$ 72

   g. $-$ 55, $-$ 121, 33

   h. 60, 140, 180

2. Find the greatest common divisor of the integers in each of the sets in Ex. 1.

3. If r, s, and t are distinct prime integers, what is their GCF?

4. If a, b, c, and d represent distinct prime numbers, what is the GCF of each of the following sets?

   a. a^2b, a^3b, ab

   b. a^3b^2, ab^3, a

   c. abc, abd, ab^2

   d. ab^2, a^2c, ad^2

   e. a^3b^3c, $a^3b^2c^2$, $a^2b^2c^3$

   f. $ab^2c^2d^2$, ab^2cd, abc^2d, ab^2

   g. ab^3c^2d, ab^2c^2d, $a^2b^2c^2d$

   h. abc, abd, bcd, ab

5. Use Euclid's algorithm to find the GCD of 462 and 546.

6. In which of the following sets are the given integers relatively prime?

   a. 13, 11   **b.** 15, 21   **c.** 31, 51, 71   **d.** 32, 52, 72

7. Describe a procedure for finding the least common multiple of two or more integers some of which are prime numbers.

8. Complete: If 2 divides 5×6 but is relatively prime to 5, then 2 _?_.

9. Find the least common multiple of the integers in each of the following sets.

   a. 84, 24, 66, 77

   b. 180, $-$ 2700, 72

   c. 252, $-$ 66, 216, 36

   d. 300, 3500, 450, 120

10. When is the LCM of the elements of a set of integers the product of the integers?

11. Can the LCM of the elements of a set of integers be one of the elements of the set?

12. If each of the variables a, b, c, and d represents a distinct prime number, write the LCM of the elements in each of the following sets.

a. a^2bc, ab^2c, abc^2 c. a^2bd, a^3b^3d, abd^3

b. abc, abd, acd d. a^3b, a^3c, c^2d, b^2c

13. Supply the reasons for the following proof.
Prove: If a, b, $c \in I$, a divides $b + c$, and a divides b, then a divides c.
Proof.

1. a divides $b + c$ 1. Why?
2. $b + c = ka$; $k \in I$ 2. Why?
3. a divides b 3. Why?
4. $b = la$; $l \in I$ 4. Why?
5. $la + c = ka$ 5. Why?
6. $c = ka - la$ 6. Why?
7. $c = a(k - l)$ 7. Why?
8. $(k - l) \in I$ 8. Why?
9. a divides c 9. Why?

14. Prove: If a, b, c, $\in I$, a does not divide c, and a divides b, then a does not divide $b + c$.

 EXERCISES

15. Prove Theorem 6–4.

16. Prove Theorem 9–4.

17. Find integers x and y such that $156\, x + 216\, y$ is the GCD of 156 and 216.

Complete Factorization of a Polynomial over the Integers

If p, a nonzero polynomial over the integers, is the product of two other polynomials over the integers, p_1 and p_2, neither of which is 1 or -1, the polynomial p is said to be *factorable over the integers*. Each of the polynomials p_1 and p_2 is called a *proper factor* of polynomial p. If it is not possible to express p as the product of two polynomials over the integers neither of which is 1 or -1, p is *nonfactorable over the integers*. In other words, a polynomial over the integers is factorable if and only if it has proper factors. For example, the polynomials $x^2 + 2\, y$, $7\, a + 3\, b + c$, -5, x, and $x^2 - 2$ are nonfactorable over the integers.

If a nonzero polynomial over the integers is a numerical expression, then *the complete factorization* of the polynomial is obtained by using the definition of the complete factorization of integers. If a polynomial over the integers is not a numerical expression, then *a complete factorization* of the polynomial is obtained by expressing the polynomial as the indicated product of non-factorable polynomials over the integers other than the polynomials 1 and -1. When a polynomial over the integers is factored by applying either of the above procedures, we say the polynomial has been *completely factored*. Each of the factorizations shown for the following polynomials is a complete factorization.

$$-225 = (-1) \cdot 5 \cdot 5 \cdot 3 \cdot 3$$
$$14\,x^2 + 7\,x - 105 = 7(2\,x - 5)(x + 3)$$
$$x^4 - 16 = (x^2 + 4)(x + 2)(x - 2)$$
$$-7\,a - 7\,b = -7(a + b) = 7(-a - b)$$
$$15a^3b^2 = (-3)(-5)(-b)aa(-a)(b) = 3 \cdot 5 \cdot a \cdot a \cdot a \cdot b \cdot b$$
$$= (-3)(-5)(-a)aa(-b)b = (-3)(-5)aaabb$$
$$a^3x^2 - 2\,a^3x + a^3 = (-a)(-a)a(1-x)(1-x)$$
$$= (1-x)a(1-x)(-a)(-a) = aaa(x-1)(x-1)$$

If a polynomial appears more than once as a factor in an indicated product, we shall indicate this by writing the appropriate power of the polynomial rather than the expanded form that was used in the preceding examples. Had we used the power notation in the preceding examples, the last factored forms of the last two examples would have been written $(-3)(-5)a^3b^2$ and $a^3(x-1)^2$, respectively.

If a complete factorization of a polynomial over the integers which is not a numerical expression is obtained, other complete factorizations can be obtained by one or both of the following:

(1) Multiplying an even number of factors of the given complete factorization by -1.

(2) Changing the order of any number of factors.

These procedures are illustrated by the last two examples in the preceding set of examples.

If other factorizations of a polynomial over the integers which is not a numerical expression are obtained by using (1) or (2), they will be identi-cally equal factorizations and each of them will be referred to as *a complete factorization* of the given polynomial over the integers.

More about Factoring Polynomials

The factoring of monomials in P_I offers little challenge. Therefore, we shall emphasize the factoring of polynomials that have two or more terms. In such cases we are concerned with the problem of converting an indicated sum into an identically equal indicated product. This is the inverse of the operation we perform when we find the product of two polynomials. For this reason it is helpful to study certain special products of polynomials. In the following four sections we consider some procedures which are used in carrying out the operation of factoring.

Grouping before Factoring

It is easy to identify a monomial which is a factor of each term in a polynomial such as $2\,ax^2 - 4\,axy + 2\,ay^2$. We have at once $2\,ax^2 - 4\,axy + 2\,ay^2 = 2\,a(x^2 - 2\,xy + y^2)$. In some cases, however, the factoring can be accomplished only after the terms of the polynomial have been regrouped. The associative and commutative properties for addition of polynomials are used to regroup the terms of a polynomial and then the distributive property is used to factor the regrouped polynomial.

Example 1. Factor $ma - 2\,nb + mb - 2\,na$ completely.

Solution. $ma - 2\,nb + mb - 2\,na = ma + mb - 2\,na - 2\,nb = m(a + b) - 2\,n(a + b) = (a + b)(m - 2\,n)$. The complete factorization of $ma - 2\,nb + mb - 2\,na$ is $(a + b)(m - 2\,n)$.

Example 2. Factor $2\,ax + by - bx - 2\,ay$.

Solution. $2\,ax + by - bx - 2\,ay = 2\,ax - 2\,ay - bx + by = 2\,a(x - y) - b(x - y) = (x - y)(2\,a - b)$. Thus, the complete factorization of the polynomial $2\,ax + by - bx - 2\,ay$ is $(2\,a - b)(x - y)$.

Example 3. Factor the polynomial $a^2bx - by + b^2x - a^2y$ completely.
$a^2bx - by + b^2x - a^2y = a^2bx - a^2y + b^2x - by = a^2(bx - y) + b(bx - y) = (bx - y)(a^2 + b)$.

 EXERCISES

Factor each of the following completely.

1. $2\,a(r + s) - 3(r + s)$
2. $am - an - bm + bn$
3. $4\,x(a + b) - 4\,y(a + b)$
4. $2\,ar - 3\,s + 2\,as - 3\,r$
5. $ac^2 - acd + abc - abd$
6. $a^2x - 3\,a^2 + ax - 3\,a$
7. $abr - abd - acr + acd$

8. $2\,ax - 4\,x + 2\,ay - 4\,y$
9. $ax + bx + ay + by + a + b$
10. $ar - as + cr - br + bs - cs$
11. $ay + 3\,xy - ax - 3\,y^2$
12. $ax^2 - am - bx^2 + bm - x^2 + m$
13. $ax^2 + am^2 - bx^2 - bm^2 - x^2 - m^2$
14. $a^2b - abm + a^2c - a^2d - acm + adm$

15. $12\,b - 2\,ab + 6\,ac - 36\,c + 2\,a - 12$

16. $4\,a + 8\,b - 4\,c - ab - 2\,b^2 + bc$

17. $-3\,r^2 + rs + 15\,r - 2\,rt + 10\,t - 5\,s$

18. $abx - 2\,aby + 3\,ab - 3\,c - cx + 2\,cy$

Difference of Two Squares

Factorable polynomials which are expressed as the difference of the squares of two monomials are readily factored. Thus $9\,a^2b^2 - 4\,x^2 = (3\,ab + 2\,x)$. $(3\,ab - 2\,x)$ and $289 - 36 = 17^2 - 6^2 = (17 + 6)(17 - 6) = 23 \times 11$.

Sometimes a polynomial may be expressed as the difference of the squares of two other polynomials p_1 and p_2 where p_1 and p_2 are not both monomials. Thus, $(a^2 + 2\,ab + b^2) - (c^2 - 2\,cd + d^2) = (a + b)^2 - (c - d)^2$ $= [(a + b) + (c - d)][(a + b) - (c - d)] = (a + b + c - d)(a + b - c + d)$. In general, $p_1^2 - p_2^2 = (p_1 + p_2)(p_1 - p_2)$.

Example 1.   Factor $4\,x^2 + 4\,xy + y^2 - 1$.

Solution.   We write $4\,x^2 + 4\,xy + y^2 - 1$ as $(2\,x + y)^2 - 1^2$. In this form we identify p_1 as $2\,x + y$ and p_2 as 1. Then
$$4\,x^2 + 4\,xy + y^2 - 1 = (2\,x - y)^2 - 1^2$$
$$= [(2\,x + y) + 1][(2\,x + y) - 1]$$
$$= (2\,x + y + 1)(2\,x + y - 1)$$

Example 2.   Factor $9\,c^2 - 4\,x^2 + 4\,xy - y^2$.

Solution. $9\,c^2 - 4\,x^2 + 4\,xy - y^2 = 9\,c^2 - (4\,x^2 - 4\,xy + y^2)$
$$= (3\,c)^2 - (2\,x - y)^2$$
$$= [3\,c + (2\,x - y)][3\,c - (2\,x - y)]$$
$$= (3\,c + 2\,x - y)(3\,c - 2\,x + y)$$

Example 3.   Factor $x^4 + x^2y^2 + y^4$.

Solution. $x^4 + x^2y^2 + y^4 = x^4 + 2\,x^2y^2 + y^4 - x^2y^2$
$$= (x^2 + y^2)^2 - (xy)^2$$
$$= (x^2 + y^2 + xy)(x^2 + y^2 - xy)$$

Example 4.   Factor the polynomial $x^4 - y^2 + y - x^2$.

Solution. $x^4 - y^2 + y - x^2 = (x^2 + y)(x^2 - y) - (x^2 - y)$
$$= (x^2 - y)[(x^2 + y) - 1]$$
$$= (x^2 - y)(x^2 + y - 1)$$

Factor each of the following completely.

1. $9\,a^2b^2 - 16$

2. $25\,x^2 - 36\,y^2z^2$

3. $(x+4)^2 - (x-1)^2$

4. $64 - (x-3)^2$

5. $x^2 - 2\,ax + a^2 - 16$

6. $(x-b)^2 - (y-c)^2$

7. $9 + a^2 - b^2 - 6\,a - 2\,b - 1$

8. $4\,a^2 + 12\,a + 9 - b^2$

9. $4\,x^2 - 4\,xy + y^2 - 9$

10. $a^4 + a^2b^2 + b^4$

11. $x^4 + a^2x^2 + a^4$

12. $x^6 - 2\,x^3 + 1 - 16$

13. $36 - x^2 + 2\,x - 1$

14. $49 - 4\,x^2 - 4\,x - 1$

15. $x^2 + 2\,x + 1 - y^2 - 2\,y - 1$

16. $x^4 - 8\,x^2 + 16 - y^4 + 4\,y^2 - 4$

17. $a^2b^2 - 4\,b^2 - 9\,a^2 + 36$

18. $m^2y^2 + 25\,d^2 - y^2d^2 - 25\,m^2$

19. $a^3b^2 - ac^2 - 4\,a^2b^2 + 4\,c^2$

20. $x^2a^2 - 16\,x^2 - 9\,a^2 + 144$

Factoring Quadratic Polynomials

A polynomial such as $ax^2 + bx + c$ when a, b, and c are constants and $a \neq 0$ is of the second degree in x. It is called the *standard form* of a quadratic polynomial in x. If we can find numbers d, e, f, and g such that $a = df$, $b = ef + dg$, and $c = eg$, then $ax^2 + bx + c \equiv dfx^2 + (ef + dg)x + eg$. Thus $dx + e$ and $fx + g$ are factors of $ax^2 + bx + c$.

Some polynomials over the integers which are quadratic trinomials in x can be factored by a trial and error process which can be checked by finding the product of the factors obtained.

The equation $ax^2 + bx + c = 0$ when $a \neq 0$ is called the *quadratic equation in standard form*. When we solve the equation $ax^2 + bx + c = 0$ for x by factoring after completing the square, we obtain $x = \dfrac{-b \pm \sqrt{b^2 - 4\,ac}}{2\,a}$ which is the *quadratic formula*. The quadratic formula will be studied in greater detail in Chapter 7.

Example 1. Factor $6\,x^2 + 11\,x - 35$.

Solution. Since $a = 6$ we know that the coefficients of the first terms of the factors (d and f) must be two numbers whose product is 6. Since $c = -35$, we must choose for e and g two numbers whose product is -35. Also, we must have $ef + dg = 11$. After some experimentation we obtain $(3\,x - 5)\,(2\,x + 7)$ as a complete factorization of $6\,x + 11\,x - 35$.

Example 2. Solve the equation $6\,x^4 - 3\,x^3 - 9\,x^2 = 0$.

Solution.	$6\,x^4 - 3\,x^3 - 9\,x^2 = 0 \longleftrightarrow 3\,x^2(2\,x^2 - x - 3) = 0 \longleftrightarrow 3\,x^2(2\,x - 3)$ $(x + 1) = 0 \longleftrightarrow 3\,x^2 = 0$ *or* $2\,x - 3 = 0$ *or* $x + 1 = 0 \longleftrightarrow x = 0$ *or* $x = \frac{3}{2}$ *or* $x = -1$. The solution set is $\{-1, 0, \frac{3}{2}\}$. Note that although we are factoring over the integers, only the coefficients of the variables are required to be integers; the variables may represent any real numbers.

Check.

When $x = -1$,
$$6(-1)^4 - 3(-1)^3 - 9(-1)^2 \overset{?}{=} 0$$
$$+6 + 3 - 9 \overset{?}{=} 0$$
$$0 \overset{\checkmark}{=} 0$$

When $x = \frac{3}{2}$,
$$6(\tfrac{3}{2})^4 - 3(\tfrac{3}{2})^3 - 9(\tfrac{3}{2})^2 \overset{?}{=} 0$$
$$\tfrac{243}{8} - \tfrac{81}{8} - \tfrac{162}{8} \overset{?}{=} 0$$
$$0 \overset{\checkmark}{=} 0$$

When $x = 0$
$$6(0)^4 - 3(0)^3 - 9(0)^2 \overset{?}{=} 0$$
$$0 \overset{\checkmark}{=} 0$$

Example 3. Find the solution set of the inequality $x^2 - 7\,x + 12 > 0$.

Solution.
$x^2 - 7\,x + 12 > 0 \longleftrightarrow (x - 3)(x - 4) > 0$.
Since the product of the factors $(x - 3)$ and $(x - 4)$ is positive, both factors can be positive or both factors can be negative. If both factors are positive, we have

$$x - 3 > 0 \text{ and } x - 4 > 0 \longleftrightarrow x > 3 \text{ and } x > 4 \longleftrightarrow x > 4.$$

If both factors are negative, we have

$$x - 3 < 0 \text{ and } x - 4 < 0 \longleftrightarrow x < 3 \text{ and } x < 4 \longleftrightarrow x < 3.$$

Thus, $\{x \mid x^2 - 7\,x + 12 > 0\} = \{x \mid x > 4\} \cup \{x \mid x < 3\} = \{x \mid x < 3 \text{ or } x > 4\}$.

Example 4. Find the solution set of $3\,x^2 + 5\,x - 2 = 0$ using the quadratic formula.

Solution.
In the equation $3\,x^2 + 5\,x - 2 = 0$, we see that $a = 3$, $b = 5$, and $c = -2$. Substituting these values in the quadratic formula
$$x = \frac{-b \pm \sqrt{b^2 - 4\,ac}}{2\,a}, \text{ we have:}$$
$$x = \frac{-5 \pm \sqrt{25 + 24}}{6}$$
$$x = \frac{-5 \pm 7}{6}$$
$$x = x = \tfrac{1}{3} \text{ or } -2$$

Check.

When $x = \frac{1}{3}$
$$3(\tfrac{1}{3})^2 + 5(\tfrac{1}{3}) - 2 \overset{?}{=} 0$$
$$\tfrac{1}{3} + \tfrac{5}{3} - 2 \overset{?}{=} 0$$
$$0 \overset{\checkmark}{=} 0$$

When $x = -2$,
$$3(-2)^2 + 5(-2) - 2 \overset{?}{=} 0$$
$$12 + (-10) - 2 \overset{?}{=} 0$$
$$0 \overset{\checkmark}{=} 0$$

A **EXERCISES**

1. Factor completely.

   a. $6 x^2 - 7 x - 20$ **d.** $24 r^2 - 6 rs - 6 s^2$ **g.** $6 x^2 + 23 xy + 21 y^2$

   b. $6 x^2 - 31 x + 35$ **e.** $2 a^2 - 4 a - 12$ **h.** $15 x^2 - 14 cx - 8 c^2$

   c. $8 y^2 + 6 dy - 2 d^2$ **f.** $a^2 + 14 ab + 49 b^2$

2. Factor completely.

   a. $x^2 m^2 - 3 x^2 m - 4 x^2 - 9 m^2 + 27 m + 36$ **e.** $27 a^2 - 27 a^2 b - 72 ab^2$

   b. $ax^2 + 3 ax + 4 a + 2 x^2 + 6 x + 8$ **f.** $a^2 - 9 r^2 + 30 rs - 25 s^2$

   c. $x^2 + 2 xy + y^2 - 4 x^2 + 4 y^2$ **g.** $8 a^4 + 8 a^3 - 30 a^2$

   d. $x^2 + 6 xy + 9 y^2 - a^2 - 2 ac - c^2$ **h.** $25 x^5 + 16 x^4 y - 9 x^3 y^2$

3. Solve each of the following equations.

   a. $x^2 - 10 x + 24 = 0$ **e.** $a^5 + 2 a^4 + a^3 = 0$

   b. $y^2 + 2 y - 8 = 0$ **f.** $x^4 - 36 x^2 = 0$

   c. $8 y^2 = 18 y + 5$ **g.** $2 x^3 + 28 x = 18 x^2$

   d. $2 x^3 - 11 x^2 + 12 x = 0$ **h.** $4 x^4 - 12 x^3 + 9 x^2 = 0$

4. Solve each of the following inequalities.

   a. $x^2 - 10 x + 24 < 0$ **d.** $3 x^4 + 21 x^3 - 24 x^2 > 0$

   b. $x^2 + 5 x > 24$ **e.** $6 x^2 + 5 x < 4$

   c. $x^3 - 6 x^2 - 7 x > 0$ **f.** $3 x^3 - 16 x^2 - 12 x < 0$

B **EXERCISES**

5. **a.** The statements "$x < 0$" and "$x > 5$" are contrary statements. Why?

   b. $\{x \mid x < 0 \text{ and } x > 5 \text{ and } x < 2\} = \emptyset$. Why?

6. Find the solution set of the inequality $6 x^3 - 42 x^2 + 72 x > 0$.

Factoring the Sum or Difference of Two Cubes

   By long division we find that $x - 1$ is a factor of $x^3 - 1$ and $x + 1$ is a factor of $x^3 + 1$.

$$
\begin{array}{r}
x^2 + x + 1 \\
x - 1 \overline{)\, x^3 + 0\,x^2 + 0\,x - 1} \\
\underline{x^3 - x^2} \\
x^2 + 0\,x - 1 \\
\underline{x^2 - x} \\
x - 1 \\
\underline{x - 1}
\end{array}
\qquad
\begin{array}{r}
x^2 - x + 1 \\
x + 1 \overline{)\, x^3 + 0\,x^2 + 0\,x + 1} \\
\underline{x^3 + x^2} \\
- x^2 + 0\,x + 1 \\
\underline{- x^2 - x} \\
x + 1 \\
\underline{x + 1}
\end{array}
$$

We may check the correctness of these divisions by multiplying each quotient by the respective divisor. We find

$$(x - 1)(x^2 + x + 1) = x^3 + 0\,x^2 + 0\,x - 1 = x^3 - 1$$

and

$$(x + 1)(x^2 - x + 1) = x^3 + 0\,x^2 + 0\,x + 1 = x^3 + 1$$

In general we have the following identities:

$$(p_1)^3 - (p_2)^3 \equiv (p_1 - p_2)(p_1{}^2 + p_1 p_2 + p_2{}^2)$$
$$(p_1)^3 + (p_2)^3 \equiv (p_1 + p_2)(p_1{}^2 - p_1 p_2 + p_2{}^2)$$

Example. Factor $27\,a^6 b^3 - 8\,x^9$ completely.

Solution. Since $27\,a^6 b^3$ is the cube of $3\,a^2 b$, and $8\,x^9$ is the cube of $2\,x^3$, we have $3\,a^2 b$ for p_1 and $2\,x^3$ for p_2. Therefore,

$$27\,a^6 b^3 - 8 x^9 = (3\,a^2 b - 2\,x^3)[(3\,a^2 b)^2 + (3\,a^2 b)(2\,x^3) + (2\,x^3)^2]$$
$$= (3\,a^2 b - 2\,x^3)(9\,a^4 b^2 + 6\,a^2 b x^3 + 4\,x^6)$$

 A **EXERCISES**

1. Factor completely.

a. $a^3 - b^3$

b. $a^3 + b^3$

c. $r^3 - 27$

d. $s^3 - 8\,a^3$

e. $27 + 64\,a^3$

f. $3\,a^3 b^3 - 24\,c^3 d^3$

g. $2\,x^3 + 16\,y^3 z^3$

h. $a^6 - y^3$

i. $m^3 - 27\,n^6$

j. $8\,a^9 - 125\,b^6$

k. $a^6 - 8\,a^3 + a^3 b - 8\,b$

l. $m^3 r^3 + m^3 - 8\,r^3 - 8$

m. $8\,a^6 - 7\,a^3 b^3 - b^6$

n. $x^5 + x^2 - 4\,x^3 - 4$

o. $x^4 - 64\,x - x^3 + 64$

p. $a^3 b + b^4 + a^3 + b^3$

Factoring Polynomials over the Rational Numbers

Before we define "factorable" and "complete factorization" for polynomials over the rational numbers, we observe that any such polynomial which is not already a polynomial over the integers can be expressed as the product of a polynomial over the integers and a rational number. To do this we multiply our given polynomial over the rational numbers by the integer d, which is the least common multiple of the denominators of the fractions that appear in its coefficients after each fractional coefficient has been expressed in the form $\frac{a}{b}$, where $|a|$ and $|b|$ are relatively prime integers. Then we form the indicated product of the resulting polynomial over the integers p_I and the multiplicative inverse of d. The resulting expression, $\frac{1}{d} \cdot p_I$, is identically equal to the original polynomial. The process is illustrated by the following example.

$$\frac{5\,x^2}{4} + \frac{14\,xy}{18} - \frac{y^2}{27} = \frac{5\,x^2}{4} + \frac{7\,xy}{9} - \frac{y^2}{27}$$

$$= \frac{1}{108} \cdot 108 \left(\frac{5\,x^2}{4} + \frac{7\,xy}{9} - \frac{y^2}{27} \right)$$

$$= \frac{1}{108} \left(108 \cdot \frac{5\,x^2}{4} + 108 \cdot \frac{7\,xy}{9} - 108 \cdot \frac{y^2}{27} \right)$$

$$= \frac{1}{108} \left(135\,x^2 + 84\,xy - 4\,y^2 \right).$$

In this example we chose to use 108 as the multiplier because 108 is the least common multiple of the denominators of the fractions that appear in the coefficients of the given polynomial. Having multiplied by 108, we must multiply by $\frac{1}{108}$ because we want our indicated product of polynomials to be identically equal to the given polynomial. Now the polynomial in the parentheses is a polynomial over the integers and we know what it means (see page 172) to say that a polynomial over the integers is factorable or has a complete factorization.

If p_Q is a polynomial over the rational numbers which is not a polynomial over the integers, it is *factorable over the rational numbers* if and only if the polynomial over the integers which is equal to the indicated product $d \cdot p_Q$ is factorable over the integers, d being the least common multiple of the denominators of the fractions that appear in the coefficients of the polynomial after each fractional coefficient has been expressed in the form $\frac{a}{b}$ where $|\,a\,|$ and $|\,b\,|$ are relatively prime integers. We shall call the indicated product of the factor $\frac{1}{d}$ and the factors in a complete factorization of the polynomial over the integers equal to $d \cdot p_Q$ *a complete factorization* of the polynomial over the rational numbers p_Q. Other identically equal complete factorizations of a polynomial over the rational numbers are considered in the examples.

Let us consider the following questions. Does $\frac{1}{3}\,x + 7$ have factors which are polynomials over the rational numbers? Is $\frac{1}{3}\,x + 7$ factorable over the rational numbers? These two questions may seem much alike until we recall that some integers which have factors are nonfactorable according to our definition.

For example, -7 has the factors (-1) and 7, but it is nonfactorable because it cannot be expressed as the product of two integers neither of which is 1 or -1. Similarly $\frac{1}{3}x+7$ has such factors over the rational numbers as $\frac{1}{3}$ and $x+21$, but it is not factorable because the polynomial over the integers obtained by multiplying $\frac{1}{3}x+7$ by 3, namely $x+21$, is nonfactorable over the integers.

Factorizations of $\frac{1}{3}x+7$ such as $\frac{1}{3}(x+21)$ or $\frac{1}{5}(\frac{5}{3}x+35)$ are called *trivial factorizations* of $\frac{1}{3}x+7$ because they are obtainable by using only the fact that any rational number may be expressed as the product of other rational numbers in infinitely many ways.

As an example of a nontrivial factorization consider the following factorization of $\frac{2}{3}x-6$. Here the polynomial $2x-18$ obtained by multiplying the given polynomial by 3 is factorable with respect to the integers. Thus we have the following nontrivial factorization: $\frac{2}{3}x-6=\frac{1}{3}\cdot 2(x-9)$. Our definition of "factorable" for a polynomial over the rational numbers requires the polynomial to have nontrivial factorizations.

The following examples illustrate the procedures for factoring polynomials over the rational numbers.

Example 1. Factor each of the following polynomials over the rational numbers.

a. $2x^2+\frac{13}{21}x+\frac{1}{21}$

b. $x^3+\frac{1}{8}$

Solution. a. $2x^2+\frac{13}{21}x+\frac{1}{21}=\frac{1}{21}(42x^2+13x+1)=\frac{1}{21}(6x+1)(7x+1)$
Note that this factorization has many identically equal forms such as $(\frac{2}{7}x+\frac{1}{21})(7x+1)$, $(6x+1)(\frac{1}{3}x+\frac{1}{21})$, and $(2x+\frac{1}{3})(x+\frac{1}{7})$.

b. $x^3+\frac{1}{8}=\frac{1}{8}(8x^3+1)=\frac{1}{8}(2x+1)(4x^2-2x+1)$
Note that this factorization has many identically equal forms such as $(x+\frac{1}{2})(x^2-\frac{1}{2}x+\frac{1}{4})$, $(\frac{1}{4}x+\frac{1}{8})(4x^2-2x+1)$, and $(\frac{1}{2}x+\frac{1}{4})(2x^2-x+\frac{1}{2})$.

Another way to factor $x^3+\frac{1}{8}$ is to recognize that $x^3+\frac{1}{8}$ can be written $x^3+(\frac{1}{2})^3$ and then factor it as the sum of two cubes.

Example 2. Give a complete factorization of $3x^2+\frac{15}{2}x-\frac{4}{3}$.

Solution. $3x^2+\frac{15}{2}x-\frac{4}{3}=\frac{1}{6}(18x^2+45x-8)=\frac{1}{6}(6x-1)(3x+8)$.
Note that this factorization also has many identically equal forms such as $(x-\frac{1}{6})(3x+8)$, $(6x-1)(\frac{1}{2}x+\frac{8}{3})$, and $(2x-\frac{1}{3})(\frac{3}{2}x+4)$.

Give a complete factorization of each of the following polynomials over the rational numbers if one exists.

1. $x^2 - \frac{1}{16}$

2. $\frac{1}{2} a + \frac{1}{2} b - \frac{1}{2} c$

3. $x^2 + \frac{5}{6} x + \frac{1}{6}$

4. $x^2 - 81$

5. $10 m^2 + 7 m - 12$

6. $\frac{3}{4} x - \frac{5}{8}$

7. $\frac{1}{2} x + 5$

8. $\frac{2}{3} x^2 - \frac{1}{6}$

9. $5 y - \frac{y^3}{5}$

10. $x^3 - \frac{1}{8}$

11. $\frac{2}{3} a + \frac{1}{3} b + c$

12. $\frac{3}{5} x + \frac{1}{5} y + 4$

13. $x^2 - \frac{19}{3} x + 2$

14. $x^2 - \frac{1}{5} x - \frac{6}{25}$

15. $2 x^2 + \frac{1}{4} x - \frac{3}{8}$

16. $x^4 - \frac{1}{36}$

17. $\frac{ax}{2} - 3 x - \frac{1}{8} a + \frac{3}{4}$

18. $x^2 y^2 - \frac{y^2}{4} - 9 x^2 + \frac{9}{4}$

19. $ax + \frac{1}{3} x - \frac{2}{3} a - \frac{2}{9}$

20. $a^3 x^3 - \frac{a^3}{64} - \frac{x^3}{8} + \frac{1}{512}$

Factoring after Completing the Square

Completing the square is another procedure which sometimes helps us find the factors of a factorable quadratic polynomial. This process is illustrated in the following examples.

Example 1. Factor $x^2 + 20 x + 51$ after completing the square.

Solution. To $x^2 + 20 x + 51$ we add the number which will make $x^2 + 20 x$ a perfect square trinomial. Obviously this number is $(\frac{1}{2} \cdot 20)^2 = 100$. Having added 100 to $x^2 + 20 x + 51$ we must also add $- 100$ to avoid changing the value of the polynomial. Thus we have $x^2 + 20 x + 51 = x^2 + 20 x + 100 - 100 + 51 = (x^2 + 20 x + 100) - 49 = (x + 10)^2 - 7^2$. Since this expression is the difference of two squares, we see that its factors are $[(x + 10) + 7][(x + 10) - 7]$ or $(x + 17)(x + 3)$. Thus $x^2 + 20 x + 51 = (x + 17)(x + 3)$.

Example 2. Factor $6 x^2 + 11 x - 35$.

Since the coefficient of the second-degree term of a quadratic polynomial must be 1 before we can complete the square, we first remove the factor 6 as follows: $6 x^2 + 11 x - 35 = 6(x^2 + \frac{11}{6} x - \frac{35}{6})$. To $x^2 + \frac{11}{6} x - \frac{35}{6}$, we now add the number which will make $x^2 + \frac{11}{6} x$ a perfect square trinomial. We see that this number is $(\frac{1}{2} \cdot \frac{11}{6})^2 = \frac{121}{144}$. Thus we have $6(x^2 + \frac{11}{6} x + \frac{121}{144} - \frac{121}{144} - \frac{35}{6}) = 6[(x^2 + \frac{11}{6} x + \frac{121}{144}) - \frac{961}{144}] = 6[(x + \frac{11}{12})^2 - (\frac{31}{12})^2] = 6[(x + \frac{11}{12}) + \frac{31}{12}][(x + \frac{11}{12}) - \frac{31}{12}] = 6(x + \frac{42}{12})(x - \frac{20}{12}) = 6(x + \frac{7}{2})(x - \frac{5}{3}) = 2 \cdot (x + \frac{7}{2}) \cdot 3 \cdot (x - \frac{5}{3}) = (2 x + 7)(3 x - 5)$. Thus $6 x^2 + 11 x - 25 = (2 x + 7)(3 x - 5)$.

Factor each of the following polynomials after first completing the square.

1. $8 x^2 - 14 x + 3$
2. $15 x^2 + 2 x - 8$
3. $6 r^2 - 10 r + 4$
4. $6 m^2 - 19 m + 15$

5. $6 t^2 + t - 12$
6. $14 a^2 - 19 a - 3$
7. $10 a^2 + 7 a - 6$
8. $6 a^2 + 20 a + 6$

9. $12 a^2 - 16 a - 3$
10. $x^2 - 60 x + 891$
11. $y^2 - 21 y - 396$
12. $56 x^2 + 83 xy - 39 y^2$

Factor each of the following after completing the square.

13. $20 m^2 + 49 mn - 153 n^2$
14. $60 x^2 - 316 x + 143$
15. $238 x^2 - 177 x + 27$

16. $(a + b)^2 + 6(a + b) + 8$
17. $2(m - 1)^2 - 15(m - 1) + 28$
18. $4(r - s)^2 - 6(r - s) + 9 t - 9 t^2$

Factoring Polynomials over the Real Numbers

The procedure for factoring polynomials over the real numbers is similar to that used for factoring polynomials over the rational numbers. In addition to expressing all fractional coefficients in lowest terms as we did when factoring polynomials over the rational numbers, all radicals should be simplified and all denominators rationalized before proceeding to factor a polynomial over the real numbers.

The following examples illustrate the procedures for finding a complete factorization of a polynomial over the real numbers.

Example 1. Find a complete factorization of $x^2 - 2$. Consider $x^2 - 2$ to be a polynomial over the real numbers.

Solution. $x^2 - 2 = x^2 - (\sqrt{2})^2 = (x - \sqrt{2})(x + \sqrt{2})$. Note that we factored the polynomial $x^2 - 2$ as the difference of two squares.

Example 2. Find a complete factorization of $x^4 - 7$. Consider $x^4 - 7$ to be a polynomial over the real numbers.

Solution.
$$x^4 - 7 = (x^2)^2 - (\sqrt{7})^2$$
$$= (x^2 - \sqrt{7})(x^2 + \sqrt{7})$$
$$= [x^2 - (\sqrt[4]{7})^2](x^2 + \sqrt{7})$$
$$= (x - \sqrt[4]{7})(x + \sqrt[4]{7})(x^2 + \sqrt{7})$$

Note that in the third step of our solution we wrote $x^2 - \sqrt{7}$ as $x^2 - (\sqrt[4]{7})^2$ and then factored it as the difference of two squares. Since $x^2 + \sqrt{7}$ is not factorable over the real numbers, we will regard it as nonfactorable until the set of real numbers is extended.

Example 3. By factoring the polynomial $x^2 + 2x - 11$ over the real numbers after completing the square, find the solution set for $x^2 + 2x - 11 = 0$.

Solution. $x^2 + 2x - 11 = 0 \leftrightarrow x^2 + 2x + 1 - 12 = 0 \leftrightarrow (x+1)^2 - 12 = 0 \leftrightarrow (x+1)^2 - (\sqrt{12})^2 = 0 \leftrightarrow (x+1-\sqrt{12})(x+1+\sqrt{12}) = 0 \leftrightarrow (x+1-2\sqrt{3})(x+1+2\sqrt{3}) = 0 \leftrightarrow x = -1+2\sqrt{3}$ or $x = -1 - 2\sqrt{3}$

The solution set is $\{-1+2\sqrt{3}, -1-2\sqrt{3}\}$.

Example 4. Find a complete factorization of

$$\frac{x^2}{\sqrt{7}} - \frac{\sqrt{3}}{\sqrt{7}}x - \sqrt{\frac{20}{7}}x + \frac{\sqrt{60}}{\sqrt{7}}.$$

as a polynomial over the real numbers.

Solution. $\dfrac{x^2}{\sqrt{7}} - \dfrac{\sqrt{3}}{\sqrt{7}}x - \sqrt{\dfrac{20}{7}}x + \dfrac{\sqrt{60}}{\sqrt{7}}$

$$= \frac{\sqrt{7}\,x^2}{7} - \frac{\sqrt{3}\sqrt{7}\,x}{7} - \frac{2\sqrt{5}\sqrt{7}\,x}{7} + \frac{2\sqrt{7}\sqrt{15}}{7}$$

$$= \tfrac{1}{7}(\sqrt{7}\,x^2 - \sqrt{3}\sqrt{7}\,x - 2\sqrt{5}\sqrt{7}\,x + 2\sqrt{7}\sqrt{3}\sqrt{5})$$

$$= \frac{\sqrt{7}}{7}[x^2 - (\sqrt{3} + 2\sqrt{5})x + 2\sqrt{3}\sqrt{5}]$$

$$= \frac{\sqrt{7}}{7}(x - 2\sqrt{5})(x - \sqrt{3}).$$

Ⓐ **EXERCISES**

1. Find a complete factorization of each of the following polynomials. Consider each of the polynomials as a polynomial over the real numbers.

a. $x^2 - 7$ g. $x^2 + 4x - 1$

b. $y^2 - \frac{5}{2}$ h. $4x^2 + 20x + 23$

c. $9r^2 - 11$ i. $4x^2 + 4x - 5$

d. $x^2 + 2x - 2$

e. $x^2 + 4x + 2$ j. $9x^2 + 12x + 1$

f. $x^2 + 6x + 7$ k. $4x^2 - 12x - 7$

l. $\dfrac{x^2}{\sqrt{2}} - \dfrac{\sqrt{3}\,x}{\sqrt{2}} - \dfrac{\sqrt{5}\,x}{\sqrt{2}} + \dfrac{\sqrt{15}}{\sqrt{2}}$

m. $\dfrac{x^2}{\sqrt{3}} - \dfrac{\sqrt{5}}{\sqrt{3}}x - \dfrac{\sqrt{2}}{\sqrt{3}}x + \dfrac{\sqrt{10}}{\sqrt{3}}$

n. $\dfrac{x^2}{3} - \dfrac{\sqrt{7}}{3}x - \dfrac{\sqrt{2}}{3}x + \dfrac{\sqrt{14}}{3}$

2. Using factoring, find the solution set for each of the following equations. Consider the left member of each equation as a polynomial over the real numbers.

a. $x^2 - 12x + 27 = 0$ d. $2r^2 - 9r + 4 = 0$ g. $x^2 + 6x + 3 = 0$

b. $x^2 + 2x - 2 = 0$ e. $4m^2 + 12m + 4 = 0$ h. $4y^2 + 4y - 2 = 0$

c. $x^2 - 2\sqrt{5}x - 7 = 0$ f. $x^2 + 4x + 1 = 0$ i. $9t^2 + 6t - 4 = 0$

Least Common Multiple of Two or more Polynomials

A common multiple of two or more polynomials is a polynomial such that each of the given polynomials is a factor.

The *least common multiple* (LCM) of two or more polynomials is the common multiple which is a factor of all other common multiples of the given polynomials.

The following examples illustrate a procedure for finding the least common multiple of two or more polynomials.

Example 1.   Find the LCM of 54, 252, and 27.

Solution.   First we find the complete factorization of each polynomial.

$$54 = 3 \cdot 3 \cdot 3 \cdot 2$$
$$252 = 3 \cdot 3 \cdot 7 \cdot 2 \cdot 2$$
$$81 = 3 \cdot 3 \cdot 3 \cdot 3$$

Next we write the factors whose product will be the LCM of 54, 252, and 81. We use 3 as a factor four times because four is the greatest number of times that 3 appears as a factor in any of the three complete factorizations. Similarly, we use 2 as a factor twice and 7 as a factor once, Thus we have:

$$3 \cdot 3 \cdot 3 \cdot 3 \cdot 2 \cdot 2 \cdot 7 = 3^4 \cdot 2^2 \cdot 7 = 2268.$$

The LCM of 54, 252, and 81 is 2268.

Example 2.   Find the LCM of $x^2 - 1$, $x + 1$, $x^2 + 2x + 1$, and $x^3 - 2x^2 + x$.

Solution.   First we find a complete factorization of each polynomial.

$$x^2 - 1 = (x - 1)(x + 1)$$
$$x + 1 = x + 1$$
$$x^2 + 2x + 1 = (x + 1)(x + 1)$$
$$x^3 - 2x^2 + x = x(x - 1)(x - 1)$$

Next we select the factors whose product will be the LCM of $x^2 - 1$, $x + 1$, $x^2 + 2x + 1$, and $x^3 - 2x^2 + x$. We use $x + 1$ as a factor twice because the greatest number of times that $x + 1$ appears as a factor in any of the four complete factorizations is twice. We use $x - 1$ as a factor twice because the greatest number of times that $x - 1$ appears as a factor in any of the four complete factorizations is twice. And we use x as a factor once. Thus we have:

$$(x + 1)(x + 1)(x - 1)(x - 1)x = (x + 1)^2(x - 1)^2(x)$$
$$= x^5 - 2x^3 + x.$$

The LCM of $x^2 - 1$, $x + 1$, $x^2 + 2x + 1$, and $x^3 - 2x^2 + x$ is $x^5 - 2x^3 + x$.

Example 3. Find the least common multiple of $45\,x - 45\,y$, $x^3 + 3\,x^2y + 3\,xy^2 + y^3$, and $x^2 - y^2$.

Solution. Complete factorizations of each polynomial are

$$45\,x - 45\,y = 3 \cdot 3 \cdot 5(x - y) = 3^2 \cdot 5(x - y)$$
$$x^3 + 3\,x^2y + 3\,xy^2 + y^3 = (x + y)(x + y)(x + y) = (x + y)^3$$
$$x^2 - y^2 = (x + y)(x - y)$$

Next we select the factors whose product will be the LCM of the given polynomials. We use $x + y$ as a factor three times because the greatest number of times that $x + y$ appears as a factor in any of the three complete factorizations is three. Similarly, we use $x - y$ as a factor once, 3 as a factor twice, and 5 as a factor once. Thus we have:

$$(x + y)^3(x - y)(3)^2(5) = 45\,x^4 + 90\,x^3y - 90\,xy^3 - 45\,y^4$$

The LCM of $45\,x - 45\,y$, $x^3 + 3\,x^2y + 3\,xy^2 + y^3$, and $x^2 - y^2$ is $45\,x^4 + 90\,x^3y - 90\,xy^3 - 45\,y^4$.

Ⓐ **EXERCISES**

Find the LCM of each of the following sets of polynomials.

1. $x^2 + 5\,x + 6$, $x^2 + 4\,x + 4$, $x^2 - 5\,x - 14$
2. $5\,x^2 - 10\,x + 5$, $7\,x^2 - 14\,x + 7$, and $x^3 - 3\,x^2 + 3\,x - 1$
3. $2\,x^3 - 50\,x$, $3\,x^2 + 15\,x$, $x^3 + 5\,x^2$
4. $m^3 + 5\,m^2 - 6\,m$, $3\,m^2 + 9\,m - 9$, $7\,m^2 - 14\,m + 7$
5. $3\,r^2 - 12$, $2\,r^2 - 8\,r + 8$, $6\,r^2 + 12\,r$
6. $4\,a + 4\,b$, $6\,a - 6\,b$, $2\,a^2 - 2\,b^2$
7. $r^2 - 3\,r$, $-2\,r + 6$, $r^3 - 27$
8. $ab - a^2$, $b^2 - ab$, $a - b$
9. $3\,r^2 - 3\,rs$, $2\,s^2 - 2\,rs$, $6\,r^2 - 12\,rs + 6\,s^2$
10. $12 - 4\,m$, $5\,m - 15$, $27 - m^3$
11. $2\,x + 3$, $5\,x - 1$, $x + 4$
12. $4\,x^3 + 24\,x^2 + 36\,x$, $3\,x^5 + 21\,x^4 + 48\,x^3 + 36\,x^2$, $x^6 + 6\,x^5 + 10\,x^4 + 4\,x^3$
13. $x - 4$, $x - 3$, $x^2 - 7\,x + 12$

Ⓑ **EXERCISES**

14. $x^4 - 49$, $x^2 - 7$, $x^2 + 2\sqrt{5}\,x + 5$
15. $3\,x^2 - \sqrt{5}\,x + x - \dfrac{\sqrt{5}}{3}$, $6\,x^2 - 5\sqrt{5}\,x + 5$, $2\,x^2 - \sqrt{5}\,x + \tfrac{2}{3}\,x - \dfrac{\sqrt{5}}{3}$

Rational Expressions

An algebraic expression which can be written in the form $\frac{p_1}{p_2}$, where p_1 and p_2 are polynomials and p_2 is not the zero polynomial, is a *rational expression*. The following are examples of rational expressions:

$$\frac{1}{y}, \frac{a+1}{a-1}, \frac{x^3+\frac{5}{3}}{y-x}, \frac{x^2+\sqrt{7}}{xy-5}.$$

Note that the polynomials p_1 and p_2 may be polynomials over I, Q, or R. In the name "rational expression" the adjective "rational" refers to the form of the algebraic expression and not to the set of numbers used as coefficients for p_1 and p_2. Since any polynomial can be written as $\frac{p}{1}$, it is clear that the set of polynomials is a subset of the set of rational expressions.

We know that for the real numbers a, b, c, and d the following statements are true provided division by zero is excluded.

(1) $\dfrac{a}{b} = \dfrac{c}{d} \longleftrightarrow ad = bc$

(2) $\dfrac{a}{b} \cdot \dfrac{c}{d} = \dfrac{ac}{bd}$

(3) $\dfrac{ac}{bc} = \dfrac{a}{b}$

(4) $\dfrac{\frac{1}{a}}{\frac{b}{a}} = \dfrac{b}{a}$

(5) $\dfrac{a}{b} \div \dfrac{c}{d} = \dfrac{ad}{bc}$

(6) $\dfrac{a}{b} + \dfrac{c}{d} = \dfrac{ad+bc}{bd}$

(7) $\dfrac{a}{b} - \dfrac{c}{d} = \dfrac{ad-bc}{bd}$

If we interpret the a, b, c, and d of these statements as representing polynomials, we have definitions for the sum, product, difference, and quotient of rational expressions. The set of rational expressions is closed under the operations of addition and multiplication. The properties of equality and the field properties which are true for the set of real numbers are also true for the set of rational expressions.

A rational expression is in simplest form when it is written as a polynomial in simplest form or as the quotient of two polynomials over the integers that have no common factor other than 1 or -1 and the original expression is identically equal to its simplified form.

Example 1. Simplify the rational expression $\dfrac{x^4 - x^2}{ax^2 - ax}$.

Solution.   Factoring both the numerator and the denominator and applying statement (3) of this section we have:

$$\frac{x^4 - x^2}{ax^2 - ax} = \frac{x^2(x^2-1)}{ax(x-1)} = \frac{x^2(x+1)(x-1)}{ax(x-1)} = \frac{x(x+1)}{a} = \frac{x^2+x}{a}$$

Example 2. Write a simplified rational expression identically equal to the indicated product $\dfrac{2\,a+3}{a^2-1}\cdot\dfrac{3\,a^2+2\,a-1}{4\,a^2-9}$.

Solution. Making use of factoring and statements (2) and (3) of this section we have:

$$\frac{2\,a+3}{a^2-1}\cdot\frac{3\,a^2+2\,a-1}{4\,a^2-9}=\frac{2\,a+3}{(a+1)(a-1)}\cdot\frac{(3\,a-1)(a+1)}{(2\,a+3)(2\,a-3)}$$

$$=\frac{(2\,a+3)(3\,a-1)(a+1)}{(a+1)(a-1)(2\,a+3)(2\,a-3)}$$

$$=\frac{3\,a-1}{(a-1)(2\,a-3)}=\frac{3\,a-1}{2\,a^2-5\,a+3}.$$

A *complex fraction* is an algebraic expression written as a fraction whose numerator or denominator involves indicated divisions.

Examples of complex fractions are:

$$\frac{\dfrac{3\,a}{a+5}}{\dfrac{a-3}{a+5}}, \quad \frac{2\,x^2-x+7}{\dfrac{x-3}{x+4}}, \quad \frac{\dfrac{1}{a}-\dfrac{1}{b}}{\dfrac{1}{a}+\dfrac{1}{b}}, \quad \frac{\dfrac{2}{3}}{\dfrac{4}{5}}$$

Such expressions are sometimes written using the symbol $\div$, as

$$\frac{3\,a}{a+5}\div\frac{a-3}{a+5}, \quad (2\,x^2-x+7)\div\frac{x-3}{x+4},$$

and so on.

A complex fraction can be expressed as the quotient of two polynomials by using statement (3) on page 187, as shown in the following examples.

Example 3. Write $\dfrac{a+\dfrac{1}{b}}{b+\dfrac{1}{a}}$ as a rational expression in simplest form.

Solution. Since ab is the least common denominator of the denominators of the fractions in both $a+\dfrac{1}{b}$ and $b+\dfrac{1}{a}$, we let c of statement (3) equal ab. We obtain:

$$\frac{a+\dfrac{1}{b}}{b+\dfrac{1}{a}}=\frac{\left(a+\dfrac{1}{b}\right)ab}{\left(b+\dfrac{1}{a}\right)ab}=\frac{a^2b+a}{ab^2+b}=\frac{a(ab+1)}{b(ab+1)}=\frac{a}{b}$$

Example 4. Write $\dfrac{\dfrac{m}{n}+1+\dfrac{n}{m}}{\dfrac{m^2}{n^2}+1+\dfrac{n^2}{m^2}}$ as a rational expression in simplest form.

Solution. Since m^2n^2 is the least common denominator of the demoninators of the fractions in both $\dfrac{m}{n}+1+\dfrac{n}{m}$ and $\dfrac{m^2}{n^2}+1+\dfrac{n^2}{m^2}$, we let c of statement (3) equal m^2n^2. We obtain:

$$\frac{\dfrac{m}{n}+1+\dfrac{n}{m}}{\dfrac{m^2}{n^2}+1+\dfrac{n^2}{m^2}}=\frac{\left(\dfrac{m}{n}+1+\dfrac{n}{m}\right)m^2n^2}{\left(\dfrac{m^2}{n^2}+1+\dfrac{n^2}{m^2}\right)m^2n^2}=\frac{m^3n+m^2n^2+mn^3}{m^4+m^2n^2+n^4}$$

$$=\frac{mn(m^2+mn+n^2)}{m^4+2\,m^2n^2+n^4-m^2n^2}=\frac{mn(m^2+mn+n^2)}{(m^2+n^2)^2-(mn)^2}$$

$$=\frac{mn(m^2+mn+n^2)}{(m^2+mn+n^2)(m^2-mn+n^2)}=\frac{mn}{m^2-mn+n^2}$$

Addition (and subtraction) of rational expressions is based upon the statements $\dfrac{ac}{bc}=\dfrac{a}{b}$ and $\dfrac{a}{c}+\dfrac{b}{c}=\dfrac{a+b}{c}$ when a, b, and c represent polynomials.

Example 5. Write $\dfrac{1}{x}+\dfrac{x-1}{x^2}-\dfrac{3}{2\,x}$ as a rational expression in simplest form.

Solution. In problems of this kind, we want to express the given fractions as identically equal fractions having like denominators. For the common denominator we usually use the least common multiple of the denominators of the individual fractions. Here, the least common multiple is $2\,x^2$.

$$\frac{1}{x}+\frac{x-1}{x^2}-\frac{3}{2\,x}=\frac{2\,x}{2\,x^2}+\frac{2(x-1)}{2\,x^2}-\frac{3\,x}{2\,x^2}$$

$$=\frac{2\,x+2(x-1)-3\,x}{2\,x^2}$$

$$=\frac{2\,x+2\,x-2-3\,x}{2\,x^2}$$

$$=\frac{x-2}{2\,x^2}$$

Example 6. Write $\dfrac{2\,x}{5\,x-c}-\dfrac{x}{c-5\,x}$ as the quotient of two polynomials.

Solution. $\dfrac{2\,x}{5\,x-c}-\dfrac{x}{c-5\,x}=\dfrac{2\,x}{5\,x-c}+\dfrac{x}{5\,x-c}=\dfrac{3\,x}{5\,x-c}$

Example 7. Solve the equation $10 + \dfrac{18}{x-2} = \dfrac{9\,x}{x-2}$

Solution. Obviously $x \neq 2$ for otherwise we obtain a zero denominator. Thus, we should find the truth set of $10 + \dfrac{18}{x-2} = \dfrac{9\,x}{x-2}$ and $x \neq 2$.

$\left(10 + \dfrac{18}{x-2} = \dfrac{9\,x}{x-2} \text{ and } x \neq 2 \right) \longleftrightarrow \left[(x-2)\left(10 + \dfrac{18}{x-2} \right) = (x-2) \right.$

$\left. \left(\dfrac{9\,x}{x-2} \right) \text{ and } x \neq 2 \right] \longleftrightarrow (10\,x - 20 + 18 = 9\,x \text{ and } x \neq 2) \longleftrightarrow$

$(x = 2 \text{ and } x \neq 2)$. Since $\{x \mid x = 2 \text{ and } x \neq 2\} = \emptyset$, the original equation has no solution.

Example 8. Solve the equation $\dfrac{4}{x-3} - \dfrac{2}{3+x} = -\dfrac{x}{9-x^2}$

Solution. We see that $x \neq 3$ and $x \neq -3$, because substitution of either of these values in the given equation results in a zero denominator. The LCM of the denominators is $(x-3)(x+3)$.

$\left(\dfrac{4}{x-3} - \dfrac{2}{3+x} = -\dfrac{x}{9-x^2} \right) \text{ and } x \neq 3 \text{ and } x \neq -3 \longleftrightarrow$

$\left(\dfrac{4}{x-3} - \dfrac{2}{x+3} = \dfrac{x}{x^2-9} \right) \text{ and } x \neq 3 \text{ and } x \neq -3 \longleftrightarrow$

$\left[(x-3)(x+3)\left(\dfrac{4}{x-3} - \dfrac{2}{x+3} \right) = (x-3)(x+3)\left(\dfrac{x}{x^2-9} \right) \right] \text{ and } x$

$\neq 3 \text{ and } x \neq -3 \longleftrightarrow [(x+3)4 - (x-3)2 = x] \text{ and } x \neq 3 \text{ and } x$

$\neq -3 \longleftrightarrow (4\,x + 12 - 2\,x + 6 = x) \text{ and } x \neq 3 \text{ and } x \neq -3 \longleftrightarrow$

$(x = -18) \text{ and } x \neq 3 \text{ and } x \neq -3$. The solution set is $\{x \mid x = -18$

$\text{and } x \neq 3 \text{ and } x \neq -3\} = \{-18\}$. The check is left to you.

Example 9. Find the truth set for the inequality $\dfrac{3}{x} + 4 > 0$.

Solution. We see that $x \neq 0$. Consequently, we know that $x > 0$ or $x < 0$. If $x > 0$,

$\dfrac{3}{x} + 4 > 0 \text{ and } x > 0 \longleftrightarrow 3 + 4\,x > 0 \text{ and } x > 0 \longleftrightarrow 4\,x > -3$

$\text{and } x > 0 \longleftrightarrow x > -\tfrac{3}{4} \text{ and } x > 0 \longleftrightarrow x > 0.$

If $x < 0$,

$\dfrac{3}{x} + 4 > 0 \text{ and } x < 0 \longleftrightarrow 3 + 4\,x < 0 \text{ and } x < 0 \longleftrightarrow 4\,x < -3$

$\text{and } x < 0 \longleftrightarrow x < -\tfrac{3}{4} \text{ and } x < 0 \longleftrightarrow x < -\tfrac{3}{4}.$

The solution set is $\{x \mid x > 0\} \cup \{x \mid x < -\tfrac{3}{4}\}$. Thus

$$\left\{ x \,\Big|\, \dfrac{3}{x} + 4 > 0 \right\} = \left\{ x \,\Big|\, x < -\dfrac{3}{4} \text{ or } x > 0 \right\}$$

1. Simplify each of the following rational expressions.

a. $\dfrac{x^3 - 27}{x^3 + 3\,x^2 + 9\,x}$

b. $\dfrac{5\,a + 15\,b}{a^2 + 6\,ab + 9\,b^2}$

c. $\dfrac{x^5 - x^3}{x^5 - x^2}$

d. $\dfrac{m^5 - 6\,m^4 + 9\,m^3}{m^4 - 3\,m^3}$

e. $\dfrac{m^2 - 8\,m + 15}{15 + 2\,m - m^2}$

f. $\dfrac{6\,x^2 + 3\,x + \frac{1}{3}}{6\,x + 1}$

2. Write a simplified rational expression identically equal to each of the following indicated products or quotients.

a. $\dfrac{x^3 + 27}{x^3 - 9} \cdot \dfrac{x^3}{x^2 - 3\,x + 9}$

b. $\dfrac{a^3 - 3\,a^2 - 4\,a}{a + 2} \cdot \dfrac{a^2 + 5\,a + 6}{a^3 - a^2 - 12\,a}$

c. $\dfrac{r^2 - 5\,r + 6}{r^2 - 6\,r + 9} \div \dfrac{r^2 + 3\,r - 10}{r^2 + 2\,r - 15}$

d. $\dfrac{m^3 - n^3}{m^2 - n^2} \div \dfrac{m^2 + mn + n^2}{m^3 + n^3}$

e. $\left(1 + \dfrac{1}{x + 2}\right)\left(1 - \dfrac{1}{x + 3}\right)$

f. $\left(\dfrac{a}{b} - \dfrac{b}{a}\right) \div \left(\dfrac{a}{b} + \dfrac{b}{a} + 2\right)$

g. $\left(1 + \dfrac{a - 1}{a + 6}\right) \cdot \dfrac{a^2 - 27}{a^2 + a + 9}$

h. $\dfrac{m(m + 1) - 2(m - 1)}{m} \cdot \dfrac{m - 1}{m^3 - 4\,m^2 + 4\,m}$

3. Simplify each of the following complex fractions.

a. $\dfrac{\dfrac{1}{x + y}}{\dfrac{1}{x - y}}$

b. $\dfrac{a}{\dfrac{1}{a} + \dfrac{1}{b}}$

c. $\dfrac{\dfrac{r^2}{s^2} - 1}{\dfrac{r^2}{s^2} + \dfrac{2\,r}{s} + 1}$

d. $\dfrac{\dfrac{x^2 - 7\,x - 12}{x^2 - 2\,x - 3}}{\dfrac{x^2 - 2\,x - 8}{x^2 - 2\,x - 3}}$

e. $\dfrac{\dfrac{2}{a + b}}{1 + \dfrac{2}{a^2 - b^2}}$

f. $\dfrac{1 + \dfrac{1}{x} + \dfrac{1}{x^2}}{\dfrac{2}{x} + \dfrac{5}{x^2}}$

4. Write each as a rational expression in simplest form.

a. $\dfrac{3}{a-b} + \dfrac{5}{a-b} + \dfrac{x}{a^2-b^2}$

e. $\dfrac{x}{x+y} + 3 + \dfrac{1}{x-y}$

b. $\dfrac{3\,x}{x^2-4} - \dfrac{2}{4-x} + \dfrac{1}{x+4}$

f. $\dfrac{x+2}{x-3} - \dfrac{x+1}{x+3} + \dfrac{2}{x-3}$

c. $\dfrac{5\,r}{r^3-8} + \dfrac{1}{r-2} - \dfrac{r}{2}$

g. $\dfrac{m+1}{m^2+5\,m+6} + \dfrac{m}{m^2-4}$

d. $\dfrac{6}{x-3} + \dfrac{2\,x}{x^2-3\,x} + \dfrac{3\,x}{x+3}$

h. $\dfrac{x+4}{x+2} - \dfrac{x-5}{x+3}$

5. Replace each _?_ with a rational expression so that the statement formed is true.

a. $\dfrac{3}{x-1} + \dfrac{5}{x^2-1} + \_?\_ = \dfrac{4\,x+7}{x^2-1}$

b. $\dfrac{4(x+3)}{10} \cdot \_?\_ = 2\,x+4$

c. $\dfrac{x^2+5\,x+6}{x^2+3\,x+1} = (x+3)(\_?\_)$

d. $\dfrac{\dfrac{1}{x+y}}{\dfrac{2}{\_?\_}} = \dfrac{1}{2}$

e. $\dfrac{r^3+1}{1-4\,r^2} \div \dfrac{r^2-r+1}{1-2\,r} = \dfrac{r^3+1}{1-4\,r^2} \cdot (\_?\_)$

6. Solve each of the following equations and inequalities.

a. $\dfrac{a+7}{a+4} = 4 + \dfrac{a+3}{a+1}$

f. $\dfrac{m+20}{m^2-4} - \dfrac{m}{2-m} = \dfrac{m}{m+2}$

b. $\dfrac{3\,x+15}{4} = \dfrac{6\,x-2}{5}$

g. $\dfrac{4}{x} - 12 < 0$

c. $\dfrac{4\,y+19}{y+7} - \dfrac{4\,y-2}{y} = 0$

h. $\dfrac{2}{t} + \dfrac{3}{2\,t} > 0$

d. $\dfrac{1}{2\,x} + \dfrac{5}{x} > \dfrac{21\,x+2}{3\,x}$

i. $\dfrac{m^2+1}{m^2-1} - \dfrac{1}{m+1} = \dfrac{m}{m-1}$

e. $\dfrac{8}{r^2-9} - \dfrac{4}{3+r} = \dfrac{r}{r+3}$

j. $\dfrac{a+2}{a+3} - \dfrac{13}{a^2-2\,a-15} + \dfrac{a+3}{a-5} = 0$

7. If the sum of a nonzero real number and its multiplicative inverse is divided by its multiplicative inverse, the result is $\frac{5}{3}$. What is the number?

8. Find the solution set for the following sentence: If 3 is divided by a nonzero real number and 1 is added to the result, the sum is greater than zero.

Before you leave this chapter make sure that you

1. Understand the meaning of the expressions "monomial over the integers," "monomial over the rational numbers," and "monomial over the real numbers." (Page 148.)

2. Can determine the numerical coefficient of a monomial. (Pages 148–149.)

3. Understand the meaning of "polynomial over the integers," "polynomial over the rational numbers," and "polynomial over the real numbers," and know the meaning of the words associated with polynomials; for example, term, coefficients of polynomials, binomial, and trinomial. (Page 149.)

4. Understand and can use properly the words "power," "exponent," "base," "square," and "cube." (Page 150.)

5. Are able to use the laws for operating with powers. (Page 151.)

6. Can determine the degree of a polynomial and the degree of a polynomial with respect to a particular variable. (Pages 153–154.)

7. Know when monomials are "like monomials" and can simplify a polynomial by combining like terms. (Page 154.)

8. Can determine when polynomials are identically equal and can distinguish between equations whose members are identically equal and equations whose members are not identically equal (that is, conditionally equal). (Page 156.)

9. Understand the definitions for "sum" and "product" of two polynomials, the definitions for "multiplicative identity" in the set of polynomials, and "additive identity" in the set of polynomials. (Pages 157–158.)

10. Understand the operations with polynomials. (Pages 157–161.)

11. Understand the properties possessed by polynomials. (Page 158.)

12. Understand the terms "factor," "proper factor," "factorable," "composite," and "divisible" as applied to integers. (Page 164.)

13. Understand the meaning of "factored form" and "a complete factorization" of a polynomial and can carry out the processes of factorization of polynomials discussed in this chapter. (Pages 166, 172–184.)

14. Can find the greatest common factor and the least common multiple of a set of integers. (Pages 167–171.)

15. Can find a common multiple and a least common multiple of a set of polynomials. (Page 185.)

16. Understand what is meant by a "rational expression;" know the defini-
    tions for sum, product, difference, and quotient of rational expressions;
    and know which of the field properties are true for the operations of addi-
    tion and multiplication. (Pages 187–189.)

17. Can carry out operations with rational expressions and can solve equa-
    tions and inequalities involving such expressions. (Pages 187–190.)

18. Can spell the following words and phrases and use them properly.

binomial (Page 149.)	numerical coefficient (Page 148.)
coefficient (Page 149.)	polynomial (Page 149.)
composite (Page 164.)	power (Page 150.)
exponent (Page 150.)	rational expression (Page 187.)
factorization (Page 166.)	relatively prime (Page 169.)
monomial (Page 148.)	trinomial (Page 149.)

CHAPTER REVIEW

1. Which of the following are monomials?

   a. 1   **c.** $x + y$ **e.** $7 x^2 y$ **g.** $4 xyz$

   b. $2 \cdot \frac{3}{5}$ **d.** $4(5 + x)$ **f.** $5(-x)(y)$ **h.** $\sqrt{-5} \, y$

2. Which of the monomials of Ex. 1 are monomials over the integers? Which are
   monomials over the rational numbers? Which are monomials over the real
   numbers?

3. State the numerical coefficient of each of the monomials of Ex. 1.

4. Which of the following are polynomials?

   a. 5   **d.** $\frac{2}{x} + 1$ **g.** $4(a + 2b)$

   b. $4x + 6y + 5z$ **h.** $-\sqrt{5} \, a^2 b^3 c + 1$

   c. $\frac{1}{2}x + 5$ **e.** $-3\,abc$

                                      f. $\sqrt{6}\,a + \sqrt{7}\,b + c + 1$ **i.** $(x + 3)(x - 1)$

5. Which of the polynomials of Ex. 4 are monomials? Which are binomials?
   Which are trinomials? Which are polynomials that are none of these?

6. Which of the polynomials of Ex. 4 are polynomials over the integers? Which
   are polynomials over the rational numbers? Which are polynomials over the
   real numbers?

7. In the monomial x^3 what is the base? the power of the base? the exponent?

8. Simplify each of the following:

a. $(x^5)^2$

b. $a^4 \cdot a^2$

c. $(m^2 n^3)^3$

d. $(4\,a^4)^2$

e. $4\,x^2(x^3 y)$

f. $\dfrac{16\,x^3 y^2}{8\,xy^4}$

g. $a^2(2\,a^2 + 3\,a - 1)$

h. $(x^0)^3$

9. State the degree of each of the following monomials.

a. $4\,x^6$

b. $\dfrac{-15}{7}$

c. $\frac{1}{2}\,abc$

d. $(4\,x^2 y^3)^2$

10. Consider $(5\,x^3 z^2)^2$. What is its degree in x? in z?

11. In which of the following pairs are the monomials "like monomials"?

a. $4\,x^2 y$; $2\,xy^2$

b. $3\,a^2 b$; $7\,a^2 b$

c. $-9\,xy^2 z$; $5\,x^2 yz^2$

d. $-1, 6$

12. Simplify each of the following by combining like terms.

a. $7\,x + 4\,y - 9\,x + 3$

b. $4\,x^2 - 9\,x^2 + 4\,x - 3$

c. $4\,x^2 + \sqrt{5}\,x + x^2 - 2\,x$

d. $16\,x + 7 - x - 1$

13. If the two polynomials of each pair are identically equal, replace _?_ by the symbol $\equiv$, but if they are conditionally equal, replace _?_ by $=$.

a. $4\,x + 5\,y$ _?_ $x + y + 3\,x + 4\,y$

b. $3(a + b)$ _?_ $3\,a + 3\,b$

c. $3\,x^2 y + 1$ _?_ $1 + 3\,x^2 y$

d. $2\,x^2 + 4\,x - 5$ _?_ $2\,x + 4\,x^2 - 5$

14. Find the values of a, b, and c which will make the two members of the following equation identically equal polynomials. $4\,x^2 + bxy - 9\,y^2 = ax^2 - 7\,xy + cy^2$

15. a. Is the product of two polynomials always a polynomial?

b. Write the polynomial which is identically equal to $(x - 3)(x + 7)$.

16. a. Is the sum of two polynomials always a polynomial?

b. Write the polynomial which is identically equal to $(4\,x + y) + (3\,x - 7\,y)$ in simplest form.

17. a. Is the quotient of two polynomials always a polynomial?

b. Write the polynomial which is identically equal to $\dfrac{x^2 - x - 20}{x + 4}$.

18. Simplify each of the following.

a. $(4\,x^2 - 5\,x - 6)(2\,x - 1)$

b. $(2\,x - 3)(2\,x + 3)$

c. $(x^2 - 9\,x - 5)(2\,x + 4)$

d. $(3\,a^2 b - 2\,ab + 4\,b^2)(2\,a^2 b - 4\,ab + b^2)$

19. Factor each of the following completely.

a. 1052

b. -420

c. $9\,x^2 y^2$

d. 98

20. Which of the following integers are factorable?

    a. 2   **b.** 147   **c.** -18 **d.** 11

21. Name the proper factors of 16.

22. Find the greatest common factor of -12, 36, and 27.

23. Find the least common multiple of the numbers in Ex. 22.

24. Factor each of the following completely.

    a. $6x^2 + 8xy - 8y^2$ **d.** $a^2 + a + \frac{1}{4}$

    b. $16a^2b^2 - 81$ **e.** $a^4 - b^2 + a^2 - b$

    c. $ab + 4b - 3a - 12$ **f.** $ac + 3c - 2a + 4$

25. Factor each of the following completely with respect to the real numbers.

    a. $x^2 - 11$ **c.** $x^2 + 6x + 3$

    b. $\dfrac{x^2}{\sqrt{7}} + \sqrt{\dfrac{3}{7}}x + \sqrt{\dfrac{2}{7}}x + \dfrac{\sqrt{6}}{\sqrt{7}}$ **d.** $x^4 - 5$

26. Find the greatest common factor of $x^4 - 4x^3 + 4x^2$ and $x^5 - 5x^4 + 6x^3$.

27. Find the least common multiple of the polynomials in Ex. 26.

28. Simplify:

    a. $\dfrac{x^2 + 2x - 15}{x^2 - 6x + 9}$ **d.** $\dfrac{x - \dfrac{1}{y}}{y^2 - \dfrac{1}{x^2}}$

    b. $\dfrac{x^2 + x - 12}{x + 2} \cdot \dfrac{x^2 + 3x + 2}{x + 4}$ **e.** $\left(\dfrac{1}{x} + y\right) \div \left(\dfrac{1}{x} - y\right)$

    c. $\dfrac{x^2}{x^2 - 25} + \dfrac{x}{x + 5} - \dfrac{1}{5 - x}$ **f.** $\left(\dfrac{x}{y} + \dfrac{1}{4}\right)\left(x - \dfrac{x^3}{x^2 + y}\right)$

29. Solve: $\dfrac{x + 3}{x^2 - 1} - \dfrac{1}{x - 2} = 0$

30. Find the solution set for $\dfrac{4}{x} - 3 > 0$.

1. Which of the following are polynomials?

   a. 0   **c.** $\frac{3}{5} x$ **e.** $\frac{7}{x} + 2 y$

   b. $a + b$ **d.** $4(r + s)$ **f.** $ax^2 + bx + c$

2. Replace the question marks below with = or ≡ to distinguish the identities from the conditional equations.

   a. $(a - b)(a - c)$ _?_ $a^2 - ab - ac + bc$

   b. $9 x^3 + 3 x^2 y + 4 xy^2 - 2$ _?_ $3 x^2 y - 4 xy^2 - 2 + 9 x^3$

   c. $\dfrac{x^2 + 7 x + 13}{x + 3}$ _?_ $x + 4 + \dfrac{1}{x + 3}$

   d. $x^2 + 9 x + 8$ _?_ $4 x - 5$

3. Simplify each of the following:

   a. $(4 a^2 b^3)^4$

   c. $\dfrac{x - \dfrac{1}{x}}{1 + \dfrac{1}{x}}$

   b. $\dfrac{a - b}{a^2 - 1} \cdot \dfrac{a - 1}{a^2 - b^2}$

   d. $7 a^2 b - 2 ab^2 c + 6 c^2 - 4 a^2 b - 9 c^2$

4. Factor each of the following completely over the integers.

   a. $ax^2 - 9 a - bx^2 + 9 b$ **c.** $6 a^4 - 3 a^3 - 84 a^2$

   b. $16 - a^2 - 2 ab - b^2$ **d.** $x^3 - 125$

5. Factor over the rational numbers: $2 x^2 + \frac{1}{5} x - \frac{3}{25}$.

6. Factor over the real numbers: $x^4 - 13$.

7. Express as an identically equal rational expression: $\left(1 + \dfrac{1}{x + 2}\right)\left(1 - \dfrac{4}{x + 3}\right)$.

8. Solve: $\dfrac{y^2 + 1}{y^2 - 1} - \dfrac{y}{y - 1} + \dfrac{2}{y + 1} = 0$.

9. Find the solution set of $2 x^3 + 5 x^2 = 12 x$.

10. Find the truth set of the inequality $x^3 - x^2 - 6 x > 0$.

198

1. Given $N = \{-2, -\sqrt{3}, -\frac{3}{2}, -1, -\frac{1}{3}, \frac{1}{3}, 1, \frac{3}{2}, \sqrt{3}, 2\}$, by means of rosters define the following subsets of N:

a. H, the subset of integers

b. K, the subset of rational numbers

c. L, the subset of irrational numbers

d. W, the subset of whole numbers

e. T, the subset of counting numbers

2. With reference to the sets of Ex. 1 complete each of the following to form a true statement.

a. $T \cap W = \_\_?\_\_$

b. $K \cap L = \_\_?\_\_$

c. $K \cup L = \_\_?\_\_$

d. The complement of K with respect to universal set $N = \_\_?\_\_$

e. The complement of H with respect to universal set $N = \_\_?\_\_$

3. Define each of the following terms.

a. variable

b. constant

c. value of a variable

d. replacement set (domain) of a variable

4. State and illustrate the eleven properties which enable us to say that the set of real numbers forms a field.

5. Complete each of the following to form a true statement.

a. If $a, b, c \in R$, then $a - b = c$ means $\_\_?\_\_$.

b. If $a, b, c \in R$, then $\dfrac{a}{b} = c$ means $\_\_?\_\_$.

6. Draw the graph of $\{(1, -2), (2, -3), (3, -4)\}$ as a subset of $I \times I$.

7. In which of the following statements is the replacement set for the statement equal to the replacement set of the variable in the statement?

a. $x + 4 = 11; \ x \in C$

b. $5x > 15; \ x \in R$

c. $4x = 6x - 2x; \ x \in R$

d. $\dfrac{3}{x-2} = 4; \ x \in I$

8. Which of the following statements are conditional equations and which are identities? In each case $x \in R$.

a. $3x + 4x = 7x$

b. $\dfrac{1}{x} = 15; \ x \neq 0$

c. $|x+2| = 11$

d. $x^2 - 5x + 6 = 0$

9. State each of the following properties:

a. the trichotomy property

b. the transitive property of equality

c. the addition property of equality

d. the multiplication property of equality

10. Make a truth table to show the conditions under which two statements s and t are equivalent and the conditions under which they are not equivalent.

11. Which of the following statements are true and which are false? In each case $x \in R$.

a. $\frac{2}{3} x = 12 \longleftrightarrow x + 7 = 25$

b. $(x - 3)(x + 3) = 0 \longleftrightarrow x^2 = 9$

c. $\dfrac{1}{x} = \dfrac{1}{4} \longleftrightarrow 2 x = 8$

12. Assuming that $x \in R$, make a graph of the truth set of each of the following statements when a graph is possible.

a. $x > 4 \wedge x > 1$ **c.** $3 x = 6 \vee x + 2 = -3$

b. $x + 2 > 5 \wedge x + 4 > 1$ **d.** $x^2 = 9 \vee 4 x > 12$

13. Complete the truth table at the right

r	s	$r \longrightarrow s$
T	T	
T	F	
F	T	
F	F	

14. Write four other statements that have the same meaning as "If m, then n."

15. Which of the following statements are true and which are false, assuming that $x \in R$?

a. $x + 5 = 9 \longrightarrow x > 1$ **c.** $| x + 2 | = 7 \longrightarrow x = 5$

b. $x^2 = 16 \longrightarrow | x | = 4$ **d.** $3 x = 15 \longrightarrow x \not> 5$

16. Write a contradiction of each of the following statements.

a. $x < 2$ *or* $x = 5$ **b.** $x > 10 \wedge y < 3$

17. Write the converse, the inverse, and the contrapositive of the statement: If $4 x = -12$, then $x = -3$.

18. Use a truth table to show that $\sim (\sim a) \longleftrightarrow a$ is a tautology.

19. Determine whether each of the following arguments is valid.

a. When Mrs. Hughes comes to school, she always visits the school library. Mrs. Hughes came to school today. Therefore Mrs. Hughes visited the school library today.

b. If a number is a counting number, it is an integer. The number x is an integer. Therefore the number x is a counting number.

20. a. What do we mean when we say that R, the set of real numbers, is closed under addition?

b. Under which of the following other operations is R closed? (1) subtraction, (2) multiplication, (3) division, (4) evolution, (5) involution

21. a. What do we mean when we say that R, the set of real numbers, possesses the property of density?

b. Which of the following subsets of R also possess this property?
(1) the counting numbers (3) the rational numbers
(2) the integers (4) the whole numbers

22. Replace each of the following question marks with one of the symbols $>$, $<$, or $=$ to form a true statement when the variables represent real numbers.

a. $(a < b \wedge c = 1) \longrightarrow ac \underline{\ ?\ } bc$

b. $(a < b \wedge c > 1) \longrightarrow ac \underline{\ ?\ } bc$

c. $(a < b \wedge c < 0) \longrightarrow ac \underline{\ ?\ } bc$

d. $(a > b \wedge c > d) \longrightarrow (a + c \underline{\ ?\ } b + d)$

e. $a > b \longleftrightarrow -a \underline{\ ?\ } -b$ and $a < b \longleftrightarrow -a \underline{\ ?\ } -b$

f. $a > b \wedge ab > 0 \longleftrightarrow \dfrac{1}{a} \underline{\ ?\ } \dfrac{1}{b}$

g. $(a > 0 \wedge b > 0 \wedge a > b) \longleftrightarrow a^2 \underline{\ ?\ } b^2$

23. Solve each of the following:

a. $x^2 + 4 \geq 20$ **b.** $\dfrac{2x}{3+x} < 0$ **c.** $(x+2)(x-1) > 0$

24. Express each of the following with a rational denominator and in its simplest form.

a. $\sqrt{147}$

c. $\dfrac{\sqrt[3]{81}}{\sqrt[3]{3}}$

e. $\dfrac{4 + \sqrt{3}}{4 - \sqrt{3}}$

b. $-\sqrt{22}\,\sqrt{72}$

d. $\dfrac{4}{1 + \sqrt{3}}$

f. $\dfrac{\sqrt{4+a} - \sqrt{4-a}}{\sqrt{4+a} + \sqrt{4-a}}$

25. Which of the following statements are true and which are false when $a, b, x, y \in R$?

a. $4 - |x| = 4 - \sqrt{x^2}$ **b.** $|x| + |y| > 0$ **c.** $|a - b| = |a| - |b|$

26. Which of the following are polynomials?

a. $4\,r^2 st$

c. $x + 2y + 3z$

e. $5(x^2 + 2y)$

b. 11

d. $\dfrac{12\,x^2}{5}$

f. $\dfrac{2}{y} + 1$

27. Simplify each of the following.

    a. $(a^4)^2$ **b.** $7\,x^3(x^4y^2)$ **c.** $4\,x^2y^2 + (3\,xy)^2$ **d.** $(2\,a^2b)(3\,ab^2)\left(-\dfrac{1}{6\,a^3}\right)$

28. For which values of a, b, and c is the following statement true?

    $ax^2 + 7\,x + 3 \equiv -\,2\,x^2 + bx + c$

29. Perform the indicated divisions.

    a. $\dfrac{6\,x^2 - 5\,x - 4}{2\,x + 1}$ **b.** $\dfrac{10\,x^4 + 5\,x^3 + x^2 - 6\,x - 4}{5\,x^2 - 2}$

30. Factor each of the following completely as a polynomial over the real numbers.

    a. $4\,x + 4\,y - 2\,x - 2\,y$ **d.** $64\,x^9 + 125$

    b. $axy - 2\,bxy + 3\,xy - 6 + 4\,b - 2\,a$ **e.** $\dfrac{x^2}{\sqrt{7}} + x - \dfrac{42}{\sqrt{7}}$

    c. $9\,a^2 + 6\,ab + b^2 - 16$ **f.** $a^2x^2 + a^2xy - 6\,a^2y^2$

31. Simplify.

    a. $\dfrac{m^2 - 5\,m + 4}{m - 3} \cdot \dfrac{m^2 - 5\,m + 6}{m - 1}$ **d.** $\dfrac{1}{a + b} - \dfrac{1}{a - b} + \dfrac{2\,b}{a^2 - b^2}$

    b. $\left(\dfrac{x^2}{x - y} - x\right)\left(\dfrac{y^2}{x + y} - y\right)$

    c. $\dfrac{m^3 - 27}{m^2 + 2\,m + 4} \div \dfrac{m^2 + 3\,m + 9}{m^3 - 8}$ **e.** $\dfrac{\dfrac{1}{a} - \dfrac{1}{b}}{\dfrac{a^2 - b^2}{2}}$

32. Find the solution set for each of the following when a, b, $x \in R$.

    a. $\dfrac{x}{a} - a = \dfrac{x}{b} - b$ **c.** $\dfrac{4}{1 + a} - \dfrac{a + 1}{a - 1} = \dfrac{a^2 - 3}{1 - a^2}$

    b. $\dfrac{3}{x} - 15 > 0$ **d.** $\dfrac{x + 4}{x^2 + 5\,x + 6} + \dfrac{1}{x + 2} = \dfrac{x}{x + 3}$

1. In the following diagram replace each question mark with the name of one of the subsets of R, the set of real numbers, so that each subset is correctly related to R and to the other subsets.

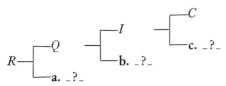

2. Draw the graph of $\{(-3,9), (-2,6), (-1,3), (0,0)\}$ as a subset of $I \times I$.

3. Assuming that $x \in R$, which of the following statements are conditional and which are identities?

   a. $x(x+3) = 4$ 　　　 b. $|x| = 6$ 　　　 c. $\dfrac{7}{x} = 7\left(\dfrac{1}{x}\right)$ 　　　 d. $5x = x + 4x$

4. Assuming that $x \in R$, which of the following statements are true and which are false?

   a. $3x = 12 \longleftrightarrow 2x = 8$ 　　　　　 c. $|x| = 4 \longleftrightarrow x^2 = 16$

   b. $\dfrac{1}{x} = 3 \longleftrightarrow 3x = 1$ 　　　　　 d. $x + 5 = -1 \longleftrightarrow x - 1 = -7$

5. Write a contradiction of the statement "$11 x < 4$ *or* $x = 4$."

6. Express each of the following statements as a true statement in either the form $p \longrightarrow q$ or the form $p \longleftrightarrow q$.

   a. $x < 4$ only if $x < 5$.

   b. a is a positive number if and only if $a > 0$.

   c. If $M \subset T$, then $M \subset S$.

   d. $xy = 0$ if $x = 0$.

7. Make a truth table which shows the conditions under which $m \longrightarrow n$ is true and the conditions under which $m \longrightarrow n$ is false.

8. Replace each of the following question marks with one of the symbols $>$, $<$, or $=$ to form a true statement.

   a. $(ab < 0 \ and \ a > 0) \longrightarrow b \ \_?\_ \ 0$.

   b. $(a > b \wedge c = d \wedge c > 0) \longrightarrow ac \ \_?\_ \ bd$.

   c. $(a < b \wedge ab > 0) \longrightarrow \dfrac{1}{a} \ \_?\_ \ \dfrac{1}{b}$.

   d. $a > b \longrightarrow -a \ \_?\_ -b$.

9. Express each of the following in simplest form.

    a. $\sqrt{448}$ b. $(3\,a^4b^3)^2a^2b$ c. $\dfrac{m^2+mn+n^2}{m^2-n^2}\cdot\dfrac{m+n}{m^3-n^3}$ d. $\dfrac{2-\sqrt{3}}{2+\sqrt{3}}$

10. Assume each of the following is a polynomial over the integers. Factor completely.

    a. $ax+ay-bx-by$ b. $27\,a^6-125$ c. $a^2-14\,ab+49\,b^2-16$

11. Find the solution set for each of the following statements, assuming that $x \in R$.

    a. $x^2-9<0$ c. $\dfrac{3}{x}-2>0$

    b. $(x^2-x)(2\,x-5)=(x^2-x)(x+9)$ d. $\dfrac{3}{2\,x+3}+\dfrac{1}{x-5}=\dfrac{8}{2\,x^2-7\,x-15}$

Introduction to Coordinate Geometry

This chapter provides an introduction to coordinate geometry. Coordinate geometry, sometimes called analytic geometry, is the study of the interrelationship of algebra and geometry resulting from the association of sets of numbers with sets of points. The French mathematician René Descartes, from whose name the word Cartesian comes, developed analytic geometry in about the year 1637.

Coordinate System in a Line

When we establish a one-to-one correspondence between the elements in the set of points in a line and the elements in the set of real numbers, we have a *coordinate system* which enables us to show the graph of the truth sets of sentences having exactly one variable. The truth set of each of the following sentences in one variable is shown at the right of the sentence.

$\dfrac{1}{x} < 1$

$|x - 1| \geq 4$

$x > 2 \land x < 5$

$|x| = 1 \lor |x - 2| = 1$

$|x| = 1 \land |x - 2| = 1$

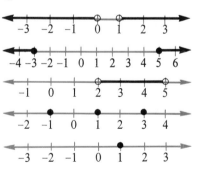

These examples remind us that the *graph* of the truth set of an open statement s_x is a set of points G for which both of the following statements are true.

(1) If a point is in G, its coordinate is a solution of the open sentence s_x.

(2) If a number is a solution of the open sentence s_x, its graph is in G.

Graph the truth set of each of the following sentences. Each variable represents a real number.

1. $x < 4 \wedge x < 0$

2. $x > 2 \wedge x > 7$

3. $\dfrac{7}{x} < 1$

4. $\dfrac{9}{x} + 2 > 3$

5. $|x + 4| < 7$

6. $|x - 1| \geq 2$

7. $|2x + 1| < 6$

8. $|x| + |-3| = 5$

9. $\left|\dfrac{1}{x}\right| = 2$

10. $\dfrac{6}{|x+1|} = 4$

11. $x > 6 \vee x < 4$

12. $x \leq -1 \vee x \leq -6$

13. $x < -5 \vee x > 5$

14. $|x| = 2 \vee |x - 5| = 2$

15. $|x| = 2 \wedge |x - 5| = 2$

16. $(2x + 6)(x - 1) = 0$

17. $\dfrac{2x + 9}{5} > 1$

18. $(x + 4)(x - 1) > 0$

19. $(x - 5)(x + 2)(x - 6) = 0$

20. $(x - 5)(x + 2)(x - 6) > 0$

The Coordinate Plane

When we establish a one-to-one correspondence between the members of the set of points in a plane and the members of the set of ordered pairs of real numbers in the manner discussed in Chapter 1, we establish a plane rectangular coordinate system which enables us to show the graphs of open statements having two variables. At this point we review the procedure for establishing a rectangular coordinate system.

First we place two number lines having the same scale so that they intersect at right angles at their origins, which we denote by O, as shown in the figure on page 206. It is customary to have one of these lines in a horizontal position and the other in a vertical position. The horizontal number line is labeled X and called the x-axis. The vertical number line is labeled Y and called the y-axis. These two lines are called the *coordinate axes*. The plane in which they are contained is called the *coordinate plane* and the intersection O is called the *origin of the coordinate system*. In the x-axis we represent positive numbers to the right of the origin and negative numbers to the left of the origin. In the y-axis we represent positive numbers above the origin and negative numbers below the origin.

We now show how a one-to-one correspondence between ordered pairs of real numbers and points in the coordinate plane can be established. Given any ordered pair of real numbers, we assign to the pair a unique point in the plane. We illustrate the process by assigning a point to the ordered pair $(-4, -2)$. In the x-axis we first locate the point S whose coordinate is -4, the first member of the ordered pair. Through S we draw a vertical line. Next, in the y-axis we locate the point T whose coordinate is -2, the second member of the ordered pair. Through T we draw a horizontal line. These lines through S and T intersect in a unique point P which corresponds to the ordered pair $(-4, -2)$ Then point P is the *graph* of the ordered pair $(-4, -2)$. The numbers -4 and -2 are called the *coordinates* of P. The first number, -4, is called the *x-coordinate* or the *abscissa* of P, and the second number, -2, is called the *y-coordinate* or *ordinate* of P.

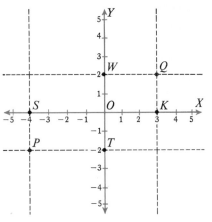

We now assign a unique ordered pair of numbers to a given point in the coordinate plane. We illustrate the process by assigning an ordered pair of real numbers to the point Q in the diagram. First we draw a vertical line through Q and read the x-coordinate of the unique point K in which this line intersects the x-axis. This is found to be 3. Next we draw a horizontal line through Q intersecting the y-axis in the unique point W. Then we read the y-coordinate of this point. This is found to be 2. We assign the ordered pair $(3, 2)$ to the point Q. The numbers 3 and 2 are the coordinates of Q, with 3 the x-coordinate or abscissa, and 2 the y-coordinate or ordinate.

Observe that the graph of the ordered pair $(-4, 0)$ is the point S in the x-axis. Indeed each point in the x-axis is the graph of an ordered pair whose second member (ordinate) is zero. Similarly, each point in the y-axis is the graph of an ordered pair whose first member (abscissa) is 0. T is the graph of $(0, -2)$ and W is the graph of $(0, 2)$. We can say that points are in the same vertical line if and only if they have the same abscissa, and points are in the same horizontal line if and only if they have the same ordinate. If we use the symbol $\overleftrightarrow{SP}$ for the line determined by points S and P, we can say that all points in $\overleftrightarrow{SP}$ have the abscissa -4. Similarly all points in the line WQ have the ordinate 2. We shall use either of the symbols $\overline{PS}$ or $\overline{SP}$ to denote the set of points in the line segment whose end points are P and S. A *ray* is the set of points consisting of a point A and all the points on one side of A in a line containing A. The point A is called the endpoint of the ray. We shall use the symbol $\overrightarrow{AB}$ to denote the ray AB with end point A and containing point B.

Given an ordered pair of real numbers, we have shown how to assign a unique point in the coordinate plane to this ordered pair. Also, given a point in the coordinate plane, we have shown how to assign a unique ordered pair of numbers to this point. Thus we can establish a one-to-one correspondence between all ordered pairs of real numbers and the points in the coordinate plane. Indeed, the coordinate plane is the graph of $R \times R$. Similar procedures may be employed to construct graphs of other sets of ordered pairs such as $Q \times Q$, $I \times I$, or $Q \times I$.

Observe that the coordinate axes divide the plane into four regions labeled I, II, III, and IV in the figure below. The region I is called the *first quadrant*, the region II is called the *second quadrant*, and so on. A point in the axis, such as point P whose coordinates are $(0, -4)$, is considered to be in the boundary lines and not in any quadrant.

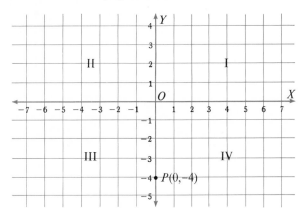

We shall frequently name a point by writing a capital letter near it or by writing a capital letter and the coordinates of the point. For example, we may name the point whose coordinates are (x_1, y_1) by writing either P_1 or $P_1(x_1, y_1)$. $P(x, y)$ represents the point whose coordinates are (x, y).

If the coordinates of point P_1 are (x_1, y_1) and the coordinates of point P_2 are (x_2, y_2), then P_1 and P_2 name the same point if and only if $x_1 = x_2$ and $y_1 = y_2$. Thus

(i) $P_1(x_1, y_1) = P_2(x_2, y_2) \longleftrightarrow (x_1 = x_2 \wedge y_1 = y_2)$

Consider the "right-to-left" implication $(x_1 = x_2 \wedge y_1 = y_2) \longrightarrow P_1(x_1, y_1) = P_2(x_2, y_2)$. This implication has two useful contrapositives:

(ii) $[P_1(x_1, y_1) \neq P_2(x_2, y_2) \wedge y_1 = y_2] \longrightarrow x_1 \neq x_2$
(iii) $[P_1(x_1, y_1) \neq P_2(x_2, y_2) \wedge x_1 = x_2] \longrightarrow y_1 \neq y_2$

The following true statements, (iv), and (v), are equivalent to (i):

(iv) $P_1(x_1, y_1) \neq P_2(x_2, y_2) \longleftrightarrow \sim (x_1 = x_2 \wedge y_1 = y_2)$
(v) $P_1(x_1, y_1) \neq P_2(x_2, y_2) \longleftrightarrow (x_1 \neq x_2 \vee y_1 \neq y_2)$

Points that are not the same are said to be *distinct* points. Statements (*iv*) and (*v*) both tell us that the coordinates of distinct points are different.

We shall continue to use the set-builder notation to indicate the truth set of an open statement. Thus $\{(x, y) \mid s_{(x,y)}\}$ represents the truth set of the open statement $s_{(x,y)}$ which has two variables x and y. Any open statement in two variables whose truth set is a nonempty subset of $R \times R$ defines a relation in $R \times R$. In the following examples, we show the graphs of the truth sets of open statements having two variables.

Example 1. Draw the graph of $\{(x, y) \mid xy = 0\}$.

Solution. The graph of $\{(x, y) \mid xy = 0\}$ is the union of the set of points in the x-axis and in the y-axis or, more briefly, the graph is the pair of coordinate axes. Is it true that any point in either axis has coordinates which belong to the truth set of the open sentence $xy = 0$? Is it true that any pair of numbers which belong to the truth set of $xy = 0$ are coordinates of a point in one of the axes?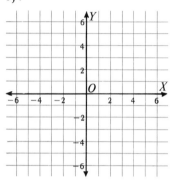

Example 2. Draw the graph of $\{(x, y) \mid xy > 0\}$.

Solution. The graph of $\{(x, y) \mid xy > 0\}$ is $Q_1 \cup Q_3$, where Q_1 is the set of points in the first quadrant and Q_3 is the set of points in the third quadrant, as shown in the diagram at the left below.

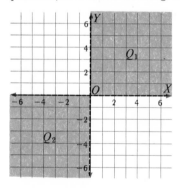 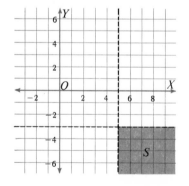

Example 3 Draw the graph of $\{(x, y) \mid x > 5 \wedge y < -3\}$.

Solution. The graph of $\{(x, y) \mid x > 5 \wedge y < -3\}$ is the shaded area S shown in the diagram at the right above. The boundary lines are shown as broken lines to indicate that they are not part of the graph.

Example 4. Draw the graph of $\{(x, y) \mid x^2 - y^2 = 0\}$.

Solution. If x, $y \in R$, the open sentence "$x^2 - y^2 = 0$" and the open sentence "$x = y \vee x = -y$" are equivalent open statements. Why? We
may indicate the equivalence of
these statements by writing $x^2 - y^2 = 0 \longleftrightarrow x = y \vee x = -y$ or by
indicating that they have the
the same truth set, thus $\{(x, y) \mid x^2 - y^2 = 0\} = \{(x, y) \mid x = y \vee x = -y\}$. The graph of this set
is shown in the diagram at the
right. It consists of the two perpendicular lines L_1 and L_2. You

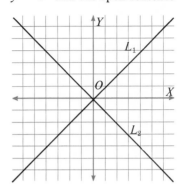

recall from your first course in algebra that the graph of the truth
set of an equation such as $x = y$ is a straight line. Each of the lines
L_1 and L_2 is, of course, a set of points. Note that L_1 is the graph of
$\{(x, y) \mid x = y\}$ and L_2 is the graph of $\{(x, y) \mid x = -y\}$.
Thus $\{(x, y) \mid x^2 - y^2 = 0\} = \{(x, y) \mid x = y \vee x = -y\} = [\{(x, y) \mid x = y\} \cup \{(x, y) \mid x = -y\}]$ and the graph of $\{(x, y) \mid x = y\} \cup \{(x, y) \mid x = -y\}$ is $L_1 \cup L_2$.

Example 5. Draw the graph of $\{(x, y) \mid x \geq y\}$.

Solution. The sentence $x \geq y$ defines a relation in $R \times R$. The graph of this
relation is shown at the left below. The graph consists of the line
L_1 and all the points below it. L_1 is the graph of $\{(x, y) \mid x = y\}$
and the shaded area is the graph of $\{(x, y) \mid x > y\}$.

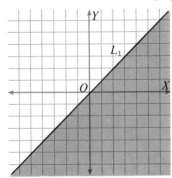
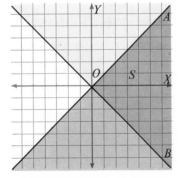

Example 6 Draw the graph of $\{(x, y) \mid x \geq y \wedge y \geq -x\}$.

Solution. The graph of the relation defined by $x \geq y \wedge y \geq -x$ is shown at
the right above. The graph is S, the set of points which consists of
the rays OA and OB and all points between them. Thus the graph
of $\{(x, y) \mid x \geq y \wedge y \geq -x\}$ is S.

We summarize the ideas illustrated by these examples as follows: The graph of an open statement $s_{(x,y)}$ in two variables x and y is S, a set of points in the coordinate plane. This means that any point P having coordinates a and b is in set S if and only if (a, b) is in the truth set of $s_{(x,y)}$. Since equivalent open statements have the same truth set, it follows that the graphs of equivalent open statements are the same. When we speak of the graph of the open statement $s_{(x,y)}$, we mean the graph of the truth set of the open statement.

Ⓐ EXERCISES

In some of the following exercises, the domain of each of the variables is specified. When the domain is not specified, it is assumed to be the set of real numbers.

1. Indicate the ordered pair of real numbers that should be assigned to each of the points $A, B, C, \cdots, G$ in the coordinate plane shown at the right.

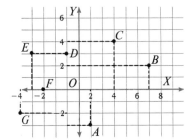

2. Indicate a coordinate plane by drawing a pair of coordinate axes. In this plane locate the graph for each of the following ordered pairs of numbers.

   a. $(-3, -1)$ **c.** $(5, 5)$ **e.** $(-1, 8)$ **g.** $(0, 0)$

   b. $(0, 6)$ **d.** $(-5, 1)$ **f.** $(8, 0)$ **h.** $(6, -5)$

3. Which of the following ordered pairs have graphs that are in the graph of the truth set of $x = 2\,y$?

   a. $(4, 8)$ **b.** $(6, 3)$ **c.** $(0, 0)$ **d.** $(-2, -1)$

4. Which of the following ordered pairs have graphs that are in the graph of the truth set of $x \geq 3\,y + 1$?

   a. $(2, 0)$ **b.** $(5, 1)$ **c.** $(-19, -7)$ **d.** $(-2, -1)$

5. Which of the graphs shown below is the graph of the relation whose membership is indicated by the inequality $y > 2 - 2\,x$?

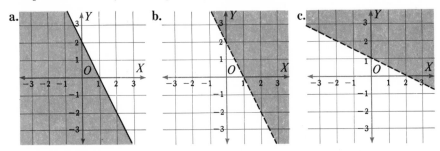

6. Which of the graphs indicated by the following black lines is the graph of the relation whose membership is indicated by $y = 2 + x$?

a.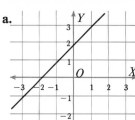

b.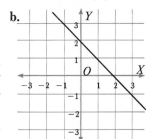

c.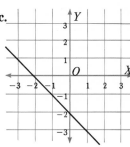

7. a. Draw the graph of $C \times C$. In this graph use heavy dots to show the subset of $C \times C$ indicated by the equation $y = x + 1$.

   b. Draw the graph of $I \times I$. In this graph use heavy dots to show the subset of $I \times I$ indicated by the equation $y = x + 1$.

   c. Show the graph of the equation $y = x + 1$ when $(x, y) \in R \times R$.

8. Make the graph of the truth set of each of the following:

   a. $y = 3x;\ x \in C,\ y \in C$

   b. $x < y$ when $(x, y) \in I \times I$

   c. $x \geq y;\ x,\ y \in I$

   d. $x \geq y;\ x,\ y \in R$

   e. $y = x + 2$ when $(x, y) \in I \times I$

   f. $y = x + 2$ when $(x, y) \in R \times R$

   g. $y = -3x;\ x \in I,\ y \in I$

   h. $y = 3x;\ x \in R,\ y \in R$

9. Which of the following sentences has its truth set indicated by the graph at the right?

   a. $x = y \lor x = -y$

   b. $x = y \land x = -y$

   c. $|x| = y$

   d. $x \geq y$

10. Show the graph of the solution set of each of the following equations.

   a. $y = x$ b. $y = x + 1$ c. $y = x + 2$ d. $y = x + 5$

11. Show the graph of the solution set of each of the following equations.

   a. $y = 2x$ b. $y = 3x$ c. $y = 4x$ d. $y = -2x$

12. Show the graph of the solution set of each of the following equations.

   a. $y = 3x + 1$ b. $y = 3x + 5$ c. $y = -3x - 6$ d. $y - 3x = 7$

The Measure of a Line Segment Between Two Points

If two points have the same ordinate or the same abscissa, it is easy to find the measure of the line segment between them. By counting spaces, we see that the measure of the line segment between $A(-11, 4)$ and $B(-3, 4)$ in the figure is 8. Similarly, the measure of the line segment between $A(-11, 4)$ and $C(6, 4)$ is 17. What is the measure of the line segment between $K(-3, 0)$ and $W(7, 0)$? Between B and C?

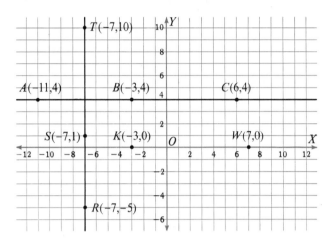

Since we are not at this point concerned with direction when we determine the distance between two points, we agree that the measure of the line segment between two points is a non-negative real number. Considering the above examples and the agreement that the measure of the line segment between two points is a non-negative real number, we rule that:

The measure of the distance between two points in a coordinate plane is the measure of the line segment between the two points.

The measure of the line segment between two points having the same ordinate is the absolute value of the difference of their abscissas. Thus for $P_1(x_1, y_1)$ and $P_2(x_2, y_1)$, $|P_1P_2| = |x_2 - x_1| = |x_1 - x_2|$. Here we use the symbol $|P_1P_2|$ to mean "the measure of the line segment between P_1 and P_2." Observe that the symbol for the measure of the line segment between two points is the familiar symbol for absolute value. This emphasizes the fact that such a measure is always non-negative. The measure is positive if the points are distinct and zero if they are the same point.

Adapting the preceding discussion to $P_3(x_3, y_3)$ and $P_4(x_3, y_4)$, that is, two points having the same abscissa, we have:

$$|P_3P_4| = |y_4 - y_3| = |y_3 - y_4|$$

Thus in the diagram on the preceding page we see that:

$$|RT| = |10 - (-5)| = 15 \text{ and } |ST| = |10 - 1| = 9.$$

Having established the measure of the line segment between two points for the special cases in which the two points have either the same ordinate or the same abscissa, let us consider how to find the measure of the line segment between two points $P_1(x_1, y_1)$ and $P_2(x_2, y_2)$ which have different ordinates and different abscissas. Our method depends on the Pythagorean theorem:

 (*i*) If one angle of a triangle is a right angle, then the square of the measure of the side opposite the right angle (that is, the hypotenuse) is equal to the sum of the squares of the measures of the other two sides.

The converse of the Pythagorean theorem can be stated as follows:

(*ii*) If the square of the measure of one side of a triangle is equal to the sum of the squares of the measures of the other two sides, then the angle opposite the first side is a right angle.

Since the Pythagorean theorem and its converse are both true, we have the following statement of equivalence:

(*iii*) An angle of a triangle is a right angle if and only if the square of the measure of the side opposite this angle is equal to the sum of the squares of the measures of the other two sides.

The standard notation for a triangle is shown at the right. In this notation, A, B, and C designate the vertices of the triangle; a, b, and c designate the measures of the sides
opposite these vertices; and α, β, and γ are the names
of the angles at the vertices A, B, and C, respectively.
Note that the side whose measure is a is opposite vertex A, the side whose measure is b is opposite vertex

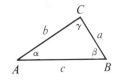

B, and the side whose measure is c is opposite vertex C. When the triangle
is a right triangle, as shown, the vertex of the right angle is labeled C.
This notation permits us to state the Pythagorean theorem in the familiar
form: If triangle ABC is a right triangle, then $c^2 = a^2 + b^2$.

The following statements are other true statements and definitions from
plane geometry that we shall find useful in our study of coordinate
geometry.

(*iv*) The measure of a right angle in degrees is 90.

(*v*) If two lines are perpendicular, they meet to form adjacent right angles.

Now consider two points $P_1(x_1, y_1)$ and $P_2(x_2, y_2)$ having different abscissas and different ordinates.

We draw L_1 a horizontal line through P_1 and L_2 a vertical line through P_2. These two lines intersect at T to form a right angle P_1TP_2. Thus triangle P_1TP_2 is a right triangle and by the Pythagorean theorem we know that $|P_1P_2|^2 = |P_1T|^2 + |TP_2|^2$. T has the same abscissa as P_2 and the same ordinate as P_1. Why? Therefore the coordinates of T are (x_2, y_1). Hence $|P_1T| = |x_2 - x_1|$ and $|TP_2| = |y_2 - y_1|$. Substituting these values in $|P_1P_2|^2 = |P_1T|^2 + |TP_2|^2$ we have $|P_1P_2|^2 = |x_2 - x_1|^2 + |y_2 - y_1|^2$.

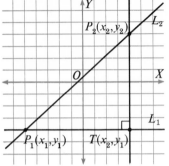

Let d represent the non-negative number $|P_1P_2|$. By the corollary to Theorem 37-3, we know that $|x_2 - x_1|^2 = (x_2 - x_1)^2$ and that $|y_2 - y_1|^2 = (y_2 - y_1)^2$. Substituting in $|P_1P_2|^2 = |x_2 - x_1|^2 + |y_2 - y_1|^2$, we have $d^2 = (x_2 - x_1)^2 + (y_2 - y_1)^2$. Since both members of $d^2 = (x_2 - x_1)^2 + (y_2 - y_1)^2$ are non-negative real numbers, we know by Theorem 28-3 that:

$$d = \sqrt{(x_2 - x_1)^2 + (y_2 - y_1)^2}$$

This is the formula (often called the distance formula) for finding the measure of the line segment between two points $P_1(x_1, y_1)$ and $P_2(x_2, y_2)$. Observe that this formula is also true for the cases in which the two points have the same abscissa or the same ordinate. For example, if the two points have the same ordinate so that $y_1 = y_2$, we have $d = \sqrt{(x_2 - x_1)^2 + 0^2} = \sqrt{(x_2 - x_1)^2} = |x_2 - x_1|$. Note that for the last step we used Theorem 35-3: If $x \in R$, then $\sqrt{x^2} = |x|$. Similarly, if $x_2 = x_1$, then $d = \sqrt{0^2 + (y_2 - y_1)^2} = \sqrt{(y_2 - y_1)^2} = |y_2 - y_1|$.

▷　**Theorem 1–5.** If $P_1(x_1, y_1)$ and $P_2(x_2, y_2)$ are any two points in the coordinate plane and d represents the measure of the line segment between them, then $d = \sqrt{(x_2 - x_1)^2 + (y_2 - y_1)^2}$.

Example 1.　Find the measure of the line segment between $R(-17, -5)$ and $S(3, 16)$.

Solution.　$d = \sqrt{(-17 - 3)^2 + (-5 - 16)^2} = \sqrt{20^2 + 21^2} = \sqrt{841} = 29$

Example 2.　If $A(-15, -26)$, $B(7, -7)$ and $C(-5, -2)$, show that triangle ABC is a right triangle.

Solution. From the figure it appears that $\angle ACB$ is the largest angle of triangle ABC. Therefore we shall use the converse of the Pythagorean theorem to test whether or not $\angle C$ is a right angle.

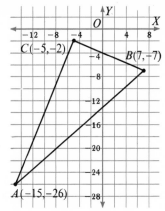

$$| AB |^2 = (-15-7)^2 + [-26 - (-7)]^2 = 22^2 + 19^2 = 845$$
$$|AC|^2 = [-15-(-5)]^2 + [-26 - (-2)]^2 = 10^2 + 24^2 = 676$$
$$| BC |^2 = [7-(-5)]^2 + [-7 - (-2)]^2 = 12^2 + 5^2 = 169.$$

Since $| AB |^2 = | AC |^2 + | BC |^2$, we conclude that $\angle C$ is a right angle and hence that triangle ABC is a right triangle.

Example 3. What equation must the coordinates (x, y) of the point P satisfy if P is the third vertex of an isosceles triangle whose base is $\overline{AB}$ with $A(-9, 7)$ and $B(-3, 11)$?

Solution. The triangle APB is an isosceles triangle with base $\overline{AB}$ if and only if $| AP | = | BP |$. Since $| AP |$ and $| BP |$ are non-negative real numbers, by Theorem 26-3 $| AP | = | BP | \longleftrightarrow | AP |^2 = | BP |^2$. Now since $d^2 = (x_2 - x_1)^2 + (y_2 - y_1)^2$, we have $| BP |^2 = (x+3)^2 + (y-11)^2$ and $| AP |^2 = (x+9)^2 + (y-7)^2$. Therefore, $(| AP |^2 = | BP |^2) \longleftrightarrow [(x+3)^2 + (y-11)^2 = (x+9)^2 + (y-7)^2] \longleftrightarrow (x^2 + 6x + 9 + y^2 - 22y + 121 = x^2 + 18x + 81 + y^2 - 14y + 49) \longleftrightarrow (3x + 2y = 0)$. Thus $P(x, y)$ is the vertex of an isosceles triangle having $\overline{AB}$ as a base if and only if x and y satisfy the equation $3x + 2y = 0$. Do you recognize the equation $3x + 2y = 0$ as the equation of a straight line? How is this line related to $\overline{AB}$?

The Midpoint of a Line Segment

The distance formula enables us to show that $x = \dfrac{x_1 + x_2}{2}$ and $y = \dfrac{y_1 + y_2}{2}$ are the formulas for finding the coordinates (x, y) of the midpoint of any line segment whose end points are $P_1(x_1, y_1)$ and $P_2(x_2, y_2)$.

Thus,
$$| P_1P | = \sqrt{\left(\frac{x_1 + x_2}{2} - x_1\right)^2 + \left(\frac{y_1 + y_2}{2} - y_1\right)^2}$$
$$= \tfrac{1}{2}\sqrt{(x_2 - x_1)^2 + (y_2 - y_1)^2}$$
$$= \tfrac{1}{2} | P_1P_2 |$$

Also

$$|P_2P| = \sqrt{\left(\frac{x_1 + x_2}{2} - x_2\right)^2 + \left(\frac{y_1 + y_2}{2} - y_2\right)^2}$$
$$= \tfrac{1}{2}\sqrt{(x_1 - x_2)^2 + (y_1 - y_2)^2}$$
$$= \tfrac{1}{2}|P_1P_2|$$

Therefore $|P_1P| = |P_2P|$. For the time being we shall assume the fact that $P \in \overleftrightarrow{P_1P_2}$. We will be able to prove this assumption later.

Example Find the coordinates of the midpoint of the line segment joining the points $P_1(-13, -5)$ and $P_2(11, 23)$.

Solution. Substituting in the midpoint formulas, we see that the required midpoint is $\left(\dfrac{-13 + 11}{2}, \dfrac{-5 + 23}{2}\right)$ or $(-1, 9)$.

 EXERCISES

1. Find the measure of the line segment between the points in each of the following pairs.

   a. $A(-2, 2)$, $B(2, -1)$ **d.** $G(-3, 2)$, $H(2, -3)$ **g.** $M(r, s)$, $N(x, y)$

   b. $C(1, 1)$, $D(7, 9)$ **e.** $I(-1, 1)$, $J(9, 10)$ **h.** $R(0, b)$, $S(a, b)$

   c. $E(-2, 7)$, $F(3, -5)$ **f.** $K(3, 4)$, $L(-3, -4)$ **i.** $T\left(0, \dfrac{a}{2}\right)$, $Q\left(\dfrac{a}{2}, 0\right)$

2. Find the coordinates of the midpoint of the line segment joining the points in each of the following pairs.

   a. $A(-2, 1)$, $B(2, 3)$ **c.** $E(-3, 4)$, $F(1, -6)$ **e.** $I(0, b)$, $J(b, 0)$

   b. $C(5, 6)$, $D(1, 8)$ **d.** $G(-3, -7)$, $H(6, -1)$ **f.** $K(a, b)$, $L(-a, -b)$

3. The coordinates of the end points of the diameter of a circle are $(-2, -1)$ and $(6, 2)$. What are the coordinates of the center of the circle?

4. Find the measure of the perimeter of a triangle having the vertices $A(-4, 0)$, $B(2, 8)$, and $C(7, 5)$.

5. Determine whether the triangle having the vertices $A(2, 0)$, $B(6, 0)$, and $C(4, 8)$ is an isosceles triangle.

6. Show that the quadrilateral having the vertices $A(-5, 0)$, $B(-1, 3)$, $C(4, -9)$, and $D(0, -12)$ is a parallelogram. (Recall that if a quadrilateral has its opposite sides of equal length the quadrilateral is a parallelogram.)

7. Find the measures of the diagonals of the quadrilateral in Ex. 6.

8. Is the quadrilateral having its vertices at $A(6, 4)$, $B(-1, 2)$, $C(3, -2)$, and $D(2, 8)$ a parallelogram?

9. Determine whether the triangle having the vertices $A(-2, -3)$, $B(4, 5)$, and $C(-4, 1)$ is a right triangle.

10. The midpoint of the line segment joining points P_1 and P_2 has the coordinates $(1, -\frac{1}{2})$. If P_1 has the coordinates $(-3, 2)$ what are the coordinates of P_2?

11. The center of a circle has the coordinates $(2, 4)$. If the circle passes through the point $A(-2, 1)$, what is the measure of the radius of the circle?

B   EXERCISES

12. Show that the points $A(3, 5)$, $B(1, 1)$, and $C(-1, -3)$ lie on one straight line. *Hint.* Compare the measures of the segments between each pair of the three points.

13. The line segment joining the points $P_1(-1, 2)$ and $P_2(7, -4)$ is divided into four equal segments. What are the coordinates of the points of division?

14. Show that the measures of the line segments between the midpoint of the hypotenuse of a right triangle and the three vertices of the triangle are equal. *Hint.* Let A, B, and C be the three vertices of the triangle with C the vertex of the right angle. Place the triangle with C at the origin, CA extending to the right along the x-axis, and B above the x-axis. From geometry you know that CB will fall along the y-axis.

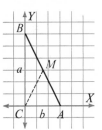

Directed Measure

We have defined the measure of the line segment between two points having the same ordinates to be the absolute value of the difference of their abscissas. In the figure at the right $|PQ| = |3 - (-9)| = 12$.

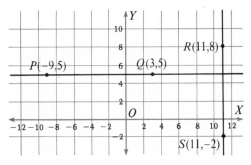

Now suppose that we are interested in the *direction* in which we move in passing from one of these points to the other along the horizontal line PQ. To indicate movement from P to Q we write PQ, and to indicate the movement from Q to P we write QP. Note that the order in which the letters are written indicates the direction of movement along the segment. The point where the move begins is called the *initial point* and the point where the move ends or terminates is called the *terminal point*.

When we move from P to Q, we move a distance of 12 units to the right. Since we have previously used positive numbers to describe movements to the right, it seems reasonable to say that the directed measure of the line segment from P to Q is 12. Note that we obtain 12 by subtracting the abscissa of the initial point P from the abscissa of the terminal point Q, $3 - (-9) = 12$. Thus $PQ = 12$. On the other hand if we move from Q to P we move a distance of 12 units to the left and use the negative number -12 to describe the movement. Note that we obtain -12 by subtracting the abscissa of the initial point Q from the abscissa of the terminal point P; that is, $-9 - 3 = -12$. Thus $QP = -12$.

On the basis of this discussion we define the *directed measures* PQ and QP for two points $P(x_1, y_1)$ and $Q(x_2, y_1)$ having the same ordinate as follows:

$PQ = x_2 - x_1 = $ (abscissa of terminal point) $-$ (abscissa of initial point)
$QP = x_1 - x_2 = $ (abscissa of terminal point) $-$ (abscissa of initial point)

Similarly for the points $R(x_1, y_1)$ and $S(x_1, y_2)$ having the same abscissa we define RS and SR as follows:

$RS = y_2 - y_1 = $ (ordinate of terminal point) $-$ (ordinate of initial point)
$SR = y_1 - y_2 = $ (ordinate of terminal point) $-$ (ordinate of initial point)

Note that when we apply this definition to find the directed measures RS and SR for the points R and S shown in the preceding diagram, we obtain $RS = (-2 - 8) = -10$ and $SR = [8 - (-2)] = 10$. Thus our definition assigns a positive number to an upward movement and a negative number to a downward movement.

For any given point $P(x, y)$ we observe that the abscissa x indicates the directed measure of the segment from the y-axis to P along a horizontal line and the ordinate y indicates the directed measure of the segment from the x-axis to P along a vertical line. We will not speak of directed measure PQ or QP unless $\overleftrightarrow{PQ}$ is either horizontal or vertical.

Ⓐ **EXERCISES**

1. Find the directed measure of the line segment between each of the following pairs of points. In each case assume that the move is from the point listed first to the point listed second.

a. $A(-6, 0)$, $B(4, 0)$ d. $G(-29, 5)$, $H(-5, 5)$

b. $C(8, 1)$, $D(3, 1)$ e. $I(c, 2)$, $J(11, 2)$

c. $E(\frac{1}{2}, 4)$, $F(\frac{3}{4}, 4)$ f. $K(1, -3)$, $L(-d, -3)$

2. Assuming that in each of the following cases the required point is a point in a vertical line passing through the given point, what are the coordinates of the required point if the directed measure of the line segment from the point

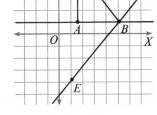

    a. $P(4, 2)$ is $- 5$?   **d.** $B(0, 0)$ is $- 6$?

    b. $Q(- 6, - 3)$ is 8?   **e.** $C(8, 0)$ is 4?

    c. $A(- 11, 2)$ is $- 1$?   **f.** $D(8, - 2)$ is 0?

3. Using the diagram at the right, explain the meaning of each of these names.

    a. AB **d.** $\overline{BA}$ **g.** AC **j.** $\overleftrightarrow{ED}$

    b. BA **e.** $\overleftrightarrow{AB}$ **h.** $|BC|$ **k.** $\overrightarrow{BD}$

    c. $\overline{AB}$ **f.** CA **i.** $\overrightarrow{EB}$ **l.** $\overline{BE}$

4. If $A, B, C,$ and D are points in a line, show that $AB \times CD + BC \times AD = AC \times BD$.

The Straight Line

You recall that in the study of geometry "straight line," like "point" and "plane," is an undefined term. (In this book we will use "line" to mean "straight line.") You are also familiar with the fact that the graph of each of the following equations is a straight line in the coordinate plane.

$$3x + 11y = 41 \qquad\qquad 0x + 4y = 11$$
$$5x = 13 \qquad\qquad 7x - 5y = 0$$

Each of these equations has the form or can be put in the form $ax + by + c = 0$ when $a, b,$ and c are constants and a and b are not both zero. Such an equation is called a linear equation. A *linear equation* in variables x and y is an equation of the form $ax + by + c = 0$ when $a, b,$ and c are constants and $a^2 + b^2 \neq 0$. (Writing $a^2 + b^2 \neq 0$ is a convenient way to state, "a and b are not both zero.")

Observe that a linear equation in x and y contains no powers of x or y greater than the first. While it is usually easy to recognize a linear equation, it is worthwhile to consider the following examples of equations that are not linear according to our definition.

$$0 \cdot x + 0 \cdot y + 5 = 0 \qquad 0 \cdot x + 0 \cdot y + 0 = 0 \qquad \frac{3}{x} + \frac{4}{y} = 1$$

The truth set for the first of these equations is $\emptyset$. The truth set for the second equation is $R \times R$ and the graph of the truth set of this equation is the entire coordinate plane. Even though the third equation contains no powers of x or y greater than the first, this equation cannot be transformed into an equivalent equation having the form $ax + by + c = 0$.

We must be very careful in making a decision on whether or not a given equation is a linear equation. Consider the following equation when x_1, x_2, y_1, and y_2 are constants: $(x_2 - x_1)(y - y_1) = (y_2 - y_1)(x - x_1)$. This equation is equivalent to $(y_1 - y_2)x + (x_2 - x_1)y + (x_1y_2 - x_2y_1) = 0$. Comparing this equation with $ax + by + c = 0$, we identify a with $y_1 - y_2$, b with $x_2 - x_1$, and c with $x_1y_2 - x_2y_1$. We see that the given equation is a linear equation if and only if $(y_1 - y_2)^2 + (x_2 - x_1)^2 \neq 0$.

In the following examples we review the procedure for drawing the graph of the truth set of a linear equation.

Example 1. Graph the solution set of $3x + 5y = 45$.

Solution. We shall use the intercept method of drawing the graph. Recall that the ordinate of the point in which a straight line intersects the y-axis is called the y-intercept of the straight line and the abscissa of the point in which the straight line intersects the x-axis is called the x-intercept of the straight line. If in the given equation we let

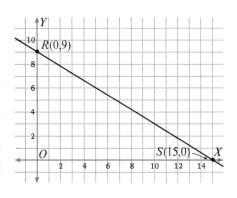

$x = 0$, then $y = 9$. If we let $y = 0$, then $x = 15$. Thus the points $R(0, 9)$ and $S(15, 0)$ are in the graph of the line. Since two points determine a line, we draw line L which intersects the y-axis at $R(0, 9)$ and the x-axis at $S(15, 0)$. The fact that the number 9 is the y-intercept for line L and the number 15 is the x-intercept for L explains why we call this method of graphing the intercept method. This method of drawing the graph of a straight line is fast and works well unless the points of intersection of the line L with the axes are too close together. If our graph is accurately drawn, we know that the ordered pair of numbers which are the coordinates of any point in L belong to the truth set of $3x + 5y = 45$, and we also know that any pair of numbers (x_1, y_1) which satisfy the equation are the coordinates of a point in L. In brief, L is the graph of $\{(x, y) \mid 3x + 5y = 45\}$.

Example 2. Draw the graph of the truth set of the equation $11x - 7y = 1$.

Solution.   We solve $11\,x - 7\,y = 1$ for y and obtain $y = \dfrac{11\,x - 1}{7}$. We choose to let
$x = -5$. Substituting -5 for x in
$y = \dfrac{11\,x - 1}{7}$ gives us $y = -\frac{54}{7}$. Thus
the ordered pair $(-5, -\frac{54}{7})$ belongs
to the truth set of the equation. In a
similar manner we find the other ordered pairs shown in the following
table. (Observe that since the graph
will be a straight line, two points are
sufficient for locating it.) We locate
the graphs of the points we have
found and draw a straight line between them. This line is the graph of all
the ordered pairs of numbers in the truth
set of the equation, not just the ordered
pairs of our table. The line is the required graph.

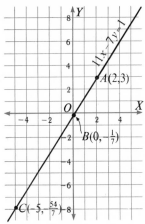

x	-5	0	2
y	$-\frac{54}{7}$	$-\frac{1}{7}$	3

Example 3.   Graph $\{(x, y) \mid 11\,x - 7\,y = 1 \land y \leq 6 \land x > -4\}$.

Solution.   The required graph is the graph of $\{(x, y) \mid 11\,x - 7\,y = 1\} \cap$
$\{(x, y) \mid y \leq 6\} \cap \{(x, y) \mid x > -4\}$. We graph $\{(x, y) \mid 11\,x -$
$7\,y = 1\}$ as in Example 2.
Next we draw the line that is
the graph of the truth set of
$y = 6$ and shade the portion
of the coordinate plane below
this line. The line and the
shaded portion of the plane
are the graph of the truth set
of $y \leq 6$. Finally we draw
the line that is the graph of
the truth set of $x = -4$. We
make this a dashed line since
it is not part of the truth set
of $x > -4$. By shading the

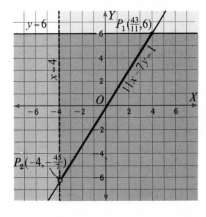

portion of the plane to the right of this dashed line, however, we do
have the graph of the truth set of $x > -4$. The graph of $\{(x, y) \mid$
$11\,x - 7\,y = 1 \land y \leq 6 \land x > -4\}$ is the set of points common
to the three graphs we have just drawn; in other words, it is that
part of the line determined by $P_1(\frac{43}{11}, 6)$ and $P_2(-4, -\frac{45}{7})$ between P_1 and P_2 including P_1 but not including P_2.

1. Using the intercept method of Example 1, draw the graph of the truth set of each of the following equations:

a. $2x - 3y = 12$

b. $5x - 4y + 20 = 0$

c. $.7x = y + 14$

d. $-5x = 3y - 45$

e. $2.1 = .6x + .3y$

f. $24 - 3y = 5x$

g. $\frac{7}{2} = 7x - 2y$

h. $-\frac{x}{4} + \frac{y}{2} = 2$

2. Using the method of Example 2, make the graph of the truth set of each of the following equations:

a. $3x + 4y = 1$

b. $5x - y = 6$

c. $4x - 3y = 0$

d. $10 = 3x - y$

e. $-4x + 6y - 9 = 0$

f. $7x + 0y = 21$

g. $0 = \frac{2}{3}x + \frac{1}{2}y - 12$

h. $.6x = 1 + .2y$

3. Draw the graph of each of the following sets:

a. $\{(x, y) \mid 4x - 2y = 6\}$

b. $\{(x, y) \mid -\frac{1}{4}x + \frac{1}{2}y = 2\}$

c. $\{(x, y) \mid -7x - 2y + 1 = 0\}$

d. $\{(x, y) \mid 2x = 6 + 4y\}$

e. $\{(x, y) \mid \frac{3}{4}x - \frac{2}{5}y = 10\}$

f. $\{(x, y) \mid 4.4x - 3.2y = 1\}$

4. Draw the graph of the truth set of each of the following equations:

a. $\frac{1}{2}x - \frac{1}{3}y = \frac{1}{4}$

b. $\frac{2}{3}x - \frac{1}{3}y = \frac{1}{6}$

c. $15x - 7y - 12 = 0$

d. $6(4x + 3y) - 25 = 0$

e. $4(2x - y) - 3(x + y) = 35$

f. $7(x - 3y) - (x + y) = 12$

5. Draw the graph of the solution set of each of the following sentences:

a. $4x + 2y = 6 \wedge x < 5 \wedge y < 4$

b. $3x + 1 = y \wedge x \geq -2 \wedge y > -1$

c. $7x + 2y = 5 \wedge -1 \leq x < 4$

d. $3y < x + 6 \wedge y < -x + 6 \wedge x - 3y = -6$

e. $(y = x \vee y = -x) \wedge y < 3 \wedge y > -2$

f. $3y = 2x + 6 \wedge (x < -2 \vee y > -1)$

g. $2y = -x + 6 \vee (y = 3 \vee y = 1)$

h. $2y = -x + 6 \wedge (y = 3 \vee y = 1)$

6. Draw the graph of each of the following sets:

a. $\{(x, y) \mid (x = y \vee x = -y \vee x = y + 6) \wedge (y \leq 4 \wedge y \geq 0)\}$

b. $\{(x, y) \mid (2y = -x + 6 \vee 2y = x + 6) \wedge y \leq 3\}$

c. $\{(x, y) \mid |x| = y \wedge y \leq 7\}$

d. $\{(x, y) \mid |x| = y + 4 \wedge y \leq -1\}$

e. $\{(x, y) \mid |x| = y + 2 \wedge y > -3\}$

7. What are the x and y intercepts of the equation $\frac{x}{a} + \frac{y}{b} = 1$?

Vertical Lines

We state the following assumption: A set of points in the coordinate plane is a straight line if and only if it is the graph of a linear equation in two variables. Sometimes one of the variables does not appear in the equation. For example, if the context makes it clear that we are to seek solutions in $R \times R$ or to draw graphs in the coordinate plane, then $x = 0$ is a linear equation of the form $ax + by + c = 0$ with $a = 1$, $b = 0$, and $c = 0$. In this case, $x = 0$ is the equation of the y-axis.

From the way in which our coordinate system is established, we know that two points are in the same vertical line if and only if they have the same abscissa. We may express this thought in a more useful form by saying:

> (i) If L is a line containing distinct points $P_1(x_1, y_1)$ and $P_2(x_2, y_2)$, then line L is vertical if and only if $x_1 = x_2$.

Since L is a straight line, we are entitled to assume that it is the graph of the linear equation $ax + by + c = 0$ for suitably chosen values of a, b, and c. It can be shown that the following statement is true.

> (ii) If (x_1, y_1), $(x_2, y_2) \in \{(x, y) \mid ax + by + c = 0\}$; $x, y \in R$; $y_1 \neq y_2$; a, b, c, x_1, x_2, y_1, and y_2 are constants; and $a^2 + b^2 \neq 0$; then $x_1 = x_2$ if and only if $b = 0$.

From (i) and (ii), we see that the following statements are equivalent:
1. Line L is a vertical line.
2. The abscissas of any two distinct points in line L are equal.
3. The equation of line L is $ax + by + c = 0$ where a, b, and c are constants, $a \neq 0$, and $b = 0$.

The following statements are also equivalent:
1. Line L is nonvertical.
2. The abscissas of any two distinct points in line L are not equal.
3. The equation of line L is $ax + by + c = 0$ where a, b, and c are constants, and $b \neq 0$.

The statement $ax + by + c = 0$ *and* $b \neq 0$ is equivalent to $y = -\dfrac{a}{b}x - \dfrac{c}{b}$.

If, in the equation $y = -\dfrac{a}{b}x - \dfrac{c}{b}$, we write m for $-\dfrac{a}{b}$ and k for $-\dfrac{c}{b}$, we have $y = mx + k$ and we can summarize our discussion of nonvertical lines with the following statement. The graph of the truth set of the equation $ax + by + c = 0$ is a nonvertical line if and only if its equation can be written in the form $y = mx + k$ with $m = -\dfrac{a}{b}$, $k = -\dfrac{c}{b}$, and $b \neq 0$.

Slope of a Nonvertical Line

We are now ready to consider the slope of a nonvertical line. To find the slope of a nonvertical line, such as L in the figure at the right, we select any two points $P_1(x_1, y_1)$ and $P_2(x_2, y_2)$ in line L. Through one of the points (let us choose P_1), we draw a line parallel to the x-axis and through the other point, P_2, we draw a line parallel to the y-axis. We call the point of intersection of these two lines $T(x_2, y_1)$. Now we give the following definition of the *slope* of line L.

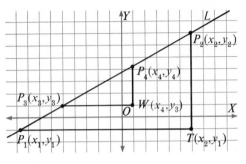

The *slope* of a nonvertical line L containing distinct points $P_1(x_1, y_1)$ and $P_2(x_2, y_2)$ is $\dfrac{y_2 - y_1}{x_2 - x_1}$.

The facts that L is nonvertical, and P_1 and P_2 are distinct points assure us that $x_1 \neq x_2$ and hence, that $x_2 - x_1 \neq 0$.

We see that $y_2 - y_1$ is the change in y obtained by moving from P_1 to P_2. Similarly $x_2 - x_1$ is the change in x obtained by moving from P_1 to P_2. The first change is sometimes called the *rise* and the second change is sometimes called the *run*. Observe that if the movement had been from P_2 to P_1, the slope would not have been affected because the rise would have been $y_1 - y_2$ and the run would have been $x_1 - x_2$. The quotient $\dfrac{y_1 - y_2}{x_1 - x_2}$ is identically equal to $\dfrac{y_2 - y_1}{x_2 - x_1}$. The selection of any other pair of distinct points in L will yield the same slope. For example, if we find the slope of L using $P_3(x_3, y_3)$ and $P_4(x_4, y_4)$ [see the preceding diagram], we get the slope $\dfrac{y_4 - y_3}{x_4 - x_3}$.

We know that $\dfrac{y_4 - y_3}{x_4 - x_3} = \dfrac{y_2 - y_1}{x_2 - x_1}$ because triangle P_1TP_2 is similar to triangle P_3WP_4 and the measures of corresponding sides of similar triangles are in proportion. Thus $\dfrac{|WP_4|}{|P_3W|} = \dfrac{|TP_2|}{|P_1T|}$ and $\dfrac{y_4 - y_3}{x_4 - x_3} = \dfrac{y_2 - y_1}{x_2 - x_1}$ because $|WP_4| = y_4 - y_3$, $|P_3W| = x_4 - x_3$, $|TP_2| = y_2 - y_1$, and $|P_1T| = x_2 - x_1$.

Example 1. Find the slope of each of the lines L_1, L_2, and L_3 if $A(-13, 7)$ and $B(4, -23)$ are in L_1; $C(-7, 5)$ and $D(-7, 31)$ are in L^2; and $E(-3, 11)$ and $F(23, 11)$ are in L_3.

Solution. Slope of $L_1 = \dfrac{-23 - 7}{4 - (-13)} = \dfrac{-30}{17}$. Slope of L_2 does not exist because both points have the same abscissa. Slope of $L_3 = \dfrac{11 - 11}{23 - (-3)} = \dfrac{0}{26} = 0$. This line is parallel to the x-axis.

Let us consider whether the "similar triangle" argument can be used to determine the slope of a horizontal line. Study of the diagram at the right shows that this argument is not applicable because no triangles are formed using the procedure described on page 224. However, the slope of a horizontal line can be determined using the coordinates of any two points in the line. For example, if $P_1(x_1, y_1)$ and $P_2(x_2, y_1)$ are any two distinct points in line L, the slope of L is $\dfrac{y_1 - y_1}{x_2 - x_1}$, or $\dfrac{0}{x_2 - x_1}$, or 0.

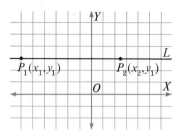

Note that the expression $\dfrac{y_2 - y_1}{x_2 - x_1}$ does not name a real number when $x_1 = x_2$. That is, the line through $P_1(x_1, y_1)$ and $P_2(x_2, y_2)$ when $x_1 = x_2$ is vertical. Therefore we say that a vertical line has no slope.

Now that we have defined what we mean by the slope of any nonvertical line and we know that any line whose equation has the form $y = mx + k$ is nonvertical, we are ready to prove the following theorem.

 Theorem 2–5. The slope of the nonvertical line L which is the graph of the equation $y = mx + k$ is m.

Proof of Theorem 2–5: The slope of the nonvertical line L which is the graph of the equation $y = mx + k$ is m. You may supply the reasons in the following ledger proof.

1. Let $P_1(x_1, y_1)$ and $P_2(x_2, y_2)$ be any two distinct points in L	1. Every line contains at least two distinct points.
2. $y_2 = mx_2 + k, \quad y_1 = mx_1 + k$	2. Why?
3. $y_2 - y_1 = m(x_2 - x_1)$	3. Why?
4. $x_2 - x_1 \neq 0$	4. Why?
5. $\dfrac{y_2 - y_1}{x_2 - x_1} = m$	5. Why?
6. $\dfrac{y_2 - y_1}{x_2 - x_1} = $ slope of L	6. Why?
7. $m = $ slope of L	7. Why?

Note that k is the y-intercept of the line L, that is, the ordinate of the point in which L intersects the y-axis. Since m indicates the slope of the non-vertical line L and k represents its y-intercept, the equation

$$y = mx + k$$

is called the *slope-intercept form* of the equation of the line.

Example 1. Given that the slope of a line is $\frac{3}{5}$ and that the y-intercept is 2, write the equation of the line.

Solution. Substituting $\frac{3}{5}$ for m and 2 for k in the slope-intercept form of the equation of a line, $y = mx + k$, we have $y = \frac{3}{5}x + 2$ or $3x - 5y + 2 = 0$. Either of the preceding equations is the equation of the line having $m = \frac{3}{5}$ and $k = 2$.

Example 2. Using the slope-intercept method, draw the graph of the truth set of the equation $y = -\frac{3}{5}x + 2$.

Solution. Since the y-intercept of the required line is 2, we locate the point $P(0, 2)$ in the y-axis. Since the slope of the required line is $-\frac{3}{5}$, we move downward 3 units from point P and to the right 5 units. We label this point Q and draw the line PQ. $\overleftrightarrow{PQ}$ is the graph of the truth set of the equation $y = -\frac{3}{5}x + 2$.

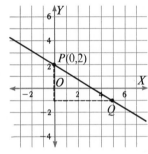

A EXERCISES

1. **a.** Explain why a horizontal line has the slope 0.
   b. Is having the slope 0 equivalent to having no slope?

2. Draw the line
   a. through the point $A(1, 2)$ and having the slope 0.
   b. through the point $B(5, 6)$ and having no slope.
   c. through the point $C(-3, 4)$ and having the slope $-\frac{1}{2}$.
   d. through the point $D(-2, 5)$ and having the slope $\frac{2}{3}$.
   e. through the point $E(-4, -5)$ and having the slope $-\frac{3}{5}$.

3. Write an equation of the line that
   a. has slope $\frac{2}{1}$ and y-intercept -2.
   b. has slope $\frac{1}{2}$ and intersects the y-axis at $P(0, 2)$.

c. intersects the y-axis at $P(0, -3)$ and has slope $\frac{4}{3}$.

d. has slope $-\frac{5}{8}$ and y-intercept 0.

4. Use the slope-intercept method to draw the graph of each of the following equations.

a. $y = 3x - 7$ **f.** $3y = 0x + 12$

b. $y = \frac{3}{5}x + 1$ **g.** $2x + y = \frac{1}{3}$

c. $y = -\frac{2}{3}x - 3$ **h.** $\frac{1}{5}y = \frac{1}{3}x - 4$

d. $y = \frac{1}{6}x$ **i.** $9x - 8y = 32$

e. $4y = -5x + 8$ **j.** $\frac{4}{3}x - \frac{3}{4}y = 10$

Two-Point Form of the Equation of a Line

The slope-intercept form of an equation enables us to write an equation when we know the slope and y-intercept of the graph of its truth set. Let us now consider how to form an equation the graph of whose truth set is the line which contains the distinct points $P_1(x_1, y_1)$ and $P_2(x_2, y_2)$. In Exercise 14, page 235 we prove that the line containing two distinct points is unique.

If the abscissas of P_1 and P_2 are equal, $x_1 = x_2$, then the line is vertical and its equation is $x = x_1$ or an equation equivalent to $x = x_1$. In this case L is the graph of $\{(x, y) \mid x + 0y = x_1\}$.

If the abscissas of P_1 and P_2 are not equal, $x_1 \neq x_2$, then the line is non-vertical and we use a drawing to help us see what the equation should be. It seems reasonable that if $P(x, y)$ is any point in L distinct from P_1 and P_2, the slope of L determined by P and P_1 is the same as the slope determined by P_1 and P_2. Hence $\dfrac{y - y_1}{x - x_1} = m$ and $\dfrac{y_2 - y_1}{x_2 - x_1} = m$.

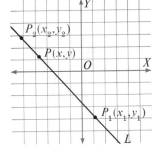

Thus $\dfrac{y - y_1}{x - x_1} = \dfrac{y_2 - y_1}{x_2 - x_1}$. This suggests that the coordinates (x, y) of any point in L satisfy the equation $\dfrac{y - y_1}{x - x_1} = \dfrac{y_2 - y_1}{x_2 - x_1}$. However, the coordinates of $P_1(x_1, y_1)$ do not satisfy this equation. Why? Since we want an equation that is satisfied by the coordinates of every point in L, we write the equation in the form (i) $(y - y_1)(x_2 - x_1) = (y_2 - y_1)(x - x_1)$ when $x, y \in R$ and x_1, y_1, x_2, and y_2 are constants. Now we need to prove that it is the equation of the straight line determined by $P_1(x_1, y_1)$ and $P_2(x_2, y_2)$. This is easy to do because we have already proved on page 220 that (i) is a linear equation and the graph of its truth set is a straight line unless "$x_1 = x_2$ and $y_1 = y_2$" is true. However, since P_1 and P_2 are distinct points, the two clauses "$x_1 = x_2$" and "$y_1 = y_2$" cannot be true simultaneously and consequently the statement "$x_1 = x_2$ and $y_1 = y_2$" cannot be true. Moreover, both (x_1, y_1) and (x_2, y_2) satisfy (i). Therefore (i) is an equation of the straight line determined by P_1 and P_2. Thus we have proved the following theorem:

> **Theorem 3–5.** If distinct points $P_1(x_1, y_1)$ and $P_2(x_2, y_2)$ are in line L, then L is the graph of the truth set of the equation $(y - y_1)(x_2 - x_1) = (y_2 - y_1)(x - x_1)$.

Observe that Theorem 3–5 applies to vertical as well as to nonvertical lines. If L is vertical, the equation is $x = x_1$ and this is the equation obtained from (i) when $x_1 = x_2$. To see this, note that when $x_1 = x_2$, statement (i) becomes $(y_2 - y_1)(x - x_1) = 0$. However, $(P_1(x_1, y_1) \neq P_2(x_2, y_2)$ and $x_1 = x_2)$ $\longrightarrow (y_1 \neq y_2) \longrightarrow (y_2 - y_1 \neq 0)$. Therefore $x - x_1 = 0$ or $x = x_1$.

Ⓐ EXERCISES

1. Using set-builder notation, indicate the set whose graph is the straight line determined by each of the following pairs of points.

a. $A(2, 6)$, $B(8, 2)$

b. $C(9, 4)$, $D(1, 11)$

c. $E(-5, 3)$, $F(-6, 3)$

d. $G(-2, 7)$, $H(6, 1)$

e. $J(-5, -2)$, $K(-8, -3)$

f. $L(-7, -2)$, $M(-7, 5)$

g. $N\left(\frac{a}{b}, c\right)$, $R\left(\frac{a}{b}, -c\right)$

h. $S\left(0, \frac{a}{2}\right)$, $T(a, 0)$

i. $X\left(\frac{a+b}{2}, c\right)$, $Y(a, -c)$

Determinants

Either equation, $\dfrac{y - y_1}{x - x_1} = \dfrac{y_2 - y_1}{x_2 - x_1}$ or $(y - y_1)(x_2 - x_1) = (y_2 - y_1)(x - x_1)$,

is referred to as "a *two-point form* for the equation of a straight line." The first of these equations is easy to remember because each of its members is an expression for the slope of the line. The second equation, in its present form, is more difficult to remember. If we express it as an equation which has zero for one of its members, $xy_1 - xy_2 - yx_1 + yx_2 - x_1y_2 - x_2y_1 = 0$, it appears that the situation is not much improved.

It happens, however, that there is a symbol for the polynomial in the left member which is very easy to remember. We introduce this symbol primarily as a mnemonic device at this stage but also with the assurance that it will be useful to you in other ways as you continue your study of mathematics.

The symbol $\begin{vmatrix} a_1 & b_1 \\ a_2 & b_2 \end{vmatrix}$ is another name for $a_1b_2 - a_2b_1$. The polynomial $a_1b_2 - a_2b_1$ is sometimes called the *value* or the *expansion* of the symbol $\begin{vmatrix} a_1 & b_1 \\ a_2 & b_2 \end{vmatrix}$. Thus $\begin{vmatrix} 5 & 3 \\ 7 & 4 \end{vmatrix} = 5(4) - 7(3) = -1$; $\begin{vmatrix} 7 & 4 \\ 5 & 3 \end{vmatrix} = 7(3) - 5(4) = 1$;

$\begin{vmatrix} 2 & -5 \\ -6 & -8 \end{vmatrix} = 2(-8) - (-6)(-5) = -46$; $\begin{vmatrix} y_1 & 1 \\ y_2 & 1 \end{vmatrix} = y_1 - y_2$; $\begin{vmatrix} 783 & 1 \\ 943 & 0 \end{vmatrix}$

$= 783(0) - 1(943) = -943.$

Now we introduce the symbol $\begin{vmatrix} a_1 & b_1 & c_1 \\ a_2 & b_2 & c_2 \\ a_3 & b_3 & c_3 \end{vmatrix}$, which is another name for

$$a_1 \cdot \begin{vmatrix} b_2 & c_2 \\ b_3 & c_3 \end{vmatrix} - b_1 \cdot \begin{vmatrix} a_2 & c_2 \\ a_3 & c_3 \end{vmatrix} + c_1 \cdot \begin{vmatrix} a_2 & b_2 \\ a_3 & b_3 \end{vmatrix}$$

Thus $\begin{vmatrix} a_1 & b_1 & c_1 \\ a_2 & b_2 & c_2 \\ a_3 & b_3 & c_3 \end{vmatrix} = a_1(b_2c_3 - b_3c_2) - b_1(a_2c_3 - a_3c_2) + c_1(a_2b_3 - a_3b_2) =$

$a_1b_2c_3 - a_1b_3c_2 - a_2b_1c_3 + a_3b_1c_2 + a_2b_3c_1 - a_3b_2c_1$. The symbol $\begin{vmatrix} a_1 & b_1 \\ a_2 & b_2 \end{vmatrix}$

or its expansion $a_1b_2 - a_2b_1$ is called a *determinant of order two*. Similarly,

the symbol $\begin{vmatrix} a_1 & b_1 & c_1 \\ a_2 & b_2 & c_2 \\ a_3 & b_3 & c_3 \end{vmatrix}$ or its expansion $a_1b_2c_3 - a_1b_3c_2 - a_2b_1c_3 + a_3b_1c_2 +$

$a_2b_3c_1 - a_3b_2c_1$ is called a *determinant of order three*. As you continue your study of determinants you will find that the pattern for expansion of determinants of order greater than three does not change. For example,

$$\begin{vmatrix} a_1 & b_1 & c_1 & d_1 \\ a_2 & b_2 & c_2 & d_2 \\ a_3 & b_3 & c_3 & d_3 \\ a_4 & b_4 & c_4 & d_4 \end{vmatrix} = a_1 \begin{vmatrix} b_2 & c_2 & d_2 \\ b_3 & c_3 & d_3 \\ b_4 & c_4 & d_4 \end{vmatrix} - b_1 \begin{vmatrix} a_2 & c_2 & d_2 \\ a_3 & c_3 & d_3 \\ a_4 & c_4 & d_4 \end{vmatrix} + c_1 \begin{vmatrix} a_2 & b_2 & d_2 \\ a_3 & b_3 & d_3 \\ a_4 & b_4 & d_4 \end{vmatrix} -$$

$d_1 \begin{vmatrix} a_2 & b_2 & c_2 \\ a_3 & b_3 & c_3 \\ a_4 & b_4 & c_4 \end{vmatrix}$ At present, however, we are concerned only with the expansion of second and third order determinants.

Now we see that

$$\begin{vmatrix} x & y & 1 \\ x_1 & y_1 & 1 \\ x_2 & y_2 & 1 \end{vmatrix} = x \begin{vmatrix} y_1 & 1 \\ y_2 & 1 \end{vmatrix} - y \begin{vmatrix} x_1 & 1 \\ x_2 & 1 \end{vmatrix} + 1 \begin{vmatrix} x_1 & y_1 \\ x_2 & y_2 \end{vmatrix}$$

$$= x(y_1 - y_2) - y(x_1 - x_2) + (x_1y_2 - x_2y_1)$$
$$= xy_1 - xy_2 - yx_1 + yx_2 + x_1y_2 - x_2y_1$$

Since the right member of this equation is the left member of $xy_1 - xy_2 - yx_1 + yx_2 + x_1y_2 - x_2y_1 = 0$, we have the following easily remembered form for the equation of a line containing distinct points $P_1(x_1, y_1)$ and $P_2(x_2, y_2)$:

$$\begin{vmatrix} x & y & 1 \\ x_1 & y_1 & 1 \\ x_2 & y_2 & 1 \end{vmatrix} = 0$$

Before we can use this form effectively, we must be able to expand a determinant easily and to understand some of the basic properties of determinants. The following examples and exercises will be of some help in these matters.

Example 1. Is $\begin{vmatrix} x & y & 1 \\ a & b & 1 \\ c & d & 1 \end{vmatrix} = 0$ a linear equation provided $(b \neq d \vee a \neq c)$?

Solution. Yes. When we expand the determinant we obtain $x(b - d) - y(a - c) + (ad - bc) = 0$. The condition $(b \neq d \vee a \neq c)$ assures us that at least one of the coefficients of x and y is not zero.

Example 2. What happens when two rows (or two columns) of a determinant are alike?

Solution. $\begin{vmatrix} a & b \\ a & b \end{vmatrix} = ab - ab = 0; \quad \begin{vmatrix} x & x \\ y & y \end{vmatrix} = xy - xy = 0;$

$\begin{vmatrix} a & b & c \\ d & e & f \\ d & e & f \end{vmatrix} = a \cdot \begin{vmatrix} e & f \\ e & f \end{vmatrix} - b \cdot \begin{vmatrix} d & f \\ d & f \end{vmatrix} + c \cdot \begin{vmatrix} d & e \\ d & e \end{vmatrix} = a \cdot 0 - b \cdot 0 + c \cdot 0$

$= 0; \quad \text{and} \quad \begin{vmatrix} a & a & d \\ b & b & e \\ c & c & f \end{vmatrix} = a \begin{vmatrix} b & e \\ c & f \end{vmatrix} - a \begin{vmatrix} b & e \\ c & f \end{vmatrix} + d \begin{vmatrix} b & b \\ c & c \end{vmatrix} = a(bf - ce)$

$- a(bf - ce) + d(bc - bc) = 0$. These and similar expansions lead us to conclude that if two rows or two columns are alike, the determinant is identically equal to zero.

 A EXERCISES

1. Expand each of the following determinants and simplify by combining like terms.

a. $\begin{vmatrix} a & r \\ b & s \end{vmatrix}$

b. $\begin{vmatrix} a & -1 \\ b & c \end{vmatrix}$

c. $\begin{vmatrix} r & -x \\ s & -y \end{vmatrix}$

d. $\begin{vmatrix} 1 & c \\ 2 & d \end{vmatrix}$

e. $\begin{vmatrix} a & b & c \\ 1 & 1 & 1 \\ d & e & f \end{vmatrix}$

f. $\begin{vmatrix} r & a & b \\ s & m & b \\ t & a & c \end{vmatrix}$

g. $\begin{vmatrix} a_1 & a_2 & 3 \\ b_1 & b_1 & 3 \\ c_1 & c_1 & 3 \end{vmatrix}$
i. $\begin{vmatrix} 5 & 1 & -1 \\ x & x & x \\ 2 & 3 & -2 \end{vmatrix}$
k. $\begin{vmatrix} 2 & 4 & -3 \\ 1 & 1 & 0 \\ -3 & 5 & 4 \end{vmatrix}$
m. $\begin{vmatrix} 5 & 4 & y \\ y & y & 3 \\ -2 & 1 & 2 \end{vmatrix}$

h. $\begin{vmatrix} 1 & a & 3 \\ 2 & b & 1 \\ -1 & a & 0 \end{vmatrix}$
j. $\begin{vmatrix} 4 & a & -a \\ 2 & b & -b \\ 5 & c & -c \end{vmatrix}$
l. $\begin{vmatrix} m & t & a \\ m & t & b \\ t & b & c \end{vmatrix}$
n. $\begin{vmatrix} 5 & -y & 4 \\ -3 & x & 2 \\ 2 & y & 1 \end{vmatrix}$

2. Find the number represented by each of the following determinants.

a. $\begin{vmatrix} 1 & 3 \\ -1 & 2 \end{vmatrix}$
c. $\begin{vmatrix} 21 & 5 \\ 10 & 2 \end{vmatrix}$
e. $\begin{vmatrix} 1 & 3 & 0 \\ 2 & 1 & 1 \\ -4 & 5 & 2 \end{vmatrix}$
g. $\begin{vmatrix} 11 & 2 & 0 \\ -4 & 0 & 3 \\ 0 & 6 & -5 \end{vmatrix}$

b. $\begin{vmatrix} 4 & 6 \\ -4 & 6 \end{vmatrix}$
d. $\begin{vmatrix} -15 & 5 \\ -4 & 0 \end{vmatrix}$
f. $\begin{vmatrix} 6 & 0 & -3 \\ -8 & 1 & 2 \\ 4 & 0 & 5 \end{vmatrix}$
h. $\begin{vmatrix} 0 & 1 & 0 \\ 1 & 0 & 1 \\ 0 & 1 & 0 \end{vmatrix}$

3. If in a second order determinant the two columns are interchanged, how does the change affect the result?

4. If in a second order determinant the two rows are interchanged, how does the change affect the result?

5. Do your conclusions of Ex. 3 and Ex. 4 hold for a third order determinant? Explain.

6. **a.** Study the arrangement of the rows and columns of the following determinants and then expand each of the determinants.

$\begin{vmatrix} a_1 & b_1 & c_1 \\ a_2 & b_2 & c_2 \\ a_3 & b_3 & c_3 \end{vmatrix}$
$\begin{vmatrix} a_1 & a_2 & a_3 \\ b_1 & b_2 & b_3 \\ c_1 & c_2 & c_3 \end{vmatrix}$

b. What conclusion do you draw about the value of the determinants?

c. Do you think your conclusion would hold for determinants of other orders but having a similar arrangement of rows and columns?

7. Write the equation of the line through $P_1(2, 7)$ and $P_2(-3, 8)$ in the "determinant equation" form and express this equation in the form $ax + by + c = 0$.

8. Write the equation the graph of whose truth set is the line containing $P_3(12, 5)$ and $P_4(52, -3)$ in the form $ax + by + c = 0$.

Point-Slope Form of the Equation for a Straight Line

If we write m for $\dfrac{y_2 - y_1}{x_2 - x_1}$ in the equation $\dfrac{y - y_1}{x - x_1} = \dfrac{y_2 - y_1}{x_2 - x_1}$ and multiply each member by $x - x_1$, we obtain $y - y_1 = m(x - x_1)$. This equation is called the *point-slope form* of an equation for a straight line.

Collinear Points

Let us look again at our "determinant form" equation, $\begin{vmatrix} x & y & 1 \\ x_1 & y_1 & 1 \\ x_2 & y_2 & 1 \end{vmatrix} = 0$,

for a line through two distinct points $P_1(x_1, y_1)$ and $P_2(x_2, y_2)$. We know that this is an equation of a line since

$$x\begin{vmatrix} y_1 & 1 \\ y_2 & 1 \end{vmatrix} - y\begin{vmatrix} x_1 & 1 \\ x_2 & 1 \end{vmatrix} + \begin{vmatrix} x_1 & y_1 \\ x_2 & y_2 \end{vmatrix} = 0$$

is a linear equation when $(x_1, y_1) \neq (x_2, y_2)$.

Moreover, $P_1(x_1, y_1)$ is in this line because when x_1 replaces x and y_1 replaces y in this equation we have a determinant which is identically equal to zero because two rows are alike. The point $P_2(x_2, y_2)$ is known to be in the line for the same reason.

From plane geometry we know that three points are *collinear* if they are in the same line. How can we determine if three points $P_1(x_1, y_1)$, $P_2(x_2, y_2)$

and $P_3(x_3, y_3)$ are collinear? Let L be the graph of $\begin{vmatrix} x & y & 1 \\ x_2 & y_2 & 1 \\ x_3 & y_3 & 1 \end{vmatrix} = 0$. The

point $P_1(x_1, y_1)$ is in this line if and only if (x_1, y_1) is a member of the truth

set of this equation, that is, if and only if $\begin{vmatrix} x_1 & y_1 & 1 \\ x_2 & y_2 & 1 \\ x_3 & y_3 & 1 \end{vmatrix} = 0$ is a true statement.

We summarize this discussion with the following theorem.

▷ **Theorem 4–5.** The points $P_1(x_1, y_1)$, $P_2(x_2, y_2)$, and $P_3(x_3, y_3)$ are collinear if

and only if $\begin{vmatrix} x_1 & y_1 & 1 \\ x_2 & y_2 & 1 \\ x_3 & y_3 & 1 \end{vmatrix} = 0$ is a true statement.

We also have the following useful corollary to Theorem 4–5.

Corollary to Theorem 4–5. Three points $P_1(x_1, y_1)$, $P_2(x_2, y_2)$, and $P_3(x_3, y_3)$ are collinear if any two of the segments P_1P_2, P_2P_3, P_1P_3 have the same slope.

We shall consider a proof of this corollary in the exercises at the end of this section.

Example 1.   Find an equation for the line L which has the slope $-\frac{3}{5}$ and passes $P(-7, -3)$.

Solution.   Since we are given a point and the slope, we will use the point-slope form of the equation of a line, $y - y_1 = m(x - x_1)$. Substituting -7

for x_1, -3 for y_1 and $-\frac{3}{5}$ for m, we obtain $y + 3 = -\frac{3}{5}(x + 7)$ or $3x + 5y + 36 = 0$. Line L is the graph of $\{(x, y) \mid 3x + 5y + 36 = 0\}$.

Example 2. Show that the points $A(-2, 1)$, $B(13, 11)$ and $C(-11, -5)$ are collinear.

Solution. There are three methods of solution available to us. (1) The equation of the line determined by $A(-2, 1)$ and $B(13, 11)$ is $\dfrac{y-1}{x+2} = \dfrac{11-1}{13+2}$, or $2x - 3y + 7 = 0$. Substituting the coordinates of C in the equation $2x - 3y + 7 = 0$, we have $2(-11) - 3(-5) + 7 = -22 + 15 + 7 = 0$. Since the coordinates of point $C(-11, -5)$ satisfy this equation, C is in the line determined by A and B, and A, B, and C are collinear.

(2) The slope of $\overline{AB}$ is $\dfrac{11-1}{13+2}$ or $\dfrac{2}{3}$. The slope of $\overline{BC}$ is $\dfrac{-5-11}{-11-13}$ or $\dfrac{2}{3}$. Therefore, A, B, and C are collinear by the corollary to Theorem 4–5.

(3) $\begin{vmatrix} -2 & 1 & 1 \\ 13 & 11 & 1 \\ -11 & -5 & 1 \end{vmatrix} = -2 \begin{vmatrix} 11 & 1 \\ -5 & 1 \end{vmatrix} - \begin{vmatrix} 13 & 1 \\ -11 & 1 \end{vmatrix} + \begin{vmatrix} 13 & 11 \\ -11 & -5 \end{vmatrix} =$

$-32 - 24 + 56 = 0$. Thus by Theorem 4-5 points A, B, and C are collinear.

Example 3. Show that $X(x_1, y_1)$, $Y(x_2, y_2)$ and $Z\left(\dfrac{x_1 + x_2}{2}, \dfrac{y_1 + y_2}{2}\right)$ are collinear.

Solution. It is readily shown that

$$\begin{vmatrix} x_1 & y_1 & 1 \\ x_2 & y_2 & 1 \\ \dfrac{x_1 + x_2}{2} & \dfrac{y_1 + y_2}{2} & 1 \end{vmatrix} = 0.$$

Therefore points X, Y, and Z are collinear by Theorem 4–5.

A EXERCISES

1. Write an equation the graph of whose truth set is the line
   a. passing through the point $A(4, -1)$ and having the slope 1.
   b. passing through the point $B(-3, 4)$ and having the slope $-\frac{2}{3}$.
   c. passing through the two points $C(2, 4)$ and $D(-3, 6)$.

d. passing through the two points $E(-1, -1)$ and $F(8, 1)$.

e. having the y-intercept 6 and the x-intercept -4.

f. having the slope $\frac{3}{4}$ and the x-intercept -2.

g. having the slope 0 and the y-intercept -5.

2. Write an equation the graph of whose truth set is the vertical line through the point $A(-6, 1)$.

3. Write an equation the graph of whose truth set is the horizontal line through the point $A(-6, 1)$.

4. Show that the points $C(-1, 6)$, $D(3, 4)$, and $E(1, 5)$ are collinear.

5. Determine whether the points $A(-8, -1)$, $B(-5, 1)$, and $C(1, 5)$ are collinear.

6. Line L is the graph of the truth set of $y - 2 = m(x - 4)$. Determine m so that the point $P(-3, -1)$ is in L.

7. Determine whether the ordered pair $(-1, 8)$ belongs to the truth set of the

$$\text{equation} \begin{vmatrix} x & y & 1 \\ 1 & 3 & 1 \\ 5 & -7 & 1 \end{vmatrix} = 0.$$

8. Determine the slope of the line through the points $R(-4, -4)$ and $S(1, 0)$.

9. Find a such that $(3, 1)$ is a member of the truth set of $ax - 4\,y = -1$.

10. Find b such that $(-2, 5)$ is a member of the truth set of $2\,x + by - 21 = 0$.

11. Write the equation $\begin{vmatrix} x & y & 1 \\ 2 & 3 & 1 \\ 7 & 5 & 1 \end{vmatrix} = 0$ in the form $ax + by + c = 0$.

12. What are the slope and y-intercept of the graph of $7\,y = -5\,x + 28$?

B **EXERCISES**

13. Supply the reasons for the following proof of the statement:

If $x, y \in R \wedge a, b, c, x_1, x_2, y_1$, and y_2 are constants $\wedge$ L is the graph of $\{(x, y) \mid ax + by + c = 0\} \wedge P_1(x_1, y_1), P_2(x_2, y_2) \in L \wedge P_1 \neq P_2 \wedge a^2 + b^2 \neq 0$, then $x_1 = x_2$ if and only if $b = 0$.

To prove this implication we use a proof of the form

$$[(p \wedge q \wedge r) \longrightarrow s \wedge (p \wedge q \wedge s) \longrightarrow r] \longrightarrow [(p \wedge q) \longrightarrow (r \longleftrightarrow s)]$$
(Refer to page 86.)

PART 1.

$$\begin{array}{c}
(1)\quad(2)\\
P_1 \in L \longrightarrow ax_1 + by_1 + c = 0\\
(3)\quad(4)\\
P_2 \in L \longrightarrow ax_2 + by_2 + c = 0\Big] \;(6)\\
(5)\\
x_1 = x_2
\end{array}$$

$$\left.\begin{array}{c}\;\\ \longrightarrow ax_1 + by_2 + c = 0\end{array}\right\}
\begin{array}{c}(7)\\ \longrightarrow by_1 = by_2 \end{array}\quad\begin{array}{c}(8)\\ \end{array}$$

$$\left. \begin{array}{c} \overset{(8)}{\longmapsto} by_1 - by_2 = 0 \overset{(9)}{\longrightarrow} b(y_1 - y_2) = 0 \\ \overset{(10)}{(P_1 \neq P_2 \wedge x_1 = x_2)} \overset{(11)}{\longrightarrow} y_1 \neq y_2 \overset{(12)}{\longrightarrow} (y_1 - y_2) \neq 0 \end{array} \right\} \overset{(13)}{\longrightarrow} b = 0$$

PART 2.

$$\left. \begin{array}{c} \overset{(1)}{P_1} \overset{(2)}{\in L} \longrightarrow ax_1 + by_1 + c = 0 \\ \overset{(3)}{P_2} \overset{(4)}{\in L} \longrightarrow ax_2 + by_2 + c = 0 \\ \overset{(5)}{b = 0} \end{array} \right\} \overset{(6)}{\longrightarrow} ax_1 + c = 0 \wedge ax_2 + c = 0 \overset{(7)}{\dashv}$$

$$\left. \begin{array}{c} \overset{(7)}{\longmapsto} ax_1 = ax_2 \overset{(8)}{\longrightarrow} a(x_1 - x_2) = 0 \\ \overset{(9)}{a^2 + b^2 \neq 0} \overset{(10)}{\atop b = 0} \longrightarrow a \neq 0 \end{array} \right\} \overset{(11)}{\longrightarrow} x_1 - x_2 = 0 \overset{(12)}{\longrightarrow} x_1 = x_2$$

$\therefore$ $(x, y \in R \wedge a, b, c, x_1, x_2, y_1,$ and y_2 are constants $\wedge$ L is the graph of

$$\{(x, y) \mid ax + by + c = 0\} \wedge a^2 + b^2 \neq 0 \wedge P_1, P_2 \in L \wedge P_1 \neq P_2) \overset{(13)}{\dashv}$$

$$\overset{(13)}{\longmapsto} [(x_1 = x_2) \longleftrightarrow (b = 0)].$$

14. Supply reasons for the proof of the statement: If two lines, L_1 and L_2, have two distinct points in common, the sets of points L_1 and L_2 are equal sets; in other words, $[P_1(x_1, y_1) \neq P_2(x_2, y_2) \wedge Pl, P_2 \in L_1 \wedge P_1, P_2 \in L_2] \longrightarrow L_1 = L_2$.

The proof of this theorem requires that we consider two cases (1) L_1 and L_2 are nonvertical, that is, $x_1 \neq x_2$, and (2) L_1 and L_2 are vertical, that is, $x_1 = x_2$.

Case 1. $x_1 \neq x_2$

Proof:

1. $x_1 \neq x_2$	1. Why?
2. Let m_1 be the slope of L_1, m_2 be the slope of L_2, k_1 be the y-intercept of L_1, and k_2 be the y-intercept of L_2	2. Nonvertical lines each have slope and a y-intercept.
3. L_1 is the graph of $\{(x, y) \mid y = m_1x + k_1\}$ L_2 is the graph of $\{(x, y) \mid y = m_2x + k_2\}$	3. Why?
4. $P_1(x_1, y_1), P_2(x_2, y_2) \in L_1$ and $P_1(x_1, y_1), P_2(x_2, y_2) \in L_2$	4. Why?
5. $m_1 = \dfrac{y_2 - y_1}{x_2 - x_1}$ and $m_2 = \dfrac{y_2 - y_1}{x_2 - x_1}$	5. Why?
6. $m_1 = m_2$	6. Why?
7. $y_1 = m_1x_1 + k_1$ and $y_1 = m_2x_1 + k_2$	7. Why?
8. $m_1x_1 + k_1 = m_2x_1 + k_2$	8. Why?
9. $m_1x_1 + k_1 = m_1x_1 + k_2$	9. Why?
10. $k_1 = k_2$	10. Why?
11. L_2 is the graph of $\{(x, y) \mid y = m_1x + k_1\}$	11. Why?
12. $L_1 = L_2$	12. Graphs of equal sets are equal.

Case 2. $x_1 = x_2$

Proof:

1. Let $\{(x, y) \mid a_1x + b_1y + c_1 = 0 \wedge a_1^2 + b_1^2$ 1. Why?
   $\neq 0\}$ be the set whose graph is L_1 and let
   $\{(x, y) \mid a_2x + b_2y + c_2 = 0 \wedge a_2^2 + b_2^2 \neq 0\}$
   be the set whose graph is L_2

2. $P_1(x_1, y_1), P_2(x_2, y_2) \in L_1$ and $P_1(x_1, y_1),$ 2. Why?
   $P_2(x_2, y_2) \in L_2$ and $x_1 = x_2$

3. $b_1 = 0$ and $b_2 = 0$ 3. Why?

4. L_1 is the graph of $\{(x, y) \mid a_1x + c_1 = 0\}$ and   4. Why?
   L_2 is the graph of $\{(x, y) \mid a_2x + c_2 = 0\}$

5. $a_1x_1 + c_1 = 0$ and $a_2x_1 + c_2 = 0$ 5. $P_1 \in L_1$ and $P_1 \in L_2$

6. $c_1 = -a_1x_1$ and $c_2 = -a_2x_1$ 6. Why?

7. L_1 is the graph of $\{(x, y) \mid a_1x - a_1x_1 = 0\}$ or   7. Why?
   $\{(x, y) \mid a_1(x - x_1) = 0\}$

8. L_2 is the graph of $\{(x, y) \mid a_2x - a_2x_1 = 0\}$ or   8. Why?
   $\{(x, y) \mid a_2(x - x_1) = 0\}$

9. $a_1 \neq 0$ and $a_2 \neq 0$ 9. Why?

10. L_1 is the graph of $\{(x, y) \mid x - x_1 = 0\}$ 10. Why?
    L_2 is the graph of $\{(x, y) \mid x - x_1 = 0\}$

11. $L_1 = L_2$ 11. Why?

ⓒ **EXERCISES**

15. Prove: If each of two sets is a set of collinear points and these sets have two distinct points in common, then their union is a set of collinear points.

16. Prove: If three points $A(x_1, y_1)$, $B(x_2, y_2)$, $C(x_3, y_3)$ are collinear with B between A and C, then $|AB| + |BC| = |AC|$. Prove this for two cases (1) A, B, and C are in the same vertical line and (2) A, B, and C are in the same non-vertical line.

17. Prove: If three distinct points $A(x_1, y_1)$, $B(x_2, y_2)$, and $C(x_3, y_3)$ are in the horizontal line L_1, then $AB + BC = AC$ regardless of the order of A, B, and C.

18. Give the reasons for the following proof: If P_1, P_2, P_3 are the distinct points whose coordinates are respectively $(x_1, y_1), (x_2, y_2), (x_3, y_3)$, then slope of $\overline{P_1P_2}$

$= \text{slope of } \overline{P_1P_3} \longrightarrow P_1, P_2, P_3$ are collinear.

$$\text{Slope } \overline{P_1P_2} \overset{(1)}{=} \text{slope } \overline{P_1P_3} \overset{(2)}{\longrightarrow} \frac{y_2 - y_1}{x_2 - x_1} = \frac{y_3 - y_1}{x_3 - x_1} \overset{(3)}{\longrightarrow} (y_2 - y_1)(x_3 - x_1) =$$

$$(x_2 - x_1)(y_3 - y_1) \overset{(4)}{\longrightarrow} (y_2 - y_1)(x_3 - x_1) - (x_2 - x_1)(y_3 - y_1) = 0 \overset{(5)}{\nrightarrow}$$

$$\overset{(5)}{\nrightarrow} y_2x_3 - y_2x_1 - y_1x_3 - x_2y_3 + x_2y_1 + x_1y_3 = 0 \overset{(6)}{\longrightarrow} \begin{vmatrix} x_1 & y_1 & 1 \\ x_2 & y_2 & 1 \\ x_3 & y_3 & 1 \end{vmatrix} = 0 \overset{(7)}{\nrightarrow}$$

$$\overset{(7)}{\nrightarrow} P_1, P_2, P_3 \text{ are collinear.}$$

Parametric Equations of a Line

In this discussion we shall see that considerations based upon the diagram at the right suggest a new and important form of the equation of a line.

In the drawing $P_1(x_1, y_1) \neq P_2(x_2, y_2)$. The line P_1P_2 is shown in a nonvertical position. $\overleftrightarrow{P_1A}$, $\overleftrightarrow{PB}$, and $\overleftrightarrow{P_2C}$ are vertical lines and $\overleftrightarrow{P_1F}$ is a horizontal line which intersects $\overleftrightarrow{PB}$ in E

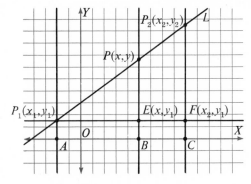

and $\overleftrightarrow{P_2C}$ in F. Since triangle P_1EP is similar to triangle P_1FP_2, we know that $\dfrac{EP}{FP_2} = \dfrac{P_1E}{P_1F}$. Setting each of these ratios equal to g, we have $EP = g \cdot FP_2$ and $P_1E = g \cdot P_1F$. Hence $y - y_1 = g(y_2 - y_1)$ or

$$(i) \quad y = y_1 + g(y_2 - y_1).$$

Similarly, $x - x_1 = g(x_2 - x_1)$ or

$$(ii) \quad x = x_1 + g(x_2 - x_1).$$

It is important to note that g can be any real number. As g changes, the position of P changes. We are interested in the path that P traces when g is allowed to "range through" all real values. For example, if $g = 0$, we have $x = x_1$ and $y = y_1$, that is, $P_1 = P$. If $g = 1$, then $P = P_2$. If we let $g = \frac{1}{2}$, equations (i) and (ii) give us the coordinates of the midpoint of $\overline{P_1P_2}$. It appears that for any real value of g, equations (i) and (ii) will name a pair of numbers x and y which are the coordinates of a point in $\overleftrightarrow{P_1P_2}$. This suggests that the graph of

$$(iii) \quad \{(x, y) \mid x = x_1 + g(x_2 - x_1) \wedge y = y_1 + g(y_2 - y_1) \wedge g \in R\}$$

is a straight line. Let us call this graph L_1. We shall find that L_1 is a straight line which can be vertical or nonvertical.

To show this we must consider three cases (1) $x_1 = x_2$ *and* $y_1 \neq y_2$, (2) $x_1 \neq x_2$ *and* $y_1 = y_2$, and (3) $x_1 \neq x_2$ *and* $y_1 \neq y_2$. We do not need to consider the case in which $x_1 = x_2$ *and* $y_1 = y_2$. Why?

If (1) is true, then the conjunctive statement $x = x_1 + g(x_2 - x_1) \wedge y = y_1 + g(y_2 - y_1) \wedge g \in R$ becomes $x = x_1 \wedge y = y_1 + g(y_2 - y_1) \wedge g \in R$. The truth set of this statement is a set of ordered pairs (x, y) such that $x = x_1$ and y is any real number. However, this is the truth set for the equation

$x + 0 \cdot y = x_1$, which we know is the equation for a vertical straight line. Therefore, if (1) is true, the graph of (*iii*) is the vertical straight line determined by (x_1, y_1) and (x_1, y_2).

Similarly if (2) is true, the graph of (*iii*) is the horizontal straight line determined by (x_1, y_1) and (x_2, y_1).

If $x_1 \neq x_2$, $y_1 \neq y_2$, and $g \in R$, then

$$x = x_1 + g(x_2 - x_1) \wedge y = y_1 + g(y_2 - y_1) \longleftrightarrow x - x_1 =$$

$$g(x_2 - x_1) \wedge y - y_1 = g(y_2 - y_1) \longleftrightarrow \frac{x - x_1}{x_2 - x_1} = g \wedge \frac{y - y_1}{y_2 - y_1} =$$

$$g \longleftrightarrow \frac{x - x_1}{x_2 - x_1} = \frac{y - y_1}{y_2 - y_1} \longleftrightarrow (y - y_1)(x_2 - x_1) = (y_2 - y_1)(x - x_1).$$

This last equation is the equation of a straight line (Theorem 3–5). Hence if (3) is true, the graph of (*iii*) is the line determined by $P_1(x_1, y_1)$ and $P_2(x_2, y_2)$.

Since one of the statements (1), (2), or (3) must be true, we conclude that the graph (*iii*) is always a straight line and we state the following theorem.

▶ **Theorem 5–5.** The graph of $\{(x, y) \mid x = x_1 + g(x_2 - x_1) \wedge y = y_1 + g(y_2 - y_1) \wedge g \in R\}$ is the straight line determined by $P_1(x_1, y_1)$ and $P_2(x_2, y_2)$ when $P_1 \neq P_2$.

The clauses $x = x_1 + g(x_2 - x_1)$ and $y = y_1 + g(y_2 - y_1)$ of the sentence $x = x_1 + g(x_2 - x_1) \wedge y = y_1 + g(y_2 - y_1) \wedge g \in R$ are said to be *parametric equations* of the line through distinct points $P_1(x_1, y_1)$ and $P_2(x_2, y_2)$ and g is said to be a *parameter*.

Example 1. If the coordinates of P_1 and P_2 are $(-6, 2)$ and $(15, 9)$ respectively, find the coordinates of the point P in $\overleftrightarrow{P_1P_2}$ such that $|P_1P| = \frac{2}{3}|P_1P_2|$.

Solution. In $x = x_1 + g(x_2 - x_1) \wedge y = y_1 + g(y_2 - y_1)$ let $x_1 = -6$, $y_1 = 2$, $x_2 = 15$, $y_2 = 9$, and $g = \frac{2}{3}$.

Then $x = -6 + \frac{2}{3}[15 - (-6)]$
$= -6 + 14 = 8$
and $y = 2 + \frac{2}{3}(9 - 2) = 6\frac{2}{3}$.
Thus the coordinates of P are $(8, 6\frac{2}{3})$.

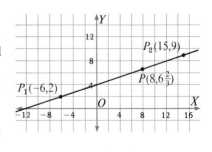

Example 2. Draw the graph of $\{(x, y) \mid x = 2 + 4k \wedge y = -2 + 5k\}$.

Solution.   We choose the values of k shown in the table below. Substituting each of these values for k in $x = 2 + 4\,k$ gives the corresponding x-values shown in the table. Similarly, substituting each value of k in $y = -2 + 5\,k$ gives the corresponding y-values shown. Now we locate the graph of each of the ordered pairs (x, y) so determined and draw the straight line connecting them. This line is the graph of the truth set of the sentence $x = 2 + 4\,k \wedge y = -2 + 5\,k$.

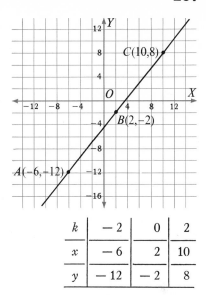

k	-2	0	2
x	-6	2	10
y	-12	-2	8

A   EXERCISES

1. For each part, write the sentence whose clauses are parametric equations and whose graph will pass through the points in each pair.

   a. $A(-4, 7)$, $B(-1, -5)$ **d.** $G(0, 2)$, $H(9, 3)$

   b. $C(2, 3)$, $D(6, -4)$ **e.** $I(8, -4)$, $J(1, 10)$

   c. $E(-4, -4)$, $F(6, 6)$ **f.** $K(\frac{1}{2}, 5)$, $L(\frac{3}{4}, -1)$

2. Draw the graph of each of the following compound sentences.

   a. $x = 5 - 3\,k \wedge y = 6 + k$

   b. $x = -2 + 4\,k \wedge y = 5 - 3\,k$

   c. $x = 1 - 5\,k \wedge y = -2 + k$

   d. $x = \frac{1}{2} - \frac{2}{3}\,k \wedge y = \frac{1}{3} - 2\,k$

   e. $x = k \wedge y = k$

   f. $x = 10 - k \wedge y = 4 + k$

3. Write each of the equations of Ex. 2 in the form $ax + by + c = 0$.

4. Use parametric equations to find the midpoint of $\overline{P_1P_2}$ if $P_1(-6, -4)$ and $P_2(8, 5)$.

5. If $P_1(-2, 11)$ and $P_2(2, 5)$, find the coordinates of the point P in $\overleftrightarrow{P_1P_2}$ such that $|P_1P| = \frac{3}{4}|P_1P_2|$.

6. If $P_1(-2, 3)$ and $P_2(13, -3)$, find the coordinates of the point P in $\overleftrightarrow{P_1P_2}$ such that $|P_2P| = \frac{2}{3}|P_2P_1|$.

Solutions of Systems of Linear Equations in Two Variables

Sometimes we wish to find an ordered pair of numbers which will satisfy two linear equations in two variables *simultaneously*. In this case, the two linear equations form a *system of equations* and any ordered pair which satisfies both equations is called a *solution of this system*. For example, $(-3, 5)$ is the solution of the system of equations $3x + 7y = 26$ *and* $5x - 3y = -30$. We generally write such a system as $\begin{cases} 3x + 7y = 26 \\ 5x - 3y = -30 \end{cases}$. The brace indicates that $3x + 7y = 26$ and $5x - 3y = -30$ are the clauses of a conjunctive open statement. We know that the truth set of an open conjunctive statement is the intersection of the truth sets of its clauses. At this point we review the procedures for solving a system consisting of two linear equations in two variables. We shall consider the reasoning which justifies these procedures when we study systems of equations in Chapter 12.

The two principal procedures are (1) the multiplication and addition method and (2) the substitution method. These are illustrated in the following examples.

Example 1. Solve the system $\begin{cases} 3x + 7y = a \\ 5x - 3y = b \end{cases}$ when a and b are constants, using the multiplication and addition method.

Solution. We wish to eliminate one of the variables and thus obtain one equation in one variable. To eliminate the variable y, we multiply both members of the first equation by 3 and multiply both members of the second equation by 7. We use the addition property of equality to obtain a third equation in which the coefficient of y is zero. We solve this equation for x.

$$3(3x + 7y) = 3(a) \qquad\qquad 9x + 21y = 3a$$
$$7(5x - 3y) = 7(b) \qquad\qquad \underline{35x - 21y = 7b}$$
$$\qquad\qquad 44x + 0y = 3a + 7b$$
$$x = \frac{3a + 7b}{44}$$

Next to eliminate the variable x, multiply both members of the first equation by 5 and multiply both members of the second equation by -3. We use the addition property and solve the resulting equation as shown:

$$5(3x + 7y) = 5(a) \qquad\qquad 15x + 35y = 5a$$
$$-3(5x - 3y) = -3(b) \qquad\qquad \underline{-15x + 9y = -3b}$$
$$\qquad\qquad 0x + 44y = 5a - 3b$$
$$y = \frac{5a - 3b}{44}$$

The ordered pair $\left(\dfrac{3\,a+7\,b}{44},\ \dfrac{5\,a-3\,b}{44}\right)$ is a solution of the given system provided it will satisfy each equation.

$$3\left(\frac{3\,a+7\,b}{44}\right)+7\left(\frac{5\,a-3\,b}{44}\right)\overset{?}{=}a$$

$$9\,a+21\,b+35\,a-21\,b\overset{?}{=}44\,a$$

$$44\,a\overset{\checkmark}{=}44\,a$$

$$5\left(\frac{3\,a+7\,b}{44}\right)-3\left(\frac{5\,a-3\,b}{44}\right)\overset{?}{=}b$$

$$15\,a+35\,b-15\,a+9\,b\overset{?}{=}44\,b$$

$$44\,b\overset{\checkmark}{=}44\,b$$

Hence $\left\{\left(\dfrac{3\,a+7\,b}{44},\ \dfrac{5\,a-3\,b}{4}\right)\right\}$ is the solution set of the given system.

Are the two equations of the given system equivalent? The answer is no, since $(\tfrac{1}{3}\,a,\,0)$ will satisfy the first equation but not the second. Can the system have other solutions?

Example 2. Solve the system $\begin{cases}5\,x+11\,y=62\\4\,x-13\,y=-103\end{cases}$ by the substitution method.

Solution. Using the substitution method, we solve one of the given equations for the expression representing the value of one of the variables and then substitute the expression thus obtained for that variable in the other equation. We solve the first equation for x and substitute the result for x in the second equation. Thus we obtain an equation in the single variable y.

$$5\,x+11\,y=62 \qquad\qquad \text{Similarly } 5\,x+11\,y=62$$

$$x=\frac{62-11\,y}{5} \qquad\qquad\qquad y=\frac{62-5\,x}{11}$$

$$4\,x-13\,y=-103 \qquad\qquad 4\,x-13\,y=-103$$

$$4\left(\frac{62-11\,y}{5}\right)-13\,y=-103 \qquad 4\,x-13\left(\frac{62-5\,x}{11}\right)=-103$$

$$248-44\,y-65\,y=-515 \qquad 44\,x-806+65\,x=-1133$$

$$y=7 \qquad\qquad\qquad\qquad x=-3$$

It is readily shown that the ordered pair $(-3,\,7)$ satisfies both equations in this system. The solution set of this system is $\{(-3,\,7)\}$.

Are the equations in this system equivalent? The answer is no because at least one ordered pair, $(8,\,2)$, will satisfy the first equation but not the second equation. Can the system have other solutions?

We have inquired twice if it were possible for the given system to have a second solution. The answer depends on whether or not the two equations in the system are equivalent. If either equation has a solution which is not a solution of the other, then the equations are, of course, not equivalent. This means that the lines L_1 and L_2 which are the graphs of these equations are not equal, that is, they are not the same line. We know that if two distinct lines have one point in common, then they do not have a second point in common. The proof of this statement is considered in an exercise. Therefore we can be assured that the solutions obtained in the above examples are unique. Thus if we can by any method (substitution, multiplication and addition, inspection, and so on) find an ordered pair which is a solution of a system consisting of a pair of nonequivalent equations, we know that the solution we have found is unique.

Some systems of nonlinear equations can be solved by the multiplication and addition method. The following is an example of the solution of such a system of equations.

Example 3.   Solve the system of equations $\begin{cases} \dfrac{4}{x} + \dfrac{2}{y} = 28 \\ \dfrac{3}{x} + \dfrac{4}{y} = 36 \end{cases}$

Solution.   When the variables appear in the denominator we usually do not try to eliminate the variables from the denominator until we have obtained an equation in one variable. In this system we shall use a combination of the multiplication and addition method and substitution. We multiply the members of the first equation by -2 and add the two equations. Thus we obtain

$$-\frac{8}{x} - \frac{4}{y} = -56$$

$$\frac{3}{x} + \frac{4}{y} = 36$$

$$\overline{-\frac{5}{x} = -20}$$

Solving for x: $-20x = -5$
$$x = \tfrac{1}{4}$$

To find the value of y we substitute $\tfrac{1}{4}$ for x in the first equation.

This gives us: $16 + \dfrac{2}{y} = 28$

$$\frac{2}{y} = 12$$

$$12y = 2$$

$$y = \tfrac{1}{6}$$

To determine if $(\frac{1}{4}, \frac{1}{6})$ also satisfies our second equation, we substitute $\frac{1}{4}$ for x and $\frac{1}{6}$ for y in the second equation.

$$\frac{3}{\frac{1}{4}} + \frac{4}{\frac{1}{6}} \overset{?}{=} 36$$

$$12 + 24 \overset{?}{=} 36$$

$$36 \overset{\vee}{=} 36$$

Since $(\frac{1}{4}, \frac{1}{6})$ satisfies both equations, it is a member of the solution set of the system of equations. Since the two equations of the system are not equivalent, $(\frac{1}{4}, \frac{1}{6})$ is the only member of the solution set.

 A EXERCISES

1. Solve the following systems of equations by use of the multiplication and addition method.

a. $\begin{cases} 2x + 3y = -17 \\ 5x - 6y = 25 \end{cases}$

b. $\begin{cases} x + 8y = 23 \\ 4x - 2y = 24 \end{cases}$

c. $\begin{cases} 3x + 4y + 7 = 0 \\ 2x - 5y = 26 \end{cases}$

d. $\begin{cases} 4(x+3) - 5(y-2) = 29 \\ 7x - 6(y+1) = -2 \end{cases}$

e. $\begin{cases} .3x + .4y = 2.6 \\ 1.2x + .3y = 7.8 \end{cases}$

f. $\begin{cases} \dfrac{x}{5} + \dfrac{y}{3} = 6 \\ x = 12 - \dfrac{y+2}{7} \end{cases}$

2. Solve the following systems of equations by use of the substitution method.

a. $\begin{cases} 8x + 3y = 34 \\ 9x + y = 24 \end{cases}$

b. $\begin{cases} 4x - y = -3 \\ -12x + 3y = 9 \end{cases}$

c. $\begin{cases} x + \dfrac{3y}{2} = -5 \\ 7x + \dfrac{y}{3} = 26 \end{cases}$

d. $\begin{cases} \dfrac{x-2}{2} - y - 3 = 0 \\ 3(x - y) - 2x = 3 \end{cases}$

e. $\begin{cases} 5(x+y) - 8x = 33 \\ \dfrac{x}{2} - \dfrac{4y}{3} = x + 1 \end{cases}$

f. $\begin{cases} \dfrac{x+1}{3} + \dfrac{2y}{5} = \dfrac{11}{5} \\ 2(x - y) + y = 1 \end{cases}$

3. Solve using the substitution or the multiplication and addition method.

a. $\begin{cases} 7(x+y) - 8(x-y) + 53 = 0 \\ 4(x+2) - 7y - 61 = 0 \end{cases}$

b. $\begin{cases} \dfrac{5x}{2} - \dfrac{4y}{3} = 22 \\ \dfrac{3x}{4} - 2y = 21 \end{cases}$

c. $\begin{cases} 3(x - y) = \dfrac{4x - y}{2} - 1 \\ x + \dfrac{3x - 2}{2} = 8y \end{cases}$

d. $\begin{cases} (9x + 5y) = -7(1 - 2y) \\ 3y - 1 = 4x + 2(y+1) \end{cases}$

e. $\begin{cases} \dfrac{2(x+3y)}{7} - \dfrac{y-x}{2} = x \\[2mm] 3x - 2y - \dfrac{2x-5y}{5} = 3y+2 \end{cases}$

g. $\begin{cases} \dfrac{3x+2y}{7} = x-2 \\[2mm] 4(x+y) = \dfrac{12x+y+1}{2} \end{cases}$

f. $\begin{cases} \dfrac{3x+2y+4}{2} - (2x-y) = 11 \\[2mm] \dfrac{2x+y}{3} + \dfrac{x-2y}{2} + \dfrac{x}{2} = 14 \end{cases}$

h. $\begin{cases} x + \dfrac{4y+6}{9} = \dfrac{5x+1}{4} \\[2mm] \dfrac{6y-5}{8} + x - \dfrac{1}{3} = \dfrac{4y-1}{3} \end{cases}$

4. Solve each of the following systems of equations.

a. $\begin{cases} \dfrac{7}{x} - \dfrac{9}{y} = 2 \\[2mm] \dfrac{12}{x} + \dfrac{6}{y} = 5 \end{cases}$

d. $\begin{cases} \dfrac{4}{x} - \dfrac{3}{y} = 2 \\[2mm] \dfrac{10}{x} - \dfrac{9}{y} = 3 \end{cases}$

b. $\begin{cases} \dfrac{16}{x} + \dfrac{15}{y} = 1 \\[2mm] \dfrac{12}{x} - \dfrac{12}{y} = \dfrac{27}{5} \end{cases}$

e. $\begin{cases} \dfrac{1}{x-2} + \dfrac{1}{y+2} = 0 \\[2mm] \dfrac{3}{x+2} - \dfrac{4}{y-2} = 0 \end{cases}$

c. $\begin{cases} \dfrac{3}{x} + \dfrac{9}{y} = 18 \\[2mm] \dfrac{1}{x} - \dfrac{6}{y} = -6 \end{cases}$

f. $\begin{cases} \dfrac{1}{x^2} + \dfrac{3}{y^2} = \dfrac{79}{100} \\[2mm] \dfrac{2}{x^2} - \dfrac{3}{y^2} = -\dfrac{67}{100} \end{cases}$

5. Prove: If two distinct lines have one point in common, then they do not have a second point in common. *Hint.* Show that this implication is a contrapositive of the statement proved in Ex. 14, page 235.

6. a. Write an equation whose graph is the line through the point $A(-5, 1)$ and having the slope $\frac{5}{3}$.

b. Write an equation whose graph is the line through the point $B(1, 4)$ and having the slope $-\frac{2}{3}$.

c. Solve the system consisting of the equations of parts **a** and **b** to find the co-ordinates of the point of intersection of their graphs.

Parallel Lines

We use the same definition for parallel lines that is used in geometry, namely: Two lines L_1 and L_2 in the same plane are *parallel* if $L_1 \cap L_2 = \emptyset$. If we use the symbol $\parallel$ for "is parallel to" and recall that a definition is reversible, we have the following equivalence:

L_1 and L_2 are in the same plane and $L_1 \cap L_2 = \emptyset \longleftrightarrow L_1 \parallel L_2$.

It is readily shown that any two distinct vertical lines are parallel. Moreover, if one of two parallel lines is vertical, so is the other. We can show that the nonvertical lines are parallel if and only if they have the same slope and different y-intercepts. We state this as

Theorem 6–5. If nonvertical lines L_1 and L_2 are the graphs of $\{(x, y) \mid y = m_1x + k_1\}$ and $\{(x, y) \mid y = m_2x + k_2\}$, respectively, then $L_1 \parallel L_2$ if and only if $m_1 = m_2$ and $k_1 \neq k_2$.

In order to establish this theorem, we must prove the following two statements. If nonvertical lines L_1 and L_2 are the graphs of $\{(x, y) \mid y = m_1x + k_1\}$ and $\{(x, y) \mid y = m_2x + k_2\}$, respectively, then (1) $L_1 \parallel L_2 \longrightarrow (m_1 = m_2 \wedge k_1 \neq k_2)$ and (2) $(m_1 = m2 \wedge k_1 \neq k_2 \longrightarrow L_1 \parallel L_2$. The proof of these two implications, that is, the proof of Theorem 6–5 is left as an exercise. (See page 244.)

Example 1. Find an equation for the line through the point $P(-5, 3)$ and parallel to the vertical line whose equation is $x = 7$.

Solution. The required line must be a vertical line through the point $P(-5, 3)$. Its equation is therefore $x = -5$.

Example 2. Find an equation for the line L_1 through the point $N(-3, 7)$ and parallel to the line L_2 which is the graph of $4x - 3y = 483$.

Solution. Solving the equation $4x - 3y = 483$ for y, we obtain $y = \frac{4}{3}x - \frac{483}{3}$. Thus the slope of L_2 is $\frac{4}{3}$. Hence the slope of L_1 is $\frac{4}{3}$ and we have $y = \frac{4}{3}x + k$, as the equation of L_1. We determine k using the fact that $N(-3, 7) \in L_1$. Substituting these values for x and y in $y = \frac{4}{3}x + k$ gives $7 = \frac{4}{3}(-3) + k$ or $k = 11$. Substituting 11 for k in $y = \frac{4}{3}x + k$ gives $y = \frac{4}{3}x + 11$, or $3y - 4x = 33$, as the required equation.

 A EXERCISES

1. In which of the following pairs will the two equations have graphs that are parallel lines?

a. $y = 3x + 4$
$\quad y = 3x - 7$

b. $y = 4x - 6$
$\quad y = 7x - 6$

c. $2x + 7y = 3$
$\quad 2x + 5y = 1$

d. $3y - 2x + 1 = 0$
$\quad 3y - 2x + 6 = 0$

e. $8y = -5x - 1$
$\quad 5x + 8y = 4$

f. $3x - 4y = 4$
$\quad y = \frac{3}{4}x - 1$

2. Write an equation whose graph is a straight line through the point $A(-1, 6)$ and parallel to the line which is the graph of the truth set of $4x - 7y = 18$.

3. Write an equation whose graph is a straight line through the point $B(-5, 4)$ and parallel to the x-axis.

4. Write an equation whose graph is a straight line through the point $C(-2, -5)$ and parallel to the line through the points $D(2, -3)$ and $E(6, 5)$.

5. Determine the values of m and k so that $\{(x, y) \mid y = mx + k\} = \{(x, y) \mid 8x - 7y = 11\}$. When m and k assume these values, are the graphs of the two sets parallel lines? Explain.

6. Write an equation the graph of whose truth set is a straight line having the y-intercept 5 and parallel to the line which is the graph of $\{(x, y) \mid y = 3x + 2\}$.

B **EXERCISES**

7. In the triangle shown at the right the line AB passes through the points $A(2, 1)$ and $B(8, 4)$. The point $P(3, 4)$ is a point in the side AC. Write an equation the graph of whose truth set is the straight line through P and parallel to $\overleftrightarrow{AB}$.

8. The vertex C of the triangle of Ex. 7 has the coordinates (5, 10). Determine the coordinates of the point in which the line of Ex. 1 intersects the side BC of the triangle.

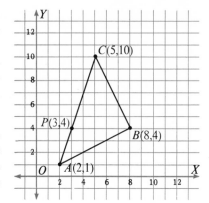

9. A parallelogram is formed by joining the points $A(-1, 2)$, $B(-3, -1)$, $C(7, 3)$, and $D(?, ?)$ in order. Write equations having truth sets whose graphs are the lines which form the sides AD and CD of the parallelogram. Solve this system of two equations to find the coordinates of the vertex D of the parallelogram.

10. Prove Theorem 6–5: If nonvertical lines L_1 and L_2 are the graphs of $\{(x, y) \mid y = m_1x + k_1\}$ and $\{(x, y) \mid y = m_2x + k_2\}$, then $L_1 \parallel L_2$ if and only if $m_1 = m_2$ and $k_1 \neq k_2$.

Perpendicular Lines

Consider two lines that intersect at $P(a, b)$. If one of these lines is vertical and the other horizontal, the two lines are, of course, perpendicular. If the two lines are non-vertical, we shall see that they are perpendicular if and only if the product of their slopes is -1. This statement is suggested by the following geometrical considerations. In the drawing at the right, L_1 and L_2 are perpendicular lines, neither of which is vertical. The vertical line $\overleftrightarrow{AB}$ intersects L_2 in A, L_1 in B, and the horizontal line through

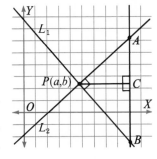

the point $P(a, b)$ in C. Since triangle PCB is similar to triangle ACP, we have:

$$\frac{|AC|}{|PC|} = \frac{|PC|}{|BC|} \quad \text{or} \quad \left|\frac{AC}{PC}\right| = \left|\frac{PC}{BC}\right| \quad \text{or} \quad \left|\frac{AC}{PC}\right| = \frac{1}{\left|\frac{BC}{PC}\right|}$$

Now if m_1 is the slope of L_1, then $|m_1|$ is equal to $\left|\frac{BC}{PC}\right|$ and if m_2 is the slope of L_2, then $|m_2|$ is equal to $\left|\frac{AC}{PC}\right|$. Therefore, $|m_2| = \frac{1}{|m_1|}$ or $|m_2| \cdot |m_1| = 1$ or $|m_1 m_2| = 1$.

Thus we see that if the nonvertical lines are perpendicular, the product of the absolute values of their slopes is 1. In the diagram $\frac{CA}{PC}$, the slope of L_2, is positive because the directed distance CA is positive and the directed distance PC is positive. Similarly, we see that $\frac{CB}{PC}$, the slope of L_1, is negative because CB is negative and PC is positive. Since m_1 and m_2 have opposite signs and the absolute value of their product is 1, we conclude that $m_1 m_2 = -1$. Thus we know that, "If L_1 and L_2 are two nonvertical perpendicular lines, then the product of their slopes is -1." A converse of this statement, "If L_1 and L_2 are two nonvertical lines and the product of their slopes is -1, then they are perpendicular," is also true.

We now state and prove:

Theorem 7–5. If two nonvertical lines L_1 and L_2 are the graphs of $\{(x, y) \mid y = m_1 x + k_1\}$ and $\{(x, y) \mid y = m_2 x + k_2\}$, respectively, then L_1 is perpendicular to L_2 if and only if $m_1 m_2 = -1$.

The proof of this theorem will be easier if we first consider a preliminary theorem, which we call a lemma. The statement of the lemma and its proof follow:

Lemma. If line L is the graph of $\{(x, y) \mid y = mx + k\}$, $P(a, b) \in L$, and the coordinates of Q are $(a + c, b + mc)$, then $Q \in L$.

Proof of lemma: $\overset{(1)}{P(a, b) \in L} \longrightarrow \overset{(2)}{b = ma + k} \longrightarrow \overset{(3)}{b + mc = ma + mc + k} \longrightarrow$
$\overset{(5)}{b + mc = m(a + c) + k} \longrightarrow Q \in L$. The reasons for the steps in this proof are left to you.

Proof of Theorem 7–5: If two nonvertical lines L_1 and L_2 are the graphs of $\{(x, y) \mid y = m_1x + k_1\}$ and $\{(x, y) \mid y = m_2x + k_2\}$, respectively, then $L_1 \perp L_2$ if and only if $m_1m_2 = -1$.

Let L_1 and L_2 be two nonvertical lines which are the graphs of $\{(x, y) \mid y = m_1x + k_1\}$ and $\{(x, y) \mid y = m_2x + k_2\}$, respectively, and which intersect in $Q(a, b)$. Let P_1 and P_2 be the points whose coordinates are $(a + c, b + m_1c)$ and $(a + c, b + m_2c)$, respectively, when $c \neq 0$, then by the lemma, $P_1 \in L_1$ and $P_2 \in L_2$ as shown in the figure.

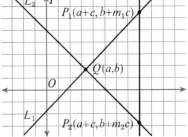

Now we can say: $L_1 \perp L_2 \longleftrightarrow |P_1P_2|^2 = |QP_1|^2 + |QP_2|^2 \longleftrightarrow [(m_1 - m_2)c]^2 = c^2 + m_1{}^2c^2 + c^2 + m_2{}^2c^2 \longleftrightarrow m_1m_2 = -1.$

Notice that the Pythagorean theorem and the distance formula are the bases of the proof.

We summarize our conclusions concerning perpendicular lines as follows: Two lines are perpendicular if one is horizontal and the other is vertical or if they are nonvertical lines the product of whose slopes is -1.

Example 1. Find the equation whose graph is the line L_1, which passes through $P(4, 1)$ and is perpendicular to line L_2 which is the graph of $4x - 7y = 31$.

Solution. The slope of L_2 is $\frac{4}{7}$. Hence the slope of L_1 is $-\frac{7}{4}$ and the equation whose graph is L_1 has the form $y = -\frac{7}{4}x + k$. To determine k, let $x = 4$ and $y = 1$.

$\therefore k = 8$ and the equation we are seeking is $y = -\frac{7}{4}x + 8$ or $4y + 7x = 32$.

If Q is in the line L, we say that the distance from point Q to line L is zero. If Q is not in L, the distance from the point Q to a line L is the measurement of the line segment QP which is perpendicular to L and intersects it in P.

Example 2. If the equation whose solution set has the graph L is $-3x + 7y = 58$, find the distance from the origin to L.

Solution.   Let (x, y) be the coordinates of P. We are to find $|OP|$. The slope of L is $\frac{3}{7}$. Hence the slope of $\overline{OP}$ is $-\frac{7}{3}$. Since $\overline{OP}$ contains the origin, the equation the graph of whose solution set contains $\overline{OP}$ is $y = -\frac{7}{3}x$. We now solve the system of equations

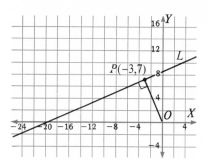

$$\text{tions} \begin{cases} -3x + 7y = 58 \\ \frac{7}{3}x + y = 0 \end{cases}$$

for x and y, the coordinates of P. We obtain $P(-3, 7)$. By the distance formula, $|OP| = \sqrt{(-3)^2 + 7^2} = \sqrt{58}$. Thus the distance from O to L is $\sqrt{58}$ units.

  EXERCISES

1. The graph of the truth set of each of the following equations is a straight line. In which of the pairs will the two lines be parallel, in which will they be perpendicular, and in which will they be neither parallel nor perpendicular?

a. $3x - 5y = -20$
   $6x - 10y = 30$

b. $2y = x - 7$
   $y = -2x + 4$

c. $7x = 8 - y$
   $7y = x - 2$

d. $3x - y - 6 = 0$
   $5x - 2y - 6 = 0$

e. $\dfrac{y}{2} = \dfrac{x}{6} + \dfrac{5}{4}$
   $\dfrac{3y}{5} = \dfrac{x}{5} + \dfrac{3}{2}$

f. $y = 8x$
   $y + \frac{1}{8}x = 0$

g. $7y = 3x + \frac{7}{2}$
   $3y = 7x + \frac{3}{2}$

h. $y = 4$
   $x = -7$

i. $7x + 4 = 0$
   $4x - 7 = 0$

j. $\dfrac{7x}{6} + \dfrac{2y}{3} = -4$
   $\dfrac{x}{2} - \dfrac{7y}{8} = -\dfrac{7}{8}$

2. Write an equation the graph of whose truth set is perpendicular to the graph of the truth set of each of the following equations and passes through the point whose coordinates are shown at the right of the given equation.

a. $4x + 3y = 9$, $P(-4, -1)$

b. $-7x + y = -2$, $R(7, -3)$

c. $11x = 15$, $S(3, 2)$

d. $y = \frac{7}{2}x - \frac{1}{2}$, $T(0, 4)$

e. $\frac{3}{5}x - \frac{5}{4}y = -1$, $W(3, -1)$

f. $\dfrac{x}{9} + \dfrac{y}{2} = \dfrac{3}{5}$, $A(-6, -2)$

3. Find the y-intercept of the line which is the graph of the solution set of $2x + 3y = 15$.

4. A triangle has the vertices $A(0, 0)$, $B(7, 7)$, and $C(3, 7)$. Find the measure of the altitude from the vertex C to the base AB.

5. Find the distance between the two parallel lines which are the graphs of $2x - 3y - 3 = 0$ and $2x - 3y + 2 = 0$. *Hint.* Select a point which is in one of the lines and find the distance from this point to the other line.   _____

6. If we consider each of the following sets of three points as the vertices of a triangle, which of the triangles are right triangles?

  a. $A(0, -2)$, $B(7, 2)$, $C(4, 4)$ **c.** $G(2, 5)$, $H(7, -2)$, $K(3, -1)$

  b. $D(-9, -2)$, $E(-2, 1)$, $F(-4, 3)$ **d.** $L(0, 3)$, $M(2, -3)$, $N(6, -2)$

7. a. Complete the following truth table.

a	b	q	$a \longrightarrow q$	$b \longrightarrow q$	$a \vee b$	$(a \longrightarrow q) \wedge (b \longrightarrow q)$	$(a \vee b) \longrightarrow q$	$[(a \longrightarrow q) \wedge (b \longrightarrow q)] \longrightarrow [(a \vee b) \longrightarrow q]$
T	T	T						
T	T	F						
T	F	T						
T	F	F						
F	T	T						
F	T	F						
F	F	T						
F	F	F						

  b. Is the statement $[(a \longrightarrow q) \wedge (b \longrightarrow q)] \longrightarrow [(a \vee b) \longrightarrow q]$ always a true statement?

 EXERCISE

8. In Theorem 7-5 we assume that P_1QP_2 is a triangle. Prove that our assumption is correct.

Sketching Graphs of Truth Sets of Open Sentences

In this section we find the geometric representation (graph) of the truth set of a given open sentence.

Consider the graph of the truth set of the equation $y = x^2$. The graph is easily obtained by identifying a few ordered pairs belonging to the truth set of the equation, locating the graphs of these ordered pairs, and drawing a smooth curve through the points which are these graphs. The table at the top of the following page shows the ordered pairs used for drawing the graph to its right.

x	-4	-3	-2	-1	0	1	2	3	4
y	16	9	4	1	0	1	4	9	16

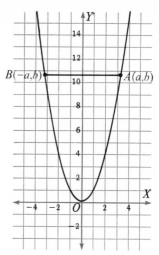

Observe that the value of y obtained when $x = -2$ is the same as the value obtained when $x = 2$. Why? We state this in a more general way by saying: If $(a, b) \epsilon \{(x, y) \mid y = x^2\}$, then $(-a, b) \epsilon \{(x, y) \mid y = x^2\}$.

We note that the y-axis is the perpendicular bisector of the segment AB which joins $B(-a, b)$ and $A(a, b)$. (Note that in the diagram we have assumed that a is positive.) Under these circumstances we say that the points A and B are symmetric with respect to the y-axis, according to the following definition: *Two points* are *symmetric with respect to a line* if that line is the perpendicular bisector of the line segment joining the points. Each of these points is called the *reflection* of the other in the line. Moreover, the curve just drawn is symmetric with respect to the y-axis according to the following definition: A *set of points S* is *symmetric with respect to a line* if the reflection in the line of every point in S is also in S.

The curve above is called a *parabola*. If we draw the graph of $S = \{(x, y) \mid y \geq x^2\}$, we have the same parabola and all points above the parabola. In this case, the graph is shown by the shaded area and the curve which bounds it below. Is $P_1(2, 7)$ in the graph of S? Is $P_2(-2, 7)$ in the graph of S? Is $P_3(2, 3)$ in the graph of S? Is $P_4(-2, 3)$ in the graph of S? Is $P_5(3, 9)$ in the graph of S? Is $P_6(-3, 9)$ in the graph of S? The set of points shown by this curve and the shaded area is symmetric with respect to the y-axis according to the second definition.

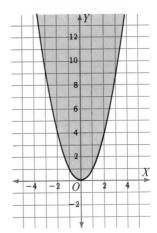

Consider the graph of $S = \{(x, y) \mid xy = 12\}$. We obtain the graph by drawing a smooth curve through the points whose coordinates are shown in the following table.

x	-12	-6	-3	-2	-1	1	2	3	6	12
y	-1	-2	-4	-6	-12	12	6	4	2	1

Observe that if $(a, b) \in S$, then $(-a, -b) \in S$. Thus we obtain a curve having one branch in the first quadrant and one in the third quadrant, as shown in the diagram at the right. Observe, also, that the origin bisects the segment AB which joins $A(2, 6)$ and $B(-2, -6)$. Thus the points $A(2, 6)$ and $B(-2, -6)$ are symmetric with respect to the origin according to the following definition: *Two points are symmetric with respect to a third point* if the third point is the midpoint of the line segment joining them. Each of the two points is called the reflection 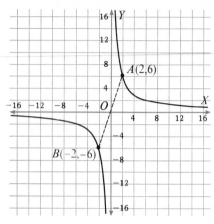 of the other in the third point. Moreover, the curve is symmetric with respect to the origin according to the following definition: A *set of points S* is *symmetric with respect to a point* if the reflection in that point of every point in S is also in S.

The preceding curve is called an *equilateral hyperbola*. The shaded area shown in the diagram at the right is the graph of the truth set of $xy > 12$. In this case the equilateral hyperbola is drawn as a dashed line to indicate that it is not part of the graph. The set of points indicated by the shaded area is symmetric with respect to the origin according to the definition of the symmetry of a set with respect to a point.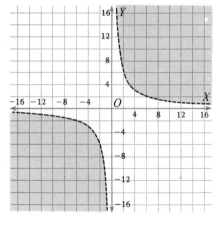

Other examples of open statements whose truth sets have graphs that are symmetric with respect to the origin are

$$x + y = 0 \qquad y = x^3 \qquad |x| + |y| < 8 \qquad xy = -12$$

We note that each of these statements is true when $-x$ is substituted for x and $-y$ is substituted for y. Thus if $x + y = 0$, then $-x - y = 0$; if $y = x^3$, then $-y = (-x)^3$, and so on.

It is not always easy to recognize that a graph will be symmetric with respect to a line or to a point. When such symmetry is recognized, it may be used to simplify the sketching of the graph of the truth set of an open statement. The graph of an open statement is symmetric with respect to the

y-axis if an equivalent open statement is obtained by replacing x by $-x$. The graph of an open statement is symmetric with respect to the x-axis if an equivalent statement is obtained by replacing y by $-y$. The graph of an open statement is symmetric with respect to the origin if an equivalent statement is obtained by replacing x by $-x$ and y by $-y$. The graph of an open statement is symmetric with respect to the graph of $\{(x, y) \mid y = x\}$ if an equivalent statement is obtained by replacing x by y and y by x.

Example 1. Test for symmetry and sketch the graph of $\{(x, y) \mid x \geq y^2 + 2\}$.

Solution. Since an equivalent sentence is obtained by replacing y by $-y$ in the sentence $x \geq y^2 + 2$, we know that the graph is symmetric with respect to the x-axis. To locate the point where the curve crosses the x-axis, we let $y = 0$ in $x = y^2 + 2$ and find $V(2, 0)$ as the point of intersection. By substituting another value of y (for example, 2) in $x = y^2 + 2$, we find that when $y = 2$, 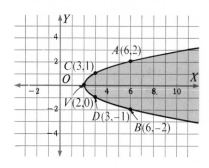 $x = 6$. Thus $A(6, 2)$ is a point in the curve and, of course, $B(6, -2)$ is also a point in the curve. In the same manner we find that $C(3, 1)$ and $D(3, -1)$ are also points in the curve. The number of such points located depends upon the amount of accuracy we need in the graph. By means of our information concerning the symmetry of the curve with respect to the x-axis, and the location of the points whose coordinates we have determined, we are able to draw the graph shown. It consists of the curve and the shaded area.

Example 2. Reflect (find the reflection of) the point $P(4, 2)$ in the x-axis, in the y-axis, in the origin, and in the point $Q(-1, -2)$.

Solution. The reflection of P in the x-axis is the point $P_1(4, -2)$. The reflection of P in the y-axis is the point $P_2(-4, 2)$. The reflection of P with respect to the origin is $P_3(-4, -2)$. The reflection of P with respect to $Q(-1, -2)$ is $P_4(-6, -6)$.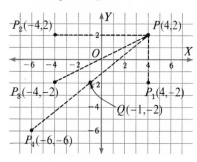

Example 3. Show that the graph of the truth set of $y = x^2 - 4x$ in $R \times R$ is symmetric with respect to the line which is the graph of $0 \, y + x = 2$.

Solution. $y = x^2 - 4x \longleftrightarrow y = x^2 - 4x + 4 - 4 \longleftrightarrow y = (x - 2)^2 - 4$.

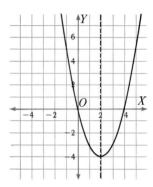

From this we see that when x is replaced by $2 + a$ we obtain the same value for y as when we replace x with $2 - a$, because $[(2 + a) - 2]^2 - 4 = [(2 - a) - 2]^2 - 4$. Thus if the graph of $(2 + a, b)$ is in the graph of $\{(x, y) \mid y = x^2 - 4\}$, then the graph of $(2 - a, b)$ is also in the graph of $\{(x, y) \mid y = x^2 - 4\}$. It is easy to show that the line which is the graph of $x = 2$ is the perpendicular bisector of the line segment joining any two points whose coordinates are $(2 + a, b)$ and $(2 - a, b)$. We know that the line segment with endpoints whose coordinates are $(2 + a, b)$ and $(2 - a, b)$ is a horizontal line, and that the coordinates of the midpoint of this line segment are $(2, b)$. Also we know that the graph of $\{(x, y) \mid x = 2\}$ is a vertical line. Thus the graph of $\{(x, y) \mid x = 2\}$ is the perpendicular bisector of any line whose endpoint coordinates are $(2 + a, b)$ and $(2 - a, b)$.

 EXERCISES

1. Make a table showing several ordered pairs belonging to the solution set of each of the following open sentences. Draw the graph of each of the ordered pairs in your table and use these as guides for estimating the location of the graph of the entire solution set.

a. $y = x^2$

b. $y = x^2 - x$

c. $y \geq 3x^2 - x$

d. $xy = 16$

e. $x(y - 1) = 2$

f. $y \geq |x|$

g. $x \leq |y|$

h. $y \leq \frac{1}{2}x^2$

i. $x = y^2$

j. $x \leq 2y^2$

k. $x = 2 \text{ or } y \geq 4$

l. $x = 2 \text{ and } y \geq -4$

2. Locate the point $A(-3, 4)$. Then give the coordinates of the reflection of A in the

a. x-axis.

b. y-axis.

c. origin.

d. point $(-1, 3)$.

e. line which is the graph of $y = -x$.

f. line which is the graph of $y = -5$.

3. Reflect each of the points of the graph of the truth set of $y = |x|$ in the x-axis.

4. Reflect each of the points of the graph of the truth set of $y = |x|$ in the origin.

5. Draw the graph of the truth set of $x > 4$. Reflect this set of points in the y-axis.

6. Test each of the following equations to see if its graph is symmetric with respect to the x-axis, the y-axis, and the origin.

a. $x^2 + y^2 = 4$ c. $x = y$

b. $xy = 6$ d. $y = (x - 3)^2$

7. Show that the graph of $y = (x - 3)^2$ is symmetric with respect to the line which is the graph of $x = 3$.

8. Show that the graph of $y = x^2 + 8x + 14$ is symmetric with respect to the graph of the truth set of $x = -4$.

9. Show that the graph of the solution set of $xy = 9$ is symmetric with respect to the graph of $\{(x, y) \mid y = x\}$.

10. Test each of following sets to see if its graph is symmetric with respect to the y-axis, the x-axis, the origin, and the graph of $\{(x, y) \mid y = x\}$. Draw the graph of each of the sets.

a. $\{(x, y) \mid y = 2 \cdot |x|\}$ e. $\{(x, y) \mid x^2 - 2x - 6 \le y\}$.

b. $\{(x, y) \mid y > x^2 - 2x\}$ f. $\{(x, y) \mid y > |x| - 3\}$

c. $\{(x, y) \mid xy = -5\}$ g. $\{(x, y) \mid 3x^2 + 2x - y = 5\}$

d. $\{(x, y) \mid 2(x - 1)^2 = y\}$ h. $\{(x, y) \mid 4x^2 - 2x - 15 < -4y\}$

Open Sentences Whose Graphs Satisfy Certain Conditions

In this section we seek the open sentence whose truth set has a graph satisfying particular geometric conditions.

Example 1.   Describe S, the set of points such that $P(x, y) \in S$ if and only if $|OP| = 1$ and the coordinates of O are $(0, 0)$.

Solution.   We can, of course, describe S as the set of points in the circle having center $O(0, 0)$ and radius 1. However, we can also give an algebraic description by using the distance formula. Since distance is non-negative, $|OP| = 1 \longleftrightarrow$
$|OP|^2 = 1 \longleftrightarrow (\sqrt{(x-0)^2 + (y-0)^2})^2$
$= 1 \longleftrightarrow x^2 + y^2 = 1$. Therefore S is the graph of $\{(x, y) \mid x^2 + y^2 = 1\}$.

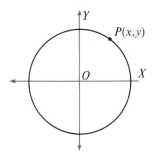

Example 2. Given $T(0, 6)$, find an open sentence whose graph is S, the set of points $P(x, y)$ each of which is twice as far from the origin as from T.

Solution. We must have $|OP| = 2|TP|$. (See the diagram at the right.) $\sqrt{(x-0)^2 + (y-0)^2} = 2\sqrt{(x-0)^2 + (y-6)^2}$ or $x^2 + y^2 = 4[x^2 + (y-6)^2] = 4x^2 + 4y^2 - 48y + 144$.

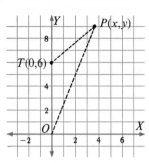

Simplifying, we obtain, $3x^2 + 3y^2 - 48y + 144 = 0$. Thus S is the graph of $\{(x, y) \mid 3x^2 + 3y^2 - 48y + 144 = 0\}$. We know that the point $C(0, 4)$ is twice as far from O as from T. Therefore $C(0, 4)$ should be in S. We find that $(0, 4)$ satisfies the equation. Even though we do not know the geometric description of S, the equation enables us to find the values of x which correspond to any given value of y. For example, if $y = 8$, $3x^2 + 192 - 384 + 144 = 0$ or $x = \pm 4$. Therefore $A(4, 8)$ and $B(-4, 8)$ are in S. Is it true that $|AO| = 2|AT|$? $|OB| = 2|BT|$?

The fact that we were able to obtain an algebraic description of S even though we are not sure about its geometric description shows the power of analytic geometry. Later we shall be able to show that S is a circle with radius 4 and center having coordinates $(0, 8)$.

Example 3. Write the equation of the line which contains the altitude $\overline{AH}$ of the triangle ABC whose vertices are $A(-4, 5)$, $B(13, 1)$, and $C(-5, 11)$.

Solution. The slope of $\overleftrightarrow{CB}$ is

$$\frac{1 - 11}{13 - (-5)} = -\frac{5}{9}.$$

Hence the slope of $\overleftrightarrow{AH}$ is $\frac{9}{5}$. Therefore $\overleftrightarrow{AH}$ is a line through $A(-4, 5)$ with slope $\frac{9}{5}$. Its equation is $y - 5 = \frac{9}{5}(x + 4)$.

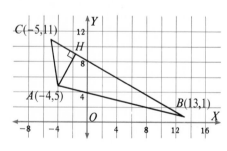

Ⓐ EXERCISES

1. Let S be the set of points $P(x, y)$ such that $|OP| = 4$. Write an equation which has S as the graph of its truth set when O is the origin.

2. Given $T(2, 3)$, find an open sentence the graph of whose truth set is the set of points $P(x, y)$ each of which is at the distance of 4 units from T.

3. Given $Q(-5, -2)$, find an open sentence whose graph is the set of points $P(x, y)$ each of which is at the distance of 2 units from Q.

4. Given $T(0, 4)$, find an equation the graph of whose truth set is the set of points $P(x, y)$ each of which is 3 times as far from the origin as from T.

5. Given $M(1, 7)$ and $N(5, 2)$, find an equation the graph of whose solution set is the set of points $P(x, y)$ equidistant from M and N.

6. Given $T(-6, 2)$ and $S(-4, 8)$, find an equation the graph of whose solution set is the set of points $P(x, y)$ each of which is half as far from T as from S.

7. Given $M_1(x_1, y_1)$ and $M_2(x_2, y_2)$, find an equation the graph of whose truth set is the set of points $P(x, y)$ equidistant from M_1 and M_2.

8. Write an equation the graph of whose solution set is the line containing the altitude CH of triangle ABC whose vertices are $A(-6, -3)$, $B(9, 3)$, and $C(3, 5)$.

9. Write an equation the graph of whose truth set is the line containing the median CM of the triangle in Ex. 8.

10. Write an equation the graph of whose truth set is the line containing the altitude BH of triangle ABC whose vertices are $A(-3, 2)$, $B(3, -3)$, and $C(6, 2)$.

11. Write an equation the graph of whose truth set is the line which is the perpendicular bisector of the line segment joining the points $A(-2, 4)$ and $B(6, -1)$.

12. Write an equation the graph of whose truth set is the line through the origin and perpendicular to the line $3x - 5y + 15 = 0$.

B **EXERCISES**

13. Write an open sentence the graph of whose truth set is the set of vertices of the right angles of the right triangles having as hypotenuse the line segment joining the points $M(-4, 0)$ and $N(0, 4)$.

14. Two vertices of a triangle are $A(-5, 0)$ and $B(3, 0)$. Write an open sentence whose graph is the set of all points $P(x, y)$ such that the area of triangle ABP is 16 square units.

15. Write the equation whose graph is the line which contains the centers of all circles tangent to the y-axis at the point $R(0, 4)$.

16. Verify that the point $B(4, 3)$ is a point of the circle which is the graph of $x^2 + y^2 = 25$. Write an equation of the line which is tangent to this circle at point B.

17. Determine the equation of the line through $A(4, -3)$ and the midpoint of the line segment between $B(1, 1)$ and $C(5, 3)$.

18. Determine the equation of the line perpendicular to the line segment between $A(-2, 4)$ and $B(6, 2)$ at its midpoint.

Using Coordinate Geometry to Prove Geometric Theorems

In the following examples we give proofs for a few well-known theorems in geometry. The reasons used in these proofs must, of course, include some theorems from geometry that we shall assume have previously been proved.

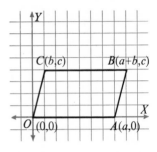

Example 1. If $A(a, 0)$, $B(a+b, c)$, $C(b, c)$ and $O(0, 0)$ are the vertices of a quadrilateral and $ac \neq 0$, prove that $OABC$ is a parallelogram.

Proof.

1. $ac \neq 0$
2. Slope $\overleftrightarrow{OA} = 0$, and slope $\overleftrightarrow{CB} = 0$
3. $\overleftrightarrow{OA}$ and $\overleftrightarrow{CB}$ are nonvertical lines

4. The y-intercept of $\overleftrightarrow{OA}$ is 0. The y-intercept of $\overleftrightarrow{CB}$ is c.
5. $\overleftrightarrow{OA} \parallel \overleftrightarrow{CB}$

6. $|CB| = |(a+b) - b| = a$
   $|OA| = |a - 0| = a$
7. $|CB| = |OA|$

8. $\therefore OABC$ is a parallelogram

1. Given
2. Definition of slope of line
3. Because none of the points that determine the lines have the same abscissa

4. Definition of y-intercept

5. Two nonvertical lines are parallel if and only if they have equal slopes and unequal y-intercepts.
6. Definition of the measure of a line segment
7. Transitive property of equality
8. Why?

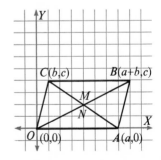

Example 2. Prove that the diagonals of the parallelogram in Example 1 bisect each other.

Proof.

1. The coordinates of M, the midpoint of $\overline{OB}$, are $\left(\dfrac{a+b}{2}, \dfrac{c}{2}\right)$ and the coordinates of N, the midpoint of $\overline{CA}$, are $\left(\dfrac{a+b}{2}, \dfrac{c}{2}\right)$.	1. The midpoint formula (Th. 1-5)
2. $M = N$	2. Why?
3. $\overleftrightarrow{BO}$ and $\overleftrightarrow{AC}$ are distinct lines	3. Why?
4. $\overline{BO}$ and $\overline{AC}$ bisect each other	4. If two distinct line segments have the same midpoint, then they bisect each other.

Is the proof above sufficient to show that the diagonals of any parallelogram bisect each other? This question requires careful consideration. The answer is yes, since we can always choose the coordinate system so that a vertex of the parallelogram is the origin and the x-axis contains one side. Moreover, there is nothing special about the parallelogram we have described.

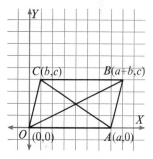

Example 3. Prove that a parallelogram with equal diagonals is a rectangle.

Proof. We use the same parallelogram we described in Example 1.

1. $|AC| = |OB|$	1. Given
2. $\sqrt{(b-a)^2 + c^2} = \sqrt{(b+a)^2 + c^2}$	2. Distance formula and substitution property of equality
3. $(b-a)^2 + c^2 = (b+a)^2 + c^2$	3. Why?
4. $b^2 - 2ab + a^2 + c^2 = b^2 + 2ab + a^2 + c^2$	4. Why?
5. $4ab = 0$	5. Why?
6. $a \neq 0$	6. Why?
7. $b = 0$	7. Why?
8. $C \in y$-axis	8. Why?
9. $\overline{OC} \perp \overline{OA}$	9. Why?
10. $OABC$ is a rectangle	10. If two sides of a parallelogram are perpendicular to each other, the parallelogram is a rectangle.

Example 4. Find the equation of L, the perpendicular bisector of $\overline{P_1P_2}$, if the coordinates of P_1 and P_2 are (x_1, y_1) and (x_2, y_2), respectively.

Solution.

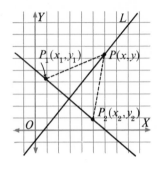

$[P(x, y) \in L$ *and* L is the perpendicular bisector of $\overline{P_1P_2}] \longleftrightarrow |PP_1| = |PP_2| \longleftrightarrow \sqrt{(x - x_1)^2 + (y - y_1)^2} = \sqrt{(x - x_2)^2 + (y - y_2)^2} \longleftrightarrow (x - x_1)^2 + (y - y_1)^2 = (x - x_2)^2 + (y - y_2)^2 \longleftrightarrow (2x_2 - 2x_1)x + (2y_2 - 2y_1)y + x_1^2 - x_2^2 + y_1^2 - y_2^2 = 0$

Thus the equation of L is

$(2x_2 - 2x_1)x + (2y_2 - 2y_1)y + x_1^2 - x_2^2 + y_1^2 - y_2^2 = 0.$

Example 5. Prove that the perpendicular bisectors of two sides of any triangle will intersect.

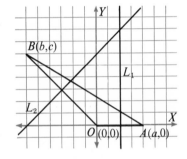

Proof.

1. Let the triangle be OAB with vertices $A(a, 0)$, $B(b, c)$, and $O(0, 0)$ and let L_1 be the perpendicular bisector of $\overline{OA}$ and L_2 be the perpendicular bisector of $\overline{OB}$.

1. Given

2. L_1 is the graph of $\left\{(x, y) \mid x = \dfrac{a}{2}\right\}$.

L_2 is the graph of $\{(x, y) \mid 2bx + 2cy = c^2 + b^2\}$

2. These defining equations were obtained using methods of Ex. 4.

3. $c \neq 0$

3. If $c = 0$, then B would be in x-axis and OAB is not a triangle.

4. 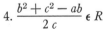 $\dfrac{b^2 + c^2 - ab}{2c} \in R$

4. Why?

5. Let P have the coordinates $\left(\dfrac{a}{2}, \dfrac{b^2 + c^2 - ab}{2c}\right)$. Then

$P \in L_1$ and $P \in L_2$

5. If the coordinates of a point satisfy the equation of a line, the point is in the line.

6. L_1 and L_2 intersect

6. Two lines that have a point in common intersect.

Note that the coordinates of P in step 5 were obtained by solving the system of equations from step 2. Note also that $L_1 \neq L_2$ because $\left(\dfrac{a}{2}, 0\right) \in L_1$ and $\left(\dfrac{a}{2}, 0\right) \notin L_2$.

Example 6. Let $O(x_1, y_1)$, $B(x_2, y_2)$, and $C(x_3, y_3)$ be the vertices of a triangle. Let L_1, L_2, and L_3 be the perpendicular bisectors of $\overline{OB}$, $\overline{BC}$, and $\overline{CO}$ respectively. Prove that L_1, L_2, and L_3 are *concurrent* (pass through a point).

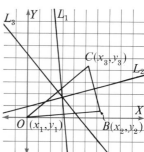

Proof.

1. L_1 is the graph of
$$\{(x, y) \mid (2\,x_2 - 2\,x_1)x + (2\,y_2 - 2\,y_1)y + x_1{}^2 - x_2{}^2 + y_1{}^2 - y_2{}^2 = 0\}$$
L_2 is the graph of
$$\{(x, y) \mid (2\,x_3 - 2\,x_2)x + (2\,y_3 - 2\,y_2)y + x_2{}^2 - x_3{}^2 + y_2{}^2 - y_3{}^2 = 0\}$$
L_3 is the graph of
$$\{(x, y) \mid (2\,x_1 - 2\,x_3)x + (2\,y_1 - 2\,y_3)y + x_3{}^2 - x_1{}^2 + y_3{}^2 - y_1{}^2 = 0\}$$

2. Let $a_1 = 2\,x_2 - 2\,x_1$, $b_1 = 2\,y_2 - 2\,y_1$, $c_1 = x_1{}^2 - x_2{}^2 + y_1{}^2 - y_2{}^2$,
$a_2 = 2\,x_3 - 2\,x_2$, $b_2 = 2\,y_3 - 2\,y_2$, $c_2 = x_2{}^2 - x_3{}^2 + y_2{}^2 - y_3{}^2$,
$a_3 = 2\,x_1 - 2\,x_3$, $b_3 = 2\,y_1 - 2\,y_3$, $c_3 = x_3{}^2 - x_1{}^2 + y_3{}^2 - y_1{}^2$
Then the equations of L_1, L_2, and L_3 are respectively:
$$a_1 x + b_1 y + c_1 = 0$$
$$a_2 x + b_2 y + c_2 = 0$$
$$a_3 x + b_3 y + c_3 = 0$$

3. $a_2 = -(a_1 + a_3)$, $b_2 = -(b_1 + b_3)$, and $c_2 = -(c_1 + c_3)$
Hence the equation of L_2 can be written
$(a_1 + a_3)x + (b_1 + b_3)y + (c_1 + c_3) = 0$, or
$(a_1 x + b_1 y + c_1) + (a_3 x + b_3 y + c_3) = 0$

4. L_1 and L_3 intersect in a point $P(i, j)$

5. $a_1 i + b_1 j + c_1 = 0$
$a_3 i + b_3 j + c_3 = 0$

6. $(a_1 + a_3)i + (b_1 + b_3)j + c_1 + c_3 = 0$

7. $P(i, j) \in L_2$

8. $\therefore$ L_1, L_2, and L_3 are concurrent.

Reasons: 1. Example 4, page 260; 2. Why? 3. Steps 1, 2, the substitution property of equality, and the distributive and commutative properties; 4. Example 5, page 260; 5. Why? 6. Addition property of equality; 7. Why? 8. Definition of concurrent

Prove each of the following theorems using the methods of coordinate geometry.

1. The median of a trapezoid is parallel to the base. (The median joins the midpoints of the nonparallel sides.)

2. The line segment joining the midpoints of two sides of a triangle is parallel to the third side of the triangle and its measure is equal to half of the measure of the third side.

3. The perpendicular bisectors of the sides of a square are concurrent.

4. The altitudes of a triangle are concurrent. (Prove for a scalene triangle only.)

5. The diagonals of a rhombus are perpendicular to each other.

6. If the diagonals of a parallelogram are perpendicular to each other, the parallelogram is a rhombus.

7. The lines joining the midpoints of the sides of a quadrilateral in order form a parallelogram.

8. In triangle ABC, M is the midpoint of $\overline{AB}$, N is the midpoint of $\overline{BC}$, $\overline{MR}$ is perpendicular to $\overline{AC}$ and $\overline{NS}$ is perpendicular to $\overline{AC}$. Prove that $|MR| = |NS|$.

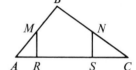

9. If the diagonals of a quadrilateral bisect each other, the quadrilateral is a parallelogram.

10. $ABCD$ is a parallelogram having M the midpoint of AB and N the midpoint of DC. Prove that $AMCN$ is a parallelogram.

11. The sum of the squares of the measures of the diagonals of a rhombus is equal to four times the square of the measure of a side.

12. The line segment joining the vertex opposite the base in an isosceles triangle to the midpoint of the base is perpendicular to the base.

ESSENTIALS

Before you leave this chapter make sure that you

1. Know that if a point is in the graph of the solution set of an open sentence s_x, then the coordinate of the point is an element of the solution set of the sentence, and that if a number is in the solution set of an open sentence s_x, then the graph of the number is in the graph of the solution set of the sentence. (Page 204.)

2. Can draw a representation of a coordinate plane and understand how to set up a one-to-one correspondence between the points of the plane and the elements of a particular Cartesian product such as $R \times R$. (Pages 205–207.)

3. Know and can use the symbolism for representing lines, line segments, rays, measures of line segments, and directed measures. (Pages 206, 212, 217).

4. Can draw the graph of the truth set of an open sentence $s_{(x,y)}$. (Page 208.)

5. Know that if a point is in the graph of the solution set of an open sentence $s_{(x,y)}$, the coordinates of the point form an ordered pair belonging to the solution set of the sentence, and if an ordered pair of numbers belongs to the solution set of an open sentence $s_{(x,y)}$, the graph of the ordered pair is in the graph of the solution set of the sentence. (Page 210.)

6. Understand that the measure of the line segment between two points is always a non-negative number, can derive the formula for finding this measure, and can use the formula. (Pages 212–215.)

7. Understand the formula for finding the coordinates of the midpoint of a line segment and can use the formula. (Pages 215–216.)

8. Know what we mean by "directed measure." (Pages 217–218.)

9. Can recognize a linear equation, know that the graph of the truth set of a linear equation is a straight line, and can draw such graphs. (Pages 219–221.)

10. Can determine whether a line is vertical or nonvertical. (Page 223.)

11. Can find the slope of a nonvertical line when the coordinates of two points in the line are known. (Page 224.)

12. Understand and can use the slope-intercept form of an equation. (Page 226.)

13. Understand and can use the two-point form of an equation. (Page 227.)

14. Know what a determinant is, can expand a determinant, and understand the basic properties of determinants which are discussed in this chapter. (Pages 228–230.)

15. Understand and can use the point-slope form of an equation. (Page 231.)

16. Understand and can use the parametric form of the equation of a line. (Pages 237–239.)

17. Can solve a system of two equations having two variables by the multiplication and addition method and by the substitution method. (Pages 240–243.)

18. Can by inspection, determine when the graphs of two linear equations will be parallel lines and can determine equations whose graphs will be parallel lines. (Pages 244–245.)

19. Can, by inspection, determine when the graphs of two linear equations will be perpendicular lines and can determine equations whose graphs will be perpendicular lines. (Pages 246–249.)

20. Can use the idea of symmetry as a guide in sketching graphs. (Page 251.)

21. Can write open sentences which satisfy certain criteria as shown in this chapter. (Pages 255–256.)

22. Can use coordinate geometry to prove theorems commonly proved in courses in synthetic geometry. (Pages 258–261.)

23. Can spell and use correctly the following words:

abscissa (Page 206.)	ordinate (Page 206.)
collinear (Page 232.)	parameter (Page 238.)
concurrent lines (Page 261.)	parallel (Page 244.)
coordinate (Page 206.)	parametric equations (Page 238.)
determinant (Page 229.)	perpendicular (Page 246.)
hypotenuse (Page 213.)	quadrant (Page 207.)
initial point (Page 217.)	symmetric (Page 251.)
intercept (Page 220.)	terminal point (Page 217.)
linear equation (Page 219.)	vertical (Page 223.)

CHAPTER REVIEW

1. Complete each of the following to form a true statement.

a. If x is a member of the solution set of the open statement s_x, then the graph of x is in _?_.

b. If P is a point in the graph of the truth set of the open statement s_x, then the coordinate of P is _?_.

c. If (x, y) is an ordered pair of numbers in the solution set of the open statement $s_{(x, y)}$, then the graph of (x, y) is in _?_.

d. If P is a point in the graph of the truth set of the open statement $s_{(x, y)}$, then the coordinates of P are _?_.

2. What do we mean when we say that there is a one-to-one correspondence between the points of a coordinate plane and the elements of $R \times R$, the set of ordered pairs of real numbers?

3. In which quadrant does the graph of each of the following ordered pairs of numbers lie?

a. $(-4, -3)$ **b.** $(6, -1)$ **c.** $(-4, 3)$ **d.** $(5, 2)$

4. What is the meaning of the symbol $P(-3, 2)$?

5. Which of the following pairs of points determine vertical lines and which determine nonvertical lines?

  a. $A(-5, 2)$, $B(-5, 3)$ c. $E(5, 3)$, $F(5, 7)$

  b. $C(-6, -1)$, $D(9, -1)$ d. $G(4, 1)$, $H(1, 4)$

6. Show the graph of the truth set of each of the following open sentences:

  a. $x < -2 \wedge y > 3$ d. $x \geq -5 \wedge y \geq 0$

  b. $x \leq -y$ e. $x = |y|$

  c. $x \leq y \wedge x < -y$ f. $y > 3 \wedge y < x$

7. Draw the graph of each of the following:

  a. $\{(x, y) \mid x = -4\}$ b. $\{(x, y) \mid x + 0\, y = -4\}$

8. Find the measure of the line segment between the two points in each of the following pairs.

  a. $P(0, 0)$, $Q(-5, -6)$ c. $M(-6, -2)$, $N(7, 1)$

  b. $R(4, -1)$, $S(5, 3)$ d. $T(4, -3)$, $S(1, -3)$

9. Which of the triangles determined by the points named below are right triangles?

  a. $A(2, 2)$, $B(5, 2)$, $C(5, -4)$ c. $G(4, -3)$, $H(8, 4)$, $J(-3, 0)$

  b. $D(-1, -1)$, $E(7, 2)$, $F(5, 5)$ d. $K(3, -9)$, $L(3, 0)$, $M(-3, -5)$

10. State the coordinates of the midpoint of the line segment joining the two points of each of the following pairs.

  a. $A(6, 1)$, $B(3, -5)$ c. $E(-5, -4)$, $F(-1, 8)$

  b. $C(2, 0)$, $D(0, 2)$ d. $G(0, 0)$, $H(9, 9)$

11. If the two symbols in each of the following pairs name the same thing, write $=$ between them. If they name different things, explain the way in which they differ.

  a. $\overleftrightarrow{PQ}$, $\overline{PQ}$ b. $\overline{PQ}$, $\overline{QP}$ c. PQ, QP d. $|PQ|$, $|QP|$

12. Which of the following equations are linear?

  a. $x = y$ c. $4\, x^2 + 2\, y = 8$ e. $\dfrac{3}{x} + 4 = \dfrac{2}{y}$

  b. $3\, x + 0\, y = 7$ d. $7\, x + 4\, y - 3 = 0$ f. $x^2 + y^2 = 1$

13. Draw the graph of the solution set for each of the following equations.

  a. $4\, x + 6\, y = 5$ c. $2\, x = -10$

  b. $y = \frac{2}{3} x - 1$ d. $4(x + 2\, y) - \dfrac{2\, x + y}{5} = 27$

14. Which of the following open sentences have truth sets whose graphs are lines, which have truth sets whose graphs are line segments, and which have truth sets whose graphs are neither lines nor line segments?

    a. $3x + 4y = 12 \land 1 \geq x \geq -3$ **c.** $x = 4$ and $y = 2$

    b. $4x + 7y - 6 = 0$ **d.** $5x + 4y \geq 2$

15. Using the intercept method, draw the graph of $4x - 3y = 24$.

16. Complete:

    a. The abscissas of all points on a vertical line are _?_.

    b. The ordinates of all points on a horizontal line are _?_.

    c. The slope of a horizontal line is _?_.

    d. The slope of a vertical line is _?_.

17. Write an equation whose graph is a line with slope -2 and y-intercept $\frac{7}{3}$.

18. What is the slope of the line which is the graph of the truth set of each of the following equations?

    a. $\frac{1}{3}x - \frac{1}{4}y = 6$ **c.** $\frac{2}{3}x + \frac{2}{3}y - 5 = 0$

    b. $7x + 5y = 18$ **d.** $y = -4$

19. State the y-intercept of each of the lines described in Ex. 18.

20. What is the value of each of the following determinants?

    a. $\begin{vmatrix} a & c \\ b & d \end{vmatrix}$ **b.** $\begin{vmatrix} 4 & -2 \\ 2 & 1 \end{vmatrix}$ **c.** $\begin{vmatrix} 3 & 5 & 1 \\ 4 & 1 & 0 \\ 5 & 2 & -1 \end{vmatrix}$ **d.** $\begin{vmatrix} 2 & 4 & 2 \\ 1 & 5 & 1 \\ 3 & -7 & 3 \end{vmatrix}$

21. Write the following equation in $ax + by + c = 0$ form: $\begin{vmatrix} x & y & 1 \\ r & m & 1 \\ s & n & 1 \end{vmatrix} = 0$

22. What can you say of the points (r_1, s_1), (r_2, s_2), and (r_3, s_3) if it is true that $\begin{vmatrix} r_1 & s_1 & 1 \\ r_2 & s_2 & 1 \\ r_3 & s_3 & 1 \end{vmatrix} = 0$?

23. Show that the points $A(-2, -10)$, $B(2, 0)$, and $C(4, 5)$ are collinear.

24. Write an equation whose graph is the line through the point $M(-6, 1)$ and having its slope $\frac{3}{4}$.

25. The equation $y = m(x - 3) + 5$ has a truth set whose graph is a straight line. Determine m so that the point $P(-2, 3)$ is in the line.

26. If P_1 and P_2 have the coordinates $(4, 1)$ and $(-5, -3)$, respectively, find the coordinates of P in $\overline{P_1P_2}$ such that $|P_1P| = \frac{1}{3}|P_1P_2|$.

27. Solve each of the following systems of equations.

a. $\begin{cases} 2x + 3y = 7 \\ x - 2y = -14 \end{cases}$

c. $\begin{cases} \dfrac{x-y}{2} - \dfrac{10(x-1)}{3} = -2 - y \\ 16x - y = 76 \end{cases}$

b. $\begin{cases} 4x - 5y = 6 \\ 3x + 2y = 1 \end{cases}$

d. $\begin{cases} \dfrac{1}{x} + \dfrac{3}{y} = \dfrac{3}{2} \\ \dfrac{5}{x} + \dfrac{2}{y} = \dfrac{19}{6} \end{cases}$

28. In which of the following pairs of equations will the truth sets have graphs that are parallel lines? Make your decision by inspection.

a. $3x + 4y = -11$
   $3x + 4y = 1$

c. $2x + 6y = 8$
   $x + 3y = 4$

b. $y = -\frac{5}{6}x + 2$
   $y = \frac{5}{6}x - 2$

d. $8x = 16$
   $x + 0y = 4$

29. Write an equation whose graph is a straight line which has the y-intercept 2 and is parallel to the line which is the graph of $\{(x, y) \mid y = -6x + 7\}$.

30. Write an equation whose graph is a straight line which has the y-intercept -3 and is perpendicular to the line which is the graph of the truth set of $y = -\frac{1}{6}x + 5$.

31. If L is the graph of $2x - 3y = 9$, what is the measure of the line segment from the origin perpendicular to L?

32. Test for symmetry and sketch the graph of the truth set of each of the following open sentences.

a. $y \geq x^2 - 5x$

c. $x^2 - x - 5 \leq y$

b. $xy = 4$

d. $x(y - 1) = -4 - x$

33. Write a sentence the graph of whose truth set is S, the set of points $P(x, y)$,

a. each of which is 2 units from the line that is the graph of the truth set of $x = 3$.

b. each of which is in the altitude $\overline{AH}$ of triangle ABC whose vertices are $A(3, 5)$, $B(-2, 3)$, and $C(14, 0)$.

c. each of which is in the perpendicular bisector of the line segment joining the points $A(-4, 1)$ and $B(1, 2)$.

34. Prove:

a. The line segments joining the midpoints of the sides of a square taken in order form a square.

b. The line segments joining the midpoints of the opposite sides of a quadrilateral bisect each other.

1. Draw the graph of the truth set of $xy < 0$.

2. Draw the graph of the truth set of $y = |x| + 3$.

3. Find the measure of the line segment between the points $P_1(-5, -2)$ and $P_2(8, 3)$.

4. State the coordinates of the midpoint of the line segment joining the points P_1 and P_2 of Ex. 3.

5. What is the slope of the line segment P_1P_2 of Ex. 3?

6. Draw the graph of the equation $4y = 3x - 5$.

7. State the y-intercept and the x-intercept of the line which is the graph of the equation $2x + 3y + 18 = 0$.

8. Find the value of the determinant: $\begin{vmatrix} 3 & -1 & 1 \\ 2 & 0 & -1 \\ 1 & 4 & 0 \end{vmatrix}$

9. Write an equation for the line through the point $(-5, 2)$ and having the slope $-\frac{1}{2}$.

10. Solve the system of equations: $\begin{cases} \frac{3}{2}x + 3y = \frac{17}{2} \\ \frac{7}{17}x + \frac{3}{17}y = 2 \end{cases}$

11. Write an equation of the line determined by the points $P_1(7, -1)$ and $P_2(-4, 5)$.

12. Write an equation whose graph will contain the point $A(-3, 2)$ and be perpendicular to the graph of $3x + 5y = 23$.

13. What will be the slope of all lines parallel to the line which is the graph of $y = -\frac{2}{3}x$?

14. Test for symmetry and sketch the graph of the truth set of $x = y^2 - 4y$.

15. Write an equation whose graph is the pespendicular bisector of the line segment joining the points $A(1, 4)$ and $B(8, 0)$.

Functions and Other Relations

More about Relations

Since a function is a special kind of relation, we review our definition of a relation before we define a function. You recall that if A and B are any nonempty sets, then every nonempty subset of $A \times B$ is a relation in $A \times B$. A *relation* is, therefore, a set of ordered pairs. The set of first members of these ordered pairs is called the *domain of the relation* and the set of second members is called the *range of the relation*. For a relation M, we denote the domain by D_M and the range by R_M. Clearly $D_M \subseteq A$ and $R_M \subseteq B$.

We define a relation M when we indicate which ordered pairs belong to it and which do not. We may indicate membership in a relation by

(1) Listing its ordered pairs. For example:

$M = \{(-6, -3), (-6, 3), (-4, -2), (-4, 2), (-2, -1), (-2, 1), (0, 0), (2, -1), (2, 1), (4, -2), (4, 2), (6, -3), (6, 3)\}$. (We see that $D_M = \{-6, -4, -2, 0, 2, 4, 6\}$ and $R_M = \{-3, -2, -1, 0, 1, 2, 3\}$.)

(2) Exhibiting its ordered pairs in a table in which the entries in the top row indicate the first member of each ordered pair and the entries in the lower row indicate the corresponding second members. For example:

First members	-6	-6	-4	-4	-2	-2	0	2	2	4	4	6	6
Second members	-3	3	-2	2	-1	1	0	-1	1	-2	2	-3	3

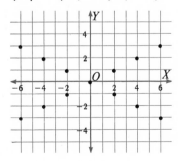

(3) Graphing each of its ordered pairs. For example, the graph of M is shown in the diagram at the right.

(4) Using the set-builder notation. For example: $M = \{(x, y) \mid |y| = \frac{1}{2}|x|; \ x \epsilon D_M\}$. We see that the relation M is a relation in $I \times I$ or, of course, in any Cartesian product of which $I \times I$ is a subset.

When an open statement $s_{(x,y)}$ is used with set-builder notation to indicate membership in a relation M and the domain and range of the relation are not specified, it will be assumed that the domain of M contains all members of R for which the sentence $s_{(x,y)}$ is meaningful. It will also be assumed that the range of M contains the corresponding members of R, that is, all members y such that (x, y) is a solution of $s_{(x,y)}$ when $x \epsilon D_M$.

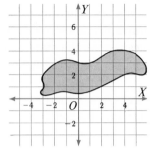

Although some relations are readily defined as the truth sets of open sentences in two variables, others are not. The relation whose membership is indicated by the graph at the right is certainly not readily defined by an open sentence.

Example 1. Find D_M and R_M of the relation $M = \{(x, y) \mid y > x^2\}$.

Solution. Since no Cartesian product is specified, M is assumed to be a relation in $R \times R$. Hence the domain of M is the set of all real numbers for which the sentence $y > x^2$ is meaningful. Thus the domain of M is R. The range of M is the set of all real numbers y such that (x, y) is a solution of $y > x^2$ when $x \epsilon R$. Hence the range is the set of all positive real numbers. The graph of M is shown at the right.

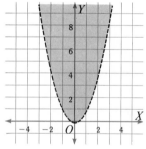

Example 2. Given $M = \{(x, y) \mid |y| \leq \sqrt{16 - x}\}$. Find D_M and R_M.

Solution. The sentence $|y| \leq \sqrt{16 - x}$ is meaningful for all real values of x that are less than or equal to 16. Therefore $D_M = \{x \mid x \leq 16\}$. When $x = 0$, then $|y| \leq \sqrt{16}$ or $|y| \leq 4$. Hence $-4 \leq y \leq 4$. Thus $\{(x, y) \mid x = 0 \wedge -4 \leq y \leq 4\}$ is a subset of M. Its graph is the segment AB in the graph of M shown at the right. Since $\sqrt{16 - x}$ increases without bound as x decreases, we see that y may have any real value. Hence the range of M is R.

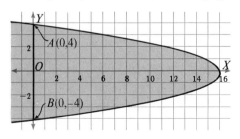

Is the graph of M symmetric with respect to the x-axis? What must be true of a statement $s_{(x,y)}$ which indicates membership in a relation in order that the graph of the relation will be symmetric with respect to the x-axis?

We say that the graph of a relation A is symmetric with respect to the graph of $\{(x, y) \mid y = x\}$ if it is true that $(a, b) \in A \longrightarrow (b, a) \in A$. This means that the statement $s_{(x,y)}$ which indicates membership in A must be such that interchanging x and y in it produces a statement equivalent to $s_{(x,y)}$; that is, $s_{(x,y)} \longleftrightarrow s_{(y,x)}$. In the following list, the graphs of the first three are symmetric with respect to the graph of $\{(x, y) \mid y = x\}$ while the graph of the last is not.

$$\{(x, y) \mid x + y = 5\}$$
$$\{(x, y) \mid x^2 + y^2 = 25\}$$
$$\{(x, y) \mid xy = 12\}$$
$$\{(x, y) \mid 2x + y = 6\}$$

A EXERCISES

1. Given the relation $\{(-2, 1), (-1, -2), (3, 3), (6, 2), (6, 4)\}$:

   a. Make a table which indicates membership in this relation.

   b. Make a graph which indicates membership in this relation.

2. Make a table which indicates membership in the relation defined by the graph at the right.

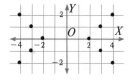

3. Make a graph which indicates membership in $\{(x, y) \mid y = x^2 - 3\}$.

4. Make a graph which indicates membership in $\{(x, y) \mid y \geq 2 \wedge x \leq -1\}$.

5. Let M be a relation in $A \times B$ when $A = \{1, 2, 3\}$ and $B = \{-3, -2, -1, 0, 1, 2, 3\}$. If the sentence $y = \dfrac{1}{x-2} \wedge x \in A$ indicates membership in M, what are the domain and range of M?

6. Let M be a relation in $A \times B$ when $A = \{1, 2, 3\}$ and $B = \{1, 2, 3, 4\}$. If the sentence $y = \dfrac{1}{x-2} \wedge x \in A$ indicates membership in M, what are the domain and range of M?

7. Let S be a relation in $A \times A$ when $A = \{1, 2, 3, \cdots, 10\}$. If the sentence $y = \sqrt{x-4}$ indicates membership in S, what are the domain and range of S?

8. Let S be a relation in $R \times R$. If the sentence $y = \sqrt{x-4}$ indicates membership in S, what are the domain and range of S?

9. Find the domain and range of the relation $M = \{(x, y) \mid y = x^2\}$ when
   a. M is a subset of $C \times C$.
   b. M is a subset of $I \times I$.
   c. M is a subset of $R \times R$.

10. Find the domain and range of the relation $\{(x, y) \mid xy = 0\}$ in
    a. $I \times I$ **b.** $R \times R$

11. Find the domain and range of the relation $\{(x, y) \mid xy = 4\}$ in
    a. $I \times I$ **b.** $R \times R$

12. If each of the following is a relation in $R \times R$, make a graph of the relation and state its domain and range.
    a. $\{(x, y) \mid y = -\frac{1}{2} x^2\}$
    b. $\{(x, y) \mid (x - y)(x + y) = 0\}$
    c. $\{(x, y) \mid (y - 3)(y - x^2) = 0\}$
    d. $\{(x, y) \mid y - 3 = 0 \wedge y - x^2 = 0\}$
    e. $\{(x, y) \mid y = x^2 + 6x + 5\}$
    f. $\{(x, y) \mid y = \sqrt{x}\}$
    g. $\left\{(x, y) \mid y = \dfrac{1}{|x - 5|}\right\}$
    h. $\left\{(x, y) \mid y = \dfrac{1}{x + 2}\right\}$
    i. $\{(x, y) \mid \sqrt{x - y} = 3\}$
    j. $\left\{(x, y) \mid \dfrac{3}{\sqrt{x - y}} = 1\right\}$

13. Sketch the graph of each of the following relations.
    a. $\{(x, y) \mid y > |x| - 5 \wedge y < -|x| + 5\}$
    b. $\{(x, y) \mid y < 2x - 3 \wedge y > 0 \wedge x = 3\}$
    c. $\{(x, y) \mid y \le 3x + 2 \wedge 2x + y \le 12 \wedge 8y + 5x \le 16\}$
    d. $\{(x, y) \mid x + 2y + 6 \ge 0 \wedge y \ge 3x - 13 \wedge 2x + 5y \le 20 \wedge 10x + 3y + 32 \ge 0\}$
    e. $\{(x, y) \mid y < 2x + 3 \wedge y > 5x - 3 \wedge y \ge 0 \wedge x \ge 0\}$

14. Which of the following relations have graphs which are symmetric with respect to the graph of $\{(x, y) \mid y = x\}$?
    a. $\{(x, y) \mid xy = -12\}$ **d.** $\{(x, y) \mid x - y = 7\}$
    b. $\{(x, y) \mid x + y = -8\}$ **e.** $\{(x, y) \mid x - y^2 = 0\}$
    c. $\{(x, y) \mid 3x + y = 7\}$ **f.** $\left\{(x, y) \mid y = \dfrac{1}{x}\right\}$

15. Compare the domains and ranges of the two relations $\{(x, y) \mid x + 2 = y\}$ and $\left\{(x, y) \mid \dfrac{x^2 - 4}{x - 2} = y\right\}$.

16. Suppose that $S = \{(x, y) \mid s_{(x,y)}\}$ and $T = \{(x, y) \mid t_{(x,y)}\}$.
    a. If $s_{(x,y)} \longleftrightarrow t_{(x,y)}$, what is true of S and T? Explain.
    b. If $S = T$, what is true of $s_{(x,y)}$ and $t_{(x,y)}$? Explain.

Functions

We now define a function.

> If A and B are any nonempty sets, then a *function* in A X B is a relation in A X B in which each member of the domain is paired with one and only one member of the range. Thus a function is a set of ordered pairs no two of which have the same first element.

The relation $K = \{(-3, 7), (-2, 5), (-1, 4), (0, 4), (1, 5), (2, 8), (3, 13), (4, 20)\}$ is a function whose domain D_K is $\{-3, -2, -1, 0, 1, 2, 3, 4\}$ and whose range R_K is $\{7, 5, 4, 8, 13, 20\}$. Any member of the domain of a function is called an *argument* of the function and the corresponding member of the range is called the *value* of the function *at* that argument. In the function K, 7 is the value of K at -3, 5 is the value of K at -2, 4 is the value of K at -1, and so on.

Let F be a function in $A \times B$ whose domain is D_F and whose range is R_F. Then D_F is the set of first members of the set of ordered pairs in F and R_F is the set of second members of these ordered pairs. Clearly $D_F \subseteq A$ and $R_F \subseteq B$.

Suppose we know that a certain number a is in the domain of F; then according to our definition there is exactly one number b in the range of F such that $(a, b) \in F$.

> Thus $a \in D_F$ implies that there is a unique number b such that $b \in R_F$ and $(a, b) \in F$. $([(a, b) \in F \wedge (a, b') \in F] \longrightarrow b = b')$

Suppose we know that a certain number b is in the range of F. Now according to our definition, the range of F contains only those numbers which are second members of ordered pairs whose first members are in the domain of F. Therefore there must be at least one a in the domain of F such that $(a, b) \in F$.

> Thus $b \in R_F$ implies that there is at least one number a such that $a \in D_F$ and $(a, b) \in F$.

Interpreted geometrically, our definition of a function means that if a is a member of the domain of F, that is, if a is an argument of the function F, then there is one and only one point in the graph of F which has a for its abscissa.

> This means that a set of points G in the coordinate plane is the graph of a function if and only if any vertical line intersects G in at most one point.

From the foregoing remarks and our definition of a function it should be clear that $N = \{(x, y) \mid y = x^3\}$ is a function, and $M = \{(x, y) \mid x = |y|\}$ is not a function. The graphs of these sets are shown in the diagrams at the right. We see that *any vertical line* will intersect the graph of N in exactly one point and that any vertical line through $P(a, 0)$ will intersect the graph of M in two points provided $a > 0$.

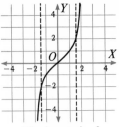

N is the graph of $\{(x, y) \mid y = x^3\}$

The graph G shown in the diagram below defines a function F whose domain and range are respectively $\{x \mid -5 \leq x \leq 16\}$ and $\{y \mid 3.5 \leq y \leq 11\}$. The graph G is a curve that seems to have been drawn without much of a plan. However, it does have the property that any vertical line intersects it in at most one point. Moreover, the approximate values of the ordered pairs which belong to F can be read from this graph. For example, we know that $(5, 3.5)$ and $(9, 8.3)$ are in F. Therefore G determines a function, namely, the function F, the set of ordered pairs whose graphs are in G. It would certainly be very difficult for us to write an equation for G. For many hundreds of years some mathematicians would not accept the idea that an arbitrary curve, such as G, could define a function.

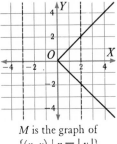

M is the graph of $\{(x, y) \mid x = |y|\}$

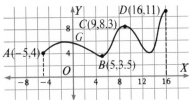

They insisted that there must be an equation involved in the definition of a function. This controversy was finally resolved by the French mathematician Fourier who showed that any arbitrary curve can be approximated as closely as we please by the graphs of increasingly complicated equations.

A glance at the eight graphs shown below should indicate that A_1, A_3, A_5, and A_7 are functions while A_2, A_4, A_6, and A_8 are not.

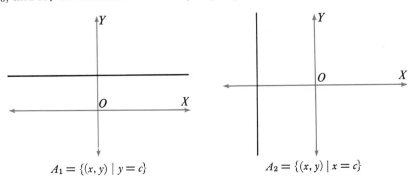

$A_1 = \{(x, y) \mid y = c\}$

$A_2 = \{(x, y) \mid x = c\}$

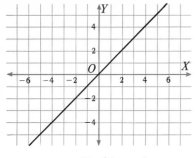

$A_3 = \{(x, y) \mid y = x\}$

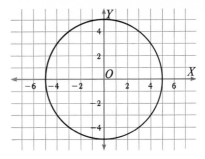

$A_4 = \{(x, y) \mid x^2 + y^2 = 25\}$

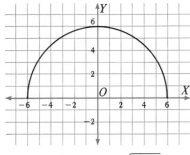

$A_5 = \{(x, y) \mid y = \sqrt{36 - x^2}\}$

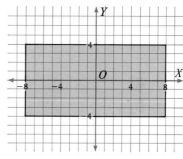

$A_6 = \{(x, y) \mid |x| \leq 8 \wedge |y| \leq 4\}$

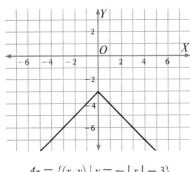

$A_7 = \{(x, y) \mid y = -|x| - 3\}$

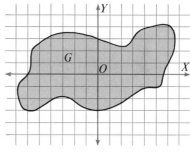

$A_8 = \{(x, y) \mid (x, y) \in G\}$

The functions A_1 and A_3 whose graphs are shown above are particularly important. A_1 is called a *constant function* and A_3 is called the *identity function*. Do you see the reasons for these names? Note that the domain of the constant function is the set of real numbers and its range is a constant. Also note that the set of real numbers is the domain and the range of the identity function.

1. Which of the following relations are functions?

    a. $\{(-3, -5), (-2, -3), (-1, -1), (0, 1), (1, 3), (2, 5), (3, 7)\}$

    b. $\{(9, -3), (4, -2), (1, -1), (0, 0), (1, 1), (4, 2), (9, 3)\}$

    c. $\{(-3, -13), (-2, -9), (-1, -5), (0, -1), (1, 3), (2, 7), (3, 11)\}$

    d. $\{(1, 1), (2, 4), (3, 9), (4, 16)\}$

2. Which of the following graphs define functions?

a.
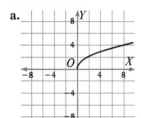

d.
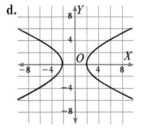

g.
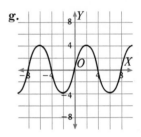

b.
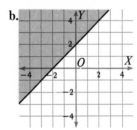

e.
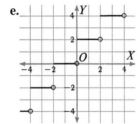

h.
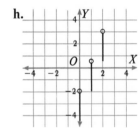

c.
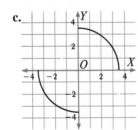

f.
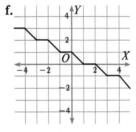

i.
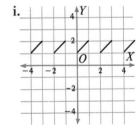

3. Which of the following indicate membership in a function?

    a. $\{(x, y) \mid y = 2x + 3 \wedge y = -x\}$ **c.** $\{(x, y) \mid y = x^2 - 1\}$

    b. $\{(x, y) \mid y = 2x + 3 \vee y = -x\}$ **d.** $\{(x, y) \mid x = y^2 + 4\}$

4. $\{(x, y) \mid y = 3x^2 - 6\}$ indicates membership in a function. Find the second member of each of the following ordered pairs so that it is an element of the function.

    a. $(0, ?)$ **b.** $(-7, ?)$ **c.** $(\frac{1}{2}, ?)$ **d.** $(2, ?)$

5. Draw the graph of each of the following functions.

   a. $\{(x, y) \mid y = 2x + 1\}$ **c.** $\{(x, y) \mid y = x^2 + 3x - 1\}$

   b. $\{(x, y) \mid y = 4x - 1\}$ **d.** $\{(x, y) \mid y = x^3\}$

6. Replace each variable below so that the ordered pair belongs to the constant function E which contains the ordered pair $(2, 3)$.

   a. $(4, y)$ **b.** $(2, y)$ **c.** $(-2, y)$ **d.** $(11, y)$

7. Replace each variable below so that the ordered pair belongs to the identity function I.

   a. $(x, -11)$ **b.** $(-\frac{1}{2}, y)$ **c.** $(x, 2)$ **d.** $(1.21, y)$

8. State the domain and range of each of the functions whose membership is indicated below.

   a. $\{(x, y) \mid y = 0x + 6\}$ **d.** $\{(x, y) \mid y = x - 4\}$

   b. $\{(x, y) \mid y = 3\}$ **e.** $\{(x, y) \mid y = 16 - x^2\}$

   c. $\left\{(x, y) \mid y = \dfrac{1}{x}\right\}$ **f.** $\left\{(x, y) \mid \dfrac{y}{x - 1} = 2\right\}$

9. Write an equation which indicates membership in each of the functions whose graphs appear below.

  a. 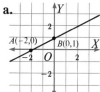   **b.** 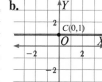   **c.** 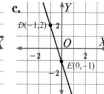   **d.**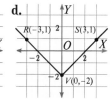

10. Each of the following indicates the ordered pairs belonging to a function in $I \times Q$. Use set-builder notation to indicate each function.

   a. $\{\cdots, (-1, -8), (0, -5), (1, -2), (2, 1), \cdots\}$

   b. $\{\cdots, (-2, 11), (-1, 9), (0, 7), (1, 5), (2, 3), \cdots\}$

   c. $\{\cdots, (-7, 1), (-6, \frac{4}{5}), (-5, \frac{3}{5}), \cdots\}$

   d. $\{\cdots, (4, \frac{38}{3}), (5, 15), (6, \frac{52}{3}), \cdots\}$

Value of a Function

When we say that the ordered pair (x, y) is in the function F, we mean that x is a member of the domain of F and y is the corresponding member of the range of F; in other words, for the function F, y is the unique value which corresponds to the argument x. We may denote this unique value y by $f(x)$

which is read "f of x." Thus given a function F, we may use the statement $y = f(x)$ to express the idea that the ordered pair (x, y) is in F. That is,

If $F = \{(x, y) \mid y = f(x)\}$, then $y_1 = f(x_1) \longleftrightarrow (x_1, y_1) \in F$.

If F is a function and a is an element in the domain of F, then the ordered pair $(a, f(a))$ is an ordered pair belonging to F. Similarly, if 5 is an element in the domain of F, the ordered pair $(5, f(5))$ is an ordered pair in F, and if $a + b$ is an element in the domain of F, then $(a + b, f(a + b))$ is an ordered pair in F. For example, if $F = \{(x, y) \mid y = x^2 - 4x - 5\}$, then $f(x) = x^2 - 4x - 5$, $f(a) = a^2 - 4a - 5$, $f(5) = 5^2 - 4(5) - 5 = 0$, and $f(a + b) = (a + b)^2 - 4(a + b) - 5 = a^2 + 2ab + b^2 - 4a - 4b - 5$.

From our definition of the symbol $f(x)$ it is clear that we may represent the function F having the domain D_F by writing $F = \{(x, y) \mid y = f(x); \ x \in D_F\}$. (As usual, instead of the semicolon in this expression, we might have used the word *and* or the symbol $\wedge$.) If no mention is made of the domain, it is assumed to be the set of all real numbers x for which $f(x)$ names a number.

When we are speaking of a specific function F there are two things that we must know before we can say that F has been defined or specified: We must know the domain of F and we must have some means, such as a rule, a graph, a table, or an equation, which will enable us to determine the member of the range of F which corresponds to any specified member of the domain.

We can usually define a function by giving an equation which enables us to determine $f(x)$ for each x in the domain of the function. We call this equation the *defining equation* for the function F. Consider the following function F_1 in $I \times I$: $F_1 = \{(x, y) \mid y = x + |x| \wedge -4 \le x \le 5\}$. We see that $f_1(x) = x + |x|$. Therefore, $f_1(-4) = -4 + |-4| = 0, f_1(-3) = -3 + |-3| = 0, \cdots, f_1(5) = 5 + |5| = 10$. Thus $F_1 = \{(-4, 0), (-3, 0), (-2, 0), (-1, 0), (0, 0), (1, 2), (2, 4), (3, 6), (4, 8), (5, 10)\}$. The graph of F_1 is shown at the right.

Let us now consider a second function also in $I \times I$: $F_2 = \{(x, y) \mid y = x + |x| \wedge 0 < x \le 5\}$. Again $f_2(x) = x + |x|$. Clearly $F_2 = \{(1, 2), (2, 4), (3, 6), (4, 8), (5, 10)\}$ and its graph consists of the five points in the first quadrant in the diagram at the right.

Since two sets are equal if and only if they have the same members, we see that $F_1 \ne F_2$ in spite of the fact that they have the same formula for $f(x)$. The functions F_1 and F_2 are equal if and only if the domain of F_1 is equal to the domain of F_2 and, for each x in the common domain, $f_1(x) = f_2(x)$.

Let us study the function $H = \left\{(x, y) \mid y = \dfrac{16}{x^2}\right\}$. In this case, $h(x) = \dfrac{16}{x^2}$.

Since the domain is not specified, we assume it to be the set of all real numbers for which $\dfrac{16}{x^2}$ names a number; that is, the set of all real numbers except 0. A few of the ordered pairs belonging to H are displayed in the following table.

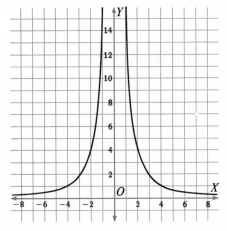

x	1	2	3	4	8
$h(x)$	16	4	$1\frac{7}{9}$	1	$\frac{1}{4}$

Since the curve is symmetric with respect to the y-axis, we know that the points whose coordinates are the ordered pairs $(-8, \frac{1}{4})$, $(-4, 1)$, $(-3, 1\frac{7}{9})$, $(-2, 4)$, and $(-1, 16)$ will also be in the graph. The graph is obtained by drawing a smooth line through the points which are the graphs of these ordered pairs. We see that R_H is the set of all positive real numbers.

In the function $\{(x, y) \mid y = x^3 - x\}$, x is the *independent* variable and y is the *dependent* variable. For the function $\{(v, s) \mid s = v^2 + 5\}$ v is the independent variable and s is the dependent variable. These names are derived from the earlier treatment of functions in which the idea of *dependence* was stressed. In a defining equation such as $y = x^3 - x$ the variable x was regarded as independent, that is, free to assume any value in its domain, while the value of y was thought of as *depending* on the value assigned to x. Thus y was considered as depending on x in much the same way that the volume v of gas in a cylinder depends on the pressure p exerted on the piston, or that the stretch s of a spring depends on the weight w which the spring supports.

Example 1. If $F = \{(x, y) \mid y = 3x + 2\}$, find $f(2)$, $f(-\frac{1}{3})$, $f(3t)$, $3f(t)$, $f(2a - 1)$, $f(t^2)$, $[f(t)]^2$.

Solution. We know that $f(x) = 3x + 2$. Thus
$$f(2) = 3(2) + 2 = 8$$
$$f(-\tfrac{1}{3}) = 3(-\tfrac{1}{3}) + 2 = 1$$
$$f(3t) = 3(3t) + 2 = 9t + 2$$
$$3f(t) = 3(3t + 2) = 9t + 6$$
$$f(2a - 1) = 3(2a - 1) + 2 = 6a - 1$$
$$f(t^2) = 3t^2 + 2$$
$$[f(t)]^2 = (3t + 2)^2 = 9t^2 + 12t + 4$$

Example 2.   Graph the function $K = \left\{ (x, y) \mid y = \dfrac{|x|}{x} \right\}$ and indicate its domain and range.

Solution.   Here $k(x) = \dfrac{|x|}{x} \wedge x \neq 0$. If $x > 0$, $k(x) = 1$. If $x < 0$, $k(x) = -1$, and if $x = 0$, $\dfrac{|x|}{x}$ does not name

a real number. Hence $D_K = R \smallsmile \{0\}$ and $R_K = \{1, -1\}$. The graph of K is shown at the right. We observe that the graph is symmetric with respect to the origin.

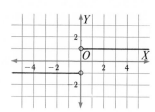

If $s_{(x,y)}$ represents the sentence $y = \dfrac{|x|}{x}$,

is $s_{(x,y)} \longleftrightarrow s_{(-x, -y)}$?

Example 3.   Draw the graph of the function G if G is $\{(x, g(x)) \mid g(x) = x^2 + 2\}$ and state its range and domain.

Solution.   The graph of G can be determined by drawing a smooth curve through the graphs of a few of the ordered pairs belonging to G. The following table shows a few of the ordered pairs.

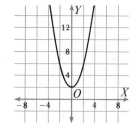

x	0	1	2	3
$g(x)$	2	3	6	11

Since the curve is symmetric to the y-axis, the points $(-1, 3)$, $(-2, 6)$ and $(-3, 11)$ will also be points in the graph. The graph of G is shown at the right. The domain of G is the set of all real numbers and the range of G is the set of real numbers which are greater than or equal to 2.

Ⓐ **EXERCISES**

1. If function $F = \{(-3, 2), (-2, 1), (-1, 0), (0, 1), (1, 2), (2, 3)\}$, what number is represented by each of the following?

   a. $f(-3)$ **b.** $f(0)$ **c.** $f(1)$ **d.** $f(-2)$

2. Each of the following ordered pairs are members of the function defined by $\{(x, y) \mid y = 3\,x^2 + 2\}$. Find the value of $f(-2), f(3), f(\sqrt{2})$, and $f(\frac{1}{3})$.

   a. $(-2, f(-2))$ **b.** $(3, f(3))$ **c.** $(\sqrt{2}, f(\sqrt{2}))$ **d.** $(\frac{1}{3}, f(\frac{1}{3}))$

3. If $f(x) = x^2 - 4x - 5$, what is the value of each of the following?

   a. $f(-3)$ **c.** $[f(4)]^2$ **e.** $f(a+2)$ **g.** $f(a^2)$

   b. $f(\frac{1}{4})$ **d.** $-3 \cdot f(4)$ **f.** $4 \cdot f(a-1)$ **h.** $f(r-s)$

4. Draw the graph of the function $\{(x, y) \mid y = 2x - 5;\ x \in I\}$.

5. Draw the graph of the function G if G is $\{(x, y) \mid y = x^2\}$.

6. Draw the graph of each of the functions defined below. State the domain and range of each function.

   a. $\left\{(x, f(x)) \mid 1 = \dfrac{f(x)}{x+1}\right\}$ **d.** $\left\{(x, h(x)) \mid h(x) = \dfrac{1}{x}\right\}$

   b. $\{(x, f(x)) \mid f(x) = x^2 - 3\}$

                               e. $\{(x, f(x)) \mid \frac{1}{2}\sqrt{x} = f(x)\}$

   c. $\left\{(x, g(x)) \mid g(x) = \dfrac{x}{|x|}\right\}$ **f.** $\{(x, k(x)) \mid k(x) = x\sqrt{x}\}$

7. M is a relation whose domain is $\{1, 2, 3, \cdots\}$. A rule exists which assigns 0 as the second member of each ordered pair whose first member is an odd number and 1 as the second member of each ordered pair whose first member is an even number.

   a. Graph the relation.

   b. Is the relation a function?

   c. What is the range of the relation?

8. N is a relation whose domain is I. A rule exists which assigns -1 as the second member of each ordered pair whose first member is negative, 1 as the second member of each ordered pair whose first member is positive, and 0 as the second member of the ordered pair whose first member is 0.

   a. Graph the relation.

   b. Is the relation a function?

   c. What is the range of the relation?

9. $F = \left\{(x, y) \mid \dfrac{1}{x} = \dfrac{1}{y}\right\}$ and $G = \{(x, y) \mid x = y\}$.

   a. Draw the graphs of both functions.

   b. How do the graphs differ?

   c. What are the domain and range of F? of G?

10. The equation $s = 16t^2$ defines the relation consisting of all ordered pairs (t, s) in which t represents the number of seconds during which an object falls and s represents the number of feet that it falls in this time.

   a. Is the relation a function?

   b. Draw the graph of the relation.

11. Choose appropriate variables and use them in an equation which defines the function which expresses the relationship between

   a. the circumference of a circle and the length of its radius.

   b. the area of a circle and the square of the length of its radius.

   c. the perimeter of a square and the length of one of its sides.

   d. the area of a square and the length of one of its sides.

   e. the temperature in Fahrenheit degrees and the corresponding temperature in Celsius (centigrade) degrees.

   f. the length of the altitude of an equilateral triangle and the length of one of its sides.

12. Let p be the measure of the perimeter of the figure at the right and let $t = a + b$.

   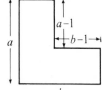

   a. Is the set of ordered pairs of the form (t, p) a function?

   b. If A represents the measure of the area of the figure, is the set of ordered pairs of the form (t, A) a function?

B **EXERCISES**

13. Draw the graph of each of the functions whose defining equation is indicated below. State the domain and the range of each function.

   a. $y = \dfrac{1}{x - 1}$ **c.** $\dfrac{x^2}{y} = 1$

   b. $\dfrac{1}{\sqrt{x - y}} = \dfrac{1}{\sqrt{x + y}}$ **d.** $y = \sqrt{16 - x^2}$

14. Write the defining equation of the constant function whose graph goes through the point of intersection of the graphs of $\{(x, y) \mid y = -2x + 8\}$ and $\{(x, y) \mid y = \frac{3}{2}x - \frac{5}{2}\}$.

15. Write the defining equation of the function whose graph is the perpendicular bisector of the line segment joining the points $A(-4, 6)$ and $B(2, 8)$.

More about Functions and Their Graphs—Special Functions

In this section, by exhibiting several special functions and their graphs, we emphasize the variety of ways in which a function can be defined.

We consider first a "step function" S whose description requires the use of the symbol $[x]$ which represents the phrase "the greatest integer that is less than or equal to x."

$$S = \{(x, y) \mid y = [x]\}$$

If $x = 3, f(x) = 3$. If $x = 3.4, f(x) = 3$. If $x = 3.99, f(x) = 3$. If $x = 4.01$, $f(x) = 4$, and so on.

The graph of the step function S is shown below.

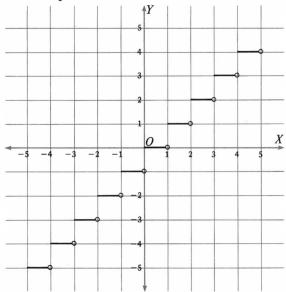

Next we study a "wrapping function" which we describe as follows. Let a square be located in the coordinate plane so that its vertices have the co-ordinates $(1, 1)$, $(-1, 1)$, $(-1, -1)$, $(1, -1)$ as shown in the diagram. Let s represent any real number. Then let a point start at $S(1, 0)$ and move without reversing its direction along a path in the square (in a *counterclockwise* direction if s is positive and in a *clockwise* direction if s is negative) until it has moved a distance $|s|$, thus arriving at the unique terminal point $P(x, y)$. Thus when $s = 1$, the coordinates of P_1 are $(1, 1)$, when $s = 3$, the coordinates of P_2 are $(-1, 1)$, when $s = 5$,

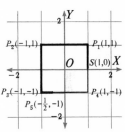

the coordinates of P_3 are $(-1, -1)$, and when $s = 5\frac{1}{2}$ (as shown in the drawing) the coordinates of P_5 are $(-\frac{1}{2}, -1)$. Had s been negative, our procedure for finding P would have been the same except that the point would move along the perimeter of the square in a *clockwise* direction starting at S. Then if $s = -2\frac{1}{2}$, the coordinates of P are $(-\frac{1}{2}, -1)$. Let us now consider the relation that exists between the variables s and y. Do you agree that for any given s the above procedure designates one and only one y? If so, you will agree that the correspondence we have established between s and y is a *function* whose independent variable is s. The expression "wrapping function" is suggested by the fact that we can think of P as one end of the cord which has been wrapped around the square after its other end was secured at S. This wrapping function, which we shall call W, is hard to define by means of the set-builder notation. However, we can describe it by means of the graph in the SY-plane shown below.

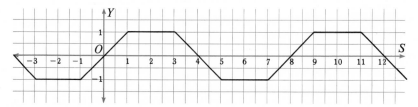

Even though we do not know the equation for $w(s)$, we can see that this graph repeats every eight units, that is, with every circuit which P makes around the square. From the graphs we read that $w(\frac{1}{2}) = \frac{1}{2}$. Also $w(8\frac{1}{2}) = \frac{1}{2}$. Indeed $w(a) = w(a + 8)$ where a is any real number. A function W which has the property that $w(s) = w(s + p)$ for all s in the domain of the function is said to be *periodic*. The smallest positive number p for which the equation $w(s) = w(s + p)$ holds is called the *period* of the function. Thus W is a periodic function having period 8. The domain of W is R and the range of W is $\{s \mid -1 \le s \le 1\}$.

Another wrapping function can be defined by reference to a unit circle with its center at the origin. This unit circle, which is the graph of $\{(x, y \mid x^2 + y^2 = 1\}$, is shown in the diagram at the right.

Let t represent any real number and let point P start at point T $(1, 0)$ and move without reversing its direction along a path in the unit circle (in a counter-clockwise direction if t is positive or in a clockwise direction if t is negative) until it has moved a distance of $|t|$ units, thus arriving at unique terminal point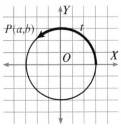

$P(x, y)$. If $t = \dfrac{\pi}{2}$, the coordinates of P are $(0, 1)$; if $t = \pi$, the coordinates of P are $(-1, 0)$; if $t = \dfrac{3\pi}{2}$, the coordinates of P are $(0, -1)$; if $t = 2\pi$, the coordinates of P are $(1, 0)$; and if $t = \dfrac{5\pi}{2}$, the co-ordinates of P are $(0, 1)$. Thus we see that the set of ordered pairs of the form (t, y) is a periodic function with period 2π.

The graph of this function is shown below.

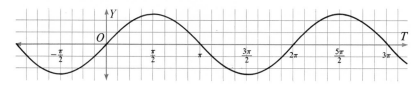

A function may have different defining equations in different parts or intervals of its domain. In order to facilitate reference to such intervals, let us adopt an appropriate notation. First we agree that A and B are distinct points on a number line and that their coordinates are respectively a and b with $a < b$. Then the symbol $\langle a, b \rangle$ represents the set of real numbers in the *closed interval* consisting of the set of real numbers whose graphs are points in the segment AB including the end points A and B. To say $x \epsilon$ $\langle a, b \rangle$ means that $a \leq x \leq b$ and that X, the graph of x, is in $\overline{AB}$. The symbol $\rangle a, b \langle$ refers to the *open interval* consisting of the real numbers whose graphs are points in the line segment AB not including A and B. To say that $x \epsilon \rangle a, b \langle$ is to say that $a < x < b$ and that X, the graph of x, is between A and B. The symbol $\rangle a, b \rangle$ refers to the interval consisting of all real numbers equal to or less than b but greater than a and the symbol $\langle a, b \langle$ refers to the interval consisting of the real numbers greater than or equal to a but less than b.

The interval which consists of the real number a and all real numbers less than a is indicated by $\rangle - \infty, a \rangle$. Note that the symbol ∞ is not a numeral. It is customary to call this symbol "infinity." Accordingly, $- \infty$ is sometimes read as "negative infinity." The interval denoted by $\rangle - \infty, a \rangle$ has no lower bound. The interval which consists of all real numbers less than a is denoted by $\rangle - \infty, a \langle$. If A is the graph of a on the number line, then $\rangle - \infty, a \langle$ is the set of numbers which are coordinates of points to the left of A. Similarly $\langle b, \infty \langle$ represents the interval which consists of the real number b and all real numbers greater than b, and $\rangle b, \infty \langle$ represents the interval consisting of all real numbers greater than b.

Recall that when the domain of a function F is not given it is said to be all real numbers for which $f(x)$ names a number. In such cases we shall not use any symbol for the interval of definition.

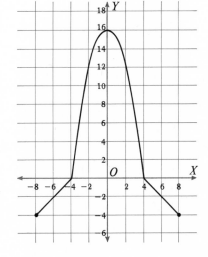

Example 1. Draw the graph of $F = \{(x, y) \mid y = x + 4 \land x \epsilon \langle -8, -4 \rangle\} \cup \{(x, y) \mid y = 16 - x^2 \land x \epsilon \langle -4, 4 \rangle\} \cup \{(x, y) \mid y = -x + 4 \land x \epsilon \langle 4, 8 \rangle\}$, and state its domain and range.

Solution. The graph of this function is shown at the right. The domain of the function is $\langle -8, 8 \rangle$ and its range is $\langle -4, 16 \rangle$.

Example 2. Graph the function $K = \{(x, y) \mid y = -4 \land x \epsilon \rangle - \infty, 0 \langle \} \cup \{(x, y) \mid y = x^2 - 4 \land x \epsilon \rangle 0, \infty \langle \}$ and state its domain and range.

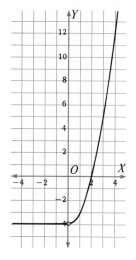

Solution. The graph is the union of the graphs of the truth sets of $\{(x, y) \mid y = -4 \land x \epsilon \rangle - \infty, 0 \langle \}$ and $\{(x, y) \mid y = x^2 - 4 \land x \epsilon \rangle 0, \infty \langle \}$. From the graph we see that the domain consists of all real numbers except 0, and the range consists of all real numbers greater than or equal to -4. That is, $D_K = \rangle - \infty, 0 \langle \cup \rangle 0, \infty \langle$ and $R_K = \langle -4, \infty \langle$.

A   **EXERCISES**

1. Sketch the graph of each of the functions defined below.

  a. $\{(x, y) \mid y = [2\,x]\}$ **e.** $\{(x, y) \mid y = |\,[x]\,|\}$

  b. $\{(x, y) \mid y = 2[x]\}$ **f.** $\{(x, y) \mid y = |-[x]\,|\}$

  c. $\{(x, y) \mid y = [\frac{1}{3}\,x]\}$ **g.** $\{(x, y) \mid y = \|\,x\,\|\}$

  d. $\{(x, y) \mid y = \frac{1}{3}[x]\}$ **h.** $\{(x, y) \mid y = [x] + 1\}$

2. A square is of such size that when its diagonals intersect in the origin of the coordinate plane, one of its vertices, A, has the coordinates $(1, 0)$. A string, the measure of whose length is l, is attached to the square at A and wrapped tightly around the square in a counterclockwise direction. Let $P(l,\ y)$ be the point at which the string ends when l is the measure of the length of the string and y is the ordinate of P.

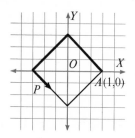

  a. Replace each y below so that the resulting ordered pair of the form $(l,\ y)$ belongs to the relations described above.

    (1) $(\sqrt{2},\ y)$ (3) $(\frac{1}{2}\sqrt{2},\ y)$ (5) $(4\sqrt{2},\ y)$

    (2) $(2\sqrt{2},\ y)$ (4) $(3\sqrt{2},\ y)$ (6) $(\frac{9}{2}\sqrt{2},\ y)$

  b. The set of ordered pairs of the form $(l,\ y)$, such as those of part **a**, is a function. Why?

  c. Draw the graph of the set of ordered pairs of the form $(l,\ y)$.

  d. What is the period of the graph of this function?

  e. What are the domain and range of this function?

  f. Is the set of ordered pairs of the form $(y,\ l)$ a function? Explain.

3. A rectangle is so located in the coordinate plane that the lines joining the midpoints of its opposite sides intersect in the origin of the plane. The midpoint A of one of the shorter sides has the coordinates $(2, 0)$. The measure of each of the shorter sides is 2. A string is attached to the rectangle at A and is wrapped tightly around the rectangle in a counterclockwise direction.

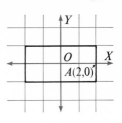

a. What will be the ordinate of $P(l, y)$, the point at which the string ends, when l, the measure of the length of the string, is

(1) 1?   (3) $\frac{5}{2}$?   (5) 5?   (7) 8?

(2) 2?   (4) 3?   (6) 6?   (8) $\frac{23}{2}$?

b. Make a graph of the set of ordered pairs of the form (l, y) if l is the measure of the length of the string and y is the ordinate of the point in which the string ends.

c. Is the set of the ordered pairs of the form (l, y) a function?

d. If the set of ordered pairs is a function, state the domain, range, and period of the function, but if the set is not a function, explain why it is not a function.

e. Is the set of ordered pairs of the form (y, l) a function? Explain.

4. Match each sentence in the column on the left with an equivalent sentence in the column on the right.

a. $x \in \,) 0, \infty \,($ (1) $-4 \le x < 0$

b. $x \in \,) -\infty, 0 \,($ (2) $-4 < x \le 0$

c. $x \in \,(-4, 0 \,($ (3) $x > 0$

d. $x \in \,) -4, 0 \,)$ (4) $-4 < x < 0$

e. $x \in \,) -4, 0 \,($ (5) $x < 0$

5. Draw the graph of each of the functions defined below. State the domain and range of each function.

a. $\{(x, y) \mid y = 2 \land x \in \,) -\infty, 2 \,)\} \cup \{(x, y) \mid y = -2x + 6 \land x \in \,) 2, \infty \,(\}$

b. $\{(x, y) \mid y = -\frac{2}{3}x + \frac{1}{3} \land x \in \,(-4, -1 \,(\} \cup \{(x, y) \mid y = 2x + 3 \land x \in \,(-1, 0 \,(\} \cup \{(x, y) \mid y = -\frac{2}{3}x + 3 \land x \in \,(0, 3 \,(\} \cup \{(x, y) \mid y = 2x - 5 \land x \in \,(3, 4 \,(\}$

c. $\{(x, y) \mid y = \sqrt{16 - x^2} \land x \in \,(-4, 4 \,)\} \cup \{(x, y) \mid y = x \land x \in \,(-6, -4 \,(\} \cup \{(x, y) \mid y = -x \land x \in \,) 4, 6 \,)\}$

d. $\{(x, y) \mid y = 3x + 6 \land x \in \,(-2, -1 \,)\} \cup \{(x, y) \mid y = 3 \land x \in \,) -1, 1 \,(\} \cup \{(x, y) \mid y = -3x + 6 \land x \in \,(1, 2 \,)\}$

e. $\{(x, y) \mid y = -\frac{1}{3}x + \frac{1}{3} \land x \in \,) -\infty, -1 \,)\} \cup \{(x, y) \mid y = 1 \land x \in \,) -1, 1 \,(\} \cup \{(x, y) \mid y = -\frac{1}{3}x + \frac{1}{3} \land x \in \,(1, \infty \,(\}$

f. $\{(x, y) \mid y = -x - 3 \wedge x \in \langle -2, -1 \rangle\} \cup \{(x, y) \mid y = \sqrt{1 - x^2} \wedge x \in \langle -1, 1 \rangle\} \cup \{(x, y) \mid y = x - 3 \wedge x \in \langle 1, 2 \rangle\}$

g. $\{(x, y) \mid y = x + 3 \wedge x \in \langle -2, -1 \rangle\} \cup \{(x, y) \mid y = \sqrt{1 - x^2} \wedge x \in \langle -1, 1 \rangle\} \cup \{(x, y) \mid y = -x + 3 \wedge x \in \langle 1, 2 \rangle\}$

6. Postal charges for third class mail are: 4 cents for the first two ounces or fraction thereof, and 2 cents for each additional ounce or fraction thereof up to but not including a total of 16 ounces.

a. Draw the graph of this function.

b. What are the domain and range of this function?

7. Rates for special handling of mail are as follows: Up to and including 2 pounds, 25¢; over 2 pounds but not over 10 pounds, 35¢; over 10 pounds, 50¢.

a. Draw the graph of this function.

b. What are the domain and range of this function?

8. A particular newspaper makes the following charges for a want ad to appear for one day: 1–9 words, $1.60; 10–15 words, $2.40; 16–21 words, $3.20; 22–27 words, $4.00; 28–33 words, $4.80; 34–39 words $5.60.

a. Draw the graph of this function.

b. What are the domain and range of the function?

 B   **EXERCISES**

9. Draw the graph of the function $\{(x, y) \mid [(f(x) = x^3 + 7) \wedge (\mid x \mid < 7)] \vee [(f(x) = 7) \wedge (\mid x \mid \geq 7)]\}$. Note that the graph has "breaks" in it. Indicate the values of x at which these "breaks" occur.

10. a. Draw the graph of the function defined by $f(x) = \dfrac{2x}{x^2 + 1}$.

b. What are the domain and range of this function?

11. Draw the graph of the function defined by each of the following sentences.

a. $y = x - \mid x - 4 \mid$ **c.** $y = x - \mid x + 4 \mid$

b. $y = x + \mid x - 4 \mid$ **d.** $y = x + \mid x + 4 \mid$

Composition of Functions

Let the function F be defined by the equation $y = 2x + 5$ and let the function G be defined by the equation $y = x^2 - 3$. Then the equation $y = (2x + 5)^2 - 3$ defines a function which we denote by $G(F)$ and call the *composition of G with F*. On the other hand the equation $y = 2(x^2 - 3) + 5$ defines a function which we denote by $F(G)$ and call the composition of F with G.

The following figure helps to explain the composition of functions. The diagram illustrates a machine for finding the values of $G(F)$. In order for all arguments of F to be processed by the machine we must be sure that the range of F is contained in the domain of G. The "Rule of F" which appears in the diagram tells us to pair each argument in F with its corresponding value. Similarly, the "Rule of G" tells us to pair each argument in G which is included in the range of F with its corresponding value.

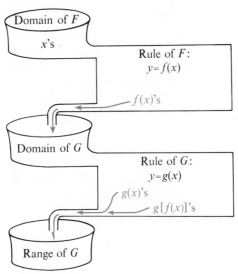

To see how the machine processes a number let us use the functions F and G described above. The number 7 is in the domain of F. After we apply the rule of F we have $f(7) = 2(7) + 5 = 19$. Now the number 19 is in the domain of G. When we apply the rule of G to 19 we obtain $g(19) = 19^2 - 3 = 358$. Recalling that $19 = f(7)$, we see that $g[f(7)] = 358$. In the same way each number a in the domain of F will be made to correspond to a unique number $g[f(a)]$ by our machine. Thus $y = g[f(x)]$ defines a function $G(F)$ whose range is included in the range of G. We summarize this discussion in the following definition:

> If F and G are the functions $\{(x, y) \mid y = f(x)\}$ and $\{(x, y) \mid y = g(x)\}$, respectively, then $\{(x, y) \mid y = g[f(x)]\}$ is called the composition of G with F and is represented by the symbol $G(F)$. Similarly, $\{(x, y) \mid y = f[g(x)]\}$ is called the composition of F with G and is represented by the symbol $F(G)$.

If $R_F \cap D_G \neq \emptyset$, then $G(F)$ is a function whose domain is a subset of the domain of F and whose range is a subset of the range of G. Note also that if the domain of G is the same as the range of F, then $y = g[f(x)]$ defines a function whose domain is the domain of F and whose range is the range of G.

The following examples show how we can obtain the composition of two functions when the functions are defined by various methods, for example, by roster, table, graph, and equation.

Example 1. Given: $F = \{(1, 2), (2, 4), (3, 6), (4, 8), (5, 10)\}$ and $G = \{(2, 4), (4, 16), (6, 36), (8, 64), (10, 100)\}$. Find the function H such that $H = G(F)$.

Solution. From the definition of the composition of two functions, we see that if $D_G = R_F$, the domain of $G(F)$ is the domain of F. Since we want $H = G(F)$, we know that $h(x) = g[f(x)]$ according to our definition of equal functions. Thus

$$\begin{aligned} h(1) &= g[f(1)] = g(2) = 4 \\ h(2) &= g[f(2)] = g(4) = 16 \\ h(3) &= g[f(3)] = g(6) = 36 \\ h(4) &= g[f(4)] = g(8) = 64 \\ h(5) &= g[f(5)] = g(10) = 100 \end{aligned}$$

Therefore $H = \{(1, 4), (2, 16), (3, 36), (4, 64), (5, 100)\}$. Another way that we can picture the composition of G with F is as follows: The function F, being a set of ordered pairs, can be thought of as *mapping* each element of its domain into one and only one element of its range. Thus, F "maps" 1 into 2. The function G in turn "maps" 2 into 4. Hence the function $G(F)$ "maps" 1 into 4. This mapping may be pictured as follows:

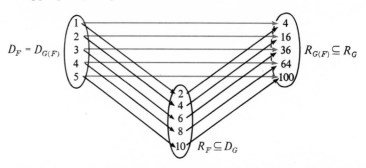

The red arrows indicate the ordered pairs in the function $G(F)$, or H, whose domain is the domain of F and whose range is, in this case, the range of G. Note that $R_F = D_G$.

Study of the ordered pairs in F and G indicates that the defining equation of F is $y = 2x$ and that the defining equation for G is $y = x^2$. Thus, $H = G(F) = \{(x, y) \mid y = 4x^2 \wedge x \in \{1, 2, 3, 4, 5\}\} = \{(1, 4), (2, 16), (3, 36), (4, 64), (5, 100)\}$ and we see that we obtain the same set of ordered pairs using the defining equations as that obtained above.

Example 2. Given: $f(x) = x^3 + 1$ and $g(x) = 3x - 2$. Find $G(F)$ and $F(G)$.

Solution. $F = \{(x, y) \mid y = x^3 + 1\}$ and $G = \{(x, y) \mid y = 3x - 2\}$

According to our definition for the composition of functions,

$G(F) = \{(x, y) \mid y = g[f(x)]\}$

$G(F) = \{(x, y) \mid y = 3(x^3 + 1) - 2\}$

$G(F) = \{(x, y) \mid y = 3x^3 + 1\}$

Similarly,

$F(G) = \{(x, y) \mid y = f[g(x)]\}$

$F(G) = \{(x, y) \mid y = (3x - 2)^3 + 1\}$

Since the domain is not specified and since both $x^3 + 1$ and $3x - 2$ name real numbers when $x \in R$, we see that R is the domain for both $G(F)$ and $F(G)$. What is the range for each?

Example 3. Let $F = \{(x, y) \mid y = \sqrt{16 + x}\}$ and $G = \{(x, y) \mid y = 4x\}$. Find $G(F)$ and $F(G)$ and sketch the graphs of F, G, $G(F)$ and $F(G)$.

Solution. Since $G(F) = \{(x, y) \mid y = g[f(x)]\}$ and $F(G) = \{(x, y) \mid y = f[g(x)]\}$, $G(F) = \{(x, y) \mid y = 4\sqrt{16 + x}\}$ and $F(G) = \{(x, y) \mid y = \sqrt{16 + 4x}\}$.

To sketch the graphs of F, G, $G(F)$ and $F(G)$, we list a few of the ordered pairs belonging to each of the functions in the table.

x	-16	-4	0	4
$f(x)$	0	$2\sqrt{3}$	4	$2\sqrt{5}$
$g(x)$	-64	-16	0	16
$g[f(x)]$	0	$8\sqrt{3}$	16	$8\sqrt{5}$
$f[g(x)]$	——	0	4	$4\sqrt{2}$

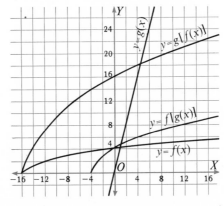

The graphs of F, G, $G(F)$ and $F(G)$ are shown above.

1. If functions F and G are defined as indicated below, find $g[f(x)]$, $D_{G(F)}$, and $R_{G(F)}$.

   a. $F = \{(x, y) \mid y = 3\,x\}$ $G = \{(x, y) \mid y = 7\,x\}$

   b. $F = \{(x, y) \mid y = \tfrac{1}{2}\,x\}$ $G = \{(x, y) \mid y = x^2\}$

   c. $F = \{(x, y) \mid y = x + 1\}$ $G = \{(x, y) \mid y = 2\,x^2 - x\}$

   d. $F = \{(x, y) \mid y = x + 2\}$ $G = \{(x, y) \mid y = x^2 - 1\}$

   e. $F = \{(x, y) \mid y = x - 3\}$ $G = \{(x, y) \mid y = x^2 + x + 2\}$

   f. $F = \left\{ (x, y) \mid y = \dfrac{1}{x} \right\}$ $G = \left\{ (x, y) \mid y = \dfrac{1}{x} \right\}$

   g. $F = \left\{ (x, y) \mid y = \dfrac{1}{\sqrt{x - 1}} \right\}$ $G = \{(x, y) \mid y = 1 + x\}$

   h. $F = \{(x, y) \mid y = |\,x\,|\}$ $G = \{(x, y) \mid y = x^2 - 2\}$

   i. $F = \left\{ (x, y) \mid y = \dfrac{1}{\sqrt{x}} \right\}$ $G = \{(x, y) \mid y = x^2 - 4\}$

   j. $F = \{(x, y) \mid y = 9\,x\}$ $G = \{(x, y) \mid y = \sqrt{99 + x}\}$

2. Using F and G as defined in Ex. 1, find $f[g(x)]$, $D_{F(G)}$, $R_{F(G)}$.

3. If $F = \{(1, 3), (2, 6), (3, 9)\}$ and $G = \{(3, 5), (4, 6), (5, 7), (6, 8), (7, 9), (8, 10), (9, 11)\}$, find $G(F)$.

4. If $H = \{(1, 4), (2, 8), (3, 12), (4, 16)\}$ and $G = \{(4, 16), (6, 36), (8, 64), (10, 100), (12, 144), (14, 196), (16, 256)\}$, find $G(H)$.

5. If $f(x) = 2\,x + 1$ and $g(x) = 3\,x + 4$, find

   a. $g[f(-2)]$ **b.** $f[g(3)]$

6. Given the graphs of the functions M and N shown at the right, draw the graph of $M(N)$.

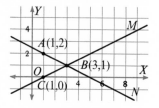

7. For each of the pairs $f(x)$, $g(x)$ defined below, draw (with respect to a single pair of coordinate axes) the graphs of $f(x)$, $g(x)$, $f[g(x)]$, and $g[f(x)]$.

   a. $f(x) = x^2$ $g(x) = x + 4$

   b. $f(x) = |\,x\,|$ $g(x) = x - 3$

   c. $f(x) = 3\,x + 12$ $g(x) = 9\,x$

   d. $f(x) = x + 2$ $g(x) = x + 4$

   e. $f(x) = x^2 - 4\,x$ $g(x) = 2\,x^2$

   f. $f(x) = |\,x\,|$ $g(x) = 2\,x + 1$

   g. $f(x) = \sqrt{9 + x}$ $g(x) = x^2 + 2$

   h. $f(x) = x - 4$ $g(x) = \sqrt{16 - x}$

Inverse Functions

Consider the following functions and their graphs shown below.

$$F = \{(x, y) \mid y = 2x - 4\} \qquad G = \{(x, y) \mid y = \tfrac{1}{2}x + 2\}$$

By substituting in the defining equations of F and G, we see that $g(10) = 7$ and $f(7) = 10$. Therefore $f[g(10)] = 10$ and $g[f(7)] = 7$. Also we see that $g(7) = 5\frac{1}{2}$ and $f(5\frac{1}{2}) = 7$. Therefore $f[g(7)] = 7$ and $g[f(5\frac{1}{2})] = 5\frac{1}{2}$. Finally we see that $f(10) = 16$ and $g(16) = 10$. Therefore $f[g(16)] = 16$ and $g[f(10)] = 10$. These results may also be verified by studying and reading the above graph.

Thus, by the transitive property of equality, $f[g(7)] = g[f(7)]$ and $f[g(10)] = g[f(10)]$. In fact we can show that "If $x \in R$, $F = \{(x, y) \mid y = 2x - 4\}$, and $G = \{(x, y) \mid y = \tfrac{1}{2}x + 2\}$, then $f[g(x)] = x = g[f(x)]$," as follows:

$$g[f(x)] = \tfrac{1}{2}(2x - 4) + 2 = x \quad \text{and} \quad f[g(x)] = 2(\tfrac{1}{2}x + 2) - 4 = x$$

Hence $G(F) = \{(x, y) \mid y = x\}$ and $F(G) = \{(x, y) \mid y = x\}$.
We recognize $\{(x, y) \mid y = x\}$ as the identity function.

If $F(G)$ is equal to the identity function and $G(F)$ is equal to the identity function as in the preceding example, F and G are called *inverse functions*. This name is suggested by the fact that the operations involved in finding $f(x)$ apparently "undo" the operations involved in finding $g(x)$. Note that the graphs of F and G are symmetrical with respect to the graph of the identity function.

The preceding discussion suggests the following definition of inverse functions.

> If F and G are functions, $R_F \subseteq D_G$, $g[f(x)] = x$ when $x \in D_F$, $R_G \subseteq D_F$, and $f[g(x)] = x$ when $x \in D_G$, then F and G are *inverse functions*.

Given the conditions stated in the preceding definition of inverse functions, it can be shown that $R_F = D_G$ and $R_G = D_F$. Thus we have the following theorem whose proof is given in Example 4.

▷ **Theorem 1–6.** If F and G are inverse functions, then $R_F = D_G$ and $R_G = D_F$.

Let us consider some additional examples of inverse functions.

Example 1. If $F = \{(x, y) \mid y = x^3\}$ and $G = \{(x, y) \mid y = \sqrt[3]{x}\}$, draw their graphs and determine if F and G are inverse functions.

Solution. Since the domains of these functions are not specified and since both x^3 and $\sqrt[3]{x}$ represent real numbers when $x \in R$, we see that $D_F = D_G = R$. Also when $x \in R$, x^3 and $\sqrt[3]{x}$ represent any value in R and we see that $R_F = R_G = R$. Also $f[g(x)] = (\sqrt[3]{x})^3 = x$ and $g[f(x)] = \sqrt[3]{x^3} = x$. Therefore F and G are inverse functions. The graphs of these functions are shown at the right. We observe that these graphs appear symmetric with respect to the graph of $\{(x, y) \mid y = x\}$.

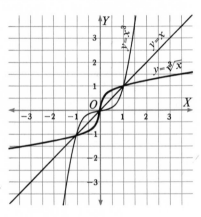

Example 2. Do $f(x) = x^2$ and $g(x) = \sqrt{x}$ define inverse functions?

First we note that $D_F = R$; $R_F = \langle 0, \infty \langle$; $D_G = \langle 0, \infty \langle$; and $R_G = \langle 0, \infty \langle$. We now check to see if the conditions of our definition of inverse functions are satisfied.
Is $R_F \subseteq D_G$? That is, is $\langle 0, \infty \langle \subseteq \langle 0, \infty \langle$? Answer: Yes.
Is $R_G \subseteq D_F$? That is, is $\langle 0, \infty \langle \subseteq R$? Answer: Yes.
When $x \in D_G$, that is, for $x \geq 0$, does $f[g(x)] = x$? That is, does $(\sqrt{x})^2 = x$? Answer: Yes.
When $x \in D_F$, that is, for $x \in R$, does $g[f(x)] = x$? That is, does $\sqrt{x^2} = x$? Answer: No. (We know that $\sqrt{x^2} = |x|$ and that $|x| \neq x$ when $x < 0$.)

Therefore, we conclude that if $F = \{(x, y) \mid y = x^2\}$ and if $G = \{(x, y) \mid y = \sqrt{x}\}$, F and G are not inverse functions. If, however, *in defining F*, we rule that $D_F = \langle 0, \infty \langle$, then D and F *are* inverse functions. Their graphs are shown in the diagram at the right. Observe that these graphs appear symmetric with respect to the graph of $\{(x, y) \mid y = x\}$.

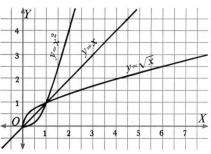

Example 3. Given $F = \{(x, y) \mid y = 2\,x^2 - 1 \land x \geq 0\}$. Find G, so that F and G are inverse functions, if G exists.

Solution. If F and G are inverse functions, we know that $f[g(x)] = x$. Hence $2[g(x)]^2 - 1 = x$. Solving for $g(x)$ we have $g(x) = \sqrt{\dfrac{x+1}{2}}$. Thus $G = \left\{(x, y) \mid y = \sqrt{\dfrac{x+1}{2}} \land x \geq -1\right\}$. From our expression for G, we see that $D_G = \{x \mid x \geq -1\}$ and from the expression for F, we see that $R_F = \{y \mid y \geq -1\}$. Thus $D_G = R_F$. In addition, for F and G to be inverse functions, D_F must be equal to R_G. D_F is the set of non-negative real numbers and R_G is the set of non-negative real numbers. Thus $D_F = R_G$. Also $g[f(x)] = g(2\,x^2 - 1) = \sqrt{\dfrac{(2\,x^2 - 1) + 1}{2}} = \sqrt{\dfrac{2\,x^2}{2}} = \sqrt{x^2} = x$. Therefore F and G are inverse functions according to the definition of inverse functions. The graphs of the functions F and G are shown in the diagram below. Note that in solving for $g(x)$, we chose the positive square root because the range of G must be the set of non-negative real numbers if it is to be equal to the domain of F.

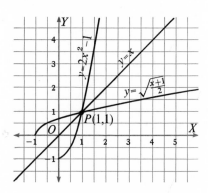

Example 4. Show that under the conditions stated in our definition for inverse functions F and G, $R_F = D_G$ and $R_G = D_F$.

Solution. We shall use an indirect essay argument. We know that $R_F \subseteq D_G$. Therefore if we can show that R_F is not a proper subset of D_G, we will know that $R_F = D_G$. Suppose $R_F \subset D_G$. Then there exists a number a such that $a \in D_G$ but $a \notin R_F$. However $a \in D_G$ implies that there is a number b in R_G such that $b = g(a)$. Now we know that $R_G \subseteq D_F$ and therefore, $b \in D_F$. Since $b \in D_F$, we know that $f(b) = f[g(a)] = a$. Hence $a \in R_F$ and this contradicts our earlier statement that $a \notin R_F$. The assumption $R_F \subset D_G$ therefore leads to a contradiction and so must be abandoned. Since R_F is a subset of D_G and is not a proper subset of D_G, we conclude that $R_F = D_G$ and our proof is complete. A similar argument will establish the fact that $R_G = D_F$.

When F and G are inverse functions, we often denote G as F^{-1} or F as G^{-1}. In this case the -1 is not to be construed as an exponent. It is, rather, an indication that the rule for one of these functions *undoes* the operations which are specified by the rule of the other. The statement $F(F^{-1}) = F^{-1}(F) = \{(x, y) \mid y = x\}$ is somewhat analogous to the statement $a \cdot a^{-1} = a^{-1} \cdot a = 1$. The last statement is true if a^{-1} is the multiplicative inverse of a; the first statement is true if F^{-1} and F are inverse functions.

We have repeatedly observed that when F and G are inverse functions, their graphs are symmetric with respect to the graph of $\{(x, y) \mid y = x\}$. This statement is equivalent to the following theorem.

▷ **Theorem 2–6.** If F and G are inverse functions, then $(a, b) \in F \longleftrightarrow (b, a) \in G$.

Proof of Theorem 2–6: If F and G are inverse functions, then $(a, b) \in F \longleftrightarrow (b, a) \in G$.

The proof of this theorem has the form $[(x \wedge y \longrightarrow z) \wedge (x \wedge z \longrightarrow y)] \longrightarrow [x \longrightarrow (y \longleftrightarrow z)]$. To prove this theorem we must prove the left-to-right implication and the right-to-left implication.

PART 1. $(a, b) \in F \longrightarrow (b, a) \in G$.

(1)
$(a, b) \in F$ —

(2)
$\longrightarrow f(a) = b$

(3)
$\longrightarrow b \in R_F$

(4)
$G = F^{-1}$

(5)
$\longrightarrow b \in D_G$

(6)
$\longrightarrow g(b) = g[f(a)] = a$

(7)
$\longrightarrow g(b) = a$

(8)

(8)
$\longmapsto (b, a) \in G$

Reasons: (1) Given, (2) If $F = \{(x, y) \mid y = f(x)\}$, then $y_1 = f(x_1) \longleftrightarrow (x_1, y_1) \in F$, (3) Definition of $f(x)$, (4) Given, (5) Definition of inverse function, (6) Definition of function, substitution property of equality, and definition of inverse function, (7) Transitive property of equality, (8) If $F = \{(x, y) \mid y = f(x)\}$, then $y_1 = f(x_1) \longleftrightarrow (x_1, y_1) \in F$.

The proof of $[(b, a) \in G \wedge F = G^{-1}] \longrightarrow (a, b) \in F$ is similar to the above proof.

Theorem 2–6 confirms our observation that the graphs of two inverse functions are symmetric with respect to the graph of the line $y = x$. Consider the graphs of $y = f(x)$ and $y = g(x)$ shown in the diagram. If G and F are inverse functions, the graph of G must be the reflection of the graph of F in line L as shown in the diagram. However, we see at once that G is not a function because some vertical line intersects it *twice*. Note that the vertical line shown is symmetric with the horizontal line, which intersects the graph of F twice. Thus we must conclude that some functions do not have inverse functions associated with them.

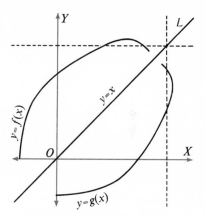

Suppose we are given a function F. Under what conditions will there be a function G such that F and G are inverse functions? Our diagram gives us a clue. If no horizontal line intersects the graph of function F more than once, then no vertical line will intersect the reflection of the graph of F in L more than once. In that case, the reflected graph will define a function which is the inverse of F. When we say that no horizontal line intersects the graph of F more than once, in effect we are stating that each member of the range of F corresponds to exactly one member of the domain. This is *not* the case for the function F whose graph is shown in the preceding diagram because one member of the range y_1 corresponds to two different members of the domain.

These observations suggest the following theorem.

Theorem 3–6. A function F has an inverse function G if and only if each member of the range of F corresponds to exactly one member of the domain of F.

On the next page we prove the left-to-right implication and give reasons for each step. The proof of the right-to-left implication is outlined in Exercise 16 on page 301.

Proof of the left-to-right part of Theorem 3–6: If a function F has an inverse function G, then each member of the range of F corresponds to exactly one member of the domain of F.

Let $F = \{(x, y) \mid y = f(x)\}$. Then there is a function $G = \{(x, y) \mid y = g(x)\}$ such that F and G are inverse functions. Why?

In order to show that each b of the range of F corresponds to exactly one member of the domain of F, we must prove two statements: (i) Each b in R_F corresponds to at least one a in D_F and (ii) each b in R_F corresponds to not more than one a in D_F. The first statement follows at once from our agreement that $b \in R_F$ implies that there is at least one number $a \in D_F$ such that $(a, b) \in F$. To prove (ii) we shall show that if $(a_1, b), (a_2, b) \in F$, then $a_1 = a_2$, as follows:

$$\overset{(1)}{[[(a_1, b) \in F} \overset{(2)}{\longrightarrow (b, a_1) \in G]} \wedge \overset{(3)}{[(a_2, b) \in F} \overset{(4)}{\longrightarrow (b, a_2) \in G]} \wedge$$

$$\overset{(5)}{(G \text{ is a function})]} \overset{(6)}{\longrightarrow a_1 = a_2.} \therefore \text{ a function } F \text{ has an inverse}$$

$$\overset{(7)}{G \longrightarrow} \text{ each member of } R_F \text{ corresponds to exactly one member of } D_F.$$

Reasons: (1) Given, (2) Definition of inverse function, (3) Given, (4) Definition of inverse function, (5) Given, (6) $[(a, b) \in F \wedge (a, b') \in F] \longrightarrow [b = b']$, (7) Transitive property of implication. Now that we have proved both (i) and (ii) true, our proof is complete, because there is one and only one a for each b.

Suppose F and G are functions whose graphs are symmetric to the graph of the identity function $\{(x, y) \mid y = x\}$ as shown in our diagram. Is it not evident that F and G are inverse functions?

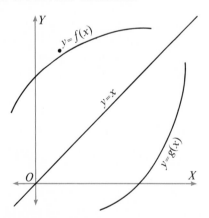

This suggests the following theorem:

Theorem 4–6. If F and G are functions and $(a, b) \in F \longleftrightarrow (b, a) \in G$, then F and G are inverse functions.

Proof of Theorem 4–6: If F and G are functions and $(a, b) \in F$ if and only if $(b, a) \in G$, then F and G are inverse functions.

$$
\begin{array}{l}
\overset{(1)}{[(b, a) \in G \longrightarrow (a, b) \in F]} \overset{(3)}{\longrightarrow R_G \subseteq D_F} \\
\overset{(2)}{[(a, b) \in F \longrightarrow (b, a) \in G]} \overset{(4)}{\longrightarrow R_F \subseteq D_G} \\
\overset{(5)}{(b, a) \in G \longrightarrow a = g(b)} \quad \overset{(7)}{} \\
\overset{(6)}{(a, b) \in F \longrightarrow b = f(a)} \longrightarrow b = f[g(b)] \wedge a = g[f(a)]
\end{array}
$$

$\overset{(8)}{\longrightarrow} G$ and F are inverse functions

Reasons: (1) Given and $(p \longleftrightarrow q) \longleftrightarrow (p \longrightarrow q \wedge q \longrightarrow p)$, (2) Same as **1**, (3) Definition of subset, (4) Definition of a subset, (5) If $F = \{(x, y) \mid y = f(x)\}$, then $y = f(x) \longleftrightarrow (x, y) \in F$, (6) Same as **5**, (7) Substitution property of equality, (8) Definition of inverse functions.

Theorem 2–6 and Theorem 4–6 can be stated as the following one theorem:

▶ **Theorem 5–6.** Functions F and G are inverses of each other if and only if $(a, b) \in F \longleftrightarrow (b, a) \in G$.

If F is a function for which the statement $(a, b) \in F \longleftrightarrow (b, a) \in F$ happens to be true, it follows from Theorem 5–6 that the function F is its own inverse, that is, it is self inverse.

If $D_F = R_F$ and $f[f(x)] = x$, then the function F defined by the equation $y = f(x)$ is self inverse because

$$(a, b) \in F \longleftrightarrow b = f(a) \longleftrightarrow f(b) = f[f(a)] \longleftrightarrow a = f(b) \longleftrightarrow (b, a) \in F.$$

Example. Let $f(x) = \dfrac{1}{x}$. Then $f[f(x)] = \dfrac{1}{\frac{1}{x}} = x$. Hence $f[f(x)] = x$ and we know that the function F defined by $y = \dfrac{1}{x}$ is self inverse provided $D_F = R_F$. Thus the function $F = \left\{(x, y) \mid y = \dfrac{1}{x}\right\}$ is a self inverse function.

Since every function is a relation, it is clear that inverse functions are also inverse relations. A *definition* of inverse relations consistent with the above discussion can be obtained by replacing the word "function" with the word "relation" in Theorem 5–6.

Ⓐ **EXERCISES**

1. Given that $F = \{(1, 6), (2, 7), (3, 8)\}$, and $G = \{(6, y), (x, 2), (x, y)\}$, replace each x and y in G so that G and F are functions.

2. Match each function indicated in the column on the left with its inverse function in the column on the right.

a. $\{(1, 1), (2, 8), (3, 27)\}$ (1) $\{(-1, -1), (-2, -2), (-3, -3)\}$

b. $\{(-2, -3), (-1, -1), (0, 1)\}$ (2) $\{(-2, -9), (-1, -4), (-6, -2)\}$

c. $\{(1, 1), (2, 2), (3, 3)\}$ (3) $\{(1, 1), (2, 8), (3, 27)\}$

d. $\{(9, -2), (4, -1), (-6, 2)\}$ (4) $\{(-2, 9), (-1, 4), (2, -6)\}$
(5) $\{(-3, -2), (-1, -1), (1, 0)\}$
(6) $\{(3, 3), (1, 1), (2, 2)\}$
(7) $\{(27, 3), (8, 2), (1, 1)\}$

3. If $F = \{(x, y) \mid y = 3x + 1\}$ and $G = \{(x, y) \mid y = \frac{1}{3}x - \frac{1}{3}\}$ show that F and G are inverse functions.

4. Each of the following graphs defines a function. Copy each of these graphs which has an inverse function and with reference to the same coordinate axes, sketch the graph of the inverse function.

a. 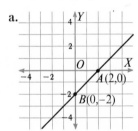   c. 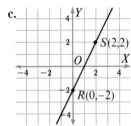   e.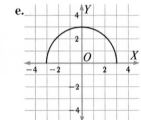

b. 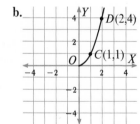   d. 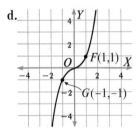   f.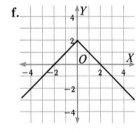

Ⓑ **EXERCISES**

5. Given $F = \{(x, y) \mid y = 3x^2 - 1\}$, find its inverse function if one exists.

6. If $F = \{(x, y) \mid y = 2\sqrt{x}\}$, determine G so that G is the function which is the inverse of F if such an inverse exists.

7. Determine the function which is the inverse of $\{(x, y) \mid y = \sqrt{x + 4}\}$ if such a function exists.

8. If F is a function and M is the identity function, prove that $F(M) = M(F) = F$.

9. If C is the constant function $\{(x, y) \mid y = c\}$ and $F = \{(x, y) \mid y = f(x)\}$, prove that $F(C) = \{(x, y) \mid y = f(c)\}$ and $C(F) = C$. Assume that $D_F = D_C = R_F$.

10. Show that the union of the graphs of inverse relations is symmetric with respect to the graph of $\{(x, y) \mid y = x\}$.

11. Prove that two relations which are inverse relations of the same relation are equal.

12. We have defined inverse functions but we have not defined the inverse of a function.

   a. Try to state a definition for the inverse of a function.

   b. According to your definition, is the inverse of a function always a function?

   c. Is the inverse of a relation always a relation?

13. Determine the function which is the inverse of $\left\{(x, y) \mid y = \dfrac{1}{x^3}\right\}$ if such a function exists.

14. Find the function which is the inverse of the function F if F is $\{(x, y) \mid xy = 6 \wedge x \in \langle 0, 2 \rangle\} \cup \{(x, y) \mid xy = 1 \wedge x \in \langle 2, 4 \rangle\}$.

15. Find the function F^{-1} which is the inverse of the function $F = \{(x, y) \mid y = x^2 \wedge x \in \langle 0, 1 \rangle\} \cup \{(x, y) \mid y = x^3 \wedge x \in \langle 1, \infty \rangle\}$. Draw the graph of F and F^{-1} on the same set of coordinate axes.

16. The right-to-left part of Theorem 3–6 may be stated as follows: If each member of the range of the function F corresponds to exactly one member of its domain, then F has an inverse function G. The proof, without reasons, is given below. You are to supply the reasons.

   Proof: Let F be the function $\{(x, y) \mid y = f(x)\}$ and G be the relation $\{(y, x) \mid (x, y) \in F\}$.

   Observe that G is a relation and we wish to prove that it is a function. To do this we must show that each y in D_G corresponds to one and only one x in R_G.

   Since $(y, x) \in G$ if and only if $(x, y) \in F$, there is at least one x for each y. Why?

   To show that there is not more than one x for each y, we prove that $[(y_1, x_1) \in G \wedge (y_1, x_2) \in G] \longrightarrow x_1 = x_2$ as follows:

$$(y_1, x_1) \in G \xrightarrow{\text{(1)}} (x_1, y_1) \in F \xrightarrow{\text{(2)}} y_1 = f(x_1) \left.\begin{array}{l} \\ \\ \end{array}\right\} \xrightarrow{\text{(5)}} f(x_1) = f(x_2) \xrightarrow{\text{(6)}}$$

$$(y_1, x_2) \in G \xrightarrow{\text{(3)}} (x_2, y_1) \in F \xrightarrow{\text{(4)}} y_1 = f(x_2)$$

$$\xrightarrow{\text{(6)}} x_1 = x_2.$$

   $\therefore$ (Each member of R_F corresponds to exactly one member of D_F) $\xrightarrow{\text{(7)}}$

   $\xrightarrow{\text{(7)}}$ (F has an inverse function G).

Linear Functions

The function L is a linear function if and only if $L = \{(x, y) \mid y = mx + k \wedge m \neq 0 \wedge x \in R\}$. We see that $D_L = R_L = R$ and that the defining equation pairs the members of D_L with the members of R_L in a one-to-one correspondence. We know, too, that the graph of L is an oblique line (a line that is neither vertical nor horizontal) whose slope is m and whose y-intercept is k.

Since each member in the range of L corresponds to exactly one member in the domain of L, we know that L has an inverse function L^{-1}. Hence $l[l^{-1}(x)] = x$ and $l[l^{-1}(x)] = ml^{-1}(x) + k$ and $x = ml^{-1}(x) + k$. Solving $x = ml^{-1}(x) + k$ for $l^{-1}(x)$, we obtain $l^{-1}(x) = \dfrac{1}{m} x - \dfrac{k}{m}$ which also defines a linear function. To be certain that the function L^{-1} is in fact the inverse of L, we need to verify that $l^{-1}[l(x)] = x$. We know that $l(x) = mx + k$. Substituting in $l^{-1}(x) = \dfrac{1}{m} x - \dfrac{k}{m}$, we have

$$l^{-1}[l(x)] = \frac{1}{m} (mx + k) - \frac{k}{m} = x + \frac{k}{m} - \frac{k}{m} = x. \text{ Thus } l^{-1}[l(x)] = x.$$

We summarize these results in the following theorem:

▶ **Theorem 6–6.** Every linear function $\{(x, y) \mid y = mx + k \wedge m \neq 0\}$ has an inverse $\left\{(x, y) \mid y = \dfrac{1}{m} x - \dfrac{k}{m}\right\}$ which is also a linear function.

Suppose that x_1 and x_2 are distinct real numbers and y_1 and y_2 are distinct real numbers. Suppose also that (x_1, y_1) and (x_2, y_2) are in the function $L = \{(x, y) \mid y = mx + k\}$. Then we have two equations $y_2 = mx_2 + k$ and $y_1 = mx_1 + k$ with which to find m and k. To find this solution we use the addition property of equality to obtain $y_2 - y_1 = m(x_2 - x_1)$. It follows that $m = \dfrac{y_2 - y_1}{x_2 - x_1}$. Substituting this expression in the first equation we obtain $y_2 = \left(\dfrac{y_2 - y_1}{x_2 - x_1}\right) x_2 + k$. Then $k = y_2 - \left(\dfrac{y_2 - y_1}{x_2 - x_1}\right) x_2$ or $k = \dfrac{y_1 x_2 - y_2 x_1}{x_2 - x_1}$. Thus if there is a linear function L which contains both (x_1, y_1) and (x_2, y_2), it is defined by the equation:

$$y = \left(\frac{y_2 - y_1}{x_2 - x_1}\right) x + \frac{y_1 x_2 - y_2 x_1}{x_2 - x_1}.$$

It can be verified by direct substitution that both (x_1, y_1) and (x_2, y_2) satisfy this equation.

Thus we have the following theorem:

▶ **Theorem 7–6.** If x_1 and x_2 are distinct real numbers and y_1 and y_2 are distinct real numbers, then there is one and only one linear function L such that $y_1 = l(x_1)$ and $y_2 = l(x_2)$.

Since any function is a set of ordered pairs, we can speak of the union of two functions or the intersection of two functions and we can depict these graphically. For linear functions $L_1 = \{(x, y) \mid y = m_1x + k_1\}$ and $L_2 = \{(x, y) \mid y = m_2x + k_2\}$, we have:

$$L_1 \cup L_2 = \{(x, y) \mid y = m_1x + k_1\} \cup \{(x, y) \mid y = m_2x + k_2\}$$
$$L_1 \cap L_2 = \{(x, y) \mid y = m_1x + k_1\} \cap \{(x, y) \mid y = m_2x + k_2\}$$

The graph of $L_1 \cup L_2$ is *two distinct lines* unless the defining equations $y = m_1x + k_1$ and $y = m_2x + k_2$ are equivalent.

The graph of $L_1 \cap L_2$ is (1) a single line if $m_1 = m_2$ and $k_1 = k_2$, (2) a single point if $m_1 \neq m_2$, and (3) nonexistent if $m_1 = m_2$ and $k_1 \neq k_2$. (When $m_1 = m_2$ and $k_1 \neq k_2$ as in (3), then $L_1 \cap L_2 = \emptyset$ and the null set does not have a graph.) In the last instance the lines which are the graphs of L_1 and L_2 are parallel according to Theorem 6–5.

Recall that the equation $y = mx + k$ is called the slope-intercept form of the equation of a straight line L. In this case "intercept" refers to the y-intercept, which is the *ordinate* of the point where L intersects the y-axis. Sometimes we are interested in the x-intercept, that is, the *abscissa* of the point where the graph of a function intersects the x-axis. For the linear function L this x-intercept can be found by solving the system: $\begin{cases} y = mx + k \\ y = 0 \end{cases}$

By substituting 0 for y in $y = mx + k$ we obtain $mx + k = 0$. Since $m \neq 0$, the equation has one and only one solution, namely $-\dfrac{k}{m}$. Substituting $-\dfrac{k}{m}$ for x and 0 for y, we see that $\left(-\dfrac{k}{m}, 0\right) \in L$. Thus the x-intercept of the function, defined by $y = mx + k$ when $m \neq 0$, is the same as the solution of the equation $0 = mx + k$. Although at the present we are concerned only with linear functions, we state the following definition which applies to all functions.

If F is a function and $(a, 0) \in F$, then a is a zero of the function F.

Thus -4 is a *zero* of the function F_1 which is defined by $y = 3x + 12$, 4 and -3 are each *zeros* of the function F_2 which is defined by $y = -x^2 + x + 12$, and 5 and -5 are each *zeros* of the function F_3 which is defined by

$y = |x| - 5$. The following graphs are graphs of F_1, F_2, and F_3.

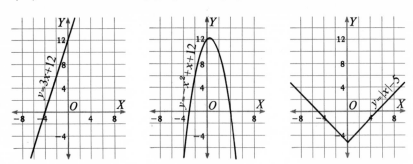

You recall that a solution of an equation is also called a *root* of the equation. Accordingly, if a function is defined by the equation $y = f(x)$, any member of $\{x \mid f(x) = 0\}$ is a *zero of the function*, an *x-intercept* of the graph of the function, and a *solution* or *root* of $f(x) = 0$.

Example 1. Find m so that 7 is the zero of the linear function defined by $y = mx - 35$.

Solution. We know that 7 is the root of the equation $0 = mx - 35$. Hence $0 = 7m - 35$ or $m = 5$. The linear function defined by the equation $y = 5x - 35$ contains the ordered pair $(7, 0)$. Then 7 is the zero of this function.

Example 2. Find the inverse L^{-1} of the linear function L defined by $y = 3x - 6$ and show that the graphs of L, L^{-1}, and $\{(x, y) \mid y = x\}$ have a point in common.

Solution. We will use the method we used in our discussion of Theorem 6–6 (page 302).

Since $l(x) = 3x - 6$ and $l[l^{-1}(x)] = x$, we have $3(l^{-1}(x)) - 6 = x$.

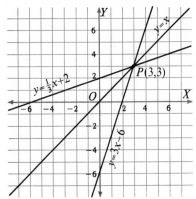

Solving for $l^{-1}(x)$, we have $l^{-1}(x) = \frac{1}{3}x + 2$. Therefore $L^{-1} = \{(x, y) \mid y = \frac{1}{3}x + 2\}$. When we solve the system $\begin{cases} y = \frac{1}{3}x + 2 \\ y = 3x - 6 \end{cases}$ we obtain $x = 3$, $y = 3$. We know that $(3, 3) \in L$ and $(3, 3) \in L^{-1}$. It is also true that $(3, 3) \in \{(x, y) \mid y = x\}$. The graphs of L, L^{-1}, and $\{(x, y) \mid y = x\}$ are shown at the right.

Example 3. Determine the defining equation for the linear function L if $l(3) = 5$ and $l(9) = 1$.

Solution. $l(x) = mx + k$. We must solve the system $\begin{cases} 5 = 3\,m + \text{k} \\ 1 = 9\,m + k \end{cases}$ for m and k. Solving we obtain $m = -\frac{2}{3}$ and $k = 7$. Therefore $l(x) = -\frac{2}{3}x + 7$.

Example 4. If $L_1 = \{(x, y) \mid 7\,x + 4\,y = 23\}$ and $L_2 = \{(x, y) \mid 3\,x - 5\,y = 30\}$, are L_1 and L_2 linear functions? If so, show the graph of $L_1 \cup L_2$ and $L_1 \cap L_2$.

Solution. Since $7\,x + 4\,y = 23 \longleftrightarrow y = -\frac{7}{4}x + \frac{23}{4}$ and $3\,x - 5\,y = 30 \longleftrightarrow y = \dfrac{3\,x}{5} - 6$, we see that L_1 and L_2 are linear functions. The graph of L_1 is the line L_1 and the graph of L_2 is the line L_2. The graph of $L_1 \cup L_2$ is the union of these two sets of points. The graph of $L_1 \cap L_2$ is the point $P(5, -3)$.

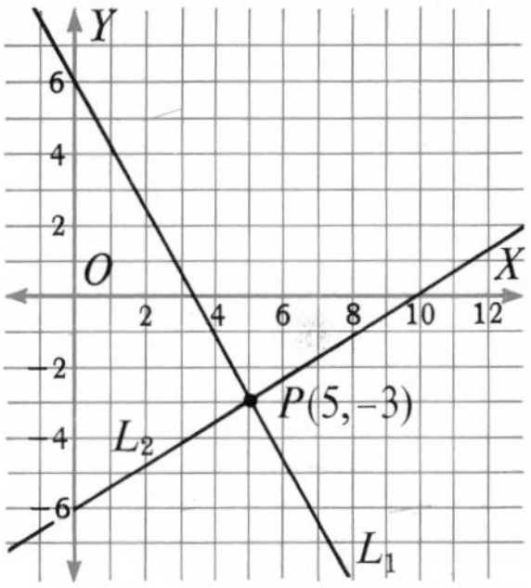

Ⓐ EXERCISES

1. Which of the following are linear functions? Assume that a, b, and c are non-zero constants.

   a. $\{(x, y) \mid 3\,x + 2\,y = 1\}$
   b. $\{(x, y) \mid 4\,x = y\}$
   c. $\{(x, y) \mid y = 18\}$
   d. $\{(x, y) \mid 7\,x + 3\,y = 2\}$
   e. $\{(x, y) \mid 7 = x\}$
   f. $\{(x, y) \mid 4\,x - 2 = y\}$
   g. $\{(x, y) \mid ax = 9\}$
   h. $\{(x, y) \mid by = 4\}$
   i. $\{(x, y) \mid ax + by = c\}$
   j. $\{(x, y) \mid y + \frac{5}{2} = 2 + \frac{1}{2}\}$

2. Which of the descriptive phrases "graph of a linear function," "graph of a constant function," or "not the graph of a function," applies to each of the following graphs?

a.
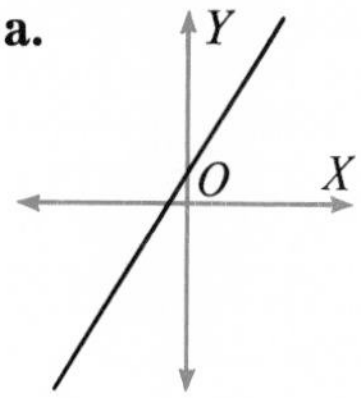

b.
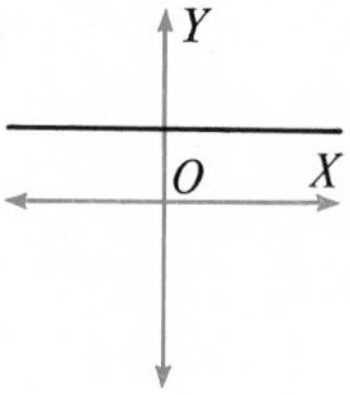

c.
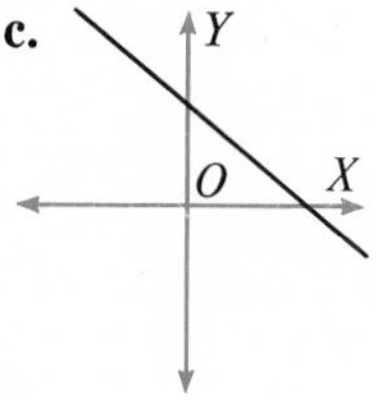

d.
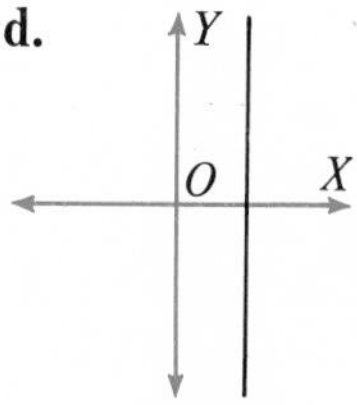

3. Find the inverse of each of the following linear functions.

a. $\{(x, y) \mid y = 2x + 1\}$ e. $\{(x, y) \mid y = -\frac{2}{3}x + \frac{5}{3}\}$

b. $\{(x, y) \mid y = -3x - 4\}$ f. $\{(x, y) \mid y = \frac{1}{2}x\}$

c. $\{(x, y) \mid y = -x + 6\}$ g. $\{(x, y) \mid y = ax + b; \ a \neq 0\}$

d. $\{(x, y) \mid y = \frac{1}{2}x - 3\}$ h. $\{(x, y) \mid y = (a + b)x + cd; \ a + b \neq 0\}$

4. By inspection, determine whether the graphs of the intersection of the two functions defined in each exercise below is a single point, a single line, or the empty set. Check your answer by drawing the graphs of the two functions in each of the following pairs.

a. $\{(x, y) \mid y = 6x + 8\}$; $\{(x, y) \mid x = \frac{1}{6}y - \frac{4}{3}\}$

b. $\{(x, y) \mid y = 3x - 2\}$; $\{(x, y) \mid y = 2x - 3\}$

c. $\{(x, y) \mid y = 7x - 1\}$; $\{(x, y) \mid y = \frac{1}{7}x - 1\}$

d. $\{(x, y) \mid y = -3x + 4\}$; $\{(x, y) \mid y = -3x - 4\}$

e. $\{(x, y) \mid 2y = 3x - 1\}$; $\{(x, y) \mid 6y = 9x - 3\}$

f. $\{(x, y) \mid 4y = -5x + 3\}$; $\{(x, y) \mid 8y = -10x - 1\}$

5. After studying the graphs you have made in Ex. 4, complete each of the following sentences.

a. If the graph of the intersection of two linear equations is a single point, the graph of the union of the two functions is

b. If the graph of the intersection of two linear functions is the null set, the graph of the union of the two functions is

c. If the graph of the intersection of two linear functions is a single line, the graph of the union of the two functions is

6. Find the zeros (if zeros exist) of the function defined by each of the following equations.

a. $y = x^2 - 4x - 12$ d. $2y = 3x + 5$ g. $y = 7$

b. $y = -x^2 - 5x + 6$ e. $y = 12x^2 - 5x - 2$ h. $y = x^2$

c. $y = 4x - 7$ f. $y = 36x^2 - 1$ i. $|x| = y - 3$

7. a. What is the greatest number of zeros that a linear function may have? What is the least number of zeros it may have?

b. Does a function that is not a linear function always have a zero? May it have more than one zero?

8. Find the x-intercept or intercepts (if they exist) of the graph of the function defined by each of the following equations.

a. $y = 7x - 5$ c. $y = x^2 + 4$

b. $y = -x^2 - 5x + 14$ d. $y = |x|$

9. Find m so that 7 is the zero of the linear function defined by $y = mx - 42$.

10. Find m so that $-\frac{11}{3}$ is the zero of the linear function defined by $y = mx - 5$.

11. Write an equation which defines the linear function having as members the ordered pairs $(-4, -1)$ and $(7, 3)$.

12. Indicate two functions which have graphs passing through the point $R(-3, 2)$. How many such functions are there?

13. Determine the linear function L for which

   a. $l(2) = 7$ and $l(5) = 16$ **b.** $l(3) = 4$ and $l(12) = 10$

14. Show that the linear equation $ax + by + c = 0$ defines a linear function provided $ab \neq 0$.

Direct Variation

You will recall that we sometimes speak of the number represented by $\frac{a}{b}$ when $a, b \in R$ and $b \neq 0$ as the *ratio* of a to b. Also, a true equation whose members are ratios is called a *proportion*.

A function defined by an equation of the form $y + b = k(x + a)^n$ when $k, a, b,$ and n are constants, $k \neq 0, x \neq -a,$ and $n > 0$, is called a *direct variation*. We say that $y + b$ *varies directly* as $(x + a)^n$ or that $y + b$ *is directly proportional to* $(x + a)^n$. The nonzero constant k is called the *constant of variation* or the *constant of proportionality*. If (x_1, y_1) and (x_2, y_2) are any two ordered pairs in this function, then $y_1 + b = k(x_1 + a)^n$ and $y_2 + b = k(x_2 + a)^n$.

Since the first member of each ordered pair is not $-a$ we have $k = \dfrac{y_1 + b}{(x_1 + a)^n}$ and $k = \dfrac{y_2 + b}{(x_2 + a)^n}$. Therefore $\dfrac{y_1 + b}{(x_1 + a)^n} = \dfrac{y_2 + b}{(x_2 + a)^n}$. The proportion $\dfrac{y_1 + b}{(x_1 + a)^n} = \dfrac{y_2 + b}{(x_2 + a)^n}$ is read "$y_1 + b$ is to $(x_1 + a)^n$ as $y_2 + b$ is to $(x_2 + a)^n$."

If $n = 1$, the direct variation defined by $y + b = k(x + a)^n$ is a *linear function* defined by $y + b = m(x + a)$.

The following pairs of equivalent statements show how we use the language of variation.

t varies directly as s^3	$t = ks^3$
$x - 3$ is directly proportional to $y + 5$	$x - 3 = k(y + 5)$
$s + 2$ varies directly as the square root of w	$s + 2 = k\sqrt{w}$
z is directly proportional to $(x - 5)^4$	$z = k(x - 5)^4$
V, the measure of the volume of a sphere, varies directly as r^3, the cube of the measure of the length of the radius.	$V = kr^3$

Example 1.   If D, the measure of the actual distance, is directly proportional to d, the measure of the scaled distance in a map, state a formula for the values of this direct variation if the constant of proportionality is 3×10^5. Also find the actual distance when the scaled distance is 3 inches.

Solution.   Since $k = 3 \times 10^5$ our defining equation for the direct variation is $D = 3 \times 10^5 \times d$. If $d = 3$, then $D = 3 \times 10^5 \times 3 = 900000$. Thus the actual distance is 900000 inches. If we wish to express this distance in miles, we have $\dfrac{900000}{63460} \approx 14.2$. Thus the actual distance is approximately 14.2 miles.

Example 2.   If A, the measure of the area of a cross section of a pyramid parallel to the base, varies directly as d^2, the square of the measure of its distance from the vertex, find the area of a cross-section five inches from the vertex if the area of a cross-section 13 inches from the vertex is 845 square inches.

Solution.   Since A varies directly as d^2, we can write $A = kd^2$ where k is a constant. Since $A = 845$ when $d = 13$, we can find k for the equation $845 = k \times 13^2$. Thus $k = 5$. Our function is described by the rule $A = 5\,d^2$. Substituting 5 for d, we obtain $A = 5(5)^2 = 125$. Thus, the area of a cross-section five inches from the vertex is 125 square inches.

Example 3.   The dependence of the volume of a gas on its absolute temperature when the pressure remains fixed is described by Charles's law, $V = kT$, which is an application of direct variation. If one gram of methane has a volume of 1513 milliliters at 298° absolute temperature, find the volume of the gas at 273° absolute temperature.

Solution.   Since $V_1 = 1513$ when $T = 298$, we have $k = \frac{1513}{298}$. Thus, substituting in $V = kT$ we have $V_2 = \frac{1513}{298}(273) \approx 1386$. Thus the volume is approximately 1386 milliliters.

Ⓐ **EXERCISES**

1. If y varies directly as x and $y = -96$ when $x = 8$, find y when $x = -3$.

2. If y varies directly as x and $y = 3$ when $x = 17$, find y when $x = 3$.

3. If C is directly proportional to r and $C = 8\pi$ when $r = 4$, find C when $r = \frac{1}{4}$.

4. If d is directly proportional to t and $d = 120$ when $t = 3$, find d when $t = 4$.

5. If y varies directly as x^2 and $y = \frac{3}{4}$ when $x = \frac{1}{2}$, find y when $x = \sqrt{3}$.

6. Each of the following tables contains a few of the ordered pairs which belong to a relation which is a direct variation. Write the equation which defines each relation.

a.

x	10	1.2×10	6.5×10^{-1}
y	10^{-3}	1.2×10^{-3}	6.5×10^{-5}

c.

x	51	10	34
y	9	$\frac{30}{17}$	6

b.

c	2	$\sqrt{5}$	$\frac{\sqrt{3}}{3}$	$\frac{\sqrt{2}}{2}$
d	$2\sqrt{3}$	$\sqrt{15}$	1	$\frac{1}{2}\sqrt{6}$

d.

r	121	-12	-33
t	-55	$\frac{11}{60}$	15

7. If s, the measure of the stretch of a rubber band within its limits of elasticity, varies directly as w, the measure of the weight which stretches it, and if a weight of 5 pounds stretches the band 4 inches, how much will a weight of 7 pounds stretch it?

8. The equation $M_a = .08\,M_b$ defines (approximately) the set of ordered pairs (M_b, M_a) in which M_b represents the measure of the weight of the part of an iceberg which floats underneath the surface of the water and M_a represents the measure of the weight of the part above the surface of the water. If 12 tons is the weight of the part of an iceberg above the surface, what is the weight of the part below the surface?

9. The measure of the volume of a sphere is directly proportional to the cube of the measure of its radius. If the volume of a sphere is $36\,\pi$ cubic inches when the length of the radius is 3 inches, find the constant of proportionality and write the equation which defines the relation.

10. Use the equation you have written for Ex. 9 to find the volume of a sphere whose radius is 6 inches long.

11. The number of feet that an object falls is directly proportional to the square of the number of seconds during which it falls. If an object has fallen 144 feet at the end of 3 seconds, how far has it fallen at the end of 5 seconds?

12. The measures of the areas of two similar polygons are directly proportional to the squares of the measures of the lengths of their corresponding sides. If the area of one polygon is 142 square inches when one of its sides is 4 inches long, what is the area of a similar polygon whose corresponding side is 6 inches long?

13. If 23 parts of sodium and 35 parts of chlorine (by weight) combine to form sodium chloride (salt), how many pounds of sodium and how many of chlorine are required to form 290 pounds of sodium chloride?

14. The measure of the time required for a complete vibration of a pendulum is directly proportional to the square root of the measure of the length of the pendulum. If a pendulum 4 centimeters long completes a vibration in .8 of a second, how long does it take a pendulum which is 16 centimeters long to complete a vibration?

15. If a pendulum completes 174,528 vibrations in 24 hours, how much must the pendulum be lengthened to produce a vibration that requires 2 seconds? Use the constant of variation found for Ex. 14.

Inverse Variation

A function defined by an equation of the form $y + b = \dfrac{k}{(x + a)^n}$ when a, b, k, and n are constants, $k \neq 0$, $x \neq -a$, and $n > 0$ is called an *inverse varia-tion*. The equation $y + b = \dfrac{k}{(x + a)^n}$ is read "$y + b$ varies inversely as $(x + a)^n$" or "$y + b$ is inversely proportional to $(x + a)^n$." As in direct variation the constant k is called the *constant of variation* or the *constant of proportionality*. When $a = 0$, $b = 0$, and $n = 1$, the defining equation $y + b = \dfrac{k}{(x + a)^n}$ becomes $y = \dfrac{k}{x}$.

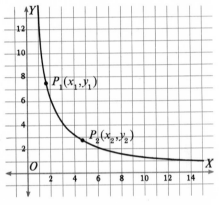

Thus $W = \left\{ (x, y) \mid y = \dfrac{k}{x} \right\}$ is an inverse variation. The graph of the truth set of $y = \dfrac{k}{x}$ when $x > 0$ and $k = 12$ is shown at the right. If $P_1(x_1, y_1)$ and $P_2(x_2, y_2)$ are any two points in the graph of this inverse variation, then $x_1 y_1 = k$ and $x_2 y_2 = k$. Hence $x_1 y_1 = x_2 y_2$. Since x_1, x_2, y_1, and y_2 are nonzero constants, we may divide both members of this equation by $x_2 y_1$ and obtain $\dfrac{x_1}{x_2} = \dfrac{y_2}{y_1}$.

Since we can form a proportion involving any two ordered pairs belonging to a function defined by $xy = k$, or $y = \dfrac{k}{x}$, we sometimes translate these sentences as "y is inversely proportional to x."

Consider the functions described by $y = \dfrac{k}{x^2}$, $y = \dfrac{k}{x + 7}$, and $y = \dfrac{k}{x^3}$. We may read the first of these as "y is inversely proportional to x^2" or as "y varies inversely as the square of x." How may we read the others?

Example. H, the measure of the intensity of light at a point, varies inversely as d^2, the square of the measure of the distance from that point to the source. The intensity at a distance of 16 feet from the source is what percent of the intensity at a distance of 12 feet?

Solution. $H = \dfrac{k}{d^2}$. Let H_1 be the measure of the intensity at a distance of 16 feet and let H_2 be the measure of the intensity at a distance of 12 feet. Then

$$H_1 = \frac{k}{16^2}$$

$$H_2 = \frac{k}{12^2}$$

$$\frac{H_1}{H_2} = \frac{k}{16^2} \div \frac{k}{12^2} = \frac{144}{256} = 0.5625$$

Therefore, the intensity at a distance of 16 feet is $56\frac{1}{4}$ percent of the intensity at 12 feet.

 A EXERCISES

1. If x varies inversely as y and $x = 12$ when $y = 18$, what is y when $x = 14$?

2. If x is inversely proportional to y and $x = 7$ when $y = 19$, find y when $x = 14$.

3. If x is inversely proportional to y and $y = 2$ when $x = .7$, write an equation which defines the relation consisting of all ordered pairs (x, y) just described.

4. Complete each of the following tables so that it expresses inverse variation.

a.

x	0.2	8	?
y	500	?	20

b.

x	5	15	?
y	$\frac{1}{600}$	?	40

5. Write an equation which defines each of the relations defined by the tables of Ex. 4.

6. Determine x or y so that each of the following statements is true.

a. $\{(2, \frac{3}{2}), (4, y)\} \subseteq \{(x, y) \mid y \text{ varies inversely as } x\}$

b. $\{(1, y), (2, \sqrt{6})\} \subseteq \{(x, y) \mid y \text{ is inversely proportional to } x^2\}$

c. $\{(x, 8), (4, 1)\} \subseteq \{(x, y) \mid y \text{ varies inversely as } x^2\}$

d. $\{(9, 5), (25, y)\} \subseteq \{(x, y) \mid y \text{ varies as } \sqrt{x}\}$

7. Draw the graph of each of the following relations.

a. $\{(x, y) \mid xy = 16\}$

b. $\left\{(x, y) \mid y = \dfrac{5}{x^2}\right\}$

c. $\left\{(x, y) \mid y + 7 = \dfrac{12}{x^2}\right\}$

d. $\left\{(x, y) \mid y + 7 = \dfrac{12}{(x-3)^2}\right\}$

8. The measure of the time required for a plane to make a trip varies inversely as the measure of the rate (ground speed) at which it travels. If a plane can make a particular trip in 2 hours traveling at the rate of 500 miles per hour, how fast must it travel to make the trip in $1\frac{3}{4}$ hours?

9. The measure of the weight of an object above the surface of the earth is inversely proportional to the square of the measure of its distance from the center of the earth. What is the weight of a man 200 miles above the surface of the earth if his weight on the surface is 180 pounds? Assume that the length of the radius of the earth is 4000 miles.

10. The number of hours required to do a piece of work is inversely proportional to the number of people doing the work, provided efficiency is not impaired by added workers and assuming that all people work at the same rate. The Fox Lake Civic Association wants to address and mail k envelopes. If two women can complete the work in 8 hours, how many hours will be needed if five women do the work?

11. The measure of the volume of air at a constant temperature varies inversely as the measure of the pressure exerted upon it. Thirty-six cubic inches of air under a pressure of 50 pounds will have what volume if the pressure is increased by 20 percent?

12. The number of revolutions of a wheel when the center moves a given distance is inversely proportional to the measure of the circumference of the wheel. If a wheel with a radius of 15 inches makes 10,560 revolutions in moving m miles, how many revolutions are made by a wheel with an 18 inch radius moving the same distance?

13. The measure of the illumination on a flat surface varies inversely as the square of the measure of its distance from the source of light. If a certain lamp bulb 3 feet from a printed page provides 30 lumens of illumination per square foot on the page, how many lumens are provided per square foot of the page if the page is held 4 feet from the light bulb?

Joint Variation and Combined Variation

If k is a nonzero constant the sentence "$z = kxy$" defines a relation in $R \times R \times R$. Using the language of variation it is read as "z varies jointly as x and y" or "z varies directly as the product of x and y." The variation of z with the product of x and y is called a *joint variation*. The sentence $z = kytx^2$ is translated as "z varies jointly as the product of y, t, and the square of x" or "z varies directly as the product of y, t, and x^2."

The equation $y = \dfrac{kx}{z}$ is read "y varies directly as x and inversely as z."

The variation of y with respect to x and z is called a *combined variation* because it involves both direct and inverse variation.

Example. M, the measure of the maximum safe load of a horizontal beam supported at its ends, varies directly as w, the measure of its width, and d^2, the square of the measure of its depth and inversely as l, the measure of the distance between supports. If the maximum safe load is 3600 pounds for a beam four inches wide and twelve inches deep, with supports 16 feet apart, find the maximum load for a beam of the same material which is three inches wide, eight inches deep, with supports 12 feet apart.

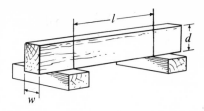

Solution. $M = \dfrac{kwd^2}{l}$

When $M = 3600$ we have $w = 4$, $d = 12$, and $l = 16$.

Thus $3600 = \dfrac{k \times 4 \times 12^2}{16}$

Thus $k = \dfrac{3600 \times 16}{4 \times 12^2} = 100$

$\therefore M = \dfrac{100\, wd^2}{l}$

Substituting 3 for w, 8 for d, and 12 for l, we obtain

$$M = \frac{100 \times 3 \times 64}{12} = 1600.$$

Thus the maximum safe load is 1600 pounds. Why was it unnecessary to express l in inches?

 EXERCISES

1. Given that m varies directly as the product of a and b and inversely as the product of c and the square of d, find m when $a = 2$, $b = -2$, $c = 3$, and $d = 5$ provided $m = \frac{10}{3}$ when $a = 4$, $b = 5$, $c = 2$, and $d = 3$.

2. The measure of the resistance of a wire to the passage of electricity varies directly as the measure of the length of the wire and inversely as the square of the measure of the diameter of a cross section of the wire. If one mile of wire, the length of the diameter of whose cross section is 0.365 inches, has a resistance of 0.420 ohms, what is the resistance of 1500 feet of wire, the length of the diameter of whose cross section is 0.420 inches?

3. Ohm's law states that I, the number of amperes of electric current, is directly proportional to E, the measure of the potential difference in volts, and inversely proportional to R, the measure of the resistance in ohms. If 110 volts of potential difference and 220 ohms of resistance causes $\frac{1}{2}$ ampere of electricity to flow, how many amperes of electricity flow if 120 volts of potential difference is combined with 100 ohms of resistance?

4. Given that n varies directly as the square root of a (provided a is non-negative) and inversely as the cube root of b, find n when $a = 4$ and $b = -8$, provided $n = 5$ when $a = 9$ and $b = 27$.

5. The measure of the volume of a pyramid varies jointly as the measures of its altitude and the area of its base. Find the length of the altitude of a pyramid the area of whose base is 10 square inches and the measure of whose volume is equal to the sum of the measures of the volumes of two pyramids P and P'. P has an altitude of $\sqrt{10}$ inches and a base of 5 square inches and P' has a base of 4 square inches, an altitude of 7 inches, and a volume of $\frac{28}{3}$ cubic inches.

6. The equation $F = \dfrac{m_1 m_2}{d^2}$ indicates that two particles, one with a mass whose measure is m_1 and the other with a mass whose measure is m_2, attract each other with a force whose measure is F and which is directly proportional to the product of the measure of their masses and inversely proportional to the square of the measure of the distance d between their centers.

a. What is the effect on F if m_1 and m_2 remain unchanged but d is tripled?

b. What is the effect on F if m_1, m_2, and d are all doubled?

c. What is the effect on F if m_1 and m_2 are each divided by 2 and d is doubled?

d. If the instrument load of a space ship weighs 100 pounds (force) on the surface of the earth what will be its weight (force) 4000 miles above the earth, assuming that the length of the diameter of the earth is 8000 miles? What will it weigh 16,000 miles above the center of the earth?

Linear Inequalities

The equation $ax + by + c = 0$ defines a linear function provided $ab \neq 0$. If, however, we replace the equality sign by another comparison symbol and replace the condition $ab \neq 0$ by $a^2 + b^2 \neq 0$, the resulting open sentence defines a relation which is not a function. In this section we again consider the graphs of such relations.

Example 1.   If $M = \{(x, y) \mid 2x + y + 5 > 0\}$, draw the graph of M.

Solution. $2x + y + 5 > 0 \longleftrightarrow y > -2x - 5$. Why? We see that the graph of $y > -2x - 5$ is the set of points in the region above the graph of the linear function defined by $y = -2x - 5$.

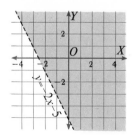

Example 2. Show the graph of A if $A = A_1 \cap A_2 \cap A_3 \cap A_4$ and $A_1 = \{(x, y) \mid y \geq 0\}$, $A_2 = \{(x, y) \mid x \geq 0\}$, $A_3 = \{(x, y) \mid 12y - 5x - 120 \leq 0\}$, $A_4 = \{(x, y) \mid y \geq 3x - 21\}$.

Solution. The region where all of the given linear inequalities are satisfied is shaded in the figure at the right. Any point whose coordinates satisfy A_2 must be on the y-axis or to the right of the y-axis. The equivalence of $12y - 5x - 120 \leq 0$ and $y \leq \frac{5}{12}x + 10$ shows that any solution of A_3 is represented by a point in $\overleftrightarrow{BP}$ or below it. Similarly any solution of A_4 is represented by a point in $\overleftrightarrow{CP}$ or above it.

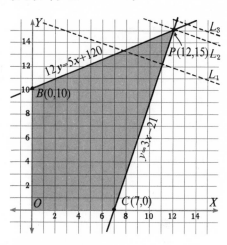

Example 3. If $V = 3y + x$, find the greatest possible value of V subject to the condition that (x, y) are the coordinates of a point in A, the region defined in Example 2.

Solution. Since $y = -\frac{1}{3}x + \frac{V}{3}$, we see that for a given V, $V = 3y + x$ is the equation of a line L having the slope $-\frac{1}{3}$ and the y-intercept $\frac{V}{3}$.

Hence $V = 3y + x$ is the equation of a family of parallel lines, L, all having the slope $-\frac{1}{3}$. Some of these are shown as the dashed lines L_1, L_2, L_3 in the figure for Example 2. Since $P(x, y) \in L$ and is also an element of A, we confine our attention to the members of this family of lines which intersect the region A. From this set of lines we must choose the one having the largest y-intercept. This is the line L_2 which contains the point $P_1(12, 15)$. Therefore the maximum value of V is obtained by substituting 12 and 15 for x and y respectively in $V = 3y + x$. Thus the maximum $V = 3 \cdot 15 + 12 = 57$.

 EXERCISES

1. Draw the graph of the relation defined by each of the following sentences.

a. $y > -2x + 3 \lor y < x$

b. $y \leq 7 \lor y \geq -3$

c. $y > 3 \lor y > x + 6 \lor y < -x - 3$

d. $3x + y > 5 \lor -2x + y < -4$

e. $y > x \lor y < 4$

f. $2 \leq y \leq 3$

g. $2x + 5 \geq y \lor y \geq -4x + 1$

h. $x - 2 \leq y \leq x + 2$

2. Draw the graph of the relation defined by each of the following sentences.

a. $y > -2x - 5 \land y > -3x + 4$

b. $3x + 1 > y \land y > -4x - 3$

c. $x \geq 0 \land y \geq 0 \land y \leq x + 4$

d. $y \leq x + 4 \land y > -x - 2 \land x > 0$

e. $y \leq 4 \land x \leq 3 \land y > -3 \land x > -3$

f. $y < \frac{1}{2}x + 2 \land y \geq 4x - 8 \land x \geq 0$

g. $y \geq -2x + 3 \land y \leq -2x + 6 \land y \geq 0 \land x \geq 0$

h. $y \geq |x| \land y \leq |x + 3| \land y \geq 0 \land -3 \leq x \leq 4$

3. Given that $A = \{(x, y) \mid y \geq x - 2\}$, $B = \{(x, y) \mid y \leq x + 2\}$, $C = \{(x, y) \mid x = -2\}$, $D = \{(x, y) \mid y \leq 4\}$, draw the graph of $A \cap B \cap C \cap D$.

4. Given that $A = \{(x, y) \mid y < 4\}$, $B = \{(x, y) \mid y > -4\}$, $C = \{(x, y) \mid x \geq 4\}$, $D = \{(x, y) \mid x \geq -4\}$, $E = \{(x, y) \mid y \leq -x + 5\}$, $F = \{(x, y) \mid y \geq x - 5\}$, $G = \{(x, y) \mid y \geq -x + 5\}$, $H = \{(x, y) \mid y < x + 5\}$, draw the graph of $A \cap B \cap C \cap D \cap E \cap F \cap G \cap H$.

5. Given $A = \{(x, y) \mid y \leq -\dfrac{5x}{3} + 7\}$, $B = \{(x, y) \mid y \geq x - 1\}$, $C = \{(x, y) \mid y \leq 9x + 39\}$, and $D = \{(x, y) \mid y \geq -7x + 25\}$, draw the graph of

a. $A \cap B \cap C$

b. $A \cap B \cap C \cap D$

6. If $M = x - y$, find the greatest possible value of M subject to the condition that (x, y) are the coordinates of a point in A the region which is the graph of $\{(x, y) \mid y = \leq -\frac{2}{5}x + 4\} \cap \{(x, y) \mid y \geq x - 3\} \cap \{(x, y) \mid y \geq 0\} \cap \{(x, y) \mid x \geq 0\}$.

7. If $K = -\frac{1}{3}x + y$, find the least possible value of K subject to the condition that (x, y) are the coordinates of a point in B the region which is the graph of $\{(x, y) \mid y \geq -2x + 8\} \cap \{(x, y) \mid y \geq \frac{2}{3}x\}$.

Sums, Products, and Quotients of Functions

For functions in $R \times R$, we define the sum of two functions F and G as follows:

> If F and G are functions and $D_F \cap D_G \neq \emptyset$, then their sum, denoted by F + G, is $\{(x, y) \mid y = f(x) + g(x) \land x \in D_F \cap D_G\}$.

Example 1.   If $F = \{(x, y) \mid y = -x^2 + 2\}$ and $G = \{(x, y) \mid y = x + 4\}$, find $F + G$. Draw the graphs of F, G, and $F + G$.

Solution. The defining equations for F and G are $y = -x^2 + 2$ and $y = x + 4$, respectively, and the common domain is the set of all real numbers. Thus

$$F + G = \{(x, y) \mid y = -x^2 + x + 6 \wedge x \in R\}$$

To draw the graphs of these functions we make a table of a few ordered pairs in each of the functions F, G, and $F + G$.

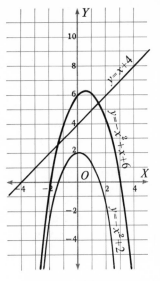

x	0	-1	1	$-\sqrt{2}$	$\sqrt{2}$	-2	2	-3	3
$f(x)$	2	1	1	0	0	-2	-2	-7	-7
$g(x)$	4	3	5	$4 - \sqrt{2}$	$4 + \sqrt{2}$	2	6	1	7
$f(x) + g(x)$	6	4	6	$4 - \sqrt{2}$	$4 + \sqrt{2}$	0	4	-6	0

We plot these points and draw a smooth solid line through the points that belong to the graphs of F and G, and draw a heavier smooth line through the points that belong to the graph of $F + G$. The graphs of F, G, and $F + G$ are shown in the diagram.

Studying the table of values used to sketch the graphs of F, G, and $F + G$ in Example 1, we see that we can add two functions graphically as follows:

In the diagram at the right $DA = f(x)$, $DB = g(x)$, and $DC = DA + DB$. In other words, the ordinate of C is equal to the ordinate of A plus the ordinate of B. C is above the x-axis because $|DB| > |DA|$. A, B, and C all have the same abscissa because they are all in the same vertical line. If we use this procedure, we can locate other points, and if we then draw a smooth curve through these points, we will find the graph is identical to the graph of $y = f(x) + g(x)$.

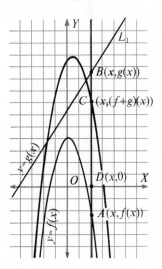

Example 2. Find the sum of the two functions F and G shown in the diagram at the right.

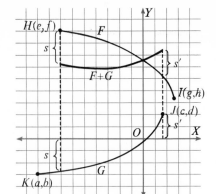

Solution. From the diagram we see that $D_F = \langle e, g \rangle$ and $D_G = \langle a, c \rangle$, therefore $D_F \cap D_G = \langle e, c \rangle$. Thus $F + G = \{(x, y) \mid y = f(x) + g(x) \land x \in \langle e, c \rangle\}$.

We define the product of two functions F and G as follows:

If F and G are functions and $D_F \cap D_G \neq \emptyset$, then their **product**, denoted by F · G, is $\{(x, y) \mid y = f(x) \cdot g(x) \land x \in D_F \cap D_G\}$.

Example 3. If $F = \{(x, y) \mid y = 2\}$ and $G = \{(x, y) \mid y = x + 4\}$, find $F \cdot G$ and draw the graphs of F, G, and $F \cdot G$.

Solution. According to the definition, $F \cdot G = \{(x, y) \mid y = 2x + 8\}$. To draw the graphs of F, G, and $F \cdot G$, we make a table of a few of the ordered pairs in each of the functions.

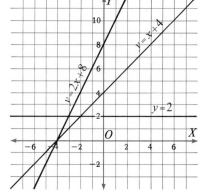

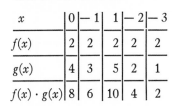

x	0	-1	1	-2	-3
$f(x)$	2	2	2	2	2
$g(x)$	4	3	5	2	1
$f(x) \cdot g(x)$	8	6	10	4	2

We plot these points and draw a smooth line through them. The graphs of F, G, and $F \cdot G$ are shown above.

We define the quotient of two functions F and G as follows:

If F and G are functions and $D_F \cap D_G \neq \emptyset$, then the **quotient** denoted by $\dfrac{F}{G}$ is $\{(x, y) \mid y = \dfrac{f(x)}{g(x)} \land x \in (D_F \cap D_G \cap \{x \mid g(x) \neq 0\})\}$.

Example 4. If $F = \{(x, y) \mid y = 1\}$ and $G = \{(x, y) \mid y = x^2 - 1\}$, find $\dfrac{F}{G}$ and draw the graphs of F, G, and $\dfrac{F}{G}$.

Solution. According to the definition, $\dfrac{F}{G} = \left\{ (x, y) \mid y = \dfrac{1}{x^2 - 1} \right\}$. Next we

make a table containing a few ordered pairs in F, G, and $\dfrac{F}{G}$ which

we can use in sketching the graphs of F, G, and $\dfrac{F}{G}$.

x	0	$\frac{1}{2}$	$-\frac{1}{2}$	1	-1	$\frac{3}{4}$	$-\frac{3}{4}$	$\frac{3}{2}$	$-\frac{3}{2}$	2	-2	3	-3
$f(x)$	1	1	1	1	1	1	1	1	1	1	1	1	1
$g(x)$	-1	$-\frac{3}{4}$	$-\frac{3}{4}$	0	0	$-\frac{7}{16}$	$-\frac{7}{16}$	$\frac{5}{4}$	$\frac{5}{4}$	3	3	8	8
$\dfrac{f(x)}{g(x)}$	-1	$-\frac{4}{3}$	$-\frac{4}{3}$	—	—	$-\frac{16}{7}$	$-\frac{16}{7}$	$\frac{4}{5}$	$\frac{4}{5}$	$\frac{1}{3}$	$\frac{1}{3}$	$\frac{1}{8}$	$\frac{1}{8}$

Notice that when $x = 1$ or -1, $g(x) = 0$ and since division by 0 is meaningless, $1, -1 \notin D_{\frac{F}{G}}$.

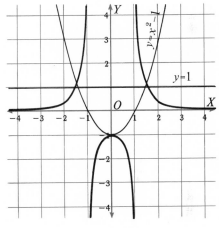

The graphs of F and G are shown by the lighter black lines in the figure. When x is an element of the interval $\rangle -1, \ 1 \langle$, $g(x) < 0$. As x approaches 1 from the left in the interval $\langle 0, \ 1 \langle$, $x^2 - 1$ becomes very small and hence $\left| \dfrac{1}{x^2 - 1} \right|$ increases without bound while $\dfrac{1}{x^2 - 1} < 0$. This explains why one branch of the curve plunges downward and seems to approach the line whose equation is $x = 1$. When x is just a little greater than 1, $g(x) > 0$ and very small. Hence the quotient is positive and large. The graph of $\dfrac{F}{G}$ is shown by the heavier black lines.

A EXERCISES

1. If $F = \{(0, 2), (1, 3), (2, 4), (3, 5)\}$ and $G = \{(2, 8), (3, 9)\}$,

   a. What is the domain of $F + G$? **d.** What is the domain of $F \cdot G$?

   b. Indicate the membership of $F + G$. **e.** Indicate the membership of $F \cdot G$.

   c. What is the range of $F + G$? **f.** What is the range of $F \cdot G$?

2. If $H = \{(-5, 25), (-4, 16), (-3, 9), (-2, 4), (-1, 1), (0, 0), (1, 1), (2, 4)\}$ and $G = \{(-4, 1), (-2, \frac{1}{2}), (-1, \frac{1}{4}), (4, 1), (6, \frac{3}{2})\}$,

a. $D_H = ?$ $D_G = ?$ $D_{H+G} = ?$ $D_{HG} = ?$

b. Indicate the membership of $H + G$.   c. Indicate the membership of $H \cdot G$.

3. Given $F = \{(x, y) \mid y = \sqrt{x - 3} \wedge (x, y) \in I \times I\}$ and $G = \{(x, y) \mid \sqrt{5 - x} \wedge (x, y) \in I \times I\}$,

a. Indicate the membership of $F + G$.

b. Indicate the membership of FG.

c. Indicate the membership of $\dfrac{F}{G}$.

4. a. If $F = \{(x, y) \mid y = 2x\}$ and $G = \{(x, y) \mid y = x + 1\}$, write the defining equation for $F \cdot G$.

b. If $F = \{(x, y) \mid y = x^2\}$ and $G = \{(x, y) \mid y = 4\}$, write the defining equation for $F + G$.

c. If $F = \{(x, y) \mid y = x\}$ and $G = \{(x, y) \mid y = 2\}$, write the defining equation for $F \cdot G$.

d. If $F = \{(x, y) \mid y = x\}$ and $G = \{(x, y) \mid y = 2\}$, write the defining equation for $\dfrac{F}{G}$.

e. If $F = \{(x, y) \mid y = x + 2\}$ and $G = \{(x, y) \mid y = x\}$, write the defining equation for $F \cdot G$.

f. If $F = \{(x, y) \mid y = \sqrt{x}\}$ and $G = \{(x, y) \mid y = 12\}$, write the defining equation for $\dfrac{F}{G}$.

5. Copy each of the following graphs on your paper with reasonable accuracy, then construct the graph of the sum of the two functions.

a.

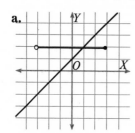

b.

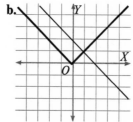

c.

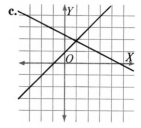

d.

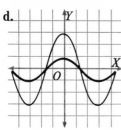

e.

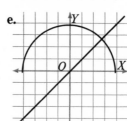

f.

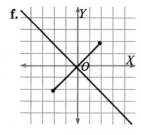

6. Given $F = \{(x, y) \mid y = x^2\}$ and $G = \{(x, y) \mid y = x + 4\}$, construct the graph of
   a. $F + G$ b. $F \cdot G$

7. If $F = \{(x, y) \mid y = 1\}$ and $G = \{(x, y) \mid y = x\}$, construct the graph of $\dfrac{F}{G}$.

B EXERCISES

8. Given $F = \{(x, y) \mid y = x^2\}$ and $G = \{(x, y) \mid y = -x^2 + 3\}$, construct the graph of
   a. $F \cdot G$ b. $\dfrac{F}{G}$

9. If $f(x) = x + 3$ and $g(x) = x^3 - 4$ are the defining equations of F and G, respectively, construct the graph of $F \cdot G$.

10. If $f(x) = 2$ and $g(x) = x^2 - 2$ are the defining equations of F and G, respectively, construct the graph of $\dfrac{F}{G}$.

Increasing and Decreasing Functions

When we say that the function $\{(x, y) \mid y = f(x)\}$ increases in a certain interval in D_F, we mean that for any x_1 and x_2 such that $x_2 > x_1$ in that interval, we have $f(x_2) > f(x_1)$. Thus the function pictured at the right is an increasing function in $\langle a, b \rangle$. Graphically this means that the graph "runs uphill" from A to the turning point T which is the highest point in the graph. Moreover, the graph "runs downhill" from T to B. We say that F is a decreasing function in $\langle b, c \rangle$ because when $x_1 \in$ $\langle b, c \rangle$, $x_2 \in \langle b, c \rangle$, and $x_1 < x_2$, we have $f(x_1) > f(x_2)$. Thus we state the following definition:

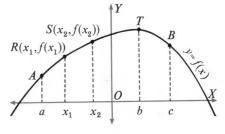

> Let F be a function and let $\langle a, b \rangle$ be an interval in its domain; then F is an increasing function in $\langle a, b \rangle$ if $[(x_1, x_2, \in \langle a, b \rangle \wedge x_1 < x_2) \longrightarrow f(x_1) < f(x_2)]$, and F is a decreasing function in $\langle a, b \rangle$ if $[(x_1, x_2, \in \langle a, b \rangle \wedge x_1 < x_2) \longrightarrow f(x_1) > f(x_2)]$.

When we say that F is an increasing function and do not specify the interval, we mean that the value of the function increases throughout its domain.

If F is an increasing function, it can be shown that $f(x_2) > f(x_1) \longrightarrow x_2 > x_1$ (see Ex. 4, page 323). This fact and Theorem 5–6 enable us to prove that if F and G are inverse functions, both are increasing functions or both are decreasing functions (see Ex. 6, page 324).

Our definition for an increasing function or a decreasing function is closely related to Theorem 3–6 because each member of the range corresponds to exactly one member of the domain only if the graph of the function has no turning point. Do you see why?

Example 1. If $f(x) = \sqrt{x}$, show that F is an increasing function.

Solution. We see that $D_F = \langle\, 0,\, \infty\, \langle$. Thus for x_1, $x_2 \in \langle\, 0,\, \infty\, \langle$ such that $0 \le x_1 < x_2$, we must show that $x_1 < x_2 \longrightarrow f(x_1) < f(x_2)$.

$$\overset{(1)}{}\qquad\overset{(2)}{}$$

We do this as follows: $0 \le x_1 < x_2 \longrightarrow$
$$\overset{(3)}{}$$
$$\sqrt{x_1} < \sqrt{x_2} \longrightarrow f(x_1) < f(x_2).$$
$$\overset{(4)}{}$$
$\therefore\ x_1 < x_2 \longrightarrow f(x_1) < f(x_2)$.

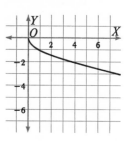

Reasons: (1) Given, (2) Corollary to Theorem 26–3, (3) Substitution property of equality, (4) Transitive property of implication. Thus by the definition of increasing function, we see that F is an increasing function.

Example 2. If $f(x) = -\sqrt{x}$, show that F is a decreasing function.

Solution. We see that $D_F = \langle\, 0,\, \infty\, \langle$. From Example 1 we know that $\sqrt{x_1} < \sqrt{x_2}$. Therefore, $-\sqrt{x_1} > -\sqrt{x_2}$ by the part of Theorem 7–3: If $a,\ b \in R$, then $a < b \longrightarrow -a > -b$. Consequently F is a decreasing function since we have shown that $x_1 < x_2 \longrightarrow f(x_1) > f(x_2)$. The graph of the function is shown at the right.

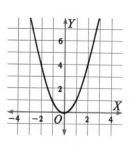

Example 3. Show that $F = \{(x, y) \mid y = x^2\}$ is increasing in $\langle\, 0,\, \infty\, \langle$ and decreasing in $\rangle -\infty,\, 0\, \rangle$.

Solution. Proof that F is increasing in $\langle\, 0,\, \infty\, \langle$:
$$\overset{(1)}{}\quad\overset{(2)}{}\qquad\qquad\overset{(3)}{}$$
$$0 \le x_1 < x_2 \longrightarrow x_1{}^2 < x_2{}^2 \longrightarrow f(x_1) <$$
$$\overset{(4)}{}$$
$f(x_2) \longrightarrow F$ is an increasing function. Reasons: (1) Given, (2) Corollary to Theorem 26–3, (3) Substitution property of equality, (4) Definition of an increasing function.

Proof that F is a decreasing function in $\langle -\infty, 0 \langle$:

$$\overset{(1)}{x_1 < x_2 \le 0} \overset{(2)}{\longrightarrow} 0 \le -x_2 < -x_1 \overset{(3)}{\longrightarrow} (-x_2)^2 < (-x_1)^2 \overset{(4)}{\longrightarrow} x_2{}^2$$

$$\overset{(5)}{< x_1{}^2 \longrightarrow} f(x_2) < f(x_1) \overset{(6)}{\longrightarrow} F \text{ is a decreasing function.}$$

Reasons: (1) Given, (2) Theorem 7–3, (3) Corollary to Theorem 26–3, (4) $(-a)^2 = a^2$, (5) Substitution property of equality, (6) Definition of decreasing function.

A function F has an *absolute minimum* at x_1 if $f(x) \ge f(x_1)$ for any x other than x_1 in the domain of F. Thus, in Example 1, $f(0) = 0$ is the absolute minimum of F. A function F has an *absolute maximum* at x_1 if $f(x) \le f(x_1)$ for any x other than x_1 in the domain of F. Thus, in Example 2, $f(0) = 0$ is the absolute maximum of F.

Ⓐ EXERCISES

1. Indicate whether each of the functions defined below is an increasing or decreasing function within the interval indicated. If no interval is mentioned, assume that it is the domain of the function.

   a. $y = 3x - 1$ e. $y = x^3$

   b. $y = -\frac{1}{2}x + 8$ f. $y = x; \ x \in \rangle -\infty, 0 \rangle$

   c. $\frac{2}{3}x + y = 4$ g. $x = \sqrt{y}$

   d. $y = x^2 + 1; \ x \in \langle 0, \infty \langle$ h. $y = \sqrt{25 - x^2}; \ x \in \langle 0, 5 \rangle$

2. Determine the absolute maximum and absolute minimum points of the graphs of the functions defined in Ex. 1, if such points exist.

3. If F is an increasing function and $f(2) = 5$, show that $f(3) \ne 0$.

4. Supply the reasons for the proof of the following statement: If F is an increasing function and $f(x_2) > f(x_1)$, then $x_2 > x_1$. We shall prove this by proving its contrapositive: (F is an increasing function $\wedge$ $x_2 \not> x_1$) $\longrightarrow f(x_2) \not> f(x_1)$.

Proof. $\overset{(1)}{x_2 \not> x_1} \overset{(2)}{\longleftrightarrow} (x_2 = x_1 \vee x_2 < x_1)$

$$\left.\begin{array}{l} x_2 = x_1 \overset{(3)}{\longrightarrow} f(x_2) = f(x_1) \\ x_2 < x_1 \overset{(4)}{\longrightarrow} f(x_2) < f(x_1) \end{array}\right\} \overset{(5)}{\longrightarrow} x_2 \le x_1 \longrightarrow f(x_2) \le f(x_1).$$

$$\overset{(6)}{f(x_2) \le f(x_1) \longleftrightarrow f(x_2) \not> f(x_1).}$$

$$\overset{(7)}{x_2 \not> x_1 \longrightarrow f(x_2) \not> f(x_1).}$$

$$\left.\begin{array}{l} F \text{ is an increasing function.} \\ f(x_2) > f(x_1) \end{array}\right\} \overset{(8)}{\longrightarrow} x_2 > x_1.$$

5. Prove: If F is an increasing function in $\langle\, a,\, b\, \rangle$ and G is an increasing function in $\langle\, a,\, b\, \rangle$, then $F + G$ is an increasing function in $\langle\, a,\, b\, \rangle$.

6. Supply the reasons for the given portion of Part 1 of the following proof, then supply the complete proof for the remainder of Part 1 and for Part 2.

If F and G are inverse functions,

(1) F is an increasing function $\longleftrightarrow G$ is an increasing function, and
(2) F is a decreasing function $\longleftrightarrow G$ is a decreasing function.

We will prove (1) from left to right.

Let (a, b) and (c, d) be in G. We must show that $a < c \longrightarrow b < d$ in order to prove that G is increasing. Why?

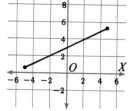
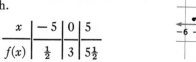

$$(a,\, b) \,\epsilon\, G \xrightarrow{\;(1)\;} (b,\, a) \,\epsilon\, F$$

$$(c,\, d) \,\epsilon\, G \xrightarrow{\;(2)\;} (d,\, c) \,\epsilon\, F$$

(3)
F is an increasing function

$\Big\} \xrightarrow{\;(4)\;} (a < c) \longrightarrow (b < d) \xrightarrow{\;(5)\;}$

(5)
$\longmapsto G$ is an increasing function

Bounded Functions

We recall that a set of real numbers S is *bounded above* if there is a number y such that for all x in S the statement $x \leq y$ is true. Likewise, S is *bounded below* if there is a number z such that for all x in S it is true that $z \leq x$. We state the following definitions:

> A function F is **bounded above** if the range of F has an upper bound. The function F is **bounded below** if its range has a lower bound. If the function F has both an upper and a lower bound it is a **bounded function**.

Example 1. Given the function $F = \{(x, y) \mid y = \frac{1}{2} x + 3 \land x \,\epsilon\, \langle\, -5, 5\, \rangle\}$. Draw the graph of F and determine if it is a bounded function.

Solution. $y = \frac{1}{2} x + 3$ is a linear equation and the graph of the truth set of a linear equation is a straight line. We graph the ordered pairs that are coordinates of three points in our graph.

x	-5	0	5
$f(x)$	$\frac{1}{2}$	3	$5\frac{1}{2}$

We see that if m_1 is any number such that $m_1 \leq \frac{1}{2}$ and m_2 is any number such that $m_2 \geq 5\frac{1}{2}$, then $m_1 \leq f(x) \leq m_2$ and F is a bounded function.

Example 2. Determine if G is a bounded function and draw its graph if

$$G = \left\{ (x, y) \mid y = \frac{3}{x} \land x \in \rangle 0, \infty \langle \right\}.$$

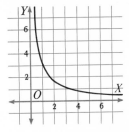

Solution. Since $x \in \rangle 0, \infty \langle$, $g(x) > 0$. Thus G is bounded below. However, if m is any positive number and $x < \frac{3}{m}$ then $f(x) > m$.

Therefore no matter how large a number we try for an upper bound, there is always an x for which the proposed bound is exceeded by the $f(x)$. Thus G is not bounded above.

Example 3. If $F = \left\{ (x, y) \mid y = \frac{2x}{x^2 + 1} \right\}$, determine if F is bounded and sketch its graph.

Solution. Since the domain of x is not specified, we assume it to be the set of all real numbers for which $\frac{2x}{x^2 + 1}$ names a real number. We use a table to display a few ordered pairs in the truth set of

$$y = \frac{2x}{x^2 + 1}.$$

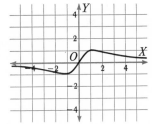

x	0	$\frac{1}{2}$	$-\frac{1}{2}$	1	-1	$\frac{3}{2}$	$-\frac{3}{2}$	2	-2	5	-5
y	0	$\frac{4}{5}$	$-\frac{4}{5}$	1	-1	$\frac{12}{13}$	$-\frac{12}{13}$	$\frac{4}{5}$	$-\frac{4}{5}$	$\frac{5}{13}$	$-\frac{5}{13}$

We see that if m_1 is any number such that $m_1 \leq -1$ and if m_2 is any number such that $m_2 \geq 1$, then $m_1 \leq f(x) \leq m_2$. Thus F is a bounded function.

Note that the absolute maximum of F is 1 and that the absolute minimum of F is -1. A proof of this is given in Exercise 9 at the end of this section.

A EXERCISES

In Exercises 1–7, state whether each of these functions is bounded above, bounded below, bounded, or not bounded. (Some exercises have more than one answer.)

1. $G = \{ (x, y) \mid xy = 5 \land x \in \rangle 0, \infty \langle \}$

2. $H = \{ (x, y) \mid xy = 5 \land x \in \rangle - \infty, 0 \langle \}$

3. $M = \{ (x, y) \mid y = \sqrt{x} \land x \in \langle 0, \infty \langle \}$

4. $N = \{ (x, f(x)) \mid f(x) = x^3 \}$

5. $S = \left\{ (x, y) \mid y = \frac{1}{x - 4} \land x > 4 \right\}$

6. $T = \left\{ (x, y) \mid y = \frac{1}{x^2 + 2} \right\}$

7. $V = \{(x, y) \mid y = 1 \wedge x \in \langle 0, \infty \langle \} \cup \{(x, y) \mid y = -1 \wedge x \in \rangle - \infty, 0 \langle \}$

8. Given that $F = \left\{(x, y) \mid y = \dfrac{2x}{x^2 + 1}\right\}$.

a. Give the reasons for the following proof which shows that 1 is the absolute maximum of F. To prove this statement, we need to prove: (*i*) $\dfrac{2x}{x^2 + 1} = 1$ is true when $x = 1$, (*ii*) $\dfrac{2x}{x^2 + 1} \leq 1$ is true. To prove (*i*) we let $x = 1$ and see that this value satisfies the equation $\dfrac{2x}{x^2 + 1} = 1$. We know that $\dfrac{2x}{x^2 + 1} \leq 1$ if $2x \leq x^2 + 1$, and that $2x \leq x^2 + 1$ is true if $0 \leq (x-1)^2$. This suggests a proof of the statement, "If $x \in R$, then $\dfrac{2x}{x^2 + 1} \leq 1$."

$$\underset{\text{(1)}}{x \in R} \overset{\text{(2)}}{\longrightarrow} (x - 1) \in R \overset{\text{(3)}}{\longrightarrow} (x - 1)^2 \geq 0 \overset{\text{(4)}}{\longrightarrow} x^2 - 2x + 1 \geq 0 \overset{\text{(5)}}{\not\longrightarrow}$$

$$\overset{\text{(5)}}{\not\longrightarrow} x^2 + 1 \geq 2x \overset{\text{(6)}}{\longrightarrow} 1 \geq \dfrac{2x}{x^2 + 1}$$

Reasons: (1) Why? (2) Why? (3) Why? (4) Why? (5) Why? (6) Why?

Note. In step (6) we assumed that $\dfrac{1}{x^2 + 1}$ was positive. This can be proved as follows:

$$\underset{\text{(1)}}{x \in R} \overset{\text{(2)}}{\longrightarrow} \left.\begin{array}{l} x^2 \geq 0 \\ \text{(3)} \\ 1 > 0 \end{array}\right\} \overset{\text{(4)}}{\longrightarrow} x^2 + 1 > 0 \overset{\text{(5)}}{\longrightarrow} \dfrac{1}{x^2 + 1} > 0$$

Reasons: (1) Why? (2) Why? (3) Why? (4) Why? (5) Why?

b. Write a similar proof to show that -1 is the absolute minimum of F.

9. Show that the absolute minimum of the function $\{(x, y) \mid y = x^2 + x + 1\}$ is $\frac{3}{4}$.

Continuous Functions

When we say that a function is *continuous*, we mean that the graph of the function has no "breaks" in it. Thus, the function whose graph is shown on the left below is not continuous and the function whose graph is shown on the right below is continuous.

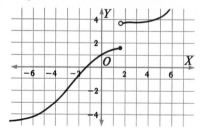
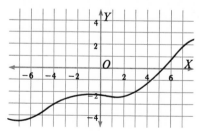

When we say that the function F is *continuous at the point* $P(a, f(a))$, we mean that there are no "breaks" in the graph of the function F close to $P(a, f(a))$.

On the other hand, the function G defined by $g(x) = \dfrac{1}{x^2}$ is not continuous since 0 is not in the domain of G. That is, the graph of G has a "break" in it at the y-axis. When $G = \left\{ (x, y) \mid y = \dfrac{1}{x^2} \right\}$, $g(x)$ becomes greater without bound as $|x|$ becomes smaller but not zero. The graph of G is shown at the right.

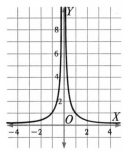

When we say that a function is *continuous in an interval J*, we mean that $J \subseteq D_F$ and that the function is continuous at every point in the interval J. This means that the graph of the function has no "breaks" in that interval.

Suppose that $A(a, f(a))$ and $B(b, f(b))$ are two points in function F which is continuous in an interval that includes $\langle a, b \rangle$. Then if c is any number between $f(a)$ and $f(b)$, the horizontal line whose equation is $y = c$ must intersect the graph of F at least once at a point whose abscissa x_1 is between a and b. The upper figure at the right shows this situation. The lower figure at the right indicates that this statement would not be true if F were not continuous in J.

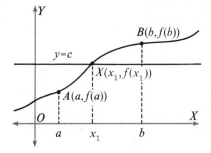

These considerations suggest a very important property of continuous functions called the *Intermediate Value Property*. The proof of this property is beyond the scope of this course in algebra but since it is easy to understand, and since we shall find it useful in later sections of this book, we state it as an assumption.

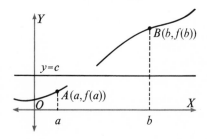

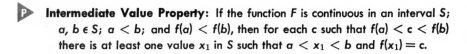

Intermediate Value Property: If the function F is continuous in an interval S; $a, b \in S$; $a < b$; and $f(a) < f(b)$, then for each c such that $f(a) < c < f(b)$ there is at least one value x_1 in S such that $a < x_1 < b$ and $f(x_1) = c$.

Example.   If $f(x) = \frac{1}{4}x + 1$, $D = \rangle 1, 14 \langle$, $f(a) = 2$, and $f(b) = 4$, show that there is at least one value x_1 in the interval D such that $f(a) < f(x_1) < f(b)$.

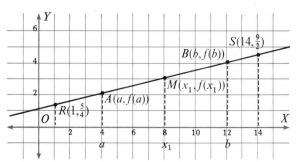

Solution.   From the graph we see that $f(a) < f(x_1) < f(b)$. Thus we have $f(4) < f(8) < f(12)$, and consequently $4 < 8 < 12$.

Ⓐ EXERCISES

1. Draw the graph of each function defined below. Indicate which of the functions are continuous within the interval indicated and which are not continuous within the interval.

   a. $\{(x, y) \mid y = -2x + 3 \wedge x \in R\}$

   b. $\{(x, y) \mid y = 4 \wedge x \in \rangle 0, 5 \langle\} \cup \{(x, y) \mid y = -3 \wedge x \in \langle -5, 0 \langle\}$

   c. $\{(x, y) \mid y = 3 \wedge x \in \rangle -\infty, -2 \rangle\} \cup \{(x, y) \mid y = 1 \wedge x \in \langle 2, \infty \langle\}$

   d. $\{(x, y) \mid y = |x| \wedge x \in \rangle -4, 4 \langle\}$

   e. $\{(x, y) \mid y = x^2 \wedge x \in R\}$

   f. $\left\{(x, y) \mid y = \frac{1}{x} \wedge x \in \langle -6, 6 \rangle\right\}$

   g. $\{(x, y) \mid y = \sqrt{x^2 - 1} \wedge x \in R\}$

   h. $\{(x, y) \mid y = 1 \wedge x \in \langle -5, 0 \langle\} \cup \{(x, y) \mid y = 2 \wedge x = 0\} \cup \{(x, y) \mid y = 3 \wedge x \in \rangle 0, 5 \rangle\}$

2. Indicate which of the following graphs are graphs of discontinuous functions and which are graphs of continuous functions for the intervals shown.

a.   **b.**   **c.**   **d.**

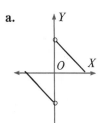 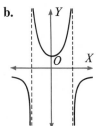 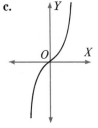 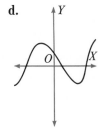

3. Given the function $F = \{(x, y) \mid y = x^2\}$, use the Intermediate Value Property to show that there is a number x_1 between 2 and 3 such that $f(x_1) = 6$.

4. Given the function $G = \{(x, y) \mid y = x^2 + 2x + 2\}$, show that there is a number x_1 between 0 and 1 such that $g(x_1) = 3$.

5. Show that the function defined by $y = x^2 + 2x - 2$ has a zero between 0 and 1. (*Hint.* What can you say about the signs of $f(0)$ and $f(1)$ if there is a zero of the function between $f(0)$ and $f(1)$?)

6. Does the function $\{(x, y) \mid y = x^2 + 2x + 1\}$ have a zero between $f(1)$ and $f(2)$?

7. Show that the function $\{(x, y) \mid y = x^3 + 3x - 6\}$ has a zero between $f(1)$ and $f(2)$.

ESSENTIALS

Before you leave this chapter make sure that you

1. Know the meanings of "relation," "domain of a relation," and "range of a relation." (Page 269.)

2. Can define a relation by any of the methods discussed in this chapter. (Page 269.)

3. Know when a relation is a function. (Page 273.)

4. Can identify constant functions, the identity function, step functions, and wrapping functions. (Pages 275, 282–284.)

5. Know the meaning of and can use such symbols as $f(x)$, $g(x)$, $f[g(x)]$, and $g[f(x)]$. (Pages 277–278, 289.)

6. Understand the composition of functions. (Pages 288–291.)

7. Know what we mean by inverse functions and can recognize the relationship of the graphs of two inverse functions to the graph of the identity function. (Pages 293–297.)

8. Recognize that the inverse of a function is not necessarily a function and can identify those functions whose inverses are not functions. (Page 297.)

9. Know the meaning of "linear function" and know that a constant function is not a linear function. (Page 302.)

10. Without making a graph can determine when the graph of the intersection of two linear functions will be a single line, when a single point, and when the empty set. (Page 303.)

11. Understand what we mean by the zeros of a function and can find them. (Pages 303–304.)

12. Can use the concepts of direct variation, inverse variation, and joint variation. (Pages 307–312.)

13. Can graph linear inequalities and the union or the intersection of two or more linear inequalities. (Page 314.)

14. Can find the sum, product, and quotient of two functions. (Page 316.)

15. Know whether a function is increasing or decreasing within a particular interval. (Pages 321–322.)

16. Know whether a function is bounded or not bounded. (Page 324.)

17. Can spell and use the following words and phrases correctly.

bounded (Page 324.)	independent variable (Page 279.)
composition (Page 288.)	interval (Page 285.)
continuous function (Page 326.)	inverse function (Page 293.)
constant function (Page 275.)	linear function (Page 302.)
dependent variable (Page 279.)	wrapping function (Page 283.)
function (Page 273.)	variation (Page 307.)
identity function (Page 275.)	

CHAPTER REVIEW

1. What is a relation?

2. When is a relation a function?

3. Given the relation defined by writing $\{(x, y) \mid y = 4x; \ x \in I\}$, show how to define the same relation in three other ways.

4. If S is a relation in $B \times B$ where $B = \{-4, -3, -2, -1, 0, 1, 2, 3\}$,

   a. What are the domain and range of S if S is defined by the sentence $y = \dfrac{1}{x}$?

   b. What are the domain and range of S if S is defined by the sentence $y = \dfrac{1}{x+2}$?

   c. Sketch the graph of each of these relations.

   d. Are either or both of these relations functions?

5. S is a relation in $A \times B$ where $A = \{1, 2, 3, 4, 5, 6\}$ and $B = \{1, 2, 3\}$.

   a. What are the domain and range of S if S is defined by the sentence $y = \sqrt{4-x}$?

   b. Is this relation a function?

6. Make a graph of each of the relations defined below, assuming that each is a subset of $R \times R$. State the domain and range of each.

   a. $\{(x, y) \mid y = x^2 + 4x + 3\}$ b. $\{(x, y) \mid x \leq -\tfrac{1}{3}y^2\}$

c. $\left\{(x, y) \dfrac{y}{x-5} = 1\right\}$ **d.** $\{(x, y) \mid x + y = 4 \wedge y = \mid x - 4 \mid\}$

7. Which of the relations of Ex. 6 are functions?

8. How do the graphs of $\left\{(x, y) \mid y = \dfrac{x^2 - 9}{x+3}\right\}$ and $\{(x, y) \mid y = x - 3\}$ differ?

9. The graphs below indicate relations. Identify the graphs which define functions.

a.   **c.** 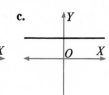   **e.** 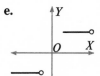   **g.**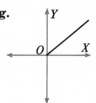

b. 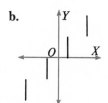   **d.** 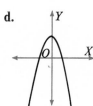   **f.** 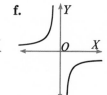   **h.**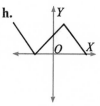

10. Which of the descriptive words *linear, nonlinear, constant, identity,* or *step* applies to each of the *functions* whose graphs are shown in Ex. 9? (More than one word applies in some cases.)

11. For what values of m and k does the equation $y = mx + k$ define the identity function?

12. The statement $y = mx + k \wedge m = 0$ identifies which special function?

13. If F represents a function whose domain is $\{\cdots, -3, -2, -1, 0, 1, 2, 3, \cdots\}$, what is the range of F if it is the function defined by each of the following equations?

   a. $y = -x^2$ **b.** $y = 6 - x^2$ **c.** $y = \sqrt{4 - x^2}$

14. If $f(x) = 2x^2 - x$, find

   a. $f(-2)$ **c.** $f[f(3)]$ **e.** $f(2a - 1)$ **g.** $f(b^2)$
   b. $f(\tfrac{1}{4})$ **d.** $f(3a)$ **f.** $[f(-1)]^2$ **h.** $f(b - 2)$

15. Draw the graph of each of the following functions, assuming that each is a subset of $R \times R$. State the domain and range of each function.

   a. $\left\{(x, f(x)) \mid f(x) = \dfrac{2x}{\mid x \mid}\right\}$ **c.** $\{(x, y) \mid y = \sqrt{x - 6}\}$

   b. $\left\{(x, f(x)) \mid 1 = \dfrac{f(x)}{x+2}\right\}$ **d.** $\left\{(x, y) \mid y = \dfrac{1}{x-7}\right\}$

16. The rectangle at the right has its vertices at the points $A(3, -1)$, $B(3, 1)$, $C(-3, 1)$, and $D(-3, -1)$. A string whose length has the measure s is fastened to the rectangle at the point $M(3, 0)$ and wrapped tightly around the rectangle counterclockwise.

a. Draw a graph of the set of ordered pairs of the form (s, y), y being the ordinate of the point on the rectangle at which the string ends.

b. What are the domain and range of the graph of part a?

c. Is the relation a function?

d. Is the relation periodic? If so, what is its period?

e. Is the set of ordered pairs (y, s) a function? Explain.

17. For each of the following, use the symbols $<$, $>$, $\leq$, or $\geq$ to write an equivalent statement.

a. $x \in \langle 0, \infty \langle$ c. $x \in \langle a, b \rangle$ e. $x \in \rangle - \infty, 0 \rangle$

b. $x \in \rangle a, b \langle$ d. $x \in \rangle a, b \rangle$ f. $x \in \rangle - \infty, 4 \langle$

18. Draw the graph of each of the relations defined below. State the domain and range of each. Which relations are functions?

a. $\{(x, y) \mid y = -2 \wedge x \in \rangle - \infty, 0 \rangle\} \cup \{(x, y) \mid y = 3 \wedge x \in \rangle 0, \infty \langle\}$

b. $\{(x, y) \mid y = 4 \wedge x \in \rangle - 7, 0 \langle\} \cup \{(x, y) \mid y = 5 \wedge x \in \rangle 0, 7 \langle\}$

c. $\{(x, y) \mid y = -x \wedge x \in \langle -5, 0 \rangle\} \cup \{(x, y) \mid y = x \wedge x \in \langle 0, 5 \langle\}$

d. $\{(x, y) \mid y = -2x \wedge x \in \langle 0, 4 \langle\} \cup \{(x, y) \mid y = 2x \wedge x \in \langle 0, 4 \rangle\}$

e. $\{(x, y) \mid y = \sqrt{9 - x^2} \wedge x \in \rangle - 3, 0 \rangle\} \cup \{(x, y) \mid y = -\sqrt{9 - x^2} \wedge x \in \rangle 0, 3 \langle\}$

19. Given $F = \{(1, 3), (2, 6), (3, 9), (4, 12), (5, 15)\}$ and $G = \{(2, -4), (3, -6), (4, -8)\}$, find H such that   a. $H = G(F)$ b. $H = F(G)$

20. Given F and G as defined below, find $G(F)$, $D_{G(F)}$, and $R_{G(F)}$ in each case.

a. $F = \{(x, y) \mid y = x^2 + 1\}$ $G = \{(x, y) \mid y = 4x + 3\}$

b. $F = \{(x, y) \mid y = x - 3\}$ $G = \{(x, y) \mid y = x^2\}$

c. $F = \left\{(x, y) \mid y = \dfrac{1}{\sqrt{x - 3}}\right\}$ $G = \{(x, y) \mid y = x^2\}$

d. $F = \{(x, y) \mid y = 4x\}$ $G = \{(x, y) \mid y = \sqrt{44 + x}\}$

21. What must be true of a function whose inverse is a function?

22. Will the function $\{(1, 5), (2, 6), (3, 6), (4, 7)\}$ have an inverse function? If there is such a function, list its members. If there is no function, explain why there is none.

23. Given $F = \{(1, 4), (2, 8), (3, 12), (4, 16)\}$, indicate the set of ordered pairs G such that G is a function which is the inverse of F.

24. Given $F = \{(x, y) \mid y = 4x - 1\}$ and $G = \{(x, y) \mid y = ?\}$, replace the question mark so that G is a function which is the inverse of F.

25. Which of the graphs below define functions whose inverses are functions?

a.
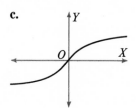

c.

e.
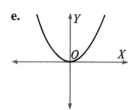

b.
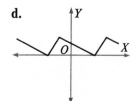

d.

f.
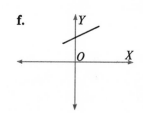

26. Indicate the zeros of the function defined by $\{(x, y) \mid y = -x^2 + 4\}$.

27. By what other names are the "zeros of a function" known?

28. Indicate the point common to the graphs of the identity function, the function defined by $y = 4x - 3$, and the inverse of this function.

29. If y varies directly as x and $y = 1.48$ when $x = 4$, find y when $x = 5$.

30. If y varies inversely as x and $y = 8$ when $x = .02$, find y when $x = 12$.

31. Each of the following tables contains a few of the ordered pairs which belong to a relation which is a direct variation. Write the equation which defines each relation.

a.

x	0.2	5	10
y	14.2	355	710

b.

x	2	0.5	-2
y	0.6	2.4	-0.6

32. Write an equation which defines the relation: y varies directly as the product of a and b and inversely as the square of c.

33. Use the equation you have written for Ex. 32 to find y when $a = 5$, $b = 3$, and $c = 6$ if $y = 2.1$ when $a = 4$, $b = 3$, and $c = 2$.

34. Draw the graph of $\{(x, y) \mid y \leq -\frac{1}{2}x + 5\} \cap \{(x, y) \mid y \geq \frac{2}{3}x - 2\} \cap \{(x, y) \mid x \geq 0\}$.

35. Draw the graph of area A such that $A = \{(x, y) \mid y \leq x + 4\} \cap \{(x, y) \mid y \leq -2x + 13\} \cap \{(x, y) \mid x \geq 0\} \cap \{(x, y) \mid y \geq 0\}$.

36. If $M = -\frac{1}{3}x + y$, find the greatest possible value of M subject to the condition that (x, y) are the coordinates of a point in A, the region which is the graph of $\{(x, y) \mid y \le x + 4\} \cap \{(x, y) \mid y \le -2x + 3\} \cap \{(x, y) \mid x \ge 0\} \cap \{(x, y) \mid y \ge 0\}$.

37. If $F = \{(1, 4), (2, 5), (3, 6), (4, 7), (5, 8)\}$ and $G = \{(2, 4), (3, 6), (4, 8)\}$,

    a. What is the domain of $F + G$? the range of $F + G$?

    b. Indicate the membership of $F + G$.

38. The lighter line in the figure at the right is the graph of function F and the heavier line is the graph of function G. Copy the figure and construct the graph of the function $F + G$.

    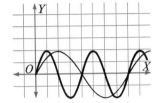

39. If $F = \{(x, y) \mid y = x^2 \wedge x \in \langle 0, \infty \rangle \}$ and $G = \{(x, y) \mid y = 9 - 6x \wedge x \in \langle 0, \infty \rangle \}$,

    a. Find $F \cdot G$.   **b.** Find $\dfrac{F}{G}$.

40. Show that the absolute minimum of the function $\{(x, y) \mid y = x^2 - 4x\}$ is -4.

41. State whether each function given below is bounded above, bounded below, bounded, or not bounded. (Some parts have more than one answer.)

    a. $\{(x, y) \mid y = 4x + 1 \wedge x \in \langle -2, 6 \rangle \}$

    b. $\{(x, y) \mid y = x \wedge x \in \langle 0, 16 \rangle \}$

    c. $\{(x, y) \mid xy = 1 \wedge x \in \langle 0, \infty \rangle \}$

    d. $\{(x, y) \mid x^3 = y \wedge x \in \rangle -\infty, 0 \rangle \}$

42. Draw the graph of each of the functions given below. Indicate which of the functions are discontinuous in the intervals indicated.

    a. $\{(x, y) \mid y = 3x - 5 \wedge x \in \rangle 0, 10 \langle \}$

    b. $\left\{ (x, y) \mid y = \dfrac{1}{x - 2} \wedge x \in \langle 0, \infty \langle \right\}$

    c. $\{(x, y) \mid y = 4x \wedge x \in \rangle 0, 1 \langle \} \cup \{(x, y) \mid y = 4x - 4 \wedge x \in \rangle -\infty, 0 \langle \}$

    d. $\{(x, y) \mid y = 4 \wedge x \in \langle -2, 2 \rangle \} \cup \{(x, y) \mid y = 2 \wedge x \in \rangle 2, 6 \rangle \}$

CHAPTER TEST

1. Indicate which of the relations defined below are functions.

    a.

x	1	1	2	2	3
y	2	5	3	6	4

    b. $\{(x, y) \mid y = \frac{1}{4}x^2; \ x \in I\}$

    c.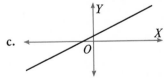

    d. $\{(1, 4), (2, 8), (3, 12), (4, 8)\}$

2. State the domain and range of each of the functions defined below.

   a. $\left\{(x, y) \mid y = \dfrac{1}{x-2}\right\}$ **b.** $\{(x, y) \mid y = \sqrt{9-x}\}$ **c.** $\{(x, y) \mid y = |x|\}$

   d. $\{(x, y) \mid y = 2 \wedge x \in \langle -5, 0 \rangle\} \cup \{(x, y) \mid y = 3x+3 \wedge x \in \rangle 0, 5 \rangle\}$

3. Given $F = \{(x, y) \mid y = x^2\}$ and $G = \{(x, y) \mid y = x+1\}$, find
   a. $F(G)$ **b.** $D_{F(G)}$ **c.** $R_{F(G)}$ **d.** $G(F)$

4. If $F = \{(x, y) \mid y = 3x^2 + 1\}$, find
   a. $f(\tfrac{1}{3})$ **b.** $f(-2)$ **c.** $f(a+1)$ **d.** $f[f(2)]$

5. Which of the functions defined below have inverses that are also functions?

   a.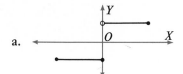

   b.

   c.

x	0	1	2	3
y	2	3	1	4

   d. $\{(x, y) \mid y = |x|\}$

6. **a.** Draw the graph of the inverse of the function defined by $\{(x, y) \mid y = x^2 \wedge x \in \langle 0, 3 \rangle\}$.

   b. Is the given function an increasing or decreasing function?

7. If y varies inversely as x and $y = \tfrac{3}{2}$ when $x = \tfrac{1}{5}$, what is the value of y when $x = 4$?

8. If y varies directly as a and inversely as the product of b and c, what is the value of y when $a = 8$, $b = 6$, and $c = 3$, if $y = \tfrac{1}{5}$ when $a = 14$, $b = 5$, and $c = 7$?

9. Draw the graph of $\{(x, y) \mid y \leq -\tfrac{1}{2}x + 3\} \cap \{(x, y) \mid y = -x - 1\} \cap \{(x, y) \mid x \geq 1\}$.

10. If $F = \{(-1, 1), (-2, 4), (-3, 9), (-4, 16), (-5, 25)\}$ and $G = \{(-2, 6), (-3, 9), (-4, 12)\}$, find $F + G$.

11. If $F = \{(x, y) \mid y = 3x \wedge x \in \langle 0, 5 \rangle\}$ and $G = \{(x, y) \mid y = x - 1 \wedge x \in \langle 0, 5 \rangle\}$, find $F \cdot G$.

12. Find the absolute minimum of the function $\{(x, y) \mid y = 2x^2 + 3 \wedge x \in \langle -2, 2 \rangle\}$.

13. Find the absolute maximum of the function $\{(x, y) \mid \tfrac{1}{4}y = -\tfrac{1}{16}x^2 + 1 \wedge x \in \langle -4, 5 \rangle\}$.

14. Identify each of the following functions as continuous or discontinuous within the specified interval.

a. $\{(x, y) \mid y = 4 \wedge x \,\epsilon\, \langle -6, 0 \rangle\} \cup \{(x, y) \mid y = 6 \wedge x \,\epsilon\, \rangle 0, 6 \rangle\}$

b. $\left\{ (x, y) \mid y = \dfrac{1}{x - 4} \wedge x \,\epsilon\, \langle 0, 5 \rangle \right\}$

15. Indicate whether either or both of the following functions can be called bounded functions.

a. $\{(x, y) \mid y = 3\,x + 4 \wedge x \,\epsilon\, \langle -2, 6 \rangle\}$

b. $\{(x, y) \mid y = x^2 \wedge x \,\epsilon\, \rangle - \infty, 0 \rangle\}$

16. If $F = \{(x, y) \mid y = 2\,x + 6 \wedge x \,\epsilon\, \langle -3, 3 \rangle\}$ and $G = \{(x, y) \mid y = -\tfrac{3}{4}x - 6 \wedge x \,\epsilon\, \langle -3, 3 \rangle\}$, find $\dfrac{F}{G}$, and draw the graphs of F, G, and $\dfrac{F}{G}$ on the same set of coordinate axes.

Quadratic Functions

Quadratic Function Defined

In this chapter we review and extend our knowledge of quadratic functions. We state the following definitions:

If a, b, and c are any real numbers such that $a \neq 0$, then the function defined by the equation $y = ax^2 + bx + c$ is a quadratic function.

If a, b, and c are any real numbers such that $a \neq 0$, then $ax^2 + bx + c = 0$ is a quadratic equation in the single variable x.

Clearly, the roots of the quadratic equation $ax^2 + bx + c = 0$ are the zeros of the quadratic function $\{(x, y) \mid y = ax^2 + bx + c\}$.

In the following examples we review procedures for obtaining the graphs and zeros for quadratic functions in which the coefficients a, b, and c have been assigned specific numerical values. The graph of a quadratic function is called a *parabola*.

Example 1. Sketch the graph of the quadratic function $F = \{(x, y) \mid y = x^2 + 4\}$. Discuss function F in terms of its graph.

Solution. According to our discussion of symmetry (page 251), the graph of this function is symmetric with respect to the y-axis. When $x \in R$, $x^2 \geq 0$ and it is clear that the point whose coordinates are $(0, 4)$ is the low point of the curve. To obtain the coordinates of other points on the curve, we make a table of ordered pairs in F.

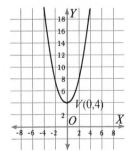

x	0	1	2	3	-1	-2	-3
y	4	5	8	13	5	8	13

Drawing a smooth curve through the graph of each of these ordered pairs, we obtain the parabola shown in the diagram. The following observations are based upon our study of this graph.

337

1. Since any real number may be substituted for x, the domain of F is R.
2. F is bounded below but is not bounded above. Any real number which is less than or equal to 4 will be a lower bound of F. What is the greatest lower bound of F?
3. F is increasing in $\langle 0, \infty \langle$ and decreasing in $\rangle - \infty, 0 \rangle$. Accordingly $f(0)$, that is 4, is the absolute minimum value of F.
4. The y-axis contains the axis of symmetry of this parabola.
5. In this case the turning point of the parabola is the lowest point, $V(0, 4)$. We call this point the *vertex* of the parabola.
6. The function F has no zeros. This corresponds to the fact that the equation $x^2 + 4 = 0$ has no solution in R.

How would the graph and the statements above be modified for the function $\{(x, y) \mid y = - x^2 + 4\}$? For the function $\{(x, y) \mid y = x^2 - 4\}$?

Example 2.

Find the roots of the quadratic equation $- \frac{1}{4} x^2 + x + 3 = 0$ by factoring. Sketch the graph of the quadratic function G defined by $y = - \frac{1}{4} x^2 + x + 3$ and discuss the function in terms of its graph.

Solution.

Considering $- \frac{1}{4} x^2 + x + 3$ as a polynomial over the rational numbers, we have $- \frac{1}{4} x^2 + x + 3 = - \frac{1}{4}(x^2 - 4 x - 12) = - \frac{1}{4}(x - 6)(x + 2)$. Thus the roots of $- \frac{1}{4} x^2 + x + 3 = 0$ are roots of $- \frac{1}{4}(x - 6)(x + 2) = 0$, namely 6 and $- 2$. Thus 6 and $- 2$ are zeros of the function G defined by $y = - \frac{1}{4} x^2 + x + 3$. It follows that $(6, 0)$ and $(- 2, 0)$ are in G. We denote the graphs of these ordered pairs as B and A, respectively. When $x > 6$ or $x < - 2$, then $y < 0$. Thus if $x = - 50$, $y = - 672$ and if $x = 50$, $y = - 572$. This suggests that G is not bounded below. The turning point, or vertex, of the parabola must therefore be its highest point. We expect the axis of symmetry of this parabola to be parallel to the y-axis. Thus it seems that this axis must pass through the point, 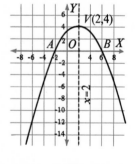 whose coordinates are $(2, 0)$, which is the midpoint of $\overline{AB}$. If this is true, then the highest point of the parabola has 2 for its abscissa. The corresponding value of y is $- \frac{1}{4}(2)^2 + 2 + 3$, or 4. Thus the point $V(2, 4)$ is the vertex of the parabola. Drawing a smooth curve through the points A, V, and B, we obtain the parabola shown in the diagram. A table of values for ordered pairs in G would confirm

our conclusion that 4 is the absolute maximum value of G. We restate our observations and make some new ones about the quadratic function G and its graph as follows:

1. The domain of G is R.
2. G is bounded above but it is not bounded below. Any real number greater than or equal to 4 is an upper bound of G. What is the least upper bound of G?
3. G is an increasing function in $\rangle - \infty, 2 \rangle$ and a decreasing function in $\langle 2, \infty \langle$. Accordingly $g(2)$, or 4, is the absolute maximum value of G.
4. The axis of symmetry of this parabola is the vertical line which is the graph of $\{(x, y) \mid x = 2\}$.
5. The vertex of the parabola is the point $V(2, 4)$.
6. The function G has two zeros, namely $- 2$ and 6. Thus
$$\{x \mid - \tfrac{1}{4} x^2 + x + 3 = 0\} = \{- 2, 6\}.$$

How do the zeros of the quadratic function $G_1 = \{(x, y) \mid y = \tfrac{1}{4} x^2 - x - 3\}$ compare with the zeros of G? How does the graph of G_1 differ from the graph of G?

Example 3. Find the roots of the quadratic equation $x^2 = - 4 x + 1$ by factoring after completing the square. Discuss the graph of the quadratic function T if T is the function $\{(x, y) \mid y = x^2 + 4 x - 1\}$.

Solution. $x^2 = - 4 x + 1 \longleftrightarrow x^2 + 4 x - 1 = 0 \longleftrightarrow x^2 + 4 x + 4 - 5 = 0 \longleftrightarrow$
$\longleftrightarrow (x + 2)^2 - 5 = 0 \longleftrightarrow (x + 2)^2 - (\sqrt{5})^2 = 0 \longleftrightarrow [(x + 2) + \sqrt{5}]$
$[(x + 2) - \sqrt{5}] = 0 \longleftrightarrow [x + (2 + \sqrt{5})][x + (2 - \sqrt{5})] = 0$. Thus
$\{x \mid x^2 = - 4 x + 1\} = \{- 2 - \sqrt{5}, - 2 + \sqrt{5}\}$. If we wish to express the decimal approximations of these

roots, we write $- 2 - \sqrt{5} \approx - 2 - 2.236$ and $- 2 + \sqrt{5} \approx - 2 + 2.236$. Expressed to the nearest tenth, these are $- 4.2$ and $.2$.

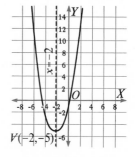

Let us now consider the equation $y = x^2 + 4 x - 1$. Since the right member is identically equal to $(x + 2)^2 - 5$, we have $y = (x + 2)^2 - 5$. Thus, when $x = - 2$, $(x + 2)^2 - 5 = - 5$, and for all other values of x, $(x + 2)^2 - 5 > - 5$. Why? Therefore the coordinates of the vertex of the parabola are $(- 2, - 5)$ and the axis of symmetry of the parabola is the line which is the graph of $x = - 2$. The range of T is $\langle - 5, \infty \langle$ and T is a decreasing function in $\rangle - \infty, - 2 \rangle$ and an increasing function in $\langle - 2, \infty \langle$.

1. For what values of a, b, and c is $y = ax^2 + bx + c$ equivalent to each of the following? Give the domain and range of the functions defined by each equation.

   a. $y = x^2 - 3x - 4$ **c.** $y = 8x^2$ **e.** $y = (x - 3)(x - 5)$

   b. $y = 9x^2 + 3$ **d.** $y = 4(x - 5)^2$ **f.** $y = (5x - 1)(x + 2)$

2. Which of the following define quadratic functions?

   a. $y = 4x^2$ **c.** $y = 3x^2 + x + 4$ **e.** $y = \dfrac{9}{x^2}$

   b. $y = 9x^2 + 18$ **d.** $3x + 7y^2 = 5$ **f.** $y = x(x + 3)(x - 1)$

3. For what values of k does each of the following define a quadratic function?

   a. $y = kx^2$ **d.** $y = (6 - k)x^2 + 4x + 3$

   b. $y = (x - 4)(x + k)$ **e.** $y = \dfrac{1}{k}x^2 + 2x + 5$

   c. $y = 4x^2 + kx - 1$ **f.** $y = x^k + 3x + 2$

4. Show that $\{(x, y) \mid y = a(x - k)^2 + p\}$ is a quadratic function when $a \neq 0$.

5. Explain why $\{(x, y) \mid y^2 = ax^2 + bx + c;\ a \neq 0\}$ is not a quadratic function.

6. Without drawing its graph, indicate the zeros, if zeros exist, of the function defined by each of the following equations.

   a. $y = (3x + 7)(x - 2)$ **d.** $x^2 + 7 = y$ **g.** $y = x^2 - 5$

   b. $y = 2x^2 - 11x + 12$ **e.** $y = 3x - 6x^2$ **h.** $y = x^2 + 2\sqrt{5}\,x - 15$

   c. $y = 2x^2 + 11x - 21$ **f.** $-8x^2 = y$ **i.** $y = x^2 + 6x + 10$

7. Find the roots of each of the following equations by factoring. Replace 0 in each equation by y and draw the graph of the function defined by the resulting equation. Discuss each function in terms of its graph.

   a. $0 = x^2 + 6x - 7$ **c.** $0 = -4x^2 + \frac{4}{3}x + \frac{1}{3}$

   b. $0 = \frac{1}{4}x^2 + 3x + 5$ **d.** $0 = x^2 + 4x + 3$

8. **a.** If in Ex. 7 each 0 is replaced by y, determine which of the functions defined by the resulting equations is bounded above. What is the least upper bound in each of these cases?

   b. State the greatest lower bound of each function which is bounded below.

9. Give the coordinates of the vertex and the equation of the axis of symmetry for the graph of each of the following functions.

   a. $\{(x, y) \mid y = x^2 - 2x\}$ **d.** $\{(x, y) \mid y = -2(x - 3)^2\}$

   b. $\{(x, y) \mid y = (x - 5)^2\}$ **e.** $\{(x, y) \mid y = 4x - x^2\}$

   c. $\{(x, y) \mid y = 8 - 6x - x^2\}$ **f.** $\{(x, y) \mid y = \sqrt{5}\,x^2\}$

10. Indicate the interval for which each function of Ex. 9 is an increasing function and the interval for which it is a decreasing function.

The Function Defined by $y = ax^2$; $a \neq 0$

To reach conclusions concerning the function $\{(x, y) \mid y = ax^2 + bx + c; a \neq 0\}$, we consider the function defined by the following cases of $y = ax^2 + bx + c$: $y = ax^2$, $y = ax^2 + p$, $y = a(x - k)^2$, and $y = a(x - k)^2 + p$. We first consider the function defined by $y = ax^2$.

If $a > 0$, the function defined by $y = ax^2$ has such graphs as those shown at the right. The graph of the function $y = 6\,x^2$ is the narrowest of the parabolas shown in the diagram. The other parabolas shown are the graphs of the functions defined by $y = x^2$, $y = \frac{1}{3}x^2$, and $y = \frac{1}{15}x^2$. Observe that as a decreases, yet remains a positive number, the curve becomes flatter. How would the graph of the function defined by $y = \frac{1}{100}x^2$ com-

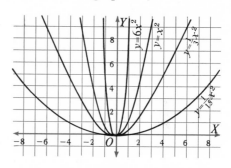

pare with the graphs shown in the diagram? How would the graph of the function defined by $y = 100\,x^2$ compare with the graphs shown?

Letting F represent the function defined by $y = ax^2$ when $a > 0$, we also conclude that:

1. The range of F is the set of all non-negative real numbers.
2. F has one zero, namely 0.
3. The graph of F is a parabola whose vertex is the origin and whose axis of symmetry is in the y-axis.
4. The absolute minimum value of F is 0.

If $a < 0$, the functions defined by $y = ax^2$ have such graphs as those shown at the right. How does the graph of the function defined by $y = -6\,x^2$ compare with the graph of the function defined by $y = 6\,x^2$?

How are the conclusions stated in the preceding paragraphs affected when the value of a in $y = ax^2$ is changed from positive to negative?

What can you say of the function defined by $y = ax^2$ when $a = 0$? Is the graph of $y = 0\,x^2$ a parabola?

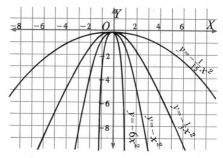

Similar Parabolas

Consider the graphs of the functions defined by $y = x^2$ and $y = \frac{1}{4} x^2$. These are shown in the figure at the right. At first glance it does not appear reasonable to ask whether these parabolas have the "same shape"; in fact at this point we have no definition of "parabolas having the same shape." Nevertheless let us consider the arcs AOB and $A'OB'$ shown in the figure. If we photographed arc AOB and enlarged it to four times its present size, the result would be congruent to arc $A'OB'$. We state the following definition of similar parabolas: Two parabolas having the y-axis as their axis of symmetry and the origin as their common vertex are *similar* provided there is a number k such that when $P_1(x_1, y_1)$ is in one graph, $P_2(kx_1, ky_1)$ is in the other. In the case under consideration, $(x_1, y_1) \in \{(x, y) \mid y = \frac{1}{4} x^2\}$ if and only if $(\frac{1}{4} x_1, \frac{1}{4} y_1) \in \{(x, y) \mid y = x^2\}$. This is true because $y_1 = \frac{1}{4} x_1{}^2 \longleftrightarrow \frac{1}{4} y_1 = (\frac{1}{4} x_1)^2$.

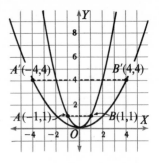

Let the parabola G_1 be the graph of the function defined by $y = a_1 x^2$ and the parabola G_2 be the graph of the function defined by $y = a_2 x^2$.

Now if $P_1(x_1, y_1)$ is in G_1, then $P_2 \left(\dfrac{a_1}{a_2} x_1, \dfrac{a_1}{a_2} y_1 \right)$

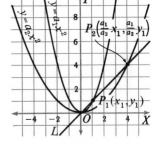

is in G_2, and conversely. This is true because $y_1 = a_1 x_1{}^2 \longleftrightarrow \dfrac{a_1}{a_2} y_1 = a_2 \left(\dfrac{a_1}{a_2} x_1 \right)^2$. Thus G_1 and G_2 are similar and $k = \dfrac{a_1}{a_2}$. It is noteworthy that P_1 and P_2 are on a line L through the origin, namely the line whose equation is $y = \dfrac{y_1}{x_1} x$. As L rotates with the origin as a pivot, P_1 and P_2 move in G_1 and G_2 in such a way that the ratio $\dfrac{OP_2}{OP_1}$ *remains constant* so long as L is oblique. Indeed, this ratio is always equal to $\dfrac{a_1}{a_2}$. Why?

Do you believe that L intersects each of the parabolas G_1 and G_2 in two distinct points if and only if L is oblique? Inasmuch as any two parabolas can be placed so that they have the y-axis as their axis of symmetry and the origin as their common vertex, we conclude that any two parabolas are similar.

Two parabolas, whose axes of symmetry lie in the y-axis and whose common vertex is the origin, are *congruent* provided that when $P_1(x_1, y_1)$ is in one parabola, $P_2(x_1, y_1)$ or $P_2(-x_1, -y_1)$ is in the graph of the other parabola. Inasmuch as any two parabolas can be placed so that they have the y-axis as their axis of symmetry and the origin as their common vertex, we can determine if they are congruent.

 EXERCISES

1. Arrange the following equations in order so that the one whose graph is the narrowest parabola is first and the one whose graph is the flattest parabola is last.

   a. $y = \frac{1}{4} x^2$　　　**b.** $y = 4 x^2$　　　**c.** $y = .2 x^2$　　　**d.** $y = -7 x^2$

2. Which of the functions indicated below will have 0 as its absolute minimum value?

   a. $\{(x, y) \mid y = \frac{5}{2} x^2\}$　　　　　**d.** $\{(x, y) \mid y = 6 x^2 + 1\}$

   b. $\{(x, y) \mid y = -8 x^2\}$　　　　**e.** $\{(x, y) \mid y = -\frac{1}{4} x^2\}$

   c. $\{(x, y) \mid 3 x^2 - y = 0\}$　　　**f.** $\{(x, y) \mid 3 y = 2 x^2\}$

3. Each of the following ordered pairs indicates the coordinates of a point. For each point, write an equation the graph of whose solution set is a parabola which contains this point, is symmetric with respect to the y-axis, and has its vertex at the origin.

   a. $(1, 2)$　　　　　　**c.** $(-4, -1)$　　　　　**e.** $(16, 1)$

   b. $(-3, 2)$　　　　　**d.** $(-5, 6)$　　　　　**f.** $(1, 16)$

4. Assuming that the domain of each of the following functions is R, state the range of the function.

   a. $\{(x, y) \mid y = -2 x^2\}$　　　　**c.** $\{(x, y) \mid y = \frac{1}{3} x^2\}$

   b. $\{(x, y) \mid y = 3 x^2\}$　　　　　**d.** $\{(x, y) \mid y = -\frac{5}{6} x^2\}$

5. Which of the parabolas whose equations are shown below are similar to the parabola whose equation is $y = 3 x^2$?

   a. $y = -3 x^2$　　　**b.** $y = x^2$　　　**c.** $y = \frac{15}{3} x^2$　　　**d.** $\frac{1}{3} y = x^2$

6. Which of the parabolas whose equations are shown in Ex. 5 are congruent to the parabola whose equation is $y = 3 x^2$?

7. If $a \in S$ when $S = \{-3, -2, -1, 1, 2, 3, 4\}$,

   a. List the members of the subset of S for which $y = ax^2$ has 0 as its absolute maximum value.

   b. List the value, or values, of a for which the graph of the function defined by $y = ax^2$ is the flattest parabola.

The Function Defined by $y = ax^2 + p$; $a \neq 0$

Let us now consider those functions defined by the equation $y = ax^2 + p$. The figure at the right shows the graphs of the functions defined by the equations $y = \frac{1}{9}x^2$, $y = \frac{1}{9}x^2 + 3$, $y = \frac{1}{9}x^2 + 6$, $y = \frac{1}{9}x^2 - 2$, and $y = \frac{1}{9}x^2 - 4$. By studying these graphs you can see that the graph of the function defined by $y = \frac{1}{9}x^2 + 6$ is congruent to the graph of the function defined by $y = \frac{1}{9}x^2$. For a given value of x there is a point $P_1(x_1, y_1)$ in the graph of the function defined by $y = ax^2$ and a point $P_2(x_1, y_1 + 6)$ in the graph of the function defined by $y = ax^2 + 6$. Thus the ordinate of P_2 is 6 greater than the ordinate of P_1. In general, $(x_1, \ y_1) \in \{(x, \ y) \mid y = ax^2\} \longleftrightarrow (x_1, y_1 + p) \in \{(x, y) \mid y = ax^2 + p\}$.

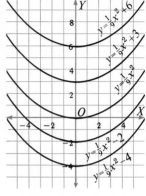

If $a > 0$, the quadratic function defined by $y = ax^2 + p$ has

1. All real numbers greater than or equal to p in its range.

2. $\sqrt{\dfrac{-p}{a}}$ and $-\sqrt{\dfrac{-p}{a}}$ as its zeros when $p \leq 0$ and no zeros when $p > 0$.

3. The point V $(0, p)$ as the vertex of its graph and the y-axis as the axis of symmetry of its graph.

4. The absolute minimum value p.

What modifications must be made in statements 1–4 if $a < 0$?

Ⓐ **EXERCISES**

1. With respect to the same pair of coordinate axes, draw the graph of the function defined by each of the following six equations.

    a. $y = 2x^2$ **c.** $y = 2x^2 + 2$ **e.** $y = 2x^2 - 3$

    b. $y = 2x^2 + 1$ **d.** $y = 2x^2 + 3$ **f.** $y = 2x^2 - 5$

2. Give the zeros of those functions in Ex. 1 which have zeros.

3. With respect to a single pair of coordinate axes, draw the graph of the function defined by each of the following six equations.

    a. $y = -\frac{1}{2}x^2$ **c.** $y = -\frac{1}{2}x^2 + 3$ **e.** $y = -\frac{1}{2}x^2 - 1$

    b. $y = -\frac{1}{2}x^2 + 1$ **d.** $y = -\frac{1}{2}x^2 + 6$ **f.** $y = -\frac{1}{2}x^2 - 4$

4. Give the zeros of those functions in Ex. 3 which have zeros.

5. Without drawing the graphs, determine which of the functions defined by each of the following equations have zeros. If zeros exist, indicate what they are.

a. $y = x^2 + 6$ d. $y = \frac{1}{2} x^2 - \frac{1}{3}$ g. $2 x^2 + 3 y = 1$

b. $y = -x^2 + 6$ e. $y = -5 x^2 - 1$ h. $5 x^2 - 7 y + 2 = 0$

c. $y = 3 x^2 - 2$ f. $y = -x^2 + 4$ i. $-3 x^2 + 2 y = 6$

6. Without drawing the parabolas, determine the coordinates of the vertex of each of the parabolas defined in Ex. 5.

7. Find the absolute minimum or absolute maximum value of the function defined by each of the following equations.

a. $y = -3 x^2$ c. $y = -\frac{1}{3} x^2 - 2$ e. $2 x^2 = y - 4$

b. $y = \frac{1}{2} x^2 + 5$ d. $y = -6 x^2 + 4$ f. $7 - x^2 = y$

B EXERCISES

8. Show that the following statement is true: If the graphs of the functions defined by $y = ax^2 + p_1$ and $y = ax^2 + p_2$ are intersected by the vertical line $x = s$ in points P_1 and P_2, respectively, and by the vertical line $x = t$ in points Q_1 and Q_2, respectively, then $P_1 P_2 Q_2 Q_1$ is a parallelogram provided $p_1 \neq p_2$ and $s \neq t$.

The Function Defined by $y = a(x - k)^2$; $a \neq 0$

Let us now consider the function defined by $y = a(x - k)^2$ in which $a \neq 0$ and $k \neq 0$.

We first consider the case in which $a > 0$. The function defined by $y = \frac{1}{4}(x - 3)^2$ is an example of such a function. The graph of this function is shown at the right together with the graph of the function defined by $y = \frac{1}{4} x^2$. We see that if $(x_1, y_1) \in \{(x, y) \mid y = \frac{1}{4} x^2\}$, then $(x_1 + 3, y_1) \in \{(x, y) \mid y = \frac{1}{4}(x - 3)^2\}$, and conversely. Thus the graph of the function defined by $y = \frac{1}{4}(x - 3)^2$ is congruent to the graph of the function defined by $y = \frac{1}{4} x^2$ and is three units *to*

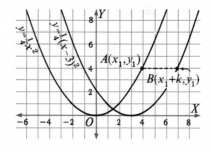

the right of it. Also the graph of the function defined by $y = \frac{1}{4}(x - 3)^2$ has $V(3, 0)$ for its vertex and the graph of $\{(x, y) \mid x = 3\}$ for its axis of symmetry. The function itself has $\langle 0, \infty \rangle$ for its range and has one zero, namely 3. This zero is called a zero of *multiplicity two* because the factor $(x - 3)$ is to the second power in the given equation.

We generalize these conclusions for the function $W = \{(x, y) \mid y = a(x - k)^2;\ a > 0\}$, whose graph is the set of points G which is a parabola, as follows:

1. The range of W is $\langle 0, \infty \rangle$.
2. W has one zero, namely k. This is a zero of multiplicity two. It is also called a root of multiplicity two for the equation $a(x - k)^2 = 0$.
3. The vertex of G is the point whose coordinates are $(k, 0)$ and the axis of symmetry of G is the graph of $\{(x, y) \mid x = k\}$.
4. The absolute minimum of W is 0.

What modifications should be made in statements 1–4 for the case in which $a < 0$?

 EXERCISES

1. Construct a pair of coordinate axes; then with respect to this one pair of axes draw the graphs of the four functions defined by the following equations.

     a. $y = x^2$ **b.** $y = (x - 4)^2$ **c.** $y = -4(x + 3)^2$ **d.** $y = -4(x - 5)^2$

2. Construct a pair of coordinate axes; then with respect to this one pair of axes construct the graphs of the four functions defined by the following equations.

     a. $y = -4x^2$ **b.** $y = -4(x + 2)^2$ **c.** $y = -4(x - 3)^2$ **d.** $y = -4(x + \frac{3}{2})^2$

3. For each of the following exercises draw a pair of coordinate axes; then with respect to these axes draw the graphs of the two functions defined in that exercise.

     a. $\{(x, y) \mid y = \frac{1}{4}x^2 - 1\}$ **c.** $\{(x, y) \mid y = 2(x + \frac{1}{2})^2\}$
        $\{(x, y) \mid y = \frac{1}{4}x^2 + 1\}$ $\{(x, y) \mid y = 2(x - \frac{1}{2})^2\}$

     b. $\{(x, y) \mid y = (x - 5)^2\}$ **d.** $\{(x, y) \mid y = (2x + 1)^2\}$
        $\{(x, y) \mid y = -(x - 5)^2\}$ $\{(x, y) \mid y = (2x - 1)^2\}$

4. Which of the following functions have zeros of multiplicity two?

     a. $\{(x, y) \mid y = 3x^2\}$ **d.** $\{(x, y) \mid y = -6x^2\}$
     b. $\{(x, y) \mid y = 2x^2 + 3\}$ **e.** $\{(x, y) \mid y = (x - 6)^2\}$
     c. $\{(x, y) \mid y = -4x^2 - 1\}$ **f.** $\{(x, y) \mid y = \frac{1}{2}(x + 4)^2\}$

5. Give the coordinates of the vertex and the equation of the axis of symmetry for the graph of each of the following functions.

     a. $\{(x, y) \mid y = (x - 3)^2\}$ **d.** $\{(x, y) \mid y = \frac{1}{2}(4 - x)^2\}$
     b. $\{(x, y) \mid y = (x - \sqrt{3})^2\}$ **e.** $\{(x, y) \mid y = (3x - 1)^2\}$
     c. $\{(x, y) \mid y = -(x + 4)^2\}$ **f.** $\{(x, y) \mid y = \sqrt{3}(2x + 1)^2\}$

6. Show that the two parabolas which are the graphs of $y = a(x - k_1)^2$ and $y = a(x - k_2)^2$ have exactly one point in common provided $k_1 \neq k_2$.

7. Determine k so that the graph of the function defined by the equation $y = 2(x+k)^2$ intersects the graph of the function defined by $y = 2x^2$ in the point whose coordinates are $(-1, 2)$.

8. Describe the location of the points common to the graphs of the functions defined by the two equations $y = a(x+k)^2$ and $y = a(x-k)^2$ as k assumes different nonzero values but a remains constant.

9. Describe the graph which is the union of all parabolas whose equations have the form $y = a(x-k)^2$, where k is a constant and a assumes all positive values.

The Function Defined by $y = a(x-k)^2 + p$; $a \neq 0$

The graph shown is the graph of the truth set of the equation $y = (x-2)^2 - 4$. Let F denote the function defined by this equation. Then $F = \{(x, y) \mid y = (x-2)^2 - 4\}$. We see that if $x \neq 2$, $f(x) > f(2)$. Therefore $f(2)$, that is, -4 is an absolute minimum for F. The range of F contains all real numbers greater than or equal to -4. Since the range of F contains 0, the function F has zeros. These are 0 and 4. The graph of F has the point V $(2, -4)$ for its vertex and the graph of $\{(x, y) \mid x = 2\}$ as its axis of symmetry.

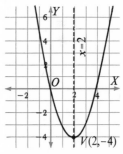

Let $f(x) = a(x-k)^2 + p$ with $a > 0$. We suspect that the vertical line L which is the graph of $\{(x, y) \mid x = k\}$ is the axis of symmetry of the graph of F. Let A be a point in the graph. If the abscissa of A is $k - c$, then the ordinate of A is $f(k-c) = a[(k-c) - k]^2 + p = ac^2 + p$. Let B be another point in the graph. If the abscissa of B is $k + c$, then the ordinate of B is $f(k+c) = a[(k+c) - k]^2 + p = ac^2 + p$. Thus the coordinates of A and B are $(k - c, ac^2 + p)$ and $(k + c, ac^2 + p)$, respectively, and hence A and B have the same ordinate. This means that $\overline{AB}$ is horizontal. Accordingly, the vertical line L is perpendicular to $\overline{AB}$ and bisects it at the point

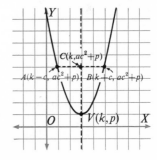

$C(k, ac^2 + p)$. Since L is the perpendicular bisector of $\overline{AB}$, we see that the reflection in the line L of any point A in the parabola is another point B in the parabola. Therefore the parabola is symmetric with respect to the line L, by definition (page 251). Therefore the line L is the axis of symmetry of the parabola.

It is readily shown that if $F = \{(x, f(x)) \mid f(x) = a(x - k)^2 + p \wedge a > 0\}$, then p is the absolute minimum of F. The proof follows and the reasons are left to you.

$$\overset{(1)}{x} \overset{(2)}{\in R} \longrightarrow (x = k \vee x \neq k)$$

When $x = k$, we have:

$$\left. \begin{array}{c} \overset{(3)}{x = k} \\ f(x) = a(x - k)^2 + p \end{array} \right\} \overset{(4)}{\longrightarrow} f(x) = f(k) = p$$

When $x \neq k$, we have:

$$\left. \overset{(5)}{x} \overset{(6)}{\neq k} \longrightarrow x - k \neq 0 \overset{(7)}{\longrightarrow} (x - k)^2 > 0 \right\} \begin{array}{c} \overset{(8)}{a > 0} \\ \end{array} \overset{(9)}{\longrightarrow} a(x - k)^2 > 0$$

$$\overset{(10)}{\longrightarrow} \left. \begin{array}{c} a(x - k)^2 + p > p \\ f(x) = a(x - k)^2 + p \end{array} \right\} \overset{(11)}{\longrightarrow} f(x) > p$$

Therefore:

$$\left. \begin{array}{c} (x \neq k \wedge f(x) > p) \\ (x = k \wedge f(x) = p) \end{array} \right\} \overset{(12)}{\longrightarrow} p \text{ is the absolute minimum.}$$

Thus the vertex of the parabola which is the graph of F is the point $V(k, p)$, and the range of F is the set of all real numbers greater than or equal to p. The function F has zeros if and only if 0 is a member of the range of F, that is, if and only if $p \leq 0$.

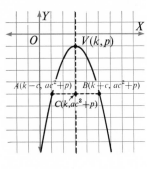

By similar reasoning we see that if $a < 0$, the line L is still the axis of the parabola and $V(k, p)$ is still the vertex of the parabola. However, in this case, p is an absolute maximum of F (the proof is left to you as an exercise) and the range of F is the set of all real numbers equal to or less than p. Also, in this case, F has zeros if and only if $p \geq 0$.

We summarize these results in the following theorem.

Theorem 1-7. If $F = \{(x, y) \mid y = a(x - k)^2 + p\}$, and G is a parabola which is the graph of F, and

If $a > 0$, then:

(1) The range of F is $\langle p, \infty \langle$.
(2) F has zeros if and only if $p \leq 0$.

(3) The axis of symmetry of G is the graph of $\{(x, y) \mid x = k\}$ and the vertex of G is the point V (k, p).

(4) F has an absolute minimum at $x = k$. This absolute minimum is p.

If $a < 0$, then

(5) The range of F is $\rangle - \infty , p \rangle$.

(6) F has zeros if and only if $p \geq 0$.

(7) The axis of symmetry of G is the graph of $\{(x, y) \mid x = k\}$ and the vertex of G is the point V (k, p).

(8) F has an absolute maximum at $x = k$. This absolute maximum is p.

There are other ways in which to express the conclusions of Theorem 1–7. For example, we can assert that if $a > 0$, F is bounded below, that its greatest lower bound is p, that G is symmetric with respect to the line $x = k$, and that if $p \leq 0$, the zeros mentioned in (2) are the roots of the equation $a(x - k)^2 + p = 0$. Corresponding assertions can be made for the case in which $a < 0$.

Ⓐ **EXERCISES**

1. Find the axis of symmetry and the coordinates of the vertex of the graph of the function defined by each of the following equations.

a. $y = 3(x - 1)^2 + 4$

b. $y = - 3(x - 1)^2 + 4$

c. $y = \frac{1}{2}(x + 5)^2 - 1$

d. $y = - \frac{1}{3}(x - 2)^2 + 3$

e. $y = - (x + 3)^2 + 2$

f. $y = \frac{2}{3}(x - 2)^2 - 3$

2. What is the range of each of the functions defined in Ex. 1?

3. Which of the functions defined in Ex. 1 have zeros? What are the zeros of these functions?

4. Sketch the graph of each of the functions defined below.

a. $\{(x, y) \mid y = 2(x + 1)^2 - 2\}$

b. $\{(x, y) \mid y = 2(x - 1)^2 - 2\}$

c. $\{(x, y) \mid y = - \frac{1}{2}(x + 2)^2 + 1\}$

d. $\{(x, y) \mid y = - \frac{1}{2}(x - 2)^2 + 1\}$

e. $\{(x, y) \mid y = 4(x + 3)^2 - 2\}$

f. $\{(x, y) \mid y = 4(x + 3)^2 + 2\}$

g. $\{(x, y) \mid y = - 4(x + 3)^2 - 2\}$

h. $\{(x, y) \mid y = - 4(x + 3)^2 + 2\}$

5. Which of the functions of Ex. 4 have absolute maxima and which have absolute minima? State the value of each absolute maximum and each absolute minimum.

6. For each of the following functions, use set-builder notation to indicate the set of all x for which the function is an increasing function.

a. $\{(x, y) \mid y = 2(x + 1)^2 - 3\}$

b. $\{(x, y) \mid y = 2(x + 1)^2 + 3\}$

c. $\{(x, y) \mid y = \frac{1}{2}(x - 2)^2 - 4\}$

d. $\{(x, y) \mid y = - \frac{1}{2}(x - 2)^2 + 4\}$

e. $\{(x, y) \mid y = (x - 3)^2 + 1\}$

f. $\{(x, y) \mid y = (x + 3)^2 + 1\}$

The inverses of the functions defined by $y = ax^2$, $y = ax^2 + p$, $y = a(x - k)^2$, and $y = a(x - k)^2 + p$ are not functions. However, these inverses and their graphs have many of the characteristics of the functions and their graphs.

7. a. State the equation of the axis of symmetry and the coordinates of the vertex of the parabola which is the graph of $\{(x, y) \mid x = ay^2\}$.

   b. Sketch representative graphs of the parabola defined by $x = ay^2$ for the case in which $a > 0$ and for the case in which $a < 0$?

   c. What is the range of the relation when $a > 0$? when $a < 0$?

   d. For a given value of y, how does the corresponding value of x change when $a > 0$ and a increases? When $a < 0$ and $|a|$ increases?

8. a. Sketch a representative graph of the parabola which is the graph of the relation defined by $x = ay^2 + p$ for each of the following cases: $a > 0$ and $p > 0$, $a > 0$ and $p < 0$, $a < 0$ and $p > 0$, $a < 0$ and $p < 0$.

   b. What are the coordinates of the vertices of the parabolas in part **a**?

   c. What is the equation of the axes of symmetry of each of the parabolas in part **a**?

   d. In which of the cases in part **a** will the parabola intersect the y-axis in two points? in no points?

   e. What is the range of each relation defined by an equation in part **a**?

   f. How is the vertex of each of the parabolas of part **a** affected when p is increased?

   g. For a given value of y how does the corresponding value of x change when $a > 0$ and a increases? when $a < 0$ and $|a|$ increases?

9. For the relation defined by $x = a(y - k)^2$,

   a. What is the axis of symmetry?

   b. What are the coordinates of the vertex?

   c. What is the range when $a > 0$? when $a < 0$?

10. For the relation $x = a(y - k)^2 + p$,

   a. What is the axis of symmetry?

   b. What are the coordinates of the vertex?

   c. What is the range when $a > 0$? when $a < 0$?

   d. If $a > 0$, under what conditions does the parabola intersect the y-axis? If $a < 0$, under what conditions does the parabola intersect the y-axis?

11. Since $x = y^2 \longleftrightarrow (y = \sqrt{x} \lor y = -\sqrt{x})$, we see that $\{(x, y) \mid x = y^2\} = \{(x, y) \mid y = \sqrt{x}\} \cup \{(x, y) \mid y = -\sqrt{x}\}$. Thus the relation can be considered as the union of two functions.

a. With respect to the same set of coordinate axes, draw the graph of $\{(x, y) \mid y = \sqrt{x}\}$ and draw the graph of $\{(x, y) \mid y = -\sqrt{x}\}$.

b. Is the union of two functions always a function?

12. **a.** Show that the relation $\{(x, y) \mid x = 4(y - 1)^2\}$ can be considered as the union of two functions.

b. Draw the graph of each of the functions you wrote in part **a.**

13. Prove: If $F = \{(x, y) \mid y = a(x - k)^2 + p \wedge a < 0\}$, then p is the absolute maximum of the function F.

The Function Defined by $y = ax^2 + bx + c$; $a \neq 0$

We observe that the quadratic trinomial $ax^2 + bx + c$ can be expressed in the form $a(x - k)^2 + p$ by performing the manipulation known as "completing the square." For example, $3x^2 + 5x - 11 = 3(x^2 + \frac{5}{3}x - \frac{11}{3}) = 3[(x^2 + \frac{5}{3}x + \frac{25}{36}) - \frac{25}{36} - \frac{11}{3}] = 3[(x + \frac{5}{6})^2 - \frac{157}{36}] = 3(x + \frac{5}{6})^2 - \frac{157}{12}$. In this case $k = -\frac{5}{6}$ and $p = -\frac{157}{12}$. For the general case, $ax^2 + bx + c$ and $a \neq 0$, we have $ax^2 + bx + c = a\left[\left(x + \dfrac{b}{2a}\right)^2 + \dfrac{4ac - b^2}{4a^2}\right] = a\left(x + \dfrac{b}{2a}\right)^2 + \dfrac{4ac - b^2}{4a}$. Thus $k = -\dfrac{b}{2a}$ and $p = \dfrac{4ac - b^2}{4a}$. We now state the following theorem.

▷ **Theorem 2–7.** If $a \neq 0$, then $ax^2 + bx + c = a(x - k)^2 + p$ where $k = -\dfrac{b}{2a}$ and $p = \dfrac{4ac - b^2}{4a}$.

Substituting these values for p and k in the conclusions of Theorem 1–7 we obtain the following corollary.

Corollary to Theorem 2–7. If $F = \{(x, y) \mid y = ax^2 + bx + c\}$, G is a parabola which is the graph of F, and

If $a > 0$, then

(1) The range of F is $\left\langle \dfrac{4ac - b^2}{4a}, \infty \right\langle$, that is, F is bounded below.

(2) F has zeros if and only if $\dfrac{4ac - b^2}{4a} \leq 0$.

(3) The axis of symmetry of G is the graph of $\left\{(x, y) \mid x = -\dfrac{b}{2a}\right\}$ and the vertex of G is the point $V\left(-\dfrac{b}{2a}, \dfrac{4ac - b^2}{4a}\right)$.

(4) F has an absolute minimum when $x = -\dfrac{b}{2a}$. This absolute minimum is $\dfrac{4ac - b^2}{4a}$.

If $a < 0$, then

(5) The range of F is $\rangle - \infty, \dfrac{4\,ac - b^2}{4\,a} \rangle$, that is, F is bounded above.

(6) F has zeros if and only if $\dfrac{4\,ac - b^2}{4\,a} \geq 0$.

(7) The axis of symmetry of G is the graph of $\left\{ (x, y) \mid x = -\dfrac{b}{2\,a} \right\}$

    and the vertex of G is the point $V\left(-\dfrac{b}{2\,a}, \dfrac{4\,ac - b^2}{4\,a}\right)$.

(8) F has an absolute maximum at $x = -\dfrac{b}{2\,a}$. This absolute maximum

    is $\dfrac{4\,ac - b^2}{4\,a}$.

Example 1.   Show that the function F defined by $y = -x^2 + 10\,x - 28$ has its absolute maximum value at $x = 5$ and that this absolute maximum value is -3. Sketch the graph of F and discuss the graph.

Solution.   Since $a = -1$, $b = 10$, and $c = -28$, we may substitute these values in the equations $x = -\dfrac{b}{2\,a}$ and $y = \dfrac{4\,ac - b^2}{4\,a}$ of the corollary to Theorem 2–7 to obtain the maximum value. Thus F has an absolute maximum at $x = -\dfrac{10}{2(-1)} = 5$ and this maximum is $y = \dfrac{4(-1)(-28) - 10^2}{4(-1)} = -3$. It follows that

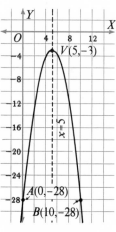

the vertex of the graph of F is the point $V(5, -3)$ and the axis of symmetry is the graph of $\{(x, y) \mid x = 5\}$. In order to obtain another point in the graph we let $x = 0$ in $y = -x^2 + 10\,x - 28$ and obtain $y = -28$. Now we sketch a parabola with the vertex $V(5, -3)$ and the y-intercept -28 as shown in the figure at the right. The reflection of the point $A(0, -28)$ in the axis of symmetry is the point $B(10, -28)$. Therefore the coordinates of B should satisfy $y = -x^2 + 10\,x - 28$. We see that they do and hence $(10, -28) \in F$.

    Instead of relying upon the equation provided in the corollary above, we could have completed the square. Doing so, we have $y = -x^2 + 10\,x - 28 = (-1)(x^2 - 10\,x + 28) = (-1)[(x^2 - 10\,x + 25) + 3] = -1[(x - 5)^2 + 3] = -(x - 5)^2 - 3$.

A study of $\{(x, y) \mid y = -(x-5)^2 - 3\}$ indicates that $y = -(x-5)^2 - 3$ defines the same function as $y = -x^2 + 10x - 28$ and that the discussion in the preceding paragraph holds for either defining equation.

Example 2. The perimeter of a rectangle is 400 feet. Find the dimensions of the rectangle which make its area as large as possible.

Solution. Let x represent the measure of the width in feet. Then the measure of the length in feet can be represented by $200 - x$. If A represents the measure of the area in square feet, $A = x(200 - x)$, or $A = -x^2 + 200x$. Comparing this equation with the general equation $y = ax^2 + bx + c$, we see that $a = -1$, $b = 200$, and $c = 0$. According to part (8) of the corollary to Theorem 2–7, the maximum value of A is at $x = -\dfrac{200}{2(-1)} = 100$ and the maximum value is $y = \dfrac{4(-1) \cdot 0 - 200^2}{4(-1)} = 10{,}000$. Thus we see that the rectangle has its maximum area 10,000 square feet when it is a square. The length is 100 feet and the width is 100 feet.

A EXERCISES

1. Change each of the following equations to the form $y = a(x-k)^2 + p$ by completing the square.

   a. $y = x^2 + 4x - 13$

   b. $y = 3x^2 - 5x - 2$

   c. $y = x^2 - \frac{14}{3}x + \frac{8}{3}$

   d. $y = x^2 - 6x$

   e. $y = x^2 - 14x + 168$

   f. $y = -2x^2 + 9x - 7$

   g. $y = -6x^2 + 5x + 1$

   h. $y = -6x^2 + 19x - 8$

2. Determine the absolute maximum or absolute minimum of the function defined by each of the equations of Ex. 1. Determine the equation of the axis of the graph of each function, and the coordinates of the vertex of the graph.

3. Use the Corollary to Theorem 2–7 as a guide for sketching the graphs of the functions defined by the following equations. State the absolute maximum or absolute minimum and the range of each function. Write the equation of the axis of symmetry for each graph. State the coordinates of the vertex of each graph.

   a. $y = 2x^2 - 8x + 12$

   b. $y = 3x^2 + 6x - 24$

   c. $y = -2x^2 - 6x - 20$

   d. $y = -6x^2 + 7x + 3$

   e. $y = x^2 + x - \frac{15}{4}$

   f. $y = -11x^2 - 24x - 4$

4. Find two numbers whose sum is 64 and whose product is the greatest possible number.

5. Find two numbers whose sum is 40 and the sum of whose squares is the least possible number.

6. Find the dimensions of the largest rectangular feeding lot that can be made using 150 feet of fencing for three sides of the lot if part of a side of the barn which is 150 feet in length is used for the fourth side of the lot.

7. A strip of metal 40 inches wide is to be folded to form an open rectangular gutter as shown at the right. Find the dimensions of the gutter which will give the maximum carrying capacity; that is, have the maximum cross section.

8. In a given triangle the sum of the measures in inches of the base and the altitude is 14. What length of the base will produce the greatest area for the triangle?

B EXERCISES

9. If an object is shot vertically upward from the surface of the earth with an initial velocity of v feet per second, it is proved in physics that $s = vt - \frac{1}{2} gt^2$ where s feet is the height of the object above the surface of the earth at the end of t seconds and g is approximately 32. (This formula neglects air resistance and other disturbing factors.) If an object is shot vertically upward from the earth's surface with an initial velocity of 256 feet per second:

(a) Draw the graph of the function defined by $s = vt - \frac{1}{2} gt^2$.

(b) Find the maximum height the object reaches.

(c) Find the time required to reach the maximum height.

(d) Find the total time the object is in flight.

10. Each month a merchant has been selling 100 of a certain article at a profit of 50 cents per article. He reasons that for each cut of 1 cent in his profit per article he will be able to sell 10 extra articles. If his reasoning is correct, what cut in price will give him the maximum total profit on his monthly sales?

11. A line segment 8 inches long is to be cut into two parts. One part is to be bent into the form of a circle and the other into the form of a square. How long should each part be if the sum of the areas of the circle and the square is to be a minimum?

12. Write the defining equation for the parabola whose vertex has the coordinates $(4, -1)$, whose y-intercept is 15, and whose axis is parallel to the y-axis.

13. Write the equation which defines the function whose maximum is 1 when $x = 5$ and whose value is -3 when $x = 7$.

Zeros of the Quadratic Function Defined by $y = ax^2 + bx + c;\ a \neq 0$

We have already learned that when $a > 0$, the quadratic function defined by $y = ax^2 + bx + c$ has zeros if and only if $\dfrac{4\,ac - b^2}{4\,a} \leq 0$; and when $a < 0$, this function has zeros if and only if $\dfrac{4\,ac - b^2}{4\,a} \geq 0$. Since the zeros of this function are the roots of the equation $ax^2 + bx + c = 0$, to find the zeros of the function we solve this equation. We assume, of course, that a, b, and c are constants, a is the coefficient of the second-degree term, b is the coefficient of the first-degree term, $a \neq 0$, and that $b^2 - 4\,ac \geq 0$. The solution by completing the square is as follows:

$$ax^2 + bx + c = 0 \overset{(1)}{\longleftrightarrow} x^2 + \frac{b}{a}x + \frac{c}{a} = 0 \overset{(2)}{\longleftrightarrow} x^2 + \frac{b}{a}x + \frac{b^2}{4\,a^2} + \frac{c}{a} - \frac{b^2}{4\,a^2} =$$

$$0 \overset{(3)}{\longleftrightarrow} \left(x + \frac{b}{2\,a}\right)^2 + \frac{4\,ac - b^2}{4\,a^2} = 0 \overset{(4)}{\longleftrightarrow} \left(x + \frac{b}{2\,a}\right)^2 - \frac{b^2 - 4\,ac}{4\,a^2} = 0 \overset{(5)}{\longleftrightarrow}$$

$$\left(x + \frac{b}{2\,a}\right)^2 - \left(\sqrt{\frac{b^2 - 4\,ac}{4\,a^2}}\right)^2 = 0 \overset{(6)}{\longleftrightarrow} \left[\left(x + \frac{b}{2\,a}\right) + \frac{\sqrt{b^2 - 4\,ac}}{2\,a}\right] \cdot \left[\left(x + \frac{b}{2\,a}\right)\right.$$

$$\left. - \frac{\sqrt{b^2 - 4\,ac}}{2\,a}\right] = 0 \overset{(7)}{\longleftrightarrow} x + \frac{b}{2\,a} + \frac{\sqrt{b^2 - 4\,ac}}{2\,a} = 0 \vee x + \frac{b}{2\,a} - \frac{\sqrt{b^2 - 4\,ac}}{2\,a} =$$

$$0 \overset{(8)}{\longleftrightarrow} x = -\frac{b}{2\,a} - \frac{\sqrt{b^2 - 4\,ac}}{2\,a} \vee x = -\frac{b}{2\,a} + \frac{\sqrt{b^2 - 4\,ac}}{2\,a} \overset{(9)}{\longleftrightarrow}$$

$$x = \frac{-b \pm \sqrt{b^2 - 4\,ac}}{2\,a}.$$ Therefore the zeros of the function defined by

$y = ax^2 + bx + c \wedge a \neq 0$ are $\dfrac{-b + \sqrt{b^2 - 4\,ac}}{2\,a}$ and $\dfrac{-b - \sqrt{b^2 - 4\,ac}}{2\,a}$.

The reasons for the steps of this proof are left to you. Thus we have proved the following theorem:

Theorem 3–7. If $F = \{(x, y) \mid y = ax^2 + bx + c\}$ and $a \neq 0$ and $b^2 - 4\,ac \geq 0$, the zeros of F are $\dfrac{-b + \sqrt{b^2 - 4\,ac}}{2\,a}$ and $\dfrac{-b - \sqrt{b^2 - 4\,ac}}{2\,a}$.

Corollary to Theorem 3–7. If $ax^2 + bx + c = 0$, $a \neq 0$, and $b^2 - 4\,ac \geq 0$, then the roots of $ax^2 + bx + c = 0$ are $\dfrac{-b + \sqrt{b^2 - 4\,ac}}{2\,a}$ and $\dfrac{-b - \sqrt{b^2 - 4\,ac}}{2\,a}$.

Recall that $x = \dfrac{-b \pm \sqrt{b^2 - 4\,ac}}{2\,a}$ is sometimes called the *quadratic formula*.

Notice that if $b^2 - 4\,ac = 0$, $-\dfrac{b}{2\,a}$ is a double root, that is, a root of multiplicity two. In this case $\{x \mid ax^2 + bx + c = 0\} = \left\{-\dfrac{b}{2\,a}\right\}$ provided $a \neq 0$.

Example 1.   Find the roots of the equation $3\,x^2 + 1.3\,x - 2.48 = 0$.

Solution.   In this equation $a = 3$, $b = 1.3$, and $c = -2.48$. Substituting these values in $\dfrac{-b + \sqrt{b^2 - 4\,ac}}{2\,a}$ and $\dfrac{-b - \sqrt{b^2 - 4\,ac}}{2\,a}$, we obtain $\dfrac{-1.3 + \sqrt{31.45}}{6}$ and $\dfrac{-1.3 - \sqrt{31.45}}{6}$. Thus $\{x \mid 3\,x^2 + 1.3\,x - 2.48 = 0\} = \left\{\dfrac{-1.3 + \sqrt{31.45}}{6}, \dfrac{-1.3 - \sqrt{31.45}}{6}\right\}$.

Let us call these roots r and s, respectively. If we seek a decimal approximation of r and s, we must perform computations which involve, among other things, finding the square roots of 31.45. We also must consider the degree of accuracy required. Let us suppose that we wish to find decimal approximations that are correct to the nearest hundredth. First we find the approximate square roots of 31.45 using the square root algorithm as follows:

$$
\begin{array}{ll}
 & 5.\ 6\ 0\ 8 \\
 & \sqrt{31.450000} \\
 & \underline{25} \\
2 \times 5 = 10 & 6\ 45 \\
10 + .6 = 10.6 & \underline{6\ 36} \\
2 \times 5.6 = 11.2 & 900 \\
11.2 + .00 = 11.20 & \underline{000} \\
2 \times 5.60 = 11.20 & 90000 \\
11.20 + .008 = 11.208 & \underline{89664} \\
 & 336
\end{array}
$$

Accordingly,

$$r \approx \frac{-1.3 + 5.608}{6} \approx .72 \text{ and } s \approx \frac{-1.3 - 5.608}{6} \approx -1.15.$$

In view of the fact that .72 and -1.15 are approximations to the roots of the equation $3\,x^2 + 1.3\,x - 2.48 = 0$, we cannot expect these values to satisfy the equation. In other words, if $f(x) = 3\,x^2 + 1.3\,x - 2.48$, we cannot expect that $f(.72) = 0$ or that $f(-1.15) = 0$. Actually we find that $f(.72) \approx .01$ and that $f(-1.15) \approx -.01$.

Example 2.   Solve the equation $m^2x^2 + 4\,x + m = 0$ where m is a nonzero constant.

Solution. When we compare the given equation with $ax^2 + bx + c = 0$, from which our formula was derived, we find that $a = m^2$, $b = 4$, and $c = m$. Accordingly,

PART 1.

$$\{x \mid m^2x^2 + 4x + m = 0\} = \left\{x \mid x = \frac{-4 \pm \sqrt{16 - 4m^3}}{2m^2}\right\}$$

$$= \left\{\frac{-2 + \sqrt{4 - m^3}}{m^2}, \frac{-2 - \sqrt{4 - m^3}}{m^2}\right\}$$

PART 2.

If $x = \dfrac{-2 + \sqrt{4 - m^3}}{m^2}$, then

$$m^2\left(\frac{-2 + \sqrt{4 - m^3}}{m^2}\right)^2 + 4\left(\frac{-2 + \sqrt{4 - m^3}}{m^2}\right) + m \stackrel{?}{=} 0$$

$$\frac{4 - 4\sqrt{4 - m^3} + 4 - m^3}{m^2} + \frac{-8 + 4\sqrt{4 - m^3}}{m^2} + \frac{m^3}{m^2} \stackrel{?}{=} 0$$

$$0 \stackrel{\checkmark}{=} 0$$

If $x = \dfrac{-2 - \sqrt{4 - m^3}}{m^2}$, then

$$m^2\left(\frac{-2 - \sqrt{4 - m^3}}{m^2}\right)^2 + 4\left(\frac{-2 - \sqrt{4 - m^3}}{m^2}\right) + m \stackrel{?}{=} 0$$

$$\frac{4 + 4\sqrt{4 - m^3} + 4 - m^3}{m^2} + \frac{-8 - 4\sqrt{4 - m^3}}{m^2} + \frac{m^3}{m^2} \stackrel{?}{=} 0$$

$$0 \stackrel{\checkmark}{=} 0$$

Therefore the solution set is $\left\{\dfrac{-2 - \sqrt{4 - m^3}}{m^2}, \dfrac{-2 + \sqrt{4 - m^3}}{m^2}\right\}$.

Note that we have assumed that $m^3 \leq 4$.

Example 3. Find the roots of $37t = t^2 + 322$.

Solution. First we write the equation in its equivalent form $t^2 - 37t + 322 = 0$. Hence $a = 1$, $b = -37$, and $c = 322$. Accordingly, $t = \dfrac{37 \pm \sqrt{(-37)^2 - 4(322)}}{2} = \dfrac{37 \pm \sqrt{1369 - 1288}}{2} = \dfrac{37 \pm \sqrt{81}}{2} = \dfrac{37 \pm 9}{2}$. Letting t_1 represent one root and t_2 the other, we have $t_1 = \dfrac{37 + 9}{2} = 23$ and $t_2 = \dfrac{37 - 9}{2} = 14$.

Therefore the solution set is $\{14, 23\}$.

Note. The fact that the roots are rational suggests that $t^2 - 37t + 322$ is factorable over the integers, and we see that the factors of $t^2 - 37t + 322$ are $(t - 23)$ and $(t - 14)$. Thus $t^2 - 37t + 322 = 0$; $(t - 23)(t - 14) = 0$; and $t = 23$ *or* $t = 14$.

1. Solve each of the following equations by using the quadratic formula.

a. $x^2 - 14x - 735 = 0$

e. $14t^2 = -9t + 15$

b. $2x^2 - 13x + 15 = 0$

f. $x + \dfrac{1}{x} = \dfrac{5}{x}(x + 3)$

c. $16x^2 - 24x + 9 = 0$

g. $(x + 8)^2 - (x - 4)^2 + x^2 = 6 + x$

d. $(x + 12)^2 + (x - 3)^2 - 293 = 0$

h. $9m^2 - 30m + 25 = 0$

2. Indicate which of the equations of Ex. 1 have roots of multiplicity two.

3. Solve using the quadratic formula and write each irrational root as a decimal approximation expressed to the nearest hundredth.

a. $x^2 + 3x + 1 = 0$

e. $5x^2 - 2\sqrt{5}x = 0$

f. $(x + 1)^2 - 2(x - 5) = 12(x - 4)$

b. $2x^2 + x - 2 = 0$

g. $\dfrac{3x}{x - 2} + \dfrac{5x}{2(x + 2)} = \dfrac{9}{2x^2 - 8}$

c. $10x = 5 - 8x^2$

d. $21m^2 - 7m = 0$

h. $\dfrac{2x - 1}{x - 1} - \dfrac{1}{x^2 - 1} = -\dfrac{x}{x + 1}$

4. Find the roots of each of the following equations and write each irrational root as a decimal approximation expressed to the nearest hundredth.

a. $x^2 - .9x - .36 = 0$

c. $.06x^2 = .7x + 3$

e. $25r^2 = .04$

b. $2x^2 - 1.3x + .15 = 0$

d. $.01x^2 + .01x - .12 = 0$

f. $.03m^2 - .6m = 0$

5. Solve for x using the quadratic formula. Assume that each radicand is a positive number.

a. $x^2 + 4a - 21a^2 = 0$

e. $r^2x^2 = 3rsx + 4s^2$

b. $x^2 = 7m - 10m^2$

f. $9a^2x^2 - 27a^2 = 0$

c. $2m^2x^2 + 5mx - 12 = 0$

g. $50a^2x^2 - 125ax + 12 = 0$

d. $t^4 - 40t^2x + 111x^2 = 0$

h. $\dfrac{(a - c)x^2}{a + c} - \dfrac{3(a + c)}{a - c} = 2x$

6. Given $W = \dfrac{I^2R}{N}$, solve for I.

7. Solve $S = 2\pi r^2 + 2\pi rh$ for r.

8. Given $V = \frac{1}{3}\pi h(r^2 + R^2 + rR)$, find R when $V = 76\pi$, $h = 12$, and $r = 2$.

9. The formula $V = \pi l[r^2 - (r - t)^2]$ gives the volume V, in cubic inches, of material required to make a cylindrical pipe when the pipe is l inches long, the outer radius is r inches, and the metal is t inches thick. If $V = 360\pi$ when $l = 75$ and $r = 10$, find the value of t to the nearest tenth.

10. Solve:

a. $|x|^2 + 2|x| - 8 = 0$

c. $|x|^2 - 7|x| + 10 = 0$

b. $|x|^2 + 8|x| + 15 = 0$

d. $|x|^2 - 4|x| - 12 = 0$

Some Properties of the Roots of a Quadratic Equation

In this section we consider the relationships that exist between the roots and the coefficients of a quadratic equation.

The equation $(x - r)(x - s) = 0$ has r and s as its roots. No number other than r or s will satisfy this equation.

For example, if t is a number which is not equal to either r or s, then t is not a root of $(x - r)(x - s) = 0$ because $t - r \neq 0$, $t - s \neq 0$, and the product of two nonzero numbers is not zero.

Since $(x - r)(x - s) = 0 \longleftrightarrow x^2 - (r + s)x + rs = 0$, it follows that the numbers r and s are roots of the equation $x^2 + px + q = 0$ if and only if $(r + s) = -p$ and $rs = q$. We state the following theorem:

▶ **Theorem 4–7.** Real numbers r and s are roots of the equation $x^2 + px + q = 0$ if and only if $r + s = -p$ and $rs = q$.

Recall that $(a \longleftrightarrow b) \longleftrightarrow (a \longrightarrow b \wedge b \longrightarrow a)$. Thus to prove an "if and only if" theorem we must prove the left-to-right implication and the right-to-left implication.

Proof of Theorem 4–7: Real numbers r and s are roots of the equation $x^2 + px + q = 0$ if and only if $r + s = -p$ and $rs = q$.

Proof of the right-to-left part: If $r + s = -p$ and $rs = q$, then real numbers r and s are roots of $x^2 + px + q = 0$.

$$\underset{(1)}{r + s = -p} \longrightarrow \underset{(2)}{r = -p - s} \left.\begin{array}{c} \\ \underset{(3)}{rs = q} \end{array}\right\} \overset{(4)}{\longrightarrow} (-p - s)s = q \overset{(5)}{\longrightarrow} \underset{(6)}{-ps - s^2 = q} \dashv$$

$$\overset{(6)}{\vdash} 0 = s^2 + ps + q \overset{(7)}{\longrightarrow} s \text{ is a root of } x^2 + px + q = 0.$$

Similarly, it can be shown that r is a root.

Proof of left-to-right part: If real numbers r and s are roots of the equation $x^2 + px + q = 0$, then $r + s = -p$ and $rs = q$.

r and s are roots of $\overset{(1)}{}$

$$\underset{}{x^2 + px + q = 0} \overset{(2)}{\longrightarrow} r = \frac{-p + \sqrt{p^2 - 4q}}{2} \text{ and } s = \frac{-p - \sqrt{p^2 - 4q}}{2} \overset{(3)}{\longrightarrow}$$

$r + s = -p$ and $rs = q$.

The reasons for the proof are left to you. Note that the reason for step 2 of the left-to-right part of the proof is Corollary to Theorem 3–7. In this case $a = 1$, $b = p$, and $c = q$.

If r and s are the roots of the quadratic equation $ax^2 + bx + c = 0$, we know that r and s are also roots of the equation $x^2 + \dfrac{b}{a}x + \dfrac{c}{a} = 0$. It follows from the left-to-right part of Theorem 4–7 that $r + s = -\dfrac{b}{a}$ and $rs = \dfrac{c}{a}$. These conclusions can also be derived directly from the Corollary to Theorem 3–7, because

$$\frac{-b + \sqrt{b^2 - 4\,ac}}{2\,a} + \frac{-b - \sqrt{b^2 - 4\,ac}}{2\,a} = -\frac{b}{a}$$

and

$$\left(\frac{-b + \sqrt{b^2 - 4\,ac}}{2\,a}\right)\left(\frac{-b - \sqrt{b^2 - 4\,ac}}{2\,a}\right) = \frac{c}{a}.$$

Thus we have the following theorem:

▷ **Theorem 5–7.** If real numbers r and s are the roots of the quadratic equation $ax^2 + bx + c = 0$ when $a \neq 0$, then $r + s = -\dfrac{b}{a}$ and $rs = \dfrac{c}{a}$.

Since $ax^2 + bx + c = a\left(x^2 + \dfrac{b}{a}x + \dfrac{c}{a}\right) = a[x^2 - (r + s)x + rs]$

$= a(x - r)(x - s)$, we have the following corollary:

Corollary to Theorem 5–7. If real numbers r and s are the roots of the quadratic equation $ax^2 + bx + c = 0$ and $a \neq 0$, then $ax^2 + bx + c = a(x - r)(x - s)$.

We have already observed that the number of roots of the quadratic equation $ax^2 + bx + c = 0$ depends upon the value of $b^2 - 4\,ac$. We summarize our conclusions in the following theorem.

▷ **Theorem 6–7.** The equation $ax^2 + bx + c = 0$ when $a \neq 0$ has two roots if and only if $b^2 - 4\,ac > 0$, one root if and only if $b^2 - 4\,ac = 0$, and no real roots if and only if $b^2 - 4\,ac < 0$.

The expression $b^2 - 4\,ac$ is called the *discriminant of the quadratic equation* $ax^2 + bx + c = 0$ and also the *discriminant of the quadratic function* defined by the equation $y = ax^2 + bx + c$. Observe that when $b^2 - 4\,ac > 0$, the graph of the function F defined by $y = ax^2 + bx + c$ intersects the x-axis in two distinct points as shown in the following figures on the left. If $b^2 - 4\,ac = 0$, the graph of F has exactly one point in common with the x-axis as shown in the following center figures. In this case we say that the parabola is *tangent* to the x-axis. If $b^2 - 4\,ac < 0$, the function has no zeros and accordingly the graph of F does not intersect the x-axis as shown in the following figures on the right.

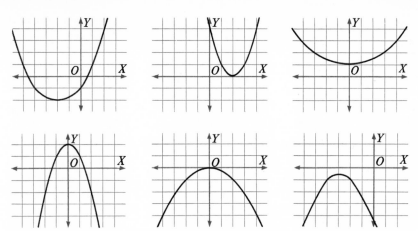

Example 1. Write a quadratic equation whose roots are $3 - \sqrt{5}$ and $3 + \sqrt{5}$.

Solution 1. According to Theorem 4–7, the equation $x^2 + px + q = 0$ is the required equation if and only if $p = -(r + s)$ and $q = rs$ when $r = 3 - \sqrt{5}$ and $s = 3 + \sqrt{5}$. We have $-(r + s) = -6$ and $rs = 4$. Therefore the required equation is $x^2 - 6x + 4 = 0$. To verify this conclusion, we find the roots of $x^2 - 6x + 4 = 0$ by the quadratic formula. We find

$$x = \frac{6 \pm \sqrt{36 - 16}}{2} = \frac{6 \pm \sqrt{20}}{2} = \frac{6 \pm 2\sqrt{5}}{2} = 3 \pm \sqrt{5}.$$

Solution 2. According to the corollary to Theorem 5–7, $ax^2 + bx + c = 0$ has the roots r and s if $a(x - r)(x - s) = 0$. Therefore $a[x - (3 - \sqrt{5})]$ $[x - (3 + \sqrt{5})] = 0$ will serve as the required equation. Performing the multiplication we obtain $a(x^2 - 6x + 4) = 0$. This equation has the given roots for any nonzero value of a.

Example 2. John solved a quadratic equation and later spilled ink on his paper so that only the first two terms, $6x^2 + 5x$, were readable. Let us call the constant term c so that the equation originally had the form $6x^2 + 5x + c = 0$. John recalled that one root was $\frac{3}{2}$. Can he find the other root and the constant c?

Solution. Yes. According to Theorem 5–7, $\frac{3}{2} + s = -\frac{5}{6}$ where s represents the other root. Thus $s = -\frac{5}{6} - \frac{3}{2} = -\frac{7}{3}$. Again, according to Theorem 5–7, $rs = \frac{c}{a}$. Therefore $\frac{3}{2}(-\frac{7}{3}) = \frac{c}{6}$. Therefore $c = -21$ and the original equation was $6x^2 + 5x - 21 = 0$.

Example 3. Why is it not possible to find the sum and the product of the roots of the equation $7x^2 + x + 21 = 0$ using Theorem 5–7?

Solution. Since $7x^2 + x + 21 = 0$ has the discriminant $1^2 - 4(7)(21) < 0$, by Theorem 6–7 we see that the equation has no real roots. Since the equation has no real roots, we see that Theorem 5–7 does not apply. When we extend the number system (Chapter 11) to include numbers other than the real numbers, we shall find that this equation does have roots and that the sum of these roots is $-\frac{1}{7}$ and their product is 3.

 A EXERCISES

1. For each of the following pairs of numbers, write a quadratic equation having the given number pair as its solution set.

   a. $3, -7$

   b. $-11, -4$

   c. $\frac{1}{2}, \frac{3}{2}$

   d. $\sqrt{5}, 3$

   e. $2 + \sqrt{3}, 2 - \sqrt{3}$

   f. $3 + a, -3 - a$

   g. $\dfrac{3 + \sqrt{2}}{2}, \dfrac{3 - \sqrt{2}}{2}$

   h. $\dfrac{-4 + \sqrt{5}}{6}, \dfrac{-4 - \sqrt{5}}{6}$

   i. $3\sqrt{3}, 4\sqrt{3}$

2. Without solving, find the sum and the product of the roots of each of the following equations.

   a. $x^2 - 12x + 35 = 0$

   b. $x^2 = 9x + 70$

   c. $2x^2 - 21x = 65$

   d. $3x^2 - 12x = 0$

   e. $5x^2 - 58x = 71$

   f. $x^2 - (2 - \sqrt{7})x - 2\sqrt{7} = 0$

3. Solve each of the following quadratic equations. Verify that the values found are roots by showing that they have the correct sum and product.

   a. $3x^2 - 23x - 105 = 0$

   b. $7x^2 - 225 = 0$

   c. $4x^2 - 12x + 9 = 0$

   d. $365x^2 - 949x = 0$

   e. $6x^2 - 6\sqrt{7}x + 7 = 0$

   f. $9x^2 + 36x + 34 = 0$

4. Determine the discriminant of each of the following equations and from it determine whether the equation has two, one, or no real solutions.

   a. $3x^2 + 16x - 35 = 0$

   b. $x^2 + .4x + .04 = 0$

   c. $x^2 - 6x = 0$

   d. $5x^2 - 14 = 0$

   e. $3x^2 - 5x + 6 = 0$

   f. $5x^2 + 3x + 1 = 0$

5. Determine k so that

   a. The equation $25x^2 + kx + 9 = 0$ has a root of multiplicity two.

   b. The equation $9x^2 + kx - 49 = 0$ has roots having opposite signs although their absolute values are equal.

   c. The sum of the roots of $6x^2 + kx - 5 = 0$ is $-\frac{7}{6}$.

   d. The sum of the roots of $(4 + k)x^2 - x - 20 = 0$ is 1.

   e. The product of the roots of $(k - 13)x^2 - 3x - 2k = 0$ is -28.

6. Find the value of c if $x^2 - 6x + c = 0$ and one root of the equation is 8.

7. For what value of a is it true that one root of $ax^2 + 36x + 18 = 0$ is double the other?

8. One root of $x^2 + mx - 25 = 0$ is the negative of the other. Find the roots and the value of m.

B **EXERCISES**

9. If r and s are the roots of $ax^2 + bx + c = 0$, show that $r^2 + s^2 = \dfrac{b^2 - 2ac}{a^2}$.

10. Prove: If $ax^2 + bx + c = 0$ and $a \neq 0$, then $ax^2 + bx + c = 0$ has at least one root which is 0 if and only if $c = 0$.

11. Prove: If $ax^2 + bx + c = 0$ and $a \neq 0$, then $ax^2 + bx + c = 0$ has one positive and one negative root if and only if a and c have opposite signs.

12. Prove: If $ax^2 + bx + c = 0$ and $a \neq 0$, then $ax^2 + bx + c = 0$ has 0 as a root of multiplicity two, if and only if $b = 0$ and $c = 0$.

13. Find the sum of the reciprocals of the roots of the equation $ax^2 + bx + c = 0$.

14. Find the product of the reciprocals of the roots of the equation $ax^2 + bx + c = 0$.

Rational and Irrational Roots

If the coefficients of the quadratic equation $ax^2 + bx + c = 0$ are integers, then the discriminant $b^2 - 4ac$ is also an integer. If $b^2 - 4ac = k^2$ where k is an integer, then $\sqrt{b^2 - 4ac} = |k|$. Thus $\sqrt{b^2 - 4ac}$ is an integer. Since $\sqrt{b^2 - 4ac} \in I$, each expression, $\dfrac{-b + \sqrt{b^2 - 4ac}}{2a}$ and $\dfrac{-b - \sqrt{b^2 - 4ac}}{2a}$, names a rational number. Accordingly, the roots of a quadratic equation having integral coefficients are rational if the discriminant of the equation is a "perfect square," that is, the square of an integer.

If $b^2 - 4ac$ is not the square of an integer $(a, b, c \in I)$, then $\sqrt{b^2 - 4ac} \notin Q$. If $\sqrt{b^2 - 4ac} \notin Q$ and $-b \in Q$, then according to Theorem 33–3, the sum $-b + \sqrt{b^2 - 4ac}$ is irrational. Moreover, if $a \neq 0$, $a \in I \longrightarrow 2a \in I \longrightarrow \dfrac{1}{2a} \in Q$.

Therefore by Theorem 34–3, we know that $\dfrac{-b + \sqrt{b^2 - 4ac}}{2a}$ is irrational.

Similarly $\dfrac{-b - \sqrt{b^2 - 4ac}}{2a}$ is irrational. Thus we have the following theorem.

▷ **Theorem 7–7.** The roots of a quadratic equation having integral coefficients are rational numbers if and only if the discriminant is the square of an integer.

Examples.   Without solving, determine which of the following equations
have rational number roots:

    a. $21\,x^2 + 4\,x = 65,$

    b. $x^2 - \frac{29}{10}\,x - \frac{21}{10} = 0,$

    a. First we write the equation in standard form as $21\,x^2 + 4\,x - 65 = 0$. Now we see that $a = 21$, $b = 4$, $c = -65$. Thus $b^2 - 4\,ac = 4^2 - 4(21)(-65) = 5476$. Taking the square root of 5476 we find that $5476 = 74^2$. Therefore the roots of $21\,x^2 + 4\,x = 65$ are rational.

    b. Any quadratic equation having rational coefficients some of which are not integers can be transformed into an equivalent equation having integral coefficients by multiplying both of its members by the least common multiple of the denominators that appear in the coefficients. Thus the given equation $x^2 - \frac{29}{10}\,x - \frac{21}{10} = 0$ is equivalent to $10\,x^2 - 29\,x - 21 = 0$. The discriminant of this equation is $b^2 - 4\,ac = (-29)^2 - 4(10)(-21) = 1681 = 41^2$. Hence the roots are rational.

1. Without solving, determine which of the following equations have rational roots.

  a. $2\,x^2 - 7\,x - 4 = 0$ **d.** $6\,x^2 - 7\,x - 4 = 0$ **g.** $6\,x^2 = 31\,x - 35$

  b. $3\,x^2 - 22\,x + 35 = 0$ **e.** $9\,x^2 - 10\,x + 1 = 0$ **h.** $5\,x^2 - 4\,x - 2 = 0$

  c. $x^2 + \frac{1}{3}\,x - \frac{2}{9} = 0$ **f.** $2\,x^2 + x = 21$ **i.** $11\,x^2 + 5\,x = 6$

2. Solve:

  a. $4\,x^2 + 29\,x - 63 = 0$ **d.** $3\,x^2 + 9\,x + 5 = 0$ **g.** $0 = 7\,x^2 - 44\,x + 12$

  b. $4\,x^2 = 5\,x + 1$ **e.** $2\,x^2 + 15\,x + 7 = 0$ **h.** $3\,x^2 - 13\,x = 30$

  c. $2\,x^2 - 11\,x - 6 = 0$ **f.** $14\,x^2 = 11\,x + 15$ **i.** $77\,x^2 - 83\,x + 20 = 0$

3. Is the following modification of Theorem 7–7 true? The roots of a quadratic equation having rational number coefficients are rational numbers if and only if the discriminant is the square of a rational number. Explain.

4. Solve for x, assuming that the constants are such that each discriminant is a positive real number.

  a. $8\,x^2 - 2\,ax - a^2 = 0$ **d.** $x^2 - cx + d = 0$

  b. $x^2 - 3\,rs + 6\,r^2 = 0$ **e.** $\dfrac{1}{4}\,x^2 - \dfrac{b}{2}\,x + c = 0$

  c. $ax^2 - bx = c$ **f.** $36 - 12(3 + x) + (3 + x)^2 = 0$

5. Solve for R: $g = \dfrac{R}{R^2 + X^2}$

6. Solve for R: $\dfrac{3R - 9}{2R - 9} - 1 = \dfrac{2R + 9}{3R + 9}$

7. For what value(s) of h does the equation $x^2 + hx + h^2 = 0$ have real roots?

8. Copy and complete the following table by filling the blanks with the proper information.

Given: $ax^2 + bx + c = 0 \wedge$ $a, b, c, z \in I \wedge a \neq 0$	Number of real roots	Roots are rational or irrational
$b^2 - 4\,ac < 0$		
$b^2 - 4\,ac = 0$		
$b^2 - 4\,ac > 0 \wedge b^2 - 4\,ac = z^2$		
$b^2 - 4\,ac > 0 \wedge b^2 - 4\,ac \neq z^2$		

9. a. Write a quadratic equation whose coefficients are integers and which has $-3 + 2\sqrt{7}$ as one of its roots.

  b. What is the other root?

10. Find the values of k for which $kx + x^2 + kx^2 - 2x = 4$ has exactly one real root.

11. a. For what values of k are the roots of $(k + 2)x^2 - 2kx + 1 = 0$ real numbers?

  b. Are there any values of k for which the roots are rational? Explain.

Equations Transformable into Quadratic Equations

In the next three sections we shall discuss equations which are transformable into the form $ax^2 + bx + c = 0$ when $a \neq 0$. Before we proceed, we consider transformations which may or may not yield equivalent equations.

We must consider transformations of equations for which the solution set S_1 of the derived equation is not always equal to the solution set S of the given equation. Specifically we shall consider transformations for which

The solution set of the derived equation is the same as the solution set of the given equation. $(S_1 = S.)$

The solution set of the derived equation is a proper subset of the solution of the given equation. $(S_1 \subset S$; that is, some roots of the original equation are lost.)

The solution set of the given equation is a proper subset of the solution set of the derived equation. $(S \subset S_1$; that is, the derived equation has at least one root which is not a root of the original equation. Such roots are sometimes called *extraneous roots*.)

We recall that there are some transformations which produce an equation which is equivalent to the given equation. These are:

Adding the same polynomial expression to each member of a given equation or subtracting the same polynomial expression from each member of a given equation, provided no new variables are introduced.

Multiplying or dividing each member of a given equation by the same nonzero number.

Replacing any polynomial expression in either member of an equation with an identically equal polynomial expression.

If we use transformations other than these we cannot be sure that the solution set of the derived equation is the same as the solution set of the given equation.

Fractional Equations Transformable into Quadratic Equations

In this section we consider some examples of fractional equations which can be transformed into the quadratic form $ax^2 + bx + c = 0$ when $a \neq 0$. By *fractional equation* we mean an equation in which a variable appears in the denominator.

Example 1. Solve the equation $x - \dfrac{12}{x} = 1$.

Solution. We assume that this equation has a solution, that is, that there is a number x for which this equality is true. We agree that $x \neq 0$ because $\dfrac{12}{x}$ is meaningless when $x = 0$.

$$x - \frac{12}{x} = 1 \longleftrightarrow x^2 - x - 12 = 0 \wedge x \neq 0 \longleftrightarrow (x-4)(x+3) = 0$$
$$\wedge \; x \neq 0 \longleftrightarrow x = 4 \vee x = -3 \wedge x \neq 0. \quad \text{The solution set is}$$
$$\{x \mid x = 4\} \cup \{x \mid x = -3\} \cap \{x \mid x \neq 0\} = \{4, -3\}.$$

Check.   When $x = 4$,   When $x = -3$,

$$4 - \tfrac{12}{4} \stackrel{?}{=} 1 \qquad\qquad\qquad -3 - \frac{12}{-3} \stackrel{?}{=} 1$$

$$1 \stackrel{\checkmark}{=} 1 \qquad\qquad\qquad\qquad 1 \stackrel{\checkmark}{=} 1$$

Since both 4 and -3 satisfy $x - \dfrac{12}{x} = 1$, we know that $\{4, -3\}$ is the solution set of this equation.

In Example 1, multiplying each member of the given equation by x produces an equation all of whose roots are roots of the given equation. This does not always happen as shown by Examples 2 and 3 on the following page.

Example 2. Find the solution set for $\dfrac{3}{x^2} = 5 - \dfrac{2\,x^2 - 3}{x^2}$.

Solution. Since the expressions $\dfrac{3}{x^2}$ and $\dfrac{2\,x^2 - 3}{x^2}$ do not name real numbers when $x = 0$, we really mean "Solve $\dfrac{3}{x^2} = 5 - \dfrac{2\,x^2 - 3}{x^2}$ *and* $x \neq 0$."

$\dfrac{3}{x^2} = 5 - \dfrac{2\,x^2-3}{x^2} \wedge x \neq 0 \longleftrightarrow x^2\left(\dfrac{3}{x^2}\right) = x^2\left(5 - \dfrac{2\,x^2-3}{x^2}\right) \wedge x \neq 0$
$\longleftrightarrow 3 = 5\,x^2 - (2\,x^2 - 3) \wedge x \neq 0 \longleftrightarrow 3 = 5\,x^2 - 2\,x^2 + 3 \wedge x \neq$
$0 \longleftrightarrow 3 = 3\,x^2 + 3 \wedge x \neq 0 \longleftrightarrow 0 = 3\,x^2 \wedge x \neq 0 \longleftrightarrow 0 = x \wedge x$
$\neq 0$. The solution set is $\{x \mid x = 0\} \cap \{x \mid x \neq 0\} = \emptyset$. Had we assumed the derived equation $3 = 5\,x^2 - (2\,x^2 - 3)$ to be equivalent to the original equation $\dfrac{3}{x^2} = 5 - \dfrac{2\,x^2 - 3}{x^2}$, we would have accepted the extraneous root 0.

Example 3. Solve $\dfrac{x+3}{x^2-1} + \dfrac{x-3}{x^2-x} = 0$.

Solution. Since substituting the values 0, 1, or -1 for x will result in a zero denominator, we really mean, "Solve $\dfrac{x+3}{x^2-1} + \dfrac{x-3}{x^2-x} = 0 \wedge x \neq 0 \wedge x \neq 1 \wedge x \neq -1$."

PART 1.
$$\frac{x+3}{x^2-1} + \frac{x-3}{x^2-x} = 0$$
$$(x-1)(x+1)(x)\left(\frac{x+3}{x^2-1} + \frac{x-3}{x^2-x}\right) = (x-1)(x+1)(x)(0)$$
$$2\,x^2 + x - 3 = 0$$
$$(2\,x+3)(x-1) = 0$$
$$x = -\tfrac{3}{2} \vee x = 1$$

PART 2.

Since we have agreed that 1 is not a solution, the only possible solution of the given equation is $-\tfrac{3}{2}$. To determine whether $-\tfrac{3}{2}$ is a solution, we substitute $-\tfrac{3}{2}$ for x in the original equation.

$$\frac{-\tfrac{3}{2}+3}{(-\tfrac{3}{2})^2-1} + \frac{-\tfrac{3}{2}-3}{(-\tfrac{3}{2})^2-(-\tfrac{3}{2})} \overset{?}{=} 0$$
$$\tfrac{12}{10} + (-\tfrac{36}{30}) \overset{?}{=} 0$$
$$0 \overset{\vee}{=} 0$$

We now see that the solution set of the original equation is $\{-\tfrac{3}{2}\}$. Observe again that the derived statement $x = -\tfrac{3}{2} \vee x = 1$ is not equivalent to the original equation. Had we assumed them to be equivalent, we would have included 1 in our solution set.

Example 4.   Solve $x^2 + 2x = 5x + 10$.

Solution.
$$x^2 + 2x = 5x + 10$$
$$x(x + 2) = 5(x + 2)$$
$$\frac{1}{x+2}\,[x(x+2)] = \frac{1}{x+2}\,[5(x+2)]$$
$$x = 5$$

When we multiplied each member of the equation $x(x + 2) = 5(x + 2)$ by $\frac{1}{x+2}$, we obtained $x = 5$. However, this equation is not equivalent to the original equation because its solution set is $\{5\}$, while the solution set of the original equation is $\{-2, 5\}$. We "lost" the root -2 when we multiplied both members of the original equation by $\frac{1}{x+2}$ thus making the assumptions that $x \neq -2$ and that the derived equation $\frac{1}{x+2}\,[x(x+2)] = \frac{1}{x+2}\,[5(x+2)]$ was equivalent to the original equation $x^2 + 2x = 5x + 10$. We would not have "lost" the root -2 had we checked this value in the original equation when we barred it to multiply by $\frac{1}{x+2}$.

 EXERCISES

1. Which of the following operations will produce an equation equivalent to the equation $x = 4$ when $x \in I$?
   a. Adding 5 to each member of $x = 4$
   b. Adding x to each member of $x = 4$
   c. Multiplying each member of $x = 4$ by 2
   d. Multiplying each member of $x = 4$ by x
   e. Squaring each member of $x = 4$

2. When $x \neq 0$ and $x \in R$, the equation $\frac{1}{x} = 6$ has the solution set $\left\{\frac{1}{6}\right\}$. Which of the following operations will produce a new equation equivalent to $\frac{1}{x} = 6$ if it is understood that in the new equation $x \in R$?

   a. Adding 1 to each member of $\frac{1}{x} = 6$

   b. Adding x to each member of $\frac{1}{x} = 6$

   c. Squaring each member of $\frac{1}{x} = 6$

d. Multiplying each member of $\dfrac{1}{x} = 6$ by 3

e. Multiplying each member of $\dfrac{1}{x} = 6$ by $3\,x^2$

3. In solving the equation $x^2 - 2\,x = x - 2$, is it permissible to divide each member of the equation by $x - 2$? Explain.

4. Solve each of the following equations.

a. $x + \dfrac{6}{x} = 5$

f. $\dfrac{x-4}{x^2} = \dfrac{1}{x^2} - 1$

b. $x + \dfrac{7}{x+1} = \dfrac{37}{6}$

g. $\dfrac{2\,x+5}{x-1} + x = \dfrac{3\,x-2}{4}$

c. $\dfrac{x}{x+3} + \dfrac{3}{x-5} = \dfrac{11}{5}$

h. $\dfrac{3\,x^2 - 19\,x + 20}{x+2} = 42$

d. $\dfrac{x}{x-3} + \dfrac{3}{x+3} = \dfrac{x^2+9}{x^2-9}$

i. $\dfrac{1}{x+3} - \dfrac{2\,x}{x^2-9} = \dfrac{4}{x-3}$

e. $\dfrac{x}{x-2} - \dfrac{x}{x+2} = 1$

j. $\dfrac{x^2+1}{x^2-1} - \dfrac{x}{x-1} = \dfrac{2}{x+1}$

5. If twice a number is divided by the sum of itself and 1, the quotient is equal to 2 decreased by the quotient which results when 5 is divided by twice the number. What is the number?

6. Solve:

a. $\dfrac{x}{x-4} - \dfrac{2\,x-1}{x+3} + \dfrac{x^2}{x^2-x-12} = \dfrac{11}{12}$

b. $\dfrac{2\,x}{1-3\,x} + \dfrac{2}{3\,x^2-7\,x+2} + \dfrac{x}{2-x} = 0$

c. $\dfrac{x^2}{(x+1)^2} - \dfrac{6\,x}{x+1} + 8 = 0$

7. One plane can make a trip of 1400 miles in $\tfrac{1}{2}$ hour less time than it takes a second plane to travel 1800 miles. What is the ground speed of each plane if the ground speed of the second is 200 miles per hour more than the ground speed of the first?

8. At approximately what air speed must a plane be flown to complete a round trip of 2500 miles in 5 hours if the flight in one direction has a head wind of 40 miles per hour and the flight in the other direction has a tail wind of 30 miles per hour? (A wind blowing in a direction opposite to the course of the plane is a head wind and a wind blowing in the same direction as the course of the plane is a tail wind.)

9. A gas station has a 10,000-gallon gasoline tank. One delivery truck takes x minutes to fill the tank and a second delivery truck takes $x + 10$ minutes to fill the tank. How long does it take each truck to fill the tank separately if the two trucks fill the tank simultaneously in 12 minutes?

Radical Equations Transformable into Quadratic Equations

By a radical equation we mean an equation in which a variable appears under a radical sign, as in the equation $\sqrt{x} = 3$. By squaring both members of $\sqrt{x} = 3$ we obtain the equation $x = 9$. In this case the derived equation $x = 9$ is equivalent to the original equation for all real values of x, but we must be aware of the fact that squaring both members of an equation does not always yield an equation equivalent to the original equation.

Example 1. Solve the equation $5 + \sqrt{n+7} = n$.

Solution. Part 1.

$5 + \sqrt{n+7} = n \longrightarrow \sqrt{n+7} = n - 5 \longrightarrow n + 7 = (n-5)^2 \longrightarrow$
$n + 7 = n^2 - 10\,n + 25 \longrightarrow n^2 - 11\,n + 18 = 0 \longrightarrow (n-9)$
$(n-2) = 0 \longrightarrow n - 9 = 0 \lor n - 2 = 0 \longrightarrow n = 9 \lor n = 2.$ We have now shown that $\{n \mid 5 + \sqrt{n+7} = n\} = \{9, 2\}$ or $\{n \mid 5 + \sqrt{n+7} = n\} \subset \{9, 2\}$.

Part 2. To determine whether 9 and 2 are members of the solution set, we substitute each, in turn, for n in the given equation.

If $n = 9$,   If $n = 2$,
$$5 + \sqrt{9+7} \overset{?}{=} 9 \qquad\qquad 5 + \sqrt{2+7} \overset{?}{=} 2$$
$$5 + \sqrt{16} \overset{?}{=} 9 \qquad\qquad\qquad 5 + 3 \overset{?}{=} 2$$
$$9 \overset{\checkmark}{=} 9 \qquad\qquad\qquad\qquad 8 \neq 2$$

Thus we see that 9 is a solution and that 2 is not a solution. The solution set of $5 + \sqrt{n+7} = n$ is $\{9\}$. Observe that had we assumed the derived equation $n + 7 = (n-5)^2$ to be equivalent to our original equation, we would have accepted 2 as a member of the solution set.

Example 2. Solve $\sqrt{2x-4} + \sqrt{3x+4} - \sqrt{10x-4} = 0$.

Solution. Part 1.

$\sqrt{2x-4} + \sqrt{3x+4} - \sqrt{10x-4} = 0$
$\sqrt{2x-4} + \sqrt{3x+4} = \sqrt{10x-4}$
Squaring both members, we have:
$2x - 4 + 2\sqrt{2x-4}\sqrt{3x+4} + 3x + 4 = 10x - 4$
$2\sqrt{2x-4}\sqrt{3x+4} = 5x - 4$
Squaring both members again, we have:
$4(2x-4)(3x+4) = 25x^2 - 40x + 16$
$24x^2 - 16x - 64 = 25x^2 - 40x + 16$
$$0 = x^2 - 24x + 80$$
$$0 = (x - 20)(x - 4)$$
$$x = 20 \ or \ x = 4$$

PART 2.

Substituting 20 and 4, in turn, for x in the given equation we find

When $x = 20$, $\sqrt{40-4} + \sqrt{60+4} - \sqrt{200-4} \overset{?}{=} 0$

$$\sqrt{36} + \sqrt{64} - \sqrt{196} \overset{?}{=} 0$$

$$6 + 8 - 14 \overset{?}{=} 0$$

$$0 \overset{\checkmark}{=} 0$$

When $x = 4$, $\sqrt{8-4} + \sqrt{12+4} - \sqrt{40-4} \overset{?}{=} 0$

$$\sqrt{4} + \sqrt{16} - \sqrt{36} \overset{?}{=} 0$$

$$2 + 4 - 6 \overset{?}{=} 0$$

$$0 \overset{\checkmark}{=} 0$$

Thus the solution set of the given equation is $\{20, 4\}$. In this case the derived equation and our original equation are equivalent as squaring did not introduce an extraneous root.

Ⓐ EXERCISES

1. By inspection, determine which of the following equations have empty solution sets, assuming that each radicand is a positive number.

   a. $\sqrt{x} = -2$ **c.** $\sqrt{x+7} + 4 = 0$

   b. $\sqrt{x+9} = 12$ **d.** $5 = -\sqrt{x} - 2$

2. Determine whether the number shown at the right of each of the following equations is a solution of the equation.

   a. $\sqrt{y} = 12$,   144   **d.** $\sqrt{n} + n = 6$,   4

   b. $\sqrt{m} = -3$, -9 **e.** $\sqrt{9-x} = 1$,   12

   c. $\sqrt{ax-b} = 1$, $\dfrac{1+b}{a}$ **f.** $\sqrt{x^2 - 5x + 6} = 0$,   3

3. Solve each of the following equations.

   a. $\sqrt{x+5} = 4$ **i.** $\sqrt{x+4} = \dfrac{20}{\sqrt{x-5}}$

   b. $\sqrt{m^2 + 3} = \sqrt{28}$

   c. $\sqrt{y^2 + 9} - 5 = 0$ **j.** $\sqrt{n+1} - \sqrt{n-2} = \sqrt{2n-5}$

   d. $\sqrt{3x+1} + \sqrt{25} = 10$

                                   k. $\sqrt{x} + \sqrt{13 + \sqrt{x}} = 7$

   e. $\sqrt{8a^2 - a} = 3a$

   f. $\sqrt{3x^2 + 9} = 3x + 3$ **l.** $\sqrt{y} - 3\sqrt{\dfrac{1}{y}} - 2 = 0$

   g. $\sqrt{x+16} + \sqrt{x} = 8$

                                m. $\sqrt{x} = \dfrac{1}{\sqrt{x}} - \dfrac{15}{4}$

   h. $\sqrt{4m-11} - 2\sqrt{m} = 1$

Other Sentences Transformable into Quadratic Form

In this section we consider sentences which are not in quadratic form but can be transformed so that they are in quadratic form.

Example 1. Find a simpler expression for $\{x \mid x^4 - 14\,x^2 + 45 = 0\}$.

Solution. PART 1.

Let us substitute z for x^2. Then the transformed equation is $z^2 - 14\,z + 45 = 0$. $z^2 - 14\,z + 45 = 0 \longrightarrow (z - 9)(z - 5) = 0 \dashv \vdash z = 9 \vee z = 5$.

Since $z = x^2$, we replace z by x^2 in $z = 9 \vee z = 5$. Thus we have $x^2 = 9 \vee x^2 = 5 \longrightarrow x = \pm 3 \vee x = \pm \sqrt{5}$.

PART 2.

Substituting each of these values, in turn, for x in the original equation $x^4 - 14\,x^2 + 45 = 0$, we find that each satisfies the equation. Thus $\{x \mid x^4 - 14\,x^2 + 45 = 0\} = \{-3, 3, -\sqrt{5}, \sqrt{5}\}$.

Example 2. Find the truth set for the conjunctive statement $2\,x - 1 - \dfrac{15}{x} > 0 \wedge x > 0$ and draw the graph of the solution set in the real number line.

Solution. $\left\{x \mid 2\,x - 1 - \dfrac{15}{x} > 0 \wedge x > 0\right\}$ is the truth set for $2\,x - 1 - \dfrac{15}{x} > 0 \wedge x > 0$ which can be changed to simpler form as follows:

$\left\{x \mid 2\,x - 1 - \dfrac{15}{x} > 0 \wedge x > 0\right\} = \{x \mid 2\,x^2 - x - 15 > 0 \wedge x > 0\}$
$= \{x \mid (x - 3)(2\,x + 5) > 0 \wedge x > 0\} = \{x \mid (x - 3 > 0 \wedge 2\,x + 5 > 0 \wedge x > 0) \vee (x - 3 < 0 \wedge 2\,x + 5 < 0 \wedge x > 0)\}$
$= [\{x \mid x > 3\} \cap \{x \mid x > -\tfrac{5}{2}\} \cap \{x \mid x > 0\}] \cup [\{x \mid x < 3\} \cap \{x \mid x < -\tfrac{5}{2}\} \cap \{x \mid x > 0\}] = \{x \mid x > 3\} \cup \phi$. The graph of the solution set is shown below.

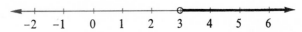

A EXERCISES

Find the solution set for each of the following equations.

1. $x^4 - 5\,x^2 + 6 = 0$

2. $x^4 - 2\,x^2 + 1 = 0$

3. $(\sqrt{x})^2 + 4\sqrt{x} + 4 = 0$

4. $x^4 - 5\,x^2 + 4 = 0$

5. $a^4 + 2\,a^2 - 6 = 0$

6. $(a^2 - 4)^2 = 25$

7. $x^4 - 8\,x^2 + 7 = 0$

8. $n^6 + 7\,n^3 - 8 = 0$

9. $\dfrac{x}{x + 3} + \dfrac{x + 3}{x} = \dfrac{17}{4}$

10. $\left(a + \dfrac{1}{a}\right)^2 = 2 - \left(a + \dfrac{1}{a}\right)$

11. $(n^2 - n)^2 - 4(n^2 - n) = -3$

13. $x - 3\sqrt{x} - 4 = 0$ *Note.* $x \geq 0$

12. $n^2 = \dfrac{1}{n^2} + \dfrac{80}{9}$

14. $a^4 = 28 - 3a^2$

15. $(\sqrt{x-5})^2 + 2\sqrt{x-5} + 1 = 0$

16. $(x^2 + 4x + 4)^2 - 2(x^2 + 4x + 4) + 1 = 0$

17. $(x^2 + x)^2 - 6(x^2 + x) + 8 = 0$

18. $12(m^2 - 3)^2 - 22(m^2 - 3) - 4 = 0$

19. $\dfrac{x^2}{(x-1)^2} + \dfrac{x}{x-1} - 6 = 0$ *Hint.* Substitute y for $\dfrac{x}{x-1}$.

Find the solution set for each of the following sentences.

20. $\sqrt{5x} - \dfrac{5}{\sqrt{5x}} > 0$

21. $(x+2)^2 + 5(x+2) + 6 > 0$

22. $\sqrt[3]{(2x-7)^2} > 9$

23. $\sqrt{\dfrac{5y+1}{y}} > 2$

24. $\dfrac{8}{a^2 - 1} - \dfrac{a}{a-1} + \dfrac{2}{a+1} > 0$

25. $x \geq 3\sqrt{x-4} + 2$

B **EXERCISES**

Solve each of the following equations.

26. $m^4 - 2m^3 - 3m^2 + 4m + 3 = 0$
    Hint. Let $x = m^2 - m$.

27. $n^4 - 2n^3 - 4n^2 + 5n + 4 = 0$

28. $\dfrac{x^2}{x+2} + \dfrac{x+2}{x^2} = 2$

29. $s^2 + 5s + 6 = 4\sqrt{s^2 + 5s + 6}$

30. $\dfrac{x-2}{x+3} + 4 = 4\sqrt{\dfrac{x-2}{x+3}}$

31. $a^2 + 6a = 5\sqrt{a^2 + 6a}$

32. $x^2 - 3x + 2 = 3\sqrt{x^2 - 3x + 2}$

33. $t^2 - 2\left(5 - \dfrac{12}{t^2}\right) = 0$

Quadratic Relations and Their Graphs

When the equality sign in a quadratic equation is replaced by the symbol $<$ or the symbol $>$, we have a *quadratic inequality*. Sentences like $x^2 + 2x \geq 0$, $x^2 - 6x + 8 \leq 0$, $y \leq x^2$, and $y \geq x^2$ which involve the symbols $\leq$ or $\geq$ are also called quadratic inequalities.

Quadratic inequalities in one variable, as well as quadratic equalities in one variable, may be solved graphically as shown in the following examples.

If S is $\{(x, y) \mid y = x^2 + 6x + 13\}$, then the graph of the quadratic relation S and the graph of its complement are shown to the left below. If T is $\{(x, y) \mid y \le -x^2 - 3x + 10\}$, then the graph of the quadratic relation T and the graph of its complement are shown to the right below.

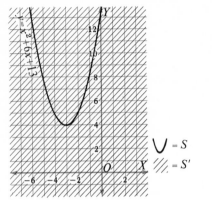
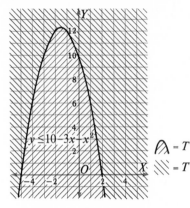

Example 1. If $S = \{(x, y) \mid y > x^2\}$ and $T = \{(x, y) \mid y < 2 - x^2\}$, show the graph of $S \cap T$.

Solution.   First we draw the graph of the solution sets of the equations $y = x^2$ and $y = 2 - x^2$ using dashed lines. The region above the graph of the solution set of $y = x^2$ is the graph of S and the region below the graph of the solution set of $y = 2 - x^2$ is the graph of T. The cross-hatched area represents the graph of $S \cap T$.

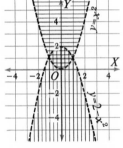

Example 2. If $S = \{(x, y) \mid y \ge \frac{1}{4} x^2\}$ and $T = \{(x, y) \mid x + 2y - 4 = 0\}$, show the graph of $S \cap T$.

Solution.   We draw the graph of S and T as shown at the right. The graph of $S \cap T$ is the segment AB shown in the figure. Note that the end points A and B are included.

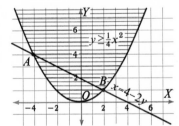

Example 3. Solve the inequality $x^2 + 2x - 15 \ge 0$ by graphical methods.

Solution.   First we let $y = x^2 + 2x - 15$ and draw the graph of
$$\{(x, y) \mid y = x^2 + 2x - 15\}.$$

Now we want to find the values of x for which $x^2 + 2x - 15 \geq 0$. Since we let $y = x^2 + 2x - 15$, we have $y \geq 0$. Thus the values of x we want are the abscissas of the points which are in the graph of

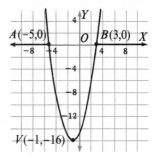

$$\{(x, y) \mid y = x^2 + 2x - 15 \wedge y \geq 0\}.$$

The graph indicates that $y \geq 0$ for any value of x which is less than or equal to -5, or greater than or equal to 3. These values of x are the abscissas of the points in the graph indicated by the heavy black lines on the x-axis. Thus,

$$\{x \mid x^2 + 2x - 15 \geq 0\} = \{x \mid x \geq 3\} \cup \{x \mid x \leq -5\}.$$

Ⓐ EXERCISES

1. Draw the graph of each of the following relations.

   a. $\{(x, y) \mid y \geq x^2\}$

   b. $\{(x, y) \mid y > x^2 + 1\}$

   c. $\{(x, y) \mid y \geq x^2 - 1\}$

   d. $\{(x, y) \mid y \geq |x^2 - 16|\}$

   e. $\{(x, y) \mid y \geq x^2 - x\}$

   f. $\{(x, y) \mid y \leq -x^2 + 3x\}$

   g. $\{(x, y) \mid y \geq x^2 - 7x + 12$

   h. $\{(x, y) \mid y < -x^2 - 6x + 8\}$

   i. $\{(x, y) \mid y \geq x^2 - 36\}$

   j. $\{(x, y) \mid y \geq |x - 3|^2\}$

2. Draw the graph of the solution set of each of the following open sentences.

   a. $y \leq \frac{1}{3}x^2 \wedge y \geq x^2 - 3$

   b. $y < x^2 + 3 \wedge y > x^2 - 4$

   c. $y < x^2 + 2x + 1 \wedge y < x^2 - 2x + 1$

   d. $y \geq x^2 - 4x + 4 \wedge y \geq 2$

   e. $y \geq x^2 - x \wedge y > \frac{1}{2}x + 3$

   f. $y < (x - 2)^2 \wedge y < (2 - x)^2$

   g. $y < x^2 - 5x + 6 \wedge y < x^2 + 5x + 6$

   h. $y \leq \frac{1}{3}x^2 \wedge y = 2x + 3$

3. Use a graph in the coordinate plane to find the solution set of each of the following inequalities as we did in Example 3.

   a. $x^2 - 5x + 4 \geq 0$ c. $x^2 - 3x > 0$ e. $2x^2 - 3x - 9 \geq 0$ g. $5x^2 - 20 \leq 0$

   b. $x^2 - 5x + 4 \leq 0$ d. $x^2 - 4x < 0$ f. $2x^2 < 8x - 6$ h. $2x^2 + 5x > 3$

Applications

In this section we study some problems whose formulation and solution involve quadratic equations. In some cases we shall find that the conditions imposed by the problem determine which of the roots of the applicable quadratic equation is to be accepted.

Example 1. On a river that flows at the rate of 4 miles per hour, a motor boat can go 16 miles downstream and return upstream in one hour and 10 minutes. What is the rate of the boat in still water.

Solution. PART 1.

Let x represent the rate of the boat in still water expressed in miles per hour. Then the boat travels downstream at the rate of $x + 4$ miles per hour. The number of hours required to go 16 miles downstream is $\dfrac{16}{x+4}$. The number of hours required to return 16 miles is $\dfrac{16}{x-4}$. The number of hours required for the entire trip is $\dfrac{16}{x+4} + \dfrac{16}{x-4}$. Since we know that the total time in hours required is $1\frac{10}{60}$, we can express the conditions of our problem in the equation $\dfrac{16}{x+4} + \dfrac{16}{x-4} = \dfrac{7}{6}$.

This equation can be transformed into a quadratic equation by multiplying both members by $(x+4)(x-4)$. The transformed equation is

$16(x-4) + 16(x+4) = \frac{7}{6}(x^2 - 16)$ or $32\,x = \frac{7}{6}(x^2 - 16)$.

Note that we have made the assumption that $x \neq 4 \wedge x \neq -4$. Next we solve the open statement $32\,x = \frac{7}{6}(x^2 - 16) \wedge x \neq 4 \wedge x \neq -4$ as follows:

$$\frac{16}{x+4} + \frac{16}{x-4} = \frac{7}{6}$$
$$32\,x = \tfrac{7}{6}(x^2 - 16) \wedge x \neq 4 \wedge x \neq -4$$
$$192\,x = 7\,x^2 - 112$$
$$0 = 7\,x^2 - 192\,x - 112$$
$$0 = (7\,x + 4)(x - 28)$$
$$x = -\tfrac{4}{7} \vee x = 28$$

PART 2.

$$\frac{16}{-\frac{4}{7}+4} + \frac{16}{-\frac{4}{7}-4} \overset{?}{=} \frac{7}{6}$$
$$\frac{112}{24} - \frac{112}{32} \overset{?}{=} \frac{7}{6}$$
$$\frac{7}{6} \overset{\vee}{=} \frac{7}{6}$$
$$\frac{16}{28+4} + \frac{16}{28-4} \overset{?}{=} \frac{7}{6}$$

$$\frac{16}{32} + \frac{16}{24} \overset{?}{=} \frac{7}{6}$$

$$\frac{7}{6} \overset{\checkmark}{=} \frac{7}{6}$$

Thus the solution set is $\{-\frac{4}{7}, 28\}$.

The number 28 is a possible solution to our problem, the number $-\frac{4}{7}$ is not. We check to see if 28 is a solution of the original problem. If 28 is the speed of the boat in still water, then the speed downstream is 32 miles per hour and the speed upstream is 24 miles per hour. The time required to go 16 miles downstream is $\frac{16}{32}$ hours and the time required to go 16 miles upstream is $\frac{16}{24}$ hours. The time for the round trip is $\frac{16}{32} + \frac{16}{24} = \frac{1}{2} + \frac{2}{3} = \frac{7}{6}$ hours $= 1$ hour and 10 minutes. We conclude that the boat must travel 28 miles per hour in still water.

Example 2. The length of line segment AB is 10 inches. If P is a point in $\overline{AB}$, find $|AP|$ and $|PB|$ such that

$$\frac{|AB|}{|AP|} = \frac{|AP|}{|PB|}.$$

Solution. Let $|AP| = x$; then $|PB| = 10 - x$. Substituting in

$\frac{|AB|}{|AP|} = \frac{|AP|}{|PB|}$, we have the equation $\frac{10}{x} = \frac{x}{10 - x}$.

PART 1.

$$\frac{10}{x} = \frac{x}{10 - x} \wedge x \neq 0 \wedge x \neq 10$$

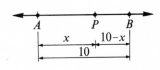

$$10(10 - x) = x^2$$
$$0 = x^2 + 10\,x - 100$$
$$x = \frac{-b \pm \sqrt{b^2 - 4\,ac}}{2\,a}$$
$$x = \frac{-10 \pm \sqrt{100 + 400}}{2}$$
$$x = -5 + 5\sqrt{5} \ or$$
$$x = -5 - 5\sqrt{5}$$

PART 2.

If $x = -5 + 5\sqrt{5}$,

$$\frac{10}{-5 + 5\sqrt{5}} \overset{?}{=} \frac{-5 + 5\sqrt{5}}{10 + 5 - 5\sqrt{5}}$$
$$(-5 + 5\sqrt{5})^2 \overset{?}{=} 10(15 - 5\sqrt{5})$$
$$150 - 50\sqrt{5} \overset{\checkmark}{=} 150 - 50\sqrt{5}$$

If $x = -5 - 5\sqrt{5}$,

$$\frac{10}{-5 - 5\sqrt{5}} \overset{?}{=} \frac{-5 - 5\sqrt{5}}{10 + 5 + 5\sqrt{5}}$$

$$(-5 - 5\sqrt{5})^2 \overset{?}{=} 10(15 + 5\sqrt{5})$$

$$150 + 50\sqrt{5} \overset{\checkmark}{=} 150 + 50\sqrt{5}$$

Thus the solution set is:

$\{x \mid x = -5 + 5\sqrt{5} \lor x = -5 - 5\sqrt{5}\} \cup \{x \mid x \neq 0 \land x \neq 10\}$,

or $\{-5 + 5\sqrt{5}, -5 - 5\sqrt{5}\}$.

The first root, being positive and less than 10, is a possible solution to our problem. The second, being a negative number, is not. Thus the length of $\overline{AP}$ is $(-5 + 5\sqrt{5})$ inches, or approximately 6.18 inches. $|PB| = 10 - x = 10 - (-5 + 5\sqrt{5})$. Thus the length of $\overline{PB}$ is $15 - 5\sqrt{5}$ inches or approximately 3.82 inches.

Example 3. The dimensions of a rectangular garden are 50 ft. by 60 ft. The garden has a border of uniform width. If the area of the border is one third the area of the entire garden, find the width of the border.

Solution. The area of the garden inside the border is evidently two thirds of the entire area. Therefore, $(60 - 2w)(50 - 2w) = \frac{2}{3}(60 \times 50)$ when $w \in \langle 0, 25 \rangle$ and is the measure of the width in feet. $(60 - 2w)(50 - 2w) = \frac{2}{3}(60 \times 50) \longleftrightarrow w^2 - 55w + 250 = 0 \longleftrightarrow (w - 5)(w - 50) = 0 \longleftrightarrow w = 5 \lor w = 50$.

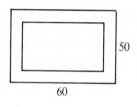

The solution set is $\{5, 50\}$. We find that 5 satisfies the conditions of the problem and that 50 does not. Thus the width of the border is 5 feet.

Ⓐ EXERCISES

1. The sum of a number and three times its reciprocal is $\frac{433}{12}$. What is the number?

2. The numerator of a fraction exceeds the denominator by 1. If the fraction exceeds its reciprocal by $\frac{17}{72}$, what is the fraction?

3. The units digit of a two-digit number is 3 more than twice the tens digit. If the sum of the squares of the digits is 53, what is the number?

4. If the length of each edge of a cube were increased by 1 inch, the volume of the resulting cube would be 169 cubic inches greater than the volume of the given cube. What is the length of an edge of the given cube?

5. A cubical box is placed on top of a larger cubical box. If the sum of the heights of the two boxes is 16 inches and the sum of the volumes of the boxes is 1456 cubic inches, what is the volume of each box?

6. A man plans to cover one wall of his office with strips of wood paneling. The wall is 14 feet long. Two widths of paneling are available, one an inch wider than the other. If the wider paneling is chosen, 4 fewer strips will be needed to cover the wall. How wide is each kind of paneling?

7. On a trip of 315 miles a bus driver, because of snow, was forced to decrease his usual speed by 10 miles per hour. If he arrived two hours late, what is his usual speed?

8. For a trip to New York, the Pleasantville History Club chartered a bus for $480, the cost to be divided equally among those making the trip. One member of the club was unable to go, so each member making the trip paid $2 extra. How many members made the trip?

9. A group of men planning a hunting trip decided to divide the cost ($245) equally among themselves. Later two other men joined the group, thereby reducing the cost for all by $14 per person. How many men made the trip?

10. On a trip to Chicago Mr. Smith drove 210 miles. He then returned home by the same route. If his rate of travel to Chicago was $\frac{5}{6}$ of his rate on the trip home and required 1 extra hour of time, how fast did he travel in each direction.

11. Eighty-four pounds of iron is molded into a beam. If the beam is made 1 foot longer, each foot will weigh 2 pounds less. What is the length of each beam?

12. Two rectangular fields are enclosed by equal amounts of fencing. One field has its length 2 rods less than 9 times the number of rods in its width and the other field is a square. If the square field contains 121 more square rods than the other field, what are the dimensions of each?

B EXERCISES

13. Two planes A and B start from the same point at the same time, A flying north and B flying east. At the end of 30 minutes plane B had traveled 65 miles farther than plane A and was approximately 402 miles from it. How fast did each plane fly?

14. The circumference of a back wheel of a truck exceeds the circumference of a front wheel by $\frac{2}{3}$ foot, and in traveling 1 mile a back wheel makes 88 less revolutions than a front wheel. Find the circumference of each wheel. (Use 1 mile $= 5280$ feet.)

15. If a given mass is thrown vertically upward with an initial velocity of v feet per second, its height at the end of t seconds is given by the equation $h = vt - 16t^2$. How long will it take the mass to reach its maximum height if thrown vertically upward from the ground with an initial velocity of 96 feet per second? What will be its maximum height?

Before you leave this chapter make sure that you

1. Know the meaning of "quadratic function" and "quadratic equation." (Page 337.)

2. Understand the relationship between the zeros of the quadratic function defined by $y = ax^2 + bx + c$ and the roots of the equation $ax^2 + bx + c = 0$. (Page 337.)

3. Can recognize the characteristics of the graph of the function by analyzing the equation which defines a quadratic function and can use the information thus obtained in sketching the graph. (Page 337.)

4. Can find the roots of the quadratic equation $ax^2 + bx + c = 0$ by factoring or by a study of the graph of the function defined by the equation $y = ax^2 + bx + c$. (Pages 337–339.)

5. Know the characteristics of the functions defined by the equations $y = ax^2$. (Page 341.); $y = ax^2 + p$. (Page 344.); $y = a(x - k)^2$. (Page 345.); $y = a(x - k)^2 + p$. (Page 347.); and $y = ax^2 + bx + c$. (Page 351.)

6. Can solve problems involving the absolute maximum or absolute minimum of a quadratic function. (Pages 351–353.)

7. Can derive the quadratic formula and can solve a quadratic equation in one variable using the quadratic formula. (Pages 355–357.)

8. Understand the relationship which exists between the roots and the coefficients of a quadratic equation. (Page 359.)

9. Can use the discriminant of a quadratic equation to determine the number of roots of the equation and whether the roots are rational, irrational, or neither. (Page 360.)

10. Can solve fractional equations that can be transformed into quadratic form. (Pages 366–368.)

11. Can solve radical equations that can be transformed into quadratic form. (Page 370.)

12. Can solve equations, other than those already mentioned above, that can be transformed into quadratic form. (Page 372.)

13. Can draw the graphs of quadratic relations and can use these graphs in finding the solution sets of sentences (both simple and compound) which define such relations. (Pages 373–374.)

14. Can solve problems involving quadratic equations. (Pages 375–378.)

15. Understand the meaning of and can spell correctly the following words and phrases.

congruent parabolas (Page 343.)   root of multiplicity two (Page 346.)
parabola (Page 337.)   similar parabolas (Page 342.)
quadratic equation (Page 337.)   zero of a function (Page 337.)
root of an equation (Page 337.)   zero of multiplicity two (Page 345.)

CHAPTER REVIEW

1. Which of the following equations define quadratic functions?

  a. $y = 3 x^2$ **c.** $y = 7 x^2 + 4$ **e.** $x^2 + y^2 = 25$
  b. $x = 3 y^2$ **d.** $- ax + y^2 = 11$ **f.** $x^2 + y = 9$

2. Indicate the zeros of the function defined by each of the following equations.

  a. $y = x^2 - 9 x + 14$ **e.** $y = - 2 x^2$
  b. $y = (2 x + 1)(x - 3)$ **f.** $1 - 3 x^2 = y$
  c. $4 x^2 - x = y$ **g.** $4 x^2 = 9 + y$
  d. $3 y = - x^2 + 12$ **h.** $y = - x^2 - x + 12$

3. For each of the following equations (1) sketch the graph of the function defined by the equation, (2) indicate the zeros of the function, (3) indicate the coordinates of the vertex of the graph of the function, (4) write the equation which defines the axis of symmetry of the graph of the function, (5) indicate the interval in which each function is an increasing function and the interval in which it is a decreasing function.

  a. $y = x^2 - 6 x + 8$ **c.** $y = 9 x^2 - 4$ **e.** $y = \frac{1}{2} x^2 + \frac{7}{2} x + 3$
  b. $y = - x^2 + 3 x + 4$ **d.** $y = (x - 3)^2$ **f.** $y = - 12 x^2 + 17 x + 5$

4. Examine each of the functions defined below; then (1) state whether the function is bounded above or below, (2) write the equation of the axis of symmetry of the graph of the function, (3) name the interval in which each function is an increasing function and the interval in which it is a decreasing function.

  a. $\{(x, y) \mid y = (x - 1)^2\}$ **d.** $\{(x, y) \mid y = 3 x - x^2\}$
  b. $\{(x, y) \mid y = - 3(x - 2)^2\}$ **e.** $\{(x, y) \mid y = - 7 x^2\}$
  c. $\{(x, y) \mid y = 2 x^2 - 5 x + 3\}$ **f.** $\{(x, y) \mid y = 2(x - 3)^2 + 5\}$

5. Which of the following equations will have the flattest parabola as its graph?

  a. $y = 3 x^2$ **b.** $y = - 3 x^2$ **c.** $y = \frac{1}{3} x^2$ **d.** $y = - 7 x^2$

6. Draw the graph of the function defined by each of the following equations.

  a. $y = 4 x^2$ **b.** $y = - 4 x^2$ **c.** $y = - 2 x^2$ **d.** $y = \frac{1}{5} x^2$

7. Which of the following equations define a function which has zero as its minimum value?

  a. $y = 3 x^2$ **b.** $y = 3 x^2 + 2$ **c.** $y = \frac{1}{4} x^2 - x - 7$ **d.** $y = - 100 x^2$

8. Each of the following ordered pairs indicates the coordinates of a point. Write an equation the graph of whose solution set contains the point, is symmetric to the y-axis, and has its vertex at the origin.

    a. $(1, 3)$ **b.** $(-2, -5)$ **c.** $(4, -3)$ **d.** $(-1, 3)$

9. Which of the parabolas whose defining equations are shown below are similar to and which are congruent to the parabola whose defining equation is $y = \frac{1}{2} x^2$?

    a. $y = -\frac{1}{2} x^2$ **b.** $y = 2 x^2$ **c.** $y = -2 x^2$ **d.** $y = -4 x^2$

10. With respect to one pair of axes draw graphs of each of the functions defined below.

    a. $\{(x, y) \mid y = \frac{1}{3} x^2 + 1\}$ **c.** $\{(x, y) \mid y = \frac{1}{3} x^2 + 7\}$

    b. $\{(x, y) \mid y = \frac{1}{3} x^2 - 1\}$ **d.** $\{(x, y) \mid y = \frac{1}{3} x^2 - 4\}$

11. Determine the absolute minimum or absolute maximum of the function defined by each of the following equations.

    a. $y = -4 x^2$ **b.** $y = \frac{1}{2} x^2 + 1$ **c.** $y = -\frac{1}{3} x^2 + 2$ **d.** $y = -5 x^2 + 3$

12. Without drawing their graphs indicate which of the following functions have zeros. If zeros exist, name them.

    a. $\{(x, y) \mid y = x^2 - 5\}$ **d.** $\{(x, y) \mid 4 y = 2 x^2 - 1\}$

    b. $\{(x, y) \mid y = -x^2 + 2\}$ **e.** $\{(x, y) \mid y = -3 x^2 + 7\}$

    c. $\{(x, y) \mid y = 4 x^2 + 3\}$ **f.** $\{(x, y) \mid 3 x^2 - 2 y = 3\}$

13. In each of the following sets of three equations, which of the equations will have a graph whose axis of symmetry is to the right of the axes of symmetry of the graphs of the other two equations?

    a. $y = x^2$, $y = (x - 1)^2$, $y = (x + 1)^2$

    b. $y = -2 x^2$, $y = -2(x + 3)^2$, $y = -2(x - 3)^2$

    c. $y = (x + 2)^2$, $y = (x + 3)^2$, $y = (x + 4)^2$

14. The graph of which of the following sets will have an absolute minimum point whose ordinate is the greatest value? The graph of which of the following sets will have an absolute minimum point whose ordinate is the least value?

    a. $\{(x, y) \mid y = x^2\}$ **d.** $\{(x, y) \mid y = (x + 3)^2 - 4\}$

    b. $\{(x, y) \mid y = x^2 + 5\}$ **e.** $\{(x, y) \mid y(x - 4)^2 + 2\}$

    c. $\{(x, y) \mid y = (x - 3)^2\}$ **f.** $\{(x, y) \mid y = (x + 5)^2 - 3\}$

15. What is the equation of the axis of symmetry of the graph of each of the following equations?

    a. $y = -\frac{1}{4} x^2$ **c.** $y = 3(x - 1)^2$

    b. $y = 2 x^2$ **d.** $y = 2(x + 4)^2 - 1$

16. Sketch the graph of each of the functions indicated below.

   a $\{(x, y) \mid y = 2(x - 1)^2 + 3\}$ c. $\{(x, y) \mid y = \frac{1}{2}(x + 2)^2 - 1\}$

   b. $\{(x, y) \mid y = 2(x - 1)^2 - 3\}$ d. $\{(x, y) \mid y = (x + 4)^2 + 3\}$

17. Indicate the interval in which each of the functions of Ex. 16 is an increasing function and the interval in which it is a decreasing function.

18. Use the method of completing the square to transform each of the following equations into the form $y = a(x - k)^2 + p$.

   a. $y = x^2 + 6x - 7$ c. $y = 3x^2 + 4x + \frac{1}{3}$

   b. $y = x^2 - 8x + 7$ d. $y = -2x^2 + 6x - 4$

19. Determine the absolute minimum or absolute maximum of the function defined by each of the equations of Ex. 18.

20. Use Corollary to Theorem 2–7 as a guide in sketching the graph of the solution set of each of the following equations.

   a. $y = -3x^2 + 4x + 1$ b. $y = 2x^2 - 3x - 2$ c. $y = x^2 - 7x + 1$

21. Find the maximum rectangular area that can be enclosed with 169 rods of fence?

22. Find two numbers, whose sum is 20, such that the square of one of the numbers minus twice the square of the other number is maximum.

23. Use the quadratic formula to find the roots of each of the following equations.

   a. $x^2 - 10x + 21 = 0$

   b. $2x^2 - 11x + 12 = 0$ e. $\dfrac{1}{x - 3} + \dfrac{x - 1}{x + 3} = \dfrac{10}{x^2 - 9}$

   c. $x - \dfrac{1}{x} = 7$

   d. $\dfrac{x + 1}{4} - \dfrac{x - 3}{12} = \dfrac{x^2 - 1}{4}$ f. $\dfrac{4}{x} + \dfrac{2}{x^2 + x} - \dfrac{4x + 1}{x} = 0$

24. For each of the following pairs of numbers, write an equation having the pair as its solution set.

   a. $\sqrt{3}, 2$ b. $\frac{1}{3}, -\frac{2}{3}$ c. $2 + a, 2 - a$ d. $\dfrac{1 - \sqrt{3}}{2}, \dfrac{1 + \sqrt{3}}{2}$

25. Without solving, find the sum and the product of the roots of each of the following equations.

   a. $3x^2 - 5x - 2 = 0$ b. $x^2 - 5x = 0$

26. Use the discriminant of each of the following equations to determine the number of real roots of each equation. For each equation determine whether the roots are rational or irrational.

   a. $x^2 + 4x - 6 = 0$ c. $-x^2 + 5x + 1 = 0$

   b. $x^2 - 2\sqrt{3}x + 3 = 0$ d. $3x^2 - 2x - 2 = 0$

27. Solve each of the following equations by any method you wish to use.

a. $\sqrt{x+4} - \sqrt{2x+6} = -1$ c. $y^4 + 2y^2 - 3 = 0$

b. $x - 3\sqrt{x} + 2 = 0$ d. $x + 1 + 4\sqrt{x+1} - 12 = 0$

28. Use a graph to find the solution set of each of the following:

a. $y \geq \frac{1}{2}x^2 \wedge x \leq 3$ c. $y > \frac{1}{9}x^2 \wedge x > \frac{1}{9}y^2$

b. $y \geq x^2 + 3x + 2 \wedge y \leq -x^2 - 3x + 4$ d. $y \geq \frac{1}{4}x^2 \wedge y = \frac{1}{4}x^2 + 3$

29. A steel cube rests on a table and a smaller steel cube rests on the larger cube. If the sum of the heights of the two cubes is 5 inches and the area of the exposed surface of the cubes is 61 square inches, how long is the edge of each cube?

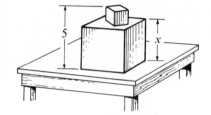

CHAPTER TEST

1. Given the function defined by $y = 2(x+1)^2 - 3$.

     a. State the equation of the axis of symmetry.

     b. State the coordinates of the vertex of the graph of the function.

     c. Indicate whether the function has an absolute maximum or an absolute minimum and state its value.

     d. List the zeros of the function, if zeros exist.

2. Write a quadratic equation whose roots are $\dfrac{1+\sqrt{5}}{4}$ and $\dfrac{1-\sqrt{5}}{4}$.

3. For what values of k and p will the graph of the function which is defined by $y = 3(x+k)^2 + p$ have its vertex at the origin?

4. For what interval is the function defined by $y = -3x^2 - 2x + 1$ an increasing function and for what interval is it a decreasing function?

5. What is the maximum rectangular area that can be enclosed with 120 rods of fence?

6. What are the sum and the product of the roots of the equation $m^2x^2 + 3mx - 4 = 0$?

7. Solve: $3x^2 - 5x - 2 = 0$

8. Solve: $\dfrac{2x+3}{x} + \dfrac{x-5}{2x-3} - \dfrac{1}{x} = 0$

9. Solve: $\sqrt{x} = \sqrt{6x-5} - \sqrt{2x+1}$

10. Solve: $y^4 - 7y^2 - 18 = 0$

11. Use a graph to find the solution set of the sentence $y \geq \frac{1}{4}x^2 - 6 \wedge y < x + 3$.

1. Assuming that $x \in R$, draw the graph of the truth set of each of the following statements.

   a. $x < 0 \wedge x > -4$ **c.** $x \geq 2 \vee x \leq -3$ **e.** $(x+6)(x-1) < 0$

   b. $x > 1 \wedge x > 3$ **d.** $|x+3| < 5$ **f.** $\dfrac{1}{x} < 3$

2. For each of the following draw the graph of $C \times C$. Use heavy dots to show the subset of $C \times C$ defined by each of the following statements.

   a. $y = 2x + 3$ **b.** $y \leq x + 4$ **c.** $y \geq 3x \wedge y < 4$

3. Find the coordinates of the midpoints of the sides of the triangle formed by joining the points $A(-4, 1)$, $B(1, -5)$, and $C(3, 7)$.

4. Determine whether the quadrilateral formed by joining the following points, in succession, is a parallelogram: $A(-2, 5)$, $B(3, -1)$, $C(9, 0)$, and $D(4, 6)$.

5. Using the intercept method, draw the graph of the solution set of the equation $2x + 3y = 6$.

6. Complete: If L is a line containing distinct points $P_1(x_1, y_1)$ and $P_2(x_2, y_2)$, then L is vertical if and only if _?_.

7. State the slope and y-intercept of the graph of the solution set of each of the following equations.

   a. $y = 4x - 3$ **b.** $3y = 2x + 4$ **c.** $2x - 4y = 7$

8. What is true of the three points $P_1(x_1, y_1)$, $P_2(x_2, y_2)$, and $P_3(x_3, y_3)$ if their coordinates make the equation $\begin{vmatrix} x_1 & y_1 & 1 \\ x_2 & y_2 & 1 \\ x_3 & y_3 & 1 \end{vmatrix} = 0$ true?

9. What is the slope of the line through the points $A(-5, 1)$ and $B(4, 6)$?

10. Determine whether the points $A(0, 6)$, $B(1, 9)$, and $C(3, 15)$ are collinear.

11. Solve by the multiplication and addition method.

   a. $\begin{cases} 3x + 2y = 4 \\ -2x - 3y = -11 \end{cases}$

   b. $\begin{cases} \dfrac{x+y}{5} + \dfrac{y-x}{4} = 1 \\ \dfrac{x}{2} - \dfrac{y}{2} = 5 \end{cases}$

12. Solve by the substitution method.

   a. $\begin{cases} 2x - 5y = -78 \\ -x + 2y = 3 \end{cases}$

   b. $\begin{cases} x - 2y = -1 \\ 4x - y = 10 \end{cases}$

13. Write an equation the graph of whose solution set is a straight line through the point $P(4, 1)$ and perpendicular to the line which is the graph of the solution set of $y = -\frac{3}{2}x + 2$.

14. Show that the graph of $y = x^2 - 6x$ is symmetric with respect to the line which is the graph of $0 y + x = 3$.

15. Find the reflection of the point $P(-3, -4)$ in:

    a. The y-axis
    b. The graph of $\{(x, y) \mid y = x\}$

16. Which of the following equations has a graph which is symmetric with respect to the y-axis?

    a. $|x| = y$
    b. $y = 2 x^2$
    c. $xy = 12$

17. Given $P(-2, 6)$ and $Q(4, 3)$, write an equation the graph of whose solution set is the set of points $R(x, y)$ equidistant from P and Q.

18. In the right triangle ABC whose vertices are $A(0, 3)$, $B(4, 0)$, and $C(0, 0)$, the altitude to the hypotenuse intersects the hypotenuse at point D. Find the coordinates of D.

19. What are the domain and the range of the relation $M = \{(x, y) \mid y \leq \sqrt{25 - x}\}$?

20. Which of the following relations are functions?

    a. $\{(-2, 0), (-1, 1), (0, 2), (1, 3), (2, 4)\}$
    c. $\{(x, y) \mid y = x^2\}$
    b. $\{(x, y) \mid x = |2 y|\}$
    d. $\{(x, y) \mid x = y^2\}$

21. What do we mean by the *value of a function*?

22. If $F = \{(x, y) \mid y = 4x - 1\}$, find:

    a. $f(2)$
    b. $f(t^2)$
    c. $[f(t)]^2$
    d. $f[f(x)]$

23. Draw the graph of each of the functions defined below.

    a. $\left\{(x, f(x)) \mid 1 = \dfrac{f(x)}{x + 2}\right\}$
    b. $\{(x, y) \mid y = -\sqrt{4 - x^2} \wedge x \in (-2, 2)\} \cup \{(x, y) \mid y = 2 - x \wedge x \in \rangle 2, \infty \langle\}$

24. State the domain and range of each of the functions of Ex. 23.

25. If functions F and G are defined as indicated below, find $F(G)$, $D_{F(G)}$ and $R_{F(G)}$.

    a. $F = \{(x, y) \mid y = 3x + 4\}$ $G = \{(x, y) \mid y = 2 x^2\}$
    b. $F = \{(x, y) \mid y = 2x\}$ $G = \{(x, y) \mid y = x^2 - 3\}$
    c. $F = \{(x, y) \mid y = \sqrt{9 - x}\}$ $G = \{(x, y) \mid y = 9x\}$

26. Complete: Functions F and G are inverses of each other if and only if $(a, b) \in F \longleftrightarrow \_?\_$.

27. Which of the following sets are linear functions?

    a. $\{(x, y) \mid y = 3x - 7\}$
    b. $\{(x, y) \mid x = 5\}$
    c. $\{(x, y) \mid ay = 4x; \ a \neq 0\}$

28. Find the inverse of each of the following functions.

    a. $\{(x, y) \mid y = 3x + 1\}$
    b. $\{(x, y) \mid 3y = -2x + 4\}$
    c. $\{(x, y) \mid y = \frac{1}{2} x\}$

29. Find the zeros (if zeros exist) of the function defined by each of the following equations.   **a.** $y = x^2 - 7x + 6$ **b.** $y = 4$ **c.** $y = 4 x^2$

30. If y varies directly as x and $y = 1$ when $x = 10$, find y when $x = 2$.

31. Determine y so that $\{(3, \frac{1}{2}), (5, y)\} \subseteq \{(x, y) \mid y \text{ varies inversely as } x\}$.

32. Given that n varies directly as the cube root of a and inversely as twice the square root of b (assuming that $b > 0$), find n when $a = 27$ and $b = 81$, if $n = \frac{3}{10}$ when $a = 125$ and $b = 625$.

33. If $A = \{(x, y) \mid y \leq -\frac{3}{5}x + 3\} \cap \{(x, y) \mid y \geq x - 2\} \cap \{(x, y) \mid y \geq 0\} \cap \{(x, y) \mid x \geq 0\}$, find the maximum value of V when $V = x + y$ and $(x, y) \in A$.

34. With respect to one pair of coordinate axes, draw the graphs of $F = \{(x, y) \mid y = 3 x\}$, and $G = \{(x, y) \mid y = x\}$; then with respect to the same pair of axes draw the graphs of $F + G$ and $F \cdot G$.

35. Is the function $\{(x, y) \mid y = x^2 + 2\}$ an increasing or a decreasing function within each of the following intervals?

   a. $\rangle - 8, 0 \rangle$ **b.** $\langle 0, 4 \rangle$

36. Indicate an interval (if one exists) within which the function $\{(x, y) \mid y^3 = x\}$ is an increasing function.

37. **a.** What do we mean when we say that a function is bounded above?

   b. What do we mean when we say that a function is bounded below?

   c. What do we mean by *a bounded function*?

38. Indicate which of the following functions is continuous within the interval indicated.

   a. $\{(x, y) \mid y = 3 x^2\}$, in $\langle - 3, 3 \rangle$ **b.** $\left\{(x, y) \mid y = \dfrac{1}{3 x}\right\}$, in $\langle - 3, 3 \rangle$

39. Which of the following equations define quadratic functions?

   a. $(x - 2)(x + 1) = 0$ **c.** $y = - 2 x^2 + 1$ **e.** $y = x(x - 3)(x - 4)$

   b. $y^2 = x$ **d.** $y = \dfrac{8}{x^2}$ **f.** $4 x + 8 y^2 = 1$

40. For what value of k does each of the following define a quadratic function?

   a. $y = kx^2$ **b.** $y = (x + 2)(x - k)$ **c.** $y = kx^2 - 3 x + 2$

41. Without drawing its graph indicate the zeros, if zeros exist, of each of the following functions.

   a. $\{(x, y) \mid y = 3 x^2 - 1\}$ **c.** $\{(x, y) \mid y = 2 x^2 + 4 x + 2\}$
   b. $\{(x, y) \mid y = - 2 x^2 + 3\}$ **d.** $\{(x, y) \mid y = - 3 x^2 - 2 x + 1\}$

42. Which of the functions of Ex. 41 are bounded below but not above, which are bounded above but not below, and which, if any, do not fall into either of these classifications?

43. What is the equation of the axis of symmetry of the graph of each of the following functions?

a. $\{(x, y) \mid y = x^2 - 3\,x\}$

b. $\{(x, y) \mid y = (x - 2)^2\}$

c. $\{(x, y) \mid y = -x^2\}$

d. $\{(x, y) \mid y = \frac{1}{2}\,x^2\}$

e. $\{(x, y) \mid y = 2(x - 3)^2 + 2\}$

f. $\{(x, y) \mid y = -(x - 2)^2 - 1\}$

44. State the coordinates of the vertex of the graph for each part of Ex. 43.

45. The relation $\{(x, y) \mid 2\,x = 3\,y^2 - 1\}$ is the union of two functions. Use set-builder notation to indicate the two functions.

46. By completing the square, change each of the following equations to the form $y = a(x - k)^2 + p$.

a. $y = x^2 - 6\,x + 7$

b. $y = x^2 - 5\,x + 3$

c. $y = 4\,x^2 - 36\,x - 5$

d. $y = -3\,x^2 - 5\,x + 2$

47. Solve each of the following equations by use of the quadratic formula.

a. $x^2 - 2\,x - 7 = 0$

b. $3\,x^2 - 5\,x + 1 = 0$

c. $(x + 5)^2 + (x - 2)^2 = 65$

d. $\frac{4}{3}\,x^2 + \frac{1}{2}(x - 1) = \frac{1}{3}(3\,x + 1)$

48. Write each irrational root of the equations in Ex. 47 as a decimal approximation expressed to the nearest hundredth.

49. Solve: $\mid x \mid^2 - 3 \mid x \mid - 35 = 0$

50. Without solving, find the sum and the product of the roots of each of the following equations.

a. $x^2 - 6\,x - 16 = 0$ b. $x^2 - x\sqrt{5} = 10$ c. $x^2 = 25\,a^2$

51. Find the discriminant of each of the following equations and from it determine whether the equation has two, one, or no real solutions.

a. $x^2 + 5\,x + 3 = 0$

b. $2\,x^2 - x = -3$

c. $2\,x^2 + 3\,x + 3 = 0$

d. $3\,x^2 + 5\,x + 2 = 0$

e. $4\,x^2 - 20\,x + 25 = 0$

f. $9\,x^2 - 6\,x + 1 = 0$

52. Find the solution set of each of the following equations.

a. $\dfrac{2\,x}{x - 1} - \dfrac{19}{x^2 - 1} = \dfrac{x - 3}{x + 1}$

b. $\sqrt{x - 1} = x - 1$

c. $x^4 - 13\,x^2 + 36 = 0$

d. $\sqrt{x + 2} + \sqrt{3 - x} = 3$

e. $\dfrac{4\,x - 10}{x + 5} + \dfrac{3\,x - 7}{x} = \dfrac{7}{2}$

f. $x + 2\sqrt{x} - 8 = 0$

g. $6\,x^2 + (3\sqrt{5} - 2\sqrt{7})x - \sqrt{35} = 0$

h. $x^6 + 9\,x^3 + 8 = 0$

53. Given $S = \{(x, y) \mid y \leq x^2\}$ and $T = \{(x, y) \mid y \leq 4 - x^2\}$, draw the graph of $S \cap T$.

54. Solve by graphing: $x^2 - x - 12 \geq 0$.

1. What is the measure of the line segment PQ when P and Q are points having the coordinates $(1, 7)$ and $(5, -3)$, respectively?

2. Write an equation whose graph is the line through the points $A(3, 4)$ and $B(-6, -1)$.

3. Write an equation whose graph is the line through the point $(0, 5)$ and perpendicular to the line which is the graph of $\{(x, y) \mid y = \frac{2}{3}x + 4\}$.

4. Which of the following indicate membership in a function?

   a. $\{(x, y) \mid y = 2x + 3\}$ c. $\{(x, y) \mid y = x^2 - 2\}$

   b. $\{(x, y) \mid y = \mid x \mid\}$ d. $\{(x, y) \mid y^2 = 4x\}$ e. $\left\{(x, y) \mid y = \frac{1}{x}\right\}$

5. If $F = \{(x, y) \mid y = \sqrt{4 + x}\}$ and $G = \{(x, y) \mid y = 2x\}$, find

   a. $F(G)$ b. $D_{F(G)}$ c. $R_{F(G)}$ d. $G(F)$ e. $G(F^2)$

6. Write the coordinates of the vertex and the equation of the axis of symmetry of the graph of $\{(x, y) \mid y = x^2 - 6x + 11\}$.

7. Without solving, write the sum and the product of the roots of the equation $2x^2 - 5x + 3 = 0$.

8. Solve: $x^4 - 10x^2 = 24$.

9. a. Find the discriminant of the equation $3x^2 - 4x - 6 = 0$.
   Use the discriminant to state:

   b. The number of real roots of the equation

   c. Whether the roots are rational or irrational

   d. Whether the roots are equal or unequal

   e. How many real roots has the equation $3x^2 - 4x + 6 = 0$?

10. Solve: $\sqrt{x + 2} = \sqrt{2x + 13} - 3$.

Exponential and Logarithmic Functions

Whole Numbers as Exponents

In Chapter 4 we stated that if $a \in R$ and $n \in W$, the symbol a^n is another name for $\underbrace{a \cdot a \cdot a \cdots a}_{n \text{ factors}}$. We also stated that 0^0 is undefined; that is, 0^0 is not a meaningful expression.

With these statements in effect, each of the following statements is an identity when $a, b \in R$ and $m, n \in W$.

1W. $a^m \cdot a^n = a^{m+n}$

2W. $(a^m)^n = a^{mn}$

3W. $(ab)^n = a^n \cdot b^n$

4W. a. $\dfrac{a^m}{a^n} = a^{m-n} \, ; \, m > n$

     b. $\dfrac{a^m}{a^n} = \dfrac{1}{a^{n-m}}; \, m < n$

     c. $\dfrac{a^m}{a^n} = a^0 = 1; \, m = n$

5W. $\left(\dfrac{a}{b}\right)^n = \dfrac{a^n}{b^n}$

We denote these identities with the symbols **1W**, **2W**, **3W** and so on, to indicate that the exponents m and n are whole numbers. These identities are known as the *laws of exponents*.

In this chapter we shall define a^m for integral exponents, rational number exponents, and real number exponents and shall consider the validity of the laws stated above for each of these kinds of exponent. We shall also study the *exponential function* and its inverse.

Example 1. Simplify each of the following:

> **a.** $(-3)^3 \cdot (-3)^5$ **d.** $(\frac{2}{3})^0$
>
> **b.** $\dfrac{(\sqrt{2})^5}{(\sqrt{2})^3}$
>
> **c.** $(-5a^2b)^4$ **e.** $\left(\dfrac{-2a}{5}\right)^3$

Solution.

> **a.** $(-3)^3 \cdot (-3)^5 = (-3)^8 = 6561$
>
> **b.** $\dfrac{(\sqrt{2})^5}{(\sqrt{2})^3} = (\sqrt{2})^2 = 2$
>
> **c.** $(-5\,a^2b)^4 = (-5)^4(a^2)^4b^4 = 625\,a^8b^4$
>
> **d.** $(\frac{2}{3})^0 = 1$
>
> **e.** $\left(\dfrac{-2a}{5}\right)^3 = \dfrac{(-2a)^3}{5^3} = \dfrac{(-2)^3a^3}{5^3} = \dfrac{-8\,a^3}{125}$

Note. We regard $\dfrac{a^n}{b^n}$ as simpler than $\left(\dfrac{a}{b}\right)^n$.

Example 2. Verify that $\left(\dfrac{a}{b}\right)^x = \dfrac{a^x}{b^x}$ is an identity when $x \,\epsilon\, W$ and $a,\,b \,\epsilon\, R$.

Solution. If $b = 0$, neither member of the above equation is defined. If $b \neq 0$, then $\dfrac{a}{b} \,\epsilon\, R$. By our definition of a^x, when $a \neq 0$ and $x = 0$, we have,

$\left(\dfrac{a}{b}\right)^0 = 1 = \dfrac{1}{1} = \dfrac{a^0}{b^0}.$ Therefore $\left(\dfrac{a}{b}\right)^0 = \dfrac{a^0}{b^0}.$

For $x = 1$ we have, $\left(\dfrac{a}{b}\right)^1 = \dfrac{a}{b} = \dfrac{a^1}{b^1}.$

For $x > 1$, $\left(\dfrac{a}{b}\right)^x = \overbrace{\left(\dfrac{a}{b}\right)\left(\dfrac{a}{b}\right)\cdots\left(\dfrac{a}{b}\right)}^{x \text{ factors}} = \dfrac{\overbrace{a \cdot a \cdots a}^{x \text{ factors}}}{\underbrace{b \cdot b \cdots b}_{x \text{ factors}}} = \dfrac{a^x}{b^x}.$

$\therefore \left(\dfrac{a}{b}\right)^x = \dfrac{a^x}{b^x}$ is an identity.

Ⓐ EXERCISES

1. Use the laws of exponents to write identically equal expressions for each of the following:

> **a.** $(-2)^3$ **d.** $(6\,a^2b^3)(3\,a^4b^2)$ **g.** $(-9\,m^2n)^3$
>
> **b.** $(-1)^4$ **e.** $(\frac{1}{2}\,rs)^4 \cdot (2\,r^2s)^3$ **h.** $(\frac{3}{4})^0$
>
> **c.** $(5\,a^2)^3$ **f.** $(\sqrt{5})^2$ **i.** $(-8\,mn^2)^2$

j. $\left(\dfrac{3\,a^2}{4}\right)^3$ **l.** $\left(\dfrac{\sqrt{3}}{\sqrt{2}}\right)^4$ **n.** $\left(\dfrac{-7\,a}{5}\right)^3$

k. $\left(\dfrac{-5\,a}{2}\right)^4$ **m.** $(-24\,r^2s^2t)(-2\,rs^3t^2)$ **o.** $\left(-\dfrac{3\,x^2}{5}\right)(15\,x^3y^2)$

2. Simplify, assuming that no denominator is zero.

a. a^3a^2 **f.** $\dfrac{15\,ab^3}{3\,ab^5}$ **k.** $\left(\dfrac{12\,abc}{7}\right)^3 \cdot \left(\dfrac{2}{3\,a}\right)^2$

b. $(2\,a^3b)^2 \cdot (4\,ab)^0;\;\; ab \neq 0$ **g.** $10\,rs \cdot \dfrac{15\,r^2s}{3\,r}$ **l.** $\dfrac{a^{15}}{a^{12}} \cdot 12\,a^2$

c. $(3\,mn^2)^2 \cdot (-2\,m^2)^3$

d. $\dfrac{8\,r^2s}{2\,rs}$ **h.** $(\sqrt{5})^2 \cdot \frac{1}{15}\,l^3$ **m.** $(\sqrt{5}\,x)^2 \cdot (\sqrt{3}\,x^3)^2$

i. $a^4 \cdot (a^2bc^2)^3$ **n.** $\dfrac{4(x+y)^2}{2(x+y)^3}$

e. $\left(\dfrac{16\,a^2b^3}{-8\,ab}\right)^3$ **j.** $\dfrac{3\,m^2n}{5\,m^3} \cdot \dfrac{10\,m^2}{9\,n^2}$ **o.** $\dfrac{(r^2-5)^3}{3(r^2-5)}$

3. Simplify, assuming that each exponent represents a whole number and that no denominator is zero.

a. $(3^a)^2$ **f.** $4\,a^x \cdot 2\,a^3$ **k.** $\dfrac{a^{3m}}{a^{5m}}$

b. $(4^m)^n$ **g.** $(-5\,ab)^x \cdot (-2\,ab)^y$

c. $a^m \cdot a^r \cdot a$ **h.** $\dfrac{(4\,m^2n)^2}{6\,m^3n^c};\; c > 2$ **l.** $\dfrac{12(x+y)^c}{-4(x+y)};\; c > 1$

d. $\dfrac{5^x}{5^y};\; x > y$ **i.** $(e^x)^2$ **m.** $\dfrac{10\,x^{3m}}{4\,x^{2m}} \cdot 12\,x$

e. $\dfrac{5^x}{5^y};\; x < y$ **j.** $(2\,a^y)^3$ **n.** $a^5(4\,a^2b - 5\,a^m)$

o. $-2\,a^2b(a^xb^y - 3\,a^{2x}b^{3y})$

4. Which of the following represents the greatest number?

$(4001)^0$ $(-18)^0$ $(-300)^0$ $\frac{3}{2}$

5. Verify that $a^x \cdot a^y = a^{x+y}$ is an identity when $x,\, y \in W$ and $a \in R$.

6. Verify that $(a^x)^y = a^{xy}$ is an identity when $x,\, y \in W$ and $a \in R$.

7. Verify that $(ab)^x = a^x \cdot b^x$ is an identity when $x \in W$ and $a,\, b \in R$.

8. Verify that $\dfrac{a^x}{a^y} = a^{x-y}$ is an identity when $x,\, y \in W,\; x > y,\; a \neq 0$, and $a \in R$.

Integers as Exponents

Having defined a^x when $x \in W$, we now consider the meaning that should be assigned to a^x when $x \in I$. In this section and in subsequent sections, in which we consider $x \in Q$ and $x \in R$, our principal objective is to state definitions of a^x in such a way that the five laws of exponents remain valid.

With this objective in mind, let us consider the meaning that should be given to the expression 5^{-3}.

If our first law of exponents is to be valid for integral exponents, it must hold for expressions such as $5^{-3} \cdot 5^3$. That is, it should be true that $5^3 \cdot 5^{-3} = 5^{3+(-3)} = 5^0 = 1$. Thus 5^{-3} must be a multiplicative inverse of 5^3. Therefore $5^{-3} = \dfrac{1}{5^3}$. Accordingly, we state the following definition:

$$\text{If } x \in I, x > 0, a \in R, \text{ and } a \neq 0, \text{ then } a^{-x} = \frac{1}{a^x} = \underbrace{\frac{1}{a \cdot a \cdot a \cdots a}}_{x \text{ factors}}. \tag{i}$$

Why is a^x not defined when $a = 0$ and x is a nonpositive integer?
From (i) it can readily be shown that,

$$\text{If } x \in I, x < 0, a \in R, \text{ and } a \neq 0, a^x = \frac{1}{a^{-x}}. \tag{ii}$$

and that,

$$\text{If } x \in I, x > 0, a, b \in R, \text{ and } ab \neq 0, \left(\frac{a}{b}\right)^{-x} = \left(\frac{b}{a}\right)^{x}. \tag{iii}$$

Using (i) and (ii) we can show that all the laws of exponents are valid for integral exponents. Let us first establish that Law 4, "If $a \in R$, $a \neq 0$, then $\dfrac{a^x}{a^y} = a^{x-y}$," is true for integral exponents. To do this we need to consider the following cases when $x, y \in I$:

1. $x \geq 0$ and $y \geq 0$, either when $x \geq y$ or when $x < y$
2. $x \geq 0$ and $y < 0$
3. $x < 0$ and $y \geq 0$
4. $x < 0$ and $y < 0$, either when $x \geq y$ or when $x < y$

Case 1, when $x \geq 0$, $y \geq 0$, and $x \geq y$ is established by Law **4W.a.** and **c.** and when $x \geq 0$, $y \geq 0$, and $x < y$ is established by Law **4W.b.** and (ii).

Case 2, when $x \geq 0$ and $y < 0$, is established as follows:

$$\left. \begin{array}{l} (1) \\ a \in R \\ a \neq 0 \\ x \geq 0 \\ y < 0 \end{array} \right\} \xrightarrow{(2)} \frac{a^x}{a^y} = \frac{a^x}{\dfrac{1}{a^{-y}}} \xrightarrow{(3)} \frac{a^x}{a^y} = \frac{a^x}{\dfrac{1}{a^{-y}} \cdot a^{-y}} \xrightarrow{(4)} \frac{a^x}{a^y} = \frac{a^{x+(-y)}}{1} \xrightarrow{(5)} \frac{a^x}{a^y} = a^{x-y}$$

You may supply the reasons.

Case 3, $x < 0$ and $y \geq 0$, and case 4, $x < 0$ and $y < 0$, can be similarly established.

Accordingly, when the exponents are integers, the fourth law of exponents

is the identity **4I.** $\dfrac{a^x}{a^y} = a^{x-y}$; $x, y \in I, a \in R$

Note that we have denoted this law with the symbol **4I**. The **I** indicates that the exponents are integers. Observe that one statement suffices for Law 4 when the exponents are integers whereas three cases were required for the whole number exponents.

We state the five laws of exponents when the exponents are integers and suggest the general proof of each with a specific example.

If $x, y \in I$, and $a, b \in R$, then each of the following is an identity:

1I. $a^x \cdot a^y = a^{x+y}$

Example. $3^{-5} \cdot 3^{-2} = \dfrac{1}{3^5} \cdot \dfrac{1}{3^2} = \dfrac{1}{3^7} = 3^{-7} = 3^{(-5)+(-2)}$

2I. $(a^x)^y = a^{xy}$

Example. $(3^{-2})^4 = \left(\dfrac{1}{3^2}\right)^4 = \dfrac{1}{3^8} = 3^{-8} = 3^{(-2)4}$

3I. $(ab)^x = a^x b^x$

Example. $(2 \cdot 3)^{-2} = \dfrac{1}{(2 \cdot 3)^2} = \dfrac{1}{2^2 \cdot 3^2} = \dfrac{1}{2^2} \cdot \dfrac{1}{3^2} = 2^{-2} \cdot 3^{-2}$

4I. $\dfrac{a^x}{a^y} = a^{x-y}$

Example. $\dfrac{2^3}{2^{-2}} = \dfrac{2^3}{\dfrac{1}{2^2}} = 2^3 \cdot 2^2 = 2^5 = 2^{3-(-2)}$

5I. $\left(\dfrac{a}{b}\right)^x = \dfrac{a^x}{b^x}$

Example. $\left(\tfrac{3}{5}\right)^{-3} = \dfrac{1}{\left(\tfrac{3}{5}\right)^3} = \dfrac{1}{\dfrac{3^3}{5^3}} = \dfrac{1 \cdot \dfrac{1}{3^3}}{\dfrac{3^3}{5^3} \cdot \dfrac{1}{3^3}} = \dfrac{\dfrac{1}{3^3}}{\dfrac{1}{5^3}} = \dfrac{3^{-3}}{5^{-3}}$

We recall that,

If $a \in R$, then $\sqrt[n]{a^n} = a$ when n is an odd counting number, and $\sqrt[n]{a^n} = |a|$ when n is an even counting number.   (iv)

Using the laws of exponents we may write simpler forms of some algebraic expressions involving integral exponents. Some of the procedures are shown in the following examples.

Examples. Simplify **a.** $(s^{-2}t^3)^{-2}$ **b.** $\left(\dfrac{3\,x^2y^3}{4\,x^{-3}}\right)^{-3}$ **c.** $\dfrac{x^{-1}-y^{-1}}{x^{-2}-y^{-2}}$

Solutions.

a. $(s^{-2}t^3)^{-2} \overset{(1)}{=} (s^{-2})^{-2}(t^3)^{-2} \overset{(2)}{=} s^4t^{-6} \overset{(3)}{=} s^4 \cdot \dfrac{1}{t^6} \overset{(4)}{=} \dfrac{s^4}{t^6}$

Reasons: (1) **3I**, (2) **2I**, (3) $a^{-x}=\dfrac{1}{a^x}$, (4) $a \cdot \dfrac{1}{b}=\dfrac{a}{b}$

b. $\left(\dfrac{3\,x^2y^3}{4\,x^{-3}}\right)^{-3} \overset{(1)}{=} \left(\dfrac{4\,x^{-3}}{3\,x^2y^3}\right)^3 \overset{(2)}{=} \dfrac{(4\,x^{-3})^3}{(3\,x^2y^3)^3} \overset{(3)}{=} \dfrac{4^3(x^{-3})^3}{3^3(x^2)^3(y^3)^3} \overset{(4)}{=}$

$\dfrac{64\,x^{-9}}{27\,x^6y^9} \overset{(5)}{=} \dfrac{64}{27\,x^{15}y^9}.$

Reasons: (1) $\left(\dfrac{a}{b}\right)^{-x}=\left(\dfrac{b}{a}\right)^x$, (2) **5I**, (3) **3I**, (4) **2I**, (5) $a^{-x}=\dfrac{1}{a^x}$

and **1I**

c. $\dfrac{x^{-1}-y^{-1}}{x^{-2}-y^{-2}} \overset{(1)}{=} \dfrac{(x^{-1}-y^{-1})x^2y^2}{(x^{-2}-y^{-2})x^2y^2} \overset{(2)}{=} \dfrac{x^{-1} \cdot x^2y^2 - y^{-1} \cdot x^2y^2}{x^{-2} \cdot x^2y^2 - y^{-2} \cdot x^2y^2} \overset{(3)}{=}$

$\dfrac{xy^2-x^2y}{y^2-x^2} \overset{(4)}{=} \dfrac{xy(y-x)}{(y+x)(y-x)} \overset{(5)}{=} \dfrac{xy}{y+x}.$

Reasons: (1) $\dfrac{a}{b}=\dfrac{ac}{bc}$, (2) Distributive property, (3) Commuta-

tive property of multiplication and **1I**, (4) Distributive property,

(5) $\dfrac{ac}{bc}=\dfrac{a}{b}.$

Another solution of **c.** follows:

$\dfrac{x^{-1}-y^{-1}}{x^{-2}-y^{-2}} \overset{(1)}{=} \dfrac{\dfrac{1}{x}-\dfrac{1}{y}}{\dfrac{1}{x^2}-\dfrac{1}{y^2}} \overset{(2)}{=} \dfrac{\dfrac{y-x}{xy}}{\dfrac{y^2-x^2}{x^2y^2}} \overset{(3)}{=} \dfrac{y-x}{xy} \cdot \dfrac{x^2y^2}{y^2-x^2} \overset{(4)}{=}$

$\dfrac{x^2y^2(y-x)}{xy(y+x)(y-x)} \overset{(5)}{=} \dfrac{xy}{y+x}.$

Reasons: (1) $a^{-x}=\dfrac{1}{a^x}$, (2) $\dfrac{a}{b}+\dfrac{c}{d}=\dfrac{ad+cb}{bd}$, (3) $\dfrac{\dfrac{a}{b}}{\dfrac{c}{d}}=\dfrac{ad}{bc}$, (4)

Commutative property, $a^2-b^2=(a-b)(a+b)$, and $\dfrac{a}{b} \cdot \dfrac{c}{d}=\dfrac{ac}{bd}$,

(5) $\dfrac{ac}{bc}=\dfrac{a}{b}.$

1. Simplify each of the following assuming that each variable in an exponent is an integer.

a. $a^{-2} \cdot a^5$

b. $\dfrac{4\,m^3}{9\,m^{-2}}$

c. $\dfrac{12\,x^{-5}}{4\,x^{-5}}$

d. $\dfrac{14\,x^{-7}}{2\,x^4 y}$

e. $(-\,3\,a^{-5})^2$

f. $(\tfrac{2}{3}\,a^3 b^{-4})^{-2}$

g. $\dfrac{64\,x^{-2}}{8\,x^5 y^6}$

h. $\dfrac{9(x+y)^2}{12(x+y)^5}$

i. $\dfrac{(3\,r^2 s t^3)^{-3}}{5\,r^3 s t}$

j. $(-\,3\,m^3 n^{-4})^0; \quad mn \neq 0$

k. $(14\,a^3 b^{-2})(7\,a^{-5} b^{-1})$

l. $2^a \cdot 2^{3a-5}$

m. $2^x \cdot 4^{x+3}$

n. $\dfrac{(3\,b)^2}{9\,b^a}$

o. $\dfrac{r^{2(x+1)}}{r^2}$

p. $\dfrac{(-\,5\,r^{-2}s)^{-2}}{r}$

q. $\left(\dfrac{9\,x^{-2}y}{12\,x^3 y^{-3}}\right)^{-1}$

r. $\dfrac{2^{-1}+3^{-1}}{6^{-1}}$

s. $\dfrac{x^{-2}-y^{-2}}{x^{-1}+y^{-1}}$

t. $\dfrac{a+a^{-1}}{1+a^{-1}}$

u. $\dfrac{a^{-1}+b^{-1}}{(a^2-b^2)(ab)^{-1}}$

2. Prove that $(a^x)^y = a^{xy}$ when x, $y \,\epsilon\, I$ and $a \,\epsilon\, R$.

3. Prove that $(ab)^x = a^x b^x$ when $x \,\epsilon\, I$ and a, $b \,\epsilon\, R$.

4. Prove that $\left(\dfrac{a}{b}\right)^x = \dfrac{a^x}{b^x}$ when $x \,\epsilon\, I$ and a, $b \,\epsilon\, R$.

Scientific Notation

Any positive number y which has been expressed in the decimal system can be written as n times an integral power of 10 where $1 \leq n < 10$. We call this notation the *scientific notation* because it is widely used in science. We define scientific notation as follows: If a positive number y is written in the form $n \times 10^k$ where k represents an integer and $1 \leq n < 10$, the number is written in scientific notation. For example, 3,800,000 can be written in scientific notation as 3.8×10^6. Also, $0.0416 = 4.16 \times 10^{-2}$ and $5.13 = 5.13 \times 10^0$. The decimal expression of 7.1328×10^{-5} is 0.000071328. Observe that the first zero serves only to emphasize the location of the decimal point. The product of 3.18×10^5 and 4.72×10^{-9} is 15.0096×10^{-4}. In scientific notation this product is 1.50096×10^{-3}.

In order to express a number in scientific notation we need some information about significant digits. We define *significant digits* in the decimal representation of a number as follows:

    Any nonzero digit is significant.
    All zeros appearing between two nonzero digits are significant.

Zeros that are not between two nonzero digits can be classified into three disjoint sets:

Initial zeros—those to the left of the first nonzero digit.
Terminal zeros—those to the right of the last nonzero digit.
Zeros appearing alone.

Initial zeros are never significant.

Terminal zeros appearing on the right of the decimal point are always significant.

Terminal zeros appearing on the left of the decimal point are not significant unless one of them is indicated as significant by a mark such as an *underline* or unless at least one zero is on the right of the decimal point. If any terminal zero is on the right of the decimal point, or if a terminal zero is underlined, it and all terminal zeros to its left are regarded as significant.

Zeros appearing alone—all such zeros to the right of the decimal point are significant.

Zeros appearing alone—if at least one such zero appears on the left of the decimal point, it is not significant if a zero appears to the right of the decimal point.

Zeros appearing alone—if all such zeros appear on the left of the decimal point, they are counted as one significant digit.

These definitions are illustrated by the following examples.

	Number of significant digits	y in scientific notation
3,600,000	Two (3, 6)	3.6×10^6
3,600,000	Four (3, 6, 0, 0)	3.600×10^6
0.075	Two (7, 5)	7.5×10^{-2}
800	One (8)	8×10^2
8.00	Three (8, 0, 0)	8.00×10^0
0.0750	Three (7, 5, 0)	7.50×10^{-2}
0.0006	One (6)	6×10^{-4}
.004150	Four (4, 1, 5, 0)	4.150×10^3
77700	Five (7, 7, 7, 0, 0)	7.7700×10^4
0	One (0)	Inexpressible
200.00	Five (2, 0, 0, 0, 0)	2.0000×10^2
0.00	Two (last two zeros)	Inexpressible
700.01	five (7, 0, 0, 0, 1)	7.0001×10^2
0.6	infinitely many	6.6×10^{-1} (See page 111)
0.200	three (2, 0, 0)	2.00×10^{-1}

Note. To write a negative number using scientific notation, we express its opposite in scientific notation and then multiply the result by negative one.

EXERCISES

1. How many significant digits are there in each of the following numbers? Express each number in scientific notation.

   a. 4,700,000   **g.** 400.00   **m.** 0.00053
   b. 500,000,000   **h.** 64.3000   **n.** 0.0000000852
   c. 17.85   **i.** 0.24785   **o.** 7542.78
   d. 938.4   **j.** 64,321,571   **p.** 9.0
   e. 0.8331   **k.** 0.83   **q.** 93,482,000
   f. 8.7130   **l.** 0.4710   **r.** 888,000

2. Write the decimal which is equal to each of the following:

   a. 3.2×10^{-3} **d.** 3.00×10^5 **g.** 7.000×10^4 **j.** 4.003×10^{-6}
   b. 3.2×10^3 **e.** 7.44×10^6 **h.** 7.00×10^4 **k.** 8.044×10^5
   c. 6.5×10^{-7} **f.** 9.000×10^{-2} **i.** 8.002×10^3 **l.** 3.412×10^{-5}

3. The escape velocity of a rocket from the earth is 25,000 mph. Express this escape velocity in scientific notation.

4. The time required for one addition on a certain computer is 4.4×10^{-4} second. Write 4.4×10^{-4} in decimal form.

5. The radius of a hydrogen atom is 1.74×10^{-10} feet. Express 1.74×10^{-10} in decimal form.

Rational Numbers as Exponents

Having defined a^x when $a \in R$, $x \in I$, and $a \neq 0$, our next step is to inquire if a^x can be defined in a meaningful way when x is a rational number. We would like to define a^x in such a way that our five laws of exponents remain valid for rational exponents.

If $a \in R$, $m \in C$, the radical expression $\sqrt[m]{a}$ denotes the least upper bound of the set S which contains all rational numbers whose mth powers are less than a provided $S \neq \emptyset$. We accept this statement for $m = 1$ with the understanding that $\sqrt[1]{a} = a$. (Although this symbol is convenient at this point, we will not use it hereafter.)

Thus when $S \neq \emptyset$ and $a \in R$, the radical expression $\sqrt[m]{a}$ denotes a unique real number for each $m \in C$ and it can be shown that $(\sqrt[m]{a})^m = a$.

If $a \geq 0$, then $\sqrt[m]{a}$ denotes the unique non-negative real number whose mth power is a. This number is called the *principal* mth *root of a*.

If $a < 0$ and m is odd, then $\sqrt[m]{a}$ denotes the unique real number (negative in this case) whose mth power is a. Again this number is called the principal mth root of a.

Sometimes $\sqrt[m]{a}$ names a rational number such as $\sqrt[3]{-\frac{8}{27}}$, or $-\frac{2}{3}$, sometimes it names an irrational number such as $\sqrt{7}$ and sometimes it is not defined, as when we write $\sqrt[4]{-5}$. Observe that in the last case the set of rational numbers whose fourth powers are less than -5 is empty and therefore its least upper bound is not defined. Thus the symbol $\sqrt[4]{-5}$ is not defined, which is appropriate in view of the fact that there is no real number whose fourth power is -5.

If $a^s \in R$, $s \in I$, and $m \in C$, we define $\sqrt[m]{a^s}$ as the least upper bound of the set S of all rational numbers whose mth powers are less than a^s, provided $S \neq \emptyset$. Thus when $S \neq \emptyset$, the expression $\sqrt[m]{a^s}$ denotes a unique real number for each $(m, s) \in C \times I$ and it can be proved that:

$$\left(\sqrt[m]{a^s}\right)^m = a^s \qquad (i)$$

If $\sqrt[m]{a}$, $\sqrt[m]{a^s} \in R$, $m \in C$, and $s \in I$, we define $a^{\frac{s}{m}}$ as another name for $\sqrt[m]{a^s}$. Thus under the conditions stated,

$$a^{\frac{s}{m}} = \sqrt[m]{a^s} \qquad (ii)$$

If $\sqrt[m]{a}$, $\sqrt[m]{a^s} \in R$, it can be shown that the two numbers represented by $\sqrt[m]{a^s}$ and $(\sqrt[m]{a})^s$ either agree in sign or are both 0. (See Example 1 below.) Now by our laws for integral exponents,

$$[(\sqrt[m]{a})^s]^m = [(\sqrt[m]{a})^m]^s = a^s \qquad (iii)$$

From (i) and (iii), we have $\left(\sqrt[m]{a^s}\right)^m = [(\sqrt[m]{a})^s]^m$. Thus $\sqrt[m]{a^s}$ and $(\sqrt[m]{a})^s$ have equal m^{th} powers. Since they agree in sign or are both 0, we conclude by the generalization of Theorem 14–3 contained in Ex. 4, page 143, that when $\sqrt[m]{a}$, $\sqrt[m]{a^s} \in R$:

$$\sqrt[m]{a^s} = \left(\sqrt[m]{a}\right)^s \qquad (iv)$$

From (ii) and (iv) we have the following theorem:

▷ **Theorem 1–8.** If $\sqrt[m]{a}$, $\sqrt[m]{a^s} \in R$, $m \in C$, and $s \in I$, then $a^{\frac{s}{m}} = \sqrt[m]{a^s} = \left(\sqrt[m]{a}\right)^s$.

Example 1. Show that $\sqrt[m]{a^s}$ and $(\sqrt[m]{a})^s$ either agree in sign or are both zero provided a, $\sqrt[m]{a}$, $\sqrt[m]{a^s} \in R$, $m \in C$, and $s \in I$.

Solution. The following statements are readily verified:
1. If $a > 0$, then $(\sqrt[m]{a})^s$ and $\sqrt[m]{a^s}$ are both positive for $m \in C$ and $s \in I$.
2. If $a = 0$ and $\sqrt[m]{a}$, $\sqrt[m]{a^s} \in R$, then s is positive and it follows that $(\sqrt[m]{a})^s$ and $\sqrt[m]{a^s}$ are both 0.
3. If $a < 0$ and $\sqrt[m]{a}$, $\sqrt[m]{a^s} \in R$, then m is odd. In this case $\sqrt[m]{a^s}$ and $(\sqrt[m]{a})^s$ are both positive when s is even and both negative when s is odd.

Thus in all cases where $\sqrt[m]{a}$, $\sqrt[m]{a^s} \in R$, the radical expressions $\sqrt[m]{a^s}$ and $(\sqrt[m]{a})^s$ are either 0 or they agree in sign.

Example 2. Evaluate each of the following:

    a. $8^{-\frac{1}{3}}$ **b.** $(-32)^{-\frac{4}{5}}$ **c.** $(.0081)^{\frac{3}{4}}$

Solutions.   **a.** $8^{-\frac{1}{3}} = 8^{\frac{-1}{3}} = \sqrt[3]{8^{-1}} = \sqrt[3]{\frac{1}{8}} = \frac{1}{2}$

           b. $(-32)^{-\frac{4}{5}} = (-32)^{\frac{-4}{5}} = \sqrt[5]{(-32)^{-4}} = (\sqrt[5]{-32})^{-4}$

$$= (-2)^{-4} = \frac{1}{(-2)^4} = \frac{1}{16}$$

           c. $(.0081)^{\frac{3}{4}} = \sqrt[4]{(.0081)^3} = (\sqrt[4]{.0081})^3$

$$= [\sqrt[4]{(.3)^4}]^3 = .3^3 = .027$$

Example 3. Find a solution in R for each of the following equations:

    a. $(-27)^x = 9$ **b.** $x^{-\frac{3}{2}} = \frac{27}{8}$

Solution.   **a.** $(-27)^x = 9$

$$[(-3)^3]^x = 9$$
$$(-3)^{3x} = 9$$
$$(-3)^{3x} = (-3)^2$$

This equation will be true if $3x = 2$; that is, if $x = \frac{2}{3}$. By substitution it can be shown that $\frac{2}{3}$ satisfies the given equation.

     b. $x^{-\frac{3}{2}} = \frac{27}{8}$

$$(\sqrt{x})^{-3} = \frac{27}{8}$$
$$\frac{1}{(\sqrt{x})^3} = \frac{27}{8}$$
$$(\sqrt{x})^3 = \frac{8}{27} = (\frac{2}{3})^3$$

Thus $\sqrt{x} = \frac{2}{3}$ and $x = \frac{4}{9}$.

Again we can verify by substitution that this value of x satisfies the given equation.

Example 4. Does $\sqrt[n]{a} \in R$ imply that $\sqrt[n]{a^s} \in R$ when $n \in C$ and $s \in I$?

Solution.   No. $\sqrt[4]{0} \in R$ but $\sqrt[4]{(0)^{-3}}$ does not name a number.

Example 5. By (ii) $(-8)^{\frac{1}{3}} = \sqrt[3]{(-8)} = -2$. Also by (ii) $(-8)^{\frac{2}{6}} = \sqrt[6]{(-8)^2} = \sqrt[6]{64} = 2$. What is wrong?

Solution.   It is true that $(-8)^{\frac{1}{3}} = \sqrt[3]{-8} = -2$ by (ii) because $\sqrt[3]{-8} \in R$. However, $(-8)^{\frac{2}{6}}$ is *not defined* by (ii) because $\sqrt[6]{-8} \notin R$. In order for $(-8)^{\frac{2}{6}}$ to be defined by (ii) we must have *both* $\sqrt[6]{-8}$ and $\sqrt[6]{(-8)^2}$ in R.

Example 6. Which of the following equations is a true statement according to definition (ii)?

    a. $(-8)^{-1} = (-8)^{\frac{-3}{3}}$ **b.** $(-8)^{-1} = (-8)^{\frac{-2}{2}}$

Solutions. **a.** According to (ii) page 399, **a.** is a true statement because both $\sqrt[3]{-8}$ and $\sqrt[3]{(-8)^{-3}}$ are in R. We have $(-8)^{\frac{-3}{3}} = \sqrt[3]{(-8)^{-3}} =$

$$\sqrt[3]{\frac{1}{(-8)^3}} = \frac{1}{-8} = -\frac{1}{8} = (-8)^{-1}.$$

b. We have no information about **b.** from (ii) because $\sqrt{-8} \notin R$. Thus (ii) does not apply.

While $\sqrt[3]{8^2} = 4 = \sqrt[6]{8^4}$, Example **5** above suggests that $\sqrt[m]{a^s}$ and $\sqrt[mq]{a^{sq}}$ do not always name the same number for $m, q \in C$ and $s \in I$. For example, $\sqrt[3]{-27} \neq \sqrt[6]{(-27)^2}$. However, if $a > 0$ we can prove that $\sqrt[m]{a^s} = \sqrt[mq]{a^{sq}}$. We have $(\sqrt[m]{a^s})^{mq} = [(\sqrt[m]{a^s})^m]^q = (a^s)^q = a^{sq}$ and $[\sqrt[mq]{a^{sq}}]^{mq} = a^{sq}$. Since $\sqrt[m]{a^s}$ and $\sqrt[mq]{a^{sq}}$ are both positive, we conclude, by the generalization of Theorem 14–3 noted above, that $\sqrt[m]{a^s} = \sqrt[mq]{a^{sq}}$. Thus we have the following theorem:

▷ **Theorem 2–8.** If a is a positive real number, $m, q \in C$, and $s \in I$, then
$$\sqrt[m]{a^s} = \sqrt[mq]{a^{sq}}.$$

Another important equation involving radicals is suggested by considering an expression such as $\sqrt[5]{\sqrt[4]{a}}$ where $a \geq 0$. We observe that $(\sqrt[5]{\sqrt[4]{a}})^{20} = [(\sqrt[5]{\sqrt[4]{a}})^5]^4 = (\sqrt[4]{a})^4 = a$. Accordingly, $\sqrt[5]{\sqrt[4]{a}}$ must be another name for $\sqrt[20]{a}$. Such an observation leads us to state the following theorem:

▷ **Theorem 3–8.** If $a \in R, a \geq 0, m, n \in C$, then $\sqrt[m]{\sqrt[n]{a}} = \sqrt[mn]{a}$.

Proof of Theorem 3–8: If $a \in R, a \geq 0, m, n \in C$, then $\sqrt[m]{\sqrt[n]{a}} = \sqrt[mn]{a}$.

$$(\sqrt[m]{\sqrt[n]{a}})^{mn} \overset{(1)}{=} [(\sqrt[m]{\sqrt[n]{a}})^m]^n \overset{(2)}{=} (\sqrt[n]{a})^n \overset{(3)}{=} a.$$

Also $(\sqrt[mn]{a})^{mn} \overset{(4)}{=} a.$

$(\sqrt[mn]{a})^{mn} \overset{(5)}{=} (\sqrt[m]{\sqrt[n]{a}})^{mn}$, and $\sqrt[mn]{a}$ and $\sqrt[m]{\sqrt[n]{a}}$ are both positive or both 0. $^{(6)}$

$\therefore \sqrt[m]{\sqrt[n]{a}} \overset{(7)}{=} \sqrt[mn]{a}.$

You may supply the reasons.

Looking back at our definition for $a^{\frac{s}{m}}$, we see that if $a > 0$, then $(\sqrt[m]{a})^s$ and $\sqrt[m]{a^s}$ are names for real numbers. Thus for $a > 0$ and $(m, s) \in C \times I$, we can write:

$$a^{\frac{s}{m}} = \sqrt[m]{a^s} = (\sqrt[m]{a})^s \tag{v}$$

1. Express with rational number exponents:

a. $\sqrt[3]{a^2}$ **b.** $\sqrt{\sqrt{a}}$ **c.** $\sqrt[4]{\sqrt{3}}$ **d.** $(\sqrt[5]{5})^3$ **e.** $\sqrt[3]{\sqrt[3]{a}}$ **f.** $\sqrt[4]{5}$

2. Replace each question mark with a numeral to form a true statement.

a. $a^{\frac{3}{4}} = \sqrt[?]{a^?}$; $a \geq 0$ **d.** $\sqrt[4]{a^5} = a^?$; $a \geq 0$

b. $\sqrt[6]{a^4} = a^?$; $a \geq 0$ **e.** $a^{\frac{1}{15}} = \sqrt[?]{\sqrt[3]{a}}$

c. $a^{\frac{10}{6}} = \sqrt[?]{a^5}$; $a > 0$ **f.** $\dfrac{1}{(\sqrt[3]{-8})^2} = (-2)^?$

3. Which of the following expressions do not represent real numbers?

a. $\sqrt[3]{0^2}$ **c.** $\sqrt[4]{(-3)^2}$ **e.** $0^{\frac{3}{4}}$ **g.** $4^{-\frac{1}{2}}$ **i.** $(-4)^{\frac{2}{3}}$

b. $\sqrt[3]{0^{-2}}$ **d.** $\sqrt[4]{(-3)^3}$ **f.** $0^{-\frac{5}{6}}$ **h.** $(-4)^{\frac{3}{2}}$ **j.** $(-4)^{-\frac{2}{3}}$

4. Which of the following are irrational numbers?

a. $16^{\frac{1}{2}}$ **c.** $0.4^{\frac{1}{2}}$ **e.** $8^{\frac{2}{3}}$ **g.** $9^{\frac{5}{2}}$ **i.** $(-64)^{-\frac{3}{2}}$

b. $5^{\frac{1}{3}}$ **d.** $\sqrt[3]{6^2}$ **f.** $.0027^{\frac{1}{3}}$ **h.** $(-6)^{\frac{5}{2}}$ **j.** $\sqrt[3]{-6^2}$

5. Write the common name for each of the following:

a. $125^{\frac{1}{3}}$ **d.** $\sqrt{\sqrt{625}}$ **g.** $(-\frac{1}{8})^{-\frac{2}{3}}$ **j.** $9^{-\frac{5}{2}}$

b. $16^{-\frac{1}{2}}$ **e.** $4^{-\frac{5}{2}}$ **h.** $\sqrt{\sqrt[3]{64}}$ **k.** $1.21^{\frac{3}{2}}$

c. $(\sqrt[3]{27})^2$ **f.** $\sqrt[4]{81^{-3}}$ **i.** $\sqrt[5]{(-32)^3}$ **l.** $81^{-\frac{3}{4}}$

6. Find the value of x which satisfies each of the following equations.

a. $2^x = 8$ **d.** $2^x = \frac{1}{8}$ **g.** $(\frac{1}{2})^x = 8$

b. $(-32)^x = 1024$ **e.** $(-27)^x = \frac{1}{729}$ **h.** $(-125)^x = 15625$

c. $(\frac{4}{3})^x = \frac{27}{64}$ **f.** $(\frac{3}{4})^x = \frac{256}{81}$ **i.** $(-\frac{7}{10})^x = \frac{10000}{2401}$

7. Find the values of x for which the following equations are true.

a. $x^{\frac{2}{3}} = 16$ **d.** $x^{-\frac{3}{4}} = \frac{1}{27}$ **g.** $(x)^{\frac{5}{3}} = 0.00032$

b. $x^{-\frac{2}{5}} = \frac{1}{4}$ **e.** $\sqrt{x^3} = \frac{27}{512}$ **h.** $\sqrt[3]{x} = 2\sqrt{2}$

c. $\sqrt[3]{x^4} = 0.0625$ **f.** $x^{-\frac{1}{2}} = \frac{4}{5}$ **i.** $x^{\frac{5}{2}} = 25\sqrt{5}$

8. Is the following converse of Theorem 2–8, "If $\sqrt[m]{a^s} = \sqrt[mq]{a^{sq}}$, then a is a positive real number, m, $q \in C$, and $s \in I$," true? Give an example.

9. Find the solution set for each of the following equations.

a. $\sqrt[3]{(x+1)^2} = 27$ **d.** $\sqrt{(a+4)^3} = 3^3$

b. $\sqrt{\sqrt{x+2}} = 25$ **e.** $\sqrt{(2\,r^2 - 8)^3} = 512$

c. $(\sqrt{4\,x + 9})^3 = 125$ **f.** $\sqrt[3]{\sqrt[4]{x}} = 2$

More About Rational Numbers as Exponents

With Theorem 1–8 established, our five laws of exponents are valid for those rational number exponents that meet the conditions of the theorem. Thus: If $a \in R$ and each of the numbers x and y represents a rational number in the form $\dfrac{s}{m}$ where $m \in C$ and $s \in I$, then each of the following equations is an identity:

1Q. $a^x \cdot a^y = a^{x+y}$

2Q. $(a^x)^y = a^{xy}$

3Q. $(ab)^x = a^x b^x$

4Q. $\dfrac{a^x}{a^y} = a^{x-y}$

5Q. $\left(\dfrac{a}{b}\right)^x = \dfrac{a^x}{b^x}$

Since every rational number can be named by writing a fraction of the form $\dfrac{s}{m}$ where $m \in C$ and $s \in I$, we call these the *laws for rational number exponents*. We will not prove them for $a \leq 0$. Proofs of statements **1Q** and **2Q** for the cases in which $a > 0$ are shown below. Proofs of **3Q**, **4Q**, and **5Q** for $a > 0$ are left as exercises.

Proof that **1Q**, when $a > 0$, $a^x \cdot a^y = a^{x+y}$, is an identity:

Let $x = \dfrac{s}{m}$ and $y = \dfrac{n}{v}$ where $m, v \in C$ and $s, n \in I$. Then $a^x \cdot a^y$ or $a^{\frac{s}{m}} \cdot a^{\frac{n}{v}}$ is

defined for $m, v \in C$ and $s, n \in I$. Also $x + y = \dfrac{s}{m} + \dfrac{n}{v} = \dfrac{sv + mn}{mv}$ where m,

$v, mv \in C$ and $sv + mn \in I$. Therefore $a^{x+y} = a^{\frac{sv+mn}{mv}}$ is also defined for $m, v \in C$ and $s, n \in I$. For any such values of m, v, s, n, each of the following equations is a true statement.

$$\overset{(1)}{a^x \cdot a^y} = \overset{(2)}{a^{\frac{s}{m}} \cdot a^{\frac{n}{v}}} = \overset{(3)}{\sqrt[m]{a^s} \cdot \sqrt[v]{a^n}} = \overset{(4)}{\sqrt[mv]{a^{sv}} \cdot \sqrt[mv]{a^{mn}}} = \overset{(5)}{\sqrt[mv]{a^{sv} \cdot a^{mn}}} =$$

$$\overset{(6)}{\sqrt[mv]{a^{sv+mn}}} = \overset{(7)}{a^{\frac{sv+mn}{mv}}} = \overset{(8)}{a^{\frac{s}{m}+\frac{n}{v}}} = a^{x+y}.$$

Reasons: (1) Substitution property of equality, (2) Theorem 1–8, (3) Theorem 2–8, (4) Theorem 30–3, (5) Law **1I**, (6) Theorem 1–8, (7) Theorem 20–2, (8) Substitution property of equality.

If in **1Q** we let $y = -x$, we have $a^x \cdot a^{-x} = a^{x+(-x)} = a^0 = 1$. Accordingly, the following statement is true. If $a > 0$ and $x = \dfrac{s}{m}$ where $m \in C$ and $s \in I$, then $a^x \cdot a^{-x} = 1$.

Note that if $a \not> 0$, then a^x may not be defined. Thus $(-4)^{\frac{5}{2}}$ and $0^{\frac{-3}{4}}$ are not defined, but $(-4)^{\frac{5}{3}}$ and $0^{\frac{3}{4}}$ are defined.

Proof that **2Q**, when $a > 0$, $(a^x)^y = a^{xy}$, is an identity:

Let $x = \dfrac{s}{m}$ and $y = \dfrac{n}{v}$ for $m, v \in C$ and $s, n \in I$. Thus $(a^x)^y$ or $(a^{\frac{s}{m}})^{\frac{n}{v}}$ is defined

for $m, v \in C$ and $s, n \in I$. Also $xy = \dfrac{s}{m} \cdot \dfrac{n}{v} = \dfrac{sn}{mv}$ with $mv \in C$ and $sn \in I$.

Therefore $(a^x)^y = a^{\frac{sn}{mv}}$ is also defined for $m, v \in C$ and $s, n \in I$. For any such values of m, v, s, n, each of the following equations is a true statement.

$$\underset{(1)}{(a^x)^y} = \underset{(2)}{(a^m)^{\frac{s}{v}}} = \underset{(3)}{(\sqrt[m]{a^s})^{\frac{n}{v}}} = \underset{(4)}{(\sqrt[v]{(\sqrt[m]{a^s})})^n} = \underset{(5)}{(\sqrt[vm]{a^s})^n} = \underset{(6)}{\sqrt[vm]{(a^s)^n}}$$

$$= \underset{(7)}{\sqrt[vm]{a^{sn}}} = \underset{(8)}{a^{\frac{sn}{mv}}} = \underset{(9)}{a^{\frac{s}{m} \cdot \frac{n}{v}}} = a^{xy}.$$

Reasons: (1) Substitution, (2) Theorem 1–8, (3) Theorem 1–8, Theorem 3–8, (5) Theorem 1–8, (6) Law **2I**, (7) Theorem 1–8, (8) Theorem 6–2, (9) Substitution property of equality.

Example 1. Express $27^{\frac{2}{3}}$ in the form of a rational number.

Solution. $27^{\frac{2}{3}} = (3^3)^{\frac{2}{3}} = 3^2 = 9$

Example 2. Express each of the following in simplest radical form.

a. $81^{-\frac{3}{4}} \cdot 3^{\frac{1}{2}}$

b. $x^{\frac{2}{5}} \cdot x^{\frac{3}{4}}; \quad x > 0$

c. $\sqrt[4]{a^2 b^6}; \quad a, b \in R; \quad a > 0; \quad b > 0$

Solutions. a. $81^{-\frac{3}{4}} \cdot 3^{\frac{1}{2}} = (3^4)^{-\frac{3}{4}} \cdot (3)^{\frac{1}{2}} = 3^{-3} \cdot 3^{\frac{1}{2}} = \dfrac{3^{\frac{1}{2}}}{3^3} = \dfrac{\sqrt{3}}{27}$

b. $x^{\frac{2}{5}} \cdot x^{\frac{3}{4}} = x^{\frac{2}{5} + \frac{3}{4}} = x^{\frac{23}{20}} = x^{1 + \frac{3}{20}} = x \cdot x^{\frac{3}{20}} = x^{\frac{20}{2}}\sqrt[20]{x^3}$

c. $\sqrt[4]{a^2 b^6} = (a^2 b^6)^{\frac{1}{4}} = a^{\frac{1}{2}} b^{\frac{3}{2}} = b a^{\frac{1}{2}} b^{\frac{1}{2}} = b(ab)^{\frac{1}{2}} = b\sqrt{ab}$

Example 3. Express each of the following as identically equal expressions in simplest form with no negative exponents.

a. $(a^{-6})^{-\frac{5}{3}}$

b. $\left(\dfrac{8 a^4}{27 a^{-2} y^3}\right)^{\frac{1}{3}}$

Solutions. a. $(a^{-6})^{-\frac{5}{3}} = a^{10}$

b. $\left(\dfrac{8 a^4}{27 a^{-2} y^3}\right)^{\frac{1}{3}} = \left(\dfrac{8 a^6}{27 y^3}\right)^{\frac{1}{3}}$

$$= \dfrac{(8 a^6)^{\frac{1}{3}}}{(27 y^3)^{\frac{1}{3}}}$$

$$= \dfrac{2 a^2}{3 y}$$

Example 4. Solve: $x^{\frac{4}{5}} - 9\,x^{\frac{2}{5}} + 18 = 0$

Solution. PART 1.
$$x^{\frac{4}{5}} - 9\,x^{\frac{2}{5}} + 18 = 0$$
$$(x^{\frac{2}{5}} - 3)(x^{\frac{2}{5}} - 6) = 0$$
$$x^{\frac{2}{5}} - 3 = 0 \ \lor \ x^{\frac{2}{5}} - 6 = 0$$
$$x^{\frac{2}{5}} = 3 \ \lor \ x^{\frac{2}{5}} = 6$$
$$x = 3^{\frac{5}{2}} \ \lor \ x = 6^{\frac{5}{2}}$$
$$x = 9\sqrt{3} \ \lor \ x = 36\sqrt{6}$$

PART 2. If $x = 9\sqrt{3}$,
$$x^{\frac{4}{5}} - 9\,x^{\frac{2}{5}} + 18 = 0$$
$$(9\sqrt{3})^{\frac{4}{5}} - 9(9\sqrt{3})^{\frac{2}{5}} + 18 \overset{?}{=} 0$$
$$(3^{\frac{5}{2}})^{\frac{4}{5}} - 9(3^{\frac{5}{2}})^{\frac{2}{5}} + 18 \overset{?}{=} 0$$
$$3^2 - 9(3) + 18 \overset{?}{=} 0$$
$$9 - 27 + 18 \overset{?}{=} 0$$
$$0 \overset{\checkmark}{=} 0$$

If $x = 36\sqrt{6}$,
$$x^{\frac{4}{5}} - 9\,x^{\frac{2}{5}} + 18 = 0$$
$$(36\sqrt{6})^{\frac{4}{5}} - 9(36\sqrt{6})^{\frac{2}{5}} + 18 \overset{?}{=} 0$$
$$(6^{\frac{5}{2}})^{\frac{4}{5}} - 9(6^{\frac{5}{2}})^{\frac{2}{5}} + 18 \overset{?}{=} 0$$
$$6^2 - 9(6) + 18 \overset{?}{=} 0$$
$$36 - 54 + 18 \overset{?}{=} 0$$
$$0 \overset{\checkmark}{=} 0$$

The solution set is $\{9\sqrt{3},\ 36\sqrt{6}\}$.

Ⓐ EXERCISES

1. Express each of the following in the form of a rational number.

   a. $(8^{\frac{2}{3}})^3$

   b. $(-32)^{\frac{4}{5}}$

   c. $[(-3)^3]^{-\frac{2}{3}}$

   d. $(4^3)^{-\frac{2}{3}}$

   e. $\sqrt[3]{8^4}$

   f. $\sqrt[5]{(-32)^3}$

   g. $(\sqrt[6]{3})^{12}$

   h. $(\sqrt[3]{\frac{1}{3}})^{-9}$

   i. $[(-3)^5]^{-\frac{1}{5}}$

   j. $(64)^{-\frac{3}{2}}$

   k. $(625^{\frac{1}{2}})^{\frac{1}{2}}$

   l. $[(-6)^3]^{\frac{2}{3}}$

2. Write a simpler expression identically equal to each of the following.

   a. $a^{\frac{2}{3}} \cdot a^{\frac{1}{3}}$

   b. $m^{\frac{1}{2}} \cdot m^{\frac{1}{3}};\ m \geq 0$

   c. $a \cdot a^{\frac{3}{2}};\ a \geq 0$

   d. $(a^{-3})^{\frac{1}{2}};\ a > 0$

   e. $(a^2 b^3)^{-\frac{1}{2}};\ a \neq 0 \text{ and } b > 0$

   f. $(a^{\frac{1}{3}})^{-\frac{3}{4}};\ a > 0$

   g. $(8\,a)^{\frac{1}{2}} \cdot (8\,b^3)^{\frac{1}{3}};\ a > 0$

   h. $(16\,x^{\frac{1}{2}})^{\frac{1}{2}} \cdot (8\,x^3)^{\frac{4}{3}};\ x \geq 0$

   i. $\sqrt[3]{a^2} \cdot \sqrt[3]{a^3} \cdot \sqrt[3]{a};\ a \geq 0$

   j. $\left(\dfrac{24\,a^2 b^3 c^5}{3\,a^3 bc}\right)^{\frac{1}{3}}$

   k. $\left(\dfrac{216\,a^3 b^5 c}{125\,b^2 c}\right)^{\frac{2}{3}}$

   l. $\dfrac{(625\,r^8 y^{\frac{1}{3}})^{\frac{1}{4}}}{(25\,r^2 y^{\frac{1}{2}})^{\frac{1}{2}}};\ y > 0$

3. Simplify:

a. $10^{3.2} \times 10^{2.1}$

b. $\dfrac{10^{0.453}}{10^{0.156}}$

c. $\dfrac{10^{2.35} \times 10^{4.13}}{10^{3.24}}$

d. $(10^{3.28})^2$

e. $\dfrac{3^{2.3} \times 3^{4.2}}{3^{1.2} \times 3^{2.5}}$

f. $(7^{4.38})^{0.5}$

4. Simplify, when the domain of each variable is the set of positive real numbers.

a. $\sqrt[3]{-0.125\, x^6 y}$

b. $\sqrt[4]{0.0081\, r^2 s^4}$

c. $\sqrt[3]{-8\, a^3 b^2} \cdot \sqrt[6]{729\, a^6 b^2}$

d. $\dfrac{\sqrt{144\, a^2 b^6}}{\sqrt[4]{144\, a^2 b^6}}$

B EXERCISES

5. Simplify, when the domain of each variable is the set of positive real numbers.

a. $(x^{-\frac{1}{2}} - y^{-\frac{1}{2}})^2$

b. $(a^{\frac{2}{3}} - b^{\frac{1}{3}})(a^{\frac{2}{3}} + b^{\frac{1}{3}})$

c. $\dfrac{t^{\frac{2}{3}} - s^{\frac{2}{3}}}{t^{\frac{1}{3}} + s^{\frac{1}{3}}}$

d. $\left(\dfrac{r^{x+1}}{r^x}\right)^x$

e. $(a^{\frac{1}{2}} + r^{\frac{1}{3}})(a^{\frac{1}{2}} + s^{\frac{2}{3}})$

f. $\left(\dfrac{1}{a^{x-1}} \cdot \dfrac{1}{a^{x-1}}\right)^{\frac{1}{x}}$

g. $\left(\dfrac{1}{a^{x-1}} + \dfrac{1}{a^{x-1}}\right)^2$

h. $\dfrac{3\sqrt{2} + \sqrt{a}}{\sqrt{2} + \sqrt{a}}$

6. Given the formula $pv^{\frac{2}{3}} = 32{,}400$, find the value of p when $v = 27$.

7. The graph of the equation $x^{\frac{2}{3}} + y^{\frac{2}{3}} = a^{\frac{2}{3}}$ (called a hypocycloid) is shown at the right. If $a = 64$, find the value of y when $x = 8$.

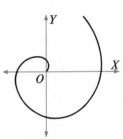

8. The graph of the equation $x^{\frac{1}{2}} + y^{\frac{1}{2}} = a^{\frac{1}{2}}$ is a parabola. If $a = 16$, what is the y-coordinate of the point in the graph having the x-coordinate 4?

9. The radius of curvature of a spiral of Archimedes is given by the formula $r = \dfrac{(p^2 + a^2)^{\frac{3}{2}}}{p^2 + 2 a^2}$. What is the value of r when $p = 4$ and $a = 3$?

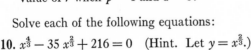

Solve each of the following equations:

10. $x^{\frac{4}{3}} - 35\, x^{\frac{2}{3}} + 216 = 0$ (Hint. Let $y = x^{\frac{2}{3}}$.)

11. $x^{\frac{2}{3}} + 27\, x^{-\frac{2}{3}} = 28$

12. $-y^{-\frac{4}{5}} + y^{-\frac{2}{5}} + \frac{5}{16} = 0$

13. Prove law **3Q** for the case in which $a > 0$ and $b > 0$.

14. Prove law **4Q** for the case in which $a > 0$.

15. Prove law **5Q** or the case in which $a > 0$ and $b > 0$.

Exponential Functions

x	2^x
0.00	1.000
0.01	1.007
0.02	1.014
0.03	1.021
0.04	1.028
0.05	1.035
0.10	1.072
0.15	1.110
0.20	1.149
0.25	1.189
0.30	1.231
0.35	1.275
0.40	1.320
0.45	1.366
0.50	1.414
0.55	1.464
0.60	1.516
0.65	1.569
0.70	1.625
0.75	1.682
0.80	1.741
0.85	1.803
0.90	1.866
0.95	1.932
1.00	2.000

If a is a constant positive real number not equal to one, we call the function $\{(x, y) \mid y = a^x\}$ an *exponential function* and denote it by the symbol E_a when a is the base of the exponential expression a^x. In this section we will consider the graphs of some exponential functions, each having the domain Q.

Consider the function $\{(x, y) \mid y = 2^x; \ x \in Q\}$. The table at the right shows some of the values of 2^x when $x \in Q$. By locating points corresponding to the ordered pairs $(x, 2^x)$ shown in this table, we obtain a few of the points of the graph of $y = 2^x$ when $x \in Q$. For example, from the table we see that when $x = .10$, $2^{.10} \approx 1.07$. Thus the point whose coordinates are approximately $(.10, 1.07)$ is a point of the graph. Similarly, when $x = .20$, $2^{.20} \approx 1.15$. Thus with the understanding that the numerical value of the y-coordinate is an approximation, we say that the point whose coordinates are $(.20, 1.15)$ is a point of the graph.

We can easily find more points of the graph by extending the table through the use of the first law of exponents—$a^x \cdot a^y = a^{x+y}$. For example, $2^{1.8} = 2 \times 2^{0.8} \approx 2 \times 1.741 \approx 3.48$. Thus the point whose coordinates are $(1.8, 3.48)$ is a point of the graph. Also $2^{3.7} = 2^3 \times 2^{0.7} \approx 8 \times 1.625 \approx 13.00$. Thus the point whose coordinates are $(3.7, 13.00)$ is a point of the graph. Similarly, $2^{-0.1} = 2^{-1} \times 2^{0.9} \approx \frac{1}{2} \times 1.866 \approx 0.93$. Thus the point whose coordinates are $(-0.1, 0.93)$ is a point of the graph.

Since infinitely many of these points can be determined, it is impossible to graph each individually. Instead, we locate the points corresponding to several of these ordered pairs, then draw a smooth curve joining them. We must recognize, however that although all points of the graph of $y = 2^x$ (when $x \in Q$) are in this curve, some points of the curve are not points of the graph. Some of these points are points in the graph of $y = 2^x$ where x is in $R \frown Q$. Sometimes, to indicate that we are interested in only those points $P(x, 2^x)$ for which x is in Q, we make the graph a gray line rather than a solid black line.

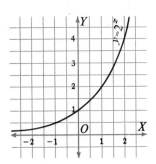

The graph shows us that the function defined by $y = 2^x$; $x \in Q$ is an increasing function. Indeed, we can prove that $a^r < a^s \longleftrightarrow r < s$ provided r and s are rational numbers and $a > 1$. We shall prove this in the following section.

If $0 < a < 1$, we find that the function defined by $y = a^x$ when $x \in Q$ is a decreasing function. Let us examine the function defined by $y = (\frac{1}{2})^x$ when $x \in Q$. We can use the table on page 407 and the first law of exponents to find ordered pairs which satisfy the equation $y = (\frac{1}{2})^x$. For example, $(\frac{1}{2})^{-2.3} = 2^{2.3} = 2^2 \times 2^{.3} \approx 4 \times 1.231 \approx 4.92$. Thus the point whose coordinates are $(-2.3, 4.92)$ is a point of the graph. Similarly,

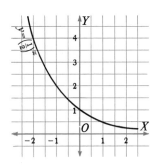

$$(\tfrac{1}{2})^{1.4} = 2^{-1.4} = 2^{-1} \times 2^{-0.4} \approx \frac{1}{2} \times \frac{1}{1.32} = 0.38.$$

Thus the point whose coordinates are $(1.4, .38)$ is a point of the graph. The graph of $y = (\frac{1}{2})^x$ is shown at the right.

Example 1. Draw the graph of the exponential function defined by

$$y = 2^x; \quad x \in W.$$

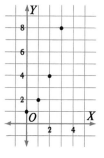

Solution. If $x = 0$, $y = 2^0 = 1$; if $x = 1$, $y = 2^1 = 2$; if $x = 2$, $y = 4$; and so on. Thus $E_2 = \{(x, y) \mid y = 2^x; \ x \in W\} = \{(0, 1), (1, 2), (2, 4), (3, 8), \cdots\}$. The graph is shown at the right.

Example 2. Draw the graph of the exponential function defined by

$$y = (\tfrac{3}{2})^x; \quad x \in I.$$

Solution. If $x = -3$, $y = (\frac{3}{2})^{-3} = (\frac{2}{3})^3 = \frac{8}{27}$; if $x = -2$, $y = \frac{4}{9}$; and so on. Thus $E_{\frac{3}{2}} = \{(x, y) \mid y = (\frac{3}{2})^x; \ x \in I\} = \{\cdots (-3, \frac{8}{27}), (-2, \frac{4}{9}), (-1, \frac{2}{3}), (0, 1), (1, \frac{3}{2}), (2, \frac{9}{4}), (3, \frac{27}{8}), \cdots\}$. The graph is shown at the right.

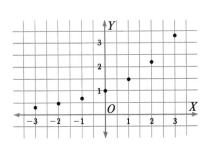

1. Using the table of values of 2^x when $x \in Q$, find approximate decimal values of each of the following:

   a. $2^{0.55}$ **c.** $2^{0.45}$ **e.** $2^{0.95}$ **g.** 2^0

   b. $2^{0.7}$ **d.** $2^{0.01}$ **f.** $2^{0.35}$ **h.** $2^{1.0}$

2. Using computation and the table of values of 2^x when $x \in Q$, find an approximate decimal equivalent of each of the following:

   a. $2^{1.5}$ **d.** $2^{-1.5}$ **g.** $2^{1.25}$ **j.** $2^{3.3}$

   b. $2^{2.5}$ **e.** $2^{-2.5}$ **h.** $2^{-3.25}$ **k.** $2^{-3.6}$

   c. $2^{3.5}$ **f.** $2^{-3.5}$ **i.** $2^{-0.75}$ **l.** $2^{-0.04}$

3. Evaluate each of the following:

   a. $4^{2.3}$ **c.** $(\frac{1}{2})^{1.5}$ **e.** $(\frac{1}{16})^{-3.3}$ **g.** $0.25^{1.5}$

   b. $8^{-1.6}$ **d.** $0.125^{2.1}$ **f.** $16^{4.5}$ **h.** $64^{-1.2}$

4. Use the table of values of 2^x when $x \in Q$ to find approximate decimal values of each of the following:

   a. $2\sqrt{2}$ **c.** $\sqrt{\sqrt{2}}$ **e.** $\sqrt{\sqrt{8}}$ **g.** $(\sqrt{2})^3$

   b. $4\sqrt{2}$ **d.** $2\sqrt{\sqrt{2}}$ **f.** $8\sqrt{\sqrt{\frac{1}{8}}}$ **h.** $(\sqrt[4]{8})^3$

5. Which of the following sentences can be used to define exponential functions as explained in this section?

   a. $y = 3^x$; $x \in W$ **c.** $y = (\frac{1}{2})^x$; $x \in W$

   b. $y = 1^x$; $x \in W$ **d.** $y = (-2)^x$; $x \in W$

6. Draw the graph of the function defined by $y = 3^x$ when $x \in \{0, 1, 2, 3, 4\}$.

7. Draw the graph of the function defined by $y = 4^x$ when $x \in \{0, 1, 2, 3, 4\}$.

8. Draw the graph of the function defined by $y = (\frac{2}{3})^x$ when $x \in \{0, 1, 2, 3, 4\}$.

9. Draw the graph of the truth set of each of the following equations. In each case $x \in Q$.

   a. $y = (\frac{1}{2})^{3x}$ **b.** $y = 4^x$ **c.** $y = (\frac{1}{4})^x$ **d.** $y = 8^x$

10. Draw the graph of each of the following functions.

   a. $\{(x, y) \mid y = 2^x; x \in I\}$ **b.** $\{(x, y) \mid y = (\frac{1}{2})^x; x \in I\}$

More about the Exponential Function

In this section we shall prove that the exponential function $\{(x, y) \mid y = a^x;$ $x \in Q\}$ is an increasing function when $a \in R$ and $a > 1$ and a decreasing function when $a \in R$ and $0 < a < 1$. Before we prove this theorem, we prove another theorem which is needed.

Using the identity $a^n - 1 = (a - 1)(a^{n-1} + a^{n-2} + \cdots + a + 1)$, if a is a positive real number and $n \in C$, we can prove:

$$1.\ 0 < a < 1 \longrightarrow 0 < a^n < 1$$
$$2.\ a = 1 \longrightarrow a^n = 1$$
$$3.\ a > 1 \longrightarrow a^n > 1$$

These proofs follow easily from the fact that the factor $(a^{n-1} + a^{n-2} + \cdots + a + 1)$ is positive for $a > 0$. Thus if $a \in R$, $0 < a < 1$, and $n \in C$ then $a^n - 1 < 0$ because it is the product of the negative factor $a - 1$ and the positive factor $(a^{n-1} + a^{n-2} + \cdots + a + 1)$. Accordingly, $0 < a^n < 1$. The proofs of statements 2 and 3 are based upon similar considerations.

If $a > 0$, the trichotomy property tells us that exactly one of the following statements is true: $0 < a < 1$, $a = 1$, $a > 1$. If $a > 0$, $a^n > 0$, and this fact combined with the trichotomy property tells us that exactly one of the following is true: $0 < a^n < 1$, $a^n = 1$, $a^n > 1$. With these facts in mind, let us consider the converses of statements 1, 2, and 3 above. Let us consider the converse of statement 1: If $0 < a^n < 1$, then $0 < a < 1$. From the hypothesis of this statement it follows that $a^n \neq 1$ *and* $a^n \not> 1$. According to the contrapositive of statement 2, $a^n \neq 1 \longrightarrow a \neq 1$. By the contrapositive of statement 3, $a^n \not> 1 \longrightarrow a \not> 1$. The conjunction of the statements $a > 0$, $a \neq 1$, and $a \not> 1$ implies that $0 < a < 1$. The converses of statements 2 and 3 can be established in a similar manner. Thus we have:

> **Theorem 4–8.** If $a \in R$, $a > 0$ and $n \in C$, then
> (1) $0 < a < 1 \longleftrightarrow 0 < a^n < 1$
> (2) $a = 1 \longleftrightarrow a^n = 1$
> (3) $a > 1 \longleftrightarrow a^n > 1$

If $m, n \in C$ and $a \in R$, we have: $a > 1 \longleftrightarrow a^m > 1 \longleftrightarrow (a^{\frac{m}{n}})^n > 1 \longleftrightarrow a^{\frac{m}{n}} > 1$. Similarly, we have: $0 < a < 1 \longleftrightarrow 0 < a^m < 1 \longleftrightarrow 0 < (a^{\frac{m}{n}})^n < 1 \longleftrightarrow 0 < a^{\frac{m}{n}} < 1$. It is also true that $a = 1 \longleftrightarrow a^{\frac{m}{n}} = 1$. Thus we have:

Corollary 1 to Theorem 4–8. If $a > 0$, $x \in Q$, and $x > 0$, then
1. $a > 1 \longleftrightarrow a^x > 1$
2. $a = 1 \longleftrightarrow a^x = 1$
3. $0 < a < 1 \longleftrightarrow 0 < a^x < 1$

Observe that Corollary 1 tells us that $(a > 0 \wedge x \in Q \wedge x > 0) \longrightarrow a^x > 0$. Since $a^x \cdot a^{-x} = 1$ when $x \in Q$, it follows that a^x and a^{-x} have the same sign. Thus we have:

Corollary 2 to Theorem 4–8. If $a > 0$ and $x \in Q$, then $a^x > 0$.

We are now in a position to prove the following theorem:

⊳ **Theorem 5–8.** If $a \in R$, $x \in Q$, $E_a = \{(x, y) \mid y = a^x\}$, and

    1. If $a > 1$, then E_a is an increasing function.
    2. If $0 < a < 1$, then E_a is a decreasing function.

Note. Theorem 5–8 is actually two theorems. Each theorem has the original hypothesis and one of the numbered conclusions.

Proof of Theorem 5–8. If $a \in R$, $x \in Q$, $E_a = \{(x, y) \mid y = a^x\}$, and
    1. If $a > 1$, then E_a is an increasing function.
    2. If $0 < a < 1$, then E_a is a decreasing function.

Before we begin the proof of Theorem 5–8(1), we should recall that according to our definition of an increasing function, we must prove that $x_1 < x_2 \longrightarrow e_a(x_1) < e_a(x_2)$ when $x_1, x_2 \in Q$.

1. $x_1 < x_2$; $x_1, x_2 \in Q$	1. Given
2. $0 < x_2 - x_1$	2. Theorem 5–3
3. $x_2 - x_1 \in Q$	3. Q is closed under subtraction
4. $x_2 - x_1$ is a positive rational number	4. Steps 2 and 3; a conjunctive statement is true if and only if each of its clauses is true.
5. $a > 1 \wedge 1 > 0$	5. Given; Theorem 8–3, Corollary 2.
6. $a^{x_2 - x_1} > 1$	6. Corollary 2 to Theorem 4–8.
7. $a > 0$	7. Transitive property of inequality
8. $a^{x_1} > 0$	8. Corollary 2 to Theorem 4–8.
9. $a^{x_1} \cdot a^{x_2 - x_1} > a^{x_1}$	9. Multiplication property of inequality
10. $a^{x_2} > a^{x_1}$	10. Law of exponents 1Q
11. $e_a(x_2) > e_a(x_1)$	11. Definition of function notation and substitution property of equality.
12. $\therefore E_a$ is an increasing function	12. Definition of an increasing function

A similar proof can be given for Theorem 5–8(2).

Since E_a is an *increasing function* for $a > 1$, we know that each member of the range of E_a corresponds to exactly one rational number in the domain of E_a. Accordingly we know by Theorem 3-6 that the function defined by $y = a^x$ when $x \in Q$, $a \in R$, and $a > 1$ has an *inverse function* which we can denote by the symbol E_a^{-1}.

Also, since E_a is a *decreasing function* for $0 < a < 1$, we know that each member of the range of E_a corresponds to exactly one rational number in the domain of E_a. Again we can assert by Theorem 3-6 that the function defined by $y = a^x$ when $x \in Q$, $a \in R$, and $0 < a < 1$ has an inverse function E_a^{-1}.

Thus if $a > 0$ and $a \neq 1$, the exponential function $E_a = \{(x, y) \mid y = a^x;$ $x \in Q\}$ has an inverse function $E_a{}^{-1}$. The domain of $E_a{}^{-1}$ consists of those real numbers which are in the range of E_a. Therefore the domain of $E_a{}^{-1}$ includes only those real numbers that are values of a^x when x is a rational number. The range of $E_a{}^{-1}$ is, of course, Q which is the domain of E_a. If we let E be the function defined by $y = 2^x$, then the function which is the inverse of E is $x = 2^y$. The graphs of $y = 2^x$ and $x = 2^y$ are shown at the right. Notice that these two graphs are symmetric with respect to the graph of $\{(x, y) \mid y = x\}$, as is always the case for the graphs of two inverse functions.

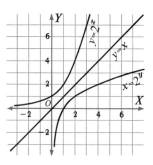

A EXERCISES

1. By inspection determine which of the following functions are increasing functions and which are decreasing functions.

   a. $\{(x, y) \mid y = 3^x; \ x \in Q\}$ **d.** $\{(x, y) \mid y = 8^x; \ x \in Q\}$

   b. $\{(x, y) \mid y = (\frac{1}{3})^x; \ x \in Q\}$ **e.** $\{(x, y) \mid y = 7^{-x}; \ x \in Q\}$

   c. $\{(x, y) \mid y = (\frac{3}{4})^x; \ x \in Q\}$ **f.** $\{(x, y) \mid y = (\frac{1}{2})^{-x}; \ x \in Q\}$

2. Write the inverse of each of the following functions.

   a. $\{(x, y) \mid y = (\frac{1}{2})^x; \ x \in Q\}$ **c.** $\{(x, y) \mid y = 8^{-x}; \ x \in Q\}$

   b. $\{(x, y) \mid y = 4^x; \ x \in Q\}$ **d.** $\{(x, y) \mid y = (\frac{1}{4})^x; \ x \in Q\}$

3. For each part of Ex. 2 draw the graph of the given function and its inverse. Use a single pair of coordinate axes for the two graphs of each pair.

4. Draw the graph of the function defined by each of the following equations. Also draw the graph of the inverse of each function.

   a. $y = 3^x$ **b.** $y = (\frac{1}{3})^x$ **c.** $y = 5^{-x}$ **d.** $y = (\frac{5}{3})^{-x}$

5. Why are exponential functions not defined for $a < 0$? for $a = 0$? for $a = 1$?

Irrational Numbers as Exponents

We have defined a^x in such a way that when $a > 0$, $a \neq 1$, and $x \in Q$, the equation $y = a^x$ defines a function whose domain is Q. Using the table for $y = 2^x$ when $x \in Q$ we were able to obtain many points in the graph of $y = 2^x$. However, we know that the smooth curve which we drew through these points must be regarded as having many "holes" in it because 2^x has not been defined when x is an irrational number. Nevertheless our graph suggests a reasonable definition for $2^{\sqrt{5}}$ and other expressions of the form 2^x when x is an irrational number. If we draw a vertical line through A $(\sqrt{5}, 0)$ we observe that the line intersects the smooth curve at the point P whose ordinate appears to be approximately 4.7. Thus we would like to define $2^{\sqrt{5}}$ in such a way that the point whose coordinates are $(\sqrt{5}, 2^{\sqrt{5}})$ would "plug a hole" in this graph. The definition which we give in the next paragraph has this effect.

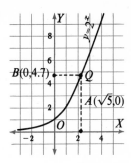

Let S be the set of rth powers of 2 where r is a rational number less than $\sqrt{5}$. Thus $S = \{y \mid y = 2^r;\ r \,\epsilon\, Q;\ r < \sqrt{5}\}$. Some of the elements of S are 2^2, $2^{2.2}$, $2^{2.23}$, $2^{2.236}$, $2^{2.2360}$, and $2^{2.23606}$. Each of these has been defined. For example, $2^{2.2} = 2^{\frac{11}{5}} = \sqrt[5]{2^{11}}$, $2^{2.23} = 2^{\frac{223}{100}} = \sqrt[100]{2^{223}}$, and so on. We know, therefore, that S is not empty. Also, by Theorem 5–8(1) we know that 2^r increases as r increases. Therefore such a number as 2^3 would serve as an upper bound of S because 3, being greater than $\sqrt{5}$, is greater than any exponent used in writing any element of S. Since S is a nonempty set of real numbers which has an upper bound, it must, according to the completeness property, have a least upper bound. We define $2^{\sqrt{5}}$ as the least upper bound of the set S. This means that $2^{\sqrt{5}}$ names a unique positive real number. It can be shown that $2^{\sqrt{5}}$ is indeed the ordinate of the point in our curve whose abscissa is $\sqrt{5}$. We state a general definition:

If $a \,\epsilon\, R, r \,\epsilon\, Q, x$ is an irrational number, and

1. If $a > 1$, then a^x is the least upper bound of the set of all rational powers a^r where $r < x$.
2. If $a = 1$, then $a^x = 1$
3. If $0 < a < 1$, then a^x is the greatest lower bound of the set of all rational powers a^r where $r < x$.

The greatest lower bound is used in part 3 of this definition because $y = a^x$ defines a decreasing function when $0 < a < 1$. This is illustrated by the graph of $\{(x, y) \mid y = (\frac{2}{3})^x;\ x \,\epsilon\, R\}$ in the diagram at the right. If we draw a vertical line through the point whose coordinates are $(-\sqrt{2}, 0)$, the line intersects the graph in a point T whose ordinate is seen to be the greatest lower bound of the set of numbers which are ordinates of points in the curve whose abscissas are less than $-\sqrt{2}$.

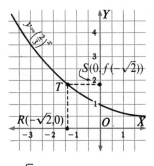

We shall not prove the laws of exponents for irrational number exponents or any other statements based directly on the above definition. However we assert that these laws are proved in more advanced courses where a^x is defined as it has been in this chapter.

We state the five laws of exponents for real number exponents.

If a, b, x, and $y \in R$, each of the following is an identity:

1R. $a^x \cdot a^y = a^{x+y}$

4R. $\dfrac{a^x}{a^y} = a^{x-y}$

2R. $(a^x)^y = a^{xy}$

3R. $(ab)^x = a^x b^x$

5R. $\left(\dfrac{a}{b}\right)^x = \dfrac{a^x}{b^x}$

Since statement **1R** above is true for all positive values of a, it is true when $a > 0$ *and* $a \neq 1$. In this case we can write $e_a(x) = a^x$ and $e_a(y) = a^y$. Also $a^{x+y} = e_a(x + y)$. Thus we have the following statement.

If a, x, $y \in R$, $a > 0$, $a \neq 1$, then $e_a(x) \cdot e_a(y) = e_a(x + y)$.

Similar restatements of **2R, 3R, 4R,** and **5R** in the notation of the exponential function E_a can be made.

The following "extension" of Theorem 5–8 for real number exponents can be proved.

Theorem 6–8. If a, $x \in R$, and

1. If $a > 1$, then the equation $y = a^x$ defines an increasing function whose domain is R and whose range is P (the set of all positive real numbers).
2. If $0 < a < 1$, then the equation $y = a^x$ defines a decreasing function whose domain is R and whose range is P.

According to Theorem 6–8(1), the function defined by $y = a^x$ is an increasing function when a, $x \in R$ and $a > 1$. Therefore the following three statements are true:

(*i*) If $x_1 < x_2$, then $a^{x_1} < a^{x_2}$ Definition of increasing function

(*ii*) If $x_1 = x_2$, then $a^{x_1} = a^{x_2}$ Definition of function— there is a unique value for each argument

(*iii*) If $x_1 > x_2$, then $a^{x_1} > a^{x_2}$ Definition of decreasing function

We can establish the converses of these statements as follows: If $a^{x_1} < a^{x_2}$, then according to the trichotomy property $a^{x_1} \neq a^{x_2}$ and $a^{x_1} \not> a^{x_2}$. If $a^{x_1} \neq a^{x_2}$, then by the contrapositive of (*ii*) $x_1 \neq x_2$. If $a^{x_1} \not> a^{x_2}$, then by the contrapositive of (*iii*) $x_1 \not> x_2$. Since $x_1 \not> x_2$ and $x_1 \neq x_2$ we know, again by the trichotomy property, that $x_1 < x_2$ and our proof of the converse of $x_1 < x_2 \longrightarrow a^{x_1} < a^{x_2}$ is complete. Similar arguments can be given for the converses of $x_1 = x_2 \longrightarrow a^{x_1} = a^{x_2}$ and $x_1 > x_2 \longrightarrow a^{x_1} > a^{x_2}$.

Thus we have established:

Corollary 1 to Theorem 6–8(1). If $a, x \in R$ and $a > 1$, then

1. $x_1 < x_2 \longleftrightarrow a^{x_1} < a^{x_2}$
2. $x_1 = x_2 \longleftrightarrow a^{x_1} = a^{x_2}$
3. $x_1 > x_2 \longleftrightarrow a^{x_1} > a^{x_2}$

Let E_a represent the function defined by $y = a^x (a > 0,\ a \neq 1)$ so that $E_a = \{(x, y) \mid y = a^x\}$. Observe that part 2 of Corollary 1 asserts that each member of the range of E_a corresponds to exactly one member of its domain. According to Theorem 3–6 this fact guarantees the existence of a function K, such that E_a and K are inverse functions. We shall denote K by the symbol $E_a{}^{-1}$ to indicate that it is the inverse of the function E_a. By Theorem 2–6 we know that $(a, b) \in E_a \longleftrightarrow (b, a) \in E_a{}^{-1}$. Therefore the domain of $E_a{}^{-1}$ is the range of E_a and the range of $E_a{}^{-1}$ is the domain of E_a. Moreover it follows that $E_a{}^{-1}$ is an *increasing function* because E_a is an increasing function and inverse functions are either both increasing or both decreasing. (See Ex. 6, page 324.) Thus we have:

Corollary 2 to Theorem 6–8(1). If $a, x \in R$ and $a > 1$, then the function $E_a = \{(x, y) \mid y = a^x\}$ has an inverse function $E_a{}^{-1}$ which is an increasing function having domain P and range R.

Similar corollaries can, of course, be stated for Theorem 6–8(2). An argument similar to that for Corollary 1 establishes the following corollary:

Corollary 3 to Theorem 6–8(2). If $a, x \in R$, $0 < a < 1$, then

1. $x_1 < x_2 \longleftrightarrow a^{x_1} > a^{x_2}$
2. $x_1 = x_2 \longleftrightarrow a^{x_1} = a^{x_2}$
3. $x_1 > x_2 \longleftrightarrow a^{x_1} < a^{x_2}$

Example 1. Sketch the graph of $E_{\frac{1}{2}} = \{(x, y) \mid y = (\frac{1}{2})^x;\ x \in R\}$ and its inverse.

Solution. Referring to page 407, we know that the points whose coordinates are given in the table

x	-3	-2	-1	0	1	2	3
y	8	4	2	1	$\frac{1}{2}$	$\frac{1}{4}$	$\frac{1}{8}$

are in the graph of $E_{\frac{1}{2}}$. Accordingly, the points whose coordinates are given

in the table

y	-3	-2	-1	0	1	2	3
x	8	4	2	1	$\frac{1}{2}$	$\frac{1}{4}$	$\frac{1}{8}$

are in the graph of

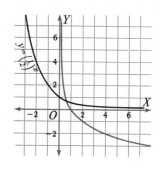

$E_{\frac{1}{2}}^{-1}$. Next we locate the points whose coordinates are given in each of the tables and draw a smooth curve through each set of points to obtain the graphs of $E_{\frac{1}{2}}$ and $E_{\frac{1}{2}}^{-1}$ shown at the right. We observe from these graphs that both functions are decreasing functions. Also we know that the domain of $E_{\frac{1}{2}}$ is R and its range is P, and that the domain of $E_{\frac{1}{2}}^{-1}$ is P and its range is R.

Example 1 suggests the following corollary to Theorem 6–8.

Corollary 4 to Theorem 6–8(2). If a, $x \in R$ and $0 \prec a < 1$, then the function $E_a = \{(x, y) \mid y = a^x\}$ has an inverse function E_a^{-1} which is a decreasing function having domain P and range R.

Example 2. Solve $5^{2x^2} = 5^{3x+3}$

Solution. By Corollary 1 to Theorem 6–8, we know that $5^{2x^2} = 5^{3x+3}$ is equivalent to $2\,x^2 = 3\,x + 3$.
$$2\,x^2 = 3\,x + 3 \longleftrightarrow 2\,x^2 - 3\,x = 3 \longleftrightarrow x^2 - \tfrac{3}{2}\,x = \tfrac{3}{2} \longleftrightarrow x^2 -$$
$$\tfrac{3}{2}\,x + \tfrac{9}{16} = \tfrac{33}{16} \longleftrightarrow (x - \tfrac{3}{4})^2 = \tfrac{33}{16} \longleftrightarrow x - \tfrac{3}{4} = \pm \tfrac{1}{4}\sqrt{33} \longleftrightarrow x =$$
$\tfrac{1}{4}(3 \pm \sqrt{33})$. Thus the solution set is $\{\tfrac{1}{4}(3 + \sqrt{33}), \tfrac{1}{4}(3 - \sqrt{33})\}$.

Check. If $x = \tfrac{1}{4}(3 + \sqrt{33})$,

$5^{2[\frac{1}{4}(3 + \sqrt{33})]^2} \overset{?}{=} 5^{3[\frac{1}{4}(3 + \sqrt{33})] + 3}$

$5^{\frac{3}{4}(7 + \sqrt{33})} \overset{\checkmark}{=} 5^{\frac{3}{4}(7 + \sqrt{33})}$

If $x = \tfrac{1}{4}(3 - \sqrt{33})$,

$5^{2[\frac{1}{4}(3 - \sqrt{33})]^2} \overset{?}{=} 5^{3[\frac{1}{4}(3 - \sqrt{33})] + 3}$

$5^{\frac{3}{4}(7 + \sqrt{33})} \overset{\checkmark}{=} 5^{\frac{3}{4}(7 + \sqrt{33})}$

Ⓐ EXERCISES

1. Draw the graph of each of the following:

   a. $E_{2.5}$ **b.** $E_{.75}^{-1}$ **c.** E_4^{-1} **d.** $E_{\frac{2}{3}}$

2. With respect to one pair of coordinate axes draw the graphs of the function defined by $y = (\tfrac{1}{5})^x$ and its inverse.

3. With respect to one pair of coordinate axes draw the graphs of E_5 and its inverse.

4. With respect to one pair of coordinate axes draw the graphs of the functions defined by $y = 3^x$ and $y = (\tfrac{1}{3})^x$.

5. Show that the graphs of the functions defined by $y = a^x$ and $y = \left(\frac{1}{a}\right)^x$, where $a > 1$ and $x \in R$, are symmetric with respect to the y-axis.

6. With respect to one pair of coordinate axes draw the graphs of the functions defined by $x = 2^y$ and $x = \left(\frac{1}{2}\right)^y$.

7. Show that the graphs of the functions defined by $x = a^y$ and $x = \left(\frac{1}{a}\right)^y$, where $a > 1$ and $x \in R$, are symmetric with respect to the x-axis.

8. Simplify:

a. $3^{\sqrt{2}} \cdot 3^{-\sqrt{2}}$

b. $\dfrac{5^{\sqrt{3}}}{5^{-\sqrt{3}}}$

c. $(4^{\sqrt{3}})^{-\sqrt{3}}$

d. $\left[\left(\frac{1}{2}\right)^{\sqrt{2}}\right]^{\frac{1}{\sqrt{2}}}$

e. $\dfrac{10^{\sqrt{12}}}{10^{\sqrt{3}}}$

f. $\dfrac{2^{\sqrt{12}}}{2^{\sqrt{48}}}$

g. $\left(6^{-\frac{2}{\pi}}\right)^{\pi}$

h. $10^{3-2\sqrt[3]{5}} \cdot 10^{2\sqrt[3]{5}}$

i. $\left(2^{\sqrt[3]{5}}\right)^{\sqrt[3]{\frac{9}{5}}}$

j. $2^{\sqrt{3}} \cdot 4^{\sqrt{3}}$

k. $\dfrac{3^{\sqrt{2}}}{9^{\sqrt{2}}}$

l. $\dfrac{2^{\sqrt{3}+2}}{2^{2-\sqrt{3}}}$

9. Solve each of the following equations.

a. $3^5 = 3^{2x+1}$

b. $2^2 = 2^{x-1}$

c. $7^{-x} = 7^{2x^2-2}$

d. $5^{x^2} = 5^{5-x}$

e. $4^{m^2} = \left(\frac{1}{4}\right)^{2m-3}$

f. $4^{3x} = 2^{2x+1}$

g. $25^n = 5^{n^2-1}$

h. $2^{m^2} = \left(\frac{1}{2}\right)^{-1}$

10. Sketch a graph of $\{(x, y) \mid y = 3^x; \ x \in R\}$ (preferably one in which each unit of length on the axes is divided into tenths). Use the graph you have drawn to find the approximate values of 3^x when

a. $x = 0.5$

b. $x = -1.7$

c. $x = \sqrt{2}$

d. $x = 2.1$

e. $x = 0.4$

f. $x = 1.3$

11. Solve graphically, estimating roots to the nearest half unit.

a. $y = 2^x$ and $y = -x + 5$

b. $y = \left(\frac{1}{2}\right)^x$ and $y = x + 2$

The Logarithmic Function $\{(x, y) \mid y = \log_a x\}$

We know that the exponential function $E_a = \{(x, y) \mid y = a^x; \ x \in R, \ a \in P,$ and $a \neq 1\}$ has an inverse function which we have represented by the symbol E_a^{-1}. Observe that the defining equation for the exponential function is $y = e_a(x)$, when $e_a(x) = a^x$. Thus,

$$e_a(0) = 1 \text{ because } e_a(0) = a^0 = 1 \qquad (i)$$
$$e_a(1) = a \text{ because } e_a(1) = a^1 = a \qquad (ii)$$
$$e_a(x) \cdot e_a(y) = e_a(x + y) \qquad (iii)$$
$$\text{because } e_a(x) \cdot e_a(y) = a^x \cdot a^y = a^{x+y} = e_a(x + y)$$

Since E_a and $E_a{}^{-1}$ are inverse functions, we know that $e_a[e_a{}^{-1}(x)] = e_a{}^{-1}[e_a(x)] = x$. It follows that:

$$e_a{}^{-1}(1) = 0 \text{ because } e_a(0) = 1 \text{ and } e_a{}^{-1}[e_a(0)] = 0 \qquad (iv)$$
$$e_a{}^{-1}(a) = 1 \text{ because } e_a(1) = a \text{ and } e_a{}^{-1}[e_a(1)] = 1 \qquad (v)$$

or

$$e_a{}^{-1}(1) = 0 \text{ because } e_a{}^{-1}(1) = e_a{}^{-1}[e_a(0)] = 0 \qquad (iv)$$
$$e_a{}^{-1}(a) = 1 \text{ because } e_a{}^{-1}(a) = e_a{}^{-1}[e_a(1)] = 1 \qquad (v)$$

We note that there is another commonly accepted name for the *inverse of the exponential function having base a*, namely, *the logarithmic function having base a*. We may write the defining equation of this function in either of two equivalent forms:

$$y = e_a{}^{-1}(x) \qquad \text{or} \qquad y = \log_a x$$

Also, $E_a{}^{-1} = \{(x, y) \mid y = e_a{}^{-1}(x)\} = \{(x, y) \mid y = \log_a x\}$.

We recall that the exponential function E_a is defined for only positive values of a other than 1. Accordingly, its inverse function $E_a{}^{-1}$ (that is, $\{(x, y) \mid y = \log_a x\}$) is defined for only positive values of a other than 1. We read the expression $\log_a x$ as "the logarithm of x to the base a" or more briefly as "the log of x to the base a." Observe that in writing this expression it is not customary to enclose x in parentheses.

We know by Theorem 6–8 that the equation $y = a^x$ when $a \in P$ and $a \neq 1$ defines a function having domain R and range P. Moreover, according to part 2 of Corollary 1 and part 2 of Corollary 3 to Theorem 6–8, we know that each member of the range of E_a corresponds to exactly one member of its domain. Thus if $y > 0$, $a > 0$, and $a \neq 1$, we can write the equation $a^x = y$ with the assurance that there is a unique $x \in R$ which satisfies it. (See the figure at the right.) Also we can prove:

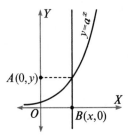

If $a, y \in P$, $a \neq 1$, $x \in R$, and $a^x = y$, then $x = \log_a y$. $\qquad (vi)$

The proof follows:

$$\overset{(1)}{a^x = y} \longrightarrow \overset{(2)}{e_a(x) = y} \longrightarrow \overset{(3)}{e_a{}^{-1}(e_a(x)) = e_a{}^{-1}(y)} \longrightarrow \overset{(4)}{x = e_a{}^{-1}(y)} \longrightarrow \overset{(5)}{x = \log_a y}.$$

Reasons: (1) Given, (2) $e_a(x)$ is another name for a^x, (3) $E_a{}^{-1}$ is a function, hence if $c = d$, then $e_a{}^{-1}(c) = e_a{}^{-1}(d)$; in this case $c = e_a(x)$ and $d = y$, (4) Definition of inverse function (5) $e_a{}^{-1}(y)$ is another name for $\log_a y$.

The converse of (vi):

$$\text{If } a, y \in P, a \neq 1, x \in R, \text{ and } x = \log_a y, \text{ then } a^x = y, \qquad (vii)$$

is readily proved by reversing the steps in the deductive sequence above. (See Ex. 11, page 422.)

From statements (vi) and (vii) and the preceding discussion, we have the following theorem:

▷ **Theorem 7–8.** If $a, y \in P, a \neq 1$, and $x \in R$, then $a^x = y \longleftrightarrow x = \log_a y$.

Using the substitution property of equality, we obtain the following corollary to Theorem 7–8.

Corollary to Theorem 7–8. If $a, y \in P, a \neq 1$, $x \in R$, and $y = a^x$, then (1) $a^{\log_a y} = y$ and (2) $x = \log_a a^x$.

Observe that the statement $a^{\log_a y} = y$ can be obtained directly from the fact that E_a and E_a^{-1} are inverse functions. Thus $e_a[e_a^{-1}(y)] = y$. Also since $\log_a y$ is another name for $e_a^{-1}(y)$, we have: $e_a[e_a^{-1}(y)] = a^{e_a^{-1}(y)} = a^{\log_a y}$. Therefore $y = a^{\log_a y}$. The statement $x = \log_a a^x$ can be similarly obtained.

Since $a^x = y$ and $x = \log_a y$ are equivalent equations, *logarithms* are frequently defined as *exponents*.

From Theorem 7–8 and its corollary, we see that $\log_a y$ is the unique solution of the equation $a^x = y$. Thus $\{x \mid a^x = y\} = \{\log_a y\}$.

Consider the graph of the function E_a^{-1} for $a > 1$ (see figure at the right). From Corollary 2 of Theorem 6–8 we know that E_a^{-1} is an *increasing function*. We state the following theorem:

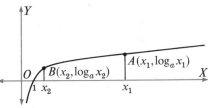

▷ **Theorem 8–8.** If $a > 1$, a, x_1, $x_2 \in P$, $y \in R$ and $y = \log_a x$, then

(1) $x_1 < x_2 \longleftrightarrow \log_a x_1 < \log_a x_2$
(2) $x_1 = x_2 \longleftrightarrow \log_a x_1 = \log_a x_2$
(3) $x_1 > x_2 \longleftrightarrow \log_a x_1 > \log_a x_2$

The proof of Theorem 8–8(3) is left as an exercise.

Note. Theorem 8–8 is actually three theorems. Each theorem has the original hypothesis and one of the numbered conclusions.

We now state the following theorem for the case when $0 < a < 1$:

▶ **Theorem 9–8.** If $0 < a < 1$, $x_1, x_2 \in P$, $y \in R$ and $y = \log_a x$, then

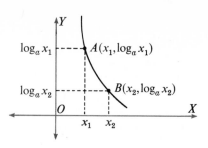

1. $x_1 < x_2 \longleftrightarrow \log_a x_1 > \log_a x_2$
2. $x_1 = x_2 \longleftrightarrow \log_a x_1 = \log_a x_2$
3. $x_1 > x_2 \longleftrightarrow \log_a x_1 < \log_a x_2$

The proof of Theorem 9–8 is left as an exercise.

We observe that any exponential equation such as $a^y = x$ has an equivalent logarithmic form, $y = \log_a x$. Some equivalent exponential and logarithmic forms of equations are shown in the following table:

Exponential Form	Logarithmic Form
$a^x = y$	$x = \log_a y$
$a^0 = 1$	$0 = \log_a 1$ (See (iv) page 418.)
$a^1 = a$	$1 = \log_a a$ (See (v) page 418.)
$a^{\log_a x} = x$	$\log_a x = \log_a x$
$a^x = a^x$	$x = \log_a a^x$
$2^5 = 32$	$5 = \log_2 32$
$10^{-4} = 0.0001$	$-4 = \log_{10} 0.0001$
$\sqrt[4]{10} = 10^{\frac{1}{4}} = 1.778$	$.25 = \log_{10} 1.778$
$10^{.25} \times 10^2 = 177.8$	$2.25 = \log_{10} 177.8$
$16^{-\frac{3}{4}} = 0.125$	$-.75 = \log_{16} 0.125$

Example 1. Find the solution set for $\log_2(x^2 - x) = \log_2 12$

Solution. By Theorem 8–8(2)

$\log_2 (x^2 - x) = \log_2 12 \longleftrightarrow x^2 - x = 12 \longleftrightarrow x^2 - x - 12 = 0 \longleftrightarrow$
$\longleftrightarrow (x - 4)(x + 3) = 0 \longrightarrow x = 4 \lor x = -3$
$\therefore \{x \mid \log_2 (x^2 - x) = \log_2 12\} = \{4, -3\}$

Check. If $x = 4$,

$\log_2 (16 - 4) \overset{?}{=} \log_2 12$
$\log_2 12 \overset{\checkmark}{=} \log_2 12$

If $x = -3$,

$\log_2 [9 - (-3)] \overset{?}{=} \log_2 12$
$\log_2 12 \overset{\checkmark}{=} \log_2 12$

Example 2. Find the solution set for each of the following equations:

    a. $\log_x 81 = 4$ **b.** $\log_3 x = -4$ **c.** $\log_9 27 = x$

Solutions. **a.** $\log_x 81 = 4 \longleftrightarrow x^4 = 81 \land x > 0 \land x \neq 1 \longleftrightarrow x = 3 \lor x = -3 \land x > 0$. Note that $\log_x 81 = 4 \longleftrightarrow x^4 = 81 \land x > 0 \land x \neq 1$ because $\log_a y$ is defined only for $a > 0 \land a \neq 1$. Thus the solution set is $\{3\}$.

    b. $\log_3 x = -4 \longleftrightarrow 3^{-4} = x \longleftrightarrow x = \frac{1}{81}$. The solution set is $\{\frac{1}{81}\}$.

    c. $\log_9 27 = x \longleftrightarrow 9^x = 27 \longleftrightarrow 3^{2x} = 3^3 \longleftrightarrow x = \frac{3}{2}$. The solution set is $\{\frac{3}{2}\}$.

Ⓐ **EXERCISES**

1. Write each of the following in exponential form.

a. $\log_{10} 100 = 2$ d. $\log_5 125 = 3$ g. $\log_{10} 100,000 = 5$

b. $\log_3 27 = 3$ e. $\log_{25} 5 = \frac{1}{2}$ h. $\log_4 \frac{1}{64} = -3$

c. $\log_4 16 = 2$ f. $\log_{10} .1 = -1$ i. $\log_{36} \frac{1}{6} = -\frac{1}{2}$

2. Write each of the following in logarithmic form.

a. $3^2 = 9$ d. $(\frac{1}{4})^2 = \frac{1}{16}$ g. $25^{\frac{3}{2}} = 125$

b. $25^{\frac{1}{2}} = 5$ e. $3^4 = 81$ h. $5^{-2} = \frac{1}{25}$

c. $10^3 = 1000$ f. $125^{\frac{1}{3}} = 5$ i. $27^{-\frac{1}{3}} = \frac{1}{3}$

3. Complete each of the following:

a. $3^{\log_3 9} = ?$ b. $4^{\log_4 64} = ?$ c. $(\sqrt{2})^{\log_{\sqrt{2}} 1} = ?$

4. Write the inverse of $y = a^x$ in two different notations.

5. Find the value of x in each of the following:

a. $\log_x 9 = 2$ f. $\log_3 x = -2$ k. $\log_6 36 = x$

b. $\log_x 625 = 4$ g. $\log_{\sqrt{3}} x = 3$ l. $\log_{\sqrt{12}} 12 = x$

c. $\log_x 16 = 4$ h. $\log_{.4} x = 2$ m. $\log_{.5} .125 = x$

d. $\log_x \frac{1}{3} = -1$ i. $\log_2 x = -5$ n. $\log_4 8 = x$

e. $\log_x 4 = 4$ j. $\log_4 x = -3$ o. $\log_5 \frac{1}{25} = x$

6. Use the table of values of 2^x on page 407 to find the values of x in each of the following:

a. $\log_2 x \approx 0.05$ d. $\log_2 x \approx 0.80$

b. $\log_2 1.149 \approx x$ e. $\log_2 1.00695 \approx x$

c. $\log_2 1.464 \approx x$ f. $\log_2 x \approx 0.45$

7. Insert $>$ or $<$ to make each of the following a true statement.

a. $\log_3 9$ _?_ $\log_3 27$ c. $\log_{\frac{1}{3}} \frac{1}{27}$ _?_ $\log_{\frac{1}{3}} \frac{1}{9}$

b. $\log_{\frac{1}{2}} \frac{1}{16}$ _?_ $\log_{\frac{1}{2}} \frac{1}{4}$ d. $\log_5 25$ _?_ $\log_5 125$

e. $\log_a b$ _?_ $\log_a c$; $a > 1$ and $b > c > 0$

f. $\log_a b$ _?_ $\log_a c$; $0 < a < 1$ and $b > c > 0$

Ⓑ **EXERCISES**

8. Find the value of x in each of the following:

a. $\log_5 .04 = x$ d. $\log_{\sqrt[4]{3}} 3\sqrt{3} = x$ g. $\log_{\sqrt[3]{3}} 3\sqrt[3]{3} = x$

b. $\log_{\sqrt{2}} x = 3$ e. $\log_x 27 = 0.75$ h. $\log_x 784 = 4$

c. $\log_x \sqrt{5} = 0.5$ f. $\log_x 54\sqrt{2} = 3$ i. $\log_x 288\sqrt{3} = 5$

9. Draw the graph of each of the following:

a. $\{(x, y) \mid y = \log_3 x\}$ **b.** $\{(x, y) \mid y = \log_{\frac{1}{3}} x\}$

10. With respect to one pair of coordinate axes draw the graph of $\{(x, y) \mid y = 2^x\}$ and $\{(x, y) \mid y = \log_2 x\}$.

11. Prove: If $a, y \in P$, $a \neq 1$, $x \in R$, and $x = \log_a y$, then $a^x = y$.

12. Prove Theorem 8–8(3).

13. If $e_a(x) = a^x$ and $e_a(y) = a^y$, then the first law of exponents for real numbers becomes $e_a(x) \cdot e_a(y) = e_a(x + y)$. Use this notation to restate each of the other four laws of exponents for real numbers.

14. Prove Theorem 9–8.

Laws of Logarithms

If a and z are positive, a is not equal to 1, and $x \in R$, then the equation $a^x = z$ has a unique solution, namely $\log_a z$. Thus $a^{\log_a z} = z$ as stated in the corollary to Theorem 7–8. Similarly if a and y are positive and $a \neq 1$ we have $a^{\log_a y} = y$. We can use these facts and the law of exponents for multiplication to show that $\log_a zy = \log_a z + \log_a y$. We use a flow diagram proof.

$$
(1)\ \begin{array}{l} z > 0 \\ a > 0 \\ a \neq 1 \\ y > 0 \end{array}\Bigg\}
\begin{array}{l} (2) \\ \xrightarrow{} z = a^{\log_a z} \\ (2) \\ \xrightarrow{} y = a^{\log_a y} \end{array}\Bigg\}
\xrightarrow{(3)} zy = a^{\log_a z} \cdot a^{\log_a y} \xrightarrow{(4)} zy = a^{\log_a z + \log_a y} \xrightarrow{(5)}
$$

$$
\xrightarrow{(5)} \log_a zy = \log_a z + \log_a y
$$

Reasons: (1) Given, (2) Corollary to Theorem 7–8, (3) Multiplication property of equality, (4) Law of exponents **1R**, (5) Theorem 7–8.

Observe that the hypothesis of the second implication in the above proof justifies the statement $\dfrac{z}{y} = \dfrac{a^{\log_a z}}{a^{\log_a y}}$. Why? From this and the law of exponents **4R** it follows that $\log_a \dfrac{z}{y} = \log_a z - \log_a y$.

Since $y = a^{\log_a y}$ when $y > 0$, $a > 0$, and $a \neq 1$, it follows that when $x \in R$ we have $y = (a^{\log_a y})^x = a^{x \log_a y}$. Therefore, $\log_a y^x = x \log_a y$. We summarize these results in the following theorem:

▷ **Theorem 10–8.** If a, z, and y are positive real numbers, and $a \neq 1$, then

(1) $\log_a zy = \log_a z + \log_a y$

(2) $\log_a \dfrac{z}{y} = \log_a z - \log_a y$

(3) $\log_a y^x = x \log_a y$ when $x \in R$

Note. Theorem 10-8 is actually three theorems. Each has the original hypothesis and one of the numbered conclusions. These three theorems are called the *laws of logarithms.*

If in Theorem 10–8(2) we let $z = 1$, we obtain:

Corollary 1 to Theorem 10–8. If a and y are positive real numbers and $a \neq 1$, then $\log_a \dfrac{1}{y} = - \log_a y$.

If we apply Theorem 10–8(3) to the identity $x = b^{\log_b x}$, we obtain $\log_a x = \log_a b^{\log_b x}, = \log_b x \cdot \log_a b$. This proves:

Corollary 2 to Theorem 10–8. If a, b, and x are positive real numbers, $a \neq 1$, and $b \neq 1$, then $\log_a x = \log_b x \cdot \log_a b$.

Example 1. If $y = \dfrac{a^5 b^2}{\sqrt[3]{c}}$, express $\log_{10} y$ in terms of the logarithms of a, b, and c.

Solution.
$$y = \frac{a^5 b^2}{\sqrt[3]{c}} = \frac{a^5 b^2}{c^{\frac{1}{3}}} = a^5 b^2 c^{-\frac{1}{3}}$$
$$\log_{10} y = \log_{10} a^5 b^2 c^{-\frac{1}{3}} = \log_{10} a^5 + \log_{10} b^2 + \log_{10} c^{-\frac{1}{3}} = 5 \log_{10} a + 2 \log_{10} b - \tfrac{1}{3} \log_{10} c.$$

A logarithmic equation in the variable x is an equation which involves the logarithms of an expression in x. Thus $\log_8 (2x - 3) = 3$ and $\frac{1}{5} \log_2 x = 2$ are logarithmic equations.

Example 2. Solve the following logarithmic equations:

   a. $\log_8 (2x - 3) = 3$ **c.** $\log_4 (x - 3) + \log_4 x = \log_4 28$

   b. $\frac{1}{5} \log_2 x = 2$

Solutions.

   a. $\log_8 (2x - 3) = 3 \longleftrightarrow 2x - 3 = 8^3 \longleftrightarrow 2x - 3 = 512 \longleftrightarrow 2x = 515 \longleftrightarrow x = 257.5$

   b. $\frac{1}{5} \log_2 x = 2 \longleftrightarrow \log_2 x = 10 \longleftrightarrow x = 2^{10} \longleftrightarrow x = 1024$

   c. In solving the equation $\log_4 (x - 3) + \log_4 x = \log_4 28$, we should remember that we must have $x - 3 > 0$ because $\log_a t$ is not defined when $t \leq 0$. If $x - 3 > 0$ then $\log_4 (x - 3) + \log_4 x = \log_4 (x - 3)x$.
Hence $\log_4 (x - 3)x = \log_4 28$. Again using the fact that $\log_a x_1 = \log_a x_2 \longleftrightarrow x_1 = x_2$ (Theorem 8–8) we obtain $x(x - 3) = 28$. Then $x^2 - 3x - 28 = 0$, or $(x - 7)(x + 4) = 0$. The roots of this equation are 7 and -4. Note that 7 satisfies the original equation and that -4 must be rejected for the reason indicated above.

1. a. $\log_{10} 2 + \log_{10} 9 = \log_{10} x \longrightarrow x = ?$

b. $\log_4 16 - \log_4 2 = \log_4 x \longrightarrow x = ?$

c. $\log_2 6 = \frac{1}{2} \log_2 x \longrightarrow x = ?$

d. $\log_8 10 = \log_8 x - \log_8 2 \longrightarrow x = ?$

e. $\log_{10} 12 = \log_{10} x + \log_{10} 2 \longrightarrow x = ?$

f. $x = \log_4 16 \longrightarrow x = ?$

g. $x = \log_2 16 \longrightarrow x = ?$

h. $x = \log_{\frac{1}{6}} 36 \longrightarrow x = ?$

i. $\log_x 27 = 3 \longrightarrow x = ?$

j. $\log_x \frac{1}{9} = -2 \longrightarrow x = ?$

2. Assuming that a, b, and c are positive real numbers, express the logarithms of each of the following in terms of base 10 logarithms of a, b, and c.

a. $a^2 b^3$

b. $a\sqrt{b}$

c. $\dfrac{a^2}{b^3}$

d. $a^{-\frac{1}{2}} b^2 c$

e. $\dfrac{a^2}{\sqrt[3]{b}}$

f. $\dfrac{1}{a^2}$

g. $\sqrt{abc}$

h. $c\sqrt[5]{a^2 b^3}$

i. $\sqrt[3]{\dfrac{ac}{b}}$

j. $\dfrac{a(\sqrt[3]{b})^4}{c}$

k. $\sqrt{\dfrac{a^3 b}{c^5}}$

l. $\left(\dfrac{a\sqrt[3]{b}}{\sqrt{c}}\right)^{\frac{2}{3}}$

3. Write each of the following without using logarithms.

a. $\log_{10} A = \log_{10} b + \log_{10} h - \log_{10} 2$

b. $\log_{10} A = \log_{10} \pi + 2 \log_{10} r$

c. $\log_{10} V = \log_{10} 4 + \log_{10} \pi + 3 \log_{10} r - \log_{10} 3$

d. $\log_{10} t = \log_{10} \pi + \frac{1}{2}(\log_{10} l - \log_{10} g)$

e. $\log_{10} V = \frac{1}{2}(\log_{10} 2 + \log_{10} g + \log_{10} d)$

4. Express each of the following as a single logarithm.

a. $\log_{10} a + \log_{10} 5 - \log_{10} 3$

b. $\frac{1}{3} \log_2 x - \log_2 (x + 2)$

c. $\log_2 3 + 2 \log_2 x + \frac{1}{2} \log_2 y$

d. $\frac{1}{3} \log_{10} x^2 + \frac{4}{3} \log_{10} y - \log_{10} 5$

e. $2 \log_3 (x - 2) + \frac{1}{2} \log_3 (x + 3) - 3 \log_3 x$

5. Solve each of the following equations.

a. $\log_2 (x + 4) = 5$

b. $\frac{1}{3} \log_2 x = 9$

c. $\frac{1}{4} \log_3 x = 2$

d. $5 \log_2 (x + 1) = 10$

e. $\log_2 (x - 2) + \log_2 x = 3$

f. $\log_{10} (x^2 - 9) - \log_{10} (x + 3) = 10$

g. $x^{\log_2 5} = 5$

h. $\log_{10} (x + 1) - \log_{10} x = \log_{10} 6$

6. Prove: If a, $b \in P$, $a \neq 1$, and $b \neq 1$, then $\log_a b = \dfrac{1}{\log_b a}$.

Hint. In Corollary 2 to Theorem 8–10, let $x = a$.

7. If $a = \log_c b$, $b = \log_a c$, and $c = \log_b a$, prove that $abc = 1$.

8. Solve for y: $\log_a y = \frac{1}{2} \log_a x + b$.

9. If $\log_b y_1 = \frac{1}{2} \log_b x_1 + c$, what is the value of c?

10. Solve for x: $\log_{10}(x + 3) = \log_{10} 8 - \log_{10}(x - 9)$

11. Solve for x: $\log_{10} 12 - \frac{1}{2}\log_{10} 5\, x + 6 = \frac{1}{2}\log_{10} 2\, x + 5$

Tables of Common Logarithms

Since our number system employs the base 10, logarithms having base 10 are commonly used in making computations. Accordingly, the logarithmic function defined by the equation $y = \log_{10} x$ is called the common logarithm function and the symbol $\log_{10} x$ is read the *logarithm of x to the base 10* or the *common logarithm of x*. Since it is customary when using base 10 to omit writing the base, we shall hereafter use $\log x$ to mean $\log_{10} x$ and we shall specify the base in other cases.

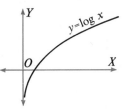

We know that the common logarithm function is a continuous, increasing function having domain P, range R, and x-intercept 1. (See the figure at the right.)

The common logarithms of integral powers of 10 are readily obtained as shown in the following table which pairs equivalent exponential and logarithmic statements.

Exponential		Logarithmic
$0.001 = 10^{-3}$	$\longleftrightarrow$	$\log 0.001 = -3$
$0.01 = 10^{-2}$	$\longleftrightarrow$	$\log 0.01 = -2$
$0.1 = 10^{-1}$	$\longleftrightarrow$	$\log 0.1 = -1$
$1 = 10^{0}$	$\longleftrightarrow$	$\log 1 = 0$
$10 = 10^{1}$	$\longleftrightarrow$	$\log 10 = 1$
$100 = 10^{2}$	$\longleftrightarrow$	$\log 100 = 2$
$1000 = 10^{3}$	$\longleftrightarrow$	$\log 1000 = 3$

Observe that in writing the decimal representation of a number whose absolute value is less than one, we write one zero just to the left of the decimal point. This emphasizes the location of the decimal point.

Since the common logarithmic function is an increasing function to which the Intermediate Value Property applies, we know that

$$0.001 < y < 0.01 \longleftrightarrow -3 < \log y < -2$$
$$0.01 < y < 0.1 \longleftrightarrow -2 < \log y < -1$$
$$0.1 < y < 1 \longleftrightarrow -1 < \log y < 0$$

It is particularly important to observe that

$$1 \leq y < 10 \longleftrightarrow 0 \leq \log y < 1. \qquad (i)$$

Accordingly when $y \in \langle 1, 10 \rangle$, $\log y$ can be expressed approximately by a decimal fraction which represents a non-negative number less than one.

The table on this page is an excerpt from the table on page 760 which gives the first four decimal places of log N when $N \in \langle 1, 10 \langle$.

N	0	1	2	3	4	5	6	7	8	9
70	8451	8457	8463	8470	8476	8482	8488	8494	8500	8506
71	8513	8519	8525	8531	8537	8543	8549	8555	8561	8567
72	8573	8579	8585	8591	8597	8603	8609	8615	8621	8627
73	8633	8639	8645	8651	8657	8663	8669	8675	8681	8686
74	8692	8698	8704	8710	8716	8722	8727	8733	8739	8745

To find log 7.27 look for 7 2 under N and move along this row to the column headed 7, where you find the entry 8615. Since log 7.27 is a positive number less than one, we see that we must regard each entry in this table (except those in the column headed N) as being preceded by a decimal point. Accordingly log 7.27 $\approx$ 0.8615. Although approximations are usually involved, it is customary in working with logarithms to use the equality sign instead of the symbol $\approx$. We may use the scientific notation (page 396) to find the common logarithm of *any* positive number. Thus,

$$\log 727 = \log (7.27 \times 10^2) = \log 7.27 + \log 10^2 = 0.8615 + 2$$
$$\log 0.00727 = \log (7.27 \times 10^{-3}) = \log 7.27 + \log 10^{-3} = 0.8615 - 3.$$

If $z > 0$, $1 \le y < 10$, and $k \in I$, then $z = y \times 10^k$. Therefore log $z = \log (y \times 10^k) = \log y + k \log 10 = \log y + (k \times 1) = \log y + k$ when $0 \le \log y < 1$ according to (*i*) above. Thus the common logarithm of a positive number can be expressed as the sum of an *integer* and a *non-negative number less than one*. This expression is called the standard form of the logarithm. The integer is called the *characteristic* of the logarithm and the non-negative number is called the *mantissa*. Observe that the characteristic of log y is the exponent of 10 in the scientific notation for y. Observe also that if a numeral is to be considered as the standard form of a logarithm, it must be the indicated sum of an integer and a *non-negative number less than one*. Thus $-3 + 0.8615$ is the standard form of log 0.00727. It is not correct to write log 0.00727 $= -3.8615$. Why? It is, of course, permissible to use $2 + 0.8615$ or 2.8615 instead of $0.8615 + 2$ for log 727. Why?

In order to use logarithms in computation, we frequently have to find a number having a given logarithm. If log $y = 4.8681$, we find y as follows using the above table. First we consider the mantissa .8681. We find 8681 in column 8 of row 73 so the digits of y are 738. Since the characteristic is 4, $y = 73,800$. This follows from the fact that $y = 10^{4.8681}$. Therefore, $10^4 < y < 10^5$ or $10,000 < y < 100,000$.

The process of finding the number whose logarithm is the known number b is called finding the antilogarithm of b. Thus 73,800 is the antilogarithm of 4.8681 which is frequently written as "antilog 4.8681." In general if $\log x = b$, then x is the *antilogarithm* of b.

The mantissa of $\log y$ determines the sequence of digits in the decimal representation of y and the characteristic of $\log y$ indicates where the decimal point should be placed.

A number in decimal form is said to have its decimal point in standard position if the decimal point is located just to the right of the first nonzero digit. Such a number is in $\langle 1, 10 \langle$ and the characteristic of its common logarithm is zero. It follows that the characteristic of $\log y$ is k, 0, or $-k$ accordingly as the decimal point in the decimal representation of y is k places to the right, in, or to the left of the standard position.

Example 1. Find the characteristic n and the mantissa m of $\log y$ for each of the following.

    a. $\log y = 0.7163$ **c.** $\log y = -2.3162$

    b. $\log y = 3.7162 + 1.6319$ **d.** $\log y = 8.3392 - 10$

Solutions.

    a. 0.7163 is the sum of the integer 0 and 0.7163, which is a nonnegative number less than 1. Therefore the characteristic n of $\log y$ is 0 and the mantissa m for $\log y$ is 0.7163.

    b. $\log y = 3.7162 + 1.6319 = 5.3481 = 5 + 0.3481$; hence 5 is the characteristic n and 0.3481 is the mantissa m.

    c. $\log y = -2.3162$. If we write $\log y = -2 + (-0.3162)$, we observe that the decimal fraction is negative and therefore cannot be regarded as a mantissa, which, by definition, is a non-negative number less than one. We see that $-3 < \log y < -2$. Therefore $\log y$ can be expressed as -3 plus some positive number less than one. This positive number is the required mantissa m. Thus

$$\log y = -3 + m$$
$$-2.3162 = -3 + m$$
$$0.6838 = m$$

Now we have $\log y = -3 + 0.6838$. We see that $n = -3$ and $m = 0.6838$. Observe that we could have obtained this result more quickly by adding $(3 - 3)$, another name for 0.

$$\log y = -2.3162$$
$$\log y = (-2.3162 + 3) - 3$$
$$\log y = 0.6838 - 3$$
$$\log y = -3 + 0.6838$$

    d. $\log y = 8.3392 - 10 = 0.3392 + (8 - 10) = 0.3392 - 2$. Therefore $n = -2$ and $m = 0.3392$.

Example 2. Find the characteristic n of log y for each of the following values of y.

  a. $y = 4567$ **b.** $y = 81.5 \times 10^7$ **c.** $y = 0.00041$

Solutions.   **a.** $y = 4.567 \times 10^3$, therefore $n = 3$
              b. $y = 8.15 \times 10^8$, therefore $n = 8$
              c. $y = 4.1 \times 10^{-4}$, therefore $n = -4$.

Example 3. Find the mantissa m and the characteristic n for log y if $4 \log y = 2 \log a + 3 \log b$, where $\log a = 0.1372$ and $\log b = 0.2718 - 3$.

Solution. $4 \log y = 2 \times (0.1372) + 3 \times (0.2718 - 3)$
                     $= 0.2744 + 3 \times (-2.7282)$
                     $= 0.2744 - 8.1846$
                     $= -7.9102$
             $\log y = -1.9776$
                     $= -1.9776 + 2 - 2$
                     $= 0.0224 - 2$
     Thus $m = 0.0224$ and $n = -2$.

If the decimal expression of y has not more than three significant digits log y can be read directly from Table II. All entries in the body of Table II are mantissas of common logarithms. Observe that all decimal points are omitted.

Example 4. Verify the following statements using Table II.

           $\log 300 = 2.4771$
           $\log 0.031 = 0.4914 - 2 = -1.5086$
           $\log 3160 = 3 + 0.4997 = 3.4997$

If the mantissa of log y can be found in Table II, y is readily determined.

Example 5. Verify the following statements using Table II and state each in the form log $x = y$.

  a. antilog $2.3909 = 246$
  b. antilog $(0.3909 - 2) = 0.0246$
  c. antilog $(8.3909 - 10) = 0.0246$
  d. antilog $(7.9581 - 10) =$ antilog $(0.9581 - 3) = 0.00908$
  e. antilog $(-3.2284) =$ antilog $[(-3.2284 + 4) - 4] =$ antilog $(0.7716 - 4) = 0.000591$

Solutions.   **a.** $\log 246 = 2.3909 \longleftrightarrow$ antilog $2.3909 = 246$

b. $\log 0.0246 = 0.3909 - 2 \longleftrightarrow$ antilog $(0.3909 - 2) = 0.0246$

c. $\log 0.0246 = 8.3909 - 10 \longleftrightarrow$ antilog $(8.3909 - 10) = 0.0246$

d. $\log 0.00908 = 7.9581 - 10 \longleftrightarrow$ antilog $(7.9581 - 10) = 0.00908$

e. $\log 0.000591 = -3.2284 \longleftrightarrow$ antilog $(-3.2284) = 0.000591$

A **EXERCISES**

1. What are the characteristic and the mantissa of $\log y$ in each of the following cases?

a. $\log y = 0.7404$ **e.** $\log y = 2.5092 + 1.2175$

b. $\log y = 1.8136$ **f.** $\log y = -3.9330$

c. $\log y = 3.8457$ **g.** $\log y = 1.9042 + 0.9547 + (-2)$

d. $\log y = -1 + 0.8457$ **h.** $\log y = 8.3927 - 10$

2. Find the characteristic of $\log y$ for each of the following values of y.

a. $y = 7483$ **e.** $y = 342$ **i.** $y = 8.43 \times 10^3$

b. $y = 74.83$ **f.** $y = 2.87$ **j.** $y = 0.384 \times 10^{-4}$

c. $y = 7.483$ **g.** $y = 847{,}000$ **k.** $y = 1.47 \times 10^5$

d. $y = 0.07483$ **h.** $y = 0.00072$ **l.** $y = 6.999$

3. Use Table II to complete each of the following to form a true statement.

a. $\log 343 = \_?\_$ **e.** $\log 45{,}700 = \_?\_$ **i.** $\log 3000 = \_?\_$

b. $\log 1.47 = \_?\_$ **f.** $\log 0.389 = \_?\_$ **j.** $\log 2780 = \_?\_$

c. $\log 0.280 = \_?\_$ **g.** $\log 0.999 = \_?\_$ **k.** $\log 71.3 = \_?\_$

d. $\log 0.0041 = \_?\_$ **h.** $\log 0.0004 = \_?\_$ **l.** $\log 1.23 = \_?\_$

4. Use Table II to complete each of the following to form a true statement.

a. antilog $1.5289 = \_?\_$ **g.** antilog $0.3365 = \_?\_$

b. antilog $8.4871 - 10 = \_?\_$ **h.** antilog $3.0000 = \_?\_$

c. antilog $4.3747 = \_?\_$ **i.** antilog $0.0000 - 6 = \_?\_$

d. antilog $0.5729 - 2 = \_?\_$ **j.** antilog $4.8904 = \_?\_$

e. antilog $0.8779 - 5 = \_?\_$ **k.** antilog $0.5775 = \_?\_$

f. antilog $2.4048 = \_?\_$ **l.** antilog $0.7135 - 1 = \_?\_$

5. Find the characteristic n and the mantissa m for $\log y$ if

a. $2 \log y = 3 \log a + 2 \log b$ where $\log a = 0.3010$ and $\log b = 0.6990$.

b. $2 \log y = \log a + \log b - 2 \log c$ where $\log a = 0.4771$, $\log b = 1.8751$, and $\log c = 0.6990$.

6. Write the logarithm of the given expression in terms of the logarithm of its factors.

   a. $(741)(3.20)$ **b.** $(15.5)(8.30)^2$ **c.** $12\sqrt[3]{183}$ **d.** $\sqrt{(346)(8.12)}$

B **EXERCISES**

7. Give the reason for each of the steps in the following deductive sequence.

$$\overset{(1)}{y > 0 \wedge n \in \langle 1, 10 \rangle \wedge k \in I} \overset{(2)}{\longrightarrow} y = n \times 10^k \overset{(3)}{\longrightarrow} \log y = \log (n \times 10^k) \overset{(4)}{\longrightarrow}$$

$$\overset{(5)}{\log y = \log n + \log 10^k} \longrightarrow \log y = \log n + k. \text{ Is ``} 0 \leq \log n < 1\text{'' true?}$$

8. Supply reasons for the following proof that $(a = 10^n(b); \; n \in I) \longleftrightarrow (\log a$ and $\log b$ have the same mantissa).

$$\overset{(1)}{a = 10^n \cdot b} \overset{(2)}{\longleftrightarrow} \log a = \log (10^n \cdot b) \overset{(3)}{\longleftrightarrow} \log a = \log 10^n + \log b \overset{(4)}{\longleftrightarrow}$$
$$\qquad\qquad (10)\qquad\qquad\qquad\qquad\quad (9)\qquad\qquad\qquad\qquad (8)$$

$$\overset{(5)}{\log a = n + \log b} \longleftrightarrow \text{mantissa} \log a = \text{mantissa} \log b.$$
$$\qquad (7)\qquad\qquad\qquad\qquad (6)$$

9. Sketch the graph of $y = \log_{\frac{1}{2}} x$ and the graph of $y = (\frac{1}{2})^x$ with respect to the same pair of coordinate axes. How are these graphs related?

10. Sketch with respect to the same set of axes:

    a. $y = \log_{\frac{1}{4}} x$ **b.** $y = \log_{\frac{1}{2}} x$ **c.** $y = \log_2 x$ **d.** $y = \log_4 x$

11. Show that the graphs of $y = \log_a x$ and $y = \log_{\frac{1}{a}} x$ when $a \in P$ and $a \neq 1$ are symmetric with respect to the x-axis.

    Hint. $d = \log_a c \longleftrightarrow -d = \log_{\frac{1}{a}} c$ because $a^d = c \longleftrightarrow \left(\frac{1}{a}\right)^{-d} = c$.

12. Solve the inequality $\log (x^2 - 3x) > 1$.

Interpolation

We conclude our discussion of the table of common logarithms by describing a procedure for "reading between the lines" in this table. This process, known as *interpolation*, is illustrated by the following example.

Example 1. Find log 2.677.

Solution.   From the table we see that $\log 2.670 = 0.4265$ and $\log 2.680 = 0.4281$, but the arrangement of digits 2677 does not appear in column N.

Since $x_1 < x_2 \longleftrightarrow \log x_1 < \log x_2$ and $2.670 < 2.677 < 2.680$, then $0.4265 < \log 2.677 < 0.4281$. This statement suggests that log 2.677 is nearer to 0.4281 than to 0.4265. An examination of a considerably magnified (though not drawn to scale) picture of the portion of the graph of $y = \log x$ (see page 445) in the figure below suggests a plan for estimating log 2.677.

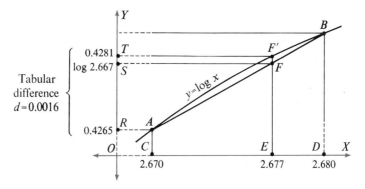

If A and B are two points on this graph, then the line segment joining A and B lies very close to the graph of $y = \log x$ provided A and B are close together. Thus, in order to find log 2.677, the graph $y = \log x$ will be approximated by the straight line through A (2.670, 0.4265) and B (2.680, 0.4281).

Observe that when x increases from 2.670 to 2.680, log x increases by 0.0016. The number 0.0016, the difference between the ordinates, is called the *tabular difference*. Since three or more parallel lines intercept proportional segments on any two transversals, we have $\dfrac{|CE|}{|CD|} = \dfrac{|AF|}{|AB|} = \dfrac{|RS|}{|RT|}$. Therefore $\dfrac{0.007}{0.010} = \dfrac{RS}{0.0016}$.

Hence $RS = \frac{7}{10} \times 0.0016 = 0.00112$. Since it is not possible to obtain five-place accuracy from a four-place table, the number 0.00112 is rounded to 0.0011. Finally we add 0.0011 to 0.4265 to obtain the ordinate of F. Thus log 2.677 = 0.4276.

Rules for Rounding Numbers

1. If the first digit to the right of the last digit to be retained is greater than 5, increase the preceding digit by one.

2. If the first digit to the right of the last digit to be retained is less than 5, leave the preceding digit unchanged.

3. If the first digit to the right of the last digit to be retained is 5 and any digit to the right of this 5 is nonzero, increase by one the last digit to be retained. When the digits to the right of the 5 are zero, increase by one the last digit to be retained if it is an odd integer and leave it unchanged if it is an even integer.

Observe that, by replacing the curve AB with $\overline{AB}$, we found the ordinate of F rather than the ordinate of F'. We are assuming that the difference $|FF'|$ is so small that it will not appreciably affect our computation.

If we let z represent the measure of line segment RS, which is the difference $(\log 2.677 - \log 2.670)$, we can arrange our work as follows:

x	$\log x$

$$0.010\left[0.007\begin{bmatrix}2.680 \\ 2.677 \\ 2.670\end{bmatrix}\right. \qquad \left.\begin{bmatrix}0.4281 \\ \log 2.677 \\ 0.4265\end{bmatrix}z\right]0.0016$$

$$\frac{0.007}{0.010} = \frac{z}{0.0016}$$

$$z = \frac{7}{10} \times 0.0016$$

$$= 0.0011$$

$$\therefore \log 2.677 = 0.4265 + 0.0011$$

$$= 0.4276$$

Example 2. Find antilog $0.6966 - 3$.

Solution. We are to find the four-digit sequence which corresponds to the mantissa 0.6966. After we have done this we shall use the characteristic -3 to locate the decimal point. From the table we see that 0.6966 lies between 0.6964 and 0.6972 whose corresponding four-digit sequences are 4970 and 4980, respectively. We arrange our work as follows:

x	$\log x$

$$0.010\left[w\begin{bmatrix}4.980 \\ \text{antilog } 0.6966 \\ 4.970\end{bmatrix}\right. \qquad \left.\begin{bmatrix}0.6972 \\ 0.6966 \\ 0.6964\end{bmatrix}0.0002\right]0.0008$$

$$\frac{w}{0.010} = \frac{0.0002}{0.0008}$$

$$\frac{w}{0.010} = \frac{1}{4}$$

$$w = 0.0025$$

Rounding w to 0.002, antilog $0.6966 = 4.970 + 0.002 = 4.972$. Since the characteristic is -3, we have antilog $0.6966 - 3 = 0.004972$.

Observe that the value of w was rounded to 0.002 because interpolation in a four-place table yields at most four significant digits for x when $\log x$ is given.

1. Find log x when

a. $x = 43.25$	**d.** $x = 981.3$	**g.** $x = 0.6545$	**j.** $x = 83.352$
b. $x = 61.82$	**e.** $x = 0.004387$	**h.** $x = 47820$	**k.** $x = 0.06367$
c. $x = 342.6$	**f.** $x = 0.0003821$	**i.** $x = 0.04783$	**l.** $x = 34828$

2. Find the antilog of each of the following:

   a. log $x = 1.4327$ **e.** log $x = 9.0000 - 10$ **i.** log $x = 8.6034 - 10$

   b. log $x = 2.3724$ **f.** log $x = 4.3811$ **j.** log $x = 3.6300$

   c. log $x = 9.3312 - 10$ **g.** log $x = 1.4137$ **k.** log $x = 2.5000$

   d. log $x = 8.4727 - 10$ **h.** log $x = 0.2862$ **l.** log $x = 0.3262$

3. **a.** Interpolate between log 0.1 and log 1 to find log 0.30.

   b. Interpolate between log 0.25 and log 0.35 to find log 0.30.

   c. Which of the values that you found in parts **a** and **b** represents more truly the real value of log 0.30? The sketch at the right shows a portion of the graph of $y = \log x$. Copy the drawing on your paper and use it to explain your answer to part **c.**

4. A curve is said to be concave upward (concave downward) at a point $P(a, b)$ if there exists an interval containing a such that every chord connecting two points whose abscissas are in the interval lies above (lies below) the curve at P.

   Which of the following phrases correctly completes the statement, "The graph of $y = \log x$ is _?_."
   (1) always concave downward
   (2) always concave upward
   (3) sometimes concave upward and sometimes concave downward

Computation with Common Logarithms—Multiplication and Division

The procedures for computation with common logarithms are illustrated by the following examples. They are based on two fundamental ideas: (1) If a numerical expression involving the numbers $a, b, c, \cdots$, does not involve addition or subtraction, then the logarithm of the numerical expression can be expressed in terms of log a, log b, log $c, \cdots$, by using the laws of logarithms (Theorem 10–8). (2) If the logarithm of a number is known, the number can be found by using Table II.

Example 1. Find y if $y = 3.15 \times 0.02167$.

Solution.
$$y = 3.15 \times 0.02167$$
$$\log y = \log 3.15 + \log 0.02167$$
$$\log 3.15 = 0.4983$$
$$\log 0.02167 = 0.3359 - 2$$
$$\log y = 0.8342 - 2$$
$$y = 0.06827$$

Example 2. Evaluate $\dfrac{43.12}{0.00517}$.

Solution. Let $y = \dfrac{43.12}{0.00517}$.

$$\text{then } \log y = \log 43.12 - \log 0.00517$$
$$\log 43.12 = 1.6347$$
$$\log 0.00517 = 0.7135 - 3$$
$$\log y = 0.9212 + 3$$
$$y = 8340$$

Example 3. Compute $\dfrac{-0.05172}{0.000923}$.

Solution. Let $y = \dfrac{-0.05172}{0.000923}$. We know that negative numbers have no logarithms. Why? However, we can use logarithms to compute $|y|$. Thus

$$|y| = \frac{|-0.05172|}{|0.000923|}$$
$$\log|y| = \log 0.05172 - \log 0.000923$$
$$\log 0.05172 = 0.7137 - 2$$
$$\log 0.000923 = 0.9652 - 4$$
$$\log|y| = (0.7137 - 2) - (0.9652 - 4)$$
$$= 0.7137 - 2 - 0.9652 + 4.$$
$$= 4.7137 - 2.9652$$
$$= 1.7485.$$

Therefore $|y| = 56.04$. We know that $y < 0$ because the quotient of a positive number and a negative number is negative. Therefore $y = -56.04$.

Example 4. Find x if $x = \dfrac{78.1 \times 4.32}{3.17 \times 764000}$

Solution.
$$\log x = \log 78.1 + \log 4.32 - (\log 3.17 + \log 764000)$$
$$\log 78.1 = 1.8927$$
$$\log 4.32 = 0.6355$$
$$\log 78.1 + \log 4.32 = 2.5282$$

$$\log 3.17 = 0.5011$$
$$\log 764,000 = 5.8831$$
$$\overline{\log 3.17 + \log 764,000 = 6.3842}$$
$$\log x = 2.5282 - 6.3842 = -3.8560$$
$$= -3 + (-0.8560)$$

Recall that a decimal fraction must be non-negative, that is in $\langle 0, 1 \langle$ in order for it to be acceptable as the mantissa of $\log x$. In order to express $\log x$ in standard form we may add zero expressed as $(4 - 4)$.

Then
$$\log x = (-3.8560 + 4) - 4$$
$$\log x = 0.1440 - 4$$
$$x = \text{antilog } (0.1440 - 4) = 0.0001393$$

Ⓐ **EXERCISES**

1. Use logarithms to evaluate each of the following:

a. 43.6×914

b. $724 \div 48.2$

c. 0.00324×0.0293

d. $\dfrac{0.0756}{-0.831}$

e. $\dfrac{362 \times 94.7}{-8.42}$

f. 8932×7436

g. 0.04794×0.9365

h. $\dfrac{98.75 \times 123.6}{17.25 \times 371.3}$

i. $475.2 \times 98.41 \times (-32.46)$

j. $\dfrac{128.4}{23.62 \times 75.86 \times 2.371}$

2. Find the value of x for which each of the following equations is true.

a. $\log x = \log 3 - \log 81$

b. $\log (x + 16) = 1 + \log (x - 2)$

c. $\log x + 2 \log x = \log 27$

d. $\log x + \log (x + 4) = \log 5$

e. $\log x - \log (x + 1) = \log 7 - \log 8$

f. $\log x = \log \pi + \log 12$

3. Use logarithms to find the decimal approximation of the reciprocal of each of the following numbers.

a. 749   b. 9.382   c. 0.1132   d. $\frac{7842}{9318}$

Ⓑ **EXERCISES**

4. Evaluate:

a. $\dfrac{7413}{1526} \times \dfrac{-3621}{1978} \times \dfrac{-4756}{1251}$

b. $\dfrac{3245}{7652} \div \dfrac{1728}{4675}$

c. $\dfrac{(0.3456)(0.9375)(3407)}{3.751}$

d. $17\frac{1}{2} \times 936\frac{2}{3} \times 841$

5. Find the value of x for which each of the following statements is true.

    a. $\log_4 x + \log_4 (x + 6) = \frac{3}{2}$

    b. $\log_2 x + \log_2 (x - 6) = -3$

    c. $\log x = 2(\log 3 - \log 5) + 3 \log 5$

    d. $\log x = 3(\log 3 - \log 4) + 2 \log 8 + 2(\log 2 - \log 3)$

Computations Involving Powers and Roots

The following examples show procedures for using logarithms to find powers and roots.

Example 1.   Using logarithms, find each of the following:

    a. $(1.317)^{15}$ **b.** $\sqrt[3]{517}$ **c.** $(-0.0912)^{\frac{1}{5}}$

Solutions.   **a.** $x = (1.317)^{15}$

        $\log x = 15 \log 1.317$

             $= 15 \times 0.1196 = 1.7940$

        $x = 62.23$

    b. $y = \sqrt[3]{517} = 517^{\frac{1}{3}}$

        $\log y = \frac{1}{3} \log 517 = \frac{1}{3} \times 2.7135 = 0.9045$

        $y = 8.026$

    c. $z = (-0.0912)^{\frac{1}{5}}$. We see that $z < 0$.

However, $\log |z| = \frac{1}{5} \log (0.0912) = \frac{1}{5}(0.9600 - 2)$

                        $= \frac{1}{5} \times (-1.0400)$

        $\log |z| = -0.2080 = -0.2080 + 1 - 1 = 0.7920 - 1$

        $|z| = 0.6194$. Therefore z is a negative number whose absolute value is 0.6194

        $z = -0.6194$

Observe that we could have written:

        $\log |z| = \frac{1}{5}(0.9600 - 2) = \frac{1}{5}(3.9600 - 5) = 0.7920 - 1$

        $z = -0.6194$

Example 2.   Find x if $x = \sqrt[5]{(1.317)^5 + (2.14)^4}$.

Solution.   We cannot add two numbers by using logarithms. We can, however, evaluate 1.317^5 and 2.14^4 by means of logarithms:

    $\log (1.317)^5 = 5 \log 1.317 = 5 \times (0.1196) = 0.5980$

        $(1.317)^5 = $ antilog $0.5980 = 3.963$

    Similarly $(2.14)^4 = $ antilog $1.3216 = 20.97$

    $(1.317)^5 + (2.14)^4 = 24.933$

    Rounding the antilog we have:

        $x = (24.93)^{\frac{1}{5}}$

        $\log x = \frac{1}{5} \log 24.93 = \frac{1}{5}(1.3967)$

             $= 0.2793$

        $x = 1.902$

Example 3. Evaluate $\sqrt[3]{\dfrac{41.7 \times (-0.821)}{(9.73)^3}}$.

Solution. If $y = \sqrt[3]{\dfrac{41.7 \times (-0.821)}{(9.73)^3}}$, then $y < 0$. Since logarithms are not defined for negative numbers, we shall find the logarithm of the absolute value of y.

$\log |y| = \frac{1}{3}[\log 41.7 + \log 0.821 - 3 \log 9.73]$

$\log |y| = \frac{1}{3}[1.6201 + (0.9143 - 1) - 3 \times 0.9881]$

$\log |y| = \frac{1}{3}[1.6201 + (-0.0857) + (-2.9643)]$

$\qquad = \frac{1}{3} \times (-1.4299) = -0.4766$

$\qquad = 0.5234 - 1$

$\qquad |y| = 0.3338$

$\therefore \qquad y = -0.3338$

A EXERCISES

1. Use logarithms to evaluate the following powers and roots.

a. $(3.24)^3$ g. $\sqrt{45.8}$ m. $(7.345)^{\frac{1}{2}}$

b. $(72.3)^4$ h. $\sqrt[3]{0.937}$ n. $(593.71)^2$

c. $(0.934)^3$ i. $\sqrt[4]{2.47}$ o. $(2.476)^{\frac{3}{2}}$

d. $(0.0807)^6$ j. $(157.7)^{\frac{1}{3}}$ p. $\sqrt{5324.8}$

e. $(3.47)^5$ k. $(0.475)^3$ q. $(1.07)^{\frac{1}{4}}$

f. $(74850)^{\frac{1}{3}}$ l. $(0.2486)^{\frac{2}{5}}$ r. $\sqrt[6]{175400}$

2. Use logarithms to evaluate each of the following.

a. $(347.2)^2(46.13)^3$

b. $\sqrt{(4.731)^3}$

c. $\sqrt{98.47} \cdot \sqrt[3]{6421}$

d. $\dfrac{24.60}{9350} \cdot \sqrt{3841}$

e. $\sqrt{\dfrac{475 \times 483}{347}}$

f. $\sqrt[3]{943210 \times 1458000}$

g. $\dfrac{(\frac{75}{49})^2 \times \frac{189}{73}}{\frac{841}{727}}$

h. $(-\frac{14}{83})^2 \cdot \sqrt{731.6}$

i. $\dfrac{(3.000)(75.4)^3}{783 \cdot \sqrt[3]{251}}$

j. $\dfrac{13.340 \times 0.9831}{\sqrt[3]{16.8 \times 195}}$

k. $\sqrt{\dfrac{246 \times 981 \times 1.4}{3.6}}$

l. $\sqrt{6\sqrt{431.2}}$

3. Evaluate.

a. $\sqrt[3]{9.434} + \sqrt{62.3}$

b. $(7.843)^3 + (96.12)^2$

c. $\sqrt{841.4} - (2.371)^3$

d. $13\sqrt{0.4281} - 5\sqrt{17.83}$

e. $(2.6) \cdot \sqrt[3]{7.821}$

f. $(415)^{\frac{1}{3}} - 6\sqrt{2473}$

Exponential and Logarithmic Equations

Let us consider examples in which we evaluate some expressions for a^b where $a \in P$ and $b \in R$.

Example 1. Evaluate each of the following:

    a. $33^{0.4}$ **b.** $(0.85)^{1.4}$ **c.** $(0.015)^{-1.3}$ **d.** $3^{\sqrt{3}}$

Solutions.   **a.** $\log 33^{0.4} = 0.4 \log 33 = 0.4 \times 1.5185 = 0.6074$
        $\therefore 33^{0.4} = $ antilog $0.6074 = 4.049$

    b. $\log (0.85)^{1.4} = 1.4 \log 0.85 = 1.4(0.9294 - 1)$
        $= 1.4 \times (-0.0706) = -0.0988 = 0.9012 - 1$
        $\therefore (0.85)^{1.4} = $ antilog $(0.9012 - 1) = 0.7965$

    c. $\log (0.015)^{-1.3} = -1.3 \log 0.015 = -1.3(0.1761 - 2)$
        $= (-1.3) \times (-1.8239) = 2.3711$
        $\therefore (0.015)^{-1.3} = 235$

    d. $\log 3^{\sqrt{3}} = \sqrt{3} \log 3 = \sqrt{3} \times (0.4771)$
        To find the product of $\sqrt{3}$ and 0.4771, we use logarithms.
        $\log \sqrt{3}(0.4771) = \frac{1}{2} \log 3 + \log (0.4771)$
            $\frac{1}{2} \log 3 = 0.2386$
           $\log 0.4771 = \underline{0.6786 - 1}$
        $\log \sqrt{3}(0.4771) = 0.9172 - 1$
        antilog $0.9172 - 1 = 0.8264$
        Thus the $\log 3^{\sqrt{3}} = 0.8264$
        antilog $0.8264 = 6.705$
            $3^{\sqrt{3}} = 6.705$

Some exponential equations can be solved by taking the logarithm of both members. We know this because when
$a, b \in P$, $a \neq 1$, and $b \neq 1$, then $a = b \longleftrightarrow \log a = \log b$. Thus, if $c, y \in P$,
and $c \neq 1$, then $c^x = y \longleftrightarrow x \log c = \log y \longleftrightarrow x = \dfrac{\log y}{\log c}$.

Example 2. Solve $(0.83)^x = 100$ for x.

Solution. $(0.83)^x = 100 \longleftrightarrow x \log (0.83) = \log 100 \longleftrightarrow x = \dfrac{2}{\log 0.83} \longleftrightarrow$

        $x = \dfrac{2}{0.9191 - 1} \longleftrightarrow x = \dfrac{2}{-0.0809}$

    We use logarithms to perform the division $\dfrac{2}{-0.0809}$.

        $x = \dfrac{2}{-0.0809}$

    $\log |x| = \log 2 - \log 0.0809 = 0.3010 - (0.9079 - 2) = 1.3931$
        $|x| = 24.72$
    Since $x < 0$, $x = -24.72$.

Example 3. Find x, if $x = \log_3 7$.

Solution. $x = \log_3 7 \longleftrightarrow 3^x = 7 \longleftrightarrow x \log 3 = \log 7 \longleftrightarrow x = \dfrac{\log 7}{\log 3} \longleftrightarrow$

$x = \dfrac{0.8451}{0.4771} \longleftrightarrow \log x = \log 0.8451 - \log 0.4771 \longleftrightarrow \log x =$

$(0.9270 - 1) - (0.6786 - 1) \longleftrightarrow \log x = 0.2484 \longleftrightarrow x = 1.772$

Example 4. Solve $\log_a (x + 1) = \log_a x + 3$ for x.

Solution. Since $x > 0$, we have: $\log_a (x + 1) = \log x_a + 3 \longleftrightarrow$

$\log_a (x + 1) - \log_a x = 3 \longleftrightarrow \log_a \dfrac{x+1}{x} = 3 \longleftrightarrow a^3 = \dfrac{x+1}{x} \longleftrightarrow$

$a^3 x = x + 1 \longleftrightarrow a^3 x - x = 1 \longleftrightarrow x(a^3 - 1) = 1 \longleftrightarrow x = \dfrac{1}{a^3 - 1}$

Ⓐ **EXERCISES**

1. Evaluate each of the following:

   a. $(57)^{0.7}$ **b.** $(0.43)^{2.6}$ **c.** $(0.176)^{-3.7}$ **d.** $72^{\sqrt 7}$

   e. $(1 + r)^{-10}$ when $r = 0.07$

2. Solve each of the following for x:

   a. $2^x = 14$ **d.** $7^x = 42$ **g.** $6^{2x-3} = 216$ **j.** $5^{3x^2-1} = 4$

   b. $0.043^x = 1.20$ **e.** $0.23^x = 64$ **h.** $4^{3x} = 16$ **k.** $9^{2x} = 3^{x^2-12}$

   c. $1000^x = 231$ **f.** $7^{2x-3} = 343$ **i.** $6^{2x-3} = 5$ **l.** $4^x = 2^{x+7}$

3. Solve each of the following for x:

   a. $x = \log_5 8$ **f.** $8^{\log_x 3} = 3$

   b. $x = \log_3 1000$ **g.** $9^{\log_x 0.625} = 0.625$

   c. $x = \log 7.342$ **h.** $3^{\log_3 4} + 5^{\log_5 7} = 2^{\log_2 x}$

   d. $5^{\log_5 x} = 9$ **i.** $7^{\log_7 3} + 0.5^{\log_{0.5} 9} = 3^{\log_3 x}$

   e. $5^{\log_5 x} = \frac{1}{4}$ **j.** $10^{\log 2} + 10^{\log 3} = 10^{\log x}$

4. Find the value of x for which each of the following statements is true.

   a. $x = \log \dfrac{\sqrt[5]{1000}}{(0.001)^3}$ **d.** $\log (x^2 - 1) - \log (x + 1) = \log 4$

   b. $x \log \sqrt[3]{42.90} = (437.5)^2$ **e.** $2 \log (3 x + 1) - \log (3 x + 1) = \log 13$

   c. $\log (x - 1) + \log x = \log 10$ **f.** $\log_2 (x - 2) + \log_2 (x - 1) = 1$

5. Find the solution set for each of the following equations.

   a. $2^{x^2-6} = 4^{\frac{1}{2}x}$ **b.** $2^{x^2+\frac{1}{4}} = 8^{\frac{1}{3}x}$ **c.** $7^{x+\frac{1}{2}} = 3^x$ **d.** $5^{x+3} = 2^x$

6. Solve for x.

   a. $\log_6 \sqrt{\dfrac{4x+5}{x}} = 0$ **b.** $\log_3 \sqrt{\dfrac{2x^2+1}{3x}} = 0$

7. Show that $(2 \log_5 5)(\log_{25} 5 + \log_{25} 25) = 3$ without using tables.

8. Show that $\log \dfrac{\sqrt{x^2+1}+x}{\sqrt{x^2+1}-x} = 2 \log (\sqrt{x^2+1}+x)$.

Using Logarithms in Problem Solving

Logarithms enable us to perform many computations which are otherwise extremely difficult or even impossible. The following examples illustrate how logarithms can be used to evaluate formulas.

Example 1. If a, b, c, are the measures of the sides of a triangle whose area is S, then $S = \sqrt{s(s-a)(s-b)(s-c)}$ when $s = \frac{1}{2}(a+b+c)$. Find the area of a triangle whose sides have the measures in inches of 31.9, 41.2, and 63.5.

Solution. Let $a = 31.9$, $b = 41.2$ and $c = 63.5$; then $s = 68.3$.

$$\log S = \tfrac{1}{2}[\log s + \log (s-a) + \log (s-b) + \log (s-c)]$$
$$= \tfrac{1}{2}(\log 68.3 + \log 36.4 + \log 27.1 + \log 4.8)$$
$$= \tfrac{1}{2}(1.8344 + 1.5611 + 1.4330 + 0.6812)$$
$$= \tfrac{1}{2}(5.5097) = 2.7548$$
$$S = 568.6$$

Thus the area is 568.6 square inches.

Example 2. In the formula $V = \frac{4}{3}\pi r^3$, V represents the measure of the volume of a sphere and r represents the measure of a radius of the sphere. Find the length of the radius of a sphere whose volume is 1000 cubic inches. Use $\pi = 3.142$.

Solution.

$$V = \tfrac{4}{3}\pi r^3$$
$$1000 = \tfrac{4}{3}\pi r^3$$
$$\log 1000 = \log 4 - \log 3 + \log \pi + 3 \log r$$
$$\log r = \frac{\log 1000 - \log 4 + \log 3 - \log \pi}{3}$$
$$= \frac{3.000 - 0.6021 + 0.4771 - 0.4972}{3} = \frac{2.3778}{3}$$
$$= 0.7926$$
$$r = 6.203$$

The length is approximately 6.2 inches.

Compound Interest. If P dollars are invested at an annual rate of interest of r percent and at the end of each year the interest is computed and added to the principal (compounded annually), then after n years the total amount A_n is given by $A_n = P(1+r)^n$.

Example 3. If a principal of \$1000 is invested at 5% interest compounded annually, what is the amount of the investment after 20 years?

Solution.

$$A_{20} = 1000(1.05)^{20}$$
$$\log A_{20} = \log 1000 + 20 \log 1.05 = 3 + (20 \times 0.0212) = 3.4240$$
$$\text{antilog } 3.4240 = 2655$$

Thus the amount at the end of 20 years is $2655.

If interest is added to the principal twice each year the rate of interest is $\frac{r}{2}$ for each half-year period. If the interest is compounded quarterly, that is, computed and added to the principal four times each year, the rate of interest is $\frac{r}{4}$ for each 3 month period. In general if the interest is compounded q times per year, the rate for each period is $\frac{r}{q}$ and the number of periods in n years is nq. Accordingly, the amount A_{nq} is given by $A_{nq} = P\left(1 + \frac{r}{q}\right)^{nq}$.

Example 4. How much should be invested now in order that the amount of the investment will be $500 in ten years if interest is compounded semi-annually at 6%?

Solution. In this case P is to be found. We know $A_{nq} = 500, r = 0.06, n = 10$ and $q = 2$.
Thus $500 = P(1 + \frac{6}{200})^{20} = P(1.03)^{20}$
$$\log 500 = \log P + 20 \log 1.03$$
$$\log 500 - 20 \log 1.03 = \log P$$
$$2.6990 - 20 \times 0.0128 = \log P$$
$$2.4430 = \log P$$
$$277.3 = P$$

Thus the amount that should be invested now is $277.30.

Example 5. How long will it take for an investment P to double in value if interest is compounded quarterly at 8%?

Solution.

$$2P = P(1.02)^{4x}$$
$$2 = (1.02)^{4x}$$
$$\log 2 = 4x \log (1.02)$$
$$x = \frac{\log 2}{4 \log 1.02} = \frac{0.3010}{4 \times 0.0086}$$

Performing this computation by logarithms, we obtain:
$$\log x = \log 0.3010 - (\log 4 + \log 0.0086)$$
$$= 0.4771 - 1 - (0.6021 + 0.9345 - 3) = 0.9405$$
$$x = 8.72$$

From this result we conclude that an investment will double in value, under the given conditions, in approximately $8\frac{3}{4}$ years or by the end of the 35th interest period.

The Logarithmic Scale. A logarithmic scale may be constructed by proceeding as follows:

1. Draw a line 10 inches long and calibrate it into 10 equal parts.
2. On another sheet of paper draw another line 10 inches long and align
   it with the first line.
3. Use the following table to calibrate the second line (shown in red below).
   Since the log 1 is 0, mark 1 on the second line opposite 0 on the first
   line, mark 2 on the second line opposite .30, the log 2, on the first line,
   and so on.

n	1	2	3	4	5	6	7	8	9	10
$\log n$	0	.30	.48	.60	.70	.78	.85	.90	.95	1.0

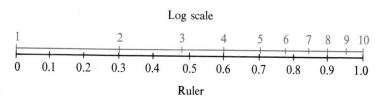

Log scale

Ruler

The second line (red line) thus calibrated is a logarithmic scale.

Example. Use two logarithmic scales to make a slide rule and explain how
such a rule can be used to perform multiplication and division.

Solution. Let us use $2 \times 3 = 6$ and $6 \div 2 = 3$, as examples. $2 \times 3 = 6$. Using
the two logarithmic scales, place the second scale so that the multi-
plicand 3 is aligned with the index 1 on the first scale. Then on the
first scale the multiplier 2 is aligned with the product 6 on the second
scale.

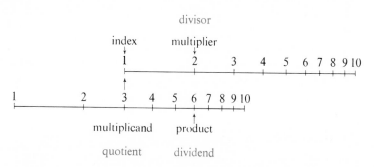

$6 \div 2 = 3$. Using the same logarithmic scales, we see that if we place
the first scale so that the divisor 2 is aligned with the dividend 6 on
the second scale, then the quotient 3 is aligned with the index 1.

1. At sea level the number of seconds, t, required for a pendulum to make a complete vibration is given by the formula $t = 2\pi\sqrt{\dfrac{l}{g}}$ where l represents the measure of the length of the pendulum and g the measure of the force of gravity. Using 3.142 for π and 32.16 for g, find the time required for a pendulum of length $1\frac{1}{2}$ feet to make a complete vibration.

2. Find the volume of a sphere whose radius is 13 inches long. (See Example 2, page 440.)

3. Find the length of the radius of a sphere whose volume is 3054 cubic inches.

4. The measure of the area, S, of a spherical triangle (a triangle in a sphere) may be found by the formula $S = \dfrac{\pi r^2 E}{180}$. In the formula, E represents the number of degrees by which the sum of measures of the angles of the triangle exceeds 180 and r represents the measure of the length of the radius of the sphere. Find the area of a spherical triangle having three 90° angles if the sphere has a radius 9 inches long.

5. If the measures in degrees of the angles of a spherical triangle are 85, 75, and 100, and the length of the radius of the sphere which contains the triangle is 14 inches, what is the area of the triangle?

6. Find the area of a plane triangle (a triangle in a plane) whose sides have the following lengths: 21.4 inches, 14.2 inches, and 11.6 inches.

7. Find the area of a plane triangle whose sides have the lengths 1621 inches, 1963 inches, and 1842 inches.

8. In the formula $V = \frac{1}{3}Bh$, V represents the measure of the volume of a pyramid whose base has an area of B square units and whose altitude has a length of h units—the units being like units, that is, both inches, both feet, and so on. Find the volume of a pyramid whose altitude is 19.5 inches long and whose base is a square each of whose sides is 8.25 inches long.

9. The volume of a pyramid is 626.81 cubic inches. If the base is a right triangle whose legs have the lengths 12.6 inches and 18.2 inches, what is the length of the altitude of the pyramid?

10. Use the formula $A_n = P\left(1 + \dfrac{r}{q}\right)^{nq}$ to find the amount A_n.

   a. When \$800 is compounded annually for 8 years at 4% per year,

   b. When \$3600 is compounded annually for 20 years at $4\frac{1}{2}$% per year.

11. Approximately 350 years ago Manhattan Island was purchased from the Indians for \$24. Had the \$24 been invested at 4% compounded semiannually, what amount would have accumulated to date?

12. What amount will accumulate when $5000 is invested at 5% compounded semiannually for

   a. 10 years?

   b. 20 years?

13. A certain bank pays $3\frac{1}{2}\%$ interest compounded semiannually. If $2000 is deposited and left to draw interest for 20 years, what amount will there be in the account at the end of 20 years if no interest has been withdrawn?

14. A certain loan company pays 4% interest compounded quarterly. If you were to deposit $1200 in the loan company today and leave it to accumulate interest, how much would you have in the account at the end of 15 years if no interest were withdrawn?

15. How much money should you deposit in the loan company of Ex. 14 if you want the money to amount to $2000 after 10 years?

16. When his grandson was 1 year old Mr. Jones deposited $2000 in a savings company at 4% compounded semiannually. At the end of the grandson's 21st year he will receive the amount which has accumulated in the account. How much will the grandson receive?

17. How long will it take $1000 invested at 5% compounded semiannually to double itself?

18. How long will it take $1000 invested at 4% compounded quarterly to double itself?

19. In the formula $A = \dfrac{P(1+r)^n}{r}$, P represents the number of dollars paid at the end of each year to purchase an annuity, r is the annual rate of interest paid on the investment, and n is the number of years during which the money accumulates. If Mr. Wilhelm purchases an annuity in which $P = 1000$, $r = 0.04$, and $n = 20$, what is the amount he will receive when he has completed his purchase?

20. Compute H if $H = I^2 \, Rt \, (4.18)^{-1}$, $I = 5.0$, $R = 22.0$, and $t = 1.01$.

21. Use logarithms and the formula $h = \dfrac{d^3 n}{50}$ where h is the number of horsepower units transmissible by cold-rolled shafting, n is the number of revolutions of the shaft per minute, and d is the diameter of the shaft in inches, to find n if a shaft whose diameter is $1\frac{1}{2}$ inches is to deliver 15 horsepower.

22. Construct a coordinate system using logarithmic scales on the coordinate axes instead of the usual linear scales. (Let the origin be 1 on both scales.) In this coordinate system plot $y = x^2$ when $x \geq 1$. Explain the result.

23. Construct a coordinate system using a logarithmic scale on the axis of ordinates and the usual linear scale on the axis of abscissas. In this system plot $y = 2^x$. Explain the result.

Before you leave this chapter make sure that you

1. Understand and can use the laws of exponents for whole numbers. (Page 390.)

2. Understand and can use the laws of exponents for integral exponents. (Page 393.)

3. Understand and can use scientific notation. (Page 396.)

4. Understand and can use the laws of exponents for rational number exponents. (Page 398.)

5. Understand the nature of the inverse of an exponential function having rational exponents. (Page 412.)

6. Understand the laws of exponents for irrational number exponents. (Page 413.)

7. Understand the nature of the inverse of an exponential function involving real exponents. (Page 415.)

8 Know that a logarithmic function is the inverse of an exponential function, and can give the defining equation of the exponential function in both the exponential and logarithmic forms. (Page 418.)

9. Understand and can use the laws of logarithms. (Page 422.)

10. Understand and can use a table of logarithms. This includes being able to interpolate. (Page 425.)

11. Understand the rules for rounding numbers. (Page 431.)

12. Can use logarithms in multiplication and division and in finding powers and roots. (Page 433.)

13. Can solve equations involving logarithms. (Page 438.)

14. Can use logarithms in solving such word problems as those given in this chapter. (Page 440.)

15. Can spell and use properly the following words and phrases.

antilogarithm (Page 427.) logarithms (Page 419.)
characteristic (Page 426.) logarithmic function (Page 418.)
exponent (Page 390.) mantissa (Page 426.)
exponential function (Page 407.) scientific notation (Page 396.)
interpolation (Page 430.) significant digit (Page 396.)

1. For which of the following values of a and x is the exponential function $\{(x, y) \mid y = a^x\}$ not defined?

a. $a = 1$ and $x = 0$ d. $a = 4$ and $x = 0$

b. $a = 0$ and $x = 0$ e. $a = \frac{1}{2}$ and $x = 5$

c. $a = -4$ and $x = 2$ f. $a = 8$ and $x = \frac{1}{2}$

2. Assuming that each variable in the following expressions represents a positive real number, simplify each expression.

a. $r^4 \cdot r^{-5}$ e. $(16\, a^4)^{\frac{1}{4}}$ h. $a^{\sqrt{2}} \cdot a$

b. $(\frac{3}{4}\, a^3)^2$

c. $(4\, x^{-3})^{-2}$ f. $\dfrac{9\, r^{-3}}{3\, r^2}$ i. $\dfrac{25 - a^{-2}}{5 - a^{-2}}$

d. $\left(\dfrac{7\, ab^3}{14\, a^2 b}\right)^{-1}$ g. $\dfrac{54\, a^{-2} b^{\frac{1}{2}}}{6\, a^3 b^{-\frac{1}{2}}}$

3. Express in scientific notation.

a. 3560000   c. 0.00005   e. 87.60.

b. 827000   d. 4.3200   f. 0.4$\dot{3}$

4. State the common name for each of the following:

a. 3.2×10^4 c. 4.81×10^{-5} e. 4.300×10^5

b. 8.5×10^{-1} d. 6.09×10^{-1} f. 8×10^3

5. Assuming that $a \in R$, under what circumstances is each of the following expressions not defined?

a. $a^{\frac{1}{2}}$ d. $(\sqrt{a})^2$ g. $\sqrt{a^3}$

b. a^{-1} e. $\sqrt{a^{-2}}$ h. $(\sqrt[4]{a})^{-2}$

c. $(\sqrt[6]{a})^4$ f. $\sqrt[4]{a^3}$ i. $a^{\frac{1}{6}} (\sqrt[4]{a})^{-2}$

6. Express with rational exponents.

a. $\sqrt[3]{x}$ b. $\sqrt{\sqrt{r}};\ r > 0$ c. $\sqrt[3]{m} \cdot \sqrt[4]{m};\ m > 0$ d. $\sqrt[5]{a}$

7. Solve each of the following equations for x.

a. $4^x = 256$ c. $\sqrt{x^5} = 4\sqrt{2}$ e. $x^{\frac{5}{2}} = 16$

b. $(\frac{3}{5})^x = \frac{125}{27}$ d. $x^{-\frac{1}{4}} = 81$ f. $(x + 1)^{\frac{2}{3}} = 4$

8. a. If $y = a^x$ is to define an exponential function, what restriction must be placed on a?

b. What additional restriction must be placed on a if the function of part **a** is to be an increasing function?

9. Which of the functions described below are increasing functions and which are decreasing functions?

a. $\{(x, y) \mid y = 10^x; \; x \in Q\}$

b. $\{(x, y) \mid y = (0.01)^x; \; x \in Q\}$

c. $\{(x, y) \mid y = (5.1)^x; \; x \in R\}$

d. $\{(x, y) \mid y = (0.7)^x; \; x \in C\}$

10. a. If $y = a^x; \; x \in R$ defines an increasing function, is its inverse function an increasing function or a decreasing function?

b. If $y = a^x; \; x \in R$ defines a decreasing function, is its inverse function an increasing function or a decreasing function?

11. Sketch the graphs of the function defined by $y = (\frac{3}{4})^x$ and its inverse function, assuming that $x \in R$. Use one pair of coordinate axes for the two graphs.

12. Sketch the graphs of the function defined by $y = (\frac{4}{3})^x$ and its inverse function, assuming that $x \in R$. Use one pair of coordinate axes for the two graphs.

13. Solve each of the following equations.

a. $5^x = 5^{2x+1}$

b. $3^{m^2} = 3^{2m-1}$

c. $9^{x^2} = 3^{4-2x}$

14. Simplify.

a. $2^{\sqrt{5}} \cdot 4^{\sqrt{10}}$

b. $(5^{\sqrt{3}})^{-\sqrt{3}}$

c. $\dfrac{2^{\sqrt{8}}}{4^{\sqrt{2}}}$

15. Indicate the inverse of each of the following in two forms.

a. $\{(x, y) \mid y = 2^x; \; x \in R\}$

b. $\{(x, y) \mid y = (\frac{1}{2})^x; \; x \in R\}$

16. Write each of the following equations in logarithmic form.

a. $a^x = y$

b. $2^4 = 16$

c. $3^{-1} = \frac{1}{3}$

d. $\sqrt{10} = 3.162$

e. $10^{-2} = 0.01$

f. $3^{\log_a x} = x$

17. Write each of the following in exponential form.

a. $\log_2 32 = 5$

b. $\log_{10} 1000 = 3$

c. $\log_{10} 0.0001 = -4$

d. $\log_{49} \frac{1}{7} = -\frac{1}{2}$

e. $\log_2 \frac{1}{2} = -1$

f. $\log_3 r = s$

18. Find the value of x for which each of the following equations is true.

a. $\log_x 0.001 = -3$

b. $\log_x 81 = 4$

c. $\log_2 x = 6$

d. $\log x = -2$

e. $\log 10000 = x$

f. $\log_3 243 = x$

19. Complete each of the following to form a true statement.

a. If $\log y = \log 2 + \log 3 - \log c$, then $y = ?$

b. If $\log 12 = \log a + 2 \log b$, then $12 = ?$

c. If $\log z = \frac{3}{4} \log a$, then $z = ?$

20. Solve each of the following equations for x.

a. $\log_2 (x + 5) = 4$

b. $\frac{3}{2} \log_3 x = 3$

c. $\log (x^2 - 4) - \log (x + 4) = \log 8$

d. $\log_3 (x^2 - 4) - \log_3 (x + 4) = 4$

21. Use logarithms to evaluate each of the following.

    a. 314×912 **d.** 758.2×9.831 **g.** $\sqrt[4]{8270 \times 943.1}$

    b. $\dfrac{75.3}{946}$ **e.** $\dfrac{672.8}{12.53}$ **h.** $\pi\sqrt[3]{(75.46)^2}$

    c. $\sqrt[5]{627}$ **f.** $(45.71)^5$ **i.** $\dfrac{0.4516}{0.0032}$

22. Find the area of a triangle whose sides have the lengths 4.32 inches, 3.81 inches, and 2.91 inches.

23. Find the volume of a sphere whose radius is 24.7 inches long. Use $\pi = 3.142$.

24. The surface, S, of a sphere is found by the formula $S = 4\pi r^2$ in which r represents the length of the radius. Find the surface area of the sphere in Ex. 23.

25. If \$8500 is invested at 5% compounded annually, what amount will have accumulated at the end of 20 years if no money is withdrawn?

CHAPTER TEST

Which of the equations in Exercises 1–4 define exponential functions and which do not?

1. $y = 4^x; \; x \in R$ **3.** $y = (-4)^x; \; x \in Q$

2. $y = (\tfrac{1}{2})^x; \; x \in R$ **4.** $y = 1^x; \; x \in R$

Evaluate each expression in Exercises 5–8.

5. $4^{\frac{1}{2}} \cdot 16^{\frac{3}{4}}$ **6.** $(\sqrt[3]{-5})^3$ **7.** $(25)^{-\frac{1}{2}}$ **8.** $4^{0} \cdot 9^{\frac{1}{2}}$

Read each of the statements in Exercises 9–12. If the statement is always true, write "T" on your paper. If the statement is not always true, write "F" on your paper.

9. $\sqrt{a^6} = a^3$ **10.** $\sqrt[3]{a} = \sqrt[6]{a^2}$ **11.** $(a^{\frac{1}{3}})^3 = a$ **12.** $a^5 \cdot a^3 = a^8$

13. Simplify: $(2^{\sqrt{2}} \cdot 8^{\sqrt{2}})^{\frac{1}{2}}$

Solve each of the equations in Exercises 14–17 for x.

14. $5^x = \frac{1}{625}$ **15.** $\log_6 216 = x$ **16.** $\log_9 x = \frac{1}{2}$ **17.** $9^{x+2} = 3^x$

State whether each of the following equations (Ex. 18–19) defines an increasing function or a decreasing function.

18. $y = (\tfrac{7}{8})^x$ **19.** $y = (\tfrac{2}{3})^x$

20. Indicate the inverse of the function defined by $y = 3^x$.

21. If $\log y = \log 2 + 3 \log b$, then $y = ?$

Use logarithms to evaluate each of the following expressions.

22. $\sqrt[3]{0.432}$ **23.** 754.2×93.84 **24.** $\dfrac{6283}{0.0053}$ **25.** $\sqrt{(237.1)^3}$

9

Trigonometric Functions

Paths in a Circle

Let P and Q be two distinct points in a circle whose radius has the measure r. These points separate the circle into two *arcs*, the sum of whose measures is $2\pi r$. The measure of the length of any arc of a circle whose radius has the measure r is a non-negative real number less than or equal to $2\pi r$.

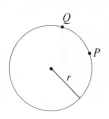

If we are given a point P in a circle C whose center is Q and whose radius has the measure r and are also given a real number s, we can determine a point S in C as follows: Let a point start at P and move, without reversing its direction, along a path in C in a counterclockwise direction if s is positive, and in a clockwise direction if s is negative, until it has moved a distance whose measure is $|s|$, thus arriving at the point S. (Observe that $|s|$ may be greater than the circumference of the circle.) Then P is the *initial* point and S is the *terminal* point of the path and the real number s is its *directed measure*. Clearly, if $s = 0$, then S and P are the same point. Q, the center of the circle C, is called the *center of this path* and the radius of circle C is called the *radius of this path*. We shall use the symbol (QP, s) to indicate a path having center Q, radius QP, initial point P, and directed measure s. We shall use O, rather than Q, to indicate the center of the path if and only if the center is the origin of the coordinate plane.

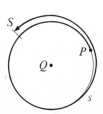

Two paths (AP, u) and (BT, v) are *equal* if and only if A and B are the same point, P and T are the same point, and $u = v$. These two paths are *equivalent* if and only if $|AP| = |BT|$ and $u = v$. Thus two paths are equivalent if and only if they are in the same circle or in congruent circles and have the same directed measure. Note that equal paths are equivalent but equivalent paths are not necessarily equal.

449

In the drawing below each of the three paths, shown as heavy black curves, is equivalent to each of the other two. P', S', and Q' are the terminal points of these paths.

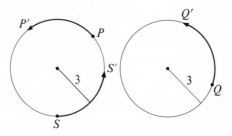

We now define the addition of two paths in the same circle as follows: If $|AP| = |AQ|$, then $(AP, u) + (AQ, v) = (AP, u + v)$. Also, $(AQ, v) + (AP, u) = (AQ, v + u)$. Observe that paths $(AP, u + v)$ and $(AQ, v + u)$ are not equal unless P and Q are the same point, but the paths are equivalent.

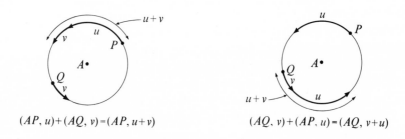

$(AP, u) + (AQ, v) = (AP, u+v)$ $(AQ, v) + (AP, u) = (AQ, v+u)$

Two paths in the same circle are called *coterminal paths* if they have the same initial point and the same terminal point. In each of the figures below, the path shown as a solid black curve is coterminal with the path shown as a dashed black curve. If r is the measure of the radius of a circle, then the directed measures of any two coterminal paths in this circle differ by $2\pi r k$

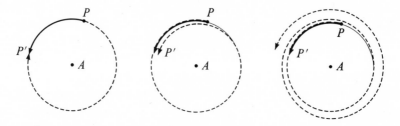

where k is an integer. Moreover, if two paths in the same circle have the same initial point, then they have the same terminal point if and only if their directed measures differ by $2\pi r k$ where $k \in I$ and r is the measure of the radius of the circle.

1. If a, b, and c are the measures of three arcs of a circle the length of whose radius has the measure r, which of the following statements can, under certain circumstances, be true?

a. $a+b+c > 2\pi r$ **c.** $a = -b$ **e.** $a+b+c = 2\pi$

b. $b = 2\pi r$ **d.** $a+b+c = 2\pi r$ **f.** $a < 0$

2. If a, b, and c are the measures of three paths in the circle described in Ex. 1, which of the statements of the exercise can be true?

3. The black curves, arrow heads, and letters in the drawings below combine to indicate directed paths in a circle. The letter written beside each path indicates the measure of the path.

a. Write the name of each path.

b. State whether the measure of the path is positive or negative.

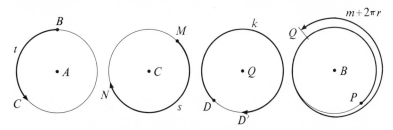

4. Copy each of the drawings of Ex. 3 and in each use a dashed line to show a path equivalent to the path already indicated.

5. Copy each of the drawings of Ex. 3 and in each use a dashed line to show a path coterminal with the path already drawn.

6. For each of the following draw a circle whose radius is one unit long and picture the indicated path.

a. (AB, π) **b.** $\left(AC, -\dfrac{\pi}{2}\right)$ **c.** $(OA, 3\pi)$ **d.** $(OA, -4\pi)$

7. Copy the figure at the right and in it show the following paths.

a. $(QC, t+s)$ **b.** $(QA, s+t)$

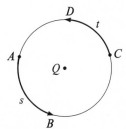

Trigonometric Functions of Real Numbers

A circle is in standard position if and only if it lies in the coordinate plane and has its center at the origin. If the radius of a circle in standard position has the measure r, then the equation of the circle is $x^2 + y^2 = r^2$.

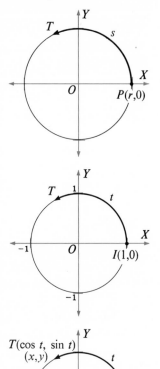

A path is in *standard position* if and only if it is in a standard-position circle and has for its initial point the point P where this circle intersects the positive x-axis. The coordinates of this point are $(r, 0)$ if the circle has a radius whose measure is r.

Let C be a unit circle (a unit circle is a circle whose radius has the measure 1) in standard position. Then C is the graph of the equation $x^2 + y^2 = 1$ and C intersects the positive x-axis at the point $I(1, 0)$. We now recall the procedure we used in Chapter 6 to show how each number t can be used to determine a unique point T in C. In view of our discussion of paths in the preceding section this procedure can now be described simply. All we need to do is to take T as the terminal point of the path (OI, t) when the coordinates of I are $(1, 0)$. Therefore each real number t determines a unique point T in a unit circle in standard position if we agree that t is to serve as the *directed measure* of a path in this circle and that the point $I(1, 0)$ is to be the initial point of this path. Accordingly, each real number t also determines a unique real number y which is the ordinate of T, and a unique real number x which is the abscissa of T.

We state the following definition: If t is the measure of a standard position path in the unit circle and (x, y) are the coordinates of the terminal point of the path, then $y = $ sine t and $x = $ cosine t. We often abbreviate the word "sine" as "sin" and the word "cosine" as "cos." Thus the coordinates of T may be given either as (x, y) or as $(\cos t, \sin t)$.

Since, by the procedure described above, each real number t corresponds to a unique real number sin t, $\{(t_1, \sin t_1), (t_2, \sin t_2), (t_3, \sin t_3), \ldots\}$ is a function. We call this function the *sine function*. Also, since each real number t corresponds to a unique real number cos t, $\{(t_1, \cos t_1), (t_2, \cos t_2), (t_3, \cos t_3), \ldots\}$ is a function. We call this function the *cosine function*.

Since T may move around the unit circle C in either a clockwise or a counterclockwise direction, we see that t may assume any real-number value. On the other hand, sin t and cos t are each restricted to $\langle -1, 1 \rangle$. Therefore each of the functions sine and cosine has R for its domain and $\langle -1, 1 \rangle$ for its range.

The real number t serves to determine four other numbers: tangent t, cosecant t, secant t, and cotangent t, which are often written in the abbreviated forms tan t, csc t, sec t, and cot t. These are defined as follows:

$$\tan t = \frac{\sin t}{\cos t}; \quad t \in R, \cos t \neq 0$$

$$\csc t = \frac{1}{\sin t}; \quad t \in R, \sin t \neq 0$$

$$\sec t = \frac{1}{\cos t}; \quad t \in R, \cos t \neq 0$$

$$\cot t = \frac{\cos t}{\sin t}; \quad t \in R, \sin t \neq 0$$

We now define the tangent function, the cosecant function, the secant function, and the cotangent function as follows:

$$\text{tangent function} = \left\{ (t, \tan t) \mid \tan t = \frac{\sin t}{\cos t}; \ t \in R, \cos t \neq 0 \right\}$$

$$\text{cosecant function} = \left\{ (t, \csc t) \mid \csc t = \frac{1}{\sin t}; \ t \in R, \sin t \neq 0 \right\}$$

$$\text{secant function} = \left\{ (t, \sec t) \mid \sec t = \frac{1}{\cos t}; \ t \in R, \cos t \neq 0 \right\}$$

$$\text{cotangent function} = \left\{ (t, \cot t) \mid \cot t = \frac{1}{\tan t}; \ t \in R, \tan t \neq 0 \right\}$$

The functions sine, cosine, tangent, secant, cosecant, and cotangent are called *trigonometric functions*.

Example 1. Make a table showing the values of sin t, cos t, tan t, csc t, sec t, and cot t when $t \in \left\{ 0, \dfrac{\pi}{2}, \pi, \dfrac{3\pi}{2}, \dfrac{7\pi}{2} \right\}$.

Solution. We draw a unit circle in standard position. This circle intersects the x-axis in the points $B(-1, 0)$ and $I(1, 0)$ and intersects the y-axis in the points $A(0, 1)$ and $C(0, -1)$. Let us assume that the points I, A, B, and C separate the circle into four equivalent paths whose measures have the sum 2π.

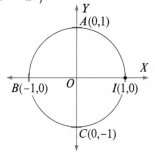

We have said that (x, y), the coordinates of the terminal point T of a path in the unit circle in standard position, can be expressed in the form $(\cos t, \sin t)$ when t is the directed measure of the path. When $t = 0$, the path $(OI, 0)$ has the initial point $I(1, 0)$, or $I(\cos 0, \sin 0)$, as its terminal point. Thus we see that $\cos 0 = 1$ and $\sin 0 = 0$. Also, by the definitions of $\tan t$, $\sec t$, $\csc t$, and $\cot t$, we have $\tan 0 = \frac{0}{1} = 0$, $\sec 0 = \frac{1}{1} = 1$, and $\csc 0$ and $\cot 0$ are undefined because $\frac{1}{0}$ is meaningless.

Similarly, by determining the terminal points of the paths whose initial point is I and whose directed measures are $\frac{\pi}{2}, \pi, \frac{3\pi}{2}$, and $\frac{7\pi}{2}$, we can find the other values required. These are shown in the table below.

$t =$	$\sin t$	$\cos t$	$\tan t$	$\cot t$	$\sec t$	$\csc t$
0	0	1	0	undefined	1	undefined
$\dfrac{\pi}{2}$	1	0	undefined	0	undefined	1
π	0	-1	0	undefined	-1	undefined
$\dfrac{3\pi}{2}$	-1	0	undefined	0	undefined	-1
$\dfrac{7\pi}{2}$	-1	0	undefined	0	undefined	-1

Observe that the last two rows are the same. Why is this so?

Example 2. $T(-0.6, 0.8)$ is a point in a unit circle in standard position. If T is the terminal point of the path (OI, t), find $\sin t$, $\cos t$, $\tan t$, $\csc t$, $\sec t$, and $\cot t$.

Solution.   The value of x which corresponds to $\cos t$ is -0.6 and the value of y which corresponds to $\sin t$ is 0.8. Therefore,

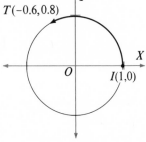

$$\tan t = \frac{\sin t}{\cos t} = \frac{0.8}{-0.6} = -\frac{4}{3},$$

$$\csc t = \frac{1}{\sin t} = \frac{1}{0.8} = \frac{5}{4},$$

$$\sec t = \frac{1}{\cos t} = \frac{1}{-0.6} = -\frac{5}{3}, \text{ and } \cot t = \frac{\cos t}{\sin t} = \frac{-0.6}{0.8} = -\frac{3}{4}.$$

1. If a unit circle is in standard position, each of the points T whose coordinates are given below is a point in the circle. Assume that each point T is the terminal point of a path (OI, t) in the circle. Recall that the point I has the coordinates $(1, 0)$. Find $\sin t$, $\cos t$, $\tan t$, $\csc t$, $\sec t$, and $\cot t$ in each case.

　a. $T(\frac{3}{5}, \frac{4}{5})$

　b. $T(-\frac{5}{13}, \frac{12}{13})$

　c. $T(-\frac{5}{13}, -\frac{12}{13})$

　d. $T\left(\frac{\sqrt{3}}{2}, \frac{1}{2}\right)$

　e. $T\left(-\frac{\sqrt{2}}{2}, \frac{\sqrt{2}}{2}\right)$

　f. $T(\frac{2}{3}, -\frac{1}{3}\sqrt{5})$

2. What are the numerical values of $\sin t$, $\cos t$, $\tan t$, $\csc t$, $\sec t$, and $\cot t$ when

　a. $t = 3\pi$　　　**b.** $t = 6\pi$　　　**c.** $t = \dfrac{5\pi}{2}$　　　**d.** $t = 4\pi$

Directed Angles

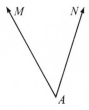

　The rays AM and AN form the geometric angle NAM whose vertex is A as shown in the figure at the right. We now consider how paths in a unit circle can be used to extend the elementary notion of an angle.

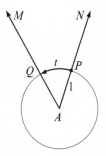

　Consider the unit circle whose center is at the vertex A of the angle formed by $\overrightarrow{AN}$ and $\overrightarrow{AM}$. The figure at the right shows that the path (AP, t) can be associated with this angle. However, it is clear that other paths could be associated with this elementary angle. To overcome this difficulty we introduce the idea of *directed angle*.

　Let a path (AP, t) in the unit circle be given and let Q be the terminal point of this path (see figure). The ray AN, which contains P, is the *initial side* of the corresponding directed angle; the ray AM, which contains Q, is its *terminal side* and the point A is its vertex. The path (AP, t) indicates how the directed angle is generated in the following sense. The ray AW is placed in the initial position $\overrightarrow{AN}$ and then rotated about A without reversing its direction of rotation so that R, its point of intersection with the unit circle, traces the path (AP, t). The terminal position of $\overrightarrow{AW}$ is then $\overrightarrow{AM}$. The directed angle NAM consists of $\overrightarrow{AN}$, $\overrightarrow{AM}$ and the *rotation* described by $\overrightarrow{AW}$ as R traced the path (AP, t).

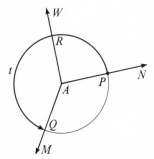

This path is called the *corresponding path in the unit circle* or, briefly, the *corresponding path* for the directed angle *NAM*. We see that this directed angle is completely determined by its initial ray *AN* and the real number *t*, which is the directed measure of its corresponding path in the unit circle. We will denote the directed angle *NAM* by the symbol $(\overrightarrow{AN}, t)$. We will denote the vertex of a directed angle with the letter *O* if and only if the angle is in the coordinate plane and its vertex is at the origin.

The *rotation* involved in a directed angle is positive or negative according as *t*, the measure of its corresponding path in the unit circle, is positive or negative. We say that a directed angle is positive if its rotation is positive and negative if its rotation is negative.

Example 1.   Draw the directed angles $\left(\overrightarrow{BF}, \dfrac{\pi}{2}\right)$, $(\overrightarrow{AZ}, 2)$, $(\overrightarrow{CK}, -2)$, and $(\overrightarrow{DM}, -10)$.

Solution.   We are given the ray $\overrightarrow{BF}$ and the number $\dfrac{\pi}{2}$. We draw a unit circle with *B* as center and which intersects $\overrightarrow{BF}$ at *R*. We locate *Q*, the terminal point of the path $\left(BR, \dfrac{\pi}{2}\right)$ and draw ray $\overrightarrow{BW}$ through *Q*. The angle *FBW* with the counterclockwise rotation of $\dfrac{\pi}{2}$ from initial side $\overrightarrow{BF}$ is the required directed angle.

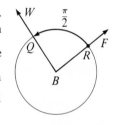

In the second case we are given the ray $\overrightarrow{AZ}$ and the number 2. We draw a unit circle with *A* as center and which intersects $\overrightarrow{AZ}$ at *B*. We locate *S*, the terminal point of the path $(AB, 2)$ as accurately as we can. (Since 2 is twice the measure of the radius of the circle, it is easy to get a reasonably close approximation to the actual directed measure of the path.) We draw ray $\overrightarrow{AS}$. The angle whose initial side is $\overrightarrow{AZ}$, whose terminal side is $\overrightarrow{AS}$, and having the counterclockwise rotation of 2 is the required directed angle.

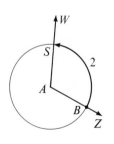

The other required directed angles are shown below.

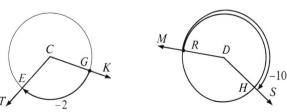

We say that two directed angles $(\overrightarrow{A_1P_1}, t_1)$ and $(\overrightarrow{A_2P_2}, t_2)$ are equal if and only if $\overrightarrow{A_1P_1} = \overrightarrow{A_2P_2}$ and $t_1 = t_2$. This is equivalent to saying that two directed angles are equal if and only if their corresponding paths are equal. Note that equal directed angles have the same vertex, the same initial side, and the same terminal side. However, directed angles with the same vertex, the same initial side, and the same terminal side are not necessarily equal.

Two directed angles with the same vertex, the same initial side, and the same terminal side are called *coterminal angles*. Clearly, two directed angles are coterminal if and only if their corresponding paths are coterminal. If $(\overrightarrow{A_1P_1}, t_1)$ and $(\overrightarrow{A_2P_2}, t_2)$ are two coterminal directed angles, then $t_1 = t_2 + 2\pi k$ when $k \in I$.

Two directed angles are equivalent if and only if their corresponding paths are equivalent. Thus angles $(\overrightarrow{A_1P_1}, t_1)$ and $(\overrightarrow{A_2P_2}, t_2)$ are equivalent if and only if $t_1 = t_2$.

A directed angle is in *standard position* if and only if its corresponding unit circle path is in standard position. This means that the vertex of the angle is at the origin and the initial side lies in the positive x-axis. The symbol $(\overrightarrow{OI}, t)$ denotes a directed angle in standard position. If $0 \leq t < 2\pi$, then (OI, t) or any path equivalent to (OI, t) is a *primary path*. Any directed angle which corresponds to a primary path is called a primary directed angle. Thus if

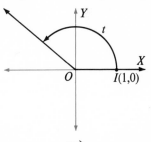

$0 \leq t < 2\pi$, then $(\overrightarrow{OI}, t)$ or any directed angle equivalent to $(\overrightarrow{OI}, t)$ is called a *primary directed angle*. It is clear that the angle $(\overrightarrow{OI}, t)$ is completely determined by the real number t.

Example 2. Draw the following angles:

$$\left(\overrightarrow{OI}, \frac{3\pi}{4}\right), (\overrightarrow{OI}, 1), \text{ and } \left(\overrightarrow{OI}, -\tfrac{4}{3}\pi\right).$$

Draw two other directed angles which are coterminal with each of these angles.

Solution. The first row of drawings on the following page shows $\left(\overrightarrow{OI}, \frac{3\pi}{4}\right)$ and two angles coterminal with it, the second row shows $(\overrightarrow{OI}, 1)$ and two angles coterminal with it, and the third row shows $\left(\overrightarrow{OI}, -\frac{4\pi}{3}\right)$ and two angles coterminal with it.

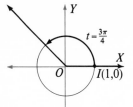

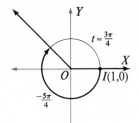

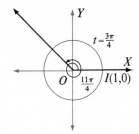

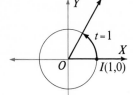

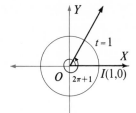

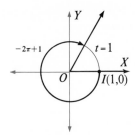

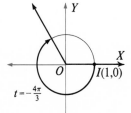

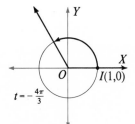

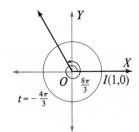

Ⓐ **EXERCISES**

1. Draw each of the following directed angles.

   a. $\left(\overrightarrow{MN}, \dfrac{\pi}{3}\right)$ c. $\left(\overrightarrow{OA}, \dfrac{5}{6}\pi\right)$ e. $(\overrightarrow{AC}, -3\pi)$

   b. $\left(\overrightarrow{OA}, -\dfrac{\pi}{3}\right)$ d. $(\overrightarrow{QB}, -1)$ f. $\left(\overrightarrow{DE}, \dfrac{\pi}{2}\right)$

2. Draw each of the following directed angles. Note that each must be in standard position.

   a. $(\overrightarrow{OI}, \pi)$ d. $\left(\overrightarrow{OI}, \dfrac{2\pi}{3}\right)$ g. $(\overrightarrow{OI}, 4)$

   b. $\left(\overrightarrow{OI}, -\dfrac{\pi}{4}\right)$ e. $\left(\overrightarrow{OI}, \dfrac{5\pi}{3}\right)$ h. $\left(\overrightarrow{OI}, -\dfrac{11\pi}{4}\right)$

   c. $\left(\overrightarrow{OI}, \dfrac{5\pi}{4}\right)$ f. $\left(\overrightarrow{OI}, -\dfrac{8\pi}{3}\right)$ i. $(\overrightarrow{OI}, -3)$

3. Draw two other directed angles each equivalent to $\left(\overrightarrow{OI}, \frac{\pi}{4}\right)$. Draw the directed angle $\left(\overrightarrow{OI}, \frac{\pi}{4}\right)$.

4. Draw two negative directed angles coterminal with directed angle $\left(\overrightarrow{OI}, -\frac{\pi}{6}\right)$. How many such angles are there?

5. Draw two positive directed angles coterminal with directed angle $\left(\overrightarrow{OI}, -\frac{\pi}{6}\right)$. How many such directed angles are there?

6. Are equal directed angles always coterminal? Are coterminal directed angles always equal?

7. Each of the following real numbers is the directed measure of a path in a unit circle. Draw, in standard position, the directed angle corresponding to each measure.

a. $-\pi$ **b.** $\frac{7\pi}{4}$ **c.** -1 **d.** $-\frac{7\pi}{6}$ **e.** 2π **f.** 6π **g.** 2 **h.** $-\frac{2\pi}{3}$

8. Which of the directed angles that you drew in Ex. 7 can be described as primary angles?

Radian Measurement

We have said that the real number t is the directed measure of the uni. circle path that corresponds to the angle $(\overrightarrow{QA}, t)$. The real number t is also called the *radian measure* of this angle. It follows from the definition of equivalent directed angles that any two equivalent directed angles have the same radian measure.

There is a useful relationship between the radian measure of a directed angle and the directed measure of its corresponding path in any circle which has the vertex of the angle as its center. Such an angle is called a directed central angle. In the figure at the right, $(\overrightarrow{QA}, t)$ is a directed angle whose corresponding path (QA, t) in the unit circle C has B for its terminal point. Let C' be a circle whose radius has the measure r and which is concentric and coplanar with the unit circle C. Let the points of intersection of $\overrightarrow{QA}$ and $\overrightarrow{QB}$ with C' be called A' 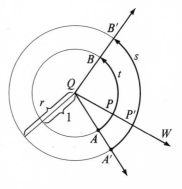 and B' respectively. Then $|QA'| = |QB'| = r$. Any ray QW which intersects C in a point P will intersect C' in a point P'. As P traces the path

(QA, t) in C, point P' traces the path (QA', s) in C'. Thus (QA', s) is the path in C' which corresponds to the directed angle $(\overrightarrow{QA}, t)$.

A path is said to *correspond* to an *arc* of a circle if a point which traces the path while moving in the counterclockwise (positive) direction also traces the arc. The measure of an arc is the measure of its corresponding path. Thus s is the measure of arc AB ($\overset{\frown}{AB}$) in the figure at the right because (OA, s) is its corresponding path. Two arcs are congruent if and only if their corresponding paths are equivalent. A central angle and an arc which corresponds to the same path are said to correspond to each other. In this case we say that the angle *intercepts* the arc and that the arc, or its chord, *subtends* the angle.

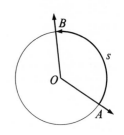

From the theorem on similar sectors in geometry we have $\dfrac{t}{s} = \dfrac{1}{r}$ when t is the measure of the arc intercepted by a central angle of a unit circle and s is the measure of the arc intercepted by the same central angle of a concentric circle whose radius has the measure r. If "central angle" in the preceding statement is replaced by "directed central angle," the equation $\dfrac{t}{s} = \dfrac{1}{r}$ remains valid. Thus the equation $t = \dfrac{s}{r}$ gives the radian measure t of a directed central angle in terms of the measure r of the radius of any circle which has the vertex of the directed angle as its center and the directed measure s of the path which corresponds to the directed central angle in that circle. Equation $t = \dfrac{s}{r}$ can be written as $s = rt$.

If $0 \leq t < 2\pi$, then $(\overrightarrow{QA}, t)$ is a primary directed angle. Why? A path in any circle is called a primary path if and only if it corresponds to a primary directed central angle. Since $0 \leq t < 2\pi$, we know that $0 \leq rt < 2\pi r$. It follows that $0 \leq s < 2\pi r$. Therefore the measure of any primary path in a circle whose radius has the measure r is a non-negative number less than $2\pi r$.

Example 1.   If a circle is divided into five congruent arcs, find the measure in radians of the central angle which corresponds to each arc.

Solution.   Since the arcs are equivalent, their central angles are equivalent. Let each of the five central angles have the measure t and the radius have the measure r. Then each arc has the measure rt. Thus $5\,rt = 2\pi r \longrightarrow t = \dfrac{2\pi}{5}$.

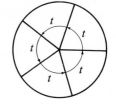

Example 2. The radius of a circle is 12 inches long and an arc of the circle subtends a central angle of 2.5 radians. Find s the length of the arc.

Solution. $s = 12 \times 2.5 = 30$. The arc is 30 inches long.

Ⓐ EXERCISES

1. If a circle is divided into n equivalent paths, find the measure in radians of the central angle subtended by each path when

 a. $n = 3$ **b.** $n = 4$ **c.** $n = 90$ **d.** $n = 360$

2. A path in a circle, the measure of whose radius is r, subtends a directed central angle whose measure in radians is t. Find the measure of the path when

 a. $r = 6$ and $t = 3\frac{1}{3}$

 b. $r = 5$ and $t = \frac{1}{5}$

 c. $r = 1$ and $t = 0.5\,\pi$

 d. $r = 18\frac{2}{3}$ and $t = \dfrac{3\,\pi}{4}$

 e. $r = 13$ and $t = 0.2$

 f. $r = 15$ and $t = \dfrac{2\,\pi}{5}$

3. Find r, the measure of the radius of each of the following circles, if the directed measure of a path in the circle is s and the path subtends a directed central angle whose measure in radians is t.

 a. $s = 12$ and $t = \frac{1}{2}$

 b. $s = -15\,\pi$ and $t = -\pi$

 c. $s = 26.5\,\pi$ and $t = 5\,\pi$

 d. $s = 23$ and $t = 2.6$

 e. $s = -20$ and $t = -1.4$

 f. $s = 15$ and $t = \frac{3}{5}\,\pi$

4. Find t, the radian measure of the directed central angle which corresponds to a path whose directed measure is s, assuming that the measure of the radius of the circle is r and that r and s are directed measures involving like units (both feet, both inches, and so on).

 a. $s = 60$ and $r = 30$

 b. $s = 90\,\pi$ and $r = 3$

 c. $s = -12.5$ and $r = 12.5$

 d. $s = 18\,\pi$ and $r = 6$

 e. $s = -10\,\pi$ and $r = 100$

 f. $s = \dfrac{180\,\pi}{17}$ and $r = \dfrac{9}{17}$

5. Find the measure in radians of a central angle of a circle whose radius is 6 inches long if the angle intercepts an arc which is 14 inches long.

6. The length of the radius of a circle is 4 inches. If the measure of a central angle of the circle in radians is 2.3, how long is the arc intercepted by the angle?

7. An arc of a circle is 7.875 inches long and subtends a central angle whose measure in radians in 4.5. Find the length of the radius of the circle.

Other Angle Measurement

In the preceding section we found t, the radian measure of a directed central angle in a circle whose radius has the length r, by dividing the directed measure of its corresponding path by r; in other words, we found t by use of the equation $t = \dfrac{s}{r}$.

If we use the circumference of a circle as the unit for measuring paths in a circle, we obtain another system for measuring directed central angles—a system whose basic unit is one *revolution*. We sometimes abbreviate the word "revolution" by writing "rev." Since the measure of the path which corresponds to the entire circle is $2\,\pi r$, we write $2\,\pi r$ for s in the equation $t = \dfrac{s}{r}$ to obtain the radian measure of the directed central angle whose corresponding arc is the entire circle. Thus,

$$1 \text{ revolution} = \frac{2\,\pi r}{r} \text{ radians} = 2\,\pi \text{ radians}$$

If we divide a circle into 360 equivalent arcs, the central angle subtended by each arc is said to have a measurement of one *degree*. We sometimes abbreviate the word "degree" by the symbol °. Thus the entire circle subtends a central angle whose measurement is 360°. Therefore 360°, 1 revolution, and $2\,\pi$ radians are all measurements of the central angle which corresponds to the entire circle. Thus when we write:

$$1 \text{ revolution} = 2\,\pi \text{ radians} = 360 \text{ degrees}$$

we indicate that these three denominate numbers are measurements of the same angle; just as when we write:

$$100 \text{ yards} = 300 \text{ feet} = 3600 \text{ inches}$$

to indicate that these three denominate numbers are measurements of the same length. Observe that,

$$\pi \text{ radians} = 180 \text{ degrees}$$

$$1 \text{ radian} = \frac{180}{\pi} \text{ degrees} \approx 75.3°$$

$$1 \text{ degree} = \frac{\pi}{180} \text{ radians} \approx 0.0175 \text{ radians}$$

Recall that the symbol $(\overrightarrow{AB}, t)$ represents the directed angle whose initial ray is $\overrightarrow{AB}$ and whose radian measure is t. We will use the symbol $(\overrightarrow{AB}, d°)$ to represent the directed angle whose initial ray is $\overrightarrow{AB}$ and whose degree measure is d.

If the angle whose measurement is one degree is divided into 60 equivalent angles, each of these angles has a measurement of one *minute*. We abbreviate the word "minute" by writing "min" or the symbol ′. Thus 30′ is read "thirty minutes." Each of the sixty equivalent angles whose sum is one minute has a measurement called one *second*. We abbreviate the word "second" by writing "sec" or the symbol ″. Thus 20″ is read "twenty seconds." Accordingly, $1° = 60'$ and $1' = 60''$.

Table IV, page 762, can be used to convert radian measurements into degree measurements and conversely. The first two columns of this table show the number of radians, expressed to the nearest ten-thousandth, which corresponds to each tenth of a degree for degree measures in $\langle 0, 45 \rangle$ and the last two columns show similar correspondences for degree measures in $\langle 45, 90 \rangle$. Observe that the last two columns are read upward from the bottom of the page.

Example 1. Express $16° \ 15'$ in radians.

Solution. $16° \ 15' = 16.25°$

We do not find $16.25°$ in the table but we do find $16.2°$ and $16.3°$, between which $16.25°$ lies. We then use the table as follows:

$$0.10°\begin{bmatrix} 16.3° = 0.2845 \text{ radians} \\ 0.05°\begin{bmatrix} 16.25° = \_?\_ \text{ radians} \\ 16.2° = 0.2827 \text{ radians} \end{bmatrix} n \text{ radians} \end{bmatrix} 0.0018 \text{ radians}$$

$$\frac{0.05}{0.10} = \frac{n}{0.0018}$$

$$n = 0.0009$$

$$16.25° = (0.2827 + 0.0009) \text{ radians} = 0.2836 \text{ radians}$$

Example 2. Convert 1.2890 radians to the nearest hundredth of a degree.

Solution. 1.2890 radians does not appear in the table but we do find 1.2881 radians and 1.2898 radians, between which 1.2890 radians lies. By use of the table we find:

$$0.1\begin{bmatrix} 73.9° = 1.2898 \text{ radians} \\ d\begin{bmatrix} \_?\_° = 1.2890 \text{ radians} \\ 73.8° = 1.2881 \text{ radians} \end{bmatrix} 0.0009 \end{bmatrix} 0.0017$$

$$\frac{d}{0.1} = \frac{0.0009}{0.0017}$$

$$d = 0.05$$

$$73.8 + 0.05 = 73.85$$

Therefore 1.2890 radians $= 73.85°$.

1. Complete the following table so that the numbers shown in each of the three columns are measures of the same angle in radians, degrees, and revolutions, respectively.

radians	degrees	revolutions
$\frac{\pi}{6}$	?	?
$\frac{1}{2}$	?	?
?	?	$-\frac{1}{4}$
?	240	?
?	?	2.5
?	60	?
-4π	?	?
?	?	$-\frac{1}{360}$
$\frac{3}{4}\pi$	?	?

2. Express each of the following in revolutions.
   a. $14°$
   b. $31° \, 40'$
   c. $-115°$
   d. $8° \, 15'$
   e. $1040°$
   f. $-425°$
   g. $60''$
   h. $12° \, 14' \, 5''$

3. Express each of the following in degrees. Express fractional parts of a degree in decimal form to the nearest hundredth.
   a. 4.5 rev   b. $\frac{5}{6}$ rev   c. -0.1 rev   d. -1.5 rev   e. $\frac{5}{8}$ rev   f. $\frac{1}{7}$ rev

4. Use $1° = 0.0175$ radians to express each of the following in radians.
   a. $30'$ b. $-12°$ c. $750°$ d. $16.1°$

5. Use Table IV to express each of the following to the nearest ten-thousandth of a radian.
   a. $4.2°$
   b. $-17°$
   c. $32.34°$
   d. $45.17°$
   e. $67.55°$
   f. $72° \, 30'$
   g. $18° \, 15'$
   h. $67° \, 12'$

6. Use Table IV to express each of the following in degrees. When interpolation is necessary, express fractional parts of a degree to the nearest hundredth.
   a. 0.0506 radians
   b. 1.2008 radians
   c. 1.4608 radians
   d. 0.7854 radians
   e. 0.1126 radians
   f. 0.3880 radians
   g. -0.1789 radians
   h. -1.4050 radians
   i. 1.5700 radians

Some Applications of Angle Measurements and Linear Measurements

One important application of the radian measure of an angle is the finding of the area of a sector of a circle. Let k represent the measure of the area of the sector $Q\text{-}\overset{\frown}{AB}$ shown at the right, let t represent the measure in radians of the central angle, and let its intercepted arc AB have the measure s. Then from geometry we know that

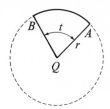

$$\frac{k}{\pi r^2} = \frac{s}{2\,\pi r}$$

From this

$$k = \tfrac{1}{2}\,rs$$

Since $s = rt$, $k = \tfrac{1}{2}r^2t$. Observe that when $t = 2\,\pi$, the right member of $k = \tfrac{1}{2}r^2t$ becomes πr^2, the equation for finding the area of a circle the measure of whose radius is r.

Example 1. Find the area of a sector of a circle if the central angle of the sector contains $50°$ and the radius of the sector is 10.0 inches long.

Solution When we say that the radius of the sector is 10.0 inches long, we mean that the radius of the circle containing the sector is 10.0 inches long. Since the $k = \tfrac{1}{2}r^2t$ is valid only if the central angle is measured in radians, we convert $50°$ to radians. Thus $50° = \dfrac{5\,\pi}{18}$ radians. Then $k = \dfrac{1}{2}\cdot(10.0)^2\cdot\dfrac{5\,\pi}{18} = \dfrac{250\,\pi}{18} = \dfrac{125\,\pi}{9}$. If we use $\pi = 3.1416$, we have $k = \dfrac{125\times 3.1416}{9} \approx 43.63$. Therefore the required area is approximately 43.6 square inches.

Radian measure also helps us to describe the motion of a particle in a circle. Let a particle move along a circle a distance whose directed measure is s. We know that $s = rt$ where s is the directed measure of a path whose radius is r, and t is the radian measure of the directed central angle which intercepts this path. If this directed distance is covered in m units of time, the average velocity is $\dfrac{s}{m}$ and the average change in t per unit of time is $\dfrac{t}{m}$. Dividing both members of $s = rt$ by m, we have $\dfrac{s}{m} = r\cdot\dfrac{t}{m}$. If we let $v = \dfrac{s}{m}$ and ω (the Greek letter omega) $= \dfrac{t}{m}$, we have $v = r\omega$ where v is the *linear velocity* of the particle, that is, the average change in *s* per unit of time, and ω is the *angular velocity* of the particle, that is, the average change in *t* per unit of time.

Example 2. The diameter of a fly-wheel is 4 feet long. If the wheel is rotating at the rate of 3600 revolutions per minute, what is its angular velocity in radians per second? What is the linear velocity of a point in its rim in feet per second?

Solution. Since 1 revolution = 2 π radians, 3600 revolutions per minute = 3600 × 2 π or 7200 π radians per minute. 7200 π radians per minute = $\frac{7200\,\pi}{60}$ or 120 π radians per second. Thus the angular velocity of the wheel is 120 π radians per second.

From the result just obtained, we see that ω = 120 π. Since *r* = 2 and *v* = *r* ω, *v* = 2 × 120 π = 240 π. Thus the linear velocity of a point on the rim of the wheel is 240 π feet per second.

 Ⓐ **EXERCISES**

1. Through how many radians does the hour hand of a clock pass in 40 minutes?

2. Assuming that the length of the diameter of the earth's equator is 7912 miles, what is the length of the portion of the equator intercepted by a central angle whose measure in degrees is 1?

3. A protractor is to be made so that a central angle whose measure in degrees is 1 intercepts a path of ⅛ inch in the outer circular edge of the protractor. How long should the radius of the protractor be made?

4. The length of the diameter of a wheel is 24 inches. If the wheel makes 4 revolutions per second, what is the linear velocity of a point on the rim of the wheel in inches per second?

5. **a.** What is the angular velocity in radians per second of a wheel that makes 1800 revolutions per minute?

   b. If the wheel of part **a** has a radius which is 6 inches long, what is the linear velocity in feet per second of a point in the rim of the wheel?

   c. What is the linear velocity in feet per second of a point midway between the rim and the center of the wheel described above?

6. The wheel, including the tire, on one make of automobile has a diameter 28 inches long. How many revolutions does the wheel make in traveling one mile?

7. What is the angular velocity in radians per second of the wheel of Ex. 6 when the wheel makes 28,800 revolutions per hour?

8. The propeller blade of an airplane is 10 feet long. If a point in the tip of the blade moves with a linear velocity of 250 feet per second, what is the angular velocity of the blade in radians per second?

9. What is the length of the diameter of a wheel whose angular velocity is 3 radians per second when the linear velocity of a point in the circumference of the wheel is 90 feet per second?

10. As the minute hand of a clock passes through an angle of 24°, its tip travels a distance of $\frac{2\pi}{5}$ inches. What is the length of the minute hand?

11. What is the area of a sector of a circle whose radius is 8 inches long and whose central angle contains 40°?

12. What is the area of a sector of a circle whose radius is 12 inches long and whose central angle measures $\frac{4\pi}{3}$ radians?

13. A belt is used to make a wheel with a 6-inch radius turn a wheel with a 15-inch radius. What is the angular velocity of the larger wheel if the angular velocity of the smaller wheel is 24π radians per second?

14. One of two belt-driven wheels has a 12-inch radius and the other has a 4-inch radius.

a. If the angular velocity of the smaller wheel is 6 radians per second, what is the angular velocity in radians per second of the larger wheel?

b. What is the linear velocity in feet per second of a point in the rim of the smaller wheel? of a point in the rim of the larger wheel?

Trigonometric Functions Associated With Angles

We have defined the trigonometric functions as *sets of ordered pairs of real numbers.* Corresponding to each real number t, which is not an integral multiple of $\frac{\pi}{2}$, there are six real numbers, sin t, cos t, tan t, cot t, sec t, and csc t, which are the values of the six trigonometric functions. This interpretation of the trigonometric functions is the one that you will encounter in many practical situations as well as in more advanced courses in mathematics such as calculus. In the remaining sections of this chapter we consider trigonometry as it was first developed for the purpose of computing unknown distances and unknown angles. In order to do this we must define the trigonometric functions of angles.

Let θ be a variable whose domain is the set of directed angles. Then θ can represent any member of $\{(\overrightarrow{A_1B_1}, t_1), (\overrightarrow{A_2B_2}, t_2) \ldots\}$. *To every angle θ there corresponds a real number t* which is the measure of the angle in radians.

To every real number t there corresponds a number sin t, which is the unique value of the sine function which corresponds to the argument *t*. *Thus for every angle θ there corresponds a real number sin t*. This correspondence defines a function whose domain is the set of angles and whose range is the set of real numbers in $\langle -1, 1 \rangle$. We define $\sin \theta$ to be the same as $\sin t$, where *t* is the radian measure of θ. Thus we have the sine function $\{(\theta, \sin \theta)\}$. The other five trigonometric functions of angles are similarly defined. Thus we have the following definition: If θ is an angle whose radian measure is *t*, then

$$\sin \theta = \sin t \qquad \tan \theta = \tan t \qquad \csc \theta = \csc t$$
$$\cos \theta = \cos t \qquad \sec \theta = \sec t \qquad \cot \theta = \cot t$$

Let the symbol $\angle t$ represent the directed angle whose radian measure is *t*, and let the symbol $\angle d°$ represent the directed angle whose degree measure is *d*. If θ is the directed angle whose radian measure is *t* and whose degree measure is *d*, we have: $\theta = \angle t = \angle d°$.

(i) If $\theta = \angle t = \angle d°$ where *t* is the radian measure of θ and *d* is the degree measure of θ, we know that:

$$\sin \theta = \sin \angle t = \sin \angle d° = \sin \frac{\pi d}{180} = \sin t.$$

A similar statement can be made about the values of each of the other five trigonometric functions.

Note that *t*, the radian measure of an angle whose degree measure is *d*, is $\frac{\pi d}{180}$. Thus $t = \frac{\pi d}{180}$.

The definition above enables us to find a unique ratio, called a trigonometric ratio, associated with any angle θ in terms of x_0 and y_0, the coordinates of the point where the terminal ray OT of an equivalent directed angle in standard position intersects the unit circle.

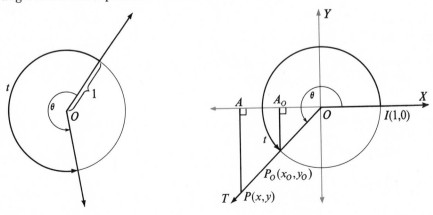

If θ is equivalent to $(\overrightarrow{OI}, t)$, and (x_o, y_o) are the coordinates of the intersection of the terminal ray of $(\overrightarrow{OI}, t)$ with the unit circle, then each of the following statements is true:

A

$$\sin \theta = \sin t = y_o \qquad\qquad \csc \theta = \csc t = \frac{1}{y_o} \quad (y_o \neq 0)$$

$$\cos \theta = \cos t = x_o \qquad\qquad \sec \theta = \sec t = \frac{1}{x_o} \quad (x_o \neq 0)$$

$$\tan \theta = \tan t = \frac{y_o}{x_o} \quad (x_o \neq 0) \qquad \cot \theta = \cot t = \frac{x_o}{y_o} \quad (y_o \neq 0)$$

Now we would like to express the trigonometric ratios associated with θ in terms of x and y the coordinates of any point, other than the origin, in the terminal ray OT. We draw vertical lines through P and P_o intersecting the x-axis in points A and A_o respectively.

Thus when right triangles OAP and OA_oP_o are similar, the measures of their corresponding sides are proportional; that is,

$$\frac{|AP|}{|OP|} = \frac{|A_oP_o|}{|OP_o|}, \quad \frac{|OA|}{|OP|} = \frac{|OA_o|}{|OP_o|}, \quad \frac{|AP|}{|OA|} = \frac{|A_oP_o|}{|OA_o|}, \quad \frac{|OP|}{|AP|} = \frac{|OP_o|}{|A_oP_o|},$$

$$\frac{|OP|}{|OA|} = \frac{|OP_o|}{|OA_o|}, \quad \frac{|OA|}{|AP|} = \frac{|OA_o|}{|A_oP_o|}.$$

For $\overrightarrow{OT}$, as shown in the preceding diagram, $|AP| = -y, |OA| = -x, |OP| = \sqrt{x^2 + y^2}, |A_oP_o| = -y_o, |OA_o| = -x_o$, and $|OP_o| = 1$. Substituting these values in the preceding equations and using the multiplication property of equality, we obtain:

B

$$\frac{y}{\sqrt{x^2 + y^2}} = y_o \qquad\qquad \frac{\sqrt{x^2 + y^2}}{y} = \frac{1}{y_o}$$

$$\frac{x}{\sqrt{x^2 + y^2}} = x_o \qquad\qquad \frac{\sqrt{x^2 + y^2}}{x} = \frac{1}{x_o}$$

$$\frac{y}{x} = \frac{y_o}{x_o} \qquad\qquad \frac{x}{y} = \frac{x_o}{y_o}$$

If we agree to let $r = |OP| = \sqrt{x^2 + y^2}$, the equations in **A** and **B** establish the following important theorem.

▷ **Theorem 1–9.** If θ is any angle, $P(x, y)$ is any point other than the origin in the terminal side of an angle in standard position equivalent to θ, and $|OP| = r$, then

(1) $\sin \theta = \dfrac{y}{r}$ 　　　　　 (4) $\csc \theta = \dfrac{r}{y}$ 　$(y \neq 0)$

(2) $\cos \theta = \dfrac{x}{r}$ 　　　　　 (5) $\sec \theta = \dfrac{r}{x}$ 　$(x \neq 0)$

(3) $\tan \theta = \dfrac{y}{x}$ 　$(x \neq 0)$ 　　 (6) $\cot \theta = \dfrac{x}{y}$ 　$(y \neq 0)$

Note. Theorem 1–9 is actually six theorems. Each of the six theorems has the original hypothesis and one of the numbered conclusions.

The six ratios $\dfrac{y}{r}, \dfrac{x}{r}, \dfrac{y}{x}, \dfrac{r}{y}, \dfrac{r}{x}$, and $\dfrac{x}{y}$, whose values depend on the angle θ but do not depend on the choice of r, are called the *trigonometric ratios* associated with θ.

From Theorem 1–9 (1) and (2), we obtain the following important corollary.

> **Corollary to Theorem 1–9.** If θ is any angle, $P(x, y)$ is any point other than the origin in the terminal side of an angle in standard position equivalent to θ, and $|OP| = r$, then $x = r \cos \theta$ and $y = r \sin \theta$.

Example 1. Write the other five trigonometric ratios associated with the angle α if $\tan \alpha = \frac{5}{3}$ and $\cos \alpha$ is negative.

Solution. Since $\tan \alpha$ is positive and $\cos \alpha$ is negative, we know that the terminal ray of α lies in Quadrant 3. Thus there is a point $P(x, y)$ in the terminal ray of α whose coordinates are $x = -3$ and $y = -5$. $|OP| = r = \sqrt{x^2 + y^2} = \sqrt{(-3)^2 + (-5)^2} = \sqrt{34}$. Therefore

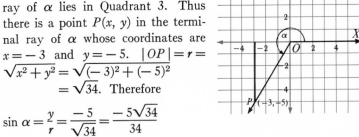

$$\sin \alpha = \frac{y}{r} = \frac{-5}{\sqrt{34}} = \frac{-5\sqrt{34}}{34}$$

$$\cos \alpha = \frac{x}{r} = \frac{-3}{\sqrt{34}} = \frac{-3\sqrt{34}}{34} \qquad \csc \alpha = \frac{r}{y} = \frac{\sqrt{34}}{-5} = -\frac{\sqrt{34}}{5}$$

$$\cot \alpha = \frac{x}{y} = \frac{-3}{-5} = \frac{3}{5} \qquad \sec \alpha = \frac{r}{x} = \frac{\sqrt{34}}{-3} = -\frac{\sqrt{34}}{3}$$

Example 2. Sketch two primary angles θ_1 and θ_2 for which the statement $\sin \theta = \frac{2}{3}$ is true.

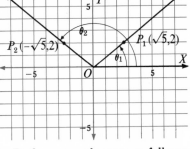

Solution. Since $\sin \theta$ is positive in Quadrants 1 and 2, the terminal rays of θ will be in Q_1 and Q_2.

Since $\sin \theta = \frac{y}{r}$, $y = 2$ and $r = 3$. To find the values of x when x is the abscissa of a point P with ordinate 2 in the terminal ray of θ, we use the Pythagorean theorem as follows:

$$x = \pm \sqrt{r^2 - y^2}$$
$$x = \pm \sqrt{3^2 - 2^2}$$
$$x = \pm \sqrt{5}$$

Therefore the coordinates of P_1, a point in the terminal ray of θ_1, are $(\sqrt{5}, 2)$ and the coordinates of P_2, a point in the terminal ray of θ_2, are $(-\sqrt{5}, 2)$. θ_1 and θ_2 are shown in the diagram.

Example 3. If the angle θ is in standard position and $P(-6, 2)$ is a point in the terminal side of θ, find the six trigonometric ratios associated with θ.

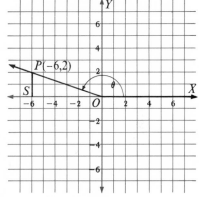

Solution. We draw a vertical line through P intersecting the x-axis at $S(-6, 0)$. Since triangle OSP is a right triangle, $|OP|$ is readily found by means of the Pythagorean theorem to be $2\sqrt{10}$. Substituting -6, 2, and $2\sqrt{10}$ for x, y, and r respectively in statements (1) through (6) of Theorem 1–9 we have

$$\sin \theta = \frac{2}{2\sqrt{10}} = \frac{1}{\sqrt{10}} = \frac{\sqrt{10}}{10} \qquad \cot \theta = \frac{-6}{2} = -3$$

$$\cos \theta = \frac{-6}{2\sqrt{10}} = -\frac{3}{\sqrt{10}} = \frac{3\sqrt{10}}{10} \qquad \sec \theta = \frac{2\sqrt{10}}{-6} = -\frac{\sqrt{10}}{3}$$

$$\tan \theta = \frac{2}{-6} = -\frac{1}{3} \qquad \csc \theta = \frac{2\sqrt{10}}{2} = \sqrt{10}$$

When $P(x, y)$ is a point in the terminal side of the directed angle $(\overrightarrow{OI}, t)$ in standard position, t is the radian measure of $(\overrightarrow{OI}, t)$ and $r = |OP|$, the symbol $P^R(r, t)$ is read "the point P with *circular coordinates r and t.*" The R written as a superscript indicates that the angle $(\overrightarrow{OI}, t)$ is measured in radians. Thus

$$P(x, y) = P^R(r, t) \longleftrightarrow x = r \cos t \wedge y = r \sin t \wedge r = \sqrt{x^2 + y^2}.$$

When d is the degree measure of $(\overrightarrow{OI}, d°)$ and $|OP| = r$, the symbol $P°(r, d)$ is read, "the point P with *circular coordinates r and d.*" The degree symbol (°) indicates that $(\overrightarrow{OI}, d°)$ is measured in degrees. Thus

$$P(x, y) = P°(r, d) \longleftrightarrow x = r \cos \angle d° \wedge y = r \sin \angle d° \wedge r = \sqrt{x^2 + y^2}.$$

Example 4. Find x and y so that

$$\textbf{a.}\ P(x, y) = P^R\!\left(10, \frac{\pi}{3}\right)\quad \textbf{b.}\ P(x, y) = P^{\circ}(10, 315)$$

Solution. **a.** $P^R\!\left(10, \frac{\pi}{3}\right)$ is the point in the terminal ray of $\left(\overrightarrow{OI}, \frac{\pi}{3}\right)$ such that $|OP| = 10$ as shown in the drawing below. From P we draw a

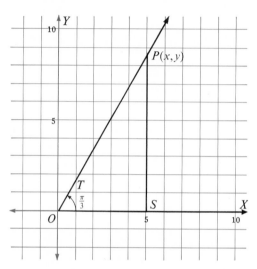

line perpendicular to the x-axis and intersecting it at S. Using the right triangle OPS and the fact from geometry that the measure of the side opposite an acute angle of a right triangle whose radian measure is $\frac{\pi}{6}$ is one half the measure of the hypotenuse, we see that $|x| = 5$. Then using the Pythagorean theorem, we have: $y = \pm\sqrt{r^2 - x^2} = \pm\sqrt{100 - 25} = \pm\sqrt{75}$ $= \pm 5\sqrt{3}$. Since the terminal side of $\left(\overrightarrow{OI}, \frac{\pi}{3}\right)$ lies in Q_1, we know that both x and y are positive. Therefore $P^R\!\left(10\ \frac{\pi}{3}\right) = P(5, 5\sqrt{3})$.

b. $P^{\circ}(10, 315)$ is the point in the terminal ray $\left(\overrightarrow{OI}, \frac{7\pi}{4}\right)$ uch that $|OP| = 10$. From P we draw a line perpendicular to the x-axis and intersecting it at S. Using the right triangle OSP and the fact from geometry that if the radian measure of an acute angle of a right triangle is $\frac{\pi}{4}$, the right triangle is isosceles, we see that $|x| = |y|$. Then using the Pythagorean theorem, we have:

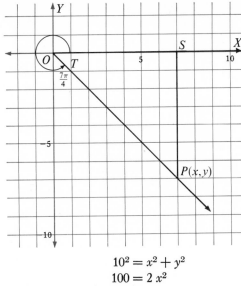

$$10^2 = x^2 + y^2$$
$$100 = 2\,x^2$$
$$50 = x^2$$
$$\pm 5\sqrt{2} = x$$

Since the terminal side of $\left(\overrightarrow{OI}, \dfrac{7\,\pi}{4}\right)$ lies in Q_4, we know that x is positive and y is negative. Therefore, $x = 5\sqrt{2}$ and $y = -5\sqrt{2}$ or $P(5\sqrt{2}, -5\sqrt{2})$.

Ⓐ EXERCISES

1. In each figure below, the coordinates of a point P in the terminal side $\overrightarrow{OT}$ of an angle θ in standard position are indicated. Write the value of each of the six trigonometric functions of each angle if this number is defined.

a.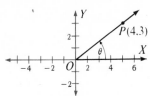

b.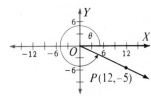

c.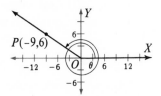

d.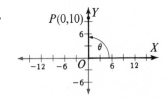

2. Angle θ has its terminal side in the first quadrant and $\sin \theta = \frac{4}{5}$. Sketch the angle.

3. In which quadrant or quadrants are the terminal sides of the angles when
   a. $\tan \theta$ is positive?   **d.** $\sin \theta$ and $\tan \theta$ are both positive?
   b. $\tan \theta$ is negative?   **e.** $\sin \theta$ and $\tan \theta$ are both negative?
   c. $\sin \theta$ is positive?   **f.** $\cos \theta$ and $\sin \theta$ are both positive?

4. In which quadrant is the terminal side of the angle θ located when $\sin \theta$ is positive and $\cos \theta$ is negative? when $\cos \theta$ is negative and $\tan \theta$ is positive?

5. Write the other five trigonometric ratios associated with the angle θ when
   a. $\cos \theta = \frac{2}{3}$ and $\sin \theta$ is positive.   **c.** $\sin \theta = -\frac{5}{6}$ and $\tan \theta$ is positive.
   b. $\cos \theta = \frac{2}{5}$ and $\sin \theta$ is negative.   **d.** $\sin \theta = -\frac{1}{2}$ and $\cos \theta$ is negative.

6. Sketch two primary angles θ for which each of the following statements is true. Write the six trigonometric ratios associated with each of the angles you draw.
   a. $\tan \theta = \frac{1}{2}$ **d.** $\cos \theta = -\frac{5}{7}$ **g.** $\sin \theta = \dfrac{\sqrt{2}}{\sqrt{5}}$ **i.** $\cos \theta = -\dfrac{\sqrt{3}}{2}$
   b. $\tan \theta = -\frac{1}{2}$ **e.** $\tan \theta = 3$
   c. $\sin \theta = -\frac{3}{4}$ **f.** $\csc \theta = -4$ **h.** $\sin \theta = -\dfrac{3}{\sqrt{58}}$

7. Complete: If $\sin \theta = \cos \theta$, then the angle θ has its terminal side in quadrant _?_ or in quadrant _?_.

8. Complete: If $\sin \theta = -\cos \theta$, then the angle θ has its terminal side in quadrant _?_ or in quadrant _?_.

9. Find the value of $\sin^2 \theta + \cos^2 \theta$ when $\tan \theta = \frac{5}{12}$. *Note.* $\sin^2 \theta$ means $(\sin \theta)^2$ and $\cos^2 \theta$ means $(\cos \theta)^2$.

10. Find the value of $\dfrac{2 \tan \theta}{1 - \tan^2 \theta}$ when $\sin \theta = \dfrac{1}{\sqrt{5}}$ and $\cos \theta$ is positive.

11. Find x and y so that:
   a. $P(x, y) = P^R\left(6, -\dfrac{5\pi}{6}\right)$ **b.** $P(x, y) = P^\circ(10, -300)$

12. Find r, d, and t so that:
   a. $P^R(r, t) = P(-1, \sqrt{3})$ **b.** $P^\circ(r, d) = P(1, 1)$

B **EXERCISES**

13. Show that for any angle θ,
   a. $\sin^2 \theta + \cos^2 \theta = 1$ **c.** $1 + \cot^2 \theta = \csc^2 \theta$
   b. $1 + \tan^2 \theta = \sec^2 \theta$

14. Find $|P_1P_2|$ if $P_1 = P^\circ(6, 30)$ and $P_2 = P^\circ(12, 120)$.

Trigonometric Ratios of Quadrantal Angles and of Angles in the Various Quadrants

If the terminal side of $(\overrightarrow{OI}, t)$ lies in one of the coordinate axes, we say that $(\overrightarrow{OI}, t)$ or any angle equivalent to $(\overrightarrow{OI}, t)$ is a *quadrantal angle*. Thus angles whose radian measures are integral multiples of $\frac{\pi}{2}$ such as $0, \frac{\pi}{2}, \pi,$ $\frac{3\pi}{2}, 2\pi, -\frac{\pi}{2},$ and $-\frac{5\pi}{2}$ are in the set of quadrantal angles. Therefore $(\overrightarrow{OI}, t)$ or any angle equivalent to $(\overrightarrow{OI}, t)$ is a quadrantal angle if and only if $t = k \cdot \frac{\pi}{2}$ when $k \,\epsilon\, I$.

If $t = \pi$, the terminal side of $(\overrightarrow{OI}, t)$ lies along the negative x-axis and hence intersects the unit circle at the point whose coordinates are $(-1, 0)$. (See the figure at the right.) Applying the statements in **A**, page 469, we have $\sin \pi = 0$, $\cos \pi = -1$, $\tan \pi = 0$, and $\sec \pi = -1$ while $\cot \pi$ and $\csc \pi$ are undefined.

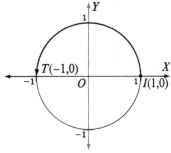

If we let t represent the radian measure of a quadrantal angle, θ, (x_0, y_0) be the coordinates of the intersection of the terminal side of the quadrantal angle in standard position with the unit circle, and "—" represent *undefined*, we have the following table of functions for quadrantal angles.

t	x_0	y_0	$\sin \angle t$ or $\sin \theta$	$\cos \angle t$ or $\cos \theta$	$\tan \angle t$ or $\tan \theta$	$\cot \angle t$ or $\cot \theta$	$\sec \angle t$ or $\sec \theta$	$\csc \angle t$ or $\csc \theta$
0	1	0	0	1	0	$-$	1	$-$
$\frac{\pi}{2}$	0	1	1	0	$-$	0	$-$	1
π	-1	0	0	-1	0	$-$	-1	$-$
$\frac{3\pi}{2}$	0	-1	-1	0	$-$	0	$-$	-1

You can verify the entries in this table by using the statements in **A** on page 469.

If the terminal ray of a directed angle in standard position does not lie in one of the coordinate axes, we say that the terminal side lies in a quadrant.

Thus if the terminal ray of $(\overrightarrow{OI}, t)$ lies in the third quadrant, and θ is any angle equivalent to $(\overrightarrow{OI}, t)$, we say that θ is a *third quadrant angle* and write $\theta \in Q_3$. Similarly, $\theta \in Q_4$ means that the terminal side of the equivalent angle $(\overrightarrow{OI}, t)$ lies in the fourth quadrant. Since t is the radian measure of θ we have:

C

$\theta \in Q_1 \longleftrightarrow 2\pi n < t < (2n + \frac{1}{2})\pi \wedge n \in I \wedge t$ is the radian measure of θ

$\theta \in Q_2 \longleftrightarrow (2n + \frac{1}{2})\pi < t < (2n + 1)\pi \wedge n \in I \wedge t$ is the radian measure of θ

$\theta \in Q_3 \longleftrightarrow (2n + 1)\pi < t < (2n + \frac{3}{2})\pi \wedge n \in I \wedge t$ is the radian measure of θ

$\theta \in Q_4 \longleftrightarrow (2n + \frac{3}{2})\pi < t < (2n + 2)\pi \wedge n \in I \wedge t$ Is the radian measure of θ

Since π radians $= 180°$ the statements in **C** are true when π is replaced by 180 and t denotes the degree measure of θ.

The following statements are readily verified.

D

$\theta \in Q_1 \longleftrightarrow \sin \theta > 0 \wedge \cos \theta > 0 \wedge \tan \theta > 0 \wedge \cot \theta > 0 \wedge \sec \theta > 0 \wedge \csc \theta > 0$

$\theta \in Q_2 \longleftrightarrow \sin \theta > 0 \wedge \cos \theta < 0 \wedge \tan \theta < 0 \wedge \cot \theta < 0 \wedge \sec \theta < 0 \wedge \csc \theta > 0$

$\theta \in Q_3 \longleftrightarrow \sin \theta < 0 \wedge \cos \theta < 0 \wedge \tan \theta > 0 \wedge \cot \theta > 0 \wedge \sec \theta < 0 \wedge \csc \theta < 0$

$\theta \in Q_4 \longleftrightarrow \sin \theta < 0 \wedge \cos \theta > 0 \wedge \tan \theta < 0 \wedge \cot \theta < 0 \wedge \sec \theta > 0 \wedge \csc \theta < 0$

Trigonometric Ratios Associated with Acute Angles

The definitions of the six trigonometric functions associated with angles can be stated in a special way that is very useful when we are dealing with the acute angles of a right triangle. An acute angle is an angle whose measure in degrees is in $\rangle 0, 90 \langle$. The figure shows the *standard notation* for a right triangle. Its vertices are the points A, B, and C. Let α and β represent the acute angles of this triangle whose vertices are at A and B, respectively, and let γ represent the angle at vertex C. The square in angle γ indicates that it is a

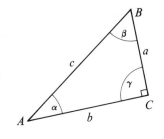

right angle, that is, its measurement can be expressed as $90°$ or $\dfrac{\pi}{2}$ radians.

We call $\overline{AC}$ and $\overline{BC}$ the legs of right triangle ABC to distinguish them from the hypotenuse $\overline{AB}$. Observe that line segment AC can be called the leg opposite β, or the leg adjacent to α. We denote $|BC|, |AC|$, and $|AB|$, the measures of the lengths of the sides, by a, b, and c, respectively. By the Pythagorean theorem $c = \sqrt{a^2 + b^2}$. Note that the measures of the angles of any polygon are positive numbers.

In order to find the trigonometric ratios associated with α we first take an equivalent angle in standard position as shown at the right. We know that $\overrightarrow{OW}$, the terminal ray of this angle, will fall in the first quadrant. Select P in $\overrightarrow{OW}$ so that $|OP| = c$ and draw $\overline{PC'}$ perpendicular to $\overrightarrow{OX}$. Now $\triangle OC'P \cong \triangle ACB$ because these triangles are right triangles whose hypotenuses have the same measure and acute angles α and $\angle C'OP$ have the same measure. Since

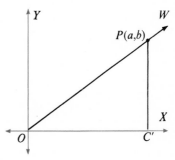

$\triangle OC'P \cong \triangle ACB$, we know that $|OC'| = b$ and $|C'P| = a$. Therefore, the coordinates of P are (b, a). Using Theorem 1–9 and the substitution property of equality, we have:

$$\sin \alpha = \frac{a}{c} \qquad \cos \alpha = \frac{b}{c} \qquad \tan \alpha = \frac{a}{b} \qquad \cot \alpha = \frac{b}{a} \qquad \csc \alpha = \frac{c}{a} \qquad \sec \alpha = \frac{c}{b}$$

Using words instead of letters, we can state the following theorem.

▷ **Theorem 2–9.** If α is an acute angle of a right triangle, then

$$\sin \alpha = \frac{|\text{leg opposite } \alpha|}{|\text{hypotenuse}|} \qquad \csc \alpha = \frac{|\text{hypotenuse}|}{|\text{leg opposite } \alpha|}$$

$$\cos \alpha = \frac{|\text{leg adjacent } \alpha|}{|\text{hypotenuse}|} \qquad \sec \alpha = \frac{|\text{hypotenuse}|}{|\text{leg adjacent } \alpha|}$$

$$\tan \alpha = \frac{|\text{leg opposite } \alpha|}{|\text{leg adjacent } \alpha|} \qquad \cot \alpha = \frac{|\text{leg adjacent } \alpha|}{|\text{leg opposite } \alpha|}$$

Example. If α is an acute angle and $\sin \alpha = \frac{1}{2}$, find the other five trigonometric ratios associated with α.

Solution. Since $\sin \alpha = \frac{1}{2}$,

$$\frac{|\text{leg opposite } \alpha|}{|\text{hypotenuse}|} = \frac{1}{2}.$$

If in right $\triangle ABC$, we let $a = 1$ and $c = 2$, then by the Pythagorean the-

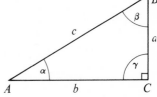

orem $b = \sqrt{3}$. Therefore by Theorem 2–9, $\cos \alpha = \dfrac{\sqrt{3}}{2}$, $\tan \alpha = \dfrac{\sqrt{3}}{3}$,

$\cot \alpha = \sqrt{3}$, $\sec \alpha = \dfrac{2\sqrt{3}}{3}$, and $\csc \alpha = 2$.

1. Angles α and β are the acute angles of the right $\triangle ABC$ shown. Find the numerical value of c and each of the following:

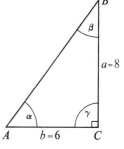

a. sin α	**e.** sec α	**i.** tan β
b. cos α	**f.** cot α	**j.** csc β
c. tan α	**g.** sin β	**k.** sec β
d. csc α	**h.** cos β	**l.** cot β

2. Verify the fact that each of the triangles shown in parts **a.**, **b.**, and **c.** is a right triangle and then for each part write the six trigonometric ratios for α and the six trigonometric ratios for β.

a.

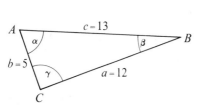

b. **c.**

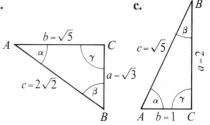

3. In the right triangle shown at the right, x and $90 - x$ are the degree measures of acute angles α and β, respectively. Find $\sin \angle x°$ and $\cos \angle (90 - x)°$ and compare them. Also find and compare $\tan \angle x°$ and $\cot \angle (90 - x)°$.

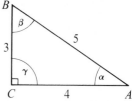

4. If $ABCD$ is a square each of whose sides has the measure 1, then its diagonal has the measure $\sqrt{2}$. Also $\angle BAC \cong \angle BCA$ and the degree measure of each of these angles is 45. Complete each of the following statements with the correct numerical value.

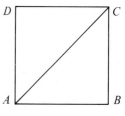

a. sin $\angle 45° = \_?\_$	**d.** csc $\angle 45° = \_?\_$
b. cos $\angle 45° = \_?\_$	**e.** sec $\angle 45° = \_?\_$
c. tan $\angle 45° = \_?\_$	**f.** cot $\angle 45° = \_?\_$

5. Triangle ABC is equilateral. From geometry we know that the measure in degrees of each angle of an equilateral triangle is 60. Also, from geometry, we know that if $\overline{CD}$ is perpendicular to $\overline{AB}$ then $|DB| = |AD| = \frac{1}{2}|AB|$. Therefore if $|CB| = 1$, then $|DB| = \frac{1}{2}$, and by the Pythagorean theorem $|CD| = \frac{1}{2}\sqrt{3}$.

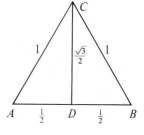

a. Use these facts to write the numerical values of the six trigonometric ratios associated with ∠ 60°. (Note $\sin \angle 60° = \sin \angle BAC = \frac{1}{2}\sqrt{3}$)

b. Use the above facts and the fact that the degree measure of ∠ BCD is 30 to write the numerical values of the six trigonometric ratios associated with ∠ 30°.

6. Draw a triangle whose sides have lengths 0.8 in., 1.5 in., and 1.7 in. and prove that it is a right triangle. Write the six trigonometric ratios associated with each of the acute angles in this right triangle.

7. Each of the following ratios is the sine of an acute angle in a right triangle. Find the other five trigonometric ratios associated with the acute angle.

a. $\frac{1}{2}$ b. $\frac{1}{3}$ c. $\frac{5}{6}$ d. $\frac{5}{8}$

8. If α is an acute angle in right triangle ABC and $\cos \alpha = a$, we know that $a \in$ $\rangle 0, 1 \langle$. Why? Express each of the following in terms of a.

a. $\sin \alpha$ b. $\tan \alpha$ c. $\cot \alpha$ d. $\sec \alpha$ e. $\csc \alpha$

9. The two bases of an isosceles trapezoid have lengths 8 inches and 10 inches, respectively. Let θ be the angle the nonparallel sides make with the larger base. If $\cos \theta = \frac{1}{2}$, what is the altitude of the trapezoid?

10. A regular hexagon has vertices $A, B, C, D, E,$ and F. A line is drawn connecting A and D, and sides AB and DC are extended to meet at a point G, thus forming triangle ADG. If each side of the hexagon is 3 units long, find the altitude of the triangle from G to AD. If θ is the angle between this altitude and side GA, find $\sin \theta$, $\cos \theta$ and $\tan \theta$.

Special Acute Angles

In this section we review and summarize the facts we have learned about the trigonometric ratios associated with acute angles whose degree measures are 30, 45, or 60. The diagrams at the right help us determine the trigonometric ratios shown in the following table.

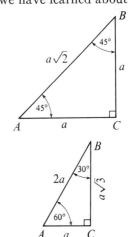

If $\theta =$	$\sin \theta$	$\cos \theta$	$\tan \theta$	$\cot \theta$	$\sec \theta$	$\csc \theta$
∠ 30°	$\frac{1}{2}$	$\frac{\sqrt{3}}{2}$	$\frac{1}{\sqrt{3}}$	$\sqrt{3}$	$\frac{2}{\sqrt{3}}$	2
∠ 45°	$\frac{\sqrt{2}}{2}$	$\frac{\sqrt{2}}{2}$	1	1	$\sqrt{2}$	$\sqrt{2}$
∠ 60°	$\frac{\sqrt{3}}{2}$	$\frac{1}{2}$	$\sqrt{3}$	$\frac{1}{\sqrt{3}}$	2	$\frac{2}{\sqrt{3}}$

Example   Find the values of the six trigonometric ratios associated with
$\angle\,240°$.

Solution.   Let P be a point in the terminal side
of a directed angle in standard position
equivalent to $\angle\,240°$. Draw $\overline{PQ}$ perpendicular to the x-axis. Then $\triangle\,QOP$
is a right triangle whose acute angle
QOP has 60 for its measure in degrees.
If we let $|OP| = 2$, then $|OQ| = 1$
and $|QP| = \sqrt{3}$. Why? Since the
terminal side of a directed angle in
standard position equivalent to $\angle\,240°$
is in Quadrant III, the coordinates of
P are $(-1, -\sqrt{3})$. By Theorem 1–9,
we have:

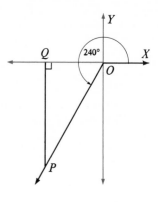

$$\sin\angle\,240° = -\frac{\sqrt{3}}{2} \qquad \csc\angle\,240° = -\frac{2}{\sqrt{3}} = -\frac{2\sqrt{3}}{3}$$

$$\cos\angle\,240° = -\tfrac{1}{2} \qquad \sec\angle\,240° = -2$$

$$\tan\angle\,240° = \sqrt{3} \qquad \cot\angle\,240° = \frac{1}{\sqrt{3}} = \frac{\sqrt{3}}{3}$$

We can use an argument involving similar triangles to prove the following
statement: If α_1 and α_2 are acute angles, then $\alpha_1 \cong \alpha_2 \longleftrightarrow \tan\alpha_1 = \tan\alpha_2$.
Similar statements may be proved for each of the other five trigonometric
ratios associated with α_1 and α_2. Thus we have the following theorem:

▶ **Theorem 3–9.** If α_1 and α_2 are acute angles, then

(1) $\alpha_1 \cong \alpha_2 \longleftrightarrow \sin\alpha_1 = \sin\alpha_2$
(2) $\alpha_1 \cong \alpha_2 \longleftrightarrow \cos\alpha_1 = \cos\alpha_2$
(3) $\alpha_1 \cong \alpha_2 \longleftrightarrow \tan\alpha_1 = \tan\alpha_2$
(4) $\alpha_1 \cong \alpha_2 \longleftrightarrow \cot\alpha_1 = \cot\alpha_2$
(5) $\alpha_1 \cong \alpha_2 \longleftrightarrow \sec\alpha_1 = \sec\alpha_2$
(6) $\alpha_1 \cong \alpha_2 \longleftrightarrow \csc\alpha_1 = \csc\alpha_2$

Note. Theorem 3–9 is actually six theorems. Each of the six theorems
has the original hypothesis and one of the numbered conclusions.

If α_1 and α_2 are two acute angles whose measures in radians are respectively t_1 and t_2 and whose measures in degrees are respectively d_1 and d_2, then
using Theorem 3–9 and the following statement,

Two acute angles are congruent if and only if they have the same measure in degrees (or measure in radians).

Thus we may write:

E

If d_1 and d_2 are the degree measures of acute angles α_1 and α_2, respectively, and t_1 and t_2 are the radian measures of acute angles α_1 and α_2, respectively, then $\alpha_1 \cong \alpha_2 \longleftrightarrow d_1 = d_2 \longleftrightarrow t_1 = t_2 \longleftrightarrow \sin \angle d_1{}^\circ = \sin \angle d_2{}^\circ \longleftrightarrow \sin \angle t_1 = \sin \angle t_2$

A similar statement can be made for each of the other five trigonometric functions.

The sum of two given angles is an angle whose degree measure is the sum of the degree measures of the two given angles. Thus, the sum of an angle whose degree measure is 30 and an angle whose degree measure is 70 is an angle whose degree measure is 100. We can write this as $\angle 30^\circ + \angle 70^\circ = \angle 100^\circ$. In general $\angle d_1{}^\circ + \angle d_2{}^\circ = \angle (d_1 + d_2)^\circ$. Also $\angle d_1{}^\circ - \angle d_2{}^\circ = \angle d_3{}^\circ$ means $\angle d_1{}^\circ = \angle d_2{}^\circ + \angle d_3{}^\circ$ and it follows that $\angle d_1{}^\circ - \angle d_2{}^\circ = \angle d_1{}^\circ + \angle (- d_2)^\circ$.

The product of a real number k and a given angle is an angle whose degree measure is the product of k and the degree measure of the given angle. Thus $\frac{1}{2} \cdot \angle 60^\circ = \angle (\frac{1}{2} \cdot 60)^\circ = 30^\circ$. In general $k \angle d^\circ = \angle (k \cdot d)^\circ = \angle kd^\circ$.

For example, $\sin (\angle 30^\circ + \angle 60^\circ) = \sin \angle 90^\circ = 1$ and $\sin \angle (2 \cdot 45)^\circ = \sin \angle 90^\circ = 1$. Note that $\sin \angle (45 + 45)^\circ \neq \sin \angle 45^\circ + \sin \angle 45^\circ$ because the left member has the value 1, the value of the right member is $\sqrt{2}$, and $1 \neq \sqrt{2}$.

A EXERCISES

1. Sketch each of the following angles in standard position. Without using a table determine the six trigonometric ratios associated with each angle.
   a. $\angle 135^\circ$ c. $\angle 120^\circ$ e. $\angle 315^\circ$ g. $\angle 210^\circ$
   b. $\angle 150^\circ$ d. $\angle (- 60)^\circ$ f. $\angle 225^\circ$ h. $\angle (- 210)^\circ$

2. For each of the following find the primary angles that make the statement true.
   a. $\sin \angle x^\circ = \frac{1}{2}\sqrt{3}$ c. $\cos \angle x^\circ = -\frac{1}{2}\sqrt{2}$ e. $\cos \angle x^\circ = -1$
   b. $\tan \angle x^\circ = \sqrt{3}$ d. $\sin \angle x^\circ = 1$ f. $\tan \angle x^\circ = 1$

3. Evaluate each of the following.
   a. $\sin \angle 60^\circ \cdot \tan \angle 30^\circ$

   b. $\tan^2 \angle 45^\circ$

   c. $\cos \angle 120^\circ \cdot \cos \angle 30^\circ$

   d. $\cos \angle 150^\circ \cdot \tan \angle 30^\circ$

   e. $\dfrac{\sin \angle 30^\circ}{\sin \angle 45^\circ}$

   f. $\sin \angle 225^\circ \cdot \sec \angle 45^\circ - \cos \angle 225^\circ$

   g. $\sin \angle 90^\circ + \cos \angle 180^\circ + \sin \angle 270^\circ$

   h. $\sin \angle 270^\circ - \sin \angle 330^\circ - \cos \angle 300^\circ$

   i. $\cos \angle (- 225)^\circ \cdot \sin \angle 135^\circ - \tan \angle 60^\circ$

   j. $(\tan \angle 60^\circ + \cos \angle 30^\circ)(- \tan \angle 45^\circ)$

4. Show that

   a. $\sin (\angle 30° + \angle 30°) \neq \sin \angle 30° + \sin \angle 30°$

   b. $\cos (\angle 90° + \angle 30°) \neq \cos \angle 90° + \cos \angle 30°$

   c. $\cos (\angle 180° + \angle - 60°) \neq \cos \angle 180° - \cos \angle 60°$

   d. $\sin \left(\angle \dfrac{\pi}{4} + \angle \dfrac{\pi}{4} \right) \neq \sin \angle \dfrac{\pi}{4} + \sin \angle \dfrac{\pi}{4}$

5. Which of the following statements are true and which are false?

   a. $\cos \angle 150° \cdot \sin \angle 210° = 1$ **e.** $\sin \angle 180° = 2 \sin \angle 90°$

   b. $\cos \angle 225° + \sin \angle 135° = 0$ **f.** $\dfrac{\sin \angle 300°}{\tan \angle 300°} = \cos \angle 300°$

   c. $\cos \angle 300° = \cos \angle 120°$ **g.** $\sin \angle 30° + \sin \angle 60° = \sin \angle 90°$

   d. $\cos \angle 120° = 2 \cos \angle 60°$ **h.** $\sin \angle 45° \cdot \cos \angle 45° = \tfrac{1}{2} \sin \angle 90°$

Functions of Complementary Angles

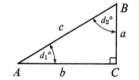

Two acute angles are complementary if and only if the sum of their degree measures is 90. Thus we know that $\angle d_1°$ and $\angle d_2°$ are complementary $\longleftrightarrow$ $d_1 + d_2 = 90 \longleftrightarrow d_2 = 90 - d_1$.

If $\angle d_1°$ and $\angle d_2°$ are the acute angles in right triangle ABC at vertices A and B, respectively, then

$$\sin \angle d_1° = \frac{a}{c} = \cos \angle d_2° = \cos \angle(90 - d_1)°$$

$$\cos \angle d_1° = \frac{b}{c} = \sin \angle d_2° = \sin \angle(90 - d_1)°$$

$$\tan \angle d_1° = \frac{a}{b} = \cot \angle d_2 = \cot \angle(90 - d_1)°$$

$$\cot \angle d_1° = \frac{b}{a} = \tan \angle d_2° = \tan \angle(90 - d_1)°$$

$$\sec \angle d_1° = \frac{c}{b} = \csc \angle d_2° = \csc \angle(90 - d_1)°$$

$$\csc \angle d_1° = \frac{c}{a} = \sec \angle d_2° = \sec \angle(90 - d_1)°$$

If we let $T \angle d_1° = co\text{-}T \angle d_2°$ represent any of the following statements: $\sin \angle d_1° = \cos \angle d_2°$, $\cos \angle d_1° = \sin \angle d_2°$, $\tan \angle d_1° = \cot \angle d_2°$, $\cot \angle d_1° = \tan \angle d_2°$, $\sec \angle d_1° = \csc \angle d_2°$, and $\csc \angle d_1° = \sec \angle d_2°$, the preceding discussion can be summarized by the following statement.

(*i*) If $\angle d_1°$ and $\angle d_2°$ are two acute angles and $d_1 + d_2 = 90$, then $T \angle d_1° = co\text{-}T \angle d_2°$.

In Exercise 10, page 484, we prove a converse of one of the implications obtainable from (i), namely: If $\angle d_1$ and $\angle d_2$ are acute angles and $\sin \angle d_1{}^\circ = \cos \angle d_2{}^\circ$, then $d_1 + d_2 = 90$. The five other converses of this type obtainable from (i) can be proved in the same manner. Thus we establish:

(ii) If $\angle d_1{}^\circ$ and $\angle d_2{}^\circ$ are acute angles and $T \angle d_1{}^\circ = co\text{-}T \angle d_2{}^\circ$, then $d_1 + d_2 = 90$.

Statements (i) and (ii) are combined in the following theorem:

▶ **Theorem 4–9.** If $\angle d_1{}^\circ$ and $\angle d_2{}^\circ$ are acute angles, then $d_1 + d_2 = 90 \longleftrightarrow$ $T \angle d_1{}^\circ = co\text{-}T \angle d_2{}^\circ$.

If in Theorem 4–9 we replace d_1 and d_2 with x_1 and x_2, the radian measures of two acute angles, we have the statement: If $\angle x_1$ and $\angle x_2$ are acute angles, then $x_1 + x_2 = \dfrac{\pi}{2} \longleftrightarrow T \angle x_1 = co\text{-}T \angle x_2$.

Example. When $\angle x^\circ$ and $\angle (45 + x)^\circ$ are acute angles, find the value of x for which $\tan \angle x^\circ = \cot \angle (45 + x)^\circ$ is true.

Solution. Since tangent and cotangent are co-functions, we know that $\angle x^\circ + \angle (45 + x)^\circ = \angle 90^\circ$. Thus $x + (45 + x) = 90$. Therefore $x = 22\frac{1}{2}$. Thus $\{x \mid \tan \angle x^\circ = \cot \angle (45 + x)^\circ\} = \{22\frac{1}{2}\}$.

Ⓐ **EXERCISES**

1. For each of the following find x so that the statement is true when $0 < x < 90$.

a. $\cos \angle 59^\circ = \sin \angle x^\circ$

b. $\cot \angle 21^\circ = \tan \angle x^\circ$

c. $\tan \angle 81^\circ = \cot \angle x^\circ$

d. $\sin \angle 42^\circ = \cos \angle x^\circ$

e. $\sin \angle 34^\circ = \cos \angle x^\circ$

f. $\cos \angle 12.3^\circ = \sin \angle x^\circ$

g. $\sec \angle 27.1^\circ = \csc \angle x^\circ$

h. $\tan \angle 77.9^\circ = \cot \angle x^\circ$

2. If t is the radian measure of θ, for what value of t in $\rangle 0, \dfrac{\pi}{2} \langle$ is it true that $\sin \theta = \cos \theta$?

3. The table at the right is a part of a table of trigonometric functions. Find the numerical values of each of the following.

a. $\sin \angle 69^\circ$

b. $\cos \angle 69^\circ$

c. $\sin \angle 68^\circ$

d. $\cot \angle 67^\circ$

e. $\cos \angle 68^\circ$

f. $\cot \angle 68^\circ$

g. $\sin \angle 67^\circ$

h. $\cos \angle 67^\circ$

θ	$\sin \theta$	$\cos \theta$	$\tan \theta$
21	0.3584	0.9336	0.3839
22	0.3746	0.9272	0.4040
23	0.3907	0.9205	0.5245

4. For each of the following, find a value for x that will make a true statement.

a. $\sin \angle 2\,x° = \cos \angle (45 - x)°$ e. $\sec \angle x° = \csc \angle 4\,x°$

b. $\cot \angle 2\,x° = \tan \angle 3\,x°$ f. $\sin \angle (3\,x + 10)° = \cos \angle (2\,x - 20)°$

c. $\cos \angle 3\,x° = \sin \angle x°$ g. $\tan \angle (3\,x + 20)° = \cot \angle (5\,x - 10)°$

d. $\cos \angle x° = \sin \angle 5\,x°$ h. $\sec \angle (4\,x + 20)° = \csc \angle 3\,x°$

B EXERCISES

In Ex. 5–7 triangle ABC is a right triangle labeled in standard notation.

5. a. If $\sin \alpha = \frac{3}{4}$, and $a = 6$, find c.   b. If $\cos \beta = \frac{1}{5}$, and $c = \frac{5}{2}$, find a.

6. If $\cot \beta = 0.75$ and $a = 1.8$, find b and c.

7. If $\cot \alpha = 1.5$ and $c = 2\sqrt{13}$, find a and b.

8. If $0 \leq x \leq 60$, show that $\sin \angle (60 - x)° = \cos \angle (30 + x)°$.

9. Show that if x, y and z are the radian measures of the angles of any triangle, then $\tan \frac{1}{2} \angle (x + y) = \cot \frac{1}{2} \angle z$.

10. Supply reasons for the following proof of the statement: If $\angle d_1°$ and $\angle d_2°$ are acute angles and $\sin \angle d_1° = \cos \angle d_2°$, then $d_1 + d_2 = 90$.

1. d_1 and d_2 are the degree measures of acute angles and $\sin \angle d_1° = \cos \angle d_2°$ 1. Why?

2. $\sin \angle d_1° = \cos \angle (90 - d_1)°$ 2. Why?

3. $\cos \angle d_2° = \cos \angle (90 - d_1)°$ 3. Why?

4. $d_2 = 90 - d_1$ 4. Why?

5. $d_1 + d_2 = 90$ 5. Why?

Tables of Trigonometric Functions

Approximations of the values of the trigonometric functions associated with positive acute angles have been calculated and are available in tables. Table IV, beginning on page 762, is such a table. Observe that the column on the left in this table contains angle measures for each tenth of a degree in $\langle\, 0.0, 45.0\,\rangle$ and the column on the right contains angle measures for each tenth of a degree in $\langle\, 45.0, 90.0\,\rangle$. The second and seventh columns show the measures in radians which correspond to each of these measures in degrees. The third, fourth, fifth, and sixth columns show the sin, cos, tan, and cot ratios to the nearest ten-thousandth for angles having each of these measures. To find the ratios for angles with degree measures in $\langle\, 0.0, 45.0\,\rangle$ (or angles with radian measure in $\langle\, 0, 0.7854\,\rangle$), we use the headings at the tops of the columns, and to find the ratios for angles with degree measures in $\langle\, 45.0, 90.0\,\rangle$ (or angles with radian measures in $\langle\, 0.7854, 1.5708\,\rangle$), we use the headings at the bottoms of the columns.

For your convenience in learning to use the table, a few lines of the table are reproduced below.

Measures in		Sin	Cos	Tan	Cot		
Degrees	Radians						
30.0	0.5236	0.5000	0.8660	0.5774	1.7321	1.0472	**60.0**
.1	0.5253	0.5015	0.8652	0.5797	1.7251	1.0455	.9
.2	0.5271	0.5030	0.8643	0.5820	1.7182	1.0437	.8
.3	0.5288	0.5045	0.8634	0.5844	1.7113	1.0420	.7
.4	0.5306	0.5060	0.8625	0.5867	1.7045	1.0402	.6
.5	0.5323	0.5075	0.8616	0.5890	1.6977	1.0385	.5
.6	0.5341	0.5090	0.8607	0.5914	1.6909	1.0367	.4
.7	0.5358	0.5105	0.8599	0.5938	1.6842	1.0350	.3
.8	0.5376	0.5120	0.8590	0.5961	1.6775	1.0332	.2
.9	0.5393	0.5135	0.8581	0.5985	1.6709	1.0315	.1
31.0	0.5411	0.5150	0.8572	0.6009	1.6643	1.0297	**59.0**
.1	0.5428	0.5165	0.8563	0.6032	1.6577	1.0280	.9
.2	0.5445	0.5180	0.8554	0.6056	1.6512	1.0263	.8
.3	0.5463	0.5195	0.8545	0.6080	1.6447	0.0245	.7
.4	0.5480	0.5210	0.8536	0.6104	1.6383	1.0228	.6
.5	0.5498	0.5225	0.8526	0.6128	1.6319	1.0210	.5
		Cos	Sin	Cot	Tan	Radians	Degrees
						Measures in	

To find the approximation to the nearest ten-thousandth of the value of any trigonometric function of an angle whose degree measure is in $\langle 0, 90 \rangle$, we proceed as in the following examples.

Example 1. Find sin $\angle 31.3°$.

Solution. We scan the left column to find 31.3. We then move horizontally in this row until we reach the column headed "Sin." Here we find 0.5195. Hence sin $\angle 31.3° = 0.5195$.

Note. Obviously some entries in the table are exact. For example, sin 30° is exactly 0.5000. For convenience, however, we usually do not try to distinguish between those which are exact and those which are approximate. We may, therefore, write sin $\angle 31.3° = 0.5195$ even though we realize that 0.5195 may only be an approximation of the true value of sin $\angle 31.3°$.

Example 2. Find the numerical value of cos $\angle 59.4°$.

Solution. We scan the column on the right until we find 59.4. We then move horizontally to the column headed "Cos" at the bottom of the column (bottom, because $45 \leq 59.4 \leq 90$). Here we find 0.5090. Therefore, if 59.4 is the measure in degrees of an angle, cos $\angle 59.4° = 0.5090$.

Observe that each entry in the third, fourth, fifth, and sixth columns does double duty. For example, $\cos \angle 59.4° = 0.5090 = \sin \angle 30.6°$.

Observe that if θ is an acute angle and its degree measure increases from 0 to 90, the values of $\sin \theta$ and $\tan \theta$ increase while the values of $\cos \theta$ and $\cot \theta$ decrease. We must keep these facts in mind when we use linear interpolation to find approximate values of the trigonometric functions of an angle whose measure is between consecutive entries in the table.

Example 3. Find $\sin \angle 31.14°$.

Solution. In the column labeled "Degrees" we find consecutive entries such that $31.1 < 31.14 < 31.2$. The sine ratios for $\angle 31.1°$ and $\angle 31.2°$ are 0.5165 and 0.5180, respectively. We proceed as follows:

$$\angle 0.10° \left[\angle 0.04° \left[\begin{array}{c|c} \angle d° & \sin \angle d° \\ \hline \angle 31.20° & 0.5180 \\ \angle 31.14° & ? \\ \angle 31.10° & 0.5165 \end{array} \right]_c \right]$$

$0.5180 - 0.5165 = 0.0015$ (a positive number because $\sin \angle 31.2° > \sin \angle 31.1°$).

$$\frac{0.04}{0.10} = \frac{c}{0.0015}$$

$$c = \tfrac{4}{10}(0.0015) = 0.0006$$

$$\therefore \sin \angle 31.14° = 0.5165 + 0.0006 = 0.5171$$

Example 4. Find $\cos 1.0353$.

Solution. Since the real number 1.0353 is the radian measure of $\angle 1.0353$, we use the column labelled "Radians" and find consecutive entries such that $1.0350 < 1.0353 < 1.0367$. We proceed as follows:

$$0.0017 \left[0.0003 \left[\begin{array}{c|c} t & \cos t \\ \hline 1.0367 & 0.5090 \\ 1.0353 & ? \\ 1.0350 & 0.5105 \end{array} \right]_c \right]$$

$0.5090 - 0.5105 = -0.0015$ (a negative number because $\cos 1.0367 < 1.0350$.

$$\frac{0.0003}{0.0017} = \frac{c}{-0.0015}$$

$$c = -0.0003$$

$$\therefore \cos 1.0353 = 0.5105 - 0.0003 = 0.5102$$

If we are given an approximation to the nearest ten-thousandth of the value of a trigonometric function of an angle, Table IV enables us to find the approximate degree measure of an angle to the nearest hundredth of a degree.

Example 5. If α is an acute angle and $\tan \alpha = 0.6020$, find the measurement of α correct to the nearest hundredth of a degree.

Solution. In the columns labeled "Tan" we find the consecutive entries such that $0.6009 < 0.6020 < 0.6032$. We see that entries 0.6009 and 0.6032 are the tangent ratios for $\angle 31.0°$ and $\angle 31.1°$, respectively. We proceed as follows:

$$\angle 0.1° \left[\angle n° \left[\begin{array}{c|c} \alpha & \tan \alpha \\ \hline \angle 31.1° & 0.6032 \\ ? & 0.6020 \\ \angle 31.0° & 0.6009 \end{array} \right] 0.0011 \right] 0.0023$$

$$\frac{n}{0.1} = \frac{0.0011}{0.0023}$$

$$n = 0.05$$

$$\angle 31.0° + \angle 0.05° = \angle 31.05°$$

The measurement of α is $31.05°$.

Example 6. If $\cot t = 0.8648$, find the measure of the acute angle to the nearest hundredth of a degree.

Solution. Since the small portion of the table on page 485 does not contain the entry 0.8648 in either column headed "Cot," we refer to the complete table. On page 768 we find the consecutive entries 0.8662 and 0.8632 such that $0.8632 < 0.8648 < 0.8662$. We then proceed as shown below.

$$0.0017 \left[n \left[\begin{array}{c|c} t & \cot t \\ \hline 0.8587 & 0.8632 \\ ? & 0.8648 \\ 0.8570 & 0.8662 \end{array} \right] -0.0014 \right] -0.0030$$

$$\frac{n}{0.0017} = \frac{-0.0014}{-0.0030}$$

$$n = 0.0008$$

$$0.8570 + 0.0008 = 0.8578$$

$$\text{Thus } t = 0.8578$$

Table IV is called a four-place table. Such a table is appropriate for making computations with linear measures that are given to four significant digits. We will use the rules for rounding given on page 431.

Ⓐ **EXERCISES**

1. Find the numerical value of each of the following:

a. $\sin \angle 15.6°$
b. $\tan \angle 21.5°$
c. $\cos \angle 81.3°$

d. $\sin \angle 88.7°$
e. $\cot \angle 35.2°$
f. $\cot \angle 21.93°$

g. $\sin \angle 39.82°$
h. $\cos \angle 44.17°$
i. $\sin \angle 16.35°$

j. $\sin \angle 84.21°$
k. $\cos \angle 72.46°$
l. $\tan \angle 46.98°$

2. Find the measurement of the acute angle θ for each of the following to the nearest tenth of a degree:

a. $\sin \theta = 0.3090$	**d.** $\tan \theta = 0.4286$	**g.** $\sin \theta = 0.2080$
b. $\cos \theta = 0.9259$	**e.** $\cot \theta = 2.8239$	**h.** $\cos \theta = 0.9591$
c. $\sin \theta = 0.8870$	**f.** $\tan \theta = 6.1742$	**i.** $\tan \theta = 3.6830$

3. Find the measurement of the acute angle θ to the nearest hundredth of a degree when:

a. $\cos \theta = 0.9387$	**e.** $\cot \theta = 1.8068$	**i.** $\sin \theta = 0.9236$
b. $\tan \theta = 0.1771$	**f.** $\sin \theta = 0.9927$	**j.** $\cos \theta = 0.6700$
c. $\sin \theta = 0.0355$	**g.** $\tan \theta = 2.4635$	**k.** $\tan \theta = 0.5100$
d. $\cos \theta = 0.8672$	**h.** $\cot \theta = 0.8791$	**l.** $\cot \theta = 1.1375$

4. For each of the following, find the number represented by the indicated ratio to the nearest ten-thousandth.

a. $\sin t$ when $t = 0.1134$	**d.** $\sin t$ when $t = 0.4762$
b. $\tan t$ when $t = 0.3892$	**e.** $\cot t$ when $t = 0.7045$
c. $\tan t$ when $t = 0.1870$	**f.** $\cos t$ when $t = 0.7850$

5. For each of the following statements, find to the nearest ten-thousandth the value of the real number t which makes each statement true, assuming that $t \in \langle 0, \frac{\pi}{2} \rangle$.

a. $\tan t = 0.7285$	**e.** $\cos t = 0.1960$	**i.** $\tan t = 1.1163$
b. $\sin t = 0.6647$	**f.** $\tan t = 2.1563$	**j.** $\cot t = 0.7847$
c. $\cos t = 0.7622$	**g.** $\sin t = 0.6831$	**k.** $\cot t = 5.6147$
d. $\sin t = 0.9366$	**h.** $\cos t = 0.1865$	**l.** $\sin t = 0.9753$

Angles of Elevation and Depression

In many practical problems an angle is described as an angle of elevation or an angle of depression.

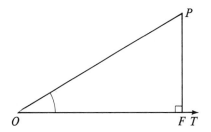
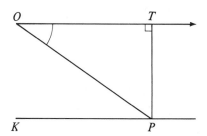

When we work with angles of elevation and depression, we always have a point O of observation and a point P at which we are looking. In the figure at the left on the preceeding page, FP represents a vertical flagpole and point O is the point of observation.

We define *angles of elevation and depression* as follows: If the vertical line through point P intersects the horizontal ray $\overrightarrow{OT}$, then angle TOP is the angle of elevation of the point P with respect to the point of observation O if P is above $\overrightarrow{OT}$. If P is below $\overrightarrow{OT}$, then the angle TOP is the angle of depression of P with respect to O.

Example. In the figure at the right, $\angle TOP$ is the angle of depression of point P with respect to the point of observation O. If $\angle TOP = \angle 37.2°$ and $|OK| = 205$, find $|KP|$ and $|OP|$.

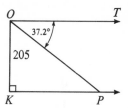

Solution. In right triangle OKP, the degree measure of $\angle KOP$ is $90 - 37.2 = 52.8$.

$$\tan \angle 52.8° = \frac{|KP|}{|OK|}$$
$$1.3175 = \frac{|KP|}{205}$$
$$|KP| = 1.3175 \times 205 \approx 270$$
$$\cos \angle 52.8° = \frac{|OK|}{|OP|}$$
$$0.6046 = \frac{205}{|OP|}$$
$$|OP| = \frac{205}{0.6046} \approx 339$$

Ⓐ EXERCISES

1. An observer standing 90 feet from the foot of a radio tower finds the angle of elevation of the top of the tower to be 73°. If the observer's eyes are 6 feet from the ground, how tall is the tower?

2. At the East Ridge shopping center, an escalator carries the shoppers from the lower level to a mall 25 feet above this level. If the angle of elevation the escalator forms with the lower level is $\angle 34°$, how far do the shoppers ride from the lower level to reach the mall?

3. At intervals around Higgins stadium, ramps lead from the ground to the entrances to the middle level seats. If these entrances are 30 feet above ground level and visitors must walk 50 feet up the ramps to reach them, what is the angle of elevation formed by a ramp and the ground level?

4. When Flight 173 was directly over the town of West Bend a passenger on the plane sighted the village of Traders Point in the distance. He knew Traders Point to be 21 miles from West Bend and he had just heard the pilot announce that the plane was flying at an altitude of 6000 feet above the ground. He wondered about the measure of the angle his line of sight to Traders Point was making with the vertical line from the plane to the ground. What was the measurement in degrees of the angle?

5. The floor in the Hartford Theatre of the Performing Arts is designed to put the eye level of people in any one row of seats 6 inches above the eye level of people in the row in front of them, assuming that the people have the same height. If the rows of seats are 40 inches apart, at what angle, measured to the nearest hundredth of a degree, does the floor slope upward from the front of the auditorium?

6. An airplane is flying a straight course with a ground speed of 420 miles per hour and at a height of 7000 feet above the ground. What will be the angle of elevation of the airplane with respect to an observer on the ground 1 minute after the plane passes directly above the observer.

7. From the top of a building 246 feet tall the angle of depression of the center of the intersection of two roads is $\angle 16.4°$. How far from the building is the intersection?

8. How high on the side of a building will a 16 foot ladder reach if it is inclined at an angle of 75° with the ground?

B   EXERCISES

9. From the top of the Trimble Building (424 feet from the ground) the angle of depression of the tops of two church spires each known to be 75 feet above the ground and in the same vertical plane with the point of observation are found to be $\angle 4.9°$ and $\angle 2.7°$. How far apart are the spires?

10. To see the top of the radar antenna at the top of a tower, Mr. Blume must raise his line of sight through an angle whose degree measurement is 32.1° above the horizontal. His son Jimmy, standing in the same spot, can see the top of the antenna when he raises his line of sight through an angle whose degree measurement is 33.2° above the horizontal. If Mr. Blume is 6.0 feet tall and Jimmy is 4.5 feet tall, how far above the ground is the top of the antenna?

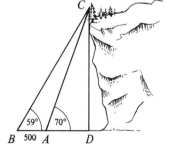

11. From point A the measurement of the angle of elevation of C is 70° and from point B, which is 500 feet from A, the measurement of the angle of elevation of C is 59°. Find the length of $\overline{CD}$.

Logarithms of the Values of the Trigonometric Functions

Each value of a trigonometric function associated with an acute angle is a positive number and therefore has a logarithm. For example,

$$\tan \angle 27° = 0.5095 \qquad \text{(Table IV)}$$
$$\log 0.5095 = 0.7072 - 1 \quad \text{(Table II)}$$
$$\therefore \log \tan \angle 27° = 0.7072 - 1$$

and we say "the logarithm of the tangent of $\angle 27°$ is $0.7072 - 1$."

The logarithms of the values of the sine, cosine, tangent, and cotangent functions can be read directly from Table V; in fact, each entry in columns two through five of Table V is the common logarithm of the corresponding entry in columns three through six of Table IV. In Table V, -10 is to be appended to logarithms of all values of sine and cosine, to logarithms of all values of tangents for angles whose measures in degrees are in $\rangle\, 0, 45 \,\langle$, and to the logarithms of all values of cotangents for angles whose measures in degrees are in $\rangle\, 45, 90 \,\langle$. For example, in finding $\log \tan \angle 27°$ directly from Table V we move down the column on the left until we find the entry 27. We then move horizontally to the column headed "L.Tan." Here we find 9.7072 to which we append -10 to obtain $\log \tan \angle 27° = 9.7072 - 10$.

Note. $9.7072 - 10$ is equal to $0.7072 - 1$, the number obtained above.

Example 1. Use Table V to find $\log \sin \angle 22.55°$.

Solution.

$\angle d°$	$\log \sin \angle d°$
$\angle 22.6°$	$9.5847 - 10$
$\angle 22.55°$	?
$\angle 22.5°$	$9.5828 - 10$

$$\angle 0.1° \left[\angle 0.05° \left[\begin{array}{c} \angle 22.6° \\ \angle 22.55° \\ \angle 22.5° \end{array} \right] c \right] 0.0019$$

$$\frac{0.05}{0.1} = \frac{c}{0.0019}$$
$$c = 0.0010$$
$$\therefore \log \sin \angle 22.55° = 9.5828 - 10 + 0.0010 = 9.5838 - 10.$$

Example 2. Use Table V to find $\log \cos \angle 63.24°$.

Solution.

$\angle d°$	$\log \cos \angle d°$
$\angle 63.30°$	$9.6526 - 10$
$\angle 63.24°$	
$\angle 63.20°$	$9.6541 - 10$

$$\angle 0.1° \left[\angle 0.04° \left[\begin{array}{c} \angle 63.30° \\ \angle 63.24° \\ \angle 63.20° \end{array} \right] c \right] -0.0015$$

$$\frac{0.04}{0.1} = \frac{c}{-0.0015}$$
$$c = -0.0006$$
Hence $\log \cos \angle 63.24° = 9.6541 - 10 + (-0.0006) = 9.6535 - 10.$

Example 3. In right triangle ABC, the measurements of a and b are 2048 feet and 5280 feet, respectively. Find the measurement of α in degrees.

Solution.

$$\tan \alpha = \tfrac{2048}{5280}$$
$$\log \tan \alpha = \log 2048 - \log 5280$$
$$= 3.3114 - 3.7226$$
$$= -0.4112 = 0.5888 - 1 = 9.5888 - 10$$

Now we find the measurement of α to the nearest hundredth of a degree by using Table V and interpolating as follows:

$$
\angle 0.1° \left[\angle n° \left[
\begin{array}{c|c}
\alpha & \log \tan \alpha \\ \hline
\angle 21.3° & 9.5909 \\
? & 9.5888 - 10 \\
\angle 21.2° & 9.5887 - 10
\end{array}
\right] 0.0001 \right] 0.0022
$$

$$\frac{n}{0.1} = \frac{0.0001}{0.0022}$$
$$n = 0.01$$
$$\alpha = \angle 21.2° + \angle 0.01° = \angle 21.21°$$

Example 4. In right triangle ABC described in standard notation $a = 241.7$ and $c = 721.3$. Find the measures of the remaining parts and the area of the triangle.

Solution.

First we draw a sketch of the triangle. We are required to find b, α, β, and K, the measure of the area of the triangle. We express each of these in terms of a and c.

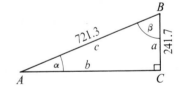

$$b^2 = c^2 - a^2$$
$$b^2 = (c+a)(c-a)$$
$$= (721.3 + 241.7)(721.3 - 241.7)$$
$$= (963.0)(479.6)$$
$$b = \sqrt{963.0 \times 479.6}$$
$$\log b = \tfrac{1}{2}(\log 963.0 + \log 479.6) = \tfrac{1}{2}(2.9836 + 2.6808)$$
$$= 2.8322$$
$$b = \text{antilog } 2.8322 = 679.5$$
$$\sin \alpha = \frac{241.7}{721.3}$$
$$\log \sin \alpha = \log 241.7 - \log 721.3 = 2.3833 - 2.8581$$
$$= 9.5252 - 10$$

Therefore the degree measure of α is 19.58.

Since the measure in degrees of γ is 90 and if we let the measure in degrees of β equal x, then

$$90 = x + 19.58$$
$$70.42 = x$$

Therefore the degree measure of β is 70.42.

$$K = \tfrac{1}{2} ab$$
$$\log K = \log a + \log b - \log 2$$
$$= \log 241.7 + \log 679.5 - \log 2$$
$$= 2.3833 + 2.8322 - 0.3010 = 4.9145$$
$$K = 82130$$

Therefore the measure of the area of $\triangle ABC$ is 82130.

 EXERCISES

1. If a, b, and c are the measures of the sides of triangle ABC shown at the right, α, β, and γ are the angles opposite these sides, respectively, and $\gamma = \angle 90°$, find the measures of the three missing parts in each of the following cases:

a. $a = 78.3$, $c = 148.2$

b. $b = 4.531$, $\beta = \angle 28.18°$

c. $a = 36.43$, $b = 14.37$

d. $b = 241.2$, $\alpha = \angle 35.70°$

e. $a = 241.2$, $c = 352.8$

f. $\alpha = \angle 74.18°$, $c = 12.13$

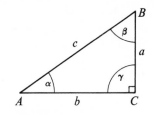

2. Find K, the measure of the area, for each triangle in Ex. 1.

3. Two vertical poles, one 16.7 feet tall and the other 25.6 feet tall, are 78.5 feet from each other. How long is a taut wire connecting their tops?

4. The perimeter of a regular pentagon is 181.4 inches. Find the length of the radius of its circumscribed circle.

5. Two lines tangent to a circle meet at an angle whose measurement is 54.6°. Find the length of the radius of the circle if the distances from the intersection of the lines to the points at which they touch the circle are each 38.6 inches.

6. In a circle whose radius is 14.54 inches long, what is the degree measure of the central angle which intercepts a chord which is 13.32 inches long?

7. What is the area of a parallelogram the lengths of whose sides are respectively 14.53 inches and 27.96 inches if two of the sides form an angle of 31.17°?

8. The lengths of the bases of an isosceles trapezoid are 18.4 feet and 6.2 feet and the length of the altitude is 4.4 feet. What is the measurement of each angle in the trapezoid?

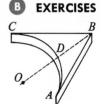

B EXERCISES

9. A metal plate is to be shaped as shown. $\overset{\frown}{AC}$ is the arc of a circle and AB and BC are tangents to the circle at A and C. If a line is drawn from B to O, the center of the circle, it intersects $\overset{\frown}{AC}$ in D. If the length of $\overline{BD}$ is 9.53 inches and the length of $\overline{BO}$ is 13.45 inches, how long is $\overline{AB}$?

10. The Preston Clay Products Company has accepted an order to manufacture some small porcelain pieces which are frustums of right circular cones. The length of the radius of each upper base is to be 0.375 of an inch, the length of the radius of each lower base is to be 0.425 of an inch, and the height of the frustum is to be 0.750 of an inch. At what angle will the slant height of each piece meet a radius of the base?

11. The circumference of the earth at the equator is approximately 24,902 miles. What is the circumference of the 40th parallel of latitude?

12. Highway A lies 50 feet lower than the ground on either side of the road. Originally the inclination of the bank was $\angle\,40°$ but when the road was improved it was decided to cut back the bank so that the angle of inclination would be $\angle\,30°$. How many cubic feet of earth had to be removed for each linear foot of highway?

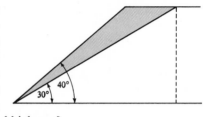

13. From the top of a 250 foot tower a forest ranger sees smoke coming from the ground at a point whose angle of depression from the observation point is $\angle\,2.3°$. How far away from the foot of the tower is the smoke originating?

Reference Angles

Corresponding to each angle θ there is a unique angle called the reference angle of θ whose degree measure is in $\langle\,0, 90\,\rangle$ or whose radian measure is in $\langle\,0, \dfrac{\pi}{2}\,\rangle$. The use of reference angles facilitates the process of using Tables IV and V for angles having any measure.

Let $P(a, b)$ be any point, other than the origin, in the terminal ray of the standard position directed angle that is equivalent to θ and let Q be the point whose coordinates are $(|\,a\,|, |\,b\,|)$. Clearly, point Q is in the first quadrant or in $\overrightarrow{OX} \cup \overrightarrow{OY}$. The primary directed angle in standard position having ray OQ as its terminal side is the *reference angle* of θ and is labeled θ_r. From the diagrams we see that the degree measure of θ_r is in $\langle\,0, 90\,\rangle$ or that the radian measure of θ_r is in $\langle\,0, \dfrac{\pi}{2}\,\rangle$.

a.

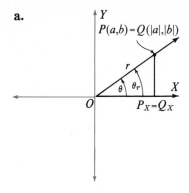

b.

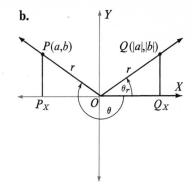

c.

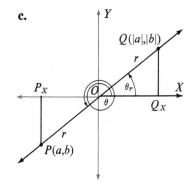

d.

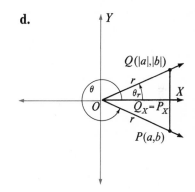

We now consider the relationships between the values of the trigonometric functions of θ and the values of the trigonometric functions of θ_r. First we observe that $|OP| = \sqrt{a^2 + b^2} = \sqrt{|a|^2 + |b|^2} = |OQ|$. Therefore we may use r to represent each of the numbers $|OP|$ and $|OQ|$.

Observe that the angle θ shown in figure **a** is a first quadrant angle and that $\theta = \theta_r$. Accordingly, $\sin \theta = \dfrac{b}{r} = \dfrac{|b|}{r} = \sin \theta_r$. Also observe that the angle θ shown in figure **b** is a second quadrant angle. Accordingly, $\sin \theta = \dfrac{b}{r} = \dfrac{|b|}{r} = \sin \theta_r$. The angle θ shown in figure **c** is a third quadrant angle. In this case $\sin \theta = \dfrac{b}{r} = -\dfrac{|b|}{r} = -\sin \theta_r$. And in figure **d** the angle θ is shown as a fourth quadrant angle, and in this case $\sin \theta = \dfrac{b}{r} = -\dfrac{|b|}{r} = -\sin \theta_r$.

Thus for every primary angle θ, $\sin \theta = \sin \theta_r$ *or* $\sin \theta = -\sin \theta_r$. Hence $|\sin \theta| = \sin \theta_r$. Similarly, $|\cos \theta| = \cos \theta_r$, $|\tan \theta| = \tan \theta_r$, $|\cot \theta| = \cot \theta_r$, $|\sec \theta| = \sec \theta_r$, and $|\csc \theta| = \csc \theta_r$.

Let vertical lines through P and Q in figures **a**, **b**, **c**, and **d** intersect the x-axis in P_X and Q_X, respectively. If θ is not a quadrantal angle, $\triangle\, Q_X O Q \cong \triangle\, P_X O P$. Therefore acute angles $P_X O P$ and $Q_X O Q$ have the same degree measure because they are congruent. This means that when θ is not a quadrantal angle, we can find the degree or radian measure of θ_r by finding the degree or radian measure of the acute angle formed by the x-axis and the terminal side of θ.

The sign of the value of each trigonometric function of θ is determined by the position of its terminal ray. The steps for finding the value of each trigonometric function of θ can be stated as follows:

(1) Determine the position of the terminal side of the standard position angle equivalent to θ.
(2) Calculate the degree or radian measure of the reference angle θ_r.
(3) Use Table IV to obtain the appropriate trigonometric ratio associated with θ_r which is the absolute value of the same trigonometric ratio associated with θ.
(4) Affix the proper sign to obtain the trigonometric ratio associated with θ.

Example 1.   Find $\sin \angle\, (-160)°$.

Solution.   The terminal side of $\angle\, (-160)°$ lies in the third quadrant and its reference angle θ_r is $\angle\, 180° - \angle\, 160°$ or $\angle\, 20°$. From Table IV $\sin \angle\, 20° = 0.3420$ and hence $|\sin \angle\, (-160)°| = 0.3420$. The sine of an angle whose terminal side lies in the third quadrant is negative so we know that $\sin \angle\, (-160)°$ is a negative number whose absolute value is 0.3420. Therefore, $\sin \angle\, (-160)° = -0.3420$.

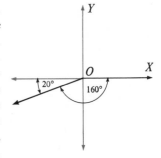

Example 2.   Find $\cot \angle\, 1000°$.

Solution.   Since $\angle\, 1000° = 2 \angle\, 360° + \angle\, 280°$, we know that $\cot \angle\, 1000° = \cot \angle\, 280°$. The terminal side of the given angle therefore lies in the fourth quadrant and the reference angle $\theta_r = 360° - 280° = 80°$. From Table IV, $\cot \angle\, 80° = 0.1763$. Thus $|\cot \angle\, 1000°| = 0.1763$. The cotangent of an angle whose terminal side lies in the fourth quadrant is negative. Therefore $\cot 1000°$ is a negative number whose absolute value is 0.1763. Hence $\cot \angle\, 1000° = -0.1763$.

If $\overrightarrow{OT}$ and $\overrightarrow{OT'}$ are the terminal rays of two directed angles in standard position whose degree measures are respectively x and $(180 - x)$, then the set $\overrightarrow{OT} \cup \overrightarrow{OT'}$ is symmetrical with respect to $\overleftrightarrow{OY}$. Thus if $P(a, b)$ is an element of $\overrightarrow{OT}$, then $P'(- a, b)$ is an element of $\overrightarrow{OT'}$ and is the reflection of P in $\overleftrightarrow{OY}$ (see the figure at the right). Also $|OP| = \sqrt{a^2 + b^2}$ and $|OP'| = \sqrt{(- a)^2 + b^2}$.

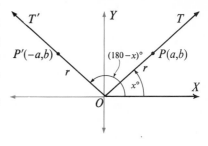

Thus if $|OP| = r$, then $|OP'| = r$. By Theorem 1–9 $\sin \angle x° = \dfrac{b}{r}$ and $\sin \angle (180 - x)° = \dfrac{b}{r}$. Also $\cos \angle x° = \dfrac{a}{r}$, $\cos \angle (180 - x)° = -\dfrac{a}{r}$, $\tan \angle x° = \dfrac{b}{a}$, and $\tan \angle (180 - x)° = -\dfrac{b}{a}$.

Therefore the following statements are true:

$$\sin \angle (180 - x)° = \sin \angle x° \qquad \csc \angle (180 - x)° = \csc \angle x°$$
$$\cos \angle (180 - x)° = - \cos \angle x° \qquad \sec \angle (180 - x)° = - \sec \angle x°$$
$$\tan \angle (180 - x)° = - \tan \angle x° \qquad \cot \angle (180 - x)° = - \cot \angle x°$$

 A EXERCISES

1. Sketch each of the following angles in standard position and find the reference angle for each. Then sketch the reference angle.

   a. $\angle 120°$ e. $\angle 300°$ i. $\angle 390°$

   b. $\angle 145°$ f. $\angle 330°$ j. $\angle - 750°$

   c. $\angle 210°$ g. $\angle 225°$ k. $\angle 150°$

   d. $\angle - 60°$ h. $\angle - 145°$ l. $\angle - 315°$

2. Complete each of the following three tables by supplying the decimal approximation for each trigonometric ratio associated with the angle shown.

a.

θ	$\sin \theta$	$\cos \theta$	$\tan \theta$
$\angle 30°$			
$\angle 150°$			
$\angle 210°$			
$\angle 330°$			

b.

θ	$\sin \theta$	$\cos \theta$	$\tan \theta$
$\angle 60°$			
$\angle 120°$			
$\angle 240°$			
$\angle 300°$			

c.

θ	$\sin\theta$	$\cos\theta$	$\tan\theta$
$\angle 45°$			
$\angle 135°$			
$\angle 225°$			
$\angle 315°$			

3. Give the degree measure of the reference angle for each of the following angles:

  a. $\angle 93°$ **d.** $\angle 275°$ **g.** $\angle 200°$ **j.** $\angle(-7)°$

  b. $\angle 104°$ **e.** $\angle(-15)°$ **h.** $\angle 540°$ **k.** $\angle 600°$

  c. $\angle 190°$ **f.** $\angle(-366)°$ **i.** $\angle 4°$ **l.** $\angle 169°$

4. Express each of the following as the value of a trigonometric function of an acute angle.

  a. $\sin\angle 100°$ **d.** $\tan\angle 240°$ **g.** $\cos\angle 453°$ **j.** $\sec\angle 170°$

  b. $\cos\angle 100°$ **e.** $\tan\angle(-30)°$ **h.** $\sin\angle 235°$ **k.** $\tan\angle 221°$

  c. $\cos\angle 200°$ **f.** $\sin\angle(-104)°$ **i.** $\cos\angle(-110)°$ **l.** $\cot\angle 312°$

5. By use of Table IV state the decimal approximation of each of the following:

  a. $\sin\angle 110°$ **e.** $\sin\angle 99°$ **i.** $\sin\angle 745°$

  b. $\cos\angle(-80)°$ **f.** $\cos\angle 99°$ **j.** $\tan\angle 318°$

  c. $\tan\angle 200°$ **g.** $\tan\angle 217°$ **k.** $\cos\angle 248°$

  d. $\sin\angle 230°$ **h.** $\tan\angle(-81)°$ **l.** $\cos\angle(-12)°$

6. By use of Table IV find two primary angles that make each of the following statements true:

  a. $\sin\angle d° = -0.1219$ **d.** $\tan\angle d° = -0.8693$ **g.** $\cos\angle d° = 0.7638$

  b. $\cos\angle d° = 0.8572$ **e.** $\tan\angle d° = 0.7002$ **h.** $\tan\angle d° = -0.9131$

  c. $\sin\angle d° = 0.8090$ **f.** $\sin\angle d° = 0.6561$ **i.** $\cos\angle d° = -0.9542$

7. By use of Table IV state the decimal approximation of each of the following:

  a. $\tan\angle 140.6°$ **d.** $\cos\angle(-75.5)°$ **g.** $\tan\angle 154.36°$

  b. $\cos\angle 211.4°$ **e.** $\cos\angle 348.1°$ **h.** $\sin\angle 300.42°$

  c. $\sin\angle(-94.2)°$ **f.** $\tan\angle(-64.7)°$ **i.** $\cos\angle 575.51°$

8. By use of Table IV find the primary angles that make each of the following statements true:

  a. $\tan\angle t = -0.3385$ **d.** $\sin\angle t = -0.9190$ **g.** $\sin\angle t = 0.0446$

  b. $\tan\angle t = 0.4111$ **e.** $\cos\angle t = 0.9754$ **h.** $\cos\angle t = 0.4230$

  c. $\sin\angle t = 0.3934$ **f.** $\tan\angle t = -3.2810$ **i.** $\cos\angle t = -0.4246$

9. If $P(a, b)$ is a point in the terminal side of $(\overrightarrow{OX}, d°)$, an angle in standard position, determine $\sin \angle d°$, $\cos \angle d°$, $\tan \angle d°$, and d.

a. $P(-3, -5)$

b. $P(5, 1)$

c. $P(-\frac{2}{3}, 4)$

d. $P(-\sqrt{5}, 2)$

e. $P(4, \sqrt{3})$

f. $P(-6, -\frac{1}{2})$

g. $P\left(-\dfrac{\sqrt{2}}{2}, \dfrac{\sqrt{2}}{2}\right)$

h. $P(-1, 0)$

i. $P(-\sqrt{3}, -2)$

10. If $P°(8, d) = P(x, 4)$, find all possible values for x, $\sin \angle d°$, $\cos \angle d°$, and $\tan \angle d°$. (See page 471.)

The Law of Sines

If in the coordinate plane we place any triangle ABC labeled in standard notation so that γ is in standard position, then by the corollary to Theorem 1–9, the coordinates of B are $x = a \cos \gamma$ and $y = a \sin \gamma$. (See figure at the right.) But y is also equal to h_b, the altitude of $\triangle ABC$ from vertex B to $\overleftrightarrow{CA}$. From geometry we know that K, the measure of the area of $\triangle ABC$, is given by the formula $K = \frac{1}{2} b \cdot h_b$. Substituting $a \sin \gamma$ for h_b, we obtain:

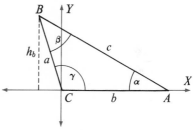

(*i*) $K = \frac{1}{2} ab \sin \gamma$

If we in turn place first α and then β in standard position, we obtain successively:

(*ii*) $K = \frac{1}{2} bc \sin \alpha$
(*iii*) $K = \frac{1}{2} ac \sin \beta$

Thus we have the following important theorem.

▶ **Theorem 5–9.** If K is the measure of the area of $\triangle$ ABC described in standard notation, then $K = \frac{1}{2}$ ab sin $\gamma = \frac{1}{2}$ bc sin $\alpha = \frac{1}{2}$ ac sin β.

Observe that when γ is a right angle, $K = \frac{1}{2} ab$.

Example 1. Find the area of $\triangle ABC$ if $\alpha = \angle 120°$, $b = 12$, and $c = 5$.

Solution. $K = \frac{1}{2} bc \sin \alpha$
$\quad\quad = \frac{1}{2}(12)(5) \sin \angle 120°$
$\quad\quad = 30 \cdot \dfrac{\sqrt{3}}{2}$
$\quad\quad = 15\sqrt{3}$

The area of the triangle is $15\sqrt{3}$ square units.

Example 2.   Find the area of an equilateral triangle if each side has s as its measure.

Solution. $K = \dfrac{1}{2} s \cdot s \cdot \sin \angle 60° = \dfrac{1}{2} s^2 \cdot \dfrac{\sqrt{3}}{2} = \dfrac{s^2\sqrt{3}}{4}$

The area of the triangle is $\dfrac{s^2\sqrt{3}}{4}$ square units.

From Theorem 5–9 we have:

$$\tfrac{1}{2} ab \sin \gamma = \tfrac{1}{2} bc \sin \alpha = \tfrac{1}{2} ac \sin \beta$$

If we divide each member of this series of equalities by $\tfrac{1}{2} abc$, we obtain:

$$\frac{\sin \gamma}{c} = \frac{\sin \alpha}{a} = \frac{\sin \beta}{b}$$

This statement is known as the *Law of Sines*. Its importance justifies its statement as the following theorem:

▶   **Theorem 6–9.** If a, b, and c are the measures of the sides of a triangle and if α, β, and γ are the angles respectively opposite these sides, then

$$\frac{\sin \alpha}{a} = \frac{\sin \beta}{b} = \frac{\sin \gamma}{c}.$$

Note that when γ is a right angle, $\sin \gamma = 1$, and we have the familiar right triangle relationships $\sin \alpha = \dfrac{a}{c}$ and $\sin \beta = \dfrac{b}{c}$.

There are six positive numbers associated with any triangle—the measures of its angles and the measures of its sides. These six numbers cannot be assigned arbitrarily. The sum of the degree measures of the three angles must be 180 and the sum of the measures of any two sides must be greater than the measure of the third side. The Law of Sines states still another relationship which must exist between these six numbers, namely: The sines of the angles of a triangle are proportional to the measures of their opposite sides, respectively.

If three of these numbers are the measures of two angles and one side or the measures of two sides and an angle opposite one of the given sides, we can find three other numbers associated with the triangle. The process of computing the other three numbers is called *solving the triangle* and a triangle which contains the given and computed parts arranged with respect to each other as required by the given data is called a *solution* determined by the *three parts whose measures are given.*

The measures of the given angles may, of course, be given in radians, but they are usually given in degrees. When we wish to represent the degree measure of the angle α, we will use the symbol $dm\ \alpha$. Thus if $\alpha = \angle d°$, we have $dm\ \alpha = d$. The radian measure of the angle α will be denoted by $rm\ \alpha$. Thus if $\alpha = \angle t$, we have $rm\ \alpha = t$.

Example 3. If in $\triangle ABC$, $\alpha = \angle 135°$, $\gamma = \angle 15°$, and $a = 40\sqrt{2}$, find b, c, and $dm\ \beta$.

Solution. Since $dm\ \alpha + dm\ \beta + dm\ \gamma = 180$, we have $dm\ \beta = 30$.
By the Law of Sines,

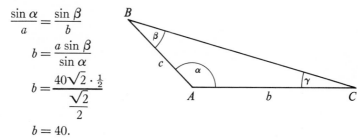

$$\frac{\sin \alpha}{a} = \frac{\sin \beta}{b}$$

$$b = \frac{a \sin \beta}{\sin \alpha}$$

$$b = \frac{40\sqrt{2} \cdot \frac{1}{2}}{\frac{\sqrt{2}}{2}}$$

$$b = 40.$$

Also

$$\frac{\sin \alpha}{a} = \frac{\sin \gamma}{c}$$

$$c = \frac{a \sin \gamma}{\sin \alpha}$$

$$c = \frac{40\sqrt{2} \times 0.2588}{\frac{\sqrt{2}}{2}}$$

$$c = 20.704 \approx 20.7$$

Example 4. If $\alpha = \angle 30°$, $a = 10$ and $b = 10\sqrt{2}$, find $dm\ \beta$, $dm\ \gamma$, and c.

Solution. By the Law of Sines
$$\frac{\sin \beta}{b} = \frac{\sin \alpha}{a}. \text{ Hence}$$

$$\sin \beta = \frac{b \sin \alpha}{a} = \frac{10\sqrt{2} \cdot \frac{1}{2}}{10} = \frac{\sqrt{2}}{2}.$$

The equation $\sin \beta = \frac{\sqrt{2}}{2}$ has two solutions whose degree measures are in $\rangle 0, 180 \langle$, namely 45 and 135.

When $\beta = \angle 45°$, we find that $\gamma = \angle 105°$, and $c = \frac{a \sin \gamma}{\sin \alpha} = \frac{10 \sin \angle 105°}{\frac{1}{2}} = 20 \times 0.9659 \approx 19.3$.

When $\beta = \angle 135°$, we find $\gamma = \angle 15°$, and $c = \frac{10 \sin \angle 15°}{\frac{1}{2}} = 20 \times 0.2588 \approx 5.18$.

Diagrams of the triangles determined in the preceding example are shown below. Note that each triangle contains the given parts in the required position relative to each other.

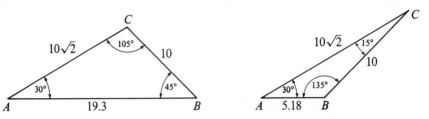

If the data given includes the degree measure of an angle θ, the measure of the side s_o opposite θ, and the measure of a side s_a adjacent to θ, we have just seen that there may be two solutions. This raises the question of the number of solutions we may have when such data is given. A study of the drawings at the right of each of the following will serve to verify that the statements are true.

(*i*) If $90 \leq dm\ \theta < 180$, then

    (a) There is one solution if and only if $s_o > s_a$.

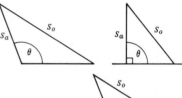

    (b) There is no solution if and only if $s_o \leq s_a$.

(*ii*) If $0 < dm\ \theta < 90$, then

    (a) There is one solution if $s_o \geq s_a$.

    (b) There is one solution, a right triangle, if $s_o = s_a \sin \theta$.

    (c) There are two solutions if and only if $s_a > s_o > s_a \sin \theta$.

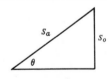

    (d) There is no solution if and only if $s_o < s_a \sin \theta$.

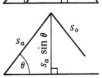

Note that when the given data (See (ii)(b)) leads to two solutions, it is called "ambiguous."

If two angles α_1 and α_2 are congruent, their corresponding trigonometric ratios are equal. This follows from the fact that if congruent angles α_1 and α_2 are placed in standard position their terminal sides intersect the unit circle in the same point $P(x, y)$. Thus $\sin \alpha_1 = y = \sin \alpha_2$, $\cos \alpha_1 = x = \cos \alpha_2$, $\tan \alpha_1 = \dfrac{y}{x} = \tan \alpha_2$, and so on.

Thus the following implications are true for any two angles α_1 and α_2:

F

$$\alpha_1 \cong \alpha_2 \longrightarrow \sin \alpha_1 = \sin \alpha_2 \qquad\qquad \alpha_1 \cong \alpha_2 \longrightarrow \cot \alpha_1 = \cot \alpha_2$$
$$\alpha_1 \cong \alpha_2 \longrightarrow \cos \alpha_1 = \cos \alpha_2 \qquad\qquad \alpha_1 \cong \alpha_2 \longrightarrow \sec \alpha_1 = \sec \alpha_2$$
$$\alpha_1 \cong \alpha_2 \longrightarrow \tan \alpha_1 = \tan \alpha_2 \qquad\qquad \alpha_1 \cong \alpha_2 \longrightarrow \csc \alpha_1 = \csc \alpha_2$$

Are the converses of these implications true?

 A EXERCISES

In the Exercises 1–5 assume that a, b, and c are the measures of the sides of a triangle and that α, β, and γ are the respective angles opposite these sides.

1. Find the measure of the area of the triangle determined by each of the following sets of data.

   a. $a = 10.37$, $b = 12.42$, $\gamma = \angle 47.2°$ c. $a = 4.781$, $c = 3.954$, $\beta = \angle 62.21°$

   b. $b = 1047$, $c = 5983$, $\alpha = \angle 71.1°$ d. $a = 45.32$, $c = 162.1$, $\beta = \angle 107.6°$

2. Given each of the following sets of data, find the measure of the side requested.

   a. $\alpha = \angle 34.2°$, $\beta = \angle 75.3°$, $a = 32.54$, find c

   b. $\beta = \angle 62.67°$, $\gamma = \angle 50.74°$, $b = 16.21$, find c

   c. $\alpha = \angle 47.4°$, $\gamma = \angle 84.5°$, $c = 1521$, find a

   d. $\beta = \angle 17.3°$, $\gamma = \angle 49.6°$, $b = 1.843$, find c

3. For each of the following sets of data, find the measures of the other parts.

   a. $\alpha = \angle 12.13°$, $\beta = \angle 43.25°$, $a = 136.1$

   b. $\alpha = \angle 64.1°$, $\gamma = \angle 21.2°$, $c = 24.33$

   c. $\beta = \angle 4.2°$, $\gamma = \angle 15.3°$, $a = 9431$

   d. $\beta = \angle 82.25°$, $\gamma = \angle 75.20°$, $c = 1.432$

   e. $\alpha = \angle 67.25°$, $\beta = \angle 27.20°$, $a = 143.2$

4. Without solving the triangle, find how many solutions are possible in each case.

   a. $\alpha = \angle 120°$, $a = 12$, $b = 7$ d. $\beta = \angle 90°$, $a = 7$, $b = 5$

   b. $\alpha = \angle 115°$, $a = 8$, $b = 18$ e. $\beta = \angle 40°$, $a = 14$, $b = 14$

   c. $\gamma = \angle 32°$, $b = 350$, $c = 170$ f. $\beta = \angle 30°$, $b = 2$, $a = 6$

5. For each of the following sets of data solve the triangle or triangles provided there is a solution.

    a. $\alpha = \angle\, 33.24°$, $a = 170.3$, $b = 355.4$

    b. $\beta = \angle\, 21.33°$, $b = 130.4$, $c = 146.2$

    c. $\beta = \angle\, 34.26°$, $\gamma = \angle\, 74.50°$, $b = 31.45$

    d. $\gamma = \angle\, 33.25°$, $b = 3551$, $c = 1704$

    e. $\alpha = \angle\, 54.26°$, $a = 8.514$, $c = 1.704$

    f. $\gamma = \angle\, 35.25°$, $b = 41.23$, $c = 24.79$

6. Two sides of a parallelogram are 15.32 and 24.71 inches long. If two of the sides meet to form an angle whose measurement is 14.5°, what is the area of the parallelogram?

7. Route 12 is a straight highway between lookout point A and lookout point B which is 15 miles ahead. When the Holcomb family stopped at lookout point A, the children wondered how far it was to the peak of Mt. Baldy (point C) in the distance. They estimated the measure in degrees of $\angle\, CAB$ to be 85. At lookout point B they stopped again and this time estimated the measure in degrees of $\angle\, CBA$ to be 70. If their estimates were correct, how far was it from A to Mt. Baldy (point C)? How far from B to Mt. Baldy (point C)?

B   **EXERCISES**

8. From a point P on the roof of an apartment building, 70 feet above the water level of a small lake, the angle of depression of a point A on the far shore of the lake is $\angle\, 6.7°$ and the angle of depression of a point B on the near shore of the lake and in the same vertical plane with the other two points, is $\angle\, 42.5°$. How wide is the lake between points A and B? (*Hint:* First determine the length of $|PA|$; then use the Law of Sines to determine the length between A and B.)

9. Prove, using the Law of Sines and statement **F**, page 503: If two angles of a triangle are congruent, the sides opposite these angles are congruent.

10. Prove, using the Law of Sines: The bisector of an angle of a triangle divides the opposite side into two segments whose lengths are proportional to the lengths of the adjacent sides.

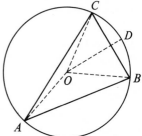

11. Prove: If d is the measure of the diameter of the circle circumscribed about a triangle ABC labeled in standard notation, then $d = \dfrac{a}{\sin \alpha} = \dfrac{b}{\sin \beta} = \dfrac{c}{\sin \gamma}$. *Hint.* Use the drawing at the right.

The Law of Cosines

At this point we state a very important generalization of the Pythagorean theorem known as the *Law of Cosines*.

> **Theorem 7–9.** If a, b, and c are the measures of the sides of a triangle and α, β, and γ are the angles opposite these sides, respectively, then
>
> (1) $a^2 = b^2 + c^2 - 2\,bc\,\cos\alpha$
> (2) $b^2 = c^2 + a^2 - 2\,ca\,\cos\beta$
> (3) $c^2 = a^2 + b^2 - 2\,ab\,\cos\gamma$.

Note. Theorem 7–9 is actually three theorems. Each theorem has the original hypothesis and one of the numbered conclusions.

Proof of Theorem 7–9(3): If a, b, and c are the measures of the sides of a triangle ABC and α, β, and γ are the angles opposite these sides, respectively, then (3) $c^2 = a^2 + b^2 - 2\,ab\,\cos\gamma$.

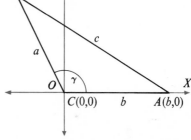

We locate any $\triangle ABC$ in the coordinate plane so that γ is in standard position and A has the coordinates $(b, 0)$ as shown at the right.

We denote the coordinates of B by (x, y). Using the distance formula we have: $c^2 = (x - b)^2 + (y - 0)^2 = x^2 + y^2 + b^2 - 2\,xb$ and $a^2 = x^2 + y^2$. It follows that $c^2 = a^2 + b^2 - 2\,xb$.

By the corollary to Theorem 1–9, we know that $x = a\cos\gamma$. Substituting $(a\cos\gamma)$ for x in the equation $c^2 = a^2 + b^2 - 2\,xb$, we have: $c^2 = a^2 + b^2 - 2\,ab\cos\gamma$. The other two theorems 7–9 (1) and 7–9 (2) can be proved similarly.

The Law of Cosines may be stated as follows: The square of the measure of a given side of a triangle is equal to the sum of the squares of the measures of the other two sides minus twice the product of the measures of these two sides and the cosine of the angle between them.

Suppose that γ is a right angle. In this case c is the hypotenuse of a right triangle and since $\cos \angle 90° = 0$ the Law of Cosines becomes $c^2 = a^2 + b^2$, which is the equation of the Pythagorean theorem. Thus we see that the Law of Cosines is a generalization of the Pythagorean theorem for arbitrary triangles.

Since, for $dm\ \gamma \in \langle 0, 180 \rangle$, $0 < dm\ \gamma < 90 \longleftrightarrow \cos \gamma > 0$ and $90 < dm\ \gamma < 180 \longleftrightarrow \cos \gamma < 0$, we can readily verify the following statements where γ is an angle in triangle ABC labeled in standard notation.

$$(i)\ dm\ \gamma < 90 \longleftrightarrow c^2 < a^2 + b^2$$
$$(ii)\ dm\ \gamma = 90 \longleftrightarrow c^2 = a^2 + b^2$$
$$(iii)\ dm\ \gamma > 90 \longleftrightarrow c^2 > a^2 + b^2$$

The Law of Cosines enables us to solve a triangle when the measures of two sides and the included angle are given or when the measures of three sides are given.

Example 1. In triangle ABC, $b = 8$, $c = 7$, and $\alpha = \angle 120°$; find a.

Solution.
$$a^2 = b^2 + c^2 - 2\ bc \cos \alpha$$
$$a^2 = 64 + 49 - 2 \cdot 8 \cdot 7(-\tfrac{1}{2})$$
$$a^2 = 169$$
$$a = 13$$

Example 2. In triangle ABC, $a = 11$, $b = 19$, and $c = 5\sqrt{3}$; find β.

Solution.
$$\cos \beta = \frac{a^2 + c^2 - b^2}{2\ ac}$$
$$= \frac{121 + 75 - 361}{2 \cdot 11 \cdot 5\sqrt{3}}$$
$$= -\frac{\sqrt{3}}{2}$$
$$\therefore\quad \beta = \angle 150°$$

 A EXERCISES

In Exercises 1 and 2, the measures of the sides of a triangle ABC are a, b, and c and α, β, and γ are the angles opposite these sides, respectively.

1. Replace each question mark with one of the symbols $<$, $=$, or $>$ to form a true statement.

a. If $a = 6$, $b = 4$, and $c = 8$, then $dm\ \gamma$ _?_ 90.

b. If $a = 12$, $b = 5$, and $c = 13$, then $dm\ \gamma$ _?_ 90.

c. If $a = 4$, $b = 9$, and $c = 12$, then $dm\ \gamma$ _?_ 90.

d. If $a = 4$, $b = 7$, and $c = 8$, then $dm\ \gamma$ _?_ 90.

2. For each of the following sets of data, solve the triangle.

a. $a = 5$, $b = 6$, $\gamma = \angle 36°$ **e.** $a = 3.6$, $b = 2.8$, $c = 1.0$

b. $b = 12$, $c = 5$, $\alpha = \angle 21°$ **f.** $a = 20$, $c = 32$, $\beta = \angle 32°$

c. $a = 121$, $c = 145$, $\beta = \angle 87°$ **g.** $a = 640$, $b = 530$, $c = 850$

d. $a = 0.80$, $b = 1.50$, $c = 1.70$ **h.** $a = 0.13$, $b = 0.15$, $c = 0.21$

3. Two roads, $\overrightarrow{AT}$ and $\overrightarrow{AW}$, form an angle TAW whose measurement is 50°. Two cars start at A at 8 A.M., one on $\overrightarrow{AT}$ and the other on $\overrightarrow{AW}$. The first travels at 50 miles per hour and the other at 70 miles per hour. Find the distance between these cars to the nearest tenth of a mile at 11 A.M.

4. The lengths of two adjacent sides of a parallelogram are 7.0 feet and 8.5 feet and the length of one of the diagonals is 6.5 feet. Find the measures of the angles of the parallelogram to the nearest tenth of a degree.

5. The lengths of the diagonals of a parallelogram are 12.3 feet and 9.2 feet and one of the angles formed by their intersection is $\angle$ 104.2°.

   a. What is the area of the parallelogram?

   b. What are the lengths of the sides of the parallelogram?

6. A piece of wire 5 feet 8 inches long is bent into the shape of a triangle. If the lengths of two sides of the triangle are 2 feet 6 inches and 1 foot 2 inches, what are the degree measures of the angles of the triangle?

7. How does the Law of Cosines show that if $a = 21$, $b = 31$, and $c = 10$, no triangle is formed?

B EXERCISES

8. The measures of sides AB and AD of a parallelogram $ABCD$ are s and t, respectively, and $dm \angle DAB = v$. Derive a general formula for:

   a. The measure d_1 of diagonal BD

   b. The measure d_2 of diagonal AC

9. Prove that in a triangle described in standard notation:

   a. $c = b \cos \alpha + a \cos \beta$

   b. $\dfrac{\cos \alpha}{a} + \dfrac{\cos \beta}{b} + \dfrac{\cos \gamma}{c} = \dfrac{a^2 + b^2 + c^2}{2\,abc}$

   c. $\dfrac{b^2}{a} \cos \alpha + \dfrac{c^2}{b} \cos \beta + \dfrac{a^2}{c} \cos \gamma = \dfrac{a^4 + b^4 + c^4}{2\,abc}$

   d. $\dfrac{\cos \alpha}{b} = \dfrac{\cos \beta}{a} \longrightarrow \triangle ABC$ is isosceles or $\triangle ABC$ is a right triangle.

10. If the measures of the sides of a triangle are a, b, and c, and if $a^2 < b^2 + c^2$, show that the angle opposite the side having measure a is an acute angle.

11. Determine the measure in degrees of the angles of the triangle ABC, whose vertices are $A(0, 0)$, $B(2, 0)$, and $C(3, -5)$.

12. If a, b, and c are the measures of the sides of an isosceles triangle, and if α is the angle opposite the side whose measure is a, show that $a^2 = 2\,b^2(1 - \cos \alpha)$.

Other Formulas Associated With the Triangle

From geometry we know that:

G   If K is the measure of the area of a triangle the measures of whose sides are a, b, and c, and $s = \frac{1}{2}(a + b + c)$, then $K = \sqrt{s(s-a)(s-b)(s-c)}$.

Suppose that O is the center of the inscribed circle of $\triangle ABC$ and that X, Y, and Z are the respective points where the sides $\overline{AB}$, $\overline{BC}$, and $\overline{CA}$ are tangent to the inscribed circle. If r is the measure of the radius of the inscribed circle, then $r = |OX| = |OY| = |OX|$ and $\overline{OX} \perp \overline{AB}$, $\overline{OY} \perp \overline{CB}$, and $\overline{OZ} \perp \overline{AC}$. Draw $\overline{AO}$, $\overline{BO}$, and $\overline{CO}$, as shown in the figure at the right. Then K, the measure of the area of $\triangle ABC$, is equal to the sum of the area of triangles AOB, BOC, and COA. Thus

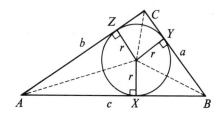

$$K = \tfrac{1}{2} rc + \tfrac{1}{2} ra + \tfrac{1}{2} rb$$
$$= r(\tfrac{1}{2} c + \tfrac{1}{2} a + \tfrac{1}{2} b)$$

H $K = rs$

From **G** and **H** we have:

$$rs = \sqrt{s(s-a)(s-b)(s-c)}$$
$$r = \frac{\sqrt{s(s-a)(s-b)(s-c)}}{s}.$$

Thus,

I $$r = \sqrt{\frac{(s-a)(s-b)(s-c)}{s}}.$$

In the figure above, $\triangle AOX \cong \triangle AOZ$. Why?   Therefore $\angle OAX = \frac{1}{2}\alpha$.

Accordingly, $\tan \frac{1}{2}\alpha = \dfrac{r}{|AX|}$.   However $|AX| = |AZ|, |XB| = |BY|$, and $|CY| = |CZ|$. Why?

Now $2s$, the perimeter of $\triangle ABC$, is given by

$$2s = |AX| + |AZ| + |BX| + |BY| + |CY| + |CZ|$$
$$2s = 2|AX| + 2|BY| + 2|CY|$$
$$2s = 2|AX| + 2(|BY| + |CY|)$$
$$2s = 2|AX| + 2a$$
$$s = |AX| + a$$
$$|AX| = s - a.$$

Therefore, $\tan \frac{1}{2} \alpha = \dfrac{r}{s-a} = \dfrac{1}{s-a} \sqrt{\dfrac{(s-a)(s-b)(s-c)}{s}}$

and (i) $\tan \frac{1}{2} \alpha = \sqrt{\dfrac{(s-b)(s-c)}{s(s-a)}}.$ By similar reasoning

J

(ii) $\tan \frac{1}{2} \beta = \sqrt{\dfrac{(s-a)(s-c)}{s(s-b)}}$ and

(iii) $\tan \frac{1}{2} \gamma = \sqrt{\dfrac{(s-a)(s-b)}{s(s-c)}}.$

The equations in **J** facilitate the logarithmic solution of a triangle when the measures of the three sides are given.

Example. Find the area and largest angle of the triangle whose sides have the measures 111.0, 145.0, and 40.0.

Solution. If $a = 111.0$, $b = 145.0$, and $c = 40.0$, then $2s = 111.0 + 145.0 + 40.0 = 296.0$, $s = 148.0$, $s - a = 37.0$, $s - b = 3.0$, and $s - c = 108.0$.

$$K = \sqrt{s(s-a)(s-b)(s-c)}$$
$$\log K = \tfrac{1}{2}[\log s + \log (s-a) + \log (s-b) + \log (s-c)]$$
$$= \tfrac{1}{2}[\log 148.0 + \log 37.0 + \log 3.0 + \log 108.0]$$
$$= \tfrac{1}{2}[2.1703 + 1.5682 + 0.4771 + 2.0334]$$
$$= 3.1245$$
$$K = 1332$$

Since the largest angle is opposite the largest side we seek $dm\ \beta$, the degree measure of the angle opposite b.

From **J**: $\tan \frac{1}{2} \beta = \sqrt{\dfrac{(s-a)(s-c)}{s(s-b)}}$

$$= \sqrt{\dfrac{37.0 \times 108.0}{148.0 \times 3.0}}$$

$$\log \tan \tfrac{1}{2} \beta = \tfrac{1}{2}[(\log 37.0 + \log 180.0) - (\log 148.0 + \log 3.0)]$$
$$= \tfrac{1}{2}[(1.5682 + 2.0334) - (2.1703 + 0.4771)]$$
$$= 0.4771$$

By Table V and interpolation:
$$\tfrac{1}{2}\beta = \angle\, 71.57°$$
$$\beta = \angle\, 143.14°$$

Ⓐ **EXERCISES**

1. If a, b, and c represent the measures of the sides of a triangle, what is the measure of the area of the triangle in each of the following cases?

a. $a = 60$, $b = 85$, $c = 95$ d. $a = 75.43$, $b = 84.22$, $c = 24.63$

b. $a = 129$, $b = 134$, $c = 191$ e. $a = 384$, $b = 276$, $c = 143$

c. $a = 33.4$, $b = 65.6$, $c = 47.2$ f. $a = 2874$, $b = 1437$, $c = 2442$

2. Find the degree measure of the largest angle in each of the triangles of Ex. 1.

3. Find r, the measure of the radius of the circle inscribed in each of the triangles of Ex. 1.

4. If r represents the measure of the radius of the circle inscribed in a triangle and s represents the measure of half the perimeter of the triangle, what is the measure of the area of the triangle in each of the following cases?

a. $r = 0.75$, $s = 14.60$ c. $r = 56.72$, $s = 173.80$

b. $r = 143.20$, $s = 2465$ d. $r = 12.7$, $s = 195.6$

5. The measures in inches of the sides of a triangle are 32, 30, and 18. What is the area of the triangle? What is the measure of the radius of the inscribed circle?

6. In triangle ABC, $a = 12$, $b = 11$, and $c = 15$. Find the radian measure of α, β, and γ.

Indicating Direction

In navigation and aviation two common methods of indicating direction are used. In one of these, directions are given in terms of the measurement of angles whose rotations are *clockwise* from north and the measure in degrees of the angle is in $\langle 0, 360 \langle$. If N is a point due north of A, then the *direction of N from A* is $0°$. The direction of B from A, in the figure at the right, is $122°$ and the direction of C from A is $258°$

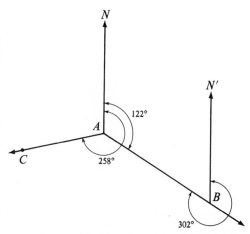

Observe that the *direction of A from B* is $122° + 180°$ or $302°$. What is the direction of A from C? If $x°$ is the direction of A from B and $y°$ is the direction of B from A, it is readily shown that $|x - y| = 180$. The direction of B from A, or the direction of ray AB is sometimes called the *bearing of B from A*.

Example.   From a navigation chart it is determined that lighthouses situated at A and B are 40 miles apart and that the direction (bearing) of B from A is $120°$ Observations taken from the ship S indicate that the direction of $\overrightarrow{SA}$ is $40°$ and the direction of $\overrightarrow{SB}$ is $70°$. Find the distance from the ship to each of the two lighthouses to the nearest tenth of a mile.

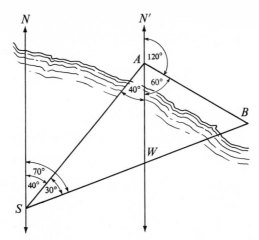

Solution. Lines drawn due north from S and A are considered to be parallel. Therefore $dm \angle WAS = 40$. $\angle WAB$ is supplementary to $\angle NAB$ and hence $dm \angle WAB = 60$.

Accordingly $dm \angle BAS = 40 + 60 = 100$. Also $dm \angle BSA = 70 - 40 = 30$. Thus in $\triangle SAB$ we know the measurements of two angles and the length of the side AB. The degree measure of the third angle ABS is $180 - (100 + 30)$. Thus $dm \angle ABS = 50$. Using the Law of Sines, we have:

$$\frac{\sin \angle 50°}{|AS|} = \frac{\sin \angle 100°}{|SB|} = \frac{\sin \angle 30°}{40} = \frac{1}{80}$$

$\therefore$ $|AS| = 80 \times \sin \angle 50° = 80 \times 0.7660 \approx 61.3$
and $|SB| = 80 \times \sin \angle 100° = 80 \times 0.9848 \approx 78.8$

Thus the distance from the ship to lighthouse A is 61.3 miles and the distance from the ship to lighthouse B is 78.8 miles.

The other method of indicating direction uses the compass points North, East, South, and West. When we use this method, the bearing of T from O is the measurement of the acute or right angle from the north or south line to $\overrightarrow{OT}$. Bearings are given in the following form: first the reference direction north or south (N or S), then the degree measurement of the angle, and finally the direction east or west (E or W) from the north or south ray. Thus the bearing of T from O, as shown at the right, is $N\ 37°\ E$, and the bearing of P from O is $S\ 76°\ W$. In what two ways may the bearing of E from O be expressed?

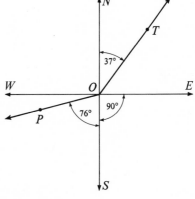

Using the second method of indicating direction, the directions in the Example on page 510 could be expressed as follows: The bearing of B from A is $S\ 60°\ E$, the bearing of A from S is $N\ 40°\ E$, and the bearing of B from S is $N\ 70°\ E$.

Ⓐ EXERCISES

1. A plane is flying in the direction $N\ 76°\ 12'\ E$ with a ground speed of 420 miles per hour. When the plane reaches point A, which is known to be 25 miles from a radio station, the bearing of the station from the plane is $S\ 12°\ 13'\ E$. After the plane has flown for 5 minutes, what is the direction of the station from the plane? How far is the plane from the station at this moment?

2. The bearing of B from A is $\angle\ 80°$. The bearing of C from A is $\angle\ 160°$ and the bearing of C from B is $\angle\ 200°$. If the distance from A to B is 2000 yards, what is the distance from A to C to the nearest yard?

3. Two planes leave Wiley airport at the same time, plane A flying a course which has the direction $10.2°$ at a ground speed of 420 miles per hour and plane B flying a course which has the direction $61.1°$ at a ground speed of 530 miles per hour. To the nearest mile, how far apart are the planes after 45 minutes if they fly straight courses?

4. An airplane flies a course which has the direction $30°$ at a ground speed of 160 miles per hour for 1 hour and 45 minutes from airport W. Then it flies a course of $130°$ at a ground speed of 185 miles per hour for 1 hour. How far is the plane from airport W at this time? At this time what is the bearing of airport W from the plane?

Vectors

A line segment is called a *directed line segment* if one of its end points is designated as its *initial point* and the other end point is designated as its *terminal point*. We use the symbol $\overrightarrow{AB}$ to denote the directed line segment whose initial point is A and whose terminal point is B. We sometimes speak of the initial and terminal points of a directed line segment as the *tail* and the *head*, respectively, of the directed line segment. Note that every directed line segment AB is part of the ray AB which has the same initial point A and the same direction.

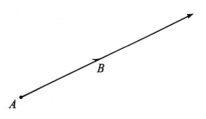

A geometrical *vector* is a directed line segment in a plane. Geometrical vectors can be used to represent quantities whose designation requires both magnitude and direction.

Consider the quantities that are paired in the following columns:

(a) A speed of 40 miles per hour

(1) A velocity of 40 miles per hour in the direction *S* 60° *W*

(b) A trip of 75 miles

(2) A trip of 75 miles in the direction 270° from north (due west)

(c) 100 cubic centimeters of water.

(3) A force of 100 grams in the direction 270° from the positive *x*-axis.

Observe that the quantities described in the column on the left have magnitude only. In physics such quantities are called *scalar* quantities. Also observe that each quantity described in the column on the right has both magnitude and direction. Such quantities are called vector quantities and are represented by geometrical vectors. If $\overrightarrow{AB}$ is used to represent a vector quantity, then $|AB|$ represents the magnitude of the quantity and the direction of $\overrightarrow{AB}$ represents its direction. As in the preceding section, the direction of $\overrightarrow{AB}$ is indicated by the measurement of the angle it makes with a ray of known direction. The following three figures show geometrical representations of the vector quantities described in statements (1), (2), and (3), respectively.

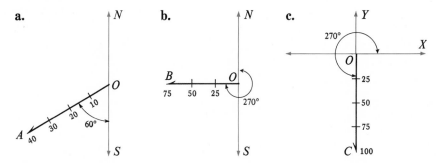

For example, in figure **a** the vector has been drawn so that $\frac{1}{4}$ inch represents 10 miles. Thus the 1-inch length of the vector represents the 40 mile distance covered in one hour. In figure **c** $\frac{1}{4}$ inch represents 25 grams. Thus the measure of the vector represents the 100 gram magnitude of the vector quantity. A vector always has a terminal point such as *A*, *B*, and *C* in figures **a**, **b**, and **c**, respectively. A ray has no terminal point. We name a vector by first naming its initial point and then naming its terminal point. Thus the vectors represented in figures **a**, **b**, and **c** are called vectors *OA*, *OB*, and *OC*, respectively.

Two vectors are *equal* if and only if they have the same magnitude, the same direction, and the same initial point. It follows that they also have the same terminal point. Thus $\overrightarrow{AB} = \overrightarrow{CD}$ if and only if A and C are the same point and B and D are the same point.

Vectors which have the same magnitude and the same direction are called *equivalent* vectors. In the figure at the right, vectors AB and CD are equivalent because $|AB| = |CD|$ and both vectors have the same direction, $N\,45°\,E$. $\overrightarrow{EF}$ is not equivalent to $\overrightarrow{AB}$ or $\overrightarrow{CD}$ even though it is parallel to them and has the same measure. This is because $\overrightarrow{EF}$ has a different direction, $S\,45°\,W$. To indicate that $\overrightarrow{AB}$ and $\overrightarrow{CD}$ are equivalent, we may

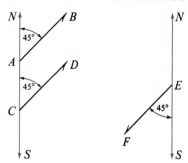

write $\overrightarrow{AB} \doteq \overrightarrow{CD}$. $\overrightarrow{AB}$ is a *zero vector* if and only if A and B are the same point; that is, if and only if $|AB| = 0$. All zero vectors are considered to be equivalent to each other.

If $\overrightarrow{AB}$ and $\overrightarrow{CD}$ are two vectors, then their sum $\overrightarrow{AB} + \overrightarrow{CD}$ is $\overrightarrow{AX}$, where X is the unique point such that $\overrightarrow{BX} \doteq \overrightarrow{CD}$. We call the operation which assigns a sum to a pair of vectors the addition operation for vectors or *vector addition*. $\overrightarrow{AX}$ is also called the *resultant* of vectors $\overrightarrow{AB}$ and $\overrightarrow{CD}$. The figures below show vector addition.

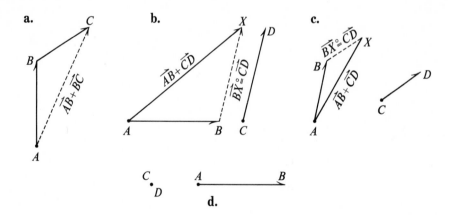

In figure **a**, since the terminal point of $\overrightarrow{AB}$ is the same point as the initial point of $\overrightarrow{BC}$, we draw $\overrightarrow{AC}$ and say $\overrightarrow{AB} + \overrightarrow{BC} = \overrightarrow{AC}$. In figure **b**, to find $\overrightarrow{AB} + \overrightarrow{CD}$ we draw $\overrightarrow{BX} \doteq \overrightarrow{CD}$ and then draw $\overrightarrow{AX}$. Now $\overrightarrow{AX} = \overrightarrow{AB} + \overrightarrow{CD}$. Similarly, in figure **c**, to find $\overrightarrow{AB} + \overrightarrow{CD}$ we draw $\overrightarrow{BX} \doteq \overrightarrow{CD}$, and then draw $\overrightarrow{AX}$. Now $\overrightarrow{AX} = \overrightarrow{AB} + \overrightarrow{CD}$. In figure **d**, since point C is the same point as D, the measure of $\overrightarrow{CD} = 0$. Accordingly, $\overrightarrow{AB} + \overrightarrow{CD} = \overrightarrow{AB}$. It can be shown that the addition of two vectors is commutative in the sense that $\overrightarrow{AB} + \overrightarrow{CD} \doteq \overrightarrow{CD} + \overrightarrow{AB}$ as shown at the right.

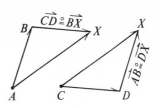

To find the sum of three vectors AB, CD, and EF, we proceed as shown at the right below. To find the sum of four or more vectors, we continue in this pattern. Thus $\overrightarrow{AB} + \overrightarrow{CD} + \overrightarrow{EF} + \overrightarrow{GH} = [(\overrightarrow{AB} + \overrightarrow{CD}) + \overrightarrow{EF}] + \overrightarrow{GH}$, and so on. It can be shown that the addition of three or more vectors is associative.

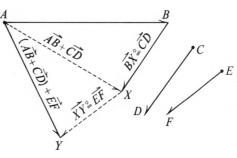

To multiply a vector by 2, we double its magnitude and leave its direction unchanged, and to multiply a vector by $\frac{1}{3}$, we make its length one third of the original length and leave its direction unchanged.

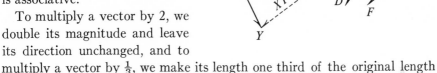

To multiply a vector by -1, we reverse its direction and leave its magnitude unchanged. To multiply a vector by -2, we first multiply by -1 and then multiply this product by 2. When we multiply a vector by a real number we say that we have multiplied the vector by a *scalar*.

$$\overrightarrow{AD} = 2\,\overrightarrow{AB}$$

$$\overrightarrow{EF} = \tfrac{1}{3}\,\overrightarrow{AB}$$

$$\overrightarrow{HG} = -\,\overrightarrow{AB}$$

Example 1. Use trigonometry to find the resultant of a trip of 40 miles in the direction 290° from north followed by a trip of 60 miles in the direction 230° from north.

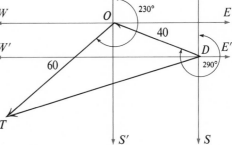

Solution. We see that $\angle W'DO = \angle 20°$ and $\angle DOT = \angle 120°$. Using the Law of Cosines, we have:

$$|DT|^2 = 60^2 + 40^2 - 2(60)(40)(-\tfrac{1}{2}) = 7600$$

$\therefore |DT| = 87.2 \approx 87$. Thus the magnitude of the resultant $\overrightarrow{DT}$ is approximately 87.

Using the Law of Sines, $\dfrac{\sin \angle ODT}{60} = \dfrac{\sin \angle 120°}{87}$.

$$\sin \angle ODT = \frac{60\left(\dfrac{\sqrt{3}}{2}\right)}{87} = 0.5972$$

$$\angle ODT = \angle 36.7°$$
$$dm \angle ODT \approx 37$$
$$dm \angle NDT = dm \angle NDO - dm \angle ODT = 290 - 37 = 253$$

Therefore the direction of $\overrightarrow{DT}$ is 253° from north. Thus the length and direction of the resultant trip are 87 miles and 253° from north, respectively.

Example 2. A force of 80 pounds and a force of 36 pounds are acting at a point in directions of 60° from each other. Find the magnitude of their resultant to the nearest pound. Also find the measure in degrees of the angle the resultant forms with the greater force.

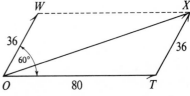

Solution. In the figure at the right let O be the point at which the forces are acting. The resultant of these two forces is the resultant of the vectors $\overrightarrow{OT}$ and $\overrightarrow{OW}$ which represent the two forces. Therefore it is the vector $\overrightarrow{OX}$ where X is the unique point such that $\overrightarrow{TX} \doteq \overrightarrow{OW}$. We are to find $|OX|$ and the measure in degrees of angle TOX. We know that $\angle OTX = \angle 120°$. Applying the Law of Cosines, we have:

$$|OX|^2 = 80^2 + 36^2 - 2 \cdot 80 \cdot 36 \cdot (-\tfrac{1}{2})$$
$$= 6400 + 1296 + 2880$$
$$= 10576.$$

Using logarithms, we obtain $|OX| \approx 103$. Thus the magnitude of $\overrightarrow{OX}$ is 103.

Applying the Law of Sines, we obtain:

$$\frac{\sin \angle XOT}{36} = \frac{\sin \angle 120°}{103}$$

$$\sin \angle XOT = \frac{36 \cdot \dfrac{\sqrt{3}}{2}}{103}$$

$$= \frac{18\sqrt{3}}{103}$$

$$\log \sin \angle XOT = \log 18 + \tfrac{1}{2} \log 3 - \log 103$$

Using Tables II and V, we obtain: $\angle XOT \approx \angle 17°$.

Thus the resultant of the two given forces is a force whose direction is approximately 17° from the greater force (on the same side of it as the smaller force) and whose magnitude is approximately 103 pounds.

Note: The parallelogram $OTXW$ shown in the diagram is often called the *parallelogram of forces* while the triangle OTX is called the *triangle of forces* or *force triangle*. Observe that the resultant of the forces, $\overrightarrow{OT}$ and $\overrightarrow{OW}$, is the diagonal $\overrightarrow{OX}$ of the parallelogram having $\overrightarrow{OT}$ and $\overrightarrow{OW}$ as adjacent sides.

In aviation, vectors are used to represent the heading of a plane and the speed and direction of the wind. The *heading* of a plane is the direction in which it is pointed and its *course* is the intended direction of the path of flight planned in advance. The *track* of a plane is the actual direction of the directed line segment traced by a point on the ground directly below the plane. The track may or may not coincide with the course. The ground speed of a plane is the speed of the plane relative to the ground; that is, the speed at which ground distances are covered. The air speed is the speed of the plane relative to the air which supports it. Thus suppose that a plane with an air speed of 300 miles per hour is flying directly into the wind which is blowing at 40 miles per hour. When we say that the wind is blowing at 40 miles per hour, we mean that the air mass which contains the plane is moving at a speed of 40 miles per hour relative to the ground. Wind direction is usually given as the direction from which the wind is blowing. Thus the ground speed of the plane would be 260 miles per hour.

If the direction and speed of the wind are represented by one vector and the heading and air speed of a plane are represented by another vector, then the resultant of these two vectors represents the track and ground speed of the plane. The following drawing which depicts this situation is called a wind diagram. The angle between the heading and the track is called the *drift angle*.

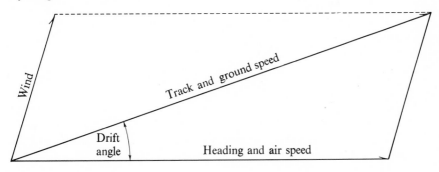

Example 3. The heading of a plane is 150° and its airspeed is 300 miles
per hour. The wind is blowing 300° from north with such speed
that the drift angle is 6°. Find to the nearest mile per hour
the ground speed of the plane and the speed of the wind.

Solution.   In our diagram $\overrightarrow{OP}$ represents the speed and di-
rection of the plane and
$\overrightarrow{PQ}$ represents the speed
and direction of the wind.
Accordingly $\overrightarrow{OQ}$, the resultant of these two vec-
tors, represents the track
and ground speed of the
plane.   If the drawing
were drawn carefully to
scale we could find $|PQ|$
and $|OQ|$ by measure-
ment.

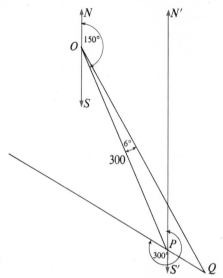

Observe that
$$dm(\angle N'PQ) = 300 - 180$$
$$= 120.$$

Also $\angle N'PO$ is supplementary to $\angle NOP$ because ON and PN' are
directed due north and are regarded as parallel. Therefore $\angle N'PO$
$= \angle 30°$ and hence $\angle OPQ = \angle 150°$. Now $dm \angle POQ + dm$
$\angle OPQ + dm \angle OQP = 180$. Thus $\angle OQP = \angle 24°$. By the Law
of Sines $\dfrac{300}{\sin \angle 24°} = \dfrac{|PQ|}{\sin \angle 6°} = \dfrac{|OQ|}{\sin \angle 150°}$. Solving by the use of
Tables II and V, we find $|OQ| = 360$ and $|PQ| = 77$. Thus the
ground speed of the plane is 360 miles per hour and the speed of the
wind is 77 miles per hour.

 EXERCISES

1. Two forces, one of 200 pounds and one of 500 pounds, act on a body and are
   perpendicular to each other. Construct the vector that represents the sum
   of the two vectors. Let $\frac{1}{4}$ inch represent 50 pounds.

2. Construct the vector that represents the sum of the two forces in Ex. 1 when
   the forces form an angle of 30° with each other.

3. Three planes leave an airport at the same time, plane A traveling N 30° E at
   500 miles per hour, plane B traveling north at 400 miles per hour, and plane C
   traveling N 60° E at 650 miles per hour. Using vectors show the paths of the
   planes during the first hour if the wind velocity is 25 miles per hour from 190°.

4. Which of the following statements is true for the figure at the right?

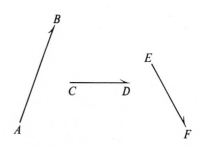

a. $\overrightarrow{AB} + \overrightarrow{AC} = \overrightarrow{BC}$ b. $\overrightarrow{AB} + \overrightarrow{BC} = \overrightarrow{AC}$

5. On your paper draw three vectors resembling those at the right. Using the vectors you have drawn, construct

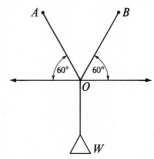

a. $\overrightarrow{AB} + \overrightarrow{CD}$ e. $\overrightarrow{AB} + \overrightarrow{EF}$

b. $\overrightarrow{CD} + \overrightarrow{AB}$ f. $\overrightarrow{EF} + \overrightarrow{AB}$

c. $\overrightarrow{CD} + \overrightarrow{EF}$ g. $\overrightarrow{AB} + \overrightarrow{CD} + \overrightarrow{EF}$

d. $\overrightarrow{EF} + \overrightarrow{CD}$ h. $\overrightarrow{EF} + \overrightarrow{AB} + \overrightarrow{CD}$

6. Draw a vector AB, and then construct each of the following:

a. $3\,\overrightarrow{AB}$ b. $-2\,\overrightarrow{AB}$ c. $\frac{2}{3}\,\overrightarrow{AB}$

7. Two forces, one of 70 pounds and one of 30 pounds, act at a point on a body and at an angle of 60° with each other. By means of trigonometry find the resultant force.

8. A jet plane with an air speed of 650 miles per hour has the heading 230° and a wind of 20 miles per hour is blowing from 90°. Find the ground speed of the plane.

9. A pilot is to fly a plane west at 450 miles per hour at a time when a wind of 30 miles per hour is blowing from the direction $N\ 80°\ E$. In what direction should he head the plane in order to stay on course?

10. The water in a river flows south at the rate of 4 miles per hour. A man on the west bank of the river wants to go by motorboat to a point in the direction 120° from north and on the opposite bank. If the boat is powered to travel 20 miles per hour in still water, in what direction should the man head the boat to reach the desired point?

11. The resultant of two forces acting at a point on a body at right angles to each other has a magnitude of 60 pounds. If the magnitude of one force is 40 pounds, what is the magnitude of the other force and what angle does it make with the resultant?

12. Two cables are attached to an object at the point O as shown in the diagram. What is the greatest weight that the two cables can support if each cable can support a maximum load of 300 pounds? Note that each cable makes an angle of 60° with a horizontal line.

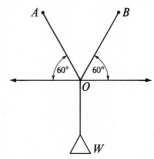

Resolving Vectors

Sometimes it is convenient to name a vector by using the symbol $\rightarrow$ above a single capital letter, such as $\overrightarrow{W}$. In such cases we use $|\overrightarrow{W}|$ to denote the magnitude of the vector. Thus if $\overrightarrow{OA} = \overrightarrow{W}$, then $|\overrightarrow{OA}| = |\overrightarrow{W}|$. Thus we say that $\overrightarrow{V} = \overrightarrow{V_1} + \overrightarrow{V_2}$ because $\overrightarrow{V_1}$ and $\overrightarrow{V_2}$ denote the vectors $\overrightarrow{OS}$ and $\overrightarrow{ST}$,

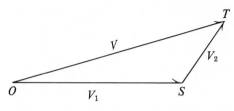

respectively, and $\overrightarrow{V}$ denotes their resultant. (See the above figure.) If $\overrightarrow{V_1} + \overrightarrow{V_2} + \overrightarrow{V_3} + \cdots + \overrightarrow{V_n} = \overrightarrow{V}$, then the n vectors $\overrightarrow{V_1} \overrightarrow{V_2} \cdots \overrightarrow{V_n}$ are called *components* of $\overrightarrow{V}$. Expressing a vector as the sum of components is called *resolving the vector*. We are usually concerned with resolving a given vector into *two* components which have specified directions. Often these directions are perpendicular to each other, as when one is horizontal and the other is vertical.

Example 1. A rope attached to the front end of a sled makes an angle of 28° with the horizontal (see figure at the right). If a man pulls on the rope with a force whose magnitude is 80 pounds, find to the nearest pound the magnitude of the force which tends to pull the sled forward along the horizontal plane and the magnitude of the force that tends to lift the front end of the sled.

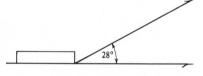

Solution. Draw the force triangle as shown at the right in which $|\overrightarrow{P}| = 80$. $\overrightarrow{H}$ and $\overrightarrow{V}$ are components of $\overrightarrow{P}$ because $\overrightarrow{H} + \overrightarrow{V} = \overrightarrow{P}$. Since $|\overrightarrow{H}| = |\overrightarrow{P}| \cos \angle 28°$ and $|\overrightarrow{V}| = |\overrightarrow{P}| \sin \angle 28°$, the magnitude of the force which pulls the sled forward is approximately 71 pounds and the magnitude of the force which lifts the front end of the sled is approximately 38 pounds.

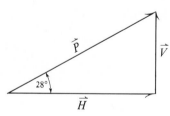

The component of $\overrightarrow{OP}$ in the direction $\overrightarrow{OW}$ which makes an angle whose measurement is $d°$, where $0 < d < 90$, with $\overrightarrow{OP}$ and the component in the direction *perpendicular* to $\overrightarrow{OW}$ can be found by a geometric construction as

follows. Draw a circle C with $\overline{OP}$ as diameter and mark its center Q (see
figure at the right). Mark A the point
of intersection of $\overrightarrow{OW}$ and C. Draw $\overrightarrow{AQ}$
and mark B the point of intersection of
C and $\overrightarrow{AQ}$. Then since $\overrightarrow{AP} \doteq \overrightarrow{OB}$, our
rule for adding vectors tells us that
$\overrightarrow{OA} + \overrightarrow{OB} = \overrightarrow{OP}$. $\overrightarrow{OA}$ is the component
of $\overrightarrow{OP}$ in the direction $\overrightarrow{OW}$ and $\overrightarrow{OB}$ is
the component of $\overrightarrow{OP}$ in the direction
which is perpendicular to $\overrightarrow{OW}$. Clearly

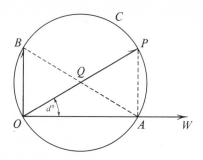

$|OA| = |OP| \cos \angle d°$ and $|OB| = |OP| \sin \angle d°$.

If three forces are in equilibrium, each is equal in magnitude but opposite
in direction to the resultant of the other two. Thus in the figure below, $\overrightarrow{OP}$
is equal in magnitude but opposite in direc-
tion to $\overrightarrow{OP'}$ which is the resultant of $\overrightarrow{OR}$ and
$\overrightarrow{OQ}$. Similarly $\overrightarrow{OR}$ is equal in magnitude but
opposite in direction to $\overrightarrow{OR'}$ the resultant of
$\overrightarrow{OP}$ and $\overrightarrow{OQ}$, and so forth.

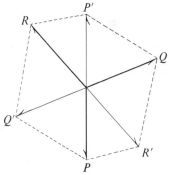

What is the sum of $\overrightarrow{OP}$, $\overrightarrow{OQ}$, and $\overrightarrow{OR}$? If
$\overrightarrow{OP}$, $\overrightarrow{OQ}$, and $\overrightarrow{OR}$ are placed so that the tail
of $\overrightarrow{OQ}$ is at the head of $\overrightarrow{OP}$ and the tail of $\overrightarrow{OR}$
is at the head of $\overrightarrow{OQ}$, what kind of a figure is
formed?

According to the laws of physics, if the sum
of all the forces acting on a body is zero, the body is either at rest or in motion in a straight line at constant speed. The converse of the foregoing
statement is also true.

Example 2.   A barrel is held in place on
an inclined plane MN by a
force $\overrightarrow{OA}$ operating parallel
to the plane and another
force $\overrightarrow{OB}$ operating perpendicular to it (see figure at
the right). If the weight of
the barrel is 300 pounds
and the plane makes an angle of 27° with the horizon-
tal, find $|OA|$ and $|OB|$.

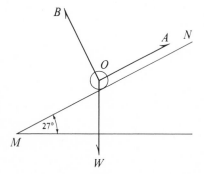

Solution.   The weight of the barrel is directed vertically downward and therefore is a force which can be represented by the vector OW. Since
the forces represented by $\overrightarrow{OW}$,
$\overrightarrow{OA}$, and $\overrightarrow{OB}$ are in equilibrium, the resultant of $\overrightarrow{OA}$ and
$\overrightarrow{OB}$ must be equal in magnitude to $\overrightarrow{OW}$ but opposite in
direction. In the drawing at
the right $\overrightarrow{OW}$ represents the
300 pound downward pull of
gravity on the barrel. Thus
$|OW| = 300$ according to our
chosen scale and $|OW| = |OW'|$. We seek two vectors
which have the directions of

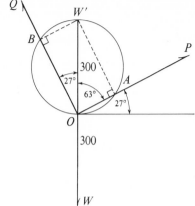

$\overrightarrow{OP}$ and $\overrightarrow{OQ}$, respectively, and whose resultant is a force of 300
pounds directed vertically upward. Applying the geometric con-
struction described on page 520, we draw a circle with $\overline{OW'}$ as diam-
eter and mark A and B, its points of intersection with $\overrightarrow{OP}$ and $\overrightarrow{OQ}$,
which have the directions of $\overrightarrow{OA}$ and $\overrightarrow{OB}$, respectively. Since
$\overrightarrow{OA} \doteq \overrightarrow{BW'}$ we see that $\overrightarrow{OW'} = \overrightarrow{OB} + \overrightarrow{OA}$. Therefore the resultant
of $\overrightarrow{OB}$ and $\overrightarrow{OA}$ is equal to a force of 300 pounds directed vertically
upward. From triangle OBW' we see that $|OB| = 300 \cdot \cos \angle 27°$
≈ 267 and from triangle $OW'A$ we see that $|OA| = 300 \cdot \cos$
$\angle 63° \approx 136$. Therefore $|OA| \approx 136$ and $|OB| \approx 267$.

Example 3.   A weight of 1000 pounds is suspended from ropes as shown in
the figure. Find the magnitude of
the force (the tension in rope OT)
exerted in the direction $\overrightarrow{OT}$ and the
magnitude of the force (the tension
in rope OS) exerted in the direction
$\overrightarrow{OS}$.

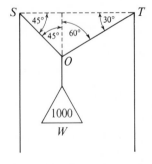

Solution.   We must be careful to note that $|OT|$
and $|OS|$ do not necessarily represent
the tension in the ropes. We construct
a force diagram as follows: Draw $\overrightarrow{OW}$ so that $|OW|$ is the length
indicated by a chosen scale. Draw $\overrightarrow{OW'}$ so that $\overrightarrow{OW}$ and $\overrightarrow{OW'}$
are opposite vectors and $|OW'| = |OW|$. Draw $\overrightarrow{OB}$ so that
$\angle BOW' = \angle 60°$ and draw $\overrightarrow{OA}$ so that $\angle AOW' = \angle 45°$. Draw
$\overleftrightarrow{W'E} \parallel \overleftrightarrow{OA}$ and intersecting $\overleftrightarrow{OB}$ at T. Draw $\overleftrightarrow{W'F} \parallel \overleftrightarrow{OB}$ intersecting

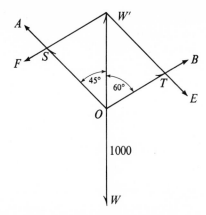

$\overrightarrow{OA}$ at S. Then $\overrightarrow{OT}$ and $\overrightarrow{OS}$ are the components of $\overrightarrow{OW'}$ in the directions indicated by $\overrightarrow{OB}$ and $\overrightarrow{OA}$, respectively. In $\triangle OTW'$, $\angle OW'T = \angle 45°$ and $\angle OTW' = \angle 75°$. By the Law of Sines

$$\frac{|OT|}{\sin \angle 45°} = \frac{|TW'|}{\sin \angle 60°} = \frac{1000}{\sin \angle 75°}$$

Thus $|OT| \approx 732$ and $|TW'| = |OS| \approx 816.5$. Therefore the tensions in ropes OT and OS are approximately 732 pounds and 816.5 pounds, respectively.

Ⓐ **EXERCISES**

1. Find the magnitude of horizontal and vertical components of each of the following vector quantities.

   a. A velocity of 400 miles per hour at 60° from north

   b. A force of 0.36 pounds at an angle of 40° counterclockwise from horizontal

   c. A displacement of 56 inches in the direction $S\ 45°\ W$

   d. A velocity of 100 miles per hour in the direction 225° from north

2. Resolve a force whose magnitude is 20 pounds into two components having equal magnitudes which form an angle of 45° with each other.

3. Resolve a force whose magnitude is 80 pounds into two components each of which makes an angle of 30° with it.

4. A force whose magnitude is 500 pounds is resolved into components of 400 pounds and 300 pounds. What angle do the components make with each other?

5. A boy pulls a sled with a rope that makes an angle of 35° with the horizontal. If a pull of 15 pounds is needed to move the sled, what is the horizontal component of the force? What is the vertical component of the force?

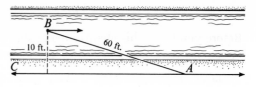

6. In early days canal boats were sometimes pulled along a canal by horses traveling a tow path parallel to the canal. In the figure at the right B represents a boat which required 200 pounds of force to move in a straight line. The boat was 10 feet from the tow path CA, and BA represents a 60 foot tow rope. If the horses at A had to exert 350 pounds of force to move the boat, how much of the force exerted by the horses was wasted?

7. A sign weighing 200 pounds is supported as shown at the right. What is the magnitude of the force along AB? along CB?

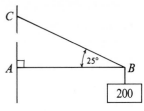

8. A block of wood weighing 8 pounds rests on an inclined plane that makes an angle of 20° with the horizontal. How much force is needed to prevent the block from sliding down the plane?

9. A weight of 800 pounds is suspended by two cables as shown at the right. If one cable makes an angle of 50° with a horizontal line and the other makes an angle of 30° with the same horizontal line, what is the tension in cable AB? in cable BC?

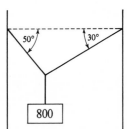

10. A block of stone weighing one ton is to be raised by means of a crane as shown at the right. When the crane is in the position shown, the angle between the crane boom CB and the tie cable AB contains 15° and the angle between cable AB and cable BD contains 45°, what force is exerted along CB? along AB?

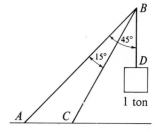

11. Find the sum of the vertical components of $\overrightarrow{AB}$, $\overrightarrow{AC}$, and $\overrightarrow{AD}$ shown at the right. What is the sum of the horizontal components of the three vectors?

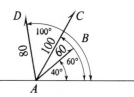

12. An iron ball weighing 20 pounds rests on two plane surfaces which meet each other and which are inclined at 30° and 45°, respectively, with the horizontal. What force does the weight of the ball exert in a direction perpendicular to each surface?

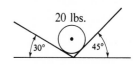

Before you leave this chapter make sure that you

1. Understand the meaning of *path in a circle* as used in this chapter and have mastered the vocabulary associated with the term. (Page 449.)

2. Understand how real numbers are used as the measures of paths and arcs in circles. (Page 449.)

3. Understand the definitions of the trigonometric functions of real numbers. (Pages 452–453.)

4. Understand the meaning of and the language associated with the term *directed angle*. (Page 455.)

5. Understand the concept of radian measurement of an angle and how it is related to the measure of a path in a circle. (Page 459.)

6. Understand the relationship among measure in radians, measure in degrees, and measure in revolutions of an angle, and can solve problems involving these relationships. (Page 462.)

7. Understand how the values of the trigonometric functions of directed angles are obtained from the values of the trigonometric functions of real numbers. (Page 467.)

8. Can solve problems involving the trigonometric ratios associated with acute angles. (Page 476.)

9. Can find, without use of a table, the trigonometric ratios associated with angles whose measures in degrees are 0, 30, 45, 60, 90, 120, 135, 150, and so on. (Page 479.)

10. Understand the relationship between values of the trigonometric functions of complementary angles. (Page 482.)

11. Can use Table IV. (Page 484.)

12. Can use Table V. (Page 491.)

13. Can solve problems involving the trigonometric ratios associated with acute angles by use of logarithms. (Page 491.)

14. Understand and can use the Law of Sines. (Page 500.)

15. Understand and can use the Law of Cosines. (Page 505.)

16. Understand and can use the methods described in this chapter for indicating direction. (Page 510.)

17. Understand the concept of vectors and can solve problems involving vectors. (Page 512.)

18. Know the meaning of, can spell, and can use correctly the following words and phrases.

angle of depression (Page 489.)
angle of elevation (Page 489.)
angular velocity (Page 466.)
circular coordinates (Page 471.)
cofunction (Page 482.)
component of vector (Page 520.)
cosecant (Page 453.)
cosine (Page 452.)
cotangent (Page 453.)
coterminal (Page 450.)
directed line segment (Page 512.)
equivalent paths (Page 449.)
initial point (Page 449.)
initial side (Page 455.)
intercepted arc (Page 460.)
linear velocity (Page 466.)

primary directed angle (Page 457.)
quadrantal angles (Page 475.)
radian measure (Page 459.)
reference angle (Page 494.)
revolution (Page 462.)
secant (Page 453.)
sine (Page 452.)
subtended angle (Page 460.)
standard position angle (Page 457.)
standard position path (Page 452.)
standard notation for a right triangle (Page 476.)
tangent (Page 453.)
terminal side (Page 455.)
vector (Page 512.)

CHAPTER REVIEW

1. For each of the following draw a unit circle in standard position and then draw the directed paths symbolized below.

   a. $\left(OI, \dfrac{\pi}{6}\right)$ b. $\left(OI, -\dfrac{2\pi}{3}\right)$ c. $(OI, -2)$ e. $(OI, 1 + 2\pi)$

   d. $(OI, 7\pi)$ f. $(OI, -2 - 4\pi)$

2. If I is the point whose coordinates are $(1, 0)$ and B is the point whose coordinates are $(0, 1)$, indicate which of the following pairs of paths in the unit circle are equal, which are equivalent, and which are neither equal nor equivalent.

   a. $\left(OI, \dfrac{\pi}{2}\right), \left(OB, \dfrac{\pi}{2}\right)$ c. $(OI, 3\pi), (OI, 5\pi)$ e. $(OB, 2\pi + 1),$

   $\qquad \qquad \qquad \qquad$ d. $(OI, -2\pi),$ $\qquad \qquad (OB, 1 + 2\pi)$

   b. $\left(OI, \dfrac{\pi}{2}\right), \left(OB, -\dfrac{\pi}{2}\right)$ $(OI, 2\pi)$ f. $\left(OI, \dfrac{\pi}{2}\right), \left(OB, -\dfrac{\pi}{2}\right)$

3. If I is the point whose coordinates are $(1, 0)$ and B is the point whose coordinates are $(0, 1)$ state which of the following pairs of paths in the unit circle are coterminal.

   a. $\left(OI, \dfrac{\pi}{6}\right), \left(OI, -\dfrac{11\pi}{6}\right)$ d. $(OB, \tfrac{2}{3}), (OI, \tfrac{2}{3} + 6\pi)$

   $\qquad \qquad \qquad \qquad$ e. $(OI, -2\pi), (OI, 4\pi)$

   b. $(OI, 3), (OI, 2\pi + 3)$

   c. $(OI, -1), (OI, 2\pi + 1)$ f. $\left(OB, \dfrac{8\pi}{3}\right), \left(OB, -\dfrac{\pi}{3}\right)$

4. Show that the point $T\left(\frac{1}{2}, \frac{\sqrt{3}}{2}\right)$ is in the unit circle in standard position.

5. If T of Ex. 4 is the terminal point of path $(\overrightarrow{OI}, t)$, find the value of each of the following.

    a. $\sin t$ **b.** $\cos t$ **c.** $\tan t$ **d.** $\csc t$ **e.** $\sec t$ **f.** $\cot t$

6. In separate diagrams, draw each of the following directed angles in standard position.

    a. $\left(\overrightarrow{OA}, \frac{\pi}{2}\right)$ **b.** $(\overrightarrow{OA}, 1)$ **c.** $(\overrightarrow{OA}, 2\pi + 2)$ **d.** $(\overrightarrow{OA}, -3\pi)$

7. If a circle is divided into 7 equivalent arcs, what is the measure in radians of the central angle subtended by each arc?

8. Find the length of the radius of a path if the path is 6 inches long and corresponds to a central angle of 2 radians.

9. Replace each of the following question marks to form a true statement.

    a. $\frac{2\pi}{3}$ radians $=$ _?_ degrees $=$ _?_ revolutions

    b. $\frac{3}{4}$ revolution $=$ _?_ radians $=$ _?_ degrees

    c. 120 degrees $=$ _?_ radians $=$ _?_ revolutions

10. Use Table IV to replace each question mark so that the statement formed is true.

    a. $14.4° =$ _?_ radians   **c.** $29.2° =$ _?_ radians

    b. 0.4854 radians $=$ _?_ °   **d.** 0.7570 radians $=$ _?_ °

11. The radius of a wheel is 13 inches long.

    a. If the wheel makes 3 revolutions per second, what is its angular velocity in radians per second?

    b. What is the linear velocity in inches per second of a point in the rim of the wheel?

12. How many revolutions per minute are made by a wheel whose angular velocity is 15 radians per second?

13. The measurement of the radius of a circle is 14 inches. Find the area of a sector of the circle if the measurement of the central angle of the sector is $\frac{2\pi}{3}$.

14. Given $(\overrightarrow{OI}, t)$, indicate the signs of each of the following in each of the four quadrants.

    a. $\sin t$ **b.** $\cos t$ **c.** $\tan t$

15. a. Sketch two primary angles θ which fit the description: $\cos\theta = \frac{3}{5}$.

    b. For each of the angles that you drew in part **a** write the values of $\sin\theta$, $\tan\theta$, $\csc\theta$, $\sec\theta$, and $\cot\theta$.

16. a. Sketch the primary angle θ which fits the description: $\sin \theta = -\frac{4}{5}$ and $\tan \theta > 0$.

b. For the angle you drew in part **a** write the values of $\cos \theta$, $\tan \theta$, $\csc \theta$, $\sec \theta$, and $\cot \theta$.

17. Given right triangle ABC:

a. If $\sin \alpha = \dfrac{1}{\sqrt{7}}$, then $\cos \beta = \_?\_$

b. If $\tan \alpha = \sqrt{3}$, then $\cot \beta = \_?\_$

c. If $\cos \beta = \frac{3}{13}\sqrt{13}$, then $\sin \alpha = \_?\_$

18. Without using a table of trigonometric functions, find the value of each of the following:

a. $\cos \angle 300°$	**c.** $\sin \angle 135°$	**e.** $\cot \angle 225°$	**g.** $\tan \angle -180°$
b. $\tan \angle 270°$	**d.** $\sin \angle -30°$	**f.** $\cos \angle 120°$	**h.** $\sin \angle 240°$

19. Without using tables, find t so that each of the following is a true statement.

a. $\sin \angle t = -\dfrac{\sqrt{3}}{2}$ **c.** $\tan \angle t = -1$ **e.** $\cos \angle t = -0.5$

b. $\cos \angle t = \dfrac{\sqrt{2}}{2}$ **d.** $\sin \angle t = -\dfrac{\sqrt{2}}{2}$ **f.** $\tan \angle t = \dfrac{\sqrt{3}}{3}$

20. Using Table IV, find the value of each of the following:

a. $\sin \angle 14.3°$	**c.** $\sin \angle 36.28°$	**e.** $\cos \angle 81.49°$	**g.** $\tan \angle 10.05°$
b. $\sin \angle 75.2°$	**d.** $\cos \angle 36.11°$	**f.** $\cos \angle 40.51°$	**h.** $\tan \angle 46.16°$

21. Use Table IV to find the measure in degrees of the acute angle θ for which

a. $\tan \theta = 0.0840$	**d.** $\sin \theta = 0.3371$	**g.** $\cos \theta = 0.9397$
b. $\tan \theta = 0.4990$	**e.** $\sin \theta = 0.7080$	**h.** $\cos \theta = 0.9976$
c. $\tan \theta = 3.7881$	**f.** $\sin \theta = 0.8100$	**i.** $\cos \theta = 0.6660$

22. In a circle whose radius is 14 inches long, a chord 12.8 inches long is drawn. What is the measure in degrees of the central angle subtended by the chord?

23. What is the measure in degrees of the angle of elevation of the sun when a vertical pole 24 feet long casts a shadow on level ground 70 feet long?

24. From the roof of a building 140 feet above the ground, the angle of depression of a bridge is $\angle 16.2°$. (Assume that the bridge and the foot of the building are in the same horizontal plane.) How far from the foot of the building is the bridge?

25. Use Table IV to find the numerical approximations of each of the following:

a. $\sin \angle 141°$	**c.** $\tan \angle 324°$	**e.** $\cos \angle -84.56°$	**g.** $\tan \angle 78.42°$
b. $\cos \angle 225°$	**d.** $\sin \angle 200.11°$	**f.** $\cos \angle 175.27°$	**h.** $\tan \angle 234.25°$

26. Find the measure in degrees of the two primary angles which θ can represent so that each of the following statements is true.

    a. $\sin \theta = 0.6840$ **c.** $\cos \theta = 0.5395$ **e.** $\tan \theta = -0.2190$

    b. $\cos \theta = -0.7442$ **d.** $\tan \theta = 0.3849$ **f.** $\sin \theta = -0.4142$

27. If $P(a, b)$ is a point in the terminal side of an angle θ in standard position, find the measure in degrees of the angle and find the values of $\sin \theta$, $\cos \theta$, and $\tan \theta$ when

    a. $P(1, 7)$ **b.** $P(-5, 2)$ **c.** $P(\sqrt{3}, -\sqrt{2})$ **d.** $P(6, -\frac{1}{2}\sqrt{2})$

In Exercises 28–30 assume that a, b, and c are the measures of the sides of a triangle and that α, β, and γ are in the angles opposite these sides, respectively.

28. Solve the triangle indicated by each of the following sets of measures.

    a. $a = 153.5$, *dm* $\alpha = 37.38$, *dm* $\beta = 60.00$ **d.** $a = 160$, $b = 120$, *dm* $\gamma = 26.3$

    b. $a = 13.15$, $b = 2041.00$, *dm* $\beta = 25.16$ **e.** $b = 181$, $c = 152$, *dm* $\alpha = 76.8$

    c. $a = 42.8$, $b = 48.5$, *dm* $\alpha = 23.20$ **f.** $a = 80$, $b = 140$, $c = 160$

29. Find the area of a triangle having angle $\alpha = \angle 26.25°$, $b = 14.3$ inches long, and $c = 24.83$ inches long.

30. Find the measure of the area of the triangle for which

    $a = 18$, $b = 21$, and *rm* $\alpha = \dfrac{\pi}{6}$.

31. If $|\vec{V}| = 37$, find the magnitude of each of the components of $\vec{V}$ in the direction of the rays $\overrightarrow{OT}$ and $\overrightarrow{OS}$ as shown in the diagram.

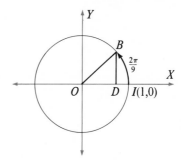

32. The airspeed of a jet aircraft is 400 miles per hour and its heading is 225°. If the track of the aircraft is 230° and the wind is blowing from 90°, find the speed of the wind and the ground speed of the plane.

CHAPTER TEST

Use the figure on the right for Exercises 1–6. Point B is the terminal point of the path $\left(OI, \dfrac{2\pi}{9}\right)$ and $\overline{BD}$ is perpendicular to $\overrightarrow{OI}$ at D.

1. Which of the following paths are coterminal with the path $\left(OI, \dfrac{2\pi}{9}\right)$?

    a. $\left(OI, 4\pi + \dfrac{2\pi}{9}\right)$ **c.** $\left(OI, \dfrac{4\pi}{9}\right)$

    b. $\left(OI, \dfrac{2\pi}{9}\right)$ **d.** $\left(OI, -\dfrac{16\pi}{9}\right)$

2. Express the measure of $\overline{OD}$ to the nearest ten thousandth. (Use Table IV.)

3. Express the measure of $\overline{BD}$ to the nearest ten thousandth. (Use Table IV.)

4. What is the area of the circular sector $O\text{-}\widehat{IB}$?

5. A rectangle is 18 inches long and 12 inches wide. What is the measurement to the nearest tenth of a degree of the angle which the diagonal forms with a shorter side?

6. Complete each of the following by inserting the approximate numerical value correct to the nearest ten thousandth. You may use a table where necessary.

  a. $\sin \angle 300° =$ _?_   c. $\tan \angle 120° =$ _?_   e. $\cos \angle 247.25°$

  b. $\cos \angle 90° =$ _?_   d. $\sin \angle 121° =$ _?_   f. $\tan \angle -12°$

7. For what values of d, $0 < d < 360$, is each of the following true?

  a. $\tan \angle d° = 0.2962$ b. $\sin \angle d° = 0.8878$ c. $\cos \angle d° = 0.9478$

8. Given that $dm\ \alpha = 34.25$, $dm\ \beta = 71.36$, and $a = 34.32$, find b, assuming that the given measures are for a triangle described in standard notation.

9. If a, b, c, and $dm\ \alpha$ are respectively the measures of the three sides and one angle of a triangle labeled in standard notation, find the value of a when $b = 123$, $c = 244$, and $dm\ \alpha = 72$.

10. In triangle ABC, $a = 21.5$, $\alpha = \angle 23.6°$, and $\beta = \angle 41.2°$. Find the area of the triangle.

11. The track of an airplane is 47° and its heading is 38°. Find the ground speed of the plane if the wind is blowing from 280° at 40 miles per hour.

12. A weight of 400 pounds is supported as shown in the figure. Find the tension in each of the cables AO and BO.

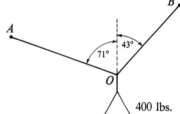

13. In triangle ABC, $a = 39.2$, $\alpha = \angle 64.7°$, and $\beta = \angle 43.6°$. Find the area of the triangle.

14. Find r, the radius of the circle inscribed in $\triangle ABC$, if $a = 24$, $b = 15$, and $c = 19$.

Properties of the Trigonometric Functions

Identities

We recall that an identity is an open statement of equality whose truth set T is equal to its replacement set E. The following equation is an algebraic identity. We continue to assume that R, the set of real numbers, is the replacement set for each variable unless otherwise specified.

$$\frac{x^3 - 1}{x - 1} = x^2 + x + 1 \qquad T = E = R \smallfrown \{1\}$$

If an algebraic expression contains at least one symbol, such as $\sin t$, $\cos \alpha$, $\csc (x + y)$, or $\tan \left(x + \dfrac{\pi}{2}\right)$, it is called a *trigonometric expression*. Thus $\sin (\theta + \alpha)$ and $\cos \left(x + \dfrac{\pi}{2}\right) + y + 3$ are trigonometric expressions. A *trigonometric equation* is an equation that contains at least one trigonometric expression.

A trigonometric equation is a conditional equation if its truth set T is a proper subset of its replacement set E. Each of the following is a conditional trigonometric equation. In each case the replacement set of the variable t is the set S of real numbers in $\langle 0, 2\pi \langle$.

$$\sin t = \tfrac{1}{2} \qquad T = \left\{\frac{\pi}{6}, \frac{5\pi}{6}\right\}; \ E = S; \ T \subset E$$

$$\tan t = 1 \qquad T = \left\{\frac{\pi}{4}, \frac{5\pi}{4}\right\}; \ E = S \smallfrown \left\{\frac{\pi}{2}, \frac{3\pi}{2}\right\}; \ T \subset E$$

$$\csc^2 t = 1 \qquad T = \left\{\frac{\pi}{2}, \frac{3\pi}{2}\right\}; \ E = S \smallfrown \{0, \pi\}; \ T \subset E$$

If a trigonometric equation is an identity, that is, if T, its truth set, is equal to E, its replacement set, it is called a trigonometric identity. Thus the trigonometric identities form a proper subset of the algebraic identities. Each of the following equations is a *fundamental trigonometric identity*. For each equation the truth set is equal to the replacement set indicated:

$$\text{I-1} \quad \sin t \csc t = 1 \qquad R \frown \{t \mid t = k\pi; \ k \in I\}$$

$$\text{I-2} \quad \cos t \sec t = 1 \qquad R \frown \left\{t \mid t = (2k+1)\frac{\pi}{2}; \ k \in I\right\}$$

$$\text{I-3} \quad \tan t \cot t = 1 \qquad R \frown \left\{t \mid t = k \cdot \frac{\pi}{2}; \ k \in I\right\}$$

$$\text{I-4} \quad \tan t = \frac{\sin t}{\cos t} \qquad R \frown \left\{t \mid t = (2k+1)\frac{\pi}{2}; \ k \in I\right\}$$

$$\text{I-5} \quad \cot t = \frac{\cos t}{\sin t} \qquad R \frown \{t \mid t = k\pi; \ k \in I\}$$

$$\text{I-6} \quad \sin^2 t + \cos^2 t = 1 \qquad R$$

$$\text{I-7} \quad \tan^2 t + 1 = \sec^2 t \qquad R \frown \left\{t \mid t = (2k+1)\frac{\pi}{2}; \ k \in I\right\}$$

$$\text{I-8} \quad 1 + \cot^2 t = \csc^2 t \qquad R \frown \{t \mid t = k\pi; \ k \in I\}$$

Each of the above equations can be written with the identically equal symbol, for example, $\sin t \csc t \equiv 1$.

Note. For convenience we will refer to the sets $R \frown \{x \mid x = k\pi; \ k \in I\}$, $R \frown \left\{x \mid x = (2k+1)\frac{\pi}{2}; \ k \in I\right\}$, and $R \frown \left\{x \mid x = k\frac{\pi}{2}; \ k \in I\right\}$ as E_1, E_2, and E_3, respectively.

The first six of these eight identities are direct consequences of the definition of the trigonometric functions of the real number t. Identity **I-7** is derived from **I-6**. If $t \in E_2$, then $\cos t \neq 0$. Hence

$$\frac{\sin^2 t}{\cos^2 t} + \frac{\cos^2 t}{\cos^2 t} = \frac{1}{\cos^2 t}$$

$$\left(\frac{\sin t}{\cos t}\right)^2 + 1 = \left(\frac{1}{\cos t}\right)^2$$

$$\therefore \tan^2 t + 1 \equiv \sec^2 t$$

Identity **I-8** can be derived by dividing both members of **I-6** by $\sin^2 t$. When $t \in R \frown \{t \mid t = k\pi; \ k \in I\}$, we are assured that $\sin t \neq 0$.

Recall that if d, $t \in R$ and $d = \dfrac{180\,t}{\pi}$, then $\sin t = \sin \angle t = \sin \angle d^\circ$, $\cos t = \cos \angle t = \cos \angle d^\circ$, $\tan t = \tan \angle t = \tan \angle d^\circ$, and so on. Therefore each of our identities remains an identity when each variable involved is replaced with a symbol which represents an angle. When such a replacement is made, the replacement set of the resulting identity involves angles. Also if θ is an angle equivalent to $(\overrightarrow{OI}, t)$ or $\theta = \angle t = \angle d°$, then $\sin t = \sin \theta$, $\cos t = \cos \theta$, $\tan t = \tan \theta$, and so on.

Trigonometric identities are often useful in *simplifying trigonometric expressions*. For example, we may use fundamental identities **I–2** and **I–5** to simplify the expression $\sin x \cot x \sec x$.

When $x \in E_2 \cap E_1$, that is, when $x \in E_3$, we have:

1. $\sin x \cot x \sec x = \sin x \cdot \dfrac{\cos x}{\sin x} \cdot \sec x$

2. $\sin x \cdot \dfrac{\cos x}{\sin x} \cdot \sec x = \sin x \cdot \left(\dfrac{\cos x}{\sin x} \cdot \sec x \right)$

3. $\sin x \cdot \left(\dfrac{\cos x}{\sin x} \cdot \sec x \right) = \sin x \left[\dfrac{1}{\sin x} (\cos x \sec x) \right]$

4. $\sin x \left[\dfrac{1}{\sin x} (\cos x \sec x) \right] = \left(\sin x \cdot \dfrac{1}{\sin x} \right)$

5. $\sin x \cdot \dfrac{1}{\sin x} = 1$

6. $\sin x \cot x \sec x = 1$

Let us examine the reasons for these steps:

1. When $x \in E_3$, by **I–5** we know that $\cot x$ and $\dfrac{\cos x}{\sin x}$ name the same number.

   By the substitution property of equality, $\dfrac{\cos x}{\sin x}$ may be substituted for $\cot x$.

2. Definition of the product of three numbers and the associative property of multiplication.
3. Theorem 4–2 and the associative property of multiplication.
4. When $x \in E_3$, by **I–2** we know that $\sec x \cdot \cos x = 1$. Associative property of multiplication.
5. The product of any nonzero real number and its multiplicative inverse is 1.
6. Transitive property of equality.

Observe that we have not established the equation $\sin x \cot x \sec x = 1$ for all x in R. We know, for example, that the left member of this equation does not name a real number when $x = \dfrac{\pi}{2}$. However, we have proved that the truth set of this equation is equal to its replacement set E_3. Thus we have shown that the members of this equation are *identically equal*.

We may arrange our work more compactly as follows:

$$\sin x \cot x \sec x = \sin x \cdot \frac{\cos x \cdot \sec x}{\sin x} = \sin x \cdot \frac{1}{\sin x} = 1.$$

Example 1. Simplify: $\sin^2 t + \sin^2 t \tan^2 t$

Solution. $\sin^2 t + \sin^2 t \tan^2 t = \sin^2 t \, (1 + \tan^2 t) = \sin^2 t \sec^2 t = \sin^2 t \cdot \dfrac{1}{\cos^2 t} = \left(\dfrac{\sin t}{\cos t}\right)^2 = \tan^2 t$. Thus we have proved that both members of $\sin^2 t + \sin^2 t \tan^2 t = \tan^2 t$ name the same real number for all values of t in E_2. In other words, $\sin^2 t + \sin^2 t \tan^2 t \equiv \tan^2 t$.

Example 2. Simplify: $\dfrac{(1 - \cos \alpha) \cos \alpha - \sin^2 \alpha}{1 - 2 \cos \alpha + \cos^2 \alpha}$

Solution. If α is an angle such that $\cos \alpha \neq 1$, we have:

$$\frac{(1 - \cos \alpha) \cos \alpha - \sin^2 \alpha}{1 - 2 \cos \alpha + \cos^2 \alpha} = \frac{(1 - \cos \alpha) \cos \alpha - (1 - \cos^2 \alpha)}{(1 - \cos \alpha)^2} =$$

$$\frac{(1 - \cos \alpha) \cos \alpha - (1 - \cos \alpha)(1 + \cos \alpha)}{(1 - \cos \alpha)^2} =$$

$$\frac{(1 - \cos \alpha)[\cos \alpha - (1 + \cos \alpha)]}{(1 - \cos \alpha)^2} = -\frac{1}{1 - \cos \alpha} = \frac{1}{\cos \alpha - 1}$$

We can check for errors by letting $\alpha = \angle t$ and substituting a specific value of $\angle t$ in the original expression and in the required expression to see if we obtain the same numerical value for each.

For example: If $\angle t = \angle \dfrac{\pi}{3}$, then

$$\frac{\left(1 - \cos \angle \frac{\pi}{3}\right) \cos \angle \frac{\pi}{3} - \sin^2 \angle \frac{\pi}{3}}{1 + \cos^2 \angle \frac{\pi}{3} - 2 \cos \angle \frac{\pi}{3}} = \frac{\left(1 - \frac{1}{2}\right) \frac{1}{2} - \frac{3}{4}}{1 + \frac{1}{4} - 1} = -2 \text{ and}$$

$$\frac{1}{\cos \angle \frac{\pi}{3} - 1} = \frac{1}{\frac{1}{2} - 1} = -2.$$

Example 3. Change each of the following into an identically equal simplified expression involving only $\sin x$ and $\cos x$.

a. $\cot x + \tan x$ **b.** $\dfrac{\tan x}{\sec x} + \dfrac{\sin x}{\tan x}$

Solutions. **a.** $\cot x + \tan x = \dfrac{\cos x}{\sin x} + \dfrac{\sin x}{\cos x} = \dfrac{\cos^2 x + \sin^2 x}{\sin x \cos x} = \dfrac{1}{\sin x \cos x}$

b. $\dfrac{\tan x}{\sec x} + \dfrac{\sin x}{\tan x} = \dfrac{\frac{\sin x}{\cos x}}{\frac{1}{\cos x}} + \dfrac{\sin x}{\frac{\sin x}{\cos x}} = \sin x + \cos x$

Example 4. Simplify: $\tan s \csc^2 s - \dfrac{1}{2}\left(\dfrac{\cot s}{\csc s - 1} - \dfrac{\cot s}{\csc s + 1}\right)$

Solution.

$$\tan s \csc^2 s - \frac{1}{2}\left(\frac{\cot s}{\csc s - 1} - \frac{\cot s}{\csc s + 1}\right) =$$

$$\tan s \csc^2 s - \frac{1}{2}\left[\frac{\cot s \,(\csc s + 1) - \cot s \,(\csc s - 1)}{\csc^2 s - 1}\right] =$$

$$\frac{\sin s}{\cos s} \cdot \frac{1}{\sin^2 s} - \frac{1}{2} \frac{\cot s + \cot s}{\cot^2 s} = \frac{1}{\cos s \sin s} - \frac{1}{\cot s} =$$

$$\frac{1}{\cos s \sin s} - \frac{1}{\dfrac{\cos s}{\sin s}} = \frac{1}{\cos s \sin s} - \frac{\sin s}{\cos s} = \frac{1}{\cos s}\left(\frac{1}{\sin s} - \sin s\right) =$$

$$\frac{1}{\cos s}\left(\frac{1 - \sin^2 s}{\sin s}\right) = \frac{1}{\cos s} \cdot \frac{\cos^2 s}{\sin s} = \frac{\cos s}{\sin s} = \cot s$$

Example 5. Express $\sin^4 z - \cos^4 z$ as an identically equal simplified expression in terms of $\cos z$.

Solution.

$$\sin^4 z - \cos^4 z = (\sin^2 z + \cos^2 z)(\sin^2 z - \cos^2 z)$$
$$= 1 \cdot (\sin^2 z - \cos^2 z)$$
$$= (1 - \cos^2 z) - \cos^2 z$$
$$= 1 - 2\cos^2 z$$

Therefore $\sin^4 z - \cos^4 z \equiv 1 - 2\cos^2 z$.

We check our work for errors by letting $z = \dfrac{\pi}{6}$.

$$\sin^4 \frac{\pi}{6} - \cos^4 \frac{\pi}{6} = \left(\frac{1}{2}\right)^4 - \left(\frac{\sqrt{3}}{2}\right)^4 \qquad 1 - 2\cos^2 \frac{\pi}{6} = 1 - 2\left(\frac{\sqrt{3}}{2}\right)^2$$
$$= \tfrac{1}{16} - \tfrac{9}{16} \qquad\qquad\qquad = 1 - \tfrac{6}{4}$$
$$= -\tfrac{1}{2} \qquad\qquad\qquad\qquad = -\tfrac{1}{2}$$

ORAL EXERCISES

Express each of the following in its simplest form.

1. $\dfrac{\cos^2 x}{\sin^2 x}$

2. $\cot t \sin t$

3. $\tan t \cos t$

4. $\dfrac{\tan x}{\sin x}$

5. $1 + \dfrac{\sin^2 t}{\cos^2 t}$

6. $\dfrac{1}{\sqrt{1 + \tan^2 x}}$

7. $\sqrt{1 + \cot^2 t}$

8. $\sqrt{\sec^2 t - 1}$

9. $\dfrac{1}{1 - \cos^2 x}$

10. $\dfrac{\csc t \sin t}{\cot t}$

11. $\dfrac{1 - \cos^2 t}{\cos^2 t}$

12. $\sin x \csc x + \tan x \cot x$

13. $\tan x \cot x + \sin^2 x + \cos^2 x$

14. $\dfrac{\sin t \cos t}{\cot t}$

15. $\dfrac{\cos t}{\sin t} \cdot \sec t$

16. $\tan t \sin t + \cos t$

17. $\dfrac{1 + \tan^2 t}{1 + \cot^2 t}$

18. $\dfrac{\cos t \csc t}{\cot t}$

1. Express each of the following in terms of $\sin t$ and leave your answers in simplest form.

   a. $\cos^2 t$ **b.** $\csc t$ **c.** $\cos t$ **d.** $\tan t$

2. Express each of the following in terms of $\cos x$ and leave your answers in simplest form.

   a. $\sec x$ **b.** $\sin^2 x$ **c.** $\sin x$ **d.** $\tan x$

3. Simplify each of the following:

   a. $\sec^2 x \tan x - \tan x$

   b. $\cos x \cot x + \sin x$

   c. $\sec x - \tan x \sin x$

   d. $\dfrac{2 \tan x}{1 + \tan^2 x}$

   e. $\dfrac{\sin x + \tan x}{1 + \sec x}$

   f. $\cot x - \sec x \csc x (1 - 2 \sin^2 x)$

   g. $\dfrac{1 - \sin^2 x}{\cos x}$

   h. $\sin x (1 + \cot^2 x)$

   i. $(\cot x + 1)^2 - 2 \cot x$

   j. $(1 - \sin^2 x)(1 + \tan^2 x)$

   k. $\sin x \sec^2 x - \sin x \tan^2 x$

   l. $(\cot^2 x - \csc^2 x)(\sec^2 x - \tan^2 x)$

4. For each of the following, find an identically equal expression involving only $\sin y$, $\cos y$, or both $\sin y$ and $\cos y$, and leave in simplest form.

   a. $\sec y \cot y$

   b. $\dfrac{\sin y}{\csc y - \cot y}$

   c. $\dfrac{1 + \csc y}{\csc y - 1}$

   d. $\dfrac{1 + \tan^2 y}{1 + \cot^2 y}$

   e. $(\tan y + \cot y)^2$

   f. $(\cot y + 1)(\cot y - 1) + 2$

   g. $\dfrac{\cot y}{1 + \cot^2 y}$

   h. $\tan y \sin y + \cos y$

5. Simplify each of the following:

   a. $\cot x + \dfrac{\sin x}{1 + \cos x}$

   b. $\dfrac{\sec x}{\cot x + \tan x}$

   c. $\dfrac{1 + \tan^2 x}{1 + \cot^2 x} + 1$

   d. $\dfrac{\cot^2 x}{\csc^2 x} + \dfrac{\tan^2 x}{\sec^2 x}$

   e. $\dfrac{\sin x}{\tan^2 x} + \dfrac{\tan x}{\sec x}$

   f. $\dfrac{\tan x - \sin x \cos x}{\sin^2 x}$

   g. $\dfrac{\csc x}{\cot x + \csc x}$

   h. $\dfrac{\sec x + \tan x}{\cos x - \tan x - \sec x}$

   i. $\dfrac{\cos x + \sin x \cot x}{\cot x}$

   j. $(1 + \tan x + \sec x)(1 + \cot x - \csc x)$

6. Prove: If $x = a \cos t - b \sin t$ and $y = a \sin t + b \cos t$, then $x^2 + y^2 = a^2 + b^2$.

7. Prove: If $m = \sec t + \csc t$ and $n = \sin t + \cos t$, then $\dfrac{m}{n} = \sec t \csc t$.

8. If $r = \dfrac{\sin t}{\tan t}$ and $s = \dfrac{\tan t}{\sec t}$, write the simplest form of the expression identically equal to $r - s$.

9. If $x = \sec t$ and $y = 1 - \cos^2 t$, write the simplest form of the expression identically equal to xy.

10. If $x = \sin t$, $y = \tan t$, and $z = \sec t$, find the simplest form of the expression identically equal to $\dfrac{x + y}{1 + z}$.

Proving Identities

We prove that an equation is an identity by showing that its solution set T is equal to its replacement set E. To do this we use the properties of real numbers, the properties of equality, and accepted definitions to show that the members of the equation are identically equal as specified on page 45. The procedure is illustrated by the following examples:

Example 1. Prove: $\dfrac{x^3 + 1}{x + 1} \equiv x^2 - x + 1$

Solution. We need to show that $\dfrac{x^3 + 1}{x + 1}$ is another name for $x^2 - x + 1$

for all members in the replacement set of $\dfrac{x^3 + 1}{x + 1} = x^2 - x + 1$.

This is accomplished as follows: $\dfrac{x^3 + 1}{x + 1} = \dfrac{(x + 1)(x^2 - x + 1)}{x + 1} =$

$\dfrac{x + 1}{x + 1}(x^2 - x + 1) = 1(x^2 - x + 1) = x^2 - x + 1$. Thus we have transformed the left member into the right member by using the rules for operating with real numbers and the properties of equality. Hence $\dfrac{x^3 + 1}{x + 1} \equiv x^2 - x + 1$.

There is no general method for proving an identity. A thorough knowledge of the various forms of the fundamental identities is, of course, essential. Sometimes a method of attack will be suggested by the form of the two given expressions. In other cases, it may be helpful to express the values of all the functions involved in terms of the values of sines and cosines.

Example 2.   Prove: $\dfrac{1+\cos x}{\sin x} \equiv \dfrac{\sin x}{1-\cos x}$

Solution. $\dfrac{1+\cos x}{\sin x} = \dfrac{(1+\cos x)(1-\cos x)}{\sin x(1-\cos x)} = \dfrac{1-\cos^2 x}{\sin x(1-\cos x)} =$

$\dfrac{\sin^2 x}{\sin x(1-\cos x)} = \dfrac{\sin x}{1-\cos x}$

Thus $\dfrac{1+\cos x}{\sin x}$ and $\dfrac{\sin x}{1-\cos x}$ name the same number for all mem-

bers in the replacement set of $\dfrac{1+\cos x}{\sin x} = \dfrac{\sin x}{1-\cos x}$.

Hence $\dfrac{1+\cos x}{\sin x} \equiv \dfrac{\sin x}{1-\cos x}$.

Example 3.   Prove: $\dfrac{1+\cot^2 z}{\sec^2 z} \equiv \cot^2 z$

Solution. $\dfrac{1+\cot^2 z}{\sec^2 z} = \dfrac{\csc^2 z}{\sec^2 z} = \dfrac{\dfrac{1}{\sin^2 z}}{\dfrac{1}{\cos^2 z}} = \dfrac{\cos^2 z}{\sin^2 z} = \left(\dfrac{\cos z}{\sin z}\right)^2 = \cot^2 z.$

Hence $\dfrac{1+\cot^2 z}{\sec^2 z} \equiv \cot^2 z$ and our proof is complete.

Example 4.   Prove: $\dfrac{1+\sin x}{1-\sin x} - \dfrac{1-\sin x}{1+\sin x} \equiv 4 \tan x \sec x$

Solution. $\dfrac{1+\sin x}{1-\sin x} - \dfrac{1-\sin x}{1+\sin x} = \dfrac{(1+\sin x)^2 - (1-\sin x)^2}{(1+\sin x)(1-\sin x)} =$

$\dfrac{(1+2\sin x+\sin^2 x)-(1-2\sin x+\sin^2 x)}{1-\sin^2 x} =$

$\dfrac{4\sin x}{\cos^2 x} = 4\dfrac{\sin x}{\cos x} \cdot \dfrac{1}{\cos x} = 4 \tan x \sec x$

$\therefore \dfrac{1+\sin x}{1-\sin x} - \dfrac{1-\sin x}{1+\sin x} \equiv 4 \tan x \sec x$

Example 5.   Prove: $\cos^6 s + \sin^6 s \equiv 1 - 3\sin^2 s \cos^2 s$

Solution. $\cos^6 s + \sin^6 s = (\cos^2 s + \sin^2 s)(\cos^4 s - \cos^2 s \sin^2 s + \sin^4 s)$

$= 1[(\cos^4 s + 2\cos^2 s \sin^2 s + \sin^4 s) - 3\cos^2 s \sin^2 s]$

$= 1[(\cos^2 s + \sin^2 s)^2 - 3\cos^2 s \sin^2 s)]$

$= 1 - 3\cos^2 s \sin^2 s$

$\therefore \cos^6 s + \sin^6 s \equiv 1 - 3\sin^2 s \cos^2 s$

We can prove that an equation is *not* an identity by exhibiting a member of its replacement set which is not a member of its truth set. The replacement set for the equation $\sin x = \sqrt{1 - \cos^2 x}$ is R. There are, however, many real numbers for which this equation is not satisfied. For example, $\dfrac{3\pi}{2}$ is a real number for which the members of this equation are not equal. Why? If we think of x as representing the measure of an angle in radians, we see that the statement $\sin \angle x = \sqrt{1 - \cos^2 \angle x}$ is false for all third and fourth quadrant angles and true for all first and second quadrant angles. Since the truth set T of the statement $\sin x = \sqrt{1 - \cos^2 x}$ is a proper subset of its replacement set R, that is, $T \subset R$, we conclude that the statement is not an identity.

Example 6. Which of the following equations is an identity?

  a. $\tan t = \sqrt{\sec^2 t - 1}$ **b.** $\tan t \sin t + \cos t = \sec t$

Solutions. **a.** The replacement set for $\tan t = \sqrt{\sec^2 t - 1}$ is $E_2 = R \smallsmile \left\{ t \mid t = (2k+1)\dfrac{\pi}{2}; \ k \, \epsilon \, I \right\}$. Since we know that $\dfrac{5\pi}{6} \, \epsilon \, E_2$, we substitute $\dfrac{5\pi}{6}$ for t in the equation $\tan t = \sqrt{\sec^2 t - 1}$ to see if $\dfrac{5\pi}{6}$ is in the truth set of the given equation.

$$\tan t = \sqrt{\sec^2 t - 1}$$
$$-\frac{1}{\sqrt{3}} \overset{?}{=} \sqrt{\left(\frac{-2}{\sqrt{3}}\right)^2 - 1}$$
$$-\frac{1}{\sqrt{3}} \neq \frac{1}{\sqrt{3}}$$

Therefore $\tan t = \sqrt{\sec^2 t - 1}$ is not an identity because we have shown that even though $\dfrac{5\pi}{6} \, \epsilon \, E_2$, $\dfrac{5\pi}{6}$ is not an element of the truth set.

  b. The replacement set for $\tan t \sin t + \cos t = \sec t$ is $E_2 = R \smallsmile \left\{ t \mid t = (2k+1)\dfrac{\pi}{2}; \ k \, \epsilon \, I \right\}$. Since we know that $\dfrac{\pi}{3} \, \epsilon \, E_2$, we substitute $\dfrac{\pi}{3}$ for t in the equation $\tan t \sin t + \cos t = \sec t$ to see if $\dfrac{\pi}{3}$ is in the truth set of the given equation.

$$\tan t \sin t + \cos t = \sec t$$
$$(\sqrt{3})\left(\frac{\sqrt{3}}{2}\right) + \frac{1}{2} \overset{?}{=} 2$$
$$\tfrac{3}{2} + \tfrac{1}{2} \overset{\checkmark}{=} 2$$

Since $\dfrac{\pi}{3}$ satisfies the given equation, we suspect that it is an identity and attempt to prove it.

$$\tan t \sin t + \cos t = \sec t$$

$$\frac{\sin t}{\cos t} \sin t + \cos t = \sec t$$

$$\frac{\sin^2 t + \cos^2 t}{\cos t} = \sec t$$

$$\frac{1}{\cos t} = \sec t$$

$$\sec t = \sec t$$

Thus we see that $\tan t \sin t + \cos t \equiv \sec t$.

Ⓐ **EXERCISES**

1. Name the replacement set for each of the following statements:

a. $\tan t = \dfrac{1}{\cot t}$

b. $\sin t = \dfrac{1}{\csc t}$

c. $\cos t \tan t = \sin t$

d. $\sin^2 t + \cos^2 t = 1$

e. $\dfrac{\sin^2 t + \cos^2 t}{\cos t} = \sec t$

f. $\dfrac{1 + \sin t}{\sin t} = 1 + \csc t$

2. Prove that each of the following statements is an identity:

a. $\sin x \sec x \cot x = 1$

b. $\tan t \cot t = 1$

c. $\dfrac{1}{1 + \sin x} + \dfrac{1}{1 - \sin x} = 2 \sec^2 x$

d. $\cot z \cos z + \sin z = \csc z$

e. $\dfrac{\cos x}{1 - \sin x} + \dfrac{\cos x}{1 + \sin x} = 2 \sec x$

f. $\dfrac{\sin y + \tan y}{1 + \sec y} = \sin y$

g. $(\csc s - \cot s)^2 = \dfrac{1 - \cos s}{1 + \cos s}$

h. $\tan x + \cot x = \dfrac{\sec x}{\sin x}$

i. $2 \cos t \sec t - \tan t \cot t = 1$

j. $\sin^2 x + \sin^2 x \cot^2 x = 1$

k. $\dfrac{\cos t \csc t}{\cot t} = 1$

l. $\csc^2 x (1 - \cos^2 x) = 1$

m. $\dfrac{\tan x - 1}{\tan x + 1} = \dfrac{1 - \cot x}{1 + \cot x}$

3. Which of the following are not identities? Why?

a. $2 \sin x = 1$

b. $\dfrac{\sin y \sec y}{\tan y} = 1$

c. $\cos x = \dfrac{\sin x}{\tan x}$

d. $\cos^2 x + 1 = 2 \cos^2 x + \sin^2 x$

e. $\sin z \cos z = 0$

f. $\cos z \csc z - \cot z = 0$

g. $\tan x = \cot x$

4. Prove that each of the following statements is true:

a. $2 \sin x (1 + \tan^2 x) \equiv \dfrac{2 \tan x}{\cos x}$

h. $\sqrt{\dfrac{1 + \cot^2 t}{1 + \tan^2 t}} \equiv |\cot t|$

b. $\sin x - 1 \equiv \cos x \, (\tan x - \sec x)$

i. $\dfrac{\tan^2 x \sin^2 x}{\tan x - \sin x} \equiv \tan x + \sin x$

c. $2 \csc^2 t - \dfrac{1 + \cos t}{\sin^2 t} \equiv \dfrac{1}{1 + \cos t}$

j. $1 - 2 \sin^2 x \cos^2 x \equiv \sin^4 x + \cos^4 x$

d. $\dfrac{1 - \tan^2 x}{1 - \sec^2 x} \equiv 1 - \cot^2 x$

k. $\dfrac{\sec x}{\sin x} - \dfrac{\cos x}{\sin x} \equiv \dfrac{\sin x}{\cos x}$

l. $(1 - \cos t)(1 + \sec t) \equiv \sin t \tan t$

e. $\dfrac{1 - \cos z}{1 + \cos z} \equiv (\csc z - \cot z)^2$

m. $\cot x \, (\sin x - \sec x) \equiv \cos x - \csc x$

f. $\cos^2 y \tan^2 y \equiv \dfrac{1}{1 + \cot^2 y}$

n. $\dfrac{\cos x - \csc x}{\sin x - \sec x} \equiv \cot x$

g. $1 - \tan^4 t \equiv 2 \sec^2 t - \sec^4 t$

o. $1 - \tan^4 x \equiv 2 \sec^2 x - \sec^4 x$

Addition Formulas

There are formulas which enable us to express the values of the trigonometric functions of $u + v$ and $u - v$ in terms of the value of the trigonometric functions of u and v. These formulas, known as *addition formulas for the trigonometric functions*, are derived in this section.

First we derive the formula for $\cos (u - v)$. Let U and V be the terminal points of paths (OI, u) and (OI, v), respectively, in the unit circle (see the figure at the right). Then the coordinates of U in the XOY-rectangular-coordinate system are $(\cos u, \sin u)$ and the coordinates of V are $(\cos v, \sin v)$. Now let lines OX and OY rotate (while remaining perpendicular to each other at O) so that the point of intersection of $\overrightarrow{OX}$ and the unit circle traverses the path (OI, v). When this rotation is complete, $\overrightarrow{OX'}$, the new position of $\overrightarrow{OX}$, will pass through V and $\overrightarrow{OY'}$, the new position

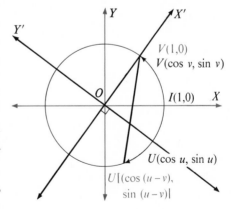

of $\overrightarrow{OY}$, is perpendicular to $\overrightarrow{OX'}$. We take $\overrightarrow{OX'}$ as the positive axis of abscissas and $\overrightarrow{OY'}$ as the positive axis of ordinates in a new coordinate system which we call the $X'OY'$-rectangular-coordinate system.

In the $X'OY'$-rectangular-coordinate system, the circular coordinates of V are $(1, 0)$ and the circular coordinates of U are $(1, (u - v))$. Accordingly, in the $X'OY'$-rectangular-coordinate system, the rectangular coordinates of V are $(1, 0)$ and the rectangular coordinates of U are $(\cos (u - v), \sin (u - v))$. Observe that these coordinates are shown in red in the figure. By using the formula for the measure of the line segment between two points, we find that:

(i) In the XOY-rectangular-coordinate system,

$$| UV |^2 = (\cos u - \cos v)^2 + (\sin u - \sin v)^2.$$

(ii) In the $X'OY'$-rectangular-coordinate system,

$$| UV |^2 = [\cos (u - v) - 1]^2 + [\sin (u - v) - 0]^2.$$

After we square the binomials as indicated in equations (i) and (ii) and use the fundamental identity $\sin^2 x + \cos^2 x = 1$, we see that (i) can be written as (iii) $| UV |^2 = 2 - 2 (\cos u \cos v + \sin u \sin v)$ and (ii) can be written as (iv) $| UV |^2 = 2 - 2 \cos (u - v)$. From ($iii$) and ($iv$), we obtain: ($v$) $\cos (u - v) = \cos u \cos v + \sin u \sin v$.

This establishes that the following equation is an identity:

I-9 $\cos (u - v) = \cos u \cos v + \sin u \sin v$ R X R

If α is an angle whose radian measure is u and β is an angle whose radian measure is v, I-9 takes the form $\cos (\alpha - \beta) = \cos \alpha \cos \beta + \sin \alpha \sin \beta$. If the $dm\alpha = a$ and $dm\beta = b$, we may also write $\cos (\angle a^\circ - \angle b^\circ) = \cos \angle a^\circ \cos \angle b^\circ + \sin \angle a^\circ \sin \angle b^\circ$.

We can use this form of I-9 to find the value of $\cos \angle 15^\circ$ as follows:

$\cos \angle 15^\circ = \cos \angle(45 - 30)^\circ = \cos \angle 45^\circ \cos \angle 30^\circ + \sin \angle 45^\circ \sin \angle 30^\circ =$
$\dfrac{\sqrt{2}}{2} \cdot \dfrac{\sqrt{3}}{2} + \dfrac{\sqrt{2}}{2} \cdot \dfrac{1}{2} = \dfrac{\sqrt{6} + \sqrt{2}}{4} \approx 0.9659$. This result agrees with the value given in Table IV.

If we let $\alpha = \angle 180^\circ$ and $\beta = \angle x^\circ$, we obtain:

$$\cos \angle(180 - x)^\circ = \cos \angle 180^\circ \cos \angle x^\circ + \sin \angle 180^\circ \sin \angle x^\circ$$
$$\cos \angle(180 - x)^\circ = (- 1) \cos \angle x^\circ + 0 \cdot \sin \angle x^\circ$$
$$\cos \angle(180 - x)^\circ = - \cos \angle x^\circ$$

This result agrees with the results obtained on page 497.

Using I-9 we can prove that when $v \in R$, $\cos \left(\dfrac{\pi}{2} - v \right) = \sin v$ is an identity as follows:

If we substitute $\dfrac{\pi}{2}$ for u in I-9, we obtain: $\cos \left(\dfrac{\pi}{2} - v \right) = \cos \dfrac{\pi}{2} \cos v +$

$\sin \dfrac{\pi}{2} \sin v$. Since $\cos \dfrac{\pi}{2} = 0$, $\sin \dfrac{\pi}{2} = 1$, and v is any real number, we have proved that the following equation is an identity:

I–10 $\cos\left(\dfrac{\pi}{2}-v\right)=\sin v$ $\qquad\qquad$ R

Using **I–10** we can prove that when $w \in R$, $\cos w = \sin\left(\dfrac{\pi}{2}-w\right)$ is an identity as follows:

When $w \in R$ and we let $w = \dfrac{\pi}{2}-v$, we see that $v = \dfrac{\pi}{2}-w$. Substituting w for $\dfrac{\pi}{2}$ -- v and $\dfrac{\pi}{2}-w$ for v in **I–10**, we have proved that the following equation is an identity:

I–11 $\cos w = \sin\left(\dfrac{\pi}{2}-w\right)$ $\qquad\qquad$ R

Using **I–9**, we can prove that when $v \in R$, $\cos(-v) = \cos v$ is an identity as follows:

If we let $u = 0$ in **I–9**, we have: $\cos(0-v) = \cos 0 \cos v + \sin 0 \sin v$. Since $\cos 0 = 1$, $\sin 0 = 0$, and v is any real number, we have established that the following equation is an identity:

I–12 $\cos(-v) = \cos v$ $\qquad\qquad$ R

Using **I–9** and **I–10**, we can prove that when $w \in R$, $\sin(-w) = -\sin w$ is an identity as follows:

If we let $v = -w$ in **I–10**, we have:

$$\cos\left[\frac{\pi}{2}-(-w)\right] = \sin(-w), \text{ or}$$

$$\cos\left(\frac{\pi}{2}+w\right) = \sin(-w).$$

We know that $\cos\left(\dfrac{\pi}{2}+w\right) = \cos\left(w+\dfrac{\pi}{2}\right)$ and using **I–9**, we have:

$$\cos\left[w-\left(-\frac{\pi}{2}\right)\right] = \cos w \cos\left(-\frac{\pi}{2}\right) + \sin w \sin\left(-\frac{\pi}{2}\right).$$

Since $\cos\left(-\dfrac{\pi}{2}\right) = 0$ and $\sin\left(-\dfrac{\pi}{2}\right) = -1$, we obtain $\cos\left(\dfrac{\pi}{2}+w\right) = -\sin w$.

Therefore, since $\cos\left(\dfrac{\pi}{2}+w\right) = \sin(-w)$ and $\cos\left(\dfrac{\pi}{2}+w\right) = -\sin w$, we have proved that the following equation is an identity:

I–13 $\sin(-w) = -\sin w$ $\qquad\qquad$ R

Observe that $\tan(-x) = \dfrac{\sin(-x)}{\cos(-x)} = \dfrac{-\sin x}{\cos x} = -\dfrac{\sin x}{\cos x} = -\tan x.$

Therefore, when $x \in R \sim \left\{ x \mid x = (2k+1)\dfrac{\pi}{2};\ k \in I \right\}$, we have established that the following equation is an identity:

I–14 $\tan(-x) = -\tan x$ $\qquad\qquad R \sim \{x \mid x = (2k+1)\dfrac{\pi}{2};\ k \in I\}$

We are now ready to derive other addition formulas from **I–9**. To obtain a formula for $\cos(u+v)$ when $u, v \in R$, we write $\cos(u+v) = \cos[u-(-v)]$ and use **I–9** to obtain:

$\cos(u+v) = \cos[u-(-v)] = \cos u \cos(-v) + \sin u \sin(-v)$. Then using **I–12**, **I–13**, and the substitution property of equality, we have proved that the following statement is an identity:

I–15 $\cos(u+v) = \cos u \cos v - \sin u \sin v$ $\qquad\qquad R \times R$

To obtain a formula for $\sin(u+v)$ when $u, v \in R$, we proceed as follows:

$$\sin(u+v) \overset{(1)}{=} \cos\left[\dfrac{\pi}{2} - (u+v)\right] \overset{(2)}{=} \cos\left[\left(\dfrac{\pi}{2} - u\right) - v\right] \overset{(3)}{=}$$

$$\cos\left(\dfrac{\pi}{2} - u\right)\cos v + \sin\left(\dfrac{\pi}{2} - u\right)\overset{(4)}{\sin v} = \sin u \cos v + \cos u \sin v$$

You may supply the reasons. Thus we have proved that the following equation is an identity:

I–16 $\sin(u+v) = \sin u \cos v + \cos u \sin v$ $\qquad\qquad R \times R$

To obtain a formula for $\sin(u-v)$, we proceed as follows:

$\sin(u-v) = \sin[u+(-v)] = \sin u \cos(-v) + \cos u \sin(-v) = \sin u \cos v - \cos u \sin v$. Hence, when $u, v \in R$, we have proved that the following equation is an identity:

I–17 $\sin(u-v) = \sin u \cos v - \cos u \sin v$ $\qquad\qquad R \times R$

Let $F = \left\{ (u, v) \mid u + v = (2k+1)\dfrac{\pi}{2};\ k \in I \right\}$,

$\qquad G = \left\{ (u, v) \mid u + 0v = (2m+1)\dfrac{\pi}{2};\ m \in I \right\}$,

$\qquad H = \left\{ (u, v) \mid 0u + v = (2n+1)\dfrac{\pi}{2};\ n \in I \right\}$,

and $\quad J = \left\{ (u, v) \mid u - v = (2k+1)\dfrac{\pi}{2};\ k \in I \right\}$.

Since $\tan(u+v) = \dfrac{\sin(u+v)}{\cos(u+v)}$, it can readily be shown that $\tan(u+v)$

and $\dfrac{\tan u + \tan v}{1 - \tan u \tan v}$ name the same number for all members of $R \times R \frown$

$(F \cup G \cup H)$. Also since $\tan (u - v) = \dfrac{\sin (u - v)}{\cos (u - v)}$, it can be readily shown

that $\tan (u - v)$ and $\dfrac{\tan u - \tan v}{1 + \tan u \tan v}$ name the same number for all members

of $R \times R \frown (J \cup G \cup H)$. Thus we have established that each of the following equations is an identity:

$$\textbf{I-18} \quad \tan (u + v) = \frac{\tan u + \tan v}{1 - \tan u \tan v} \qquad\qquad R \times R \frown (F \cup G \cup H)$$

$$\textbf{I-19} \quad \tan (u - v) = \frac{\tan u - \tan v}{1 + \tan u \tan v} \qquad\qquad R \times R \frown (J \cup G \cup H)$$

We list for reference the identities **I-9** through **I-19** and indicate the replacement set of each:

$$\textbf{I-9} \quad \cos (u - v) = \cos u \cos v + \sin u \sin v \qquad\qquad R \times R$$

$$\textbf{I-10} \quad \cos \left(\frac{\pi}{2} - v\right) = \sin v \qquad\qquad R$$

$$\textbf{I-11} \quad \sin \left(\frac{\pi}{2} - w\right) = \cos w \qquad\qquad R$$

$$\textbf{I-12} \quad \cos (- v) = \cos v \qquad\qquad R$$
$$\textbf{I-13} \quad \sin (- w) = - \sin w \qquad\qquad R$$

$$\textbf{I-14} \quad \tan (- x) = - \tan x \qquad\qquad R \frown \left\{x \mid x = (2 k + 1)\frac{\pi}{2}; \ k \in I\right\}$$

$$\textbf{I-15} \quad \cos (u + v) = \cos u \cos v - \sin u \sin v \qquad\qquad R \times R$$
$$\textbf{I-16} \quad \sin (u + v) = \sin u \cos v + \cos u \sin v \qquad\qquad R \times R$$
$$\textbf{I-17} \quad \sin (u - v) = \sin u \cos v - \cos u \sin v \qquad\qquad R \times R$$

$$\textbf{I-18} \quad \tan (u + v) = \frac{\tan u + \tan v}{1 - \tan u \tan v} \qquad\qquad R \times R \frown (F \cup G \cup H)$$

$$\textbf{I-19} \quad \tan (u - v) = \frac{\tan u - \tan v}{1 + \tan u \tan v} \qquad\qquad R \times R \frown (J \cup G \cup H)$$

Example 1. Using the addition formulas, simplify the following:

$$\textbf{a.} \ \sin \left(\frac{3 \pi}{2} - x\right) \qquad\qquad \textbf{c.} \ \tan \left(x + \frac{\pi}{2}\right)$$

$$\textbf{b.} \ \cos \left(\frac{5 \pi}{2} + x\right) \qquad\qquad \textbf{d.} \ \sin (k\pi + x); \ k \in I$$

Solutions.   **a.** $\sin \left(\dfrac{3 \pi}{2} - x\right) = \sin \dfrac{3 \pi}{2} \cos x - \cos \dfrac{3 \pi}{2} \sin x.$ Since $\sin \dfrac{3 \pi}{2} =$

$- 1$ and $\cos \dfrac{3 \pi}{2} = 0$, we have $\sin \left(\dfrac{3 \pi}{2} - x\right) = - \cos x.$

$\therefore \sin \left(\dfrac{3 \pi}{2} - x\right) \equiv - \cos x.$

b. $\cos\left(\dfrac{5\pi}{2}+x\right)=\cos\dfrac{5\pi}{2}\cos x-\sin\dfrac{5\pi}{2}\sin x.$ Since $\cos\dfrac{5\pi}{2}=0$

and $\sin\dfrac{5\pi}{2}=1$, we have $\cos\left(\dfrac{5\pi}{2}+x\right)=-\sin x.$

$\therefore\cos\left(\dfrac{5\pi}{2}+x\right)\equiv-\sin x.$

c. We cannot use **I–18** to simplify $\tan\left(x+\dfrac{\pi}{2}\right)$ because $\dfrac{\pi}{2}$ is not in the replacement set of **I–18**. We can, however, use **I–4** to write

$$\tan\left(x+\dfrac{\pi}{2}\right)=\dfrac{\sin\left(x+\dfrac{\pi}{2}\right)}{\cos\left(x+\dfrac{\pi}{2}\right)}\text{ provided }x\neq k\pi,\ k\ \epsilon\ I.$$

Thus when x is not an integral multiple of π, we have $\tan$

$$\left(x+\dfrac{\pi}{2}\right)=\dfrac{\sin x\cos\dfrac{\pi}{2}+\cos x\sin\dfrac{\pi}{2}}{\cos x\cos\dfrac{\pi}{2}-\sin x\sin\dfrac{\pi}{2}}=\dfrac{\cos x}{-\sin x}=-\cot x$$

$\therefore\tan\left(x+\dfrac{\pi}{2}\right)\equiv-\cot x.$

d. $\sin(k\pi+x)=\sin k\pi\cos x+\cos k\pi\sin x,\ k\ \epsilon\ I.$ Now $\sin k\pi=0$, $\cos k\pi=1$ when k is even, and $\cos k\pi=-1$ when k is odd. Therefore $\cos k\pi=(-1)^k.$ Hence $\sin(k\pi+x)\equiv(-1)^k\sin x$ when $k\ \epsilon\ I.$

Example 2. Let α and β represent two angles such that $\sin\alpha=\frac{4}{5}$, $\sin\beta=-\frac{7}{25}$, $90<dm\alpha<180$, and $-180<dm\beta<-90$. Find:

a. $\sin(\alpha-\beta)$ **b.** $\cos(\alpha-\beta)$ **c.** $\tan(\alpha+\beta)$

Solutions. Let $\overrightarrow{OT}$ be the terminal side of α and let $\overrightarrow{OV}$ be the terminal side of β when each of these angles is in standard position. Then $P(-3,4)\ \epsilon$ $\overrightarrow{OT}$ and $Q(-24,-7)\ \epsilon\ \overrightarrow{OV}$ where $|OP|=5$ and $|OQ|=25$. By Theorem 1–9, $\cos\alpha=-\frac{3}{5}$, $\tan\alpha=-\frac{4}{3}$, $\cos\beta=-\frac{24}{25}$, and $\tan\beta=\frac{7}{24}$. Since the addition formulas are valid when the real numbers u and v are replaced by angles α and β, we have:

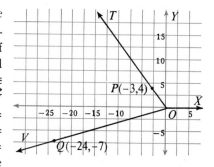

a. $\sin (\alpha - \beta) = \sin \alpha \cos \beta - \cos \alpha \sin \beta$
$$= \tfrac{4}{5} \cdot (-\tfrac{24}{25}) - (-\tfrac{3}{5})(-\tfrac{7}{25}) = -\tfrac{117}{125}$$

b. $\cos (\alpha - \beta) = \cos \alpha \cos \beta + \sin \alpha \sin \beta$
$$= (-\tfrac{3}{5})(-\tfrac{24}{25}) + (\tfrac{4}{5})(-\tfrac{7}{25}) = \tfrac{44}{125}$$

c. $\tan (\alpha + \beta) = \dfrac{\tan \alpha + \tan \beta}{1 - \tan \alpha \tan \beta} = \dfrac{-\tfrac{4}{3} + \tfrac{7}{24}}{1 - (-\tfrac{4}{3})(\tfrac{7}{24})} = -\tfrac{3}{4}$

From **a** and **b**, we know that $\alpha - \beta$ is a fourth quadrant angle. Why?

Example 3. Prove:
$$(\sin x \cos y + \cos x \sin y)^2 + (\cos x \cos y - \sin x \sin y)^2 \equiv 1$$

Solution.
$$\sin x \cos y + \cos x \sin y = \sin (x + y)$$
and
$$\cos x \cos y - \sin x \sin y = \cos (x + y).$$

Now we know that $\sin^2 (x + y) + \cos^2 (x + y) = 1$ when $x, y \, \epsilon \, R$. Therefore by the substitution property of equality,
$$(\sin x \cos y + \cos x \sin y)^2 + (\cos x \cos y - \sin x \sin y)^2 = 1.$$
$\therefore (\sin x \cos y + \cos x \sin y)^2 + (\cos x \cos y - \sin x \sin y)^2 \equiv 1$

Example 4. Prove that each of the following is an identity:

a. $\cos (\angle d_1{}^\circ + \angle d_2{}^\circ) - \cos (\angle d_1{}^\circ - \angle d_2{}^\circ) = - 2 \sin \angle d_1{}^\circ$
$\sin \angle d_2{}^\circ$

b. $\sin \left(\angle \dfrac{\pi}{6} + \theta \right) = \tfrac{1}{2} (\cos \theta + \sqrt{3} \sin \theta)$ when θ is measured in radians.

Solutions.
a. When $\angle d^\circ \, \epsilon \, \{\angle d^\circ \mid d \, \epsilon \, R\}$, we have:
$\cos (\angle d_1{}^\circ + \angle d_2{}^\circ) - \cos (\angle d_1{}^\circ - \angle d_2{}^\circ) =$
$\cos \angle d_1{}^\circ \cos \angle d_2{}^\circ - \sin \angle d_1{}^\circ \sin \angle d_2{}^\circ - \cos \angle d_1{}^\circ \cos \angle d_2{}^\circ -$
$\sin \angle d_1{}^\circ \sin \angle d_2{}^\circ = - 2 \sin \angle d_1{}^\circ \sin \angle d_2{}^\circ$
$\therefore \cos (\angle d_1{}^\circ + \angle d_2{}^\circ) - \cos (\angle d_1{}^\circ - \angle d_2{}^\circ) \equiv$
$- 2 \sin \angle d_1{}^\circ \sin \angle d_2{}^\circ$

b. When $\theta \, \epsilon \, \{\angle t \mid t \, \epsilon \, R\}$, we have:
$$\sin \left(\angle \frac{\pi}{6} + \theta \right) = \sin \angle \frac{\pi}{6} \cos \theta + \sin \theta \cos \angle \frac{\pi}{6}$$
$$= \frac{1}{2} \cos \theta + \frac{\sqrt{3}}{2} \sin \theta$$
$$= \frac{1}{2} (\cos \theta + \sqrt{3} \sin \theta)$$
$$\therefore \sin \left(\angle \frac{\pi}{6} + \theta \right) \equiv \frac{1}{2} (\cos \theta + \sqrt{3} \sin \theta)$$

Example 5. Simplify and then use a table to find the value of each of the following:

$$\text{a. } \sin \angle 120° \cos \angle 15° - \cos \angle 120° \sin \angle 15°$$

$$\text{b. } \frac{\tan \angle 40° + \tan \angle 145°}{1 - \tan \angle 40° \tan \angle 145°}$$

Solutions.

a. $\sin \angle 120° \cos \angle 15° - \cos \angle 120° \sin \angle 15° =$
$\sin (\angle 120° - \angle 15°) = \sin \angle 105° = 0.9659$

b. $\dfrac{\tan \angle 40° + \tan \angle 145°}{1 - \tan \angle 40° \tan \angle 145°} = \tan \angle 185° = 0.0875.$

Ⓐ EXERCISES

1. Without using a table find the value of each of the following:

a. $\sin \angle 15°$	c. $\sin \angle 135°$	e. $\cos \angle 75°$	g. $\cos \angle 120°$
b. $\cos \angle 105°$	d. $\tan \angle 135°$	f. $\sin \angle 195°$	h. $\sin \angle 165°$

2. Show that each of the following statements is true.

a. $\sin (\angle 270° - \theta) \equiv - \cos \theta$ d. $\tan (\angle 270° + \theta) \equiv - \cot \theta$

b. $\cos (\angle 180° + \theta) \equiv - \cos \theta$ e. $\tan (\angle 360° - \theta) \equiv - \tan \theta$

c. $\tan (\angle 180° + \theta) \equiv \tan \theta$ f. $\sin (\angle 360° - \theta) \equiv - \sin \theta$

3. Simplify and then use a table to find the value of each of the following:

a. $\sin \angle 23° \cos \angle 14° - \cos \angle 23° \sin \angle 14°$

b. $\sin \angle 27° \cos \angle 111° + \cos \angle 27° \sin \angle 111°$

c. $\cos \angle 300° \cos \angle 152° + \sin \angle 300° \sin \angle 152°$

d. $\sin \angle 15° \cos \angle 7° + \cos \angle 15° \sin \angle 7°$

e. $\dfrac{\tan \angle 81° + \tan \angle 64°}{1 - \tan \angle 81° \tan \angle 64°}$

4. Simplify:

a. $\dfrac{\sin (\angle 270° + \theta)}{\cos (\angle 180° + \theta)}$ b. $\dfrac{\tan \left(\dfrac{3\pi}{2} + t\right)}{\sin \left(\dfrac{\pi}{2} + t\right)}$ c. $\dfrac{\tan (\angle 150° - \theta)}{\cot (\angle 1080° - \theta)}$

5. If $\sin \alpha = \frac{1}{2}$ and α is an acute angle, while $\sin \beta = \frac{4}{5}$ and β is an angle in standard position whose terminal side is in the second quadrant, find the value of each of the following without use of a table.

a. $\sin (\alpha + \beta)$	c. $\cos (\alpha + \beta)$	e. $\tan (\alpha + \beta)$
b. $\sin (\alpha - \beta)$	d. $\cos (\alpha - \beta)$	f. $\tan (\alpha - \beta)$

6. If $\sin u = \dfrac{12}{13}$ and $0 < u < \dfrac{\pi}{2}$, and $\cos v = -\dfrac{4}{5}$ and $\pi < v < \dfrac{3\pi}{2}$, find:

    a. $\sin (u + v)$　　　　　　　　**c.** $\cos (u + v)$　　　　　　　　**e.** $\tan (u + v)$

    b. $\sin (u - v)$　　　　　　　　**d.** $\cos (u - v)$　　　　　　　　**f.** $\tan (u - v)$

7. Using the addition formulas, simplify the following:

    a. $\cos (k\pi - x); \ k \epsilon I$　　　　　　　　**b.** $\tan (k\pi + x); \ k \epsilon I$

8. If α is an angle in standard position whose terminal side lies in the third quadrant, β is an angle in standard position whose terminal side lies in the second quadrant, $\cos \alpha = -\frac{12}{13}$, and $\tan \beta = -\frac{8}{15}$, find the sine, cosine, and tangent of each of the following:

    a. $(\alpha + \beta)$　　　　　　　　**b.** $(\alpha - \beta)$　　　　　　　　**c.** $(\pi - \beta)$

9. Without use of a table find the value of $\sin x$, $\cos x$, and $\tan x$ when:

    a. $x = \dfrac{5\pi}{12}$　　　　**b.** $x = \dfrac{7\pi}{12}$　　　　**c.** $x = \dfrac{11\pi}{12}$　　　　**d.** $x = \dfrac{15\pi}{12}$

10. Prove that each of the following statements is an identity:

    a. $\sin \left(\dfrac{\pi}{6} + x\right) = \dfrac{1}{2} (\cos x + \sqrt{3} \sin x)$

    b. $\cos \left(\dfrac{\pi}{4} - x\right) = \dfrac{\sqrt{2}}{2} (\cos x + \sin x)$

    c. $\cos \left(\dfrac{3\pi}{2} + x\right) = \sin x$

    d. $\sin \left(\dfrac{\pi}{4} + x\right) = \dfrac{\sin x + \cos x}{\sqrt{2}}$

    e. $\sin (\angle 180° + \theta) \cot (\angle 270° - \theta) = -\dfrac{\sin^2 \theta}{\cos \theta}$

    f. $\sin \left(\dfrac{\pi}{6} + x\right) = \cos \left(\dfrac{\pi}{3} - x\right)$

    g. $\sin (\alpha - \angle 120°) = -\dfrac{\sin \alpha + \sqrt{3} \cos \alpha}{2}$

    h. $\cos (\angle 210° + \angle x°) = \frac{1}{2} (\sin \angle x° - \sqrt{3} \cos \angle x°)$

11. Prove that each of the following statements is an identity:

    a. $\sin (\phi + \theta) + \sin (\phi - \theta) = 2 \sin \phi \cos \theta$

    b. $\sin (\phi + \theta) - \sin (\phi - \theta) = 2 \cos \phi \sin \theta$

    c. $\cos (\phi + \theta) + \cos (\phi - \theta) = 2 \cos \phi \cos \theta$

12. Simplify: $\dfrac{\tan 3t + \tan 2t}{1 - \tan 2t \tan 3t}$

13. Prove that $\sin (x+y+z) \equiv \sin x \cos y \cos z + \cos x \sin y \cos z + \cos x \cos y$ $\sin z - \sin x \sin y \sin z$. *Hint.* $\sin (x+y+z) = \sin [(x+y)+z]$

14. Prove that $\cos (x+y+z) \equiv \cos x \cos y \cos z - \cos x \sin y \sin z - \sin x \cos y$ $\sin z - \sin x \sin y \cos z$.

15. Express each of the following as a single trigonometric ratio.

a. $\sin (2\,\alpha+\beta) \cos (\alpha+3\,\beta) + \cos (2\,\alpha+\beta) \sin (\alpha+3\,\beta)$

b. $\sin (3\,\alpha-2\,\beta) \cos (4\,\alpha+\beta) - \cos (3\,\alpha-2\,\beta) \sin (4\,\alpha+\beta)$

c. $\cos (\alpha+2\,\beta) \cos (2\,\alpha+\beta) + \sin (\alpha+2\,\beta) \sin (2\,\alpha+\beta)$

d. $\cos (4\,\alpha+\beta) \cos (2\,\alpha+\beta) - \sin (4\,\alpha+\beta) \sin (2\,\alpha+\beta)$

16. Prove: $\cot (y+z) = \dfrac{\cot y \cot z - 1}{\cot y + \cot z}$

17. Prove **I-18**: $\tan (u+v) = \dfrac{\tan u + \tan v}{1 - \tan u \tan v}$

Trigonometric Functions of 2 x and $\frac{1}{2}$ x

It is interesting to observe that if we let $u = v$ in identity **I-9**, we obtain the Pythagorean identity: $1 = \cos^2 u + \sin^2 u$. Other identities are obtained by letting $u = v$ in identities **I-15**, **I-16**, and **I-18**. From **I-15** we have: $\cos (u+u) = \cos^2 u - \sin^2 u$. Using the above Pythagorean identity, we see that $\cos 2\,u$ can be expressed either as $2 \cos^2 u - 1$ or $1 - 2 \sin^2 u$. Also when we substitute u for v in **I-16**, we obtain $\sin 2\,u = 2 \sin u \cos u$.

Thus when $u \in R$, each of the following equations is an identity:

I-20 $\cos 2\,u = \cos^2 u - \sin^2 u$		R
I-21 $\cos 2\,u = 2 \cos^2 u - 1$		R
I-22 $\cos 2\,u = 1 - 2 \sin^2 u$		R
I-23 $\sin 2\,u = 2 \sin u \cos u$		R

When we let $u = v$ in **I-18**, we have the following equation which is an identity:

I-24 $\tan 2\,u = \dfrac{2 \tan u}{1 - \tan^2 u}$ $\qquad R \sim \left\{ x \mid x = (2\,k+1)\dfrac{\pi}{4}\,;\ k \in I \right\}$

Now we are ready to consider formulas involving $\frac{1}{2}\,y$. If we let $y = 2\,u$ in **I-21**, we can replace u with $\frac{1}{2}\,y$ when $y \in R$, to obtain:

$$2 \cos^2 \tfrac{1}{2} y - 1 = \cos y$$

$$\cos^2 \frac{1}{2} y = \frac{\cos y + 1}{2}$$

$$\left| \cos \frac{1}{2} y \right| = \sqrt{\frac{1 + \cos y}{2}}$$

Similarly, the result of substituting y for $2u$ in **I-22** is equivalent to:

$$\left| \sin \frac{1}{2} y \right| = \sqrt{\frac{1 - \cos y}{2}}$$

Thus each of the following is an identity:

I-25 $\left| \cos \dfrac{1}{2} y \right| = \sqrt{\dfrac{1 + \cos y}{2}}$ 　　　　　 R

I-26 $\left| \sin \dfrac{1}{2} y \right| = \sqrt{\dfrac{1 - \cos y}{2}}$ 　　　　　 R

Example. Find $\cos \angle 15°$ using **I-25** and show that the result obtained is equal to the result obtained by using identity **I-9**.

Solution. $\cos \angle 15° = \cos \dfrac{1}{2} \cdot \angle 30° = \sqrt{\dfrac{1 + \cos \angle 30°}{2}} = \sqrt{\dfrac{1 + \dfrac{\sqrt{3}}{2}}{2}} =$

$\tfrac{1}{2} \sqrt{2 + \sqrt{3}}$. Note that $\cos \angle 15° = |\cos \angle 15°|$. Why? Recall that the value of $\cos \angle 15°$ obtained from **I-9** was $\dfrac{\sqrt{6} + \sqrt{2}}{4}$. (See page 542.) Is it true that $\dfrac{\sqrt{6} + \sqrt{2}}{4} = \dfrac{1}{2} \sqrt{2 + \sqrt{3}}$? The answer is "Yes."

$$(\sqrt{6} + \sqrt{2})^2 = (2 \sqrt{2 + \sqrt{3}})^2 = 8 + 4 \sqrt{3}.$$

Each of the following equations is an identity. In each case we have indicated the replacement set.

I-27 $\left| \tan \dfrac{y}{2} \right| = \sqrt{\dfrac{1 - \cos y}{1 + \cos y}}$ 　　　　 $R \frown \{y \mid y = (2k+1)\pi;\ k \in I\}$

I-28 $\tan \dfrac{y}{2} = \dfrac{1 - \cos y}{\sin y}$ 　　　　　　 $R \frown \{y \mid y = k\pi;\ k \in I\}$

I-29 $\tan \dfrac{y}{2} = \dfrac{\sin y}{1 + \cos y}$ 　　　　　　 $R \frown \{y \mid y = (2k+1)\pi;\ k \in I\}$

We present the proof of **I-28**. The proofs of **I-27** and **I-29** are left as exercises.

Proof of **I–28**:

$$\tan \frac{y}{2} \overset{(1)}{=} \frac{\sin \frac{y}{2}}{\cos \frac{y}{2}} \overset{(2)}{=} \frac{2 \sin^2 \frac{y}{2}}{2 \sin \frac{y}{2} \cos \frac{y}{2}} \overset{(3)}{=} \frac{1 - \cos y}{\sin y}$$

Reasons: (**1**) **I–4**, (**2**) We multiply the fraction $\dfrac{\sin \frac{y}{2}}{\cos \frac{y}{2}}$ by $\dfrac{2 \sin \frac{y}{2}}{2 \sin \frac{y}{2}}$.

Hence our reason is Theorem 7–2. (**3**) **I–22** and **I–23** where $u = \dfrac{y}{2}$.

A **EXERCISES**

1. If $\sin x = \frac{8}{17}$ and $0 < x < \frac{1}{2} \pi$, find:

   a. $\sin 2x$ **c.** $\tan 2x$ **e.** $\cos \frac{1}{2} x$

   b. $\cos 2x$ **d.** $\sin \frac{1}{2} x$ **f.** $\tan \frac{1}{2} x$

2. If $\cos u = -\frac{3}{5}$ and $\frac{1}{2} \pi < u < \pi$, find:

   a. $\sin 2u$ **c.** $\tan 2u$ **e.** $\cos \frac{1}{2} u$

   b. $\cos 2u$ **d.** $\sin \frac{1}{2} u$ **f.** $\tan \frac{1}{2} u$

3. If $\sin y = -\frac{4}{5}$ and $\pi < y < \frac{3}{2} \pi$, find:

   a. $\sin 2y$ **c.** $\tan 2y$ **e.** $\cos \frac{1}{2} y$

   b. $\cos 2y$ **d.** $\tan \frac{1}{2} y$ **f.** $\sin \frac{1}{2} y$

4. Using $\cos \angle 30°$ and identities **I–25** through **I–29**, find:

   a. $\sin \angle 15°$ **b.** $\cos \angle 15°$ **c.** $\tan \angle 15°$

5. Using $\sin \angle 45°$, find each of the following:

   a. $\sin \angle 22.5°$ **b.** $\cos \angle 22.5°$ **c.** $\tan \angle 22.5°$

6. Using $\sin \angle 32° = 0.53$, find each of the following:

   a. $\sin \angle 16°$ **c.** $\tan \angle 16°$ **e.** $\cos \angle 64°$

   b. $\cos \angle 16°$ **d.** $\sin \angle 64°$ **f.** $\tan \angle 64°$

7. Derive a formula for $\left| \sec \dfrac{\theta}{2} \right|$ in terms of $\sec \theta$.

8. Derive a formula for $\cot 2\theta$ in terms of $\cot \theta$.

9. Prove identity **I–27**: $\left| \tan \dfrac{\theta}{2} \right| = \sqrt{\dfrac{1 - \cos \theta}{1 + \cos \theta}}$

10. Prove identity **I–29**: $\tan \dfrac{\theta}{2} = \dfrac{\sin \theta}{1 + \cos \theta}$

11. Prove that each of the following statements is an identity:

a. $\left| \cot \dfrac{1}{2} u \right| = \sqrt{\dfrac{1 + \cos u}{1 - \cos u}}$ b. $\cot \dfrac{1}{2} u = \dfrac{\sin u}{1 - \cos u}$ c. $\cot \dfrac{1}{2} u = \dfrac{1 + \cos u}{\sin u}$

12. Show that $\sin (\angle x° + \angle 75°) \cos (\angle x° - \angle 75°) - \cos (\angle x° + \angle 75°) \sin (\angle x° - \angle 75°) = \frac{1}{2}$.

13. Let a and b be the measures of the legs of a right triangle ABC, let c be the measure of the hypotenuse, and let α, β, and γ be the angles respectively opposite these sides. Show that each of the following equations is true:

a. $\sin 2\alpha = \dfrac{2ab}{c^2}$

b. $\cos 2\alpha = \dfrac{b^2 - a^2}{c^2}$

c. $\tan 2\alpha = \dfrac{2ab}{b^2 - a^2}$

d. $\sin (\alpha - \beta) = \cos 2\beta$

e. $\cos (\alpha - \beta) = \sin 2\alpha$

14. Show that the value of $\sin 2\theta$ is less than the value of $2 \sin \theta$ when the measure in degrees of θ is in $\rangle 0, 90 \langle$.

B EXERCISES

15. Prove that each of the following statements is true:

a. $\left(\sin \dfrac{x}{2} + \cos \dfrac{x}{2} \right)^2 \equiv 1 + \sin x$

b. $\dfrac{1 - \tan^2 \dfrac{x}{2}}{1 + \tan^2 \dfrac{x}{2}} \equiv \cos x$

c. $\cot \dfrac{x}{2} + \tan \dfrac{x}{2} \equiv 2 \csc x$

d. $\dfrac{\sin x + \cos x}{\cos x - \sin x} \equiv \tan 2x + \sec 2x$

e. $\dfrac{\sin 2x}{1 + \cos 2x} \equiv \tan x$

f. $\dfrac{1 - \tan^2 x}{1 + \tan^2 x} \equiv \cos 2x$

g. $\dfrac{\tan 2x \tan x}{\tan 2x - \tan x} \equiv \sin 2x$

h. $\csc 2x - \cot 2x \equiv \dfrac{1 - \cos 2x}{\sin 2x}$

i. $\dfrac{\sin 2x - \sin x}{\cos 2x + \cos x} \equiv \tan \dfrac{x}{2}$

j. $\dfrac{\sin 2x}{\sin x} - \dfrac{\cos 2x}{\cos x} \equiv \dfrac{\tan \dfrac{x}{2} + \cot \dfrac{x}{2}}{\cot \dfrac{x}{2} - \tan \dfrac{x}{2}}$

k. $\tan x + \cot x \equiv 2 \csc 2x$

l. $\cot x - \tan x \equiv 2 \cot 2x$

16. Derive formulas for each of the following in terms of the values of the trigonometric functions of x:

a. $\sin 3x$ b. $\cos 3x$ c. $\tan 3x$ d. $\cos 4x$

17. Given that θ is a positive acute angle and $\sin \theta = \frac{3}{5}$, find:

a. $\sin 3\theta$ b. $\cos 3\theta$ c. $\tan 3\theta$ d. $\cos 4\theta$

18. Prove: If u, v, $s \in R$, then $\cos u \cos v + \sin u \sin v \equiv \cos (u + s) \cos (v + s) + \sin (u + s) \sin (v + s)$

19. If α, β, and γ are the angles of a triangle ABC, prove that each of the following is an identity:

a. $\sin^2 \alpha + \sin^2 \beta - \sin^2 \gamma = 2 \sin \alpha \sin \beta \cos \gamma$

b. $\tan \dfrac{\alpha}{2} \tan \dfrac{\beta}{2} + \tan \dfrac{\beta}{2} \tan \dfrac{\gamma}{2} + \tan \dfrac{\gamma}{2} \tan \dfrac{\alpha}{2} = 1$

20. Prove: $\cos (\alpha + \beta + \gamma) + \cos (\beta + \gamma - \alpha) + \cos (\gamma + \alpha - \beta) + \cos (\alpha + \beta - \gamma) \equiv 4 \cos \alpha \cos \beta \cos \gamma$.

Sum and Product Formulas

Using identities I–9, I–15, I–16, and I–17 and the addition property of equality, we have:

(i) $\cos (u + v) + \cos (u - v) = 2 \cos u \cos v$
(ii) $\cos (u + v) - \cos (u - v) = - 2 \sin u \sin v$
(iii) $\sin (u + v) + \sin (u - v) = 2 \sin u \cos v$
(iv) $\sin (u + v) - \sin (u - v) = 2 \cos u \sin v$.

If we let $u + v = x$, $u - v = y$, and u, $v \in R$, we obtain: $2 u = x + y$ or $u = \frac{1}{2} (x + y)$, and $2 v = x - y$ or $v = \frac{1}{2} (x - y)$. If we substitute these values in equations (i)–(iv), then each of the following is an identity:

I–30 $\cos x + \cos y = 2 \cos \frac{1}{2}(x + y) \cos \frac{1}{2}(x - y)$	R X R
I–31 $\cos x - \cos y = - 2 \sin \frac{1}{2}(x + y) \sin \frac{1}{2}(x - y)$	R X R
I–32 $\sin x + \sin y = 2 \sin \frac{1}{2}(x + y) \cos \frac{1}{2}(x - y)$	R X R
I–33 $\sin x - \sin y = 2 \cos \frac{1}{2}(x + y) \sin \frac{1}{2}(x - y)$	R X R

These identities, often called *sum formulas*, are useful in changing indicated sums into identically equal indicated products. On the other hand, it is sometimes necessary to reverse this process, that is, to change indicated products into identically equal indicated sums. To do this, we use the following identities which are derived from (i), (ii), and (iii).

I–34 $\cos u \cos v = \frac{1}{2}[\cos (u + v) + \cos (u - v)]$	R X R
I–35 $\sin u \sin v = - \frac{1}{2}[\cos (u + v) - \cos (u - v)]$	R X R
I–36 $\sin u \cos v = \frac{1}{2}[\sin (u + v) + \sin (u - v)]$	R X R

Identities I–34, I–35, and I–36 are known as the *product formulas*.

Example 1. Express each of the following indicated sums as indicated products:

a. $\cos \angle 80° + \cos \angle 50°$

b. $\sin \angle 160° - \sin \angle 80° + \sin \angle 40°$

Solutions.   **a.** From **I–30** we have:

$$\cos \angle 80° + \cos \angle 50° = 2 \cos \tfrac{1}{2}(\angle 80° + \angle 50°) \cdot$$
$$\cos \tfrac{1}{2}(\angle 80° - \angle 50°)$$
$$= 2 \cos \angle 65° \cos \angle 15°$$

b. From **I–33**, we have:

$$(\sin \angle 160° - \sin \angle 80°) + \sin \angle 40°$$
$$= 2 \cos \tfrac{1}{2}(\angle 160° + \angle 80°) \cdot$$
$$\sin \tfrac{1}{2}(\angle 160° - \angle 80°) + \sin \angle 40°$$
$$= 2 \cos \angle 120° \sin \angle 40° + \sin \angle 40°$$
$$= \sin \angle 40° \; [2(-\tfrac{1}{2}) + 1]$$
$$= \sin \angle 40° \; (0)$$

Example 2.   Prove that the following equation is an identity:

$$\tan \frac{1}{2} (x + y) \overset{?}{=} \frac{\sin x + \sin y}{\cos x + \cos y}$$

Solution.   Using **I–30** and **I–32** to transform the right member of the given equation, we obtain:

$$\frac{\sin x + \sin x}{\cos x + \cos y} = \frac{2 \sin \tfrac{1}{2}(x + y) \cos \tfrac{1}{2}(x - y)}{2 \cos \tfrac{1}{2}(x + y) \cos \tfrac{1}{2}(x - y)} = \frac{\sin \tfrac{1}{2}(x + y)}{\cos \tfrac{1}{2}(x + y)} =$$
$$\tan \tfrac{1}{2}(x + y)$$

Therefore $\tan \tfrac{1}{2}(x + y) \equiv \dfrac{\sin x + \sin y}{\cos x + \cos y}$.

Ⓐ **EXERCISES**

1. Write each of the following as an indicated product:

a. $\sin \angle 30° + \sin \angle 50°$

b. $\sin \angle 110° - \sin \angle - 70°$

c. $\cos \angle 42° + \cos \angle 70°$

d. $2 (\cos \angle - 150° - \cos \angle 24°)$

e. $\tfrac{1}{2} (\sin \angle 121° + \sin \angle 73°)$

f. $3 (\cos \angle 11° + \cos \angle 111°)$

g. $\sin \angle 74° + \sin \angle 40° + \sin \angle 57°$

h. $\sin 5\,\theta + \sin 2\,\theta$

i. $\cos \tfrac{3}{2}\,\theta - \cos \tfrac{1}{2}\,\theta$

j. $\sin 3\,x - \sin 5\,x + \sin x$

k. $\sin \dfrac{x}{2} - \sin \dfrac{3\,x}{2} - \cos x$

2. Write each of the following as an indicated sum:

a. $\cos \angle 173° \cos \angle 100°$

b. $\sin \angle 75° \sin \angle 18°$

c. $\sin \angle 12° \cos \angle 47°$

d. $\cos \angle 41° \sin \angle - 15°$

e. $2 \cos \angle 84° \cos \angle 74°$

f. $4 \sin \angle 100° \sin \angle 40°$

g. $- 6 \cos \angle - 38° \frac{1}{3} \cos \angle 100°$

h. $\sqrt{2} \sin \angle 94° \cos \angle - 15°$

i. $2 \cos 4 x \sin 2 x$

j. $\sin 6 x \cos x$

k. $4 \cos 6 x \sin 2 x$

l. $\cos x \sin \dfrac{x}{2}$

3. Prove that each of the following equations is an identity:

a. $\dfrac{2 \cos 3 x}{\sin 2 x} + \dfrac{\sin 2 x}{\cos x} = \dfrac{\cos 2 x}{\sin x}$

b. $\csc \alpha - \cot \alpha = \tan \dfrac{\alpha}{2}$

c. $\left(\sin \dfrac{\theta}{2} + \cos \dfrac{\theta}{2} \right)^2 = 1 + \sin \theta$

d. $\left(\sin \dfrac{\theta}{2} - \cos \dfrac{\theta}{2} \right)^2 = 1 - \sin \theta$

e. $\sin(\alpha + \beta) \sin (\alpha - \beta) = \sin^2 \alpha - \sin^2 \beta$

f. $\cos (\alpha + \beta) \cos (\alpha - \beta) = \cos^2 \alpha - \sin^2 \beta$

g. $\dfrac{\sin 2 \theta \cos \theta}{(1 + \cos 2 \theta)(1 + \cos \theta)} = \tan \dfrac{\theta}{2}$

h. $\dfrac{\sin u - \sin v}{\sin u + \sin v} = \dfrac{\tan \frac{1}{2}(u - v)}{\tan \frac{1}{2}(u + v)}$

i. $\dfrac{\tan (x + y) - \tan y}{1 + \tan (x + y) \tan y} = \tan x$

j. $\cot x + \tan y = \dfrac{\cos (x - y)}{\sin x \cos y}$

Graphs of the Sine and Cosine Functions

To obtain the graphs of $\{(x, y) \mid y = \sin x\}$ and $\{(x, y) \mid y = \cos x\}$, we first prepared tables (shown below) listing familiar ordered pairs belonging to each function. With respect to separate coordinate axes, we then located the points whose coordinates are given in each of these tables. Then we drew a smooth curve through the respective sets of points. The tables and graphs can, of course, be continued indefinitely.

x	$-\frac{5\pi}{6}$	$-\frac{3\pi}{4}$	$-\frac{\pi}{2}$	$-\frac{\pi}{6}$	0	$\frac{\pi}{3}$	$\frac{\pi}{2}$	$\frac{5\pi}{6}$	π	$\frac{5\pi}{4}$	$\frac{3\pi}{2}$	$\frac{11\pi}{6}$	2π	$\frac{7\pi}{3}$	$\frac{5\pi}{2}$
$y = \sin x$	$-\frac{1}{2}$	$-\frac{\sqrt{2}}{2}$	-1	$-\frac{1}{2}$	0	$\frac{\sqrt{3}}{2}$	1	$\frac{1}{2}$	0	$-\frac{\sqrt{2}}{2}$	-1	$-\frac{1}{2}$	0	$\frac{\sqrt{3}}{2}$	1

x	$-\frac{5\pi}{6}$	$-\frac{3\pi}{4}$	$-\frac{\pi}{2}$	$-\frac{\pi}{6}$	0	$\frac{\pi}{3}$	$\frac{\pi}{2}$	$\frac{5\pi}{6}$	π	$\frac{5\pi}{4}$	$\frac{3\pi}{2}$	$\frac{11\pi}{6}$	2π	$\frac{7\pi}{3}$	$\frac{5\pi}{2}$
$y = \cos x$	$-\frac{\sqrt{3}}{2}$	$-\frac{\sqrt{2}}{2}$	0	$\frac{\sqrt{3}}{2}$	1	$\frac{1}{2}$	0	$-\frac{\sqrt{3}}{2}$	-1	$-\frac{\sqrt{2}}{2}$	0	$\frac{\sqrt{3}}{2}$	1	$\frac{1}{2}$	0

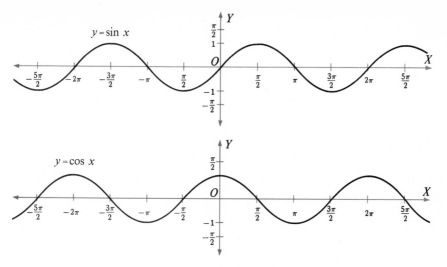

The point P with rectangular coordinates (x, y) is in the graph of $\{(x, y) \mid y = \sin x\}$ if and only if y is the ordinate of a point P' in the standard position unit circle and x is the measure of a standard position unit circle path whose terminal point is P'. Also, the point $Q(x, y)$ is in the graph of $\{(x, y) \mid y = \cos x\}$ if and only if y is the abscissa of a point Q' in the standard position unit circle and x is the measure of a standard position unit circle path whose terminal point is Q'. Thus if x, the measure of a standard position unit circle path, is $\dfrac{5\pi}{6}$, then $\left(\dfrac{5\pi}{6}, \dfrac{1}{2}\right) \epsilon \{(x, y) \mid y = \sin x\}$ and $\left(\dfrac{5\pi}{6}, -\dfrac{\sqrt{3}}{2}\right) \epsilon \{(x, y) \mid y = \cos x\}$.

We can sketch the graphs of $\{(x, y) \mid y = \sin x\}$ and $\{(x, y) \mid y = \cos x\}$ very quickly by using the following facts.

(a) The *range* of each function is $\langle -1, 1 \rangle$.

(b) The measure of the circumference of the unit circle is 2π.

(c) Each function is *periodic* with *period* 2π. (See page 284.) *Note.* When a function is periodic we say that its graph is periodic. Then we proceed as follows:

(1) Draw the guide lines which are the graphs of the equations $y = 1$ and $y = -1$. We know that all points in the graph of either $y = \sin x$ or $y = \cos x$ must lie in or between these lines.

(2) Calibrate the x-axis in multiples of $\dfrac{\pi}{2}$ starting at the origin and using $\dfrac{\pi}{2} \approx \dfrac{3.14}{2} = 1.57$.

(3) Sketch the graph of the function $\{(x, y) \mid y = \sin x\}$, or of $\{(x, y) \mid y = \cos x\}$, when $x \in \langle 0, 2\pi \rangle$ after studying the change in $\sin x$, or $\cos x$, as the point P traverses the standard position unit circle path $(OI, 2\pi)$ as shown in part in the following figures.

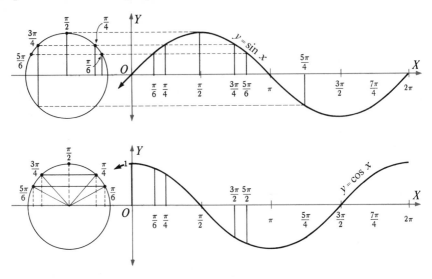

We see that:

When x increases from	$\sin x$	$\cos x$
0 to $\dfrac{\pi}{2}$	increases from 0 to 1	decreases from 1 to 0
$\dfrac{\pi}{2}$ to π	decreases from 1 to 0	decreases from 0 to -1
π to $\dfrac{3\pi}{2}$	decreases from 0 to -1	increases from -1 to 0
$\dfrac{3\pi}{2}$ to 2π	increases from -1 to 0	increases from 0 to 1

(4) Extend each curve for values of x outside $\langle 0, 2\pi \rangle$ by using the fact that each function is periodic with period 2π as noted in (c) on the preceding page. Thus we know that when $k \in I$,

$$\sin(x + 2\pi k) = \sin x \text{ and } \cos(x + 2\pi k) = \cos x.$$

The results obtained by performing these four steps will be two curves that are similar to those shown in the following figure. Each of these curves is called a *sine wave* or *sinusoid*. In the figure, we show the sine waves whose equations are $y = \sin x$ and $y = \cos x$ on the same set of axes. Since $\cos x = \sin\left(\dfrac{\pi}{2} + x\right)$, we often refer to the function defined by $y = \cos x$ as a "sine function."

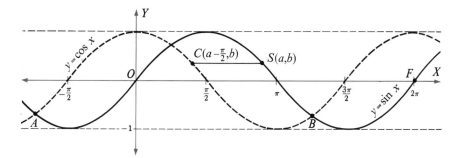

When we study these two graphs we see that (a, b) is in $\{(x, y) \mid y = \sin x\}$ if and only if $\left(a - \dfrac{\pi}{2}, b\right)$ is in $\{(x, y) \mid y = \cos x\}$. This is true because, by identities I–12 and I–10, $\cos\left(a - \dfrac{\pi}{2}\right) = \cos\left(\dfrac{\pi}{2} - a\right) = \sin a$. Thus, if we start at any point $C\left(a - \dfrac{\pi}{2}, b\right)$ in the cosine curve and move $\dfrac{\pi}{2}$ units horizontally to the right, we reach the point $S(a, b)$ in the sine curve. Clearly, these two curves are congruent   Indeed we can think of the sine curve as the cosine curve translated $\dfrac{\pi}{2}$ units to the right.

Period and Amplitude

If the graph of a function is a sine wave, an arc of this sine wave whose end points have the abscissas x_1 and x_2 is called a cycle of the sine wave provided $|x_2 - x_1|$ is equal to the period of the function. Thus, arcs AB and OF are cycles of the sine waves shown in the figure above.

If m and n are the maximum and minimum values, respectively, of a periodic function, the number $\dfrac{m - n}{2}$ is called the *amplitude* of the function or the amplitude of the graph of the function. Accordingly, the amplitude of the sine and the cosine functions is $\dfrac{1 - (-1)}{2} = 1$.

Consider the graph of $\{(x, y) \mid y = 3 \cos x\}$ shown by the dotted line in the following figure. We observe that the ordinate of each point in this graph is 3 times the ordinate of the point with the same abscissa in the graph of $\{(x, y) \mid y = \cos x\}$. Therefore this function has range $\langle -3, 3 \rangle$, amplitude 3 and period 2π. The sinusoid shown as a dashed curve in the figure is the graph of $\{(x, y) \mid y = -3 \cos x\}$.

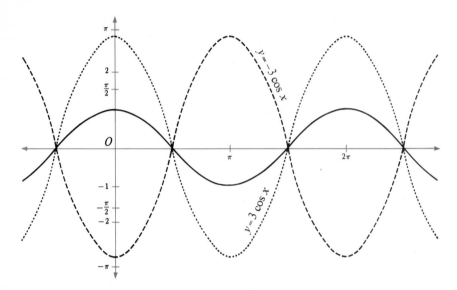

The ordinate of each point in this curve is -3 times the ordinate of the point with the same abscissa in the graph of $\{(x, y\} \mid y = \cos x\}$ which is shown as a solid line. The sinusoid shown as a dashed curve is the reflection in the x-axis of the sinusoid shown as a dotted curve. Accordingly, the function $\{(x, y) \mid y = -3 \cos x\}$ also has amplitude 3 and period 2π. In general, the graph of any function of the form $\{(x, y) \mid y = a \cos x\}$ or $\{(x, y) \mid y = a \sin x\}$ is a sinusoid with period 2π and amplitude $|a|$.

In order to sketch the graph of $\{(x, y) \mid y = \sin 3x\}$, we observe that $3x$ increases from 0 to 2π when x increases from 0 to $\dfrac{2\pi}{3}$. Therefore, the period of this function is $\dfrac{2\pi}{3}$ and the graph of $\{(x, y) \mid y = \sin 3x; \ x \in \langle 0, \dfrac{2\pi}{3} \rangle \}$ is a cycle of this sine wave. This statement is verified by the following table:

x	0	$\dfrac{\pi}{18}$	$\dfrac{\pi}{9}$	$\dfrac{\pi}{6}$	$\dfrac{2\pi}{9}$	$\dfrac{5\pi}{18}$	$\dfrac{\pi}{3}$	$\dfrac{7\pi}{18}$	$\dfrac{4\pi}{9}$	$\dfrac{\pi}{2}$	$\dfrac{5\pi}{9}$	$\dfrac{11\pi}{18}$	$\dfrac{2\pi}{3}$
$3x$	0	$\dfrac{\pi}{6}$	$\dfrac{\pi}{3}$	$\dfrac{\pi}{2}$	$\dfrac{2\pi}{3}$	$\dfrac{5\pi}{6}$	π	$\dfrac{7\pi}{6}$	$\dfrac{4\pi}{3}$	$\dfrac{3\pi}{2}$	$\dfrac{5\pi}{3}$	$\dfrac{11\pi}{6}$	2π
$y = \sin 3x$	0	0.5	0.87	1	0.87	0.5	0	-0.5	-0.87	-1	-0.87	-0.5	0

Thus the function has period $\dfrac{2\pi}{3}$ and amplitude 1 as shown by the solid curve in the following figure.

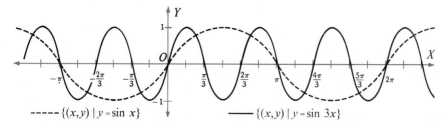

$----\{(x,y) \mid y = \sin x\}$ $\qquad\qquad$ $\overline{}\{(x,y) \mid y = \sin 3x\}$

We observe that the graph of any function having the form $\{(x, y) \mid y = a \sin px\}$ or the form $\{(x, y) \mid y = a \cos px\}$ when $ap \neq 0$ is a sinusoid with amplitude $|a|$ and period $\left|\dfrac{2\pi}{p}\right|$. We can use these facts to help us sketch a sinusoid as shown in the following examples.

Example 1. Sketch the graph of $\{(x, y) \mid y = -3 \sin 2x\}$ over two periods beginning at the origin and extending to the right.

Solution. Amplitude $= |-3| = 3$; period $= \dfrac{2\pi}{2} = \pi$. From our study of the graph of the sine function, we know that we are concerned with the abscissas of the end points and of the "quarter points" in $\langle 0, \pi \rangle$. Thus when $x = 0$, $y = 0$; when $x = \dfrac{\pi}{4}$, $y = -3$; when $x = \dfrac{\pi}{2}$, $y = 0$; when $x = \dfrac{3\pi}{4}$, $y = 3$; and when $x = \pi$, $y = 0$. Therefore, the first cycle of our sinusoid crosses the x-axis at $(0, 0)$, $\left(\dfrac{\pi}{2}, 0\right)$, and $(\pi, 0)$. We see that there

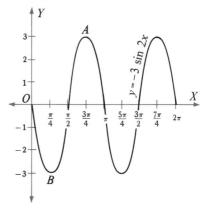

is a maximum value at A $\left(\dfrac{3\pi}{4}, 3\right)$ and a minimum value at B $\left(\dfrac{\pi}{4}, -3\right)$. Using this information, we sketch two cycles of the curve as shown in the figure.

Example 2. Sketch the functions defined by each of the following equations:

a. $y = 3 \cos \pi x$; $x \in \langle -2, 2 \rangle$

b. $y = 3 \cos \pi x + 2$; $x \in \langle -2, 2 \rangle$

Solution.

a. The amplitude is $|3|$, or 3; and the period is $\dfrac{2\pi}{\pi}$, or 2. The given interval $\langle -2, 2 \rangle$ contains two cycles of the graph of $\{(x, y) \mid y = 3 \cos \pi x\}$. The coordinates of the points where the graph intersects the x-axis in the interval $\langle -2, 2 \rangle$ are $(-\frac{3}{2}, 0)$, $(-\frac{1}{2}, 0)$, $(\frac{1}{2}, 0)$, and $(\frac{3}{2}, 0)$. The maximum of the function is 3 and there are maximums in the interval $\langle -2, 2 \rangle$ at the points whose coordinates are $(-2, 3)$, $(0, 3)$, and $(2, 3)$. The minimum of the function is -3 and in the interval $\langle -2, 2 \rangle$ there are minimums at the points whose coordinates are $(-1, -3)$ and $(1, -3)$. With this information we sketch the graph of $y = 3 \cos \pi x$. The required graph, when $x \in \langle -2, 2 \rangle$, is shown as the heavier dashed curve in the diagram.

b. Clearly the ordinate of every point in the graph of $y = 3 \cos \pi x + 2$ is 2 more than the ordinate of the corresponding point in the graph of $y = 3 \cos \pi x$. Thus the graph of $y = 3 \cos \pi x + 2$ can be traced by the upper-end of a vertical line segment of measure 2 which moves in such a way that its lower-end traces the graph of $y = 3 \cos \pi x$. Observe that the effect of the $+2$ is to "lift the graph" two units without affecting its amplitude or period. The graph of $y = 3 \cos \pi x + 2$ when $x \in \langle -2, 2 \rangle$ is shown as the heavier solid curve in the diagram.

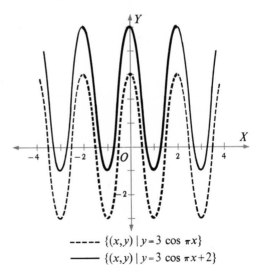

----- $\{(x,y) \mid y = 3 \cos \pi x\}$

——— $\{(x,y) \mid y = 3 \cos \pi x + 2\}$

1. Sketch the graph of each of the following when $x \in \rangle - 2\,\pi, 2\,\pi \langle$:

   a. $\{(x, y) \mid y = 2 \sin x\}$

   b. $\{(x, y) \mid y = -4 \sin x\}$

   c. $\{(x, y) \mid y = \frac{1}{2} \cos x\}$

   d. $\{(x, y) \mid y = \pi \cos x\}$

   e. $\{(x, y) \mid y = \sin 3x\}$

   f. $\left\{(x, y) \mid y = \cos \dfrac{x}{2}\right\}$

   g. $\left\{(x, y) \mid y = \sin \dfrac{\pi x}{2}\right\}$

   h. $\{(x, y) \mid y = 2 \cos 3x\}$

   i. $\left\{(x, y) \mid y = -\dfrac{1}{2} \sin \dfrac{x}{2}\right\}$

   j. $\{(x, y) \mid y = 3 + 2 \sin x\}$

   k. $\{(x, y) \mid y = -5 + 3 \cos 2x\}$

   l. $\{(x, y) \mid y = 1 + \sin \pi x\}$

   m. $\{(x, y) \mid y = \frac{1}{2} + \sin 2x\}$

   n. $\{(x, y) \mid y = \sin x + 1\}$

2. Draw the graphs of each of the following pairs of functions with respect to the same xy-coordinate system. From the graphs determine the approximate values of x (arguments) for which the two trigonometric functions have the same value.

   a. $\{(x, y) \mid y = \sin x; \ 0 < x < 2\,\pi\}$
     $\{(x, y) \mid y = \sin 2x; \ 0 < x < 2\,\pi\}$

   b. $\{(x, y) \mid y = 2 \cos 2x; \ 0 < x < 2\,\pi\}$
     $\{(x, y) \mid y = \cos x; \ 0 < x < 2\,\pi\}$

   c. $\{(x, y) \mid y = \sin x; \ -2\,\pi < x < 2\,\pi\}$
     $\left\{(x, y) \mid y = \sin \left(x + \dfrac{\pi}{2}\right); \ -2\,\pi < x < 2\,\pi\right\}$

   d. $\{(x, y) \mid y = 2 \sin 3x; \ -\pi \le x < \pi\}$
     $\{(x, y) \mid y = \sin x; \ -\pi \le x < \pi\}$

   e. $\{(x, y) \mid y = 3 \sin x; \ -2\,\pi < x < 2\,\pi\}$
     $\{(x, y) \mid y = 2 \cos 3x; \ -\pi < x < 3\,\pi\}$

3. Write an equation in x and y whose graph is a sine curve which has a minimum value of $-\dfrac{3}{2}$, a maximum value of $\dfrac{3}{2}$, period $\dfrac{3\,\pi}{4}$, and which contains point O $(0, 0)$, when $x, y \in R$.

4. Write an equation whose graph is a cosine curve which has a minimum value of -2, a maximum value of 2, period $2\,\pi$, and contains the point $P(0, 2)$.

5. We wish to draw a sine curve that crosses the x-axis at $x = \dfrac{\pi}{3}$, has a period of $\dfrac{2\,\pi}{3}$, has a minimum value of -1, and has a maximum value of 1. Write an equation whose graph is this curve.

6. If $A = \left\{(x, y) \mid y = 2 \cos 3x; \ -\dfrac{2\,\pi}{3} < x < \dfrac{2\,\pi}{3}\right\}$ and $B = \{(x, y) \mid y = 1\}$, how many elements are there in $A \cap B$?

7. Use graphs to find the approximate values of x for which each of the following statements is true.

    a. $\sin 3x > \sin x$; $0 < x < \pi$. *Hint.* Draw the graphs of $\{(x, y) \mid y = \sin 3x\}$ and $\{(x, y) \mid y = \sin x\}$.

    b. $2 \cos 2x < \cos x$; $0 < x < \pi$

    c. $\sin\left(x + \dfrac{\pi}{2}\right) = \cos x$; $-\infty < x < \infty$

    d. $\cos 2x = x + 1$; $-\pi < x < \pi$

8. Sketch the graph of the function defined by each of the following equations when $x \in \langle -2\pi, 2\pi \rangle$.

    a. $y = |\sin x|$ **c.** $y = -|\cos x|$ **e.** $y = |\sin 2x|$

    b. $y = \sin |x|$ **d.** $y = 3|\sin x|$ **f.** $y = |\cos 2x|$

Phase Shift

    To draw the graph of $F_1 = \left\{ (x, y) \mid y = \cos\left(x - \dfrac{\pi}{4}\right) \right\}$, we first make a table of a few ordered pairs belonging to $F = \{(x, y) \mid y = \cos x\}$ and a table of a few ordered pairs belonging to F_1.

x	0	$\dfrac{\pi}{4}$	$\dfrac{\pi}{2}$	$\dfrac{3\pi}{4}$	π	$\dfrac{5\pi}{4}$	$\dfrac{3\pi}{2}$	$\dfrac{7\pi}{4}$	2π
$\cos x$	1	$\dfrac{\sqrt{2}}{2}$	0	$-\dfrac{\sqrt{2}}{2}$	-1	$-\dfrac{\sqrt{2}}{2}$	0	$\dfrac{\sqrt{2}}{2}$	1

x	$\dfrac{\pi}{4}$	$\dfrac{\pi}{2}$	$\dfrac{3\pi}{4}$	π	$\dfrac{5\pi}{4}$	$\dfrac{3\pi}{2}$	$\dfrac{7\pi}{4}$	2π	$\dfrac{9\pi}{4}$
$\cos\left(x - \dfrac{\pi}{4}\right)$	1	$\dfrac{\sqrt{2}}{2}$	0	$-\dfrac{\sqrt{2}}{2}$	-1	$-\dfrac{\sqrt{2}}{2}$	0	$\dfrac{\sqrt{2}}{2}$	1

    Observe that $\left(x + \dfrac{\pi}{4}, y\right) \in F_1 \longleftrightarrow (x, y) \in F$. This tells us that a point with ordinate y_1 is in the graph of F_1 if and only if it is $\dfrac{\pi}{4}$ units *to the right* of a point with the same ordinate in the graph of F. Accordingly, F and F_1 have the same period and the same amplitude. Since the graph of F_1 is obtained by shifting the graph of F $\dfrac{\pi}{4}$ units to the right, the constant $\dfrac{\pi}{4}$ is called the *phase shift* of F_1. See the graph below.

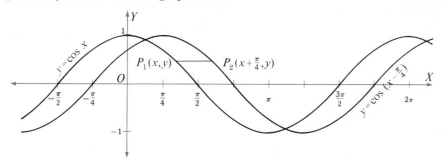

If $F_2 = \left\{ (x, y) \mid y = \cos\left(x + \dfrac{\pi}{4}\right) \right\}$, how would the graph of F be shifted to obtain the graph of F_2?

In general, we can say that the sine wave whose equation is $y = a \sin (px + s)$ or $y = a \cos (px + s)$ where $ap \neq 0$ has amplitude $\mid a \mid$, period $\dfrac{2\pi}{\mid p \mid}$, and phase shift $-\dfrac{s}{p}$. Observe that the curve is shifted $\left| \dfrac{s}{p} \right|$ units to the left of the graph of $y = a \sin px$ or $y = a \cos px$ if $\dfrac{s}{p} > 0$ and $\left| \dfrac{s}{p} \right|$ units to the right of the graph of $y = a \sin px$ or $y = a \cos px$ if $\dfrac{s}{p} < 0$.

Ⓐ **EXERCISES**

1. Without drawing the graph, state the amplitude, the period, and the phase shift of the function defined by each of the following equations:

   a. $y = 3 \sin\left(x - \dfrac{\pi}{2}\right)$ **c.** $y = \dfrac{1}{2} \cos\left(2x - \dfrac{\pi}{3}\right)$ **e.** $y - 1 = \sin x$

   b. $y = -2 \sin\left(x + \dfrac{\pi}{4}\right)$ **d.** $y = -4 \cos\dfrac{x}{2} + \pi$ **f.** $y = \dfrac{2}{3} \cos(x - 3)$

2. The graph at the right is the graph of $\{(x, y) \mid y = \sin x\}$. Write the equation of the graph obtained if

   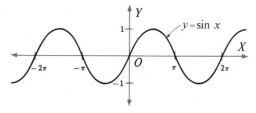

   a. the ordinate of each point in the graph shown is increased by 2.

   b. the ordinate of each point in the graph shown is multiplied by 2.

   c. each point of the graph shown is shifted $\dfrac{\pi}{3}$ units to the right.

3. Sketch the graph of the solution set of each of the following equations:

a. $y = 3 \sin \left(x - \dfrac{\pi}{3}\right)$ **c.** $y + 2 = 3 \cos (x + 1)$ **e.** $y = \frac{1}{3} \sin (2x + \pi)$

b. $y = -\frac{1}{3} \cos 3x$ **d.** $y - 4 = \cos \pi x$ **f.** $y = \frac{1}{2} \sin \left(2x - \dfrac{\pi}{2}\right)$

Graphs of the Tangent, Cotangent, Secant and Cosecant Functions

Let us consider the graph of the tangent function $\{(x, y) \mid y = \tan x\}$ whose domain is E_2, or $R \backsim \left\{x \mid x = (2k + 1)\dfrac{\pi}{2};\ k \in I\right\}$. Since $\tan x = \dfrac{\sin x}{\cos x}$, when $x \in E_2$, we can obtain the graph of the tangent function by sketching the graphs of $y = \sin x$ and $y = \cos x$ with reference to the same set of axes and then employing the method of division of ordinates as described in Chapter 6. (See Example 4, page 318.)

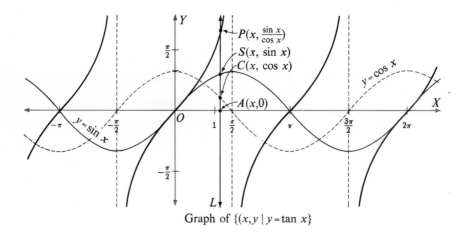

Graph of $\{(x, y \mid y = \tan x\}$

Thus in any vertical line L through $A(x, 0)$ when $x \in E_2$ we locate a point P whose ordinate is $\dfrac{\sin x}{\cos x}$ or $\dfrac{AS}{AC}$ as shown in the figure above. As the vertical line L moves horizontally the point P traces a curve which is the graph of the tangent function. Since $\tan x$ increases without bound as the abscissa of A approaches $\dfrac{\pi}{2}$ from the left, we say that the line whose equation is $x = \dfrac{\pi}{2}$ is an *asymptote* for this curve and that the curve approaches this line *asymptotically*. Observe that the curve also approaches this line asymptotically *from the right*.

Our graph suggests that the tangent function is periodic with period π. In order to confirm this conjecture, we must show that (*i*) $\tan (x + \pi) \equiv \tan x$ and (*ii*) there is no positive number a smaller than π such that $\tan (x + a) = \tan x$ for all $x \in E_2$. The proof of (*i*) follows from identity **I–18**:

$$\tan (x + \pi) = \frac{\tan x + \tan \pi}{1 - \tan x \tan \pi} = \frac{\tan x + 0}{1 - 0 \cdot \tan x} = \tan x.$$
$$\therefore \tan (x + \pi) \equiv \tan x.$$

The proof of (*ii*) is left as an exercise.

The sketch of the graph of $\{(x, y) \mid y = \cot x\}$ obtained by the method of division of ordinates is left to you.

The graphs of the secant and cosecant functions obtained by a method similar to that used to obtain the graph of tangent function are shown below:

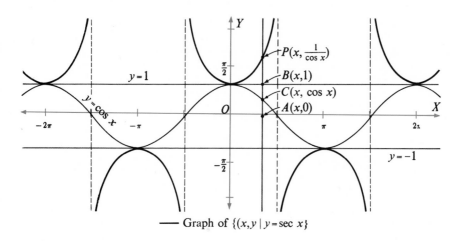

— Graph of $\{(x, y \mid y = \sec x\}$

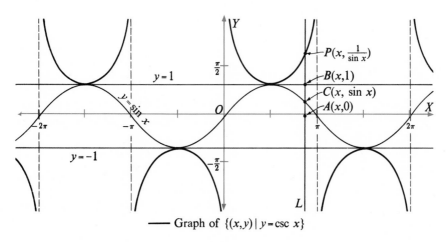

— Graph of $\{(x, y) \mid y = \csc x\}$

1. Which of the following functions have amplitudes?

a. $\{(x, y) \mid y = \sin x\}$ **c.** $\{(x, y) \mid y = \tan x\}$ **e.** $\{(x, y) \mid y = \sec x\}$
b. $\{(x, y) \mid y = \cos x\}$ **d.** $\{(x, y) \mid y = \cot x\}$ **f.** $\{(x, y) \mid y = \csc x\}$

2. Sketch the graph of the function defined by each of the following equations.

a. $y = \csc x + 1$ **f.** $3 y = 6 \sec 3 x$

b. $y = \frac{1}{2} \sec x + 3$ **g.** $y + 1 = \csc x$

c. $y = \tan \dfrac{x}{2}$ **h.** $y = \tan \pi x$

d. $y = 2 \sec x$ **i.** $y = 3 \csc \left(x + \dfrac{\pi}{2} \right)$

e. $y = - \csc x$ **j.** $y = \frac{1}{2} \cot (2 x + \pi)$

3. Find the period of the function defined by each of the following equations.

a. $y = \tan \dfrac{x}{2}$ **g.** $y = \sec 2 x$

b. $y = \cot x$ **h.** $y - 4 = \csc 2 x$

c. $y = \frac{1}{2} \tan x$ **i.** $y = 3 \sin 4 x$

d. $y + 1 = \tan 2 x$ **j.** $y = \frac{1}{2} \cos \frac{3}{4} x$

e. $y = \sec x$ **k.** $y = 3 + \frac{2}{3} \sec \frac{1}{2} x$

f. $y = \csc x$ **l.** $y - 2 = \csc 3 x$

4. Using the method of division of ordinates draw the graph of $\{(x, y) \mid y = \cot x\}$.

5. Prove that $\mid \sec x \mid \geq \mid \tan x \mid$ when $x \in R$.

6. Prove that there is no positive number a smaller than π such that $\tan (x + a) = \tan x$.

Inverses of the Trigonometric Functions

We know from our discussion in Chapter 6 that the relations U and V in $R \times R$ are the inverses of each other if and only if the statement $(a, b) \in U \leftrightarrow (b, a) \in V$ is true.

Let sine denote the sine function and let the relation which is the inverse of the sine function be denoted by either sine^{-1} or arc sine. Then $(a, b) \in$ sine $\leftrightarrow (b, a) \in$ sine$^{-1} \leftrightarrow (b, a) \in$ arc sine. Now sine $= \{(x, y) \mid y = \sin x\}$. Therefore sine$^{-1} = \{(x, y) \mid x = \sin y\} =$ arc sine. Thus each ordered pair in sine^{-1} can be written as (x, y) or $(\sin y, y)$.

The graph of the sine function and the graph of the relation sine^{-1} are shown at the right. Note that the domain of sine is R and the range of sine is $\langle -1, 1 \rangle$, and that the domain of sine^{-1} is $\langle -1, 1 \rangle$ and the range of sine^{-1} is R. Observe too that there exist vertical lines which intersect the graph of sine in one point and intersect the graph of sine^{-1} in infinitely many points. Thus we see that the relation sine^{-1} is not a function.

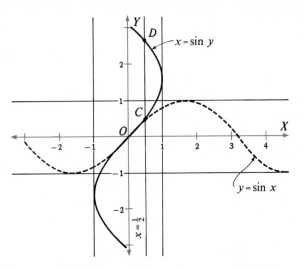

The fact that a vertical line may intersect the graph of sine^{-1} in infinitely many points corresponds to the fact that the equation $a = \sin y$ has infinitely many solutions when a is a constant in $\langle -1, 1 \rangle$. If $a = \frac{1}{2}$, we have:

$$\{y \mid \tfrac{1}{2} = \sin y\} = \left\{y \mid y = \frac{\pi}{6} + k2\pi; k \in I\right\} \cup \left\{y \mid y = \frac{5\pi}{6} + k2\pi; k \in I\right\}$$

$$= \left\{\cdots, -\frac{11\pi}{6}, -\frac{7\pi}{6}, \frac{\pi}{6}, \frac{5\pi}{6}, \frac{13\pi}{6}, \cdots\right\}.$$

We see that the ordinate of each of the points C and D in the diagram above is a member of $\{y \mid \frac{1}{2} = \sin y\}$. We observe too that each of the ordered pairs

$$\cdots, \left(\frac{1}{2}, -\frac{11\pi}{6}\right), \left(\frac{1}{2}, -\frac{7\pi}{6}\right), \left(\frac{1}{2}, \frac{\pi}{6}\right), \left(\frac{1}{2}, \frac{5\pi}{6}\right), \left(\frac{1}{2}, \frac{13\pi}{6}\right), \cdots$$

is a member of the relation sine^{-1}.

We will use either of the symbols "sin$^{-1} \frac{1}{2}$" or "arc sin $\frac{1}{2}$" as another name for $\{y \mid \frac{1}{2} = \sin y\}$. Thus sin$^{-1} \frac{1}{2} = \{y \mid \frac{1}{2} = \sin y\} = $ arc sin $\frac{1}{2}$. Each of the symbols sin$^{-1} \frac{1}{2}$, $\{y \mid \frac{1}{2} = \sin y\}$, and arc sin $\frac{1}{2}$ denotes the same infinite set of numbers. Each number in this set is the first member of an ordered pair which belongs to the sine function and has $\frac{1}{2}$ for its second member. *Note.* When you use the symbol sin$^{-1} \frac{1}{2}$ be careful not to confuse it with $(\sin \frac{1}{2})^{-1}$ which is, of course, another name for $\dfrac{1}{\sin \frac{1}{2}}$.

In general, sin$^{-1} a$ or arc sin a is the solution set of the equation $\sin y = a$ when a is a constant in $\langle -1, 1 \rangle$. We define cos$^{-1} a$, tan$^{-1} a$, and so on, when a is a constant in the appropriate interval, in a similar manner. Thus,

$\sin^{-1} a = \{y \mid a = \sin y\} = \text{arc sin } a$ provided a is a constant in $\langle -1, 1 \rangle$

$\cos^{-1} a = \{y \mid a = \cos y\} = \text{arc cos } a$ provided a is a constant in $\langle -1, 1 \rangle$

$\tan^{-1} a = \{y \mid a = \tan y\} = \text{arc tan } a$ provided a is a constant in $\rangle -\infty, \infty \langle$

Similar statements can be stated for $\csc^{-1} a$, $\sec^{-1} a$, and $\cot^{-1} a$ provided a is a constant in the appropriate interval.

The graphs of the tangent function and the relation tangent^{-1} are shown in the following diagram.

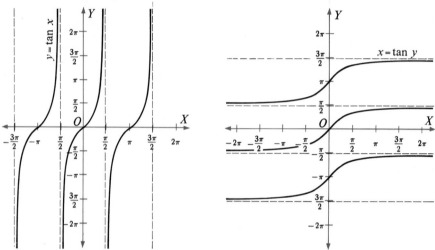

Example 1.   Specify $\cot^{-1}\sqrt{3}$ using the roster method and using set-builder notation.

Solution. $\cot^{-1}\sqrt{3} = \{y \mid \sqrt{3} = \cot y\}$

$$= \left\{\cdots, -\frac{17\pi}{6}, -\frac{11\pi}{6}, -\frac{5\pi}{6}\right\} \cup \left\{\frac{\pi}{6}, \frac{7\pi}{6}, \frac{13\pi}{6}, \cdots\right\}$$

$$= \left\{\cdots, -\frac{17\pi}{6}, -\frac{11\pi}{6}, -\frac{5\pi}{6}, \frac{\pi}{6}, \frac{7\pi}{6}, \frac{13\pi}{6}, \cdots\right\}$$

$$= \left\{y \mid y = \frac{\pi}{6} + k\pi; \ k \in I\right\}.$$

Example 2.   If $s \in \text{arc csc } \dfrac{2}{\sqrt{3}}$, find $\tan s$.

Solution. $s \in \text{arc csc } \dfrac{2}{\sqrt{3}} \longleftrightarrow s \in \left\{t \mid \dfrac{2}{\sqrt{3}} = \csc t\right\} \longleftrightarrow \csc s = \dfrac{2}{\sqrt{3}}.$

We may proceed with the solution in either of two ways:

(1) $\csc s = \dfrac{2}{\sqrt{3}} \longrightarrow \csc^2 s = \dfrac{4}{3} \longrightarrow 1 + \cot^2 s = \dfrac{4}{3} \longrightarrow \cot^2 s$

$$= \frac{1}{3} \longrightarrow \frac{1}{\tan^2 s} = \frac{1}{3} \longrightarrow \tan^2 s$$

$$= 3 \longrightarrow (\tan s = \sqrt{3} \lor \tan s = -\sqrt{3})$$

(2) $\left\{ t \mid \csc t = \dfrac{2}{\sqrt{3}} \right\} = A \cup B$ where $A = \left\{ t \mid t = \dfrac{\pi}{3} + 2\pi k; \ k \in I \right\}$

and $B = \left\{ t \mid t = \dfrac{2\pi}{3} + 2\pi k; \ k \in I \right\}$.

Thus $s \epsilon \left\{ t \mid \csc t = \dfrac{2}{\sqrt{3}} \right\} \longrightarrow s \epsilon (A \cup B) \longrightarrow s \epsilon A \vee$

$s \epsilon B \longrightarrow \tan s = \sqrt{3} \vee \tan s = -\sqrt{3}.$

Example 3. Determine $\tan (\cos^{-1} \tfrac{1}{2})$.

Solution. The problem requires us to find the value of the tangent function for the infinite set of numbers $\{ t \mid \tfrac{1}{2} = \cos t \}$. Since $\{ t \mid \tfrac{1}{2} = \cos t \} =$

$\left\{ t \mid t = \dfrac{\pi}{3} + 2\pi k \right\} \cup \left\{ t \mid t = -\dfrac{\pi}{3} + 2\pi k \right\}$, $\tan t = \pm \sqrt{3}.$

Example 4. Find the least non-negative member of arc $\sin \left(\tan \dfrac{3\pi}{4} \right)$.

Solution. arc $\sin \left(\tan \dfrac{3\pi}{4} \right) = $ arc $\sin (-1) = \{ t \mid \sin t = -1 \} =$

$\left\{ \cdots, -\dfrac{5\pi}{2}, -\dfrac{\pi}{2}, \dfrac{3\pi}{2}, \dfrac{7\pi}{2}, \cdots \right\}$. The least non-negative mem-

ber of this set is $\dfrac{3\pi}{2}$.

Ⓐ EXERCISES

1. Using the roster method, specify each of the following sets.

   a. arc $\sin \tfrac{1}{2}$ **e.** arc $\tan (-1)$ **i.** $\cos^{-1} 0$

   b. arc $\cos 1$ **f.** $\cos^{-1} \left(-\dfrac{\sqrt{3}}{3} \right)$ **j.** arc $\sin \dfrac{\sqrt{2}}{2}$

   c. $\tan^{-1} \sqrt{3}$ **g.** $\cos^{-1} \dfrac{\sqrt{3}}{2}$ **k.** arc $\csc 2$

   d. $\csc^{-1} \left(-\dfrac{2\sqrt{3}}{3} \right)$ **h.** arc $\sec 2$ **l.** $\sin^{-1} 1$

2. List those members of each of the following sets which are in the interval $\langle 0, 2\pi \langle$.

   a. $\sin^{-1} -\tfrac{1}{2}$ **d.** arc $\cos \tfrac{1}{2}$ **g.** arc $\cos \left(\sin \dfrac{5\pi}{4} \right)$

   b. arc $\tan 1$ **e.** arc $\csc \left(-\dfrac{2\sqrt{3}}{3} \right)$ **h.** arc $\sin \left(\sec \dfrac{\pi}{3} \right)$

   c. arc $\tan -\dfrac{\sqrt{2}}{2}$ **f.** $\tan^{-1} (\cos \pi)$ **i.** $\cot^{-1} (\cos \tfrac{1}{4} \pi)$

3. If s is in the given set, find the values of $\sin s$, $\cos s$, or $\tan s$ as indicated.

a. arc tan $\sqrt{3}$; $\cos s$

b. $\tan^{-1}(-1)$; $\sin s$

c. arc sin $(-\frac{1}{2})$; $\tan s$

d. arc cos $\frac{3}{5}$; $\sin s$

e. arc cos $\frac{3}{5}$; $\cos s$

f. $\cot^{-1}(-4)$; $\sin s$

g. arc tan $\frac{1}{3}\sqrt{3}$; $\sin s$

h. $\csc^{-1}(-1.1)$; $\tan s$

4. Name the least non-negative member of each set.

a. $\sin^{-1}\dfrac{\sqrt{3}}{2}$

b. $\sin^{-1}\left(-\dfrac{\sqrt{3}}{2}\right)$

c. arc sin $\left[\tan\left(-\dfrac{\pi}{6}\right)\right]$

d. arc cos $(\cos \pi)$

e. $\tan^{-1}\left(\sin\dfrac{\pi}{6}\right)$

f. arc cot $\left(\cot\dfrac{7\pi}{10}\right)$

5. Determine each of the following:

a. $\sec[\tan^{-1}(-1)]$

b. $\sec(\tan^{-1}0.3)$

c. $\cos\left[\text{arc sin}\left(-\dfrac{\sqrt{2}}{2}\right)\right]$

d. $\tan(\cot^{-1}a)$; $a \neq 0$

e. $\sec(\sin^{-1}a)$; $a \in \langle\,0, 1\,\rangle$

f. $\csc(\sin^{-1}0.4137)$

6. Sketch the graph of each of the following relations:

a. arc cosine **b.** cotangent^{-1} **c.** secant^{-1} **d.** arc cosecant

7. Sketch the graph of each of the following relations:

a. $\{(x, y) \mid x = 2\cos y\}$

b. $\{(x, y) \mid x = \frac{1}{2}\sin 3y\}$

c. $\{(x, y) \mid x = \frac{1}{2}\tan 2y\}$

d. $\left\{(x, y) \mid x = \sec\left(y + \dfrac{\pi}{2}\right)\right\}$

8. If $t \in$ arc tan $\dfrac{\sqrt{1-a^2}}{a}$, find $\cos \angle t$.

Inverse Functions Associated with the Trigonometric Functions

We know that a function has an inverse relation and if no horizontal line intersects the graph of the function in more than one point, its inverse relation is a function. Clearly, no trigonometric function has an inverse function. We may, however, restrict the domain of each of the trigonometric functions in such a way that the resulting function has an inverse function. Though there are many ways to do this, by general agreement it is done by restricting the domain of each of the functions sine, cosecant, tangent, and cotangent to $\left\langle -\dfrac{\pi}{2}, \dfrac{\pi}{2} \right\rangle$ and the domain of each of the functions cosine and secant to $\langle\,0, \pi\,\rangle$. We still use the names sine, cosine, tangent, and so on, but we begin the names with capital letters to distinguish them from the original functions. Thus,

A

Sine function $= \left\{ (x, y) \mid y = \sin x;\ x \in \langle -\frac{\pi}{2}, \frac{\pi}{2} \rangle \right\} = \{(x, y) \mid y = \text{Sin } x\}$

Cosecant function $= \left\{ (x, y) \mid y = \csc x;\ x \in \langle -\frac{\pi}{2}, \frac{\pi}{2} \rangle \right\} = \{(x, y) \mid y = \text{Csc } x\}$

Cosine function $= \{(x, y) \mid y = \cos x;\ x \in \langle 0, \pi \rangle \} = \{(x, y) \mid y = \text{Cos } x\}$

Secant function $= \{(x, y) \mid y = \sec x;\ x \in \langle 0, \pi \rangle \} = \{(x, y) \mid y = \text{Sec } x\}$

Tangent function $= \left\{ (x, y) \mid y = \tan x;\ x \in \langle -\frac{\pi}{2}, \frac{\pi}{2} \rangle \right\} = \{(x, y) \mid y = \text{Tan } x\}$

Cotangent function $= \left\{ (x, y) \mid y = \cot x;\ x \in \langle -\frac{\pi}{2}, \frac{\pi}{2} \rangle \right\} = \{(x, y) \mid y = \text{Cot } x\}$

The heavy black portion of the graph of the sine function at the right is the graph of the Sine function. The fact that any horizontal line will intersect the graph of the Sine function in at most one point indicates that the Sine function has an inverse function which we call *the inverse sine function* and denote by either the symbol arc Sine function or the symbol Sine^{-1} function. Thus the domain of the function arc Sine is $\langle -1, 1 \rangle$ and its range is

$\langle -\frac{\pi}{2}, \frac{\pi}{2} \rangle$. The graph of arc Sine is, of course,

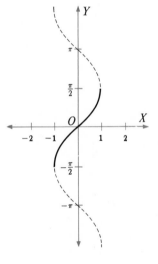

part of the graph of arc sine just as the graph of Sine is part of the graph of sine.

Since Sine and Sine^{-1} are inverse functions, we know from the discussion in Chapter 6 that (*i*) Sin^{-1} (Sin s) $= s$ and (*ii*) Sin (Sin^{-1} s) $= s$. Equation (*ii*) enables us to evaluate Sin^{-1} a when a is in $\langle -1, 1 \rangle$. If, for example, $a = -\frac{1}{2}$ and we let Sin^{-1} $(-\frac{1}{2}) = y$, then Sin [Sin^{-1} $(-\frac{1}{2})] = $ Sin y, or $-\frac{1}{2} = $ Sin y. Since $-\frac{\pi}{6}$ is the only value of y for

which this equation is true, $-\frac{\pi}{6} = y = $ Sin^{-1} $(-\frac{1}{2})$.

In general, if $a \in \langle -1, 1 \rangle$, then

1. Sin^{-1} a is the unique solution of Sin $y = a$,

2. Sin^{-1} a is the only solution of sin $y = a$ in $\langle -\frac{\pi}{2}, \frac{\pi}{2} \rangle$,

3. Sin^{-1} a is the unique member of the range of sine^{-1} in $\langle -\frac{\pi}{2}, \frac{\pi}{2} \rangle$.

$\mathrm{Sin}^{-1}\,a$ is called the *principal value* of sine^{-1}. Similarly, $\mathrm{Csc}^{-1}\,a$ is called the principal value of cosecant^{-1}, and so on. Then

$$y = \mathrm{Sin}^{-1}\,a \longleftrightarrow \sin y = a \wedge y \in \left\langle -\frac{\pi}{2}, \frac{\pi}{2} \right\rangle$$

$$y = \mathrm{Csc}^{-1}\,a \longleftrightarrow \csc y = a \wedge y \in \left\langle -\frac{\pi}{2}, \frac{\pi}{2} \right\rangle$$

B $\qquad y = \mathrm{Tan}^{-1}\,a \longleftrightarrow \tan y = a \wedge y \in \left\langle -\frac{\pi}{2}, \frac{\pi}{2} \right\rangle$

$$y = \mathrm{Cot}^{-1}\,a \longleftrightarrow \cot y = a \wedge y \in \left\langle -\frac{\pi}{2}, \frac{\pi}{2} \right\rangle$$

$$y = \mathrm{Cos}^{-1}\,a \longleftrightarrow \cos y = a \wedge y \in \left\langle 0, \pi \right\rangle$$

$$y = \mathrm{Sec}^{-1}\,a \longleftrightarrow \sec y = a \wedge y \in \left\langle 0, \pi \right\rangle$$

The graph of the Cosecant^{-1} function is part of the graph of the cosecant^{-1} relation. It consists of those points with coordinates (x, y) in the graph of cosecant^{-1} for which

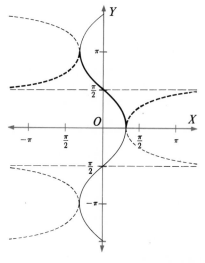

$y \in \left\langle -\dfrac{\pi}{2}, \dfrac{\pi}{2} \right\rangle$. In a similar way the graph of each of the other inverse functions, Tangent^{-1}, Cotangent^{-1}, Cosine^{-1}, and Secant^{-1}, can be identified as part of the graph of the corresponding relations tangent^{-1}, cotangent^{-1}, cosine^{-1}, and secant^{-1}. The graph of the Cosine^{-1} function is shown at the right by a heavy black curve as a part of the graph of the cosine^{-1} relation, and the graph of the Secant^{-1} function is shown by a heavy dashed curve as part of the graph of the secant^{-1} relation.

Since $y = \mathrm{Sin}^{-1}\,x$, $y = \mathrm{Cos}^{-1}\,x$, $y = \mathrm{Tan}^{-1}\,x$, $y = \mathrm{Csc}^{-1}\,x$, $y = \mathrm{Sec}^{-1}\,x$, and $y = \mathrm{Cot}^{-1}\,x$ each define a function whose graph has not more than one point of intersection with any horizontal line, we know that: $\mathrm{Sin}^{-1}\,x_1 = \mathrm{Sin}^{-1}\,x_2 \longleftrightarrow x_1 = x_2$, $\mathrm{Cos}^{-1}\,x_1 = \mathrm{Cos}^{-1}\,x_2 \longleftrightarrow x_1 = x_2$, and so on for the other inverse functions.

Example 1. Solve each of the following equations for x in terms of y and draw the graph of the equation in part **b**.

        a. $y = 4\,\mathrm{Sin}\,3x$ $\qquad\qquad\qquad$ **b.** $y = \frac{4}{3}\,\mathrm{Sin}^{-1}\frac{1}{3}x$

Solutions.   a. $y = 4 \operatorname{Sin} 3x \longleftrightarrow \dfrac{y}{4} = \operatorname{Sin} 3x \longleftrightarrow \operatorname{Sin}^{-1}\left(\dfrac{y}{4}\right) = \operatorname{Sin}^{-1}(\operatorname{Sin} 3x) \longleftrightarrow$

$\longleftrightarrow \operatorname{Sin}^{-1}\left(\dfrac{y}{4}\right) = 3x \longleftrightarrow x = \dfrac{1}{3}\operatorname{Sin}^{-1}\dfrac{y}{4}$.   The domain of the function defined by $y = 4 \operatorname{Sin} 3x$ can be determined by noting that $3x \in \left\langle -\dfrac{\pi}{2}, \dfrac{\pi}{2}\right\rangle$. Therefore $x \in \left\langle -\dfrac{\pi}{6}, \dfrac{\pi}{6}\right\rangle$. The range of this function is $\langle -4, 4\rangle$. For any value of y in $\langle -4, 4\rangle$ there is one and only one value of x.

b. $y = \dfrac{4}{3}\operatorname{Sin}^{-1}\dfrac{x}{3} \longleftrightarrow \dfrac{3y}{4} = \operatorname{Sin}^{-1}\dfrac{x}{3} \longleftrightarrow \operatorname{Sin}\dfrac{3y}{4} = \operatorname{Sin}\left(\operatorname{Sin}^{-1}\dfrac{x}{3}\right) \longleftrightarrow$

$\longleftrightarrow \operatorname{Sin}\dfrac{3y}{4} = \dfrac{x}{3} \longleftrightarrow x = 3\operatorname{Sin}\dfrac{3y}{4}$.   The domain of the function

defined by $y = \dfrac{4}{3}\operatorname{Sin}^{-1}\dfrac{x}{3}$ is

$\langle -3, 3\rangle$ and its range is

$\left\langle -\dfrac{2\pi}{3}, \dfrac{2\pi}{3}\right\rangle$. For any value

of y in $\left\langle -\dfrac{2\pi}{3}, \dfrac{2\pi}{3}\right\rangle$ there is

one and only one value of x.

Since $\left\{(x, y) \mid y = \dfrac{4}{3}\operatorname{Sin}^{-1}\dfrac{x}{3}\right\} =$

$\left\{(x, y) \mid x = 3\operatorname{Sin}\dfrac{3y}{4}\right\}$, we draw

the graph of $\left\{(x, y) \mid y = \dfrac{4}{3}\operatorname{Sin}^{-1}\dfrac{x}{3}\right\}$ by sketching the graph of

its inverse function $\left\{(x, y) \mid y = 3\operatorname{Sin}\dfrac{3x}{4}\right\}$ and then reflecting

each point in the graph of $x = y$.

Example 2.   Without using tables, find $\sin t$, $\cos t$, and $\tan t$ when $t = 2\operatorname{Sin}^{-1}\dfrac{3}{5} - \operatorname{Sin}^{-1}\dfrac{24}{25}$.

Solution.   Let $u = \operatorname{Sin}^{-1}\dfrac{3}{5}$ and $v = \operatorname{Sin}^{-1}\dfrac{24}{25}$. For $t = 2u - v$,

$\sin t = \sin(2u - v) = \sin 2u \cos v - \cos 2u \sin v$

$\qquad = 2\sin u \cos u \cos v - (1 - 2\sin^2 u)\sin v$.

Now $\sin u = \dfrac{3}{5}$, $\cos u = \dfrac{4}{5}$, $\sin v = \dfrac{24}{25}$, and $\cos v = \dfrac{7}{25}$.

$\therefore \sin t = 2 \cdot \dfrac{3}{5} \cdot \dfrac{4}{5} \cdot \dfrac{7}{25} - \left(1 - 2 \cdot \dfrac{9}{25}\right)\dfrac{24}{25} = 0$

If we evaluate $\cos(2u - v)$ by a similar procedure, we obtain $\cos t = 1$.

Thus $\tan t = \dfrac{\sin t}{\cos t} = \dfrac{0}{1} = 0$.

Example 3. Evaluate: **a.** $\cos [\text{arc Tan} (-\sqrt{3})]$ **b.** $\sin [\text{Sec}^{-1} (-\frac{13}{5})]$

Solutions.

a. Let $t = \text{Tan}^{-1} (-\sqrt{3})$. Then $\tan t = -\sqrt{3} \wedge -\frac{\pi}{2} \leq t \leq \frac{\pi}{2}$.

Thus $t = -\frac{\pi}{3}$ and we know that $\cos \left(-\frac{\pi}{3}\right) = \frac{1}{2}$.

$\therefore \cos [\text{arc Tan} (-\sqrt{3})] = \cos \left(-\frac{\pi}{3}\right) = \frac{1}{2}$.

b. Let $t = \text{Sec}^{-1} (-\frac{13}{5})$. Then $\sec t = -\frac{13}{5} \wedge 0 \leq t \leq \pi$. This means that $\frac{\pi}{2} < t < \pi$. Thus we can regard t as the radian measure of a second quadrant angle whose terminal side passes through $P(-5, 12)$. From the sketch, $\sin t = \frac{12}{13}$.

$\therefore \sin [\text{Sec}^{-1} (-\frac{13}{5})] = \sin t = \frac{12}{13}$.

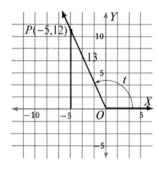

Example 4. Evaluate $\tan [\text{Sin}^{-1} (-\frac{3}{5}) + \text{Cos}^{-1} \frac{3}{5}]$.

Solution. Let $s = \text{Sin}^{-1} (-\frac{3}{5})$ and $t = \text{Cos}^{-1} \frac{3}{5}$. Then $\sin s = -\frac{3}{5}$ and $s \in \langle -\frac{\pi}{2}, \frac{\pi}{2} \rangle$, and $\cos t = \frac{3}{5}$ and $t \in \langle 0, \pi \rangle$.

We can regard s as the radian measure of a fourth quadrant angle whose terminal side passes through $A (4, -3)$ and t as the radian measure of a first quadrant angle whose terminal side passes through $B (3, 4)$ as shown at the right. Hence

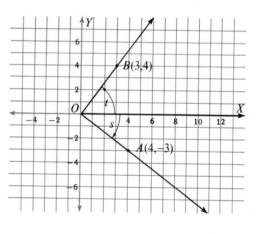

$\tan s = -\frac{3}{4}$ and $\tan t = \frac{4}{3}$ and $\tan (s + t) = \dfrac{\tan s + \tan t}{1 - \tan s \tan t} = \dfrac{-\frac{3}{4} + \frac{4}{3}}{1 - (-\frac{3}{4}) \cdot \frac{4}{3}} = \frac{7}{24}$.

$\therefore \tan [\text{Sin}^{-1} (-\frac{3}{5}) + \text{Cos}^{-1} \frac{3}{5}] = \frac{7}{24}$.

The preceding result may be obtained by using the formula $\tan (s + t) = \dfrac{(\sin s + t)}{(\cos s + t)} = \dfrac{\sin s \cos t + \cos s \sin t}{\cos s \cos t - \sin s \sin t}$.

Example 5. Prove: $\mathrm{Tan}^{-1}\frac{1}{2} = \mathrm{Sin}^{-1}\frac{1}{\sqrt{10}} + \mathrm{Cos}^{-1}\frac{7}{5\sqrt{2}}$

Solution. Both members of this equation represent non-negative numbers less than $\frac{\pi}{2}$. Why? Therefore they are equal if their tangents are equal. Why?

Let $u = \mathrm{Tan}^{-1}\frac{1}{2}$, $v = \mathrm{Sin}^{-1}\frac{1}{\sqrt{10}}$, and $w = \mathrm{Cos}^{-1}\frac{7}{5\sqrt{2}}$. Then

$\tan v = \frac{1}{3}$, $\tan w = \frac{1}{7}$, and $\tan u = \frac{1}{2}$. Hence $\tan(v+w) =$

$\frac{\tan v + \tan w}{1 - \tan v \tan w} = \frac{\frac{1}{3} + \frac{1}{7}}{1 - \frac{1}{3} \cdot \frac{1}{7}} = \frac{\frac{10}{21}}{\frac{20}{21}} = \frac{1}{2}$, and $\tan(v+w) = \tan u$.

Thus $[(\tan(v+w) = \tan u) \wedge (v+w \,\epsilon\, \langle 0, \frac{\pi}{2} \rangle) \wedge (u \,\epsilon\, \langle 0, \frac{\pi}{2} \rangle)] \rightarrow$

$\rightarrow v + w = u$.

$\therefore \mathrm{Tan}^{-1}\frac{1}{2} = \mathrm{Sin}^{-1}\frac{1}{\sqrt{10}} + \mathrm{Cos}^{-1}\frac{7}{5\sqrt{2}}$.

Ⓐ EXERCISES

1. Find the real number represented by each of the following expressions.

   a. arc Sin 0

   b. $\mathrm{Sin}^{-1}\frac{1}{2}$

   c. $\mathrm{Tan}^{-1}1$

   d. arc Tan $\frac{\sqrt{3}}{3}$

   e. arc Tan (-1)

   f. $\mathrm{Cos}^{-1}\frac{1}{2}$

2. If t represents the measure in radians of an angle, find the number of radians in each of the following:

   a. $t = \mathrm{Tan}^{-1}\sqrt{3}$

   b. $t = $ arc Cos 0

   c. $t = \mathrm{Sin}^{-1}\left(-\frac{1}{2}\right)$

   d. $t = \mathrm{Cos}^{-1}\frac{\sqrt{2}}{2}$

   e. $t = $ arc Csc 2

   f. $t = $ arc Tan $\left(\sin\frac{2\pi}{3}\right)$

3. If θ represents an angle whose radian measure is t, find the measure in degrees of θ for each of the following:

   a. $t = $ arc Tan $\sqrt{3}$

   b. $t = $ arc Sin $\frac{\sqrt{2}}{2}$

   c. $t = \mathrm{Sin}^{-1}\left(-\frac{1}{2}\right)$

   d. $t = \mathrm{Cos}^{-1}\left[\sin\left(-\frac{\pi}{3}\right)\right]$

4. Evaluate:

   a. $\cos\left[\text{arc Tan}\left(-\sqrt{3}\right)\right]$

   b. $\cot\left(\mathrm{Sin}^{-1}\frac{3}{5}\right)$

   c. $\tan\left(\text{arc Cos}\frac{1}{2}\right)$

   d. $2\sin\left[\mathrm{Tan}^{-1}\left(-\frac{5}{12}\right)\right]$

   e. $\sin\left(\text{arc Cos}\frac{\sqrt{3}}{2} + \text{arc Sin}\frac{1}{2}\right)$

   f. $\cos\left(\text{arc Sin}\frac{2}{3} + \text{arc Cos}\frac{1}{2}\right)$

   g. $\tan\left(\mathrm{Sin}^{-1}\frac{3}{5} + \mathrm{Cos}^{-1}\frac{1}{2}\right)$

   h. $\sin\left(\mathrm{Cos}^{-1}\frac{12}{13} + \mathrm{Tan}^{-1}\frac{3}{4}\right)$

5. Sketch the graphs of each of the following:

a. $y = \text{Sec } x$ d. $y = \text{Tan}^{-1} x$ g. $y = 2 \text{ Cos } \frac{1}{2} x$

b. $y = \text{Csc } x$ e. $y = \text{arc Sin } 2 x$ h. $y = \text{arc Tan } \frac{1}{2} x$

c. $y = \text{Csc}^{-1} x$ f. $y = \text{Cos}^{-1} 2 x$ i. $y = \text{arc Tan } 2 x$

6. Prove that each of the following statements is true:

a. $\text{Tan}^{-1} \dfrac{1}{2} + \text{Tan}^{-1} \dfrac{1}{3} = \dfrac{\pi}{4}$

b. $\left| \text{ arc Tan } x + \text{ arc Cot } x \right| = \dfrac{\pi}{2}$

c. $\text{arc Tan } \frac{1}{4} + \text{arc Tan } \frac{2}{9} = \frac{1}{2} \text{ arc Sec } \frac{5}{3}$

d. $\text{Sin}^{-1} x + \text{Cos}^{-1} x = \dfrac{\pi}{2}$

e. $\text{arc Sin } \frac{4}{5} + 2 \text{ arc Tan } 2 = \pi$

f. $\text{arc Tan } \frac{1}{3} + \text{arc Tan } \frac{1}{5} = \text{arc Tan } \frac{4}{7}$

g. $\text{arc Sin } 1 - \text{arc Tan } 1 = \dfrac{\pi}{4}$

7. Prove: $\text{arc Sin } (-a) = - \text{arc Sin } a$

8. Solve for x: $\text{arc Cos } \frac{3}{5} - \text{arc Sin } \frac{4}{5} = \text{arc Cos } x$

9. Solve for x: $\text{Tan}^{-1} x + 2 \text{ Tan}^{-1} 1 = \dfrac{3\pi}{4}$

Open Sentences Involving Values of the Trigonometric Functions

We can use the properties of the inverses of the trigonometric functions together with the trigonometric identities and algebraic transformations to solve open sentences involving values of trigonometric functions.

First we shall consider simple equations such as $\sin x = a$ and $\tan \theta = \dfrac{y}{x}$.

For example, if $\sin x = \dfrac{1}{2}$, we know that one solution is arc Sin $\dfrac{1}{2}$ or $\dfrac{\pi}{6}$.

We display this solution and some others in the graph below.

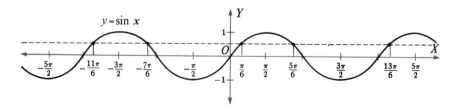

Surveying these solutions we observe an interesting pattern. To find the solution near $k\pi$, we add $\dfrac{\pi}{6}$ if k is even and subtract $\dfrac{\pi}{6}$ if k is odd. For the general case, $\sin x = a$ when $a \,\epsilon\, \langle -1, 1 \rangle$, we have:

$$\{x \mid \sin x = a\} = \{x \mid x = k\pi + (-1)^k \,(\mathrm{Sin}^{-1}\, a); \; k \,\epsilon\, I\}$$

Let $A = \{x \mid \sin x = a\}$ and $B = \{x \mid x = k\pi + (-1)^k \,\mathrm{Sin}^{-1}\, a\}$ where $k \,\epsilon\, I$ and $a \,\epsilon\, \langle -1, 1 \rangle$. We can prove that $t \,\epsilon\, B \longrightarrow t \,\epsilon\, A$ as follows: $t \,\epsilon\, B \longrightarrow t = k\pi + (-1)^k \,\mathrm{Sin}^{-1}\, a \longrightarrow \sin t = \sin [k\pi + (-1)^k \,\mathrm{Sin}^{-1}\, a] = \underline{\sin k\pi \cos (-1)^k \,\mathrm{Sin}^{-1}\, a + \cos k\pi \sin [(-1)^k \,\mathrm{Sin}^{-1}\, a]}$.

If k is even, the underlined expression becomes $0 + \sin (\mathrm{Sin}^{-1}\, a)$, or a.

If k is odd, the underlined expression becomes $0 - \sin (-\mathrm{Sin}^{-1}\, a) = \sin (\mathrm{Sin}^{-1}\, a)$, or a.

We can also prove that $t \,\epsilon\, B \longrightarrow t \,\epsilon\, A$ which is equivalent to $t \,\epsilon\, A \longrightarrow t \,\epsilon\, B$. From $t \,\epsilon\, B \longrightarrow t \,\epsilon\, A$ and $t \,\epsilon\, A \longrightarrow t \,\epsilon\, B$, we have:

$$\left. \begin{array}{c} (t \,\epsilon\, B \longrightarrow t \,\epsilon\, A) \longrightarrow B \subseteq A \\ (t \,\epsilon\, A \longrightarrow t \,\epsilon\, B) \longrightarrow A \subseteq B \end{array} \right\} \longrightarrow A = B.$$

Similar considerations based upon the definitions of the principal values of the inverse trigonometric functions lead to the following theorem which provides general solutions for trigonometric equations such as $\sin x = a$, $\cos x = b$, and so on.

> **Theorem 1–10.** If $a \,\epsilon\, R$ and $k \,\epsilon\, I$, then the solution set of
>
> 1. $\sin x = a$ is $\{x \mid x = k\pi + (-1)^k \,\text{arc Sin}\, a\}$ provided $a \,\epsilon\, \langle -1, 1 \rangle$
> 2. $\csc x = a$ is $\{x \mid x = k\pi + (-1)^k \,\text{arc Csc}\, a\}$ provided $a \,\not\epsilon\, \rangle -1, 1 \langle$
> 3. $\cos x = a$ is $\{x \mid x = 2\,k\pi \pm \text{arc Cos}\, a\}$ provided $a \,\epsilon\, \langle -1, 1 \rangle$
> 4. $\sec x = a$ is $\{x \mid x = 2\,k\pi \pm \text{arc Sec}\, a\}$ provided $a \,\not\epsilon\, \rangle -1, 1 \langle$
> 5. $\tan x = a$ is $\{x \mid x = k\pi + \text{arc Tan}\, a\}$
> 6. $\cot x = a$ is $\{x \mid x = k\pi + \text{arc Cot}\, a\}$.

If t is a solution of a trigonometric equation and $\angle t = \angle d°$, then $\angle t$ and $\angle d°$ are also solutions. If $t \,\epsilon\, \langle 0, 2\,\pi \langle$, then t, $\angle t$, or $\angle d°$ is each called a *primary solution*.

Example 1. Solve: $\cot x = \sqrt{3}$.

Solution. By Theorem 1–10 and the substitution property of equality,

$$\{x \mid \cot x = \sqrt{3}\} = \{x \mid x = k\pi + \text{arc Cot}\, \sqrt{3}\} = \left\{ x \mid x = k\pi + \frac{\pi}{6} \right\}.$$

To find particular solutions, we replace k in $x = k\pi + \dfrac{\pi}{6}$ by various integers. Thus if $k = -2$, $x = -2\,\pi + \dfrac{\pi}{6} = -\dfrac{11\,\pi}{6}$; if $k = -1$,

$$-1\pi+\frac{\pi}{6}=-\frac{5\pi}{6}; \text{ if } k=0, x=0\pi+\frac{\pi}{6}=\frac{\pi}{6}; \text{ if } k=1, x=1\pi+$$

$\frac{\pi}{6}=\frac{7\pi}{6}$; and so on. Thus the solution set (the set of general solutions) is

$$\left\{\ldots, -\frac{11\pi}{6}, -\frac{5\pi}{6}, \frac{\pi}{6}, \frac{7\pi}{6}, \ldots\right\}.$$

Example 2. Find the set of general solutions and all primary solutions for the equation $\sin 3x = 0.6626$.

Solution. $\sin 3x = 0.6626 \longleftrightarrow \text{arc} \sin 0.6626 = 3x$. From Table IV, arc Sin $0.6626 = 0.7243$. Consequently from Theorem 1–10, we know that $3x = k\pi + (-1)^k 0.7243$. Hence $x = \frac{1}{3}[k\pi + (-1)^k 0.7243] =$

$k\frac{\pi}{3} + (-1)^k 0.2414$.

Thus the solution set is $\left\{x \mid x = k\frac{\pi}{3} + (-1)^k 0.2414; \; k \in I\right\}$.

We can obtain the primary solutions by letting k take the values $0, 1, 2, 3, 4,$ and 5 in $x = \frac{\pi k}{3} + (-1)^k 0.2414$ and substituting 3.1416 for π. Thus we have: $\{x \mid \sin 3x = 0.6626\} \cap \{x \mid x \in \langle 0, 2\pi \langle \} = \{0.2414, 0.8058, 2.3358, 2.9002, 4.4302, 4.9946\}$.

If $x = 0.2414$, then

$\sin 3(0.2414) \overset{?}{=} 0.6626$

$\sin 0.7242 \overset{?}{=} 0.6626$

$0.6626 \overset{\checkmark}{=} 0.6626$

If $x = 0.8058$, then

$\sin 3(0.8058) \overset{?}{=} 0.6626$

$\sin 2.4174 \overset{?}{=} 0.6626$

$0.6626 \overset{\checkmark}{=} 0.6626$

Similarly, it can be shown that 2.3358, 2.9002, 4.4302 and 4.9946 satisfy the original equation.

Since $\frac{\pi}{3}$ radians $= 60$ degrees and 0.2414 radians $= 13.8$ degrees, we have: $\{\angle x° \mid \sin \angle (3x)° = 0.6626\} \cap \{\angle x° \mid x \in \langle 0, 360 \langle \} = \{\angle x° \mid x = k \cdot 60 + (-1)^k 13.8\}$. Thus the set of primary solutions is $\{\angle 13.8°, \angle 46.2°, \angle 133.8°, \angle 166.2°, \angle 253.8°, \angle 286.2°\}$.

Example 3. Find the solution set of the equation $2\cos^2 t - 3\sin t - 3 = 0$.

Solution. When values of two or more trigonometric functions are involved in an equation to be solved, it is generally desirable to use the trigonometric identities to obtain an equation equivalent to the given equation which involves values of only one trigonometric function. Substituting $1 - \sin^2 t$ for $\cos^2 t$, we have $2(1 - \sin^2 t) - 3\sin t - 3 = 0$. It follows that:

$\{t \mid 2(1 - \sin^2 t) - 3 \sin t - 3 = 0\} =$
$\{t \mid 2 - 2 \sin^2 t - 3 \sin t - 3 = 0\} =$
$\{t \mid 2 \sin^2 t + 3 \sin t + 1 = 0\} =$
$\{t \mid (2 \sin t + 1)(\sin t + 1) = 0\} =$
$\{t \mid 2 \sin t + 1 = 0\} \cup \{t \mid \sin t + 1 = 0\} =$
$\{t \mid \sin t = -\frac{1}{2}\} \cup \{t \mid \sin t = -1\} =$
$\{t \mid t = k\pi + (-1)^k \operatorname{Sin}^{-1}(-\frac{1}{2})\} \cup$

$\{t \mid t = k\pi + (-1)^k \operatorname{Sin}^{-1}(-1)\} = \left\{t \mid t = k\pi + (-1)^k \left(-\frac{\pi}{6}\right)\right\} \cup$

$\left\{t \mid t = k\pi + (-1)^k \left(-\frac{\pi}{2}\right)\right\}.$

Thus the solution set is:

$$\left\{t \mid t = k\pi + (-1)^k \left(-\frac{\pi}{6}\right) \vee t = k\pi + (-1)^k \left(-\frac{\pi}{2}\right); \ k \in I\right\}$$

Example 4. Find the solution set for the equation $\tan x + 3 \cot x = 2\sqrt{3}$.

Solution. The replacement set E of this equation does not include any value of x for which $\tan x = 0$. Why? Therefore, for all x in E the equation $\tan^2 x + 3 = 2\sqrt{3} \tan x$ is equivalent to the original equation. Then $\tan^2 x - 2\sqrt{3} \tan x + (\sqrt{3})^2 = 0 \longleftrightarrow (\tan x - \sqrt{3})^2 = 0 \longleftrightarrow \tan x = \sqrt{3}$. By Theorem 1–10, $\{x \mid \tan x = \sqrt{3}\} =$

$\{x \mid x = k\pi + \operatorname{Tan}^{-1} \sqrt{3}\} = \left\{x \mid x = k\pi + \dfrac{\pi}{3}\right\}.$

The solution set of the original equation is $\left\{x \mid x = k\pi + \dfrac{\pi}{3}; \ k \in I\right\}.$

Example 5. Find the primary solutions of the equation $1 + \csc x = \csc x$ $(\cos^2 x - \sin^2 x)$.

Solution. $1 + \csc x = \csc x (\cos^2 x - \sin^2 x) \wedge \sin x \neq 0 \longleftrightarrow \sin x(1 + \csc x) = \sin x [\csc x (\cos^2 x - \sin^2 x)] \wedge \sin x \neq 0 \longleftrightarrow \sin x + 1 = \cos^2 x - \sin^2 x \wedge \sin x \neq 0 \longleftrightarrow \sin x + 2 \sin^2 x = 0 \wedge \sin x \neq 0 \longleftrightarrow \sin x (1 + 2 \sin x) = 0 \wedge \sin x \neq 0 \longleftrightarrow \sin x = 0 \vee \sin x = -\frac{1}{2} \wedge \sin x \neq 0$. The solution set is $\{x \mid x = k \cdot \pi + (-1)^k \left(-\dfrac{\pi}{6}\right); \ k \in I\}.$

The solutions in $\langle 0, 2\pi \rangle$ are obtained when $k \in \{1, 2\}$. Hence the set of primary solutions is $\left\{\dfrac{7\pi}{6}, \dfrac{11\pi}{6}\right\}.$

Check. If $x = \dfrac{7\pi}{6}$, then

$1 + \csc \dfrac{7\pi}{6} \overset{?}{=} \csc \dfrac{7\pi}{6} \left(\cos^2 \dfrac{7\pi}{6} - \sin^2 \dfrac{7\pi}{6}\right)$

$1 - 2 \overset{?}{=} -2(\frac{3}{4} - \frac{1}{4})$

$-1 \overset{\checkmark}{=} -1$

If $x = \dfrac{11\pi}{6}$, then

$1 - 2 \overset{?}{=} -2(\frac{3}{4} - \frac{1}{4})$

$-1 \overset{\checkmark}{=} -1$

Example 6.   Given $\sin 3x + \sin x = 0$.

           a. Find the solution set of the given equation.

           b. Find the set of primary solutions.

Solutions.   **a.** We transform the left member of the given equation using the identity $\sin u + \sin v = 2 \sin \frac{1}{2}(u+v) \cos \frac{1}{2}(u-v)$ and proceed as follows:

$$\sin 3x + \sin x = 0 \longleftrightarrow 2 \sin \frac{3x + x}{2} \cos \frac{3x - x}{2} = 0 \leftrightarrow$$

$$\longleftrightarrow 2 \sin 2x \cos x = 0 \longleftrightarrow \sin 2x = 0 \vee \cos x = 0. \text{ Thus}$$

$$\{x \mid \sin 3x + \sin x = 0\} = \{x \mid \sin 2x = 0\} \cup \{x \mid \cos x = 0\}$$

Now $\{x \mid \sin 2x = 0\}$ is the set of integral multiples of $\frac{\pi}{2}$ (set A)

and $\{x \mid \cos x = 0\}$ is the set of all odd multiples of $\frac{\pi}{2}$ (set B).

Since $B \subset A$, we see that $A \cup B = A$. Therefore $\{x \mid \sin 3x +$

$\sin x\} = \left\{ x \mid x = k \frac{\pi}{2}; \ k \in I \right\}$.

b. The set of primary solutions is $\left\{ 0, \frac{\pi}{2}, \pi, \frac{3\pi}{2} \right\}$. We leave the check of each of these solutions to you.

Example 7.   Draw the graph of $\{(x, y) \mid (x \in \langle 0, 2\pi \rangle \wedge y \geq 0) \wedge (y \leq \tan x \wedge y \leq \cos x)\}$.

Solution.   The graph of the given set is the graph of the following:

$\{(x, y) \mid x \in \langle 0, 2\pi \rangle\} \cap \{(x, y) \mid y \geq 0\} \cap \{(x, y) \mid y \leq \tan x\} \cap \{(x, y) \mid y \leq \cos x\}$

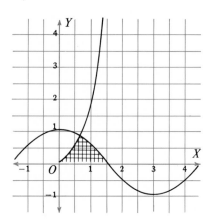

The required graph is the cross-hatched area and the boundaries of the cross-hatched area as shown above.

1. Use the roster method to indicate the solution set for each of the following equations.

a. $\cos x = -\dfrac{\sqrt{2}}{2}$

b. $\sin \angle t = 1$

c. $\tan \angle t = \frac{1}{2}$

d. $\cos x = \frac{1}{4}$

e. $\sin x = 0.0349$

f. $\cos \angle t = 0.4067$

g. $\tan x = 0.2742$

h. $\cot x = .1240$

i. $\sin \angle t = \frac{2}{3}$

2. Use set-builder notation to indicate the solution set and the roster method to indicate the set of the primary solutions for each of the following.

a. $\cos x = \dfrac{\sqrt{3}}{2}$

b. $\tan x = -1$

c. $\sin x = \dfrac{\sqrt{3}}{2}$

d. $\sin 2 x = \dfrac{\sqrt{2}}{2}$

e. $\cos 4 x = 0.9976$

f. $\tan 3 x = 0.1287$

g. $\tan \dfrac{x}{2} = 0.8098$

h. $\cos \dfrac{x}{4} = 0.8511$

i. $2 \sin 2 x = 2$

3. Solve each of the following equations. Find both the solution set and the set of primary solutions.

a. $\sin^2 x = \frac{3}{4}$

b. $\cos^2 \dfrac{x}{2} = \dfrac{3}{4}$

c. $3 \tan x + 2 = 0$

d. $\sin (\pi + x) = -\frac{1}{2}$

e. $\tan 2 x = \cot x$

f. $\tan x = \cot x$

g. $\sin \dfrac{x}{2} + \cos \dfrac{x}{2} = 1$

h. $\tan^2 x = \tan x$

i. $\sin^2 x = 1 + 2 \cos x$

j. $\sec^2 x - \tan x - 3 = 0$

4. Sketch the graph of $\{(x, y) \mid y \le \sin x \ and \ y \ge \cos x; \ x \in \langle -\pi, \pi \rangle \}$.

5. Find the set of primary solutions for each of the following:

a. $\sin \angle t = 3 \sin \angle t$

b. $\cos \angle t = \cos \dfrac{\angle t}{2}$

c. $3 \tan 2 x + 2 \cos 2 x = 0$

d. $\sin x = 1 - \cos 2 x$

e. $\dfrac{1 - 2 \tan x}{\cos x} = 4 \sec x$

f. $\dfrac{\cos \angle t}{1 + \sin \angle t} = 1 - \sin \angle t$

g. $\cos 6 x + \cos 3 x = 0$

h. $\sin 2 x \cos 2 x = -\frac{1}{2}$

i. $\cos \left(\dfrac{\pi}{4} + x\right) - \cos \left(\dfrac{\pi}{4} - x\right) = \sqrt{2}$

j. $4 \cos \angle t = 3 \sec \angle t$

k. $\cos \left(\dfrac{\pi}{3} + x\right) + \cos \left(\dfrac{\pi}{3} - x\right) = -\frac{1}{2} \sqrt{3}$

l. $\cos 3 x + \cos 2 x + \cos x = 0$

m. $2 \sin \left(\angle t - \dfrac{\pi}{6}\right) = \sqrt{3} \sin \angle t$

n. $\sin \dfrac{x}{2} \cos 2 x (1 - \tan^2 x) = 0$

6. Sketch the graph of each of the following:

    a. $\{(x, y) \mid y \leq \sin x \wedge y \geq \frac{1}{2} \sqrt{2}\}$ **b.** $\{(x, y) \mid y \geq \cos x \wedge y < \frac{1}{2}\}$

7. Draw the graph of each of the following sets:

    a. $\{x \mid \sin^2 x > \frac{1}{2}\}$ **c.** $\{x \mid 4 \cos^2 x \leq 3\}$

    b. $\{x \mid \tan^2 x - 1 \leq 0\}$ **d.** $\{x \mid \sin \frac{x}{2} > 0.4147\}$

ESSENTIALS

Before you leave this chapter make sure that you

1. Know the meanings of "trigonometric expression" and "trigonometric equation." (Page 531.)

2. Understand how to prove that a trigonometric equation is an identity. (Page 537.)

3. Understand, can prove, and can use the fundamental trigonometric identities. (Page 532.)

4. Understand and can use the addition formulas. (Page 541.)

5. Understand and can use the formulas for finding the values of trigonometric functions of $2x$ and $\frac{1}{2}x$. (Page 550.)

6. Understand and can use the sum and product formulas. (Page 554.)

7. Can draw the graphs of the sine or cosine functions by means of a table of values. (Page 556.)

8. Can draw the graphs of the sine or cosine functions by use of information about its range and period, and the fact that the measure of the unit circle is 2π. (Page 557.)

9. Understand that $|a|$ is the amplitude of the function defined by $y = a \sin x$ or $y = a \cos x$. (Page 560.)

10. Understand that the period of the function defined by $y = a \sin px$ or $y = a \cos px$ is $\dfrac{2\pi}{|p|}$. (Page 561.)

11. Understand how changes of the real number n affect the graph of the equation $y = a \sin px + n$ or $y = a \cos px + n$. (Pages 561–563.)

12. Understand how the real numbers s and p can be used to determine the phase shift of the graph of $y = \sin (px + s)$ or $y = \cos (px + s)$, with respect to the graph of $y = \sin px$ or $y = \cos px$. (Page 564.)

13. Can use the concepts of amplitude, period, and phase shift in drawing graphs of sinusoids. (Pages 557–565.)

14. Can draw the graphs of the tangent, cotangent, cosecant, and secant functions. (Page 566.)

15. Understand what is meant by the inverse of a trigonometric function and can draw the graphs of the relations which are the inverses of trigonometric functions. (Pages 568, 573, 574.)

16. Understand how to restrict the domains of the trigonometric functions so that each resulting function has an inverse which is a function. (Pages 572–577.)

17. Can find the solution set (the set of general solutions) and the set of primary solutions for a trigonometric equation and can find the solution set of a trigonometric inequality. (Page 579.)

18. Know the meaning of the following words and phrases and can spell them.

amplitude (Page 559.)   primary solutions (Page 579.)
asymptote (Page 566.)   principal value (Page 574.)
cosine curve (Page 559.)   sine curve (Page 559.)
cycle (Page 559.)   sine wave (Page 559.)
period (Page 557.)   sinusoid (Page 559.)
phase shift (Page 565.)

CHAPTER REVIEW

1. Under what conditions is a trigonometric equation a conditional equation and when is it an identity?

2. Which of the following statements are identities and which are conditional equations?

a. $\sin x \cos x = \frac{1}{2}$

e. $\tan^2 x = \sec^2 x - 1$

b. $\sin x \csc x = 1$

f. $\tan x = \dfrac{\sin x}{\cos x}$

c. $\sin^2 x + \cos^2 x = 1$

g. $\tan x \cos x = 1$

d. $\sin^2 x + \csc^2 x = 1$

h. $\sin(-x) = -\sin x$

3. Show that each of the following is an identity:

a. $\cot x \sin x = \cos x$

e. $\dfrac{\cos \theta}{\tan \theta} + \sin \theta = \csc \theta$

b. $\dfrac{\tan x}{\cot x} = \sec^2 x - 1$

f. $\tan x \csc x \cos x = 1$

c. $\dfrac{\cos x \sec x}{\cot x} = \tan x$

g. $\cos \theta \sqrt{1 + \tan^2 \theta} = 1$

d. $\tan \theta \csc \theta = \sec \theta$

h. $\tan^2 x = \dfrac{1}{\csc^2 x - 1}$

4. Simplify each of the following:

a. $\sin x \sec x$

e. $\tan^2 x \left(\dfrac{1 - \sin^2 x}{1 - \cos^2 x} \right)$

b. $\sec x (\sec^2 x - 1)$

f. $(1 - \sin x)(1 + \sin x)$

c. $\csc^2 x (1 - \sin^2 x)$

g. $\sec^2 x - \dfrac{2}{\cos^2 x} + \tan^2 x + 1$

d. $\dfrac{\cos x}{\sin x} - \dfrac{\csc x}{\cos x}$

h. $\dfrac{\cot x + \tan x}{\sec x}$

5. If r and s represent real numbers, complete each of the following to form a true statement.

a. $\sin (r + s) = \underline{\ ?\ }$ **c.** $\sin (r - s) = \underline{\ ?\ }$ **e.** $\tan (r + s) = \underline{\ ?\ }$

b. $\cos (r + s) = \underline{\ ?\ }$ **d.** $\cos (r - s) = \underline{\ ?\ }$ **f.** $\tan (r - s) = \underline{\ ?\ }$

6. Without use of a table, find the number represented by each of the following:

a. $\cos \left(\dfrac{\pi}{3} - \dfrac{\pi}{4} \right)$ **b.** $\sin \left(\dfrac{\pi}{4} + \dfrac{\pi}{6} \right)$ **c.** $\tan \left(\dfrac{\pi}{3} + \dfrac{\pi}{4} \right)$

7. Match each of the expressions in the column on the right with its identically equal expression in the column on the left.

a. $\sin 2x$

$(1)\ \dfrac{\cos x + 1}{2}$

b. $\sqrt{\dfrac{1 + \cos x}{2}}$

$(2)\ \cos^2 x - \sin^2 x$

c. $\cos 2x$

$(3)\ \dfrac{1 - \cos x}{\sin x}$

d. $\cos^2 \dfrac{x}{2}$

$(4)\ 2 \sin x \cos x$

e. $\tan \dfrac{x}{2}$

$(5)\ |\cos \tfrac{1}{2} x|$

8. If α is a third quadrant angle, β is a second quadrant angle, $\sin \alpha = -\frac{3}{5}$, and $\sin \beta = \dfrac{\sqrt{2}}{2}$, find:

a. $\sin (\alpha + \beta)$ **c.** $\sin (\alpha - \beta)$ **e.** $\tan^2 (\alpha + \beta)$

b. $\cos (\alpha + \beta)$ **d.** $\cos 2\alpha + \sin 2\beta$ **f.** $\tan^2 \alpha + \tan^2 \beta$

9. Use the identities involving trigonometric functions of $\frac{1}{2} x$ and find the number represented by each of the following:

a. $\sin \dfrac{\pi}{12}$ **b.** $\tan \dfrac{\pi}{12}$ **c.** $\cos \dfrac{\pi}{8}$ **d.** $\sin \angle 22.5°$

10. Use the addition formulas to find the number represented by each of the following:

a. $\cos \dfrac{7\pi}{12}$ **b.** $\sin \dfrac{17\pi}{12}$ **c.** $\tan \angle 75°$ **d.** $\sin \angle 105°$

11. Express each of the following as the product of the values of sines, of cosines, or of both sines and cosines.

   a. $\sin 8x - \sin 4x$

   b. $\frac{1}{2}(\sin 5x + \sin 3x)$

   c. $\frac{1}{2}(\sin \frac{3}{2}\theta - \sin \frac{1}{2}\theta)$

   d. $\frac{1}{2}(\cos 2\theta - \cos 6\theta)$

12. Express each of the following as the sum or difference of sines, of cosines, or of both sines and cosines.

   a. $2\sin 3x \cos x$ **b.** $2\cos 2x \cos x$ **c.** $-2\sin 4\theta \sin \theta$ **d.** $2\cos 4\theta \sin 2\theta$

13. Without drawing the graphs, explain how the graph of each of the following differs from the graph of $\{(x, y) \mid y = \sin x\}$.

   a. $\{(x, y) \mid y = -\sin x\}$

   b. $\{(x, y) \mid y = 2\sin x\}$

   c. $\{(x, y) \mid y = 2 + \sin x\}$

   d. $\{(x, y) \mid y = \sin 2x\}$

   e. $\{(x, y) \mid y = \sin (x + 2)\}$

   f. $\{(x, y) \mid y = |\sin x|\}$

14. Sketch the graphs of each of the following sets.

   a. $\{(x, y) \mid y = -\frac{1}{2}\sin x\}$

   b. $\{(x, y) \mid y = \cos \frac{1}{3}x\}$

   c. $\{(x, y) \mid y = 1 + 2\sin 3x\}$

   d. $\left\{(x, y) \mid y = \frac{1}{2}\cos\left(3x + \frac{\pi}{2}\right)\right\}$

   e. $\{(x, y) \mid y = 2\tan x\}$

   f. $\{(x, y) \mid y = \tan 3x\}$

15. Without sketching the graph, state the amplitude, the period, and the phase shift of each of the following functions.

   a. $\left\{(x, y) \mid y = \cos\left(x + \frac{\pi}{3}\right)\right\}$

   b. $\{(x, y) \mid y = 2\cos 4x\}$

   c. $\{(x, y) \mid y = 2\sin (3x + \pi)\}$

   d. $\{(x, y) \mid y = 1 + \frac{1}{2}\sin x\}$

16. Find the set of positive real numbers less than 2π which are members of each of the following:

   a. tangent^{-1} 1

   b. arc sine $\dfrac{\sqrt{3}}{2}$

   c. cosine$^{-1}\left(-\frac{1}{2}\right)$

   d. arc cosine $\left(-\dfrac{\sqrt{3}}{2}\right)$

   e. sine$^{-1}\left(-\frac{1}{2}\right)$

   f. arc tangent (0.1051)

17. Evaluate:

   a. $\sin (\text{arc tan } \sqrt{3})$

   b. $\cos [\text{arc tan } (-1)]$

   c. $\tan (\sin^{-1} 0)$

   d. $\cos\left[\sin^{-1}\left(-\dfrac{\sqrt{2}}{2}\right)\right]$

   e. $\cos (\text{arc Sin } \frac{1}{2} + \text{arc Cos } \frac{1}{2})$

   f. $\sin\left(\text{Sin}^{-1}\dfrac{\sqrt{2}}{2} + \text{Cos}^{-1}\dfrac{\sqrt{3}}{2}\right)$

18. State the domain and range of each of the following:

   a. arc sine relation

   b. arc Sine function

   c. cosine^{-1} relation

   d. Cosine^{-1} function

   e. tangent^{-1} relation

   f. Tangent^{-1} function

19. Show that each of the following statements is an identity.

    a. $\tan^2 x + \sec^2 x = 2 \sec^2 x - 1$ **b.** $2 \sin 2 x \cos x - \sin x = \sin 3 x$

20. Show that each of the following statements is true.

    a. $\text{Sin}^{-1} 0 + \text{Cos}^{-1} 0 = \dfrac{\pi}{2}$ **b.** $\text{Sin}^{-1} 1 = \dfrac{\pi}{4} + \text{Tan}^{-1} 1$

21. Find the solution set and the set of primary solutions for each of the following equations.

    a. $\sin^2 x - \cos^2 x - \cos x = 1$ **c.** $\tan x + \tan 2 x - \tan 3 x = 0$

    b. $\sin 2 x - 2 \sin x + \cos x - 1 = 0$

22. Sketch the graph of the function defined by each of the following equations.

    a. $y = 2 \csc x$ **b.** $y = \sec \dfrac{x}{2}$ **c.** $y = \cot 3 x$ **d.** $y = - \tan x$

23. Sketch the graph of each of the following:

    a. $\{(x, y) \mid y = \text{Cos}^{-1} 2 x\}$ **b.** $\{(x, y) \mid y = \text{arc Sin } \tfrac{1}{2} x\}$

24. Find the real number represented by each of the following:

    a. $\text{arc Tan } \dfrac{\sqrt{3}}{3}$ **b.** $\text{arc Cot } (-1)$ **c.** $\text{Sin}^{-1} \dfrac{\sqrt{3}}{2}$ **d.** $\text{arc Cos } \tfrac{1}{2}$

CHAPTER TEST

1. Prove that $\cos^2 x + \cos^2 x \tan^2 x = 1$ is an identity.

2. Find the set of primary solutions for $\tan x = \sin x \cos x$.

3. State the amplitude, the period, and the phase shift of $\{(x, y) \mid y = 2 \sin (3 x + \pi)\}$.

4. Complete: $\sin (\alpha + \beta) =$

5. If x represents the measure in radians of an angle in the second quadrant and $\sin \angle x = \dfrac{\sqrt{2}}{2}$, y represents the measure in radians of an angle in the third quadrant, and $\tan \angle y = 2$, find $\cos (\angle x + \angle y)$.

6. Which of the following statements is an identity?

    a. $\tan 2\theta = \dfrac{2 \tan \theta}{\tan^2 \theta - 1}$ **b.** $\tan 2\theta = \dfrac{2 \tan \theta}{1 - \tan^2 \theta}$ **c.** $\tan 2\theta = \sec^2 2\theta - 1$

7. Sketch the graph of $\{(x, y) \mid y = \text{Sin}^{-1} x\}$.

8. Evaluate $\tan [\text{arc Sin } (-\tfrac{1}{2})]$.

9. Sketch the graph of $\left\{(x, y) \mid y = 2 \sin \left(2 x + \dfrac{\pi}{2}\right)\right\}$.

10. Find the real number that is represented by $\sin (\text{arc Cot } \sqrt{3})$.

Complex Numbers

Complex Numbers

A number system E_s consists of a set of numbers E and two binary operations, usually addition and multiplication, defined on E so that E is closed with respect to each operation and at least the commutative, associative, and distributive properties hold.

B_s is an *extension* of A_s if and only if $A \subset B$, and the operations of addition and multiplication are defined so that the properties which are valid in A_s are valid in B_s. Also, if D_s and G_s are each extensions of A_s, then D_s is simpler than G_s if and only if $D \subset G$. B_s is the *simplest extension* of A_s when B_s has a given property not in A_s if and only if B is a proper subset of the set of elements of every other extension of A_s having that property. Thus I_s is the *simplest extension* of W_s which provides a solution for all equations of the form $x + a = 0$ where $a \in W$, and Q_s is the simplest extension of I_s which provides a solution for all equations of the form $ax = b$ where a, $b \in I$ and $a \neq 0$.

Let R_s represent the number system which consists of R, the set of real numbers, and the operations of addition and multiplication defined so that the eleven field properties are valid. (See page 22.) Although we have been working entirely within R_s, from time to time we have found equations which have no solution in R. It is the purpose of this chapter to provide an extension of R_s which will provide solutions for such equations.

The equation $x^2 + 1 = 0$ has no solution in R because it is a quadratic equation of the form $ax^2 + bx + c = 0$ whose discriminant is a negative number, namely -4. To find a solution for this equation we must extend the number system R_s so as to create a new number system which will include numbers other than the real numbers. However, we obviously want the elements of R to be among the numbers of the new system and we want the properties of the new system to be consistent with the properties of R_s. Moreover, for the sake of simplicity, we want the new system to include only the numbers and properties needed. In other words, we want the new system to be the simplest extension of R_s which will provide a solution of the equation $x^2 + 1 = 0$. Let us call the new system the system of *complex numbers* and denote it by Z_s.

In order for Z_s to be an *extension* of R_s the following statements must be true:

(1) Z must be a superset of R; that is, it must be true that $R \subset Z$.

(2) The properties pertaining to addition and multiplication that are valid in R_s must be valid in Z_s. (See properties **Z–2** through **Z–9** which follow.)

In addition we also want the following statements to be true:

(3) Z contains a solution of the equation $x^2 + 1 = 0$. (See property **Z–10** below.)

(4) Z_s must be the simplest extension of R_s that contains a solution to the equation $x^2 + 1 = 0$. (See property **Z–11**, page 592.)

We list ten of the properties of Z_s:

Z–1 Every real number is a member of Z.

Z–2 Two operations, addition (+) and multiplication (·), are defined in Z_s, and Z is closed with respect to each operation.

Z–3 Addition in Z_s is associative and commutative. The sum of two or more real numbers in Z is the same as their sum in R.

Z–4 Multiplication in Z_s is associative and commutative. The product of two or more real numbers in Z is the same as their product in R.

Z–5 Z possesses a unique additive identity which is the real number 0. Thus if $z \in Z$, then $z + 0 = z$.

Z–6 Z possesses a unique multiplicative identity which is the real number 1. Thus if $z \in Z$, then $z \cdot 1 = z$.

Z–7 Each element z in Z has an additive inverse $-z$ in Z such that $z + (-z) = 0$.

Z–8 Each element z in Z, $z \neq 0$, has a multiplicative inverse $\frac{1}{z}$ in Z such that $z \cdot \frac{1}{z} = 1$.

Z–9 Multiplication is distributive with respect to addition.

Z–10 The set Z contains a unique element i which has the property $i \cdot i = i^2 = -1$. We call the element i the *imaginary unit*. We shall use $\sqrt{-1}$ as another name for i.

The reflexive property of equality, $z = z$, is valid in Z. Moreover, when we write $z_1 = z_2$; $z_1, z_2 \in Z$, we mean that z_1 and z_2 name the same complex number. It follows that z_1 may be substituted for z_2 in any statement without changing the truth or falsity of the statement. Thus, both the reflexive and substitution properties of equality are valid in Z. Since the symmetric transitive, addition, and multiplication properties of equality are derived from the reflexive and substitution properties of equality (see page 103), it follows that all six properties of equality are valid in Z.

Since all of the eleven field properties are valid in Z_s, it follows that all theorems whose proofs depend upon these properties are valid in Z_s. This means that the theorems presented in Chapter 2 are valid when each R is replaced with a Z. We are therefore entitled to use these theorems in our proofs. For review purposes we shall occasionally prove some of them for elements in Z.

Observe that **Z–10** implies that Z contains at least one element which is not in the set of real numbers because there is no real number whose square is -1. Hence, R is a proper subset of Z; that is, $R \subset Z$.

Since Z is closed with respect to the operations of addition and multiplication, we can prove that:

Every number of the form $a + bi$ when $a, b \in R$ is in Z. The proof of this statement follows:

$$
\left.
\begin{array}{l}
\begin{array}{l}
(1) \\
i \in Z
\end{array} \\
\begin{array}{l}
(2)\quad(3) \\
b \in R \longrightarrow b \in Z
\end{array}
\end{array}
\right\}
\begin{array}{l}
(4) \\
\longrightarrow bi \in Z
\end{array}
$$

Reasons: (1) **Z–10**, (2) Given, (3) **Z–1**, (4) **Z–2** (Z is closed with respect to multiplication), (5) **Z–2** (Z is closed with respect to addition).

It is noteworthy that the number i can be written in the form $a + bi$. We have $i = 0 + 1 \cdot i$. Also, any real number a can be written in the form $a + 0 \cdot i$ because $0 \cdot i = 0$. The proof that $z \in Z \longrightarrow z \cdot 0 = 0$ is shown at the end of this section. (See Theorem 1-11.)

We have just established that all numbers of the form $a + bi$ when $a, b \in R$ and i is the imaginary unit are members of Z. If we represent this set of numbers by T, or $\{z \mid z = a + bi;\ a, b \in R\}$, then we know that $T \subseteq Z$.

As we proceed in this chapter we shall see that T is closed with respect to addition and multiplication. Indeed we shall find that:

(a) All of the properties of Z_s are valid in T_s.
   This means that T_s is an extension of R_s.
(b) T_s is the *simplest extension* of R_s which contains a solution of $x^2 + 1 = 0$.
   (See Example 4, page 593.)

This means that T contains all the numbers required by properties **Z–1** through **Z–10** and no others. However, by (4), page 590, we know that Z_s is required to be the simplest extension of R_s that contains a solution for $x^2 + 1 = 0$. Thus, Z must also be the set that contains all the numbers required by **Z–1** through **Z–10**, and no others. Therefore $Z = T$.

Accordingly we state the following property:

▶ **Z–11** $Z = \{z \mid z = a + bi;\ a, b \in R, i = \sqrt{-1}\}$

We may express **Z–11** in an equivalent form by writing:

$$z = a + bi \text{ when } a, b \in R \text{ and } i = \sqrt{-1} \longleftrightarrow z \in Z$$

From **Z–11** we see that the subset of Z obtained by letting $b = 0$ is the set of real numbers R. The subset of Z obtained by letting $a = 0$ contains numbers such as $3\,i,\ -7\,i,\ i\sqrt{3},\ -\pi i,\ 0\,i$, and so on. These numbers are called *pure imaginaries* and we shall use the symbol P_i to denote this set of numbers. Note that $R \cap P_i = \{0\}$. Note also that $(R \cup P_i) \subset Z$ because $Z \smallsmile (R \cup P_i)$ contains numbers such as $3 + 7\,i$, that is, numbers of the form $a + bi$ where $ab \neq 0$. The diagram at the right depicts the relationship $C \subset W \subset I \subset Q \subset R \subset Z$.

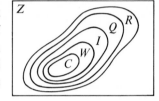

We now present the proof of the following theorem:

▶ **Theorem 1–11.** If $z \in Z$, then $z \cdot 0 = 0$.

Proof of Theorem 1–11: If $z \in Z$, then $z \cdot 0 = 0$.

$$
\begin{array}{l}
\overset{(1)}{1 \in Z} \overset{(2)}{\longrightarrow} 1 + 0 = 1 \\
\hspace{1.2cm} \overset{(3)}{z \in Z}
\end{array}
\left.
\begin{array}{l}
\\
\\
\end{array}
\right\}
\overset{(4)}{\longrightarrow} z(1 + 0) = z \cdot 1 \overset{(5)}{\longrightarrow} z \cdot 1 + z \cdot 0 = z \cdot 1 \overset{(6)}{\mathbf{\not\longrightarrow}}
$$

$$
\overset{(6)}{\mathbf{\not\longrightarrow}}\, z + z \cdot 0 = z \overset{(7)}{\longrightarrow} z \cdot 0 = 0
$$

Reasons: (1) Existence of multiplicative identity in Z, (2) Addition Property of zero, (3) Given, (4) Multiplication property of equality, (5) Distributive property, (6) Multiplication property of one, (7) Uniqueness of the additive identity.

Note that this proof is exactly the same as that given for Theorem 2–2.

From Theorem 1–11 it follows that $0 + 0\,i = 0$. Thus we have the following corollary:

    Corollary to Theorem 1–11. If $a, b \in R$, $a = 0$, $b = 0$, and i is the imaginary unit, then $a + bi = 0$.

Example 1.   Write each of the following complex numbers in the form $a + bi$ when $a, b \in R$ and i is the imaginary unit.

        a. 5   **b.** $-7\,i$ **c.** i^2

Solutions.   **a.** $5 = 5 + 0\,i$ **b.** $-7\,i = 0 + (-7)i$ **c.** $i^2 = -1 = -1 + 0\,i$

Example 2. If E is the set of non-negative even integers $\{0, 2, 4, \cdots\}$ and F is the set of negative even integers $\{\cdots, -4, -2\}$, then $E \cup F = G = \{\cdots, -4, -2, 0, 2, 4, \cdots\}$. Is E_s simpler than G_s?

Solution. Yes. We see that $E \subset G$ and all the properties of addition and multiplication that are valid in E_s are also valid in G_s. Therefore G_s is an extension of E_s. This is equivalent to saying that E_s is simpler than G_s.

Example 3. If an equation does not have a solution in a given number system, is it always possible to extend the given number system to obtain a new number system in which the equation will have a solution?

Solution. No. An equation which does not have a solution in a given number system may not have a solution in any extension of this number system. For example, the equation $x + 1 = x$, which has no solution in W_s, has no solution in any number system which is an extension of W_s.

Example 4. Prove the following implication: If T_s is an extension of R_s, then it is the simplest extension of R_s that contains a solution of $x^2 + 1 = 0$.

Solution. Let T_s' be any extension of R_s which contains a solution of $x^2 + 1 = 0$. Then T' contains all real numbers and i, and is closed with respect to addition and multiplication. Therefore, T' contains all numbers which can be expressed in the form $a + bi$ when a and b are real numbers. This means that $T \subseteq T'$ because every member of T is a member of T'. Since T_s is an extension of R_s and T is a subset of any set T' such that T_s' is an extension of R_s which contains a solution of $x^2 + 1 = 0$, and since T contains a solution of $x^2 + 1 = 0$, we see that T_s is the simplest extension of R_s that contains a solution to this equation.

Ⓐ EXERCISES

1. None of the following equations can be solved within the domain mentioned. In each case, replace the name of the given domain with the name of the set of numbers of the simplest extension of the indicated number system in which a solution can be found.

a. $3\,x = 4$; $x \in I$ **c.** $x^2 = 5$; $x \in Q$ **e.** $x + 1 = 1$; $x \in C$

b. $x + 4 = 1$; $x \in W$ **d.** $x^2 = -2$; $x \in R$ **f.** $x^2 + 4 = 0$; $x \in I$

2. **a.** Subtraction is not always possible within W_s. Name the simplest extension of W_s within which subtraction is always possible.

   b. What is the simplest extension of Q_s in which the square root of every rational number is in the set of numbers of this simplest extension?

3. If a, b, $c \in R$, then each of the following equations has a solution in R. Name the simplest extension of C_s in which each equation has a solution when a, b, and c are in that simplest extension.

   a. $a + y = b$ \qquad **b.** $ay = b$; $a \neq 0$ \qquad **c.** $ay + b = c$; $a \neq 0$

4. Write each of the following in $a + bi$ form when a, $b \in R$.

   a. 2 \qquad **c.** -6 \qquad **e.** $\sqrt{6}$ \qquad **g.** $-i$

   b. $3i$ \qquad **d.** $-2i$ \qquad **f.** $\frac{2}{3}$ \qquad **h.** 0

5. Indicate whether each of the following complex numbers is a real number, a pure imaginary number, or neither.

   a. $3i$ \qquad **d.** $5\sqrt{-1}$ \qquad **g.** $\frac{3}{4}$ \qquad **j.** $a + bi$; $a = 0$, $b \in R$, $b \neq 0$

   b. $3 + i$ \qquad **e.** $6 + 5i$ \qquad **h.** $-2i$ \qquad **k.** $a + bi$; $a \in R$, $a \neq 0$, $b = 0$

   c. 4 \qquad **f.** $4 + \sqrt{3}$ \qquad **i.** $\sqrt{6}$ \qquad **l.** $a + bi$; a, $b \in R$, $a \neq 0$, $b \neq 0$

B EXERCISES

6. Given that $S = \{x \mid x = c + d\sqrt{2}; c, d \in Q\}$. Prove that S is closed with respect to multiplication.

7. Given that $S = \{x \mid x = c + d\sqrt{2}; c, d \in Q\}$. Prove each of the following statements.

   a. Each number in S has a unique additive inverse in S.

   b. Each number in S, other than 0, has a unique multiplicative inverse in S.

   c. S contains an additive identity.

   d. S contains a multiplicative identity.

   e. S_s is an extension of Q_s.

   f. S_s is the simplest extension of Q_s which contains a solution for the equation $(bx - a)^2 = 2$ where a, $b \in Q$ and $b \neq 0$.

Addition, Multiplication, and Subtraction in Z

We now use the Z properties to establish the rules for computing with complex numbers. In this section we develop formulas for finding the *sum*, *product*, and *difference* of two complex numbers. The division of complex numbers is considered on page 602.

First, we develop a simple formula for adding $a + bi$ and $c + di$ when a, b, c, and d are in R. We have: $(a + bi) + (c + di) = (a + c) + (bi + di)$

because property **Z-3** assures us that addition is associative and commutative in Z. Property **Z-9** tells us that multiplication is distributive with respect to addition. Thus $bi + di = (b + d)i$. Hence $(a + bi) + (c + di) = (a + c) + (b + d)i$ and we have:

▶ **Theorem 2–11.** If $a, b, c, d \in R$ and i is the imaginary unit, then $(a + bi) + (c + di) = (a + c) + (b + d)i$.

Now consider the indicated product $(a + bi)(c + di)$ when $a, b, c, d \in R$. We use the distributive property to obtain $(a + bi)(c + di) = a(c + di) + bi(c + di)$. Again using the distributive property and the commutative property of multiplication, we have: $(a + bi)(c + di) = ac + adi + bci + bdi^2$. According to **Z-10**, $i^2 = -1$ and we have: $(a + bi)(c + di) = ac + adi + bci - bd$. Using the commutative property of addition and again using the distributive property, we have: $(a + bi)(c + di) = (ac - bd) + (ad + bc)i$. This completes the proof of the following theorem:

▶ **Theorem 3–11.** If $a, b, c, d \in R$ and i is the imaginary unit, then $(a + bi)(c + di) = (ac - bd) + (ad + bc)i$.

We also have the following:

Corollary to Theorem 3–11. If $a, b \in R$ and i is the imaginary unit, then $(a + bi)(a - bi) = a^2 + b^2$.

In performing addition and multiplication in Z, we do not try to remember the expressions for the sum and product of two complex numbers as stated in Theorems 2–11 and 3–11, respectively. Instead, we perform the operations by direct applications of the Z properties involved.

Example 1. Express the sum of $7 + 3i$ and $8 + 11i$ in the form $a + bi$ when a and b are real numbers.

Solution. $(7 + 3i) + (8 + 11i) = (7 + 8) + (3i + 11i) = (7 + 8) + (3 + 11)i = 15 + 14i$.

Example 2. Express the product of $3 + 5i$ and $2 - 7i$ in the form $a + bi$ when a and b are real numbers.

Solution.
$$(3 + 5i)(2 - 7i) = 3(2 - 7i) + 5i(2 - 7i)$$
$$= 6 - 21i + 10i - 35i^2$$
$$= 6 - 21i + 10i - 35(-1)$$
$$= 6 - 21i + 10i + 35$$
$$= (6 + 35) + (-21 + 10)i$$
$$= 41 - 11i.$$

This result agrees with that obtained if 3, 5, 2, and -7 are substituted for $a, b, c,$ and d, respectively, in the right member of the equation in Theorem 3–11.

Next we consider subtraction. Property **Z–7** assures us that every element z in Z has an additive inverse in Z that we denote by the symbol $-z$. That is, $z + (-z) = 0$. Theorem 8–2, which we know to be valid in Z_s, tells us that this additive inverse is unique. Just as in Chapter 1, we define $z_2 - z_1$ as the number which added to z_1 gives z_2. Accordingly,

$$z_2 = (z_2 - z_1) + z_1$$
$$z_2 + (-z_1) = [(z_2 - z_1) + z_1] + (-z_1)$$
$$z_2 + (-z_1) = (z_2 - z_1) + [z_1 + (-z_1)]$$
$$z_2 + (-z_1) = (z_2 - z_1) + 0$$
$$z_2 + (-z_1) = z_2 - z_1$$

Thus we have established that for z_1, $z_2 \in Z$, $z_2 - z_1 = z_2 + (-z_1)$, and we have done so by the same method we used to prove Theorem 9–2, which is the corresponding theorem for real numbers.

We now find $-z$ when $z = a + bi$ and a, $b \in R$. We know by **Z–7** that $-z$ is in Z and therefore we can write $-z = x + yi$ when x, $y \in R$. Since $z + (-z) = 0$, we have: $(a + bi) + (x + yi) = 0$. By Theorem 2–11 this becomes $(a + x) + (b + y)i = 0 = 0 + 0\,i$. The equation $(a + bi) + (x + yi) = 0$ is satisfied if $x = -a$ and $y = -b$. Therefore $(-a) + (-b)i$ is an additive inverse of $a + bi$. Since each number in Z has exactly one additive inverse, we have established the following theorem:

▶ **Theorem 4–11.** If $z = a + bi$, a, $b \in R$, and i is the imaginary unit, then $-z = (-a) + (-b)i$.

Now it is easy to prove the following theorem:

▶ **Theorem 5–11.** If $z_1 = a_1 + b_1 i$, $z_2 = a_2 + b_2 i$, a_1, b_1, a_2, $b_2 \in R$, and i is the imaginary unit, then $z_2 - z_1 = (a_2 - a_1) + (b_2 - b_1)i$.

The proof of Theorem 5–11 is left as an exercise.

Example 3. Express $(7 + 3\,i) - (5 + 11\,i)$ in the form $a + bi$ when a and b are real numbers.

Solution.
$$(7 + 3\,i) - (5 + 11\,i) = (7 - 5) + (3 - 11)\,i$$
$$= 2 - 8\,i$$

Example 4. If $z_1 = 3 + 7\,i$, $z_2 = 5 - 3\,i$, and $z_3 = 11 - 5\,i$, express $z_3 - z_1 \cdot z_2$ in the form $a + bi$ when a and b are real numbers.

Solution.
$$z_1 \cdot z_2 = (3 + 7\,i)(5 - 3\,i)$$
$$= (3 + 7\,i)5 + (3 + 7\,i)(-3\,i)$$
$$= 15 + 35\,i - 9\,i + 21$$
$$= 36 + 26\,i$$
$$\therefore z_3 - z_1 \cdot z_2 = (11 - 5\,i) - (36 + 26\,i) = -25 - 31\,i$$

1. Express each of the following sums and differences in the form $a + bi$ when $a, b \in R$.

   a. $(1 + 3\,i) + (2 + 4\,i)$

   b. $(5 + i) + (1 + 2\,i)$

   c. $(2 - 3\,i) + (1 + 6\,i)$

   d. $(0 + i) + (4 + 2\,i)$

   e. $i + (3 + 5\,i)$

   f. $(1 - 4\,i) - (5 + 2\,i)$

   g. $(3 + 7\,i) - (1 - 9\,i)$

   h. $(5 - 2\,i) + (-5 - 2\,i)$

   i. $(\sqrt{6} + \sqrt{-1}) + (3\sqrt{6} + \sqrt{-1})$

   j. $3\,i + \sqrt{5}\,i$

   k. $(\frac{2}{3} + \frac{1}{4}\,i) - (\frac{5}{6} - \frac{1}{2}\,i)$

   l. $2 + (3 + 6\,i)$

2. Given that $a, b, c, \cdots \in R$, we have defined the sum of three or more real numbers as follows: $a + b + c = (a + b) + c$, $a + b + c + d = (a + b + c) + d$, and so on. If we are to preserve this definition for the real numbers within the set of complex numbers, how should we define each of the following?

   a. $(a + bi) + (c + di) + (e + fi)$ when $a, b, c, d, e, f \in R$

   b. $(a + bi) + (c + di) + (e + fi) + (g + hi)$ when $a, b, c, d, e, f, g, h \in R$

3. Use the definitions that you have written in Ex. 2 to express each of the following in the form $a + bi$ when $a, b \in R$.

   a. $(3 + 2\,i) + (4 + 7\,i) + (1 + 3\,i)$

   b. $(4 - i) + (2 - 6\,i) + (7 + i)$

   c. $(3 + 2\,i) + (i) + (2\,i) + (-6 + 4\,i)$

   d. $7 + (3 + 6\,i) - (4 + 5\,i) - (-2 + i)$

   e. $(\sqrt{2} + i) + (3\sqrt{2} - i) + (2\sqrt{2}) + (6 + i)$

   f. $(u + vi) - (x + yi) + (t + si);\ u, v, x, y, s, t \in R$

4. Replace each question mark by a number of the form $a + bi$ when $a, b \in R$ to make the following statements true.

   a. $(3 + 2\,i) + \_?\_ = 0$

   b. $(-2 + 7\,i) + \_?\_ = 0$

   c. $(4 + i) + 0 = \_?\_$

   d. $(x + yi) + \_?\_ = 0;\ x, y \in R$

   e. $(u + vi) + 0 = \_?\_;\ u, v \in R$

   f. $(a + bi) + (-a - bi) = \_?\_$

5. Replace each question mark with a number of the form $a + bi$ when $a, b \in R$ to make the following statements true.

   a. $(6 + 5\,i) + \_?\_ = (4 - 2\,i)$

   b. $(8 + 3\,i) - \_?\_ = (7 + 0\,i)$

   c. $5\,i - \_?\_ = 4 + 2\,i$

   d. $(3 + 2\,i) + (6 - i) + \_?\_ = (5 + 3\,i)$

6. Express each of the following products in the form $a + bi$ when $a, b \in R$.

   a. $(2 + 3\,i)(3 + i)$

   b. $(1 - 5\,i)(1 - 2\,i)$

   c. $(4 + 7\,i)(-3 + 2\,i)$

   d. $(6 + 2\,i)^2$

   e. $(2 - i)(2 + i)$

   f. $(4 + 3\,i)(4 - 3\,i)$

g. $i(8-3\,i)$

h. $\sqrt{7}(\sqrt{7}+2\,i)$

i. $-6\,i\cdot3\,i$

j. $(a+bi)(c-di);\ a,b,c,d\in R$

k. $(x+yi)(ax-ayi);\ a,x,y\in R$

l. $(a+bi)(a+b);\ a,b\in R$

7. Recalling our definition for the product of three or more real numbers:

   a. How should we define $(a+bi)(c+di)(e+fi)$ when $a,\ b,\ c,\ d,\ e,\ f\in R$?

   b. How should we define $(a+bi)(c+di)(e+fi)(g+hi)$ when $a,\ b,\ c,\ d,\ e,\ f,\ g,$ $h\in R$?

8. Express each of the following products in the form $a+bi$ when $a,\ b\in R$.

   a. $2(2+3\,i)(2-3\,i)$

   b. $(4+6\,i)(3+2\,i)(i)$

   c. $(3+2\,i)^3$

   d. $(2-5\,i)(2+5\,i)^2$

   e. $(2+i)^2(-2+i)^2$

   f. $(a+bi)^4;\ a,b\in R$

9. Express each of the following in the form $a+bi$ when $a,\ b\in R$.

   a. i^2

   b. i^3

   c. i^4

   d. i^5

   e. i^6

   f. i^7

   g. i^8

   h. i^{19}

   i. $i^{4n};\ n\in C$

   j. $i^{4n+1};\ n\in C$

   k. $i^{4n+2};\ n\in C$

   l. $i^{4n+3};\ n\in C$

10. Show that $2+3\,i$ is a member of the solution set for the equation $x^2-5\,x+9+(-2\,x+7)i=0$

11. The following theorems are a few of those stated for real numbers in Chapter 2. State the corresponding theorems for complex numbers.

   a. Theorem 1–2. If $a\in R$ and $a\neq0$, then a has only one multiplicative inverse.

   b. Theorem 3–2: If $a,\ b\in R$ and $ab=0$, then $a=0$ or $b=0$.

   c. Theorem 11-2: If $a,\ b\in R$, then $(-a)b=-(ab)$.

   d. Theorem 12–2: If $a,\ b\in R$, then $(-a)(-b)=ab$.

Ⓑ EXERCISES

12. Write a proof for the theorem you stated in Ex. 11, part **a**.

13. Prove Theorem 5–11: If $z_1=a_1+b_1i$ and $z_2=a_2+b_2i$ when $a_1,\ b_1,\ a_2,\ b_2\in R$, then $z_2-z_1=(a_2-a_1)+(b_2-b_1)i$.

Standard Form of a Complex Number

According to the Corollary to Theorem 1–11: If $a,\ b\in R$, $a=0$, $b=0$, and i is the imaginary unit, then $a+bi=0$. Consider the following converse of this corollary: If $a,\ b\in R$, $a+bi=0$, and i is the imaginary unit, then $a=0$ and $b=0$. We can build a deductive sequence from the hypothesis to the conclusion as follows:

$$\left.\begin{matrix} \overset{(1)}{a+bi=0} \\ a,\,b\,\epsilon\,R \\ i \text{ is the imaginary unit} \end{matrix}\right\} \xrightarrow{(2)} a=-bi \xrightarrow{(3)} a^2=(-bi)^2 \overset{(4)}{\nrightarrow}$$

$$\left.\overset{(4)}{\nleftrightarrow} \begin{matrix} a^2=(-b)^2 i^2 \\ \overset{(5)}{i^2=-1} \end{matrix}\right\} \xrightarrow{(6)} a^2=b^2\cdot(-1) \xrightarrow{(7)} a^2=-b^2 \xrightarrow{(8)} a^2+b^2=0 \overset{(9)}{\nrightarrow}$$

$$\overset{(9)}{\nleftrightarrow} a=0 \wedge b=0$$

Reasons: (1) Given, (2) **Z–2, Z–7**, and Theorem 8–2, (3) $z_1=z_2 \longrightarrow z_1{}^2 = z_2{}^2$, Theorem 2–3 (valid for $a,\,b\,\epsilon\,Z$), (4) Multiplication is commutative and associative in Z_s, (5) **Z–10**, (6) Substitution property of equality, (7) Theorem 10–2, $(-1)z=-z$, (8) Addition property of equality, (9) $(a,\,b\,\epsilon\,R\,\wedge\,a^2+b^2=0) \longleftrightarrow a=0 \wedge b=0$.

The above proof and the corollary to Theorem 1–11 establish the following theorem:

▷ **Theorem 6–11.** If $a,\,b\,\epsilon\,R$ and i is the imaginary unit, then $a+bi=0 \longleftrightarrow a=0 \wedge b=0$.

Now we can prove the following important corollary:

Corollary to Theorem 6–11. If a, b, c, $d\,\epsilon\,R$ and i is the imaginary unit, then $a+bi=c+di \longleftrightarrow a=c \wedge b=d$.

Proof of Corollary to Theorem 6–11: If $a,\,b,\,c,\,d\,\epsilon\,R$ and i is the imaginary unit, then $a+bi=c+di \longleftrightarrow a=c \wedge b=d$.

If $a,\,b,\,c,\,d\,\epsilon\,R$ and i is the imaginary unit, then

$$a+bi=c+di \overset{(1)}{\longleftrightarrow}(a+bi)-(c+di)=0 \overset{(2)}{\longleftrightarrow}(a-c)+(b-d)i=0$$
$$\overset{(3)}{\longleftrightarrow}(a-c)=0 \wedge (b-d)=0 \overset{(4)}{\longleftrightarrow} a=c \wedge b=d.$$

You may supply the reasons.

The form $a+bi$ when $a,\,b\,\epsilon\,R$ and i is the imaginary unit is called the *standard form* of the complex number z. The corollary to Theorem 6–11 tells us that this form is unique; that is, given the complex number z, there is one and only one pair of real numbers a, b such that $z=a+bi$. We call the real number a the *real part* of $a+bi$ and we call the real number b the *imaginary part* of $a+bi$. Thus a complex number is a real number if and only if its imaginary part is zero. Complex numbers which are not real numbers are referred to as imaginary numbers. Also, a complex number is a *pure imaginary* number if and only if its real part is zero. Note particularly that *the imaginary part of $a + bi$ is the real number b* and not the pure imaginary number bi. Note also that zero is a pure imaginary but not an imaginary. The following table provides examples of complex numbers and their parts:

z	Real part of z	Imaginary part of z	Standard form of z
0	0	0	$0 + 0\,i$
$3 + 2\,i$	3	2	$3 + 2\,i$
$5 - i$	5	-1	$5 + (-1)\,i$ or $5 - i$
i	0	1	$0 + 1\,i$
i^3	0	-1	$0 + (-1)\,i$ or $0 - i$

Example 1. Find all pairs of real numbers x, y for which
$3\,x + 5\,yi = 6 + 30\,i$.

Solution. According to the corollary to Theorem 6–11,
$3\,x + 5\,yi = 6 + 30\,i \longleftrightarrow 3\,x = 6 \wedge 5\,y = 30$. Thus $x = 2$ and $y = 6$, and these are the only real numbers for which $3\,x + 5\,yi = 6 + 30\,i$.

Example 2. Find all pairs of complex numbers x, y for which
$3\,x + 5\,yi = 6 + 30\,i$.

Solution. Since x and y are complex numbers, we can write $x = a + bi$ when $a, b \in R$, and $y = c + di$ when $c, d \in R$. Substituting in $3\,x + 5\,yi = 6 + 30\,i$, we obtain:

$$3(a + bi) + 5(c + di)i = 6 + 30\,i, \text{ or}$$
$$(3\,a - 5\,d) + (3\,b + 5\,c)i = 6 + 30\,i$$

Since $3\,a - 5\,d$ and $3\,b + 5\,c$ are real numbers, it follows from the corollary to Theorem 6–11 that the last equation is true if and only if:

$$3\,a - 5\,d = 6 \wedge 3\,b + 5\,c = 30, \text{ or}$$
$$d = \frac{3\,a - 6}{5} \wedge c = \frac{30 - 3\,b}{5}.$$

We are now free to assign a and b any real values. Thus, all pairs of complex numbers which satisfy the equation $3\,x + 5\,yi = 6 + 30\,i$ are given by $x = a + bi$ and $y = \dfrac{30 - 3\,b}{5} + \dfrac{3\,a - 6}{5}\,i$. Therefore

$$\left\{ (x, y) \mid x = a + bi \wedge y = \frac{30 - 3\,b}{5} + \frac{3\,a - 6}{5}\,i;\ a, b \in R \right\}$$ is the

solution set of $3\,x + 5\,yi = 6 + 30\,i \wedge x, y \in Z$.

For example, if we let $a = -3$ and $b = 5$, we have $x = -3 + 5i$ and $y = 3 - 3i$. When we substitute these values for x and y in the given equation, we see that it is satisfied as follows:

$$3(-3 + 5i) + 5i(3 - 3i) = -9 + 15i + 15i + 15 = 6 + 30i$$

Note that if $a = 2$ and $b = 0$, we obtain the real solutions we had in Example 1.

A **EXERCISES**

1. Indicate the real part and the imaginary part of each of the following numbers. Note that any indicated operations must be performed before the decision is made.

a. $3 + 2i$ d. i^4 g. $m - 6i$; $m \in R$ j. $(\sqrt{5} + i)^2$

b. $4i + 5$ e. $6i$ h. $(2 + i)^2$ k. $(2 - i\sqrt{3})^2$

c. $(3 + 2i) - 4$ f. $\frac{3}{5}$ i. $5 + i^2$ l. $5 + (i\sqrt{2})^2$

2. For what value of a and of b is each of the following statements true when $a, b \in R$?

a. $a + bi = 2 - 3i$ f. $a + 1 + (2 + b)i = 4 + 10i$

b. $3a - bi = 12 + i$ g. $a + b + (a - b)i = 3 + 5i$

c. $a - 5bi = 11 - 15i$ h. $a - b - 2(a + b)i = 7 + 6i$

d. $4a - 3bi = 7 - 6i$ i. $(a + i)^2 = bi$

e. $a + 3 + bi = 5 - 6i$ j. $(a - i)^2 - bi = 0$

3. For each of the following, find three pairs of complex numbers x and y for which each statement is true.

a. $2x + 3yi = 16 + 2i$ c. $5x + 9yi = 33 + 35i$

b. $3x - 4yi = 7 - i$ d. $2x - yi = -11 - i$

B **EXERCISES**

4. The statements of the left-to-right part of an indirect proof of Theorem 6–11 and one of the reasons are given below. You are to supply the missing reasons. If $a, b \in R$ and i is the imaginary unit, then:

(1) $b = 0$ *or* $b \neq 0$ (1) Why?

(2) If $a + bi = 0$ and $b \neq 0$,   (2) Why?

then $i = -\dfrac{a}{b}$.

(3) "$i = -\dfrac{a}{b}$" is false.   (3) A real number cannot equal a nonzero pure imaginary number

(4) Hence $b = 0$ (4) Why?

(5) If $a + bi = 0$ and $b = 0$, then   (5) Why?

$a + bi = a + 0i = 0$.

(6) $0\,i = 0$ (6) Why?
(7) $a + 0 = 0$ (7) Why?
(8) $a = 0$ (8) Why?
(9) $\therefore$ If $a,\ b \epsilon R,\ i$ is the imaginary   (9) Why?
  unit, and $a + bi = 0$, then $a = 0 \wedge$
  $b = 0$.

5. In Theorem 2–11 we required that a, b, c, and d represent real numbers. Is the theorem true if a, b, c, and d represent complex numbers? Explain.

6. In Theorem 3–11 we required that a, b,/c, and d represent real numbers. Is the theorem true if a, b, c, and d represent complex numbers? Explain.

Division of Complex Numbers

We define division of complex numbers in terms of multiplication just as we defined division of real numbers in Chapter 1. Thus, if z_1 and z_2 are complex numbers and $z_2 \neq 0$, we define $z_1 \div z_2$, or $\dfrac{z_1}{z_2}$, as the complex number z_3 such that $z_1 = z_2 \cdot z_3$.

With this definition in effect, the following statements are readily proved (see exercises, page 605).

1. If z_1, $z_2 \epsilon Z$ and $z_2 \neq 0$, then $\dfrac{z_1}{z_2} = z_1 \cdot \dfrac{1}{z_2}$.

2. Each nonzero complex number has a unique multiplicative inverse.

3. If z_1, $z_2 \epsilon Z$ and $z_1 z_2 \neq 0$, then $\dfrac{1}{z_1} \cdot \dfrac{1}{z_2} = \dfrac{1}{z_1 z_2}$.

4. If z_1, z_2, z_3, $z_4 \epsilon Z$ and $z_2 z_4 \neq 0$, then $\dfrac{z_1}{z_2} \cdot \dfrac{z_3}{z_4} = \dfrac{z_1 z_3}{z_2 z_4}$.

5. If z_1, z_2, $z_3 \epsilon Z$ and $z_2 z_3 \neq 0$, then $\dfrac{z_1}{z_2} = \dfrac{z_1 z_3}{z_2 z_3}$.

6. If z_1, z_2, z_3, $z_4 \epsilon Z$ and $z_2 z_4 \neq 0$, then $\dfrac{z_1}{z_2} + \dfrac{z_3}{z_4} = \dfrac{z_1 z_4 + z_3 z_2}{z_2 z_4}$.

We may use statement **5** and the fact that the product of $c + di$ and $c - di$ is the real number $c^2 + d^2$ (Corollary to Theorem 3–11) to express $\dfrac{a + bi}{c + di}$ in standard form as follows:

$$\frac{a + bi}{c + di} = \frac{(a + bi)(c - di)}{(c + di)(c - di)} = \frac{ac + bd}{c^2 + d^2} + \frac{bc - ad}{c^2 + d^2}\,i.$$

The correctness of the statement $\dfrac{a + bi}{c + di} = \dfrac{ac + bd}{c^2 + d^2} + \dfrac{bc - ad}{c^2 + d^2}\,i$ can be verified by showing that $a + bi = (c + di)\left(\dfrac{ac + bd}{c^2 + d^2} + \dfrac{(bc - ad)}{c^2 + d^2}\,i\right).$

Thus we have the following theorem:

▶ **Theorem 7–11.** If $a, b, c, d \in R$ and $c^2 + d^2 \neq 0$, then $\dfrac{a+bi}{c+di} =$
$\dfrac{ac+bd}{c^2+d^2} + \dfrac{bc-ad}{c^2+d^2} i$.

The general formula for finding the standard form of $\dfrac{a+bi}{c+di}$ given in Theorem 7–11 is somewhat difficult to remember. In practice, it is better to use the procedure which we used in proving the theorem. This procedure is illustrated in Example 1.

Example 1. Write $\dfrac{3-7\,i}{4+5\,i}$ in standard form.

Solution.
$$\frac{3-7\,i}{4+5\,i} = \frac{(3-7\,i)(4-5\,i)}{(4+5\,i)(4-5\,i)} = \frac{12-35}{41} + \frac{-28-15}{41}\,i$$
$$= -\frac{23}{41} + \left(-\frac{43}{41}\right)i$$

Let us now consider the relationship between $a + bi$ and $a + (-b)i$. We adopt the following definition:

> If $a, b \in R$ and $z = a + bi$, then we call $a + (-b)i$ the complex conjugate of z and write $\bar{z} = \overline{a + bi} = a + (-b)i$.

Since $a + (-b)i = a - bi$, we may also write $\bar{z} = \overline{a + bi} = a - bi$. If z_1 is the conjugate of z_2, then z_2 is the conjugate of z_1, and z_1 and z_2 form a conjugate pair.

Clearly the conjugate of a conjugate of a complex number is the number itself. That is, if $z = a + bi$, then $\bar{\bar{z}} = \overline{\overline{a+bi}} = \overline{a - bi} = a + bi = z$.

Example 2. If $z_1 = 2 + 3\,i$ and $z_2 = -4 + 3\,i$, express each of the following in standard form.

    a. $\bar{z}_1$ **b.** $\bar{z}_2$ **c.** $\bar{z}_1 + \bar{z}_2$ **d.** $\overline{z_1 + z_2}$

Solution.
    a. $\bar{z}_1 = 2 - 3\,i = 2 + (-3)i$ **b.** $\bar{z}_2 = -4 - 3\,i = -4 + (-3)i$
    c. $\bar{z}_1 + \bar{z}_2 = (2 - 3\,i) + (-4 - 3\,i) = -2 - 6\,i$
    d. $z_1 + z_2 = -2 + 6\,i$. Hence $\overline{z_1 + z_2} = \overline{-2 + 6\,i} = -2 + (-6)i$.

Example 3. If $z_1, z_2 \in Z$ and $z_1 \neq 0$, prove that the equation $z_1 z = z_2$ has a unique solution.

Proof.   To prove that $z_1 \cdot z = z_2$ has a unique solution, we need show that $z_1 \cdot z = z_2$ has a solution and has exactly one solution.

We know that $z_1 \cdot z = z_2 \wedge z_1 \neq 0 \longleftrightarrow z = \dfrac{z_2}{z_1}$. Thus $z_1 \cdot z = z_2$ has a solution.

Now suppose that x and y are each solutions of the equation. Then $z_1 \cdot x = z_2$ and $z_1 \cdot y = z_2$. Hence, $z_1(x - y) = 0$. By Theorem 3–2 (which is valid in Z) this is true only if one or both factors are zero. Since $z_1 \neq 0$, $x - y = 0$, or $x = y$. Thus $z_1 \cdot z = z_2$ has a solution which is unique.

 EXERCISES

1. Name the complex number which has no multiplicative inverse.

2. Name the complex number which is its own multiplicative inverse.

3. Write the multiplicative inverse of each of the following complex numbers as a complex number in standard form.

a. 4   c. i e. $3 - 4i$ g. $(3 - 2i)^2$

b. 1   d. $2 + i$ f. $5 + i^2$ h. $-\frac{1}{2} - \frac{2}{3}i$

4. Express each of the following in standard form.

a. $\dfrac{1}{3+i}$

b. $\dfrac{2}{4-i}$

c. $\dfrac{4}{3i}$

d. $\dfrac{2+i}{1+i}$

e. $\dfrac{1+i}{3-i}$

f. $\dfrac{3-2i}{4+3i}$

g. $\dfrac{i}{4-3i}$

h. $\dfrac{2+7i}{6+5i}$

i. $\dfrac{7-3i}{i}$

j. $\dfrac{-6i}{3-2i}$

k. $\dfrac{1-\sqrt{2}i}{1+\sqrt{2}i}$

l. $\dfrac{\sqrt{5}+i}{\sqrt{5}-i}$

m. $\dfrac{\sqrt{3}+\sqrt{2}i}{1+\sqrt{3}i}$

n. $\dfrac{a-2bi}{a+bi}$; $a, b \in R$

o. $\dfrac{u+vi}{u-vi}$; $u, v \in R$

p. $\dfrac{-2c+3di}{-c+di}$; $c, d \in R$

q. $\dfrac{m+ni}{-m+ni}$; $m, n \in R$

r. $\dfrac{2u-3vi}{4u-vi}$; $u, v \in R$

5. If $z_1 = -3 + 4i$, $z_2 = 2 - 6i$, $z_3 = -1 - i$, and $z_4 = 5 + 2i$, express each of the following in standard form.

a. $\overline{z_1}$

b. $\overline{z_2}$

c. $\overline{z_1} + \overline{z_2}$

d. $-\overline{z_1}$

e. $\overline{z_1 + z_2}$

f. $\overline{z_1} \cdot \overline{z_2}$

g. $\overline{z_1 \cdot z_2}$

h. $\overline{z_1(-\overline{z_2})}$

i. $\dfrac{z_2}{z_3}$

j. $\dfrac{z_1}{z_2} \cdot \dfrac{z_3}{z_4}$

k. $\overline{z_3} \cdot \overline{z_4}$

l. $\dfrac{\overline{z_1}}{z_2} \cdot \dfrac{z_3}{z_4}$

m. $\overline{z_4}(z_1 + z_3)$

n. $z_3(\overline{z_2} + z_4)$

6. Prove: If z_1, $z_2 \in Z$ and $z_2 \neq 0$, then $\dfrac{z_1}{z_2} = z_1 \cdot \dfrac{1}{z_2}$.

7. Prove: If z_1, $z_2 \in Z$ and $z_1 z_2 \neq 0$, then $\dfrac{1}{z_1} \cdot \dfrac{1}{z_2} = \dfrac{1}{z_1 z_2}$.

8. Prove: If z_1, z_2, z_3, $z_4 \in Z$ and $z_2 z_4 \neq 0$, then $\dfrac{z_1}{z_2} \cdot \dfrac{z_3}{z_4} = \dfrac{z_1 z_3}{z_2 z_4}$.

9. Prove: If z_1, z_2, $z_3 \in Z$ and $z_2 z_3 \neq 0$, then $\dfrac{z_1}{z_2} = \dfrac{z_1 z_3}{z_2 z_3}$.

10. Prove: If z_1, z_2, z_3, $z_4 \in Z$ and $z_2 z_4 \neq 0$, then $\dfrac{z_1}{z_2} + \dfrac{z_3}{z_4} = \dfrac{z_1 z_4 + z_3 z_2}{z_2 z_4}$.

11. Prove: If two complex numbers are conjugates of each other, then their sum is a real number.

12. Prove: If two complex numbers are conjugates of each other, then their product is a real number.

13. Express $\dfrac{1}{a + bi}$ in standard form without using the conjugate of $a + bi$.

Quadratic Equations

Now we shall show that the complex number system will permit us to solve the quadratic equation $az^2 + bz + c = 0$ when $a, b, c \in R$, $a \neq 0$, $z \in Z$, and the discriminant $b^2 - 4ac$ is negative. Thus far we have considered only one quadratic equation with a negative discriminant, namely $z^2 + 1 = 0$. Since $1 = -i^2$, this equation can be written in the form $z^2 - i^2 = 0$. Hence $(z + i)(z - i) = 0$. This factorization shows that if z is a complex number which satisfies $z^2 + 1 = 0$, at least one of the factors, $z + i$ or $z - i$, must be zero and hence z must be either $-i$ or i. Conversely, if $z = i$ or $z = -i$, the equation $z^2 + 1 = 0$ is satisfied. Therefore, $\{z \mid z^2 + 1 = 0\} = \{-i, i\}$.

Now, the equation $z^2 + 1 = 0$ is a special case of the equation $z^2 = r$ when $r < 0$. If r is negative, then $-r$ is positive and $\sqrt{-r}$ is defined as the unique positive real number whose square is $-r$. Thus $r = (-1)(-r) = i^2(\sqrt{-r})^2 = (i\sqrt{-r})^2$. Hence $z^2 - r = z^2 - (i\sqrt{-r})^2 = (z + i\sqrt{-r}) \cdot (z - i\sqrt{-r})$, and we conclude that $\{z \mid z^2 = r \wedge r < 0\} = \{i\sqrt{-r}, -i\sqrt{-r}\}$. For example, the equation $z^2 = -11$ has two solutions, namely $i\sqrt{-(-11)}$, or $i\sqrt{11}$, and $-i\sqrt{-(-11)}$, or $-i\sqrt{11}$.

Recall that in Chapter 3 we used the symbol $\sqrt{2}$ to denote the unique positive solution of the equation $x^2 = 2$. Thus we were able to describe the solution set of the equation $x^2 = 2$ as $\{\sqrt{2}, -\sqrt{2}\}$. More generally, we have: $\{x \mid x^2 = r; \ r \geq 0\} = \{\sqrt{r}, -\sqrt{r}\}$.

We would like to extend the definition of $\sqrt{r}$ when r is a negative real number so that the description of the solution set of the equation $z^2 = r$ would be the same for all real numbers r. When $r < 0$, we know that the solutions are $i\sqrt{-r}$ and $-i\sqrt{-r}$. The question is: Which of these numbers shall be denoted by $\sqrt{r}$ and which by $-\sqrt{r}$?

We cannot select one of these as $\sqrt{r}$ on the grounds that it is "positive" because we have not defined the term "positive" or "negative" for nonzero complex numbers. In fact, we cannot define "positive" or "negative" for such numbers in a way that is consistent with the corresponding meaning for real numbers. However, since we must make a choice, we make it arbitrarily and choose to denote $i\sqrt{-r}$ by the symbol $\sqrt{r}$ when $r < 0$. Accordingly, we extend our interpretation of the symbol $\sqrt{r}$ when $r \in R$ by stating the following definition:

> If $r \in R$ and $r \geq 0$, then $\sqrt{r}$ is the unique non-negative real number $\sqrt{r}$ such that $(\sqrt{r})^2 = r$, and if $r < 0$, then $\sqrt{r} = i\sqrt{-r}$.

Example 1.   Simplify each of the following:

$\quad$ **a.** $\sqrt{-1}$ $\qquad\qquad$ **b.** $\sqrt{-75}$ $\qquad\qquad$ **c.** $\sqrt{(3i)^2}$

Solution. $\quad$ **a.** $\sqrt{-1} = i\sqrt{1} = i$

$\qquad\qquad$ **b.** $\sqrt{-75} = i\sqrt{75} = 5\sqrt{3}\,i$

$\qquad\qquad$ **c.** $\sqrt{(3i)^2} = \sqrt{9\,i^2} = \sqrt{-9} = i\sqrt{9} = 3i$

Example 2.   Find the product $(\sqrt{-12})(\sqrt{-3})$.

Solution. $\quad$ We have:

$$(\sqrt{-12})(\sqrt{-3}) = (i\sqrt{12})(i\sqrt{3}) = i^2\sqrt{12}\sqrt{3} = i^2\sqrt{36} = -6$$

Note that it is *not* correct to say $(\sqrt{-12})(\sqrt{-3}) = \sqrt{(-12)(-3)} = \sqrt{36} = 6$.

The statement $\sqrt{a}\sqrt{b} = \sqrt{ab}$ (Theorem 29–3(1)) has been proved only for the case where a and b are non-negative real numbers. This statement happens to be true when a and b have opposite signs. It is *not true* when a and b are both negative.

Example 3.   Find the quotient $\dfrac{\sqrt{4}}{\sqrt{-9}}$.

Solution. $\quad$ We have $\dfrac{\sqrt{4}}{\sqrt{-9}} = \dfrac{2}{3i} = \dfrac{2i}{-3} = -\dfrac{2}{3}i$.

Note that it is *not* correct to say $\dfrac{\sqrt{4}}{\sqrt{-9}} = \sqrt{\dfrac{4}{-9}} = \sqrt{(-1) \times \dfrac{4}{9}} =$ $\sqrt{-1}\sqrt{\dfrac{4}{9}} = \dfrac{2}{3}i.$

The statement $\dfrac{\sqrt{a}}{\sqrt{b}} = \sqrt{\dfrac{a}{b}}$ (Theorem 29-3 (2)) has been proved only for the case when $a, b \in R$, $a \geq 0$, and $b > 0$. This statement happens to be true when a and b have the same sign or when b is positive. It is *not true* when a is positive and b is negative.

With the definition of $\sqrt{r}$ when $r \in R$ in effect, we have the following theorem:

▷ **Theorem 8–11.** If $r \in R$ and $z \in Z$, then $\{z \mid z^2 = r\} = \{\sqrt{r}, -\sqrt{r}\}.$

Let us now consider the quadratic equation $az^2 + bz + c = 0$ when $a, b, c \in R$, $z \in Z$, and $a \neq 0$. According to the first three steps of the proof of Theorem 3–7 (page 355):

$$az^2 + bz + c = 0 \longleftrightarrow z^2 + \frac{b}{a}z + \frac{c}{a} = 0 \longleftrightarrow z^2 + \frac{b}{a}z + \frac{b^2}{4a^2} + \frac{c}{a} - \frac{b^2}{4a^2} = 0 \longleftrightarrow$$

$$\longmapsto \left(z + \frac{b}{2a}\right)^2 + \frac{4ac - b^2}{4a^2} = 0$$

Thus, $az^2 + bz + c = 0 \longleftrightarrow \left(z + \dfrac{b}{2a}\right)^2 = \dfrac{b^2 - 4ac}{4a^2}.$ If we let $x = z + \dfrac{b}{2a},$

this last equation becomes $x^2 = \dfrac{b^2 - 4ac}{4a^2}.$ Theorem 8–11 assures us that

$x^2 = \dfrac{b^2 - 4ac}{4a^2}$ has a solution whether $b^2 - 4ac$ is positive, negative,

or zero. Using Theorem 8–11, we have:

$$x = \sqrt{\frac{b^2 - 4ac}{4a^2}} \quad or \quad x = -\sqrt{\frac{b^2 - 4ac}{4a^2}}.$$

Accordingly,

$$z + \frac{b}{2a} = \frac{\sqrt{b^2 - 4ac}}{2a} \quad or \quad z + \frac{b}{2a} = -\frac{\sqrt{b^2 - 4ac}}{2a}.$$

Thus if z_1 satisfies the equation $az^2 + bz + c = 0$, then

$$z_1 = \frac{-b + \sqrt{b^2 - 4ac}}{2a} \quad or \quad z_1 = \frac{-b - \sqrt{b^2 - 4ac}}{2a}.$$

It can be shown by substitution that each of these numbers actually satisfies the equation $az^2 + bz + c = 0$. Thus we have proved the following theorem:

▶ **Theorem 9–11.** If a, b, $c \in R$, $z \in Z$, and $a \neq 0$, then

$$\{z \mid az^2 + bz + c = 0\} = \left\{ \frac{-b + \sqrt{b^2 - 4ac}}{2a}, \frac{-b - \sqrt{b^2 - 4ac}}{2a} \right\}.$$

Example. 4. Find the solutions of $z^2 + z + 2 = 0$.

Solution. $a = 1$, $b = 1$, and $c = 2$. By Theorem 9–11,

$$z = \frac{-1 + \sqrt{1-8}}{2} = \frac{-1 + i\sqrt{7}}{2}$$

or

$$z = \frac{-1 - \sqrt{1-8}}{2} = \frac{-1 - i\sqrt{7}}{2}.$$

Thus the set of solutions of $z^2 + z + 2 = 0$ is

$$\left\{ \frac{-1 + i\sqrt{7}}{2}, \frac{-1 - i\sqrt{7}}{2} \right\}.$$

Other statements about the relationships between the roots and the coefficients of the equation $az^2 + bz + c = 0$ can be proved just as they were in Chapter 7. Thus, if z_1 and z_2 are roots of this equation, then $z_1 + z_2 = \frac{-b}{a}$, $z_1 z_2 = \frac{c}{a}$, and $az^2 + bz + c = a(z - z_1)(z - z_2)$. Therefore we have extended Theorem 5–7 and the corollary to Theorem 5–7 to include all elements of Z.

Ⓐ **EXERCISES**

1. Simplify each of the following:

a. $\sqrt{-2}$ d. $\sqrt{-(-4)^2}$ g. $\sqrt{-162}$ j. $\sqrt{-(3i)^2}$

b. $\sqrt{-9}$ e. $\sqrt{(-4)^2}$ h. $\sqrt{-98}$ k. $\sqrt{-(-5i)^2}$

c. $\sqrt{-(4)^2}$ f. $\sqrt{-27}$ i. $\sqrt{(2i)^2}$ l. $\sqrt{-7i^2}$

2. Write each of the following in standard form.

a. $\sqrt{-36} + \sqrt{-4}$ e. $\sqrt{-9} \cdot \sqrt{-4}$ i. $\sqrt{-\frac{1}{9}}$

b. $\sqrt{-16} - \sqrt{-25}$ f. $\sqrt{-5} \cdot \sqrt{-1}$ j. $\frac{\sqrt{-36}}{3\sqrt{-50}}$

c. $\sqrt{-18} + \sqrt{-8}$ g. $\sqrt{-8} \cdot \sqrt{-9} \cdot \sqrt{-1}$ k. $\sqrt{\frac{16}{-9}}$

d. $-\sqrt{-49} + 3\sqrt{-7}$ h. $\sqrt{-12} \cdot \sqrt{-3}$

3. Find the solution set of each of the following equations. In each case $z \in Z$.

   a. $z^2 + 3 = 0$

   b. $z^2 - z + 1 = 0$

   c. $z^2 - 4z + 5 = 0$

   d. $z^2 + 2z + 3 = 0$

   e. $2z^2 + 4z + 5 = 0$

   f. $3z^2 - z - 1 = 0$

   g. $z^2 + 6z + 12 = 0$

   h. $3z^2 - 2z + 1 = 0$

   i. $5z^2 + 4 = 0$

   j. $3z^2 + 5 = 0$

   k. $2z^2 - 2\sqrt{2}z + 3 = 0$

   l. $3z^2 + z + \frac{1}{2} = 0$

4. For each of the following sets write an equation of the form $az^2 + bz + c = 0$ which has the given set as its solution set.

   a. $\{2i, -2i\}$

   b. $\{\frac{4}{7}i, -\frac{4}{7}i\}$

   c. $\{2+i, 2-i\}$

   d. $\{1-i, 1+i\}$

   e. $\{2+3i, 2-3i\}$

   f. $\left\{\dfrac{-2+i\sqrt{5}}{3}, \dfrac{-2-i\sqrt{5}}{3}\right\}$

B **EXERCISES**

5. If z_1 and z_2 are the two roots of the equation $az^2 + bz + c = 0$, $z \in Z$, $a, b, c \in R$, and $a \neq 0$, show that

   a. $z_1 + z_2 = -\dfrac{b}{a}$

   b. $z_1 z_2 = \dfrac{c}{a}$

6. Show that if the equation $az^2 + bz + c = 0$ when $z \in Z$, $a, b, c \in R$, and $a \neq 0$ has one root that is a nonreal complex number, then both roots of the equation are nonreal complex numbers.

7. If $3 + 5i$ is one root of a quadratic equation having real coefficients, what is the other root?

8. One root of the equation $z^3 - 8 = 0$ when $z \in Z$ is 2. What are the other two roots?

9. Supply reasons for the proof of the following statement: If $a, b \in R$, $a > 0$, and $b < 0$, then $\sqrt{a}\sqrt{b} = \sqrt{ab}$.

   $$\left.\begin{array}{c} a > 0 \\ b < 0 \end{array}\right\} \overset{(2)}{\underset{(1)}{\longrightarrow}} ab < 0 \overset{(3)}{\longrightarrow} \sqrt{ab} = i\sqrt{-ab}.$$

   $$b < 0 \overset{(1)\ (4)}{\longrightarrow} \sqrt{b} = i\sqrt{-b} \overset{(5)}{\longrightarrow} \sqrt{a}\sqrt{b} = \sqrt{a}(i\sqrt{-b}) \overset{(6)}{\longrightarrow} \sqrt{a}\sqrt{b} =$$

   $$i\sqrt{a}\sqrt{-b} \overset{(7)}{\longrightarrow} \sqrt{a}\sqrt{b} = i\sqrt{a(-b)} \overset{(8)}{\longrightarrow} \sqrt{a}\sqrt{b} = i\sqrt{-ab}.$$

   $$\therefore (\sqrt{ab} = i\sqrt{-ab} \wedge \sqrt{a}\sqrt{b} = i\sqrt{-ab}) \overset{(9)}{\longrightarrow} \sqrt{ab} = \sqrt{a}\sqrt{b}$$

10. If $a, b \in R$, $a < 0$, and $b > 0$, prove that $\dfrac{\sqrt{a}}{\sqrt{b}} = \sqrt{\dfrac{a}{b}}$.

11. What is the solution set of the equation $z^2 = i$? *Hint.* Write z in the standard form $x + yi$.

Graphical Representation; Absolute Value

Since each complex number z is uniquely expressible in the standard form $x + yi$, we see that each complex number determines, and is determined by, an ordered pair (x, y) of real numbers. Therefore, complex numbers may be assigned to points in the xy-plane (the coordinate plane) in the same way that ordered pairs of real numbers are assigned to points in the xy-plane. We agree to associate z with $P(x, y)$ if and only if $z = x + yi$ and thereby establish a one-to-one correspondence between the elements of Z and points in the xy-plane. Since the graphs of complex numbers of the form $x + 0i$ are points in the x-axis, the x-axis is called the *axis of reals*. Since the graphs of complex numbers of the form $0 + yi$ are points in the y-axis, the y-axis is called the *axis of imaginaries*. When a one-to-one correspondence is established between the points in the xy-plane and the elements in the set of complex numbers, we sometimes refer to the plane as the *complex plane*.

We use the expression "Argand diagram" to describe the graph obtained when the point $P(x, y)$ in the xy-plane is used to represent the complex number $x + yi$ given in standard form. In the Argand diagram at the right, $P_1(2, -5)$ represents the complex number z_1, or $2 - 5i$; $P_2(-4, 1)$ represents the complex number z_2, or $-4 + i$; and $P(a, b)$ represents z, or $a + bi$. What complex number does $P_3(0, 8)$ represent?

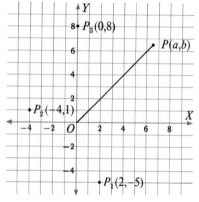

The geometric representation of complex numbers suggests a definition of the absolute value of a complex number. Recall that when a point X in a number line with origin O is the graph of a real number x, the absolute value of the real number is equal to the measure of line segment OX, that is, $|x| = |OX|$. Accordingly, we define the absolute value of the complex number z ($|z|$, or $|a + bi|$) to be the measure of the line segment from the origin to $P(a, b)$, that is, $|z| = |OP|$. Using the distance formula, we have $|OP| = \sqrt{a^2 + b^2}$, and we may state our definition algebraically as follows:

$$\text{If } a, b \in R, \text{ and } z = a + bi, \text{ then } |z| = \sqrt{a^2 + b^2}.$$

Observe that this definition is consistent with our previous understanding of the absolute value of a real number. If $z = a + bi$ and $b = 0$, we have $z = a$, from which we must have $|z| = |a|$. Note that our definition gives this result because $|z| = \sqrt{a^2 + 0} = \sqrt{a^2} = |a|$.

Recall that the sum of two complex numbers z and w when $z = a + bi$ and $w = c + di$ is the complex number $z + w$, or $(a + c) + (b + d)i$.

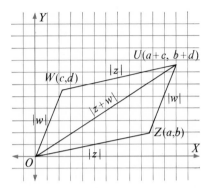

The points $Z(a, b)$, $W(c, d)$, and $U(a + c, b + d)$ which correspond to the complex numbers z, w, and $z + w$, repectively, are shown in the above Argand diagram. We draw the line segments OZ, OW, WU, and ZU and observe that

$$\left.\begin{array}{l} |OZ| = \sqrt{a^2 + b^2} \\ |WU| = \sqrt{a^2 + b^2} \end{array}\right\} \longrightarrow |OZ| = |WU| \longrightarrow \overline{OZ} \cong \overline{WU}, \text{ and}$$

$$\left.\begin{array}{l} |OW| = \sqrt{c^2 + d^2} \\ |ZU| = \sqrt{c^2 + d^2} \end{array}\right\} \longrightarrow |OW| = |ZU| \longrightarrow \overline{OW} \cong \overline{ZU}.$$

Therefore, if we assume that points O, Z, and W are not collinear, we can say that the figure $OZUW$ is a parallelogram because it is a quadrilateral having both pairs of opposite sides congruent.

Thus we have the following geometrical construction for finding the point in the Argand diagram that corresponds to the sum of two complex numbers: If Z and W are the points in the Argand diagram that correspond to the complex numbers z and w, respectively, then in the Argand diagram the point U that corresponds to $z + w$ is the fourth vertex of the parallelogram whose other three vertices are O (the origin), Z, and W.

This construction for finding the graph of the sum of two complex numbers reminds us of our definition for the *sum of two vectors* in Chapter 9. Clearly $\overrightarrow{ZU}$ is equivalent to $\overrightarrow{OW}$. Therefore $\overrightarrow{OU}$ is equal to $\overrightarrow{OZ} + \overrightarrow{OW}$. This consideration enables us to use *vector addition* to find the point which corresponds to the sum of two complex numbers as follows: If Z and W are the points in the Argand diagram that correspond to the complex numbers z and w, respectively, then the point U that corresponds to $z + w$ is the terminal point of $\overrightarrow{OU}$ where $\overrightarrow{OU} = \overrightarrow{OZ} + \overrightarrow{OW}$. Observe that this procedure is applicable whether or not O, Z, and W are collinear.

Example 1. If $u = -11 - 4i$ and $v = 4 - 2i$, locate the following points in an Argand diagram:

a. The points U and V which correspond to u and v, respectively.

b. The point S that corresponds to $u + v$.

c. The point V' that corresponds to $-v$.

d. The point D that corresponds to $u - v$.

Solution. The required points are shown in the Argand diagram below. Observe that $\overrightarrow{US} \doteq \overrightarrow{OV}$. Thus, we can locate S by starting at U and

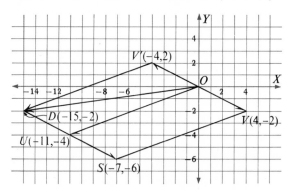

moving four units to the right and thence two units down. The coordinates of S are $(-7, -6)$. Note that $u + v = (-11 - 4i) + (4 - 2i) = -7 - 6i$. Since $-v = -(4 - 2i) = -4 + 2i$, $\overrightarrow{OV'}$ is equal in magnitude but opposite in direction to $\overrightarrow{OV}$, that is, V and V' are symmetric with respect to the origin. Since $u - v = u + (-v)$, $\overrightarrow{OD} = \overrightarrow{OU} + \overrightarrow{OV'}$. Thus, we can arrive at D by starting at U and moving a distance $|OV|$ in the direction opposite to that of $\overrightarrow{US}$. Such a move is equivalent to starting at U and moving four units to the left and thence two units up. This brings us to the point $D(-15, -2)$. Note that $u - v = (-11 - 4i) - (4 - 2i) = (-11 - 4i) + (-4 + 2i) = -15 - 2i$.

Example 2. Let Z_1, Z_2, Z_3 be distinct points in the Argand diagram which correspond to the complex numbers z_1, z_2, and z_3, respectively.

a. Prove that Z_3 is the midpoint of $\overline{Z_1 Z_2}$ if and only if $z_3 = \dfrac{z_1 + z_2}{2}$.

b. Prove that O, Z_1, and Z_2 are distinct collinear points if and only if $z_2 = kz_1$ when $k \in R$.

Proof.　**a.** Let $z_1 = a + bi$, $z_2 = c + di$, and $z_3 = x + yi$. Then $Z_3(x, y)$ is the midpoint of $\overline{Z_1 Z_2}$ $\overset{(1)}{\longleftrightarrow} x = \dfrac{a + c}{2}$ $\wedge$

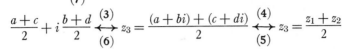

$y = \dfrac{b + d}{2} \overset{(2)}{\underset{(7)}{\longleftrightarrow}} x + yi =$

$\dfrac{a + c}{2} + i \dfrac{b + d}{2} \overset{(3)}{\underset{(6)}{\longleftrightarrow}} z_3 = \dfrac{(a + bi) + (c + di)}{2} \overset{(4)}{\underset{(5)}{\longleftrightarrow}} z_3 = \dfrac{z_1 + z_2}{2}$

Reasons: (left-to-right) (1) Midpoint formula, (2) Substitution property of equality, (3) Substitution property of equality and Z–3 and Z–9, (4) Substitution property of equality. The reasons right-to-left are left to you.

b. Let $z_1 = a + bi$ and $z_2 = c + di$. $(O, Z_1, \text{and } Z_2$ are distinct collinear points$)$ $\overset{(1)}{\underset{(12)}{\longleftrightarrow}} \begin{vmatrix} c & d & 1 \\ a & b & 1 \\ 0 & 0 & 1 \end{vmatrix} \overset{(2)}{\underset{(11)}{=}} 0 \longleftrightarrow$

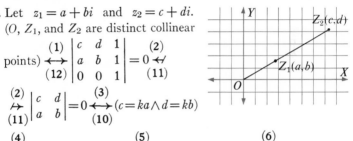

$\overset{(2)}{\underset{(11)}{\longmapsto}} \begin{vmatrix} c & d \\ a & b \end{vmatrix} = 0 \overset{(3)}{\underset{(10)}{\longleftrightarrow}} (c = ka \wedge d = kb)$

$\overset{(4)}{\underset{(9)}{\longleftrightarrow}} c + di = ka + kbi \overset{(5)}{\underset{(8)}{\longleftrightarrow}} c + di = k(a + bi) \overset{(6)}{\underset{(7)}{\longleftrightarrow}} z_2 = kz_1$

The reasons, except for (3), left-to-right are left to you. Reason 3 is considered in Example 3.

Example 3. Prove that $\begin{vmatrix} x & y \\ a & b \end{vmatrix} = 0 \longrightarrow x = ka \wedge y = kb$ if $a^2 + b^2 \neq 0$.

Proof. There are two cases to consider: Case 1 in which exactly one of the numbers a and b is zero, and case 2 in which neither of the numbers a and b is zero, that is, $ab \neq 0$.

CASE 1: Let $a \neq 0$ and $b = 0$. Then

$\begin{vmatrix} x & y \\ a & b \end{vmatrix} = 0 \overset{(1)}{\underset{(8)}{\longleftrightarrow}} \begin{vmatrix} x & y \\ a & 0 \end{vmatrix} = 0 \overset{(2)}{\underset{(7)}{\longleftrightarrow}} x \cdot 0 = ay \overset{(3)}{\underset{(6)}{\longleftrightarrow}} 0 = ay \overset{(4)}{\underset{(5)}{\longleftrightarrow}} y = 0.$

Since $x = \dfrac{x}{a} \cdot a$ and $0 = \dfrac{x}{a} \cdot 0$, $x = ka$ and $y = kb$ where $k = \dfrac{x}{a}$.

Similarly if $a = 0$ and $b \neq 0$, then $x = 0$. Since $y = \dfrac{y}{b} \cdot b$ and

$0 = \dfrac{y}{b} \cdot 0$, $y = kb$ and $x = ka$ where $k = \dfrac{y}{b}$.

CASE 2: Let $a \neq 0$ and $b \neq 0$. Then

$$\begin{vmatrix} x & y \\ a & b \end{vmatrix} = 0 \overset{(1)}{\underset{(6)}{\longleftrightarrow}} xb - ay = 0 \overset{(2)}{\underset{(5)}{\longleftrightarrow}} \left.\begin{matrix} xb = ay \\ ab \neq 0 \end{matrix}\right\} \overset{(3)}{\underset{(4)}{\longleftrightarrow}} \frac{x}{a} = \frac{y}{b}.$$

Since the numbers $\dfrac{x}{a}$ and $\dfrac{y}{b}$ are equal, we may denote each by k.

Hence $\dfrac{x}{a} = k \wedge \dfrac{y}{b} = k$, or $x = ka \wedge y = kb$. You may supply the reasons.

Example 4. If $z_1 = x_1 + y_1 i$, $z_2 = x_2 + y_2 i$, Z_1 is the graph of z_1, and Z_2 is the graph of z_2, prove that $|Z_2 Z_1| = |z_2 - z_1|$.

Proof.

$$|Z_2 Z_1| \overset{(1)}{=} \sqrt{(x_2 - x_1)^2 + (y_2 - y_1)^2}$$
$$\overset{(2)}{=} |(x_2 - x_1) + i(y_2 - y_1)|$$
$$\overset{(3)}{=} |(x_2 + y_2 i) - (x_1 + y_1 i)|$$
$$\overset{(4)}{=} |z_2 - z_1|.$$

You may supply the reasons.

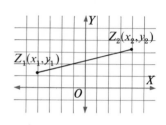

Some of the theorems pertaining to absolute value which we studied in Chapter 3 are valid for complex numbers. Two of the most useful are stated in the following theorem:

▶ **Theorem 10–11.** If z_1 and z_2 are complex numbers, then

1. $|z_1| |z_2| = |z_1 z_2|$
2. $|z_1| + |z_2| \geq |z_1 + z_2|$

We illustrate Theorem 10–11 in the following examples and we outline the proof of Theorem 10–11(1) in the exercises.

Example 5. If $z_1 = 3 + 4i$ and $z_2 = 5 - 12i$, show that $|z_1| |z_2| = |z_1 z_2|$.

Solution.

$|z_1| = \sqrt{3^2 + 4^2} = 5$, $|z_2| = \sqrt{5^2 + (-12)^2} = 13$
$\therefore |z_1| |z_2| = 65$
$z_1 z_2 = (3 + 4i)(5 - 12i) = (15 + 48) - 16i = 63 - 16i$
$\therefore |z_1 z_2| = \sqrt{63^2 + (-16)^2} = \sqrt{4225} = 65$
$\therefore |z_1| |z_2| = |z_1 z_2|$

Example 6. If $z_1 = 7 + 3i$ and $z_2 = 2 + 5i$, show both geometrically and algebraically that $|z_1| + |z_2| > |z_1 + z_2|$.

Solution. In the Argand diagram Z_1 and Z_2 are the graphs of z_1 and z_2, respectively, and Z_2' corresponds to $z_1 + z_2$. This drawing shows why the statement

$$|z_1| + |z_2| > |z_1 + z_2|$$

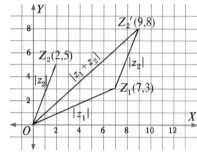

is called the triangle inequality. Since $|OZ_1| = |z_1|$, $|OZ_2| = |Z_1Z_2'| = |z_2|$, and $|OZ_2'| = |z_1 + z_2|$, the triangle inequality $|z_1| + |z_2| > |z_1 + z_2|$ merely says that the sum of the measures of two sides of a triangle is greater than the measure of the third side. If the triangle OZ_1Z_2' "collapses" so that $Z_1 \in \overline{OZ_2'}$, then $|z_1| + |z_2| = |z_1 + z_2|$. Why?

We can show algebraically that $|z_1| + |z_2| > |z_1 + z_2|$ as follows: $|z_1| = \sqrt{49 + 9} = \sqrt{58}$, $|z_2| = \sqrt{4 + 25} = \sqrt{29}$, $z_1 + z_2 = 9 + 8i$, and $|z_1 + z_2| = \sqrt{81 + 64} = \sqrt{145}$. By finding the square roots of the radical expressions involved, the inequality $\sqrt{58} + \sqrt{29} > \sqrt{145}$ can be readily established.

Ⓐ EXERCISES

1. What is the complex number that corresponds to each of the points A, B, C, D, E, and F, respectively, as shown in the figure at the right?

2. In the complex plane locate the point which corresponds to each of the following complex numbers:

   a. $1 + i$ f. 2
   b. $3 + 2i$ g. $-i$
   c. $0 + 4i$ h. $0 + 0i$
   d. $-6 - 3i$ i. $4 - 3i$
   e. $2 + 3i$ j. $-4 - 2i$

3. State the absolute value of each of the complex numbers in Ex. 2. Write your answers in simplest form.

4. Let v represent each of the following complex numbers, in turn. In the xy-plane locate the point which is the graph of each v and the point which is the graph of each $-v$.

   a. $-3 + 2i$ c. $6 - i$ e. $-4 - 5i$ g. 3
   b. $3i$ d. $2 + 2i$ f. $2 - i$ h. $4 - 3i$

5. Use geometric constructions to locate the points which correspond to each of the following sums and differences.

a. $(3 + i) + (4 + 5 i)$

b. $(4 + 2 i) + (2 - 3 i)$

c. $3 + (5 + 4 i)$

d. $(5 + 2 i) - (1 + 4 i)$

e. $(- 6 + 2 i) - (1 - 3 i)$

f. $(- 2 + 4 i) + (5 - i)$

g. $(- 7 - 2 i) + 7$

h. $(4 + i) + (6 + 4 i) + (6 - i)$

i. $(i) + (5) + (- 2 - 3 i)$

j. $(3 + 2 i) + (3 - 2 i) + 6 i$

6. Z_1 and Z_2 are points in the Argand diagram which correspond to the complex numbers z_1 and z_2, respectively. Write the complex number which corresponds to the midpoint of $\overline{Z_1 Z_2}$ in each of the following cases:

a. $z_1 = 1 + 6 i,\ z_2 = 5 + 2 i$

b. $z_1 = 2 + 4 i,\ z_2 = - 4$

c. $z_1 = 4 + 5 i,\ z_2 = 4 - 5 i$

d. $z_1 = - 3 + 2 i,\ z_2 = 3 - 2 i$

e. $z_1 = - 4 - 5 i,\ z_2 = 2 + 3 i$

f. $z_1 = 3,\ z_2 = 9$

g. $z_1 = 4 i,\ z_2 = 8$

h. $z_1 = 3,\ z_2 = - 5 i + 2$

7. Assume that O is the origin of the complex plane, that Z_1 is the point in the plane which corresponds to the complex number z_1, and that Z_2 is the point in the plane which corresponds to the complex number z_2. In which of the following cases are O, Z_1, and Z_2 collinear?

a. $z_1 = 3 + 3 i,\ z_2 = 5 + 5 i$

b. $z_1 = 3 + i,\ z_2 = - 3 - i$

c. $z_1 = 4 + 5 i,\ z_2 = - 4 + 5 i$

d. $z_1 = 2 + 4 i,\ z_2 = 3 + 6 i$

e. $z_1 = 6 - i,\ z_2 = 4 + 3 i$

f. $z_1 = - 2 + 4 i,\ z_2 = - \frac{1}{2} + i$

8. Find $|z|$ for each of the following values of z:

a. $z = - 2 + 5 i$

b. $z = 1 - 4 i$

c. $z = 3 i$

d. $z = 8$

e. $z = 1 + 2 i^2$

f. $z = i^2 + i^5$

g. $z = - \sqrt{3} + 2 i$

h. $z = - 3 - \sqrt{5} i$

9. Given that Z_1 is the point in the Argand diagram which corresponds to the complex number z_1 and that Z_2 is the point in the diagram which corresponds to the complex number z_2, show $|Z_1 Z_2|$ geometrically in each of the following cases:

a. $z_1 = 2 + i,\ z_2 = 6 + 6 i$

b. $z_1 = 4 + 2 i,\ z_2 = - 1 + 3 i$

c. $z_1 = - 2 - 2 i,\ z_2 = 5 - 2 i$

d. $z_1 = 2 - i,\ z_2 = 3 + 4 i$

e. $z_1 = - 3 - 4 i,\ z_2 = 3 + 2 i$

f. $z_1 = - 2 i,\ z_2 = 5 + i$

g. $z_1 = 3 + 2 i,\ z_2 = - 3 - 2 i$

h. $z_1 = 2,\ z_2 = - 2 + i$

10. For each of the number pairs z_1, z_2 of Ex. 9, find $|z_1 z_2|$.

11. If $z_1 = 5 + 12 i$ and $z_2 = 3 - 4 i$, show algebraically and geometrically that $|z_1| + |z_2| > |z_1 + z_2|$.

12. Supply reasons for the following proof of Theorem 10–11 (1):
    If z_1 and z_2 are complex numbers, then $|z_1||z_2| = |z_1 \cdot z_2|$.

$$\text{Proof: } z_1, z_2 \in Z \overset{(1)}{\longrightarrow} \overset{(2)}{[(z_1 = a + bi \land a, b \in R) \land (z_2 = c + di \land c, d \in R)]} \overset{(3)}{\longrightarrow}$$

$$\overset{(3)}{\longrightarrow} (|z_1| = \sqrt{a^2 + b^2} \land |z_2| = \sqrt{c^2 + d^2}) \overset{(4)}{\longrightarrow}$$

$$\overset{(4)}{\longrightarrow} |z_1||z_2| = \sqrt{a^2 + b^2}\sqrt{c^2 + d^2} \overset{(5)}{\longrightarrow}$$

$$\overset{(5)}{\longrightarrow} |z_1||z_2| = \sqrt{(a^2 + b^2)(c^2 + d^2)} \overset{(6)}{\longrightarrow} |z_1||z_2| =$$

$$\sqrt{(a^2c^2 - 2\,abcd + b^2d^2) + (a^2d^2 + 2\,abcd + b^2c^2)} \overset{(7)}{\longrightarrow}$$

$$\overset{(7)}{\longrightarrow} |z_1||z_2| = \sqrt{(ac - bd)^2 + (ad + bc)^2} \overset{(8)}{\longrightarrow}$$

$$\overset{(8)}{\longrightarrow} |z_1||z_2| = |(ac - bd) + (ad + bc)i| \overset{(9)}{\longrightarrow}$$

$$\overset{(9)}{\longrightarrow} |z_1||z_2| = |z_1 \cdot z_2|.$$

13. Prove Theorem 10–11 (2): If z_1 and z_2 are complex numbers, then $|z_1| + |z_2| \geq |z_1 + z_2|$. *Hint.* Show that $|z_1 + z_2|^2 \geq |z_1|^2 + |z_2|^2$ and use Theorem 26–3.

More about Complex Conjugates

If z is in the standard form $a + bi$, we know that its conjugate $\bar{z}$ written in standard form is $a - bi$. Since $|z| = \sqrt{a^2 + b^2}$, the corollary to Theorem 3–11: If $a, b \in R$ and i is the imaginary unit, then $(a + bi)(a - bi) = a^2 + b^2$, can be stated in the form $z \in Z \longrightarrow z \cdot \bar{z} = |z|^2$. It is also worthwhile to observe that $z_1 = z_2 \longleftrightarrow \bar{z}_1 = \bar{z}_2$.

If we graph z and $\bar{z}$, where $z = 5 + 3\,i$ and $\bar{z} = 5 - 3\,i$, in an Argand diagram as points Z and C, respectively, we see that points Z and C are symmetric with respect to the x-axis. Similarly, if N is the point which corresponds to $-\bar{z}$, or $-5 + 3\,i$, we see that N and Z are symmetric with respect to the y-axis; that is, either of the points N or Z is the reflection of the other in the y-axis. If we use the symbol P_z to name the point, in the complex plane, which corresponds to the complex number z, we can generalize this example by observing that:

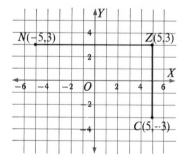

P_z and $P_{\bar{z}}$ are symmetric with respect to the x-axis and
P_z and $P_{-\bar{z}}$ are symmetric with respect to the y-axis.

Clearly, $z + \bar{z} = (a + bi) + (a - bi) = 2a$ and $z - \bar{z} = (a + bi) - (a - bi) = 2bi$. From these equations, we obtain $a = \dfrac{z + \bar{z}}{2}$ and $b = \dfrac{z - \bar{z}}{2i} = \dfrac{(z - \bar{z})i}{-2} = \dfrac{i}{2}(\bar{z} - z)$. Thus, we have the following theorem:

> **Theorem 11–11.** If z is in the standard form $a + bi$, then $z + \bar{z} = 2a$ and
> $z - \bar{z} = 2bi$, or $a = \dfrac{1}{2}(\bar{z} + z)$ and $b = \dfrac{i}{2}(\bar{z} - z)$.

Using Theorem 11–11 we have: $z \in R \longleftrightarrow b = 0 \longleftrightarrow z = \bar{z}$, and ($z$ is a pure imaginary) $\longleftrightarrow a = 0 \longleftrightarrow z = -\bar{z}$. Thus, we have:

Corollary to Theorem 11–11. If $z \in Z$, then
1. $z \in R \longleftrightarrow z = \bar{z}$,
2. z is a pure imaginary $\longleftrightarrow z = -\bar{z}$.

Theorem 11–11 enables us to state relationships between a and b, the real and imaginary parts of the complex number z, as a relationship between z and $\bar{z}$. This provides a particularly useful way to express certain statements from analytic geometry. Before considering examples, we state a theorem which enables us to simplify the writing of conjugates.

> **Theorem 12–11.** If z_1 and z_2 are complex numbers, then
> 1. $\overline{z_1 + z_2} = \bar{z}_1 + \bar{z}_2$
> 2. $\overline{z_1 z_2} = \bar{z}_1 \cdot \bar{z}_2$
> 3. $\overline{z_1 - z_2} = \bar{z}_1 - \bar{z}_2$
> 4. $\overline{\left(\dfrac{z_1}{z_2}\right)} = \dfrac{\bar{z}_1}{\bar{z}_2}$; $z_2 \neq 0$

The proofs of the four parts of Theorem 12–11 are left as exercises.

Example 1. If $z \in Z$, use the statement $z\bar{z} = |z|^2$ to prove: $|z_1||z_2| = |z_1 \cdot z_2|$.

Proof. The plan is to show that $(|z_1||z_2|)^2 = |z_1 \cdot z_2|^2$ and then apply Theorem 27–3 (If $a \geq 0 \wedge b \geq 0$, then $a^2 = b^2 \longleftrightarrow a = b$).

$$\overset{(1)}{(|z_1||z_2|)^2} = \overset{(2)}{|z_1|^2|z_2|^2} = (z_1 \cdot \bar{z}_1)(z_2 \cdot \bar{z}_2) = \overset{(3)}{(z_1 \cdot z_2)(\bar{z}_1 \cdot \bar{z}_2)} = \overset{(4)}{}$$

$$\overset{(5)}{(z_1 z_2)(\overline{z_1 z_2})} = |z_1 \cdot z_2|^2$$

$$\overset{(6)}{\therefore |z_1||z_2| = |z_1 \cdot z_2|.}$$

Reasons: (1) If $a, b \in R$, $(ab)^2 = a^2 b^2$, (2) Corollary to Theorem 3–11, (3) Multiplication is associative and commutative, (4) Theorem 12–11(2), (5) Corollary to Theorem 3–11, (6) Theorem 27–3.

Example 2. Let $z_1 = a + bi$ when $a, b \in R$ and $z = x + yi$ when $x, y \in R$. Write the z-equation of a circle having its center at $P(a, b)$ and radius r.

Solution. (P_z is a point in a circle with radius r and center P_{z_1}) $\longleftrightarrow | P_z P_{z_1} | = | z - z_1 | = r$. Accordingly, $| z - z_1 | = r$ is the required z-equation and the xy-equation is readily obtained from it. Thus,

$$| z - z_1 | = r \longleftrightarrow | (x + iy) - (a + bi) | = r$$
$$\longleftrightarrow | (x - a) + (y - b)i | = r$$
$$\longleftrightarrow \sqrt{(x - a)^2 + (y - b)^2} = r$$
$$\longleftrightarrow (x - a)^2 + (y - b)^2 = r^2.$$

Example 3. Prove that $i\bar{z} = w \longleftrightarrow z = i\bar{w}$.

Proof.
$$\overline{iz} = w \overset{(1)}{\longleftrightarrow} \overline{\overline{iz}} = \overline{w} \overset{(2)}{\longleftrightarrow} \overline{i}\,\overline{\overline{z}} = \overline{w} \overset{(3)}{\longleftrightarrow} -iz = \overline{w} \overset{(4)}{\longleftrightarrow} z = i\overline{w}$$

Reasons: (1) $z_1 = z_2 \longleftrightarrow \bar{z}_1 = \bar{z}_2$, (2) Theorem 12–11(2), (3) Definition of conjugate and $\bar{\bar{z}} = z$, (4) Multiplication property of equality (multiply each number by i). Right-to-left reasons are left to you.

Ⓐ **EXERCISES**

1. Replace each question mark below to form a true statement.
  a. If $z = 3 + 2i$, then $z + \bar{z} = \_?\_$ and $z - \bar{z} = \_?\_$
  b. If $z = -3 + 5i$, then $z + \bar{z} = \_?\_$ and $z - \bar{z} = \_?\_$
  c. If $z = -1 - i$, then $z + \bar{z} = \_?\_$ and $z - \bar{z} = \_?\_$
  d. If $z = 3i$, then $z + \bar{z} = \_?\_$ and $z - \bar{z} = \_?\_$
  e. If $z = 4$, then $z + \bar{z} = \_?\_$ and $z - \bar{z} = \_?\_$

2. Replace each of the following question marks with a number which makes the statement true.
  a. $\overline{(2 + 3i) + (3 - 4i)} = (2 - 3i) + \_?\_$
  b. $\overline{(4 - 6i)(-1 + i)} = (4 + 6i)(\_?\_)$
  c. $\overline{(-1 + 2i) - (4 - 7i)} = (-1 - 2i) + \_?\_$
  d. $\overline{\left(\dfrac{2 + 5i}{-3 - 3i} \right)} = \dfrac{2 - 5i}{\_?\_}$
  e. $\overline{(1 + 2i) + \_?\_} = (1 - 2i) + (6 + 5i)$
  f. $\overline{(\_?\_)(2 + i)} = \frac{1}{2}(2 - i)$
  g. $\overline{(7 - i) - 8i} = (7 + i) - \_?\_$
  h. $\overline{\left(\dfrac{-4 - i}{\_?\_} \right)} = \dfrac{-4 + i}{3 + 6i}$

3. When does z equal $\bar{z}$?

4. When does z equal $-\bar{z}$?

5. Prove: $|z_1|^2 = |\bar{z}_1|^2$

6. Prove that $\overline{z^2} = (\bar{z})^2$.

B EXERCISES

7. If $z,\ w \in Z$, then P_z and P_w are symmetric with respect to the graph of the identity function if and only if $i\bar{z} = w$.

a. Supply the reasons for the proof of the statement: $(z,\ w \in Z \wedge i\bar{z} = w) \longrightarrow$ (P_z and P_w are symmetric with respect to the graph of the identity function).

1. Let $w = a + bi,\ a,\ b \in R$	1. Why?
2. $P_w = P(a, b)$	2. Why?
3. $i\bar{z} = w$	3. Why?
4. $i\bar{z} = a + bi$	4. Why?
5. $-\bar{z} = ai - b$	5. Why?
6. $\bar{z} = b - ai$	6. Why?
7. $z = b + ai$	7. Why?
8. $P_z = P(b, a)$	8. Why?
9. P_z and P_w are symmetric with respect to the graph of the identity function.	9. Why?

b. Write the proof of the statement: $(z,\ w \in Z$, and P_z and P_w are symmetric with respect to the graph of the identity function) $\longrightarrow i\bar{z} = w$.

8. Prove that $z_1 \bar{z}_2$ and $z_2 \bar{z}_1$ are conjugates.

9. Prove: $|z_1 - z_2|^2 + |z_1 + z_2|^2 = 2|z_1|^2 + 2|z_2|^2$

10. Prove part (1) of Theorem 12–11.

11. Prove part (2) of Theorem 12–11.

12. Prove part (3) of Theorem 12–11.

13. Prove part (4) of Theorem 12–11.

14. Prove that the graph of $z\bar{z} = 1$ is a circle with its center at the origin and the measure of its radius is 1.

15. Prove that the graph of $(z - z_1)(\bar{z} - \bar{z}_1) = r^2$ is a circle whose center is the point P_{z_1} and whose radius has the measure r.

16. If Z_1 and Z_2 are distinct points in the complex plane which correspond to the complex numbers z_1 and z_2, respectively, prove that the line segments from the origin to the point Z_1 and to the point Z_2 are perpendicular to each other if and only if $z_1 \bar{z}_2$ is a pure imaginary number.

The Trigonometric Form of a Complex Number.

In this section we shall find that the multiplication and division of complex numbers can be greatly facilitated by first expressing each complex number involved in a form called the *trigonometric form*. In the following sections, we shall learn how the operations of involution (raising to a power) and evolution (extraction of a root) in the set of complex numbers are made relatively easy by use of this form.

We have seen that the ordered pair of real numbers (x, y) uniquely determines the point $P(x, y)$, the vector OP from the origin to point P, and the complex number z, or $x + yi$, as shown in the Argand diagram at the right.

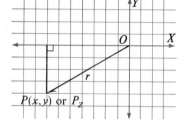

Recall that if $P(x, y) = P^R(r, t)$, we say that the point $P(x, y)$ has circular coordinates r and t. In this case, we know that,

(*i*) $r = \sqrt{x^2 + y^2}$

(*ii*) $x = r \cos t$

(*iii*) $y = r \sin t$

From (*ii*) and (*iii*), we see that the complex number z, or $x + yi$, has the *trigonometric form* $r \cos t + ri \sin t$. Thus,

(*iv*) $z = x + yi = r\,(\cos t + i \sin t)$

We sometimes abbreviate $\cos t + i \sin t$ by writing cis t, pronounced "sis *t*." We call r the *modulus* of the complex number z. Thus "modulus" is another name for $|z|$. Note that $z = 0$ if and only if $|z| = 0$. The real number t is called an *amplitude* of the complex number z.

If $P_z = P(x, y) = P^\circ(r, d) = P^R(r, t)$, we know that $x = r \cos \angle d^\circ = r \cos \angle t$, $y = r \sin \angle d^\circ = r \sin \angle t$, and hence the complex number z, or $x + yi$, has the alternate trigonometric form: $r\,(\cos \angle d^\circ + i \sin \angle d^\circ)$ or $r\,(\cos \angle t + i \sin \angle t)$.

Since the system of circular coordinates is closely related to the system of *polar coordinates* used in analytic geometry, it is customary to use "polar form" as another name for the "trigonometric form" of a complex number.

According to (*i*), (*ii*), (*iii*), and the preceding discussion, the following equations are valid for any nonzero complex number z:

$$\cos t = \frac{x}{|z|} = \frac{x}{\sqrt{x^2 + y^2}} \quad \text{and} \quad \sin t = \frac{y}{|z|} = \frac{y}{\sqrt{x^2 + y^2}}$$

Therefore the polar (trigonometric) form of z expressed in terms of x and y is simply (*v*) $z = \sqrt{x^2 + y^2}\left(\frac{x}{\sqrt{x^2 + y^2}} + i\,\frac{y}{\sqrt{x^2 + y^2}}\right) = |z|\left(\frac{x}{|z|} + i\,\frac{y}{|z|}\right).$

The polar form of a complex number z may be described by saying that it expresses z as the indicated product of two factors, one factor is the non-negative real number $|z|$, and the other factor, $\cos t + i \sin t$, or $\dfrac{x}{|z|} + i \dfrac{y}{|z|}$, is a complex number whose absolute value is one. Note that when z is expressed in the polar form $|z| \left(\dfrac{x}{|z|} + i \dfrac{y}{|z|} \right)$, no amplitude is specified.

Clearly, any given nonzero complex number z has infinitely many amplitudes because P_z is in the terminal side of infinitely many standard position angles. If $\angle t_1$ and $\angle t_2$ are two of these angles, they are coterminal angles and hence $t_1 - t_2 = 2\pi k$ when $k \in I$.

When $z = r(\cos t + i \sin t)$ and t is a real number, there is one and only one amplitude, t, of z in $\langle 0, 2\pi \langle$. This amplitude is called the *argument of z* and is written arg z. Thus: $(vi)\ t = \arg z \longleftrightarrow z = |z|\ (\cos t + i \sin t) \wedge 0 \leq t < 2\pi$. Clearly if $\angle \arg z = \angle d°$, then $0 \leq d < 360$.

Observe that arg z is the radian measure of the unique primary angle whose terminal side contains P_z. For this reason, the expression $|z|$ cis arg z is called the *primary trigonometric (polar) form* of the nonzero complex number z. The fact that z is uniquely determined by $|z|$ and arg z is indicated by the statement: $(vii)\ z_1 = z_2 \longleftrightarrow |z_1| = |z_2| \wedge$ arg $z_1 = $ arg z_2.

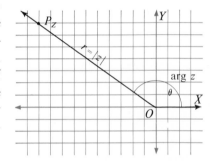

We know that cis arg $z =$ cis (arg $z + 2\pi k$) when $k \in I$. Why? This fact suggests that the expression $|z|$ cis (arg $z + 2\pi k$) be called the *general trigonometric (polar) form* of the nonzero complex number z. If $\angle \arg z = \angle d°$, then $|z|$ cis $\angle (d + k\ 360)°$ is also referred to as the general polar form, and $|z|$ cis $\angle d°$ is referred to as the primary polar form.

If we have complex numbers $\cos t_1 + i \sin t_1$ and $\cos t_2 + i \sin t_2$, we can prove that $\cos t_1 + i \sin t_1 = \cos t_2 + i \sin t_2$ if and only if $t_1 = t_2 + 2\pi k$ when $k \in I$. Thus we have the following theorem whose proof is shown in Ex. 10 on page 627.

▶ **Theorem 13–11.** If $t_1, t_2 \in R$, then
$$\cos t_1 + i \sin t_1 = \cos t_2 + i \sin t_2 \longleftrightarrow t_1 = t_2 + 2\pi k \text{ when } k \in I.$$

We also have the following corollary:

Corollary to Theorem 13–11. If $z_1 = r_1$ cis t_1, $z_2 = r_2$ cis t_2, and $z_1 \neq 0$, then $z_1 = z_2 \longleftrightarrow (r_1 = r_2 \wedge t_1 = t_2 + 2\pi k$ when $k \in I)$.

While the truth of this corollary is evident from geometric considerations, the statements of a ledger proof are given in Ex. 11 on page 628.

Now that we have a new form, which we call the *trigonometric* or *polar* form of a complex number, we shall sometimes refer to the standard form of the complex number as the *rectangular* form of the complex number because it uses the rectangular Cartesian coordinates (x, y) of the point P_z in the Argand diagram.

Before we discuss multiplication and division of complex numbers in polar form, we consider some examples involving the trigonometric form of certain complex numbers.

Example 1. Verify the given modulus for each of the following complex numbers. Also verify the argument and two other amplitudes given for each.

z	modulus	arg z	two other amplitudes
a. $3 + 4i$	5	arc Tan $\frac{4}{3}$	arc Tan $\frac{4}{3} + 2\pi$, or 7.2105
			arc Tan $\frac{4}{3} + 4\pi$, or 13.4937
b. $8 - 8i$	$8\sqrt{2}$	$\frac{7}{4}\pi$	$\frac{7}{4}\pi + 2\pi$, $\frac{7}{4}\pi + 12\pi$
c. 2.41 cis(0.5280)	2.41	0.5280	$0.5280 + 6.2832$, or 6.8112
			$0.5280 - 6.2832$, or -5.7552
d. $\sqrt{3} + i$	2	$\dfrac{\pi}{6}$	$\dfrac{\pi}{6} + 2\pi$, $\dfrac{\pi}{6} - 2\pi$

Example 2. Express each of the following complex numbers in standard (rectangular) form.

    a. $10 (\cos 0 + i \sin 0)$

    b. 8 cis π

    c. 14 cis $\frac{3}{2}\pi$

Solutions.   **a.** $10 (\cos 0 + i \sin 0) = 10(1 + 0 \cdot i) = 10 + 0i$

    b. 8 cis $\pi = 8(\cos \pi + i \sin \pi) = 8(-1 + 0 , i) = -8 + 0i$

    c. 14 cis $\frac{3}{2}\pi = 14\left(\cos \dfrac{3\pi}{2} + i \sin \dfrac{3\pi}{2}\right) = 14[0 + i(-1)] = 0 - 14i$

Example 3. Express $3 - 4i$ in the polar form without specifying an amplitude.

Solution.   Using equation (i) and the fact that $|z| = r$, we have $|z| = \sqrt{3^2 + (-4)^2} = 5$. Therefore by (v), we have: $3 - 4i = 5\left(\dfrac{3}{5} - \dfrac{4}{5}i\right)$.

Example 4. Find the primary trigonometric form for each of the following complex numbers, and also write an expression for the general trigonometric form for each.

  a. -5 **b.** $5i$ **c.** $-\sqrt{3}+i$

Solutions.   **a.** $z = -5 \longrightarrow z = -5 + 0\,i \longrightarrow P_z = P(-5, 0) \longrightarrow$
$\longrightarrow (|z| = 5 \wedge \arg z = \pi) \longrightarrow z = 5 \text{ cis } \pi.$ 5 cis π is the primary trigonometric form of z.
Also if $k \in I$, $z = 5 \text{ cis } (\pi + 2\,\pi k) = 5 \text{ cis } (2\,k + 1)\pi$.
5 cis $(2\,k + 1)\pi$ when $k \in I$ is the general trigonometric form.
For example, if $k = 5$,
$z = 5 \text{ cis } 11\,\pi = 5(\cos 11\,\pi + i \sin 11\,\pi) =$
  $5(\cos \pi + i \sin \pi) = 5(-1 + 0\,i) = -5.$

b. The primary trigonometric form of $5\,i$ is $5 \text{ cis } \dfrac{\pi}{2}$ and the general

trigonometric form is $5 \text{ cis } \left(\dfrac{\pi}{2} + 2\,\pi k\right) = 5 \text{ cis } (4\,k + 1)\dfrac{\pi}{2}$ when

$k \in I$.

c. $z = -\sqrt{3} + i \longrightarrow P_z = P(-\sqrt{3}, 1) \longrightarrow |z|$
  $= \sqrt{(-\sqrt{3})^2 + 1^2} = 2$
If θ is the primary angle whose terminal side contains
$P(-\sqrt{3}, 1)$, then $\cos \theta = -\dfrac{\sqrt{3}}{2}$ and $\sin \theta = \dfrac{1}{2}$.
$\therefore \ \theta = \angle 150°$ and $z = 2 \text{ cis } \angle 150°$, and 2 cis $\angle 150°$ is the primary trigonometric form of z. The general trigonometric form of z is 2 cis $\angle(150 + k\,360)°$, $k \in I$.

Now we turn our attention to the multiplication and division of complex numbers that have been expressed in polar form. Suppose that $z_1 = r_1$ $(\cos t_1 + i \sin t_1)$ and $z_2 = r_2 (\cos t_2 + i \sin t_2)$. If we form the product of z_1 and z_2, we obtain:

$z_1 z_2 = r_1 r_2 (\cos t_1 + i \sin t_1)(\cos t_2 + i \sin t_2)$
$z_1 z_2 = r_1 r_2 [(\cos t_1 \cos t_2 - \sin t_1 \sin t_2) + i (\sin t_1 \cos t_2 + \cos t_1 \sin t_2)]$

Using the addition formulas for cosine and sine (Formulas I–15 and I–16) we have:

$$z_1 z_2 = r_1 r_2 [\cos (t_1 + t_2) + i \sin (t_1 + t_2)] = r_1 r_2 \text{ cis } (t_1 + t_2)$$

Thus, we have proved:

$$(z_1 = r_1 \text{ cis } t_1,\ z_2 = r_2 \text{ cis } t_2) \longrightarrow z_1 z_2 = r_1 r_2 \text{ cis } (t_1 + t_2)$$

Therefore, we see that the product of two given complex numbers is a complex number whose modulus is the product of the moduli of the two given numbers and whose amplitude is the sum of their amplitudes.

To find the polar form of the quotient of z_1 and z_2, we write:

$$\frac{z_1}{z_2} = \frac{r_1\,(\cos t_1 + i \sin t_1)}{r_2\,(\cos t_2 + i \sin t_2)} = \left(\frac{r_1}{r_2}\right)\frac{\cos t_1 + i \sin t_1}{\cos t_2 + i \sin t_2} \cdot \frac{\cos t_2 - i \sin t_2}{\cos t_2 - i \sin t_2}$$

$$= \frac{r_1\,(\cos t_1 \cos t_2 + \sin t_1 \sin t_2) + i\,(\sin t_1 \cos t_2 - \cos t_1 \sin t_2)}{r_2 \qquad \cos^2 t_2 + \sin^2 t_2}$$

$$= \frac{r_1}{r_2}\left[\cos (t_1 - t_2) + i \sin (t_1 - t_2)\right] = \frac{r_1}{r_2}\operatorname{cis}(t_1 - t_2)$$

Thus we have proved:

$$(z_1 = r_1 \operatorname{cis} t_1,\ z_2 = r_2 \operatorname{cis} t_2) \longrightarrow \frac{z_1}{z_2} = \frac{r_1}{r_2}\operatorname{cis}(t_1 - t_2) \text{ provided } z_2 \neq 0.$$

Example 5. If $z_1 = 2 \operatorname{cis} \dfrac{\pi}{4}$ and $z_2 = 6 \operatorname{cis} \dfrac{3\,\pi}{4}$, find $z_1 \cdot z_2$ and $\dfrac{z_1}{z_2}$.

Solution.

$$z_1 \cdot z_2 = \left(2 \operatorname{cis}\frac{\pi}{4}\right)\left(6 \operatorname{cis}\frac{3\,\pi}{4}\right) = 12 \operatorname{cis} \pi = 12(-1 + 0\,i) = -12 + 0\,i.$$

$$\frac{z_1}{z_2} = \frac{2 \operatorname{cis}\dfrac{\pi}{4}}{6 \operatorname{cis}\dfrac{3\,\pi}{4}} = \frac{1}{3}\operatorname{cis}\left(-\frac{\pi}{2}\right) = \frac{1}{3}\left[\cos\left(-\frac{\pi}{2}\right) + i \sin\left(-\frac{\pi}{2}\right)\right]$$

$$= \frac{1}{3}\,(0 - i) = 0 - \frac{i}{3}.$$

It is instructive to verify these results by means of the standard (rectangular) forms of z_1 and z_2.

$$z_1 = 2 \operatorname{cis}\frac{\pi}{4} = 2\left(\cos\frac{\pi}{4} + i \sin\frac{\pi}{4}\right) = 2\left(\frac{1}{\sqrt{2}} + \frac{i}{\sqrt{2}}\right) = \sqrt{2} + \sqrt{2}\,i$$

$$z_2 = 6 \operatorname{cis}\frac{3\,\pi}{4} = 6\left(\cos\frac{3\,\pi}{4} + i \sin\frac{3\,\pi}{4}\right) = 6\left(-\frac{1}{\sqrt{2}} + \frac{i}{\sqrt{2}}\right) =$$
$$-3\sqrt{2} + 3\sqrt{2}\,i$$

Accordingly, $z_1 \cdot z_2 = (\sqrt{2} + \sqrt{2}\,i)(-3\sqrt{2} + 3\sqrt{2}\,i) = -12$, and

$$\frac{z_1}{z_2} = \frac{\sqrt{2} + \sqrt{2}\,i}{-3\sqrt{2} + 3\sqrt{2}\,i} = \frac{1 + i}{-3 + 3\,i} = \frac{(1 + i)(-3 - 3\,i)}{(-3 + 3\,i)(-3 - 3\,i)} = -\frac{i}{3}.$$

Ⓐ **EXERCISES**

1. Express each of the following complex numbers in its primary trigonometric form and in its general trigonometric form when the amplitude is a real number.

a. $\sqrt{3} + i$	d. $\sqrt{3} - i$	g. i	j. -2	m. $-5 + 3\,i$
b. $-\sqrt{3} + i$	e. $1 + i$	h. $3\,i$	k. $-i^4$	n. $-2 - 5\,i$
c. $-\sqrt{3} - i$	f. $2 + 2\,i$	i. 4	l. $4 - i$	o. $-5 - 5\sqrt{3}\,i$

2. Specify arg z and two other amplitudes for each of the following:

a. $z = -6 + 8i$

c. $z = \sqrt{3} + i$

e. $z = 4 \text{ cis } \dfrac{\pi}{16}$

d. $z = 3\sqrt{3} \text{ cis } \dfrac{7\pi}{3}$

b. $z = 3 + 3i$

f. $z = 3 \text{ cis } 1.0559$

3. Express each of the following complex numbers in its rectangular form.

a. $\sqrt{2}\left(\cos\dfrac{\pi}{4} + i\sin\dfrac{\pi}{4}\right)$

g. $8 \text{ cis } \dfrac{2\pi}{3}$

b. $6\left(\cos\dfrac{3\pi}{2} + i\sin\dfrac{3\pi}{2}\right)$

h. $2\sqrt{2} \text{ cis } \dfrac{5\pi}{4}$

c. $4\left(\cos\dfrac{\pi}{2} + i\sin\dfrac{\pi}{2}\right)$

i. $2 \text{ cis } \pi$

j. $5 \text{ cis } 1$

d. $2\left(\cos\dfrac{3\pi}{4} + i\sin\dfrac{3\pi}{4}\right)$

k. $\text{cis } \dfrac{19\pi}{6}$

e. $2 \text{ cis } 0$

f. $4 \text{ cis } \dfrac{5\pi}{3}$

l. $2 \text{ cis } \dfrac{9\pi}{4}$

4. Express each of the following in its polar form without specifying an amplitude.

a. $-3 + 4i$

c. $4 - 5i$

e. $4i$

g. $1.2 - 3.5i$

b. $-5 - 12i$

d. $\sqrt{2} + \sqrt{3}i$

f. 3

h. $-\frac{2}{3} + 3i$

5. Find each of the products indicated below. Express your answer in standard form.

a. $3\left(\cos\dfrac{\pi}{6} + i\sin\dfrac{\pi}{6}\right) \cdot 2\left(\cos\dfrac{\pi}{12} + i\sin\dfrac{\pi}{12}\right)$

b. $4\left(\cos\dfrac{\pi}{3} + i\sin\dfrac{\pi}{3}\right) \cdot 3\left(\cos\dfrac{\pi}{6} + i\sin\dfrac{\pi}{6}\right)$

c. $\left(\cos\dfrac{17\pi}{36} + i\sin\dfrac{17\pi}{36}\right) \cdot 4\left(\cos\dfrac{5\pi}{18} + i\sin\dfrac{5\pi}{18}\right)$

d. $6\left(\cos\dfrac{5\pi}{4} + i\sin\dfrac{5\pi}{4}\right) \cdot \left(\cos\dfrac{5\pi}{12} + i\sin\dfrac{5\pi}{12}\right)$

e. $2\left(\cos\dfrac{\pi}{6} + i\sin\dfrac{\pi}{6}\right) \cdot \dfrac{1}{2}\left(\cos\dfrac{5\pi}{6} + i\sin\dfrac{5\pi}{6}\right)$

f. $4 \text{ cis } \dfrac{3\pi}{4} \cdot 2 \text{ cis } \dfrac{\pi}{4}$

g. $3\sqrt{2} \text{ cis } \dfrac{3\pi}{2} \cdot 5\sqrt{2} \text{ cis } \left(-\dfrac{\pi}{2}\right)$

h. $7 \text{ cis } 0.2618 \cdot 3 \text{ cis } 0.3630$

i. $\text{cis } 1.1314 \cdot 5 \text{ cis } 0.9630$

6. Find each of the following quotients. Express your answer in standard form.

a. $\dfrac{6 \text{ cis } \dfrac{2\pi}{3}}{2 \text{ cis } \dfrac{\pi}{3}}$

d. $\dfrac{12 \left(\cos 2\pi + i \sin 2\pi\right)}{10 \left(\cos \dfrac{2\pi}{3} + i \sin \dfrac{2\pi}{3}\right)}$

b. $\dfrac{\text{cis } \dfrac{4\pi}{9}}{2 \text{ cis } \left(\dfrac{-2\pi}{9}\right)}$

e. $\dfrac{\sqrt{2} \left(\cos 0.2897 + i \sin 0.2897\right)}{\sqrt{2} \left(\cos 0.2443 + i \sin 0.2443\right)}$

f. $\dfrac{3 \left(\cos 1.2741 + i \sin 1.2741\right)}{3\sqrt{2} \left(\cos 0.2496 + i \sin 0.2496\right)}$

c. $\dfrac{2 \text{ cis } \pi}{3 \text{ cis } 0}$

g. $\dfrac{5 \left(\cos 0.9198 + i \sin 0.9198\right)}{4 \left(\cos 0.6510 + i \sin 0.6510\right)}$

B **EXERCISES**

7. Prove: $z = r \text{ cis } \theta \longleftrightarrow \bar{z} = r \text{ cis } (-\theta)$.

8. Prove: $z = r \text{ cis } \theta \longrightarrow \dfrac{1}{z} = \dfrac{1}{r} \text{ cis } (-\theta)$ provided $z \neq 0$.

9. Prove: If z_1 and z_2 have the same argument and $z_2 \neq 0$, then $\dfrac{z_1}{z_2}$ is a real number.

10. The statements of the left-to-right part of the proof of Theorem 13–11: If t_1, $t_2 \in R$, then $\cos t_1 + i \sin t_1 = \cos t_2 + i \sin t_2 \longleftrightarrow t_1 = t_2 + 2\pi k \wedge k \in I$, are given below. You are to supply the reasons for this part and you are to write a complete proof of the right-to-left part.

a. Proof of left-to-right part:

$$\overset{(1)}{\text{Since } \cos t_2 + i \sin t_2 \neq 0}, \overset{(2)}{\cos t_1 + i \sin t_1 = \cos t_2 + i \sin t_2} \overset{(3)}{\longrightarrow}$$

$$\overset{(3)}{\longmapsto} \dfrac{\cos t_1 + i \sin t_1}{\cos t_2 + i \sin t_2} = 1 \overset{(4)}{\longrightarrow} \cos (t_1 - t_2) + i \sin (t_1 - t_2) = 1 \overset{(5)}{\longrightarrow}$$

$$\overset{(5)}{\longmapsto} \cos (t_1 - t_2) = 1 \wedge \sin (t_1 - t_2) = 0.$$

Now $\cos (t_1 - t_2) = 1 \overset{(6)}{\longrightarrow} (t_1 - t_2) \in S_1$, or $\{\cdots, -6\pi, -4\pi, -2\pi, 0, 2\pi, 4\pi, 6\pi, \cdots\}$,

$\sin (t_1 - t_2) = 0 \overset{(7)}{\longrightarrow} (-t_2) \in S_2$, or $\{\cdots, -6\pi, -5\pi, -4\pi, -3\pi, -2\pi, -\pi, 0, \pi, 2\pi, 3\pi, 4\pi, 5\pi, 6\pi, \cdots\}$, and

$\cos (t_1 - t_2) = 1 \wedge \sin (t_1 - t_2) = 0 \overset{(8)}{\longrightarrow} (t_1 - t_2) \in S_1 \cap S_2$, or $\{\cdots, -6\pi, -4\pi, -2\pi, 0, 2\pi, 4\pi, 6\pi, \cdots\}$.

$\overset{(9)}{\therefore t_1 - t_2 = 2\pi k} \wedge k \in I$, or $\overset{(10)}{t_1 = t_2 + 2\pi k} \wedge k \in I$.

b. Prove the right-to-left part of Theorem 13–11.

11. The statements of the left-to-right part of the proof of the corollary to Theorem 13–11:   If $z_1 = r_1$ cis t_1 and $z_2 = r_2$ cis t_2, and $z_1 \neq 0$, then $z_1 = z_2 \longleftrightarrow (r_1 = r_2 \wedge t_1 = t_2 + 2\pi k, k \in I)$, are given below.

a. Complete the left-to-right part of the proof by supplying the reasons.

1. $z_1 = r_1$ cis t_1, $z_2 = r_2$ cis t_2, $z_1 = z_2$, $z_1 \neq 0$	1. Why?
2. $r_1 = \lvert z_1 \rvert$, $r_2 = \lvert z_2 \rvert$	2. Why?
3. $\lvert z_1 \rvert = \lvert z_2 \rvert$	3. Why?
4. $r_1 = r_2$	4. Why?
5. r_1 cis $t_1 = r_2$ cis t_2	5. Why?
6. r_1 cis $t_1 = r_1$ cis t_2	6. Why?
7. $r_1 \neq 0$	7. Why?
8. cis $t_1 =$ cis t_2	8. Why?
9. $t_1 = t_2 + 2\pi k \wedge k \in I$	9. Why?

b. Write the proof of the right-to-left part of the corollary to Theorem 13–11.

Powers of Complex Numbers

If $z = r (\cos t + i \sin t)$, then $z^2 = r^2 (\cos t + i \sin t)^2 = r^2 [(\cos^2 t - \sin^2 t) + 2 i \sin t \cos t]$.   Applying identities **I-20** and **I-23**, we obtain: $z^2 = r^2 (\cos 2t + i \sin 2t)$, or $z^2 = r^2$ cis $2t$.

Extending this idea, we have:

$$z^3 = z^2 \cdot z$$
$$z^3 = [r^2 (\cos 2t + i \sin 2t)] [r (\cos t + i \sin t)]$$
$$z^3 = r^3 (\cos 3t + i \sin 3t) = r^3 \text{ cis } 3t$$

In a similar way we can derive formulas for $z^4, z^5, z^6, \cdots, z^n$ for each counting number n. The general result is given by the following theorem which is known as DeMoivre's theorem:

▷ **Theorem 14–11.** If $z = r$ cis t and $n \in C$, then $z^n = r^n$ cis nt.

We can show that this theorem is true for $n = 1, 2, 3, 4, \cdots, k$ when $k \in C$, by the procedure indicated above. This, however, does not prove that the theorem is true for all counting numbers. Since it is proved in more advanced courses, we will accept it without proof.

Since DeMoivre's theorem is true for all n in C, the following discussion shows that it is also true for n in I.

Since $z^0 = 1$ when z is a nonzero real number, we shall define z^0 as another name for 1 for all nonzero complex numbers z. If we substitute 0 for n in $z^n = r^n (\cos nt + i \sin nt)$, we obtain: $z^0 = r^0 (\cos 0 + i \sin 0) = 1$.   Therefore, Theorem 14–11 is valid when $n \in W$.

When $n < 0$ and $n \in I$, we have $z^n = \dfrac{1}{z^{-n}}$ where $-n$ is a positive integer.

We can prove that $z = r \operatorname{cis} t \longrightarrow z^{-5} = r^{-5} \operatorname{cis}(-5t)$ as follows:

$$z^{-5} \overset{(1)}{=} \frac{1}{z^5} \overset{(2)}{=} \frac{1}{(r \operatorname{cis} t)^5} \overset{(3)}{=} \frac{1}{r^5 \operatorname{cis} 5t} \overset{(4)}{=} \frac{1}{r^5} \cdot \frac{1}{\operatorname{cis} 5t} \overset{(5)}{=} r^{-5} \cdot \frac{1}{\operatorname{cis} 5t} \overset{(6)}{=} r^{-5} \cdot \frac{\operatorname{cis} 0}{\operatorname{cis} 5t}$$

$$\overset{(7)}{=} r^{-5} \operatorname{cis}(0 - 5t) \overset{(8)}{=} r^{-5} \operatorname{cis}(-5t).$$

Reasons: (1) $z^n = \frac{1}{z^{-n}}$, (2) Substitution property of equality, (3) $(r \operatorname{cis} t)^n = r^n \operatorname{cis} nt$ when $n \in C$, (4) $\frac{1}{ab} = \frac{1}{a} \cdot \frac{1}{b}$, (5) Definition of a^x when $x < 0$, (6) Substitution property of equality, (7) $\frac{\operatorname{cis} t_1}{\operatorname{cis} t_2} = \operatorname{cis}(t_1 - t_2)$, (8) $0 - a = -a$. The proof that $z^n = r^n \operatorname{cis} nt$, when n is a negative integer, can be obtained from the above proof by substituting n for -5.

Example 1. Find each of the following and express each result in standard form:

    a. $\left(2 \operatorname{cis} \frac{\pi}{3}\right)^{10}$ **b.** $(-1-i)^8$ **c.** $(1 + \sqrt{3}\,i)^5$

Solutions.   **a.** $\left(2 \operatorname{cis} \frac{\pi}{3}\right)^{10} = 2^{10} \operatorname{cis} 10 \cdot \frac{\pi}{3} = 1024 \operatorname{cis} \frac{10\pi}{3}$

$$= 1024 \left(\cos \frac{10\pi}{3} + i \sin \frac{10\pi}{3}\right)$$

$$= 1024 \left(\cos \frac{4\pi}{3} + i \sin \frac{4\pi}{3}\right)$$

$$= 1024 \left(-\frac{1}{2} - \frac{\sqrt{3}}{2} i\right)$$

$$= -512 - 512 \sqrt{3}\, i$$

b. $(-1-i)^8 = \left(\sqrt{2} \operatorname{cis} \frac{5\pi}{4}\right)^8 = (\sqrt{2})^8 \operatorname{cis} 8 \left(\frac{5\pi}{4}\right) =$

    $16 \operatorname{cis} 10\pi = 16 \operatorname{cis} 0 = 16 + 0\,i$

c. $(1 + \sqrt{3}\,i)^5 = \left(2 \operatorname{cis} \frac{\pi}{3}\right)^5 = 2^5 \operatorname{cis} \frac{5\pi}{3} =$

    $32 \left(\cos \frac{5\pi}{3} + i \sin \frac{5\pi}{3}\right) = 32 \left(\frac{1}{2} - \frac{\sqrt{3}}{2} i\right) = 16 - 16 \sqrt{3}\, i$

Example 2. Using DeMoivre's theorem, find expressions for $\sin 2t$ and $\cos 2t$ in terms of $\sin t$ and $\cos t$.

Solution. $(\cos t + i \sin t)^2 = \cos 2t + i \sin 2t$

    $(\cos t + i \sin t)^2 = \cos^2 t + 2 i \sin t \cos t + i^2 \sin^2 t$

                 $= (\cos^2 t - \sin^2 t) + i(2 \sin t \cos t)$

Thus, we have: $\cos 2t + i \sin 2t = (\cos^2 t - \sin^2 t) + i(2 \sin t \cos t)$. Equating the real parts of this equation and the imaginary parts, we obtain: $\cos 2t = \cos^2 t - \sin^2 t$ and $\sin 2t = 2 \sin t \cos t$.

Ⓐ EXERCISES

1. Find each of the following powers and express each result in standard form.

a. $\left(2 \operatorname{cis} \dfrac{\pi}{4}\right)^4$

d. $\left(\dfrac{1}{2} \operatorname{cis} \dfrac{\pi}{12}\right)^3$

g. $\left(\sqrt[4]{3} \operatorname{cis} \dfrac{\pi}{16}\right)^4$

b. $\left(\sqrt{3} \operatorname{cis} \dfrac{\pi}{3}\right)^6$

e. $(2 \sqrt{3} \operatorname{cis} 0)^6$

h. $(2 \operatorname{cis} 0.5498)^2$

c. $\left(5 \operatorname{cis} \dfrac{2\pi}{3}\right)^{-3}$

f. $\left(\sqrt{2} \operatorname{cis} \dfrac{\pi}{2}\right)^{-2}$

i. $(0.5 \operatorname{cis} 0.6388)^3$

j. $\left(\sqrt{\tfrac{2}{3}} \operatorname{cis} \pi\right)^4$

2. Express each base of the following in its primary trigonometric form. Then find the required power and express in standard form.

a. $(1+i)^6$

d. $(i^2 + i^5)^{-3}$

g. $(1 + 3i)^5$

b. $(1 - i\sqrt{3})^3$

e. $(-\tfrac{1}{2} - \tfrac{1}{2}i)^8$

h. $(3 - 2i)^{-3}$

c. $(2\sqrt{3} - 2i)^4$

f. $(2 - i\sqrt{3})^4$

i. $(-2 + 7i)^4$

3. Using DeMoivre's theorem, find expressions for $\sin 3t$ and $\cos 3t$ in terms of $\sin t$ and $\cos t$.

4. Using DeMoivre's theorem, find expressions for $\sin 4t$ and $\cos 4t$ in terms of $\sin t$ and $\cos t$.

5. Given $z = 1 - i\sqrt{3}$, find z^1, z^2, z^3, z^4, and z^5 and locate the point in the xy-plane which corresponds to each of these powers.

6. Given $z = -1 + i$, find z^0, z^1, z^2, and z^3 and locate the point in the xy-plane which corresponds to each of these powers.

7. Let $z = \cos 1 + i \sin 1$. Draw the graphs of the first eight powers of z. What quadrant contains the point which is the graph of z^{80}?

Roots of Complex Numbers

The theorem of DeMoivre, Theorem 14–11, can be used to find the complex number w such that $w^n = z$, when $z \,\epsilon\, Z$, and n is a counting number. Consider the following example:

Example.   Find the solution set for the equation $w^3 = 1$ and draw its graph.

Solution.   One obvious solution is $w = 1$. To find the other solutions in Z, we use polar forms. If $w = |w| \operatorname{cis} t$, then $w^3 = |w|^3 \operatorname{cis} 3t$ by DeMoivre's theorem. If $|w| \operatorname{cis} t$ is a solution of $w^3 = 1$, then $|w|^3 \operatorname{cis} 3t = 1 \operatorname{cis} 0$. By the corollary to Theorem 13–11, $|w|^3 = 1$ and $3t = 0 + k \cdot 2\pi$.

Hence $|w| = 1$ and $t = \dfrac{k \cdot 2\pi}{3}$ where $k \,\epsilon\, I$. Thus $w \,\epsilon\, \left\{ w \mid w = 1 \cdot \text{cis}\, \dfrac{k \cdot 2\pi}{3}; \; k \,\epsilon\, I \right\}.$ The only values of k which give values of t in $\langle 0, 2\pi \langle$ are 0, 1, and 2. All other integral values of k give values of t which cannot serve as arguments for w.

If $k = 0$, $w = 1 \cdot \text{cis}\, 0 = 1 = w_0$

If $k = 1$, $w = 1 \cdot \text{cis}\, \dfrac{2\pi}{3} = \cos \dfrac{2\pi}{3} + i \sin \dfrac{2\pi}{3} = -\dfrac{1}{2} + \dfrac{\sqrt{3}}{2} i = w_1$

If $k = 2$, $w = 1 \cdot \text{cis}\, \dfrac{4\pi}{3} = \cos \dfrac{4\pi}{3} + i \sin \dfrac{4\pi}{3} = -\dfrac{1}{2} - \dfrac{\sqrt{3}}{2} i = w_2$

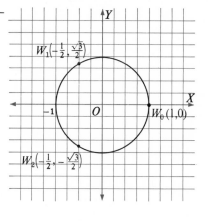

The graphs of w_0, w_1, and w_2 are equally spaced points in the unit circle as shown in the figure. It is easily shown that $w_0{}^3 = w_1{}^3 = w_2{}^3 = 1$. Therefore we have $\{w \mid w^3 = 1\} = \left\{ 1, -\dfrac{1}{2} + \dfrac{\sqrt{3}}{2} i, -\dfrac{1}{2} - \dfrac{\sqrt{3}}{2} i \right\}.$

Note. If d is the degree measure of the angle whose radian measure is t, we may write $w = |w| \text{cis}\, \angle d^\circ$. Thus $w = 1 \cdot \text{cis}\, \dfrac{k \cdot \angle 360^\circ}{3} = \text{cis}\, k \cdot \angle 120^\circ$. Substituting 0, 1, and 2 for k, we obtain the values of w_0, w_1, and w_2 shown above.

It is possible to solve the equation in the above example without using DeMoivre's theorem as follows:

$$w^3 = 1 \leftrightarrow w^3 - 1 = 0 \leftrightarrow (w - 1)(w^2 + w + 1) = 0 \leftrightarrow$$
$$\leftrightarrow (w - 1 = 0 \;\vee\; w^2 + w + 1 = 0).$$

The solution set of our equation is the union of the solution sets of the equations $w - 1 = 0$ and $w^2 + w + 1 = 0$. By the quadratic formula,

$$\{w \mid w^2 + w + 1 = 0\} = \left\{ \dfrac{-1 + \sqrt{3}\,i}{2}, \dfrac{-1 - \sqrt{3}\,i}{2} \right\}.$$

Therefore $\quad \{w \mid w^3 = 1\} = \left\{ 1, -\dfrac{1}{2} + \dfrac{i\sqrt{3}}{2}, -\dfrac{1}{2} - \dfrac{i\sqrt{3}}{2} \right\}.$

Each of these numbers is called a cube root of 1.

We now extend the procedure for obtaining roots of order n when $n \in C$ and $n \geq 2$ by the following theorem:

▶ **Theorem 15–11.** If z is a nonzero complex number, n is a counting number, and $n \geq 2$, then the solution set of $w^n = z$ is $\{w_0, w_1, w_2, \cdots, w_{n-1}\}$ where

$$w_k = \sqrt[n]{|z|} \operatorname{cis} \left(\frac{1}{n}t + k \cdot \frac{2\,\pi}{n}\right), \, k = 0, 1, 2, \cdots, n-1, \text{ and } t = \arg z.$$

By the methods used in the preceding example, we can show that:

1. Each of the numbers of $\{w_0, w_1, w_2, \cdots, w_{n-1}\}$ is a solution of $w^n = z$
2. All the numbers $w_0, w_1, \cdots, w_{n-1}$ are distinct and
3. $w^n = z$ has no solutions other than those listed.

The proof of (1) follows easily from DeMoivre's theorem:

$$\begin{aligned}
w_k{}^n &= \left[\sqrt[n]{|z|} \operatorname{cis} \left(\frac{1}{n}t + k \frac{2\,\pi}{n}\right)\right]^n \\
&= (\sqrt[n]{|z|})^n \cdot \left[\operatorname{cis} \left(\frac{t}{n} + k \cdot \frac{2\,\pi}{n}\right)\right]^n \\
&= |z| \operatorname{cis} (t + k \cdot 2\,\pi) \\
&= |z| \operatorname{cis} t \\
&= z
\end{aligned}$$

The proof of (2) follows from the fact that no two of the numbers $w_0, w_1,$ $\cdots, w_{n-1}$ have the same argument. The proof of (3) follows from the fact that any solution of $w^n = z$ must have the form $\sqrt[n]{|z|} \operatorname{cis} \left(\frac{1}{n}t + k \cdot \frac{2\,\pi}{n}\right)$ and any integral value of k not in $\{0, 1, 2, \cdots, n-1\}$ gives one of the numbers in $\{w_0, w_1, \cdots, w_{n-1}\}$ when substituted in the above expression. Thus if $k = n + 3$, we have the expression:

$$\sqrt[n]{|z|} \operatorname{cis} \left(\frac{t}{n} + (n+3) \frac{2\,\pi}{n}\right) = \sqrt[n]{|z|} \operatorname{cis} \left(\frac{t}{n} + 3 \cdot \frac{2\,\pi}{n} + 2\,\pi\right) =$$

$$\sqrt[n]{|z|} \operatorname{cis} \left(\frac{t}{n} + 3 \cdot \frac{2\,\pi}{n}\right) = w_3$$

When $n \in C$, we know by Theorem 4–4 that any integer k can be expressed as $mn + s$ where $m \in I$ and $s \in \{0, 1, 2, \cdots, n-1\}$; that is, either k is an integral multiple of n or it lies between two consecutive integral multiples of n.

If we let $k = mn + s$ in $\sqrt[n]{|z|} \operatorname{cis} \left(\frac{t}{n} + k \cdot \frac{2\,\pi}{n}\right)$, we obtain:

$$\sqrt[n]{|z|} \operatorname{cis} \left(\frac{t}{n} + (mn+s) \frac{2\,\pi}{n}\right) = \sqrt[n]{|z|} \operatorname{cis} \left(\frac{t}{n} + s \cdot \frac{2\,\pi}{n} + m \cdot 2\,\pi\right) =$$

$$\sqrt[n]{|z|} \operatorname{cis} \left(\frac{t}{n} + s \cdot \frac{2\,\pi}{n}\right) = w_s$$

We have now established the fact that each nonzero complex number z has exactly n distinct nth roots when $n \, \epsilon \, C$. The complex number 0 has only one nth root namely 0.

 EXERCISES

1. Find the cube roots of each of the following complex numbers.

   a. $1 + i$ **b.** 8 **c.** i **d.** $2 - i\sqrt{3}$

2. In each of the following cases find n distinct nth roots:

   a. $-2 - 2i$; $n = 4$ **c.** $1 - i$; $n = 5$ **e.** $16 \, i$; $n = 4$

   b. i; $n = 2$ **d.** $16 \text{ cis } \angle \, 120°$; $n = 4$ **f.** $1 + i$; $n = 3$

3. Find the solution set of each of the following equations.

   a. $x^2 = 4$ **d.** $x^3 + i = 0$ **g.** $x^5 = 32$

   b. $x^5 - 1 = 0$ **e.** $x^3 = -2 - 2\sqrt{3}\,i$ **h.** $x^4 = 81 \text{ cis } \dfrac{\pi}{3}$

   c. $x^3 = -1$ **f.** $x^4 - 4 + 4\sqrt{3}\,i = 0$ **i.** $x^2 = -9\,i$

4. Find the five distinct fifth roots of 2. Represent these roots graphically.

5. Find the three distinct cube roots of $2\,i$. Represent these roots graphically.

ESSENTIALS

Before you leave this chapter make sure that you

1. Understand why and how we extend R_s. (**Page** 589.)

2. Know the properties of Z_s, the complex number system, listed in this chapter. (**Page** 590.)

3. Can find the sum, product, and difference of any two complex numbers. (**Page** 594.)

4. Know what we mean by the standard form of a complex number. (**Page** 599.)

5. Can find the quotient of two complex numbers. (**Page** 602.)

6. Can solve quadratic equations whose roots are in Z. (**Page** 605.)

7. Can represent complex numbers graphically. (**Page** 610.)

8. Understand the theorems pertaining to the absolute values of complex numbers given in this chapter. (**Page** 614.)

9. Understand the theorems pertaining to the conjugates of complex numbers given in this chapter. (**Page** 617.)

10. Can transform the standard form of a complex number into the trigonometric (polar) form and conversely. (**Page** 621.)

11. Can use DeMoivre's theorem to find powers and roots of complex numbers. (Pages 628–630.)

12. Understand, can spell, and use correctly the following words and phrases.

amplitude (Page 621.)   modulus (Page 621.)
Argand diagram (Page 610.)   polar form (Page 621.)
argument of z (Page 622.)   primary trigonometric form (Page 622.)
axis of imaginaries (Page 610.)   pure imaginary (Page 600.)
axis of reals (Page 610.)   rectangular form (Page 623.)

CHAPTER REVIEW

1. Name the simplest extension of C_s in which a solution for each of the following equations can be found.

   a. $x^2 = -7$ **b.** $x^2 - 2\sqrt{2}\,x + 2 = 0$ **c.** $4\,x = 17$ **d.** $3\,x - 57 = -57$

2. Indicate which of the following complex numbers are real numbers, which are pure imaginary numbers, and which are neither real numbers nor pure imaginaries.

   a. 0 **c.** $\sqrt{2} + i$ **e.** i^3 **g.** $i^4 + 3$
   b. $\sqrt{3}$ **d.** $i^2 + i^5$ **f.** $\sqrt{-36}$ **h.** $2\,i - 2\sqrt{2}\,i^3$

3. Write each of the following complex numbers in standard form.

   a. 3 **b.** $4\,i$ **c.** -2 **d.** 0 **e.** $\dfrac{4 + 7\,i}{2\,i}$

4. Write in standard form the multiplicative inverse of $x + yi$.

5. Write in standard form the additive inverse of $x - yi$.

6. Write in standard form the multiplicative inverse, if one exists, for each of the following complex numbers.

   a. $2 + 3\,i$ **b.** $-\pi i$ **c.** $0 + 0\,i$ **d.** $\frac{3}{5} - \frac{1}{2}\,i$

7. What is the real part and what is the imaginary part of each of the following complex numbers?

   a. $-5 + 2\,i$ **b.** 10 **c.** $12 - i$ **d.** $4\,i$ **e.** 0

8. Express each of the following as a complex number in standard form.

   a. $(2 + 3\,i) + (4 - 6\,i)$
   b. $(6 - i) - (5 - 4\,i) + 6\,i$
   c. $(\frac{1}{2} + 6\,i) - i(3 - 5\,i)$
   d. $(2 - 3\,i)(4 - 2\,i)$
   e. $6\,i \cdot 4\,i \cdot i$
   f. $(3 - 2\,i)^2$

   g. $\dfrac{1 - i}{2 + 3\,i}$
   h. $\dfrac{5}{i} + \dfrac{3\,i}{4\,i^2}$
   i. $\dfrac{1 - \sqrt{3}\,i}{1 + \sqrt{3}\,i}$

   j. $\dfrac{(1 + i)(1 - i) + (2 + 3\,i)}{4 - 3\,i}$
   k. $\dfrac{5 + \sqrt{-3}}{2 - \sqrt{-2}}$
   l. $\dfrac{3 - 2\,i}{4 + i} + \dfrac{5 - i}{2 - 3\,i}$

9. For what real number values of a and b is each of the following true?

   a. $a + bi = 5 - 2i$ **b.** $3a + bi = 6i$ **c.** $(a + 2) + (3 - b)i = 4 - 9i$

10. Find two pairs of complex numbers x and y for which each of the following statements are true.

    a. $2x - 3yi = 6 + 2i$ **b.** $x + 2yi = 4 - i$ **c.** $3x - 4yi = 5$

11. Write each of the following in standard form.

    a. $\sqrt{-12}$

    b. $\sqrt{-(4i)^2}$

    c. $\sqrt{-5i^2}$

    d. $\sqrt{-\frac{1}{16}} \cdot \sqrt{-8}$

    e. $\sqrt{-18} + \sqrt{-2}$

    f. $\dfrac{\sqrt{-49}}{i\sqrt{-25}}$

12. Find the solution set of each of the following equations.

    a. $3z^2 + 2z + 8 = 0$ **b.** $z^2 - 32z + 10 = 0$ **c.** $z^2 - 4\sqrt{5}\,z - 1 = 0$

13. One root of $x^3 - 27 = 0$ is obviously 3. Find the other two roots.

14. Represent graphically:

    a. $-3 - 2i$ **b.** $4 - i$ **c.** $0 + 6i$ **d.** $8 - \frac{1}{2}i$

15. By means of a geometrical construction find the point in the xy-plane which corresponds to each of the following:

    a. $(-4 + 2i) + (1 - 5i)$

    b. $(4 - 3i) + (-4 + 3i)$

    c. $(1 + 2i) + (3 - 3i) + 4i$

16. Let Z_1 and Z_2 be two points in the xy-plane. If Z_1 corresponds to the complex number $3 - 2i$ and Z_2 corresponds to the complex number $-5 + 4i$, what are the (x, y) coordinates of the midpoint of $\overline{Z_1 Z_2}$ and what is the complex number which corresponds to the midpoint?

17. Find $|z|$ when z has each of the following values.

    a. $z = 5 - 2i$ **b.** $z = -3 + 4i$ **c.** $z = -5 - 12i$ **d.** $z = 7 - i$

18. Z_1 and Z_2 are two points in the xy-plane. If Z_1 corresponds to the complex number z_1 and Z_2 corresponds to the complex number z_2, show $|Z_2 Z_1|$ geometrically in each of the following cases. Also write the number which corresponds to $|Z_2 Z_1|$ in each case.

    a. $z_1 = 3 - i, z_2 = 2 + 4i$

    b. $z_1 = -5 + 2i, z_2 = 3 - 4i$

    c. $z_1 = 2i, z_2 = 3 + 6i$

    d. $z_1 = -6 - 2i, z_2 = 4$

19. If $z = 4 - 2i$, what number is represented by each of the following expressions? Express each in standard form.

    a. $-z$ **b.** $\bar{z}$ **c.** $|z|$ **d.** $|z|^2$ **e.** $|z^2|$ **f.** $\dfrac{1}{z}$

20. Express each of the following in its primary trigonometric form and in its general trigonometric form.

a. $4 + 4i$ c. $-\sqrt{3} - i$ e. $4i$ g. $4 - 5i$

b. $-2 + i$ d. $1 - \sqrt{3}i$ f. 6 h. $3 + 7i$

21. Express each of the following complex numbers in rectangular form.

a. $2\,(\cos \angle 135° + i \sin \angle 135°)$

b. $\sqrt{2}\,(\cos \angle 315° + i \sin \angle 315°)$

c. $2 \text{ cis } \angle 240°$

d. $3 \text{ cis } \dfrac{4\pi}{3}$

e. $\frac{1}{2} \text{ cis } \angle 42.35°$

f. $4 \text{ cis } 0.1222$

22. Express each of the following as the product of a positive number and a complex number whose absolute value is one.

a. $-5 + 12i$ b. $6 - 8i$ c. 5 d. $\frac{3}{4} + 2i$

23. Find each of the following products. Express your answer in standard form.

a. $\sqrt{3}\left(\cos \dfrac{\pi}{6} + i \sin \dfrac{\pi}{6}\right) \cdot 2\left(\cos \dfrac{\pi}{3} + i \sin \dfrac{\pi}{3}\right)$

b. $4\left(\cos \dfrac{3\pi}{4} + i \sin \dfrac{3\pi}{4}\right) \cdot 4\left(\cos \dfrac{\pi}{2} + i \sin \dfrac{\pi}{2}\right)$

c. $\dfrac{1}{2} \text{ cis } \dfrac{\pi}{18} \cdot 6 \text{ cis } \dfrac{2\pi}{9}$

e. $2 \text{ cis } \dfrac{5\pi}{6} \cdot \text{ cis } \dfrac{\pi}{3}$

d. $3 \text{ cis } \dfrac{\pi}{12} \cdot 5 \text{ cis } \dfrac{\pi}{4}$

f. $4 \text{ cis } 0.2820 \cdot \text{ cis } 0.4513$

24. Express each of the following powers in standard form.

a. $\left(3 \text{ cis } \dfrac{\pi}{4}\right)^4$

c. $\left(\sqrt{2} \text{ cis } \dfrac{\pi}{12}\right)^4$

e. $(\text{cis } 0.1990)^3$

b. $\left(2 \text{ cis } \dfrac{\pi}{6}\right)^3$

d. $2\sqrt{3}\,(\text{cis } \pi)^5$

f. $\left(2 \text{ cis } \dfrac{5\pi}{8}\right)^4$

25. Before finding the power, change each of the following to trigonometric form. After finding the power, express it in standard form.

a. $(\sqrt{3} - i)^4$ b. $(-1 - \sqrt{3}i)^5$ c. $(2 + 2i)^{-8}$

26. For each of the following find n distinct nth roots.

a. $8 \text{ cis } \pi; \; n = 3$ b. $16 \cos \pi; \; n = 4$ c. $1 + \sqrt{3}i; \; n = 3$

27. Solve each of the following equations:

a. $x^4 = 8$

c. $x^3 = 3 + 3i$

b. $x^3 = 2$

d. $x^4 = -4 + 4\sqrt{3}i$

1. If a solution is to be found for each of the following equations, which will require an extension of the real number system?

    a. $2x = 12$ **b.** $3x = 7$ **c.** $x^2 = 12$ **d.** $x^2 = -12$

2. Write the subset of real numbers in $T = \{3 + 4i, \sqrt{-1}, \sqrt{2} + \sqrt{3}\,i, 3 + 0\,i, 0 + 0\,i, (\sqrt{-1})^{-4}, \frac{3}{5} + i, \sqrt{6}\}$.

3. Write each of the following complex numbers in standard form:

    a. 14 **b.** $\sqrt{-9}$ **c.** i^4 **d.** $\dfrac{1}{3+i}$

    In Ex. 4–9 write each of the given expressions as a single complex number in standard form.

4. $(2 + 4i) + (6 - 2i)$ **7.** $\dfrac{2-i}{3+i}$

5. $(3 - 5i)(2 + 4i)$ **8.** $\dfrac{2 - \sqrt{3}\,i}{\sqrt{3} + \sqrt{3}\,i}$

6. $(4 - i)^2$ **9.** $\dfrac{3 + 5i}{i} + \dfrac{2 + 3i}{1 + i}$

10. For what real number values of a and b is it true that $-3a + bi = 6 - 7i$?

11. If $z = -\sqrt{3} + i$, find arg z.

12. Represent the complex number $-2 + 5i$ graphically.

13. If $z = 3 - 6i$, what number is represented by each of the following expressions? Express each in standard form.

    a. $-z$ **b.** $\bar{z}$ **c.** $|z|$ **d.** $|z|^2$

14. Express $-\sqrt{3} - i$ in its primary trigonometric form.

15. $5\,(\cos \angle 45° + i \sin \angle 45°) \cdot 2\,(\cos \angle 15° + i \sin \angle 15°) = \underline{\ ?\ }$

16. $8\left(\cos \dfrac{5\pi}{6} + i \sin \dfrac{5\pi}{6}\right) \div 2\left(\cos \dfrac{\pi}{2} + i \sin \dfrac{\pi}{2}\right) = \underline{\ ?\ }$

17. $\left(4 \operatorname{cis} \dfrac{\pi}{18}\right)^5 = \underline{\ ?\ }$ **18.** $\left(2 \operatorname{cis} \dfrac{\pi}{6}\right)^6 = \underline{\ ?\ }$

19. Find three distinct cube roots of $27 \operatorname{cis} \dfrac{\pi}{3}$.

20. Find the solution set for $x^4 = 1$.

638

1. Simplify, assuming that each variable represents a real number.

a. $\dfrac{(\sqrt{3})^5}{(\sqrt{3})^3}$

b. $\left(\dfrac{-3\,a^2}{7}\right)^{-3}$; $a \neq 0$

c. $\dfrac{(16\,x)^{-2}}{2\,x^3 y^3}$; $x \neq 0,\ y \neq 0$

d. $2^x \cdot 8^{x+2}$

e. $(125)^{\frac{2}{3}}$

f. $\dfrac{3\sqrt{8}}{9\sqrt{2}}$

g. $8^{3-\sqrt{5}} \cdot 8^{2+3\sqrt{5}}$

2. Express in scientific notation:

a. 5,200,000   b. 0.00000042   c. 75,842,000   d. 1.0000010

3. Write the decimal which is equal to each of the following:

a. 7.8×10^{-4} b. 8.004×10^5 c. 4.700×10^6 d. 3.300×10^{-2}

4. Evaluate:

a. $(216)^{-\frac{2}{3}}$ b. $\sqrt[3]{-125} \cdot \sqrt[4]{81}$ c. $(x+7)^0$; $x \neq -7$ d. $\left(\dfrac{27\,a^3 b^2 c^4}{8\,a^3 b^3 c}\right)^{\frac{1}{3}}$

5. Solve each of the following equations for x.

a. $3^x = 729$ b. $x^{\frac{3}{5}} = 64$ c. $\sqrt{x^5} = 9\sqrt{3}$ d. $4^{x^2} = 4^{3-2x}$

6. Write the inverse of $\{(x, y) \mid y = 10^x;\ x \in R\}$ in two forms.

7. Write in exponential form: $\log_2 16 = 4$.

8. Solve each of the following equations for x.

a. $\log x = 3$

b. $\log_x 81 = 2$

c. $\log_5 625 = x$

d. $\log_2 (x+5) = 3$

e. $3 \log_4 x = 15$

f. $5^x = \frac{1}{125}$

9. Use logarithms to evaluate:

a. 793×0.471 b. $\dfrac{8742}{9685}$ c. $\dfrac{0.3218\,\pi}{8.421 \times 17}$ d. $\sqrt[4]{(7.825)^3}$

10. If each of the following pairs designates two paths in a unit circle in standard position and if $I(1, 0)$ and $B\left(\dfrac{\sqrt{2}}{2}, \dfrac{\sqrt{2}}{2}\right)$ indicate two points in the circle, in which pair(s) are the two paths equal? In which pair(s) are the two paths equivalent?

a. $\left(OI, \dfrac{\pi}{4}\right), \left(OB, \dfrac{\pi}{4}\right)$ b. $\left(OI, \dfrac{\pi}{4}\right), \left(OI, \text{Sin}^{-1} \dfrac{\sqrt{2}}{2}\right)$ c. $(OB, 2\pi), \left(OI, \dfrac{9\pi}{4}\right)$

11. a. Show that the point $T\left(-\dfrac{1}{2}, \dfrac{\sqrt{3}}{2}\right)$ is in a unit circle in standard position.

b. When T of part **a.** is the terminal point of path $(\overrightarrow{OI}, t)$ in the unit circle, find:

(1) $\sin t$ (2) $\cos t$ (3) $\tan t$

12. The length of the radius of a wheel is 6 inches.

   a. If the wheel makes 3 revolutions per second, what is its angular velocity in radians per second?

   b. What is the linear velocity in inches per second of a point in the rim of the wheel?

13. In right triangle ABC in standard notation, α is the angle whose vertex is A, β is the angle whose vertex is B, and γ is the right angle whose vertex is C.

   a. $\cos \alpha = \_?\_$ **b.** $\cos \beta = \_?\_$ **c.** $\tan \alpha = \_?\_$ **d.** $\csc \beta = \_?\_$

14. Solve each of the following triangles, assuming that a, b, and c are the measures of the sides of the triangle and that α, β, and γ are the angles respectively opposite these sides.

   a. $a = 11.64$
   $c = 15.72$
   $dm\ \beta = 135$

   b. $a = 194$
   $b = 181$
   $c = 92$

   c. $a = 511.1$
   $b = 853.0$
   $dm\ \alpha = 22.90$

15. Without use of a table, state the value of each of the following:

   a. $\sin \angle 225°$ **b.** $\cos \angle 330°$ **c.** $\cot \angle 270°$

16. If a, b, and c are the measures of the three sides of a triangle and α, β, and γ are the angles respectively opposite these sides, find the area of the triangle when $a = 25.7$, $dm\ \alpha = 31.4$, and $dm\ \beta = 45.7$.

17. Which of the following statements are identities and which are conditional equations, assuming that $x \in R$?

   a. $\tan x \cot x = 1$ **c.** $\sin^2 x = 1 - \cos^2 x$ **e.** $\cos(-x) = \cos x$

   b. $\tan x \cos x = \frac{1}{2}$ **d.** $\cos x = \dfrac{1}{\sec x}$ **f.** $\cot x = \dfrac{\sin x}{\cos x}$

18. Simplify each of the following, assuming that no denominator is zero and that $x \in R$.

   a. $\cos^2 x \tan x - \tan x$ **c.** $\tan x \cot x + \sin^2 x + \cos^2 x$

   b. $\dfrac{\tan^2 x}{1 + \tan^2 x}$ **d.** $1 - \dfrac{\cos^2 x}{1 + \sin x}$

19. Find the primary solutions for the equation $\dfrac{\sec \theta}{\cot \theta + \tan \theta} = \dfrac{1}{\sqrt{2}}$.

20. Without using a table, find the value of each of the following:

   a. $\sin \angle 75°$ **b.** $\sin \angle 105°$ **c.** $\cos \angle 15°$ **d.** $\cos \dfrac{13\pi}{12}$

21. If $\sin \alpha = \frac{2}{3}$ and $0 < dm\ \alpha < 90$, find:

   a. $\sin 2\alpha$ **b.** $\cos 2\alpha$ **c.** $\sin \frac{1}{2}\alpha$ **d.** $\tan \frac{1}{2}\alpha$

22. Without drawing the graphs, explain how the graph of each of the following differs from the graph of $\{(x, y) \mid y = \sin x; \ x \, \epsilon \, R\}$.

    a. $\{(x, y) \mid y = -2 \sin x; \ x \, \epsilon \, R\}$ **c.** $\{(x, y) \mid y = \sin 3x; \ x \, \epsilon \, R]$

    b. $\{(x, y) \mid y = -2 + \sin x; \ x \, \epsilon \, R\}$ **d.** $\{(x, y) \mid y = \sin (x+1); \ x \, \epsilon \, R\}$

23. What positive real number(s) are represented by each of the following?

    a. $\sin^{-1} \dfrac{\sqrt{2}}{2}$ **b.** arc cos (-1) **c.** $\tan^{-1} \dfrac{\sqrt{3}}{3}$

24. Sketch the graph of each of the following:

    a. $\{(x, y) \mid x = \text{Cos } y]$ **b.** $\left\{(x, y) \mid x = \dfrac{2 \text{ Sin } y}{3}\right\}$

25. Given $A = \left\{\sqrt{3}, \ 7, \ 2\,i, \ 3 + 5\,i, \ -\dfrac{i}{2}, \ 4 - 6\,i, \ 3 + 0\,i, \ 0 + 6\,i, \ 50 + 2\,i\right\}$, find each of the following subsets of A.

    a. the real numbers in A **c.** the pure imaginary numbers in A

    b. the complex numbers in A

26. Simplify each of the following expressions:

    a. $(3 + 2\,i) + (4 + 2\,i)$ **d.** $(1 + i)(1 - i)$ **g.** $\dfrac{4 + 2\,i}{10 + 5\,i}$

    b. $(7 + 2\,i) - (2 - 3\,i)$ **e.** $7 + (4 - 3\,i)$ **h.** $i^7 \cdot i$

    c. $(2 + 6\,i)^2$ **f.** $2\,i(\tfrac{1}{2} + 4\,i)$ **i.** $\dfrac{5 - 2\,i}{i}$

27. Write each of the following in standard form:

    a. $2 - i - \dfrac{(3 + i)^2}{1 + i}$ **b.** $\dfrac{2 + i}{3 - i} \cdot \dfrac{3 + i}{i}$ **c.** $\dfrac{2}{3 + i} + \dfrac{i}{1 - i}$

28. Solve each of the following equations, assuming that z represents a complex number.

    a. $z^2 = 7$ **b.** $z^2 - 4z + 5 = 0$ **c.** $z^2 + 3z + 8 = 0$

29. Given that $u = 4 - 3\,i$ and $v = -1 + 6\,i$, locate in an Argand diagram:

    a. The points U and V that correspond respectively to u and v.

    b. The point S which corresponds to the sum of u and v.

30. Express in rectangular form:

    a. $2 \ (\cos \angle 45° + i \sin \angle 45°)$ **c.** $\dfrac{1}{2} \left(\cos \dfrac{3\,\pi}{4} + i \sin \dfrac{3\,\pi}{4}\right)$

    b. $6 \text{ cis } \dfrac{5\,\pi}{3}$

31. Express in polar form:

    a. $-1 + \sqrt{3}\,i$ **b.** $4 - 4\,i$ **c.** $1 + 5\,i$

32. Perform each of the following indicated operations.

    a. $3 \text{ cis } \frac{2}{3} \pi \cdot 2 \text{ cis } \frac{1}{3} \pi$ **b.** $\left(4 \text{ cis } \frac{2\pi}{3}\right)^3$

33. Find all the complex number roots of $z^5 = -1$.

CUMULATIVE TEST
[Chapters 8–11]

1. Simplify each of the following expressions:

    a. $\left(\frac{-4\,a^3}{5}\right)^{-2}$; $a \neq 0$ **b.** $4^{\sqrt{5}} \cdot 8^{\sqrt{5}}$ **c.** $16^{\frac{3}{2}}$

2. If $x \in R$, solve each of the following equations for x:

    a. $3^x = 243$ **b.** $x^{\frac{2}{3}} = 25$ **c.** $\sqrt{x^6} = 8$ **d.** $3^{x^2} = 3^{3x+4}$

3. Write the inverse of $\{(x, y) \mid y = 3^x; \ x \in R\}$.

4. Write in exponential form: $\log_4 256 = x$

5. Use logarithms to evaluate $\sqrt[3]{\dfrac{384.1 \times 742.0}{0.0056}}$.

6. If $\sin \theta = -\dfrac{\sqrt{3}}{2}$ and $0 < dm \ \theta < 270$, what number(s) are represented by

    a. $\cos \theta$?   **b.** $\tan \theta$?

7. If a, b, and c are the measures of the sides of triangle ABC, and α, β, and γ are the angles respectively opposite these sides, find γ when $a = 703$, $c = 912$, and $dm \ \alpha = 47$.

8. Simplify $\sec x \cos x - \cos^2 x$.

9. Without drawing the graphs, explain how the graph of each of the following differs from the graph of $\{(x, y) \mid y = \sin x\}$. In each case $x \in R$.

    a. $\{(x, y) \mid y = \sin 2\,x\}$ **b.** $\{(x, y) \mid x = \sin y\}$ **c.** $\{(x, y) \mid y = \text{Sin } x\}$

10. Simplify each of the following and express in standard form.

    a. $(4 - 2\,i) + (3 + 7\,i)$ **b.** $(2 + 4\,i)^2$ **c.** $\dfrac{2 - 3\,i}{2 + 3\,i}$

11. Write in rectangular form: $4 \text{ cis } \angle 390°$.

12. Write in its primary trigonometric form: $1 - \sqrt{3}\,i$.

13. Perform each of the indicated operations.

    a. $\left(3 \text{ cis } \dfrac{\pi}{4}\right)^5$ **b.** $\dfrac{18 \text{ cis } \frac{13}{18}\,\pi}{6 \text{ cis } \dfrac{5\,\pi}{9}}$ **c.** $\left(\dfrac{1 - i\sqrt{3}}{2}\right)^3$

14. Find n distinct nth roots for each of the following:

    a. $3 - 4\,i$; $n = 3$ **b.** $25 \text{ cis } \dfrac{\pi}{3}$; $n = 2$

Systems of Linear Sentences

Systems of Open Sentences

Recall that an ordered pair of numbers (a, b) satisfies the open sentence $s_{(x,y)}$ if $s_{(a,b)}$ is a true numerical statement. Thus the ordered pair $(3, 1)$ satisfies the open sentence $x^2 + y^2 = 10$ but the ordered pair $(1, 5)$ does not. Similarly, the ordered pair $(-3i, i)$ satisfies the open sentence $x^2 + y^2 + 5 < 0$ but the ordered pair (i, i) does not.

We shall assume that each of the variables in the sentences which we shall consider has R for its domain unless otherwise stated. When x, $y \in R$, a sentence $s_{(x,y)}$ will have a subset of $R \times R$ for its replacement set.

A *system of open sentences* is the conjunction of two or more open sentences. When we know that we are working in $R \times R$, that is, working with sentences whose graphs are in the xy-plane, we say that the conjunction of two or more sentences, each of which contains at least one of the variables x and y, is a *system of open sentences* in x and y. The individual sentences are called the *components* of the system.

If we are working in $R \times R$, each of the following is a two-component system of open sentences in x and y.

a. $\begin{cases} x + 3y = 4 \\ 5x - 2y = 3 \end{cases}$
c. $\begin{cases} x + 2y < 5 \\ 3x - y > 7 \end{cases}$
e. $\begin{cases} 3x - 7y = 2 \\ x + 3y \geq 5 \end{cases}$
g. $\begin{cases} x = 1 \\ x^2 + xy = 3 \end{cases}$

b. $\begin{cases} y = 5 \\ x = -2 \end{cases}$
d. $\begin{cases} x > 7 \\ x > 10 \end{cases}$
f. $\begin{cases} y \leq 2 \\ y \leq 9 \end{cases}$
h. $\begin{cases} x^2 + y^2 > 0 \\ y < x \end{cases}$

The first two systems are systems of linear equations in x and y. The next two systems are systems of linear inequalities in x and y. Each of the systems in the first three columns can be described as a system of linear sentences in x and y. This is true because when each of these sentences is written as an equivalent sentence having one member zero, the other member can be written in the form $ax + by + c$ where $a^2 + b^2 \neq 0$. Each of the last two systems involves one nonlinear sentence in x and y.

Observe that when we know that we are working in $R \times R$, we think of the sentences in system **f** as $0\,x + y \leq 2$ and $0\,x + y \leq 9$, and of the sentences in system **b** as $0\,x + y = 5$ and $x + 0\,y = -2$. Note that in systems such as those shown in **d** and **f**, we cannot tell from the appearance of the system that we are working in $R \times R$. The context, however, usually makes clear what the replacement set is.

The *replacement set of any system of open sentences* is the intersection of the replacement sets of its component sentences. The *solution set of any system of open sentences* is the intersection of the solution sets of its component sentences. Thus we see that $(1, 1)$ is in the solution set of system **a** but $(3, 6)$ is not. The solution set of system **b** is $\{(-2, 5)\}$ and the solution set of system **d** is $\{(x, y) \mid x + 0\,y > 10\}$ when we are working in $R \times R$.

Example. Draw the graph of the truth set of the system: $\begin{cases} x^2 + y^2 < 12 \\ y > x \end{cases}$

Solution. If S is the solution set of $x^2 + y^2 < 12$, T is the solution set of $y > x$, and C is the solution set of the system $x^2 + y^2 < 12 \wedge y > x$, then

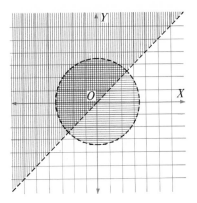

$C = T \cap S$. The graph of C is the cross-hatched region shown in the diagram. *Note.* If instead of $y > x$ the second sentence had been $y > x + 6$, we would have obtained $C = \emptyset$.

If S and T are the truth sets of the components of a two-sentence system and $S \cap T = \emptyset$, the open sentences have no common solution and the system of open sentences is said to be *inconsistent*. The following system is an example of an inconsistent system.

$$\begin{cases} 3\,x + y = 7 \\ 3\,x + y = -15 \end{cases}$$

The union of the graphs of the two equations which are components of the above system is two parallel lines.

If $S \cap T \neq \emptyset$, then there is at least one pair of numbers which satisfies both sentences. In this case the system is said to be *consistent*. Consistent systems are classified as either *dependent* or *independent*. If $S = T$, the system is dependent. If $S \neq T$, the system is independent.

Thus every system can be placed in one of the following classifications: inconsistent, consistent dependent, or consistent independent. Consistent dependent systems are generally called *dependent systems*; consistent independent systems are generally called *independent systems*. The following are examples of dependent systems:

$$\begin{cases} 4\,x + 7\,y = 16 \\ 12\,x + 21\,y = 48 \end{cases} \qquad \begin{cases} y > x - 7 \\ 3\,y > 3\,x - 21 \end{cases}$$

In each of these systems the second sentence is obtained by multiplying the members of the first sentence by 3. Clearly, any number pair (c, d) which satisfies the first sentence also satisfies the second, and conversely. An example of an independent system is the system whose graph is shown in the example on page 648.

We summarize the above statements in the following definition:

> If a system in two variables is the conjunction of two open sentences whose truth sets are S and T, then
>
> 1. The system is inconsistent if $S \cap T = \emptyset$.
> 2. The system is dependent if $S = T$.
> 3. The system is independent if $S \cap T \neq \emptyset \wedge S \neq T$.

Ⓐ EXERCISES

1. Does the ordered pair $(-4, -5)$ satisfy the first equation of the system of equations $\begin{cases} y = 2\,x + 3 \\ y = x - 1 \end{cases}$? Does it satisfy the second equation of the system? Is $(-4, -5)$ an element of the solution set of the system? Explain.

2. With respect to a single pair of axes draw the graphs of the truth sets of the component open sentences of the system $\begin{cases} 2\,x - 3\,y - 6 = 0 \\ x + y - 2 = 0 \end{cases}$. From the graphs determine what ordered pair(s) belong(s) to the intersection of these truth sets, in other words, to the truth set of the system.

3. With respect to a single pair of axes draw the graphs of the truth sets of the component open sentences of the system $\begin{cases} y = 2\,x + 5 \\ 2\,y = 4\,x + 10 \end{cases}$. What do the graphs indicate about the truth set of the system?

4. With respect to a single pair of axes draw graphs of the truth sets of the component sentences of the system $\begin{cases} 3x+y-1=0 \\ 3x+y-5=0 \end{cases}$. What do the graphs indicate about the truth set of the system?

5. Use graphing to indicate the truth set of each of the following systems of open sentences.

a. $\begin{cases} x+2y > 5 \\ 2x-y > 3 \end{cases}$

b. $\begin{cases} y > 3x+2 \\ y > -x-1 \end{cases}$

c. $\begin{cases} 4x-3y \le 8 \\ 4x \ge 5y \end{cases}$

d. $\begin{cases} y \le x-7 \\ x = 2 \end{cases}$

e. $\begin{cases} x-2y > 4 \\ y < x+3 \end{cases}$

f. $\begin{cases} x-3y > 2 \\ y < 2x+1 \end{cases}$

g. $\begin{cases} x+y > 9 \\ y < 3 \end{cases}$

h. $\begin{cases} x+y = 25 \\ x-3y \ge 21 \end{cases}$

i. $\begin{cases} x+16y = 16 \\ y = x \end{cases}$

j. $\begin{cases} y \le x-4 \\ 3y-2x \le -6 \end{cases}$

k. $\begin{cases} x+y < 4 \\ y = -x+2\sqrt{2} \end{cases}$

l. $\begin{cases} 4x+9y \le 36 \\ y > 4 \end{cases}$

6. Which of the following systems are consistent and which inconsistent? Which of the consistent systems are dependent and which independent?

a. $\begin{cases} x+y = 3 \\ 2x+2y = 6 \end{cases}$

b. $\begin{cases} 3x+4y = 1 \\ 3x+4y = 5 \end{cases}$

c. $\begin{cases} y = 2x+3 \\ y = 3x-1 \end{cases}$

d. $\begin{cases} y = 4x+3 \\ y = 4x-3 \end{cases}$

e. $\begin{cases} 2y = x+6 \\ y = \frac{1}{2}x+3 \end{cases}$

f. $\begin{cases} y > x^2 \\ y = x \end{cases}$

g. $\begin{cases} x^2+y^2 = 16 \\ x^2+y^2 = 4 \end{cases}$

h. $\begin{cases} y > 4x^2 \\ y < 4x^2+3 \end{cases}$

i. $\begin{cases} 4x^2+4y^2 = 16 \\ 3x^2+3y^2 = 12 \end{cases}$

j. $\begin{cases} x^2+y^2 = 9 \\ y = x^2+4 \end{cases}$

k. $\begin{cases} y = -x^2-3 \\ 3y-2x = -6 \end{cases}$

l. $\begin{cases} xy = -12 \\ x = 4y \end{cases}$

7. For what value of a will the solution set of the system $\begin{cases} 12x+18y = 6 \\ 10x+15y = a \end{cases}$ not be the null set?

8. By means of graphs indicate the solution set of each of the following systems.

a. $\begin{cases} y-\frac{1}{2}x-1 = 0 \\ y = 3 \end{cases}$

b. $\begin{cases} y-2x+9 = 0 \\ y = \frac{1}{2}x \end{cases}$

c. $\begin{cases} y = x-10 \\ \frac{1}{2}x+y = 2 \end{cases}$

d. $\begin{cases} y > x-10 \\ \frac{1}{2}x+y = 2 \end{cases}$

e. $\begin{cases} x+y = 4 \\ y \ge 0 \end{cases}$

f. $\begin{cases} 2x+y = 7 \\ y \le 2 \end{cases}$

g. $\begin{cases} \frac{2}{3}x+5y = 1 \\ \frac{3}{4}x+y = \frac{31}{4} \end{cases}$

h. $\begin{cases} y = 2(x-2)+3 \\ y > 2(x+2)+3 \end{cases}$

i. $\begin{cases} 3x+2y = 12 \\ y < x \end{cases}$

9. What must be true of the graphs of the truth sets of the component sentences of the system $\begin{cases} ax+by+c = 0 \\ dx+ey+f = 0 \\ gx+hy+k = 0 \end{cases}$ if the system is to have a solution set containing exactly one member provided $a, b, c, d, e, f, g, h, k \in R$?

Equivalent Open Sentences and Equivalent Systems of Open Sentences

Solving a system can be described as the process whereby we convert a given system into an equivalent system which is so simple that we can determine its truth set by inspection.

Two systems of open sentences are equivalent if they have the same replacement set and the same solution set. For example, $\begin{cases} 3x - 2y - 12 = 0 \\ 5x + 3y - 1 = 0 \end{cases}$ is equivalent to the simpler system $\begin{cases} x = 2 \\ y = -3 \end{cases}$ since both systems have the same replacement set $R \times R$ and the solution set $\{(2, -3)\}$.

If the members of an open sentence are polynomials, the sentence is called a polynomial sentence. Two polynomial sentences in the same variables have the same replacement set if their like variables have the same domain. If, for example, $s_{(x,y)}$ and $t_{(x,y)}$ are two polynomial sentences such that $x \in R$ and $y \in R$, as is the case unless otherwise specified, then $s_{(x,y)}$ and $t_{(x,y)}$ have the same replacement set, namely $R \times R$. This is true because a polynomial expression, unlike some other rational expressions such as $\dfrac{3}{(x-7)(y+3)}$, is defined for every member of $R \times R$.

Since two polynomial sentences in the same variables have the same replacement set provided their like variables have the same domains, two such sentences are equivalent if and only if they have the same solution set. We can also state that two systems whose components are polynomial sentences in the same variables have the same replacement set provided their like variables have the same domain, and are therefore equivalent if and only if they have the same solution set.

The following conclusions regarding equivalent systems of open sentences are direct consequences of the definition of equivalent systems.

1. Any system is equivalent to itself.
2. If system S is equivalent to system T, then system T is equivalent to system S.
3. Two systems that are equivalent to the same system are equivalent to each other.
4. If any component sentence in a system is replaced with an equivalent sentence, the resulting system is equivalent to the original system.

 EXERCISES

1. In which of the following pairs, are the two systems equivalent?

a. $\begin{cases} 2x + y = 7 \\ x + 3y = 11 \end{cases}$ $\begin{cases} x = 2 \\ y = 3 \end{cases}$ b. $\begin{cases} x^2 = 4 \\ y = x + 1 \end{cases}$ $\begin{cases} x = 2 \\ y = x + 1 \end{cases}$

$$\text{c.}\begin{cases}5\,x+y=-1\\2\,x-y=-6\end{cases}\qquad\begin{cases}x+1=0\\y-4=0\end{cases}\qquad\text{e.}\begin{cases}3\,x-y=10\\2\,x+3\,y=-8\end{cases}\qquad\begin{cases}x=2\\y=-4\end{cases}$$

$$\text{d.}\begin{cases}y=x^2\\y=2\,x\end{cases}\qquad\begin{cases}x^2=y\\y=2\,x\end{cases}\qquad\text{f.}\begin{cases}3\,x+y=5\\4\,x-y=2\end{cases}\qquad\begin{cases}x=1\\y=2\end{cases}$$

2. Verify that $\begin{cases}3\,x+y=1\\2\,x-y=9\end{cases}\longleftrightarrow\begin{cases}x=2\\y=-5\end{cases}$ and that

$\begin{cases}9\,x+3\,y=3\\4\,x-2\,y=18\end{cases}\longleftrightarrow\begin{cases}3\,x+y=1\\2\,x-y=9\end{cases}$.

Assuming that both of these verifications prove to be correct, according to which of the Statements 1–4 above does it follow that

$$\begin{cases}9\,x+3\,y=3\\4\,x-2\,y=18\end{cases}\longleftrightarrow\begin{cases}x=2\\y=-5\end{cases}?$$

3. Replace each "Why?" with one of the Statements 1–4 on page 646 to complete the following proof.

(1) $\begin{cases}2\,x-4\,y=2\\-3\,x+y=7\end{cases}\longleftrightarrow\begin{cases}2\,x-4\,y=2\\-3\,x+y=7\end{cases}$ (1) Why?

(2) $2\,x-4\,y=2\longleftrightarrow x-2\,y=1$ (2) Multiplication property of equality

(3) $\begin{cases}2\,x-4\,y=2\\-3\,x+y=7\end{cases}\longleftrightarrow\begin{cases}x-2\,y=1\\-3\,x+y=7\end{cases}$ (3) Why?

4. Draw the graphs of the solution sets of the component sentences of each of the following pairs of systems. From the graphs decide in which pairs the two systems are equivalent.

a. $\begin{cases}2\,x+3\,y=9\\x-4\,y=-1\end{cases}\qquad\begin{cases}4\,x-y=11\\2\,x+7\,y=13\end{cases}$

b. $\begin{cases}y=x-2\\y=5\,x-4\end{cases}\qquad\begin{cases}y=x+2\\y=-1\end{cases}$

c. $\begin{cases}y=x+3\\y=4\,x-3\end{cases}\qquad\begin{cases}y=-x-3\\y=-4\,x+3\end{cases}$

5. Which of the following statements are true?

a. $\begin{cases}3\,y>3\,x\\y>2\end{cases}\longleftrightarrow\begin{cases}y>x\\y>2\end{cases}\qquad$ c. $\begin{cases}x>y\\x=2\end{cases}\longleftrightarrow\begin{cases}x-y<0\\x=2\end{cases}$

b. $\begin{cases}x+4<y\\x<1\end{cases}\longleftrightarrow\begin{cases}x<y-4\\x<1\end{cases}\qquad$ d. $\begin{cases}x>y\\x+1=3\end{cases}\longleftrightarrow\begin{cases}y<x\\x=2\end{cases}$

6. We have accepted the definition: Two systems of open sentences are equivalent if they have the same replacement set and the same solution set. When the component open sentences are linear equations having the same variables, we prove the systems equivalent by merely proving they have the same solution set. Why may we omit mention of the replacement sets?

7. The following systems are two systems in x and y where $x, y \in R$. The systems are not equivalent. Why not?

$$\begin{cases} \dfrac{1}{x-y} = 3 \\ x = y \end{cases} \qquad \begin{cases} 1 = 3\,x - 3\,y \\ x = y \end{cases}$$

Systems of Linear Equations in Two Variables

In this section we consider examples illustrating some of the principles which explain methods for solving systems that consist of two linear equations in two variables. Some of these principles are stated as theorems and proved.

The basic procedure for solving any equation or any system of equations can be described as follows: Assume that a solution exists and find a set T that contains the solution set. Eliminate from T those members that are not solutions by substituting each member of T in the given equation or system and rejecting those that do not satisfy the given equation or system.

Example 1.   Find S, the solution set of the system $\begin{cases} 7\,x + 3\,y = 26 \\ 5\,x - 4\,y = 37 \end{cases}$.

Solution.   We begin by assuming that $S \neq \emptyset$, that is, there exists a pair of numbers a and b which satisfies each of the component equations. This means that we assume the truth of the statements in the following system:

$$\begin{cases} 7\,a + 3\,b = 26 \\ 5\,a - 4\,b = 37 \end{cases}$$

We can eliminate the b's from these equations if we multiply the members of the first equation by 4 and the members of the second equation by 3 and then apply the addition property of equality.

Thus,

$\left. \begin{array}{l} 7\,a + 3\,b = 26 \longrightarrow 28\,a + 12\,b = 104 \\ 5\,a - 4\,b = 37 \longrightarrow 15\,a - 12\,b = 111 \end{array} \right\} \longrightarrow 43\,a = 215 \longrightarrow$

$\longmapsto \left. \begin{array}{l} a = 5 \\ 7\,a + 3\,b = 26 \end{array} \right\} \longrightarrow b = -3$. Consequently, if a solution exists, it is $(5, -3)$. It follows that $S \subseteq \{(5, -3)\}$. In so far as our present discussion is concerned, we do not yet know that $(5, -3)$ is actually a solution. Therefore we substitute 5 for x and -3 for y in each component equation to see if it is satisfied. Having found that each equation is satisfied by $(5, -3)$, we know that $\{(5, -3)\} \subseteq S$.

Statements $S \subseteq \{(5, -3)\}$ and $\{(5, -3)\} \subseteq S$ imply that $\{(5, -3)\} = S$ and we are justified in saying that:

$$\begin{cases} 7x + 3y = 26 \\ 5x - 4y = 37 \end{cases} \longleftrightarrow \begin{cases} x = 5 \\ y = -3 \end{cases}$$

Note that in the example above we were not logically sure that $(5, -3)$ was a solution until we checked by substitution in the original system. While it is always a good idea to check in order to avoid numerical errors, we would like to develop methods in which a check is unnecessary from a logical point of view. This is essential since we hope that these methods will apply to the solution of systems whose components are open sentences of any kind. Indeed if some of the components of a system are linear inequalities, we are in no position to check each member of an alleged solution set.

Often in industrial and research applications of mathematics it is necessary to solve systems of linear sentences which have hundreds of components and hundreds of variables. While the actual work is done by computers, the computers are operated by persons who have a thorough knowledge of linear systems. In this chapter we seek to develop a thorough understanding of some of the simpler principles involved. The system we consider next serves to introduce some of these.

Suppose we have the system $\begin{cases} 2x + 3y = -9 \\ 5x - 2y = 25 \end{cases}$. First we write the given system as the equivalent system $\begin{cases} 2x + 3y + 9 = 0 \\ 5x - 2y - 25 = 0 \end{cases}$. The components of this system are equations of two straight lines which have different slopes. Hence these lines intersect in a unique point $P(a, b)$.

Now we choose the real numbers k_1 and k_2 which are not both zero and form the new equation: (i) $k_1(2x + 3y + 9) + k_2(5x - 2y - 25) = 0$. Simplified, this becomes $2k_1x + 3k_1y + 9k_1 + 5k_2x - 2k_2y - 25k_2 = 0$, or (ii) $(2k_1 + 5k_2)x + (3k_1 - 2k_2)y + (9k_1 - 25k_2) = 0$.

Equation (ii) is a linear equation of the form $ax + by + c = 0$ which we recognize as the equation of a straight line. Since equation (i) is equivalent to equation (ii), the graph of equation (i) must also be a straight line. We inquire if this straight line contains the point P whose coordinates (a, b) satisfy the given system. Substituting (a, b) in (i), we obtain:

$$k_1(2a + 3b + 9) + k_2(5a - 2b - 25) = 0$$

Since (a, b) satisfies the given system, we know that each of the expressions in parentheses has the value 0. Hence the last equation is equivalent to the true statement:

$$k_1(0) + k_2(0) = 0 \quad \text{or} \quad 0 = 0$$

We conclude that the number pair (a, b) satisfies equation (i) as well as each of the component equations of the system. This means that equation (i) is the equation of a straight line which passes through $P(a, b)$, the point of intersection of the graphs of the two equations of the given system. We summarize these results in the following statement:

A   If L_1 and L_2 are lines which intersect in exactly one point, and if their equations are respectively $a_1x + b_1y + c_1 = 0$ and $a_2x + b_2y + c_2 = 0$, and if k_1 and k_2 are real numbers, not both zero, then $k_1(a_1x + b_1y + c_1) + k_2(a_2x + b_2y + c_2) = 0$ is the equation of a line which passes through the intersection of L_1 and L_2.

Saying that L_1 and L_2 are lines which intersect in exactly one point is equivalent to saying that the system $\begin{cases} a_1x + b_1y + c_1 = 0 \\ a_2x + b_2y + c_2 = 0 \end{cases}$ is an independent system of linear equations. The conclusion of statement **A** is equivalent to two assertions: (1) $k_1(a_1x + b_1y + c_1) + k_2(a_2x + b_2y + c_2) = 0$ is a linear equation, and (2) $\{(a, b)\}$, the solution set of the given system, satisfies this equation.

Thus we restate **A** in algebraic terms as the following theorem:

▷ **Theorem 1–12.** If $\begin{cases} a_1x + b_1y + c_1 = 0 \\ a_2x + b_2y + c_2 = 0 \end{cases}$ is an independent system of linear equations whose solution set is S, and k_1 and k_2 are real numbers such that $k_1^2 + k_2^2 \neq 0$, then $k_1(a_1x + b_1y + c_1) + k_2(a_2x + b_2y + c_2) = 0$ is a linear equation whose solution set contains all the elements of S.

To determine the multipliers k_1 and k_2 in a way that will help us solve the system described in Theorem 1–12, we return to the system we were originally considering, namely $\begin{cases} 2x + 3y + 9 = 0 \\ 5x - 2y - 25 = 0 \end{cases}$. We know that the equation (ii) $(2k_1 + 5k_2)x + (3k_1 - 2k_2)y + (9k_1 - 25k_2) = 0$ is the equation of a straight line which contains P whose coordinates (a, b) satisfy the system. If this line is parallel to the x-axis, it must have an equation equivalent to $0 \cdot x + y = b$. Equation (ii) will have this form if $2k_1 + 5k_2 = 0$, that is, $k_1 = -\frac{5}{2} k_2$. For example, if $k_1 = 5$, then $k_2 = -2$. Substituting these values in (ii), we obtain $0 \cdot x + [3 \cdot 5 - 2(-2)]y + 9(5) - 25(-2) = 0$, or $19y + 95 = 0$. Thus $y = -5$.

If, on the other hand, the line is parallel to the y-axis, it will have an equation equivalent to $x + 0 \cdot y = a$. We see that equation (ii) will have this form if $3k_1 - 2k_2 = 0$, that is, $k_2 = \frac{3}{2} k_1$. For example, if $k_1 = 2$, then $k_2 = 3$. Substituting these values in (ii), we obtain $19x - 57 = 0$. Then $x = 3$.

Thus we have found two simple equations $x = 3$ and $y = -5$ whose graphs are parallel to the y-axis and to the x-axis, respectively, and whose graphs intersect at the point P whose coordinates $(3, -5)$ are the solution of the given system as shown in the figure.

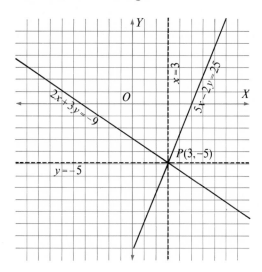

The system formed by these simple equations is equivalent to the given system; that is, $\begin{cases} x = 3 \\ y = -5 \end{cases} \longleftrightarrow \begin{cases} 2x + 3y = -9 \\ 5x - 2y = 25 \end{cases}$.

This method of solution is called the "multiplication and addition method." It depends on the following theorem.

▷ **Theorem 2–12.** The systems
$$\begin{cases} a_1x + b_1y + c_1 = 0 \\ a_2x + b_2y + c_2 = 0 \end{cases} \text{ and } \begin{cases} a_1x + b_1y + c_1 = 0 \\ k_1(a_1x + b_1y + c_1) + k_2(a_2x + b_2y + c_2) = 0 \end{cases}$$
are equivalent provided $k_2 \neq 0$.

Proof of Theorem 2–12. The systems $\begin{cases} a_1x + b_1y + c_1 = 0 \\ a_2x + b_2y + c_2 = 0 \end{cases}$ and

$\begin{cases} a_1x + b_1y + c_1 = 0 \\ k_1(a_1x + b_1y + c_1) + k_2(a_2x + b_2y + c_2) = 0 \end{cases}$ are equivalent provided $k_2 \neq 0$.

Let S and T be the solution sets of the first and second systems, respectively. To prove Theorem 2–12, we must prove that $S = T$. To do this we must prove two statements.

(1) Any ordered pair (c, d) which satisfies the first system also satisfies the second system. This is equivalent to saying that any member of S is a member of T and hence establishes that $S \subseteq T$.

(2) Any ordered pair (c, d) which satisfies the second system also satisfies the first system. This establishes that $T \subseteq S$.

Proof of (1). If $(c, d) \in S$, then this ordered pair satisfies each of the components of the first system and we have $a_1 c + b_1 d + c_1 = 0$ and $a_2 c + b_2 d + c_2 = 0$. It follows that $\overline{k_1(a_1 c + b_1 d + c_1) = 0}$ and $\overline{k_2(a_2 c + b_2 d + c_2) = 0}$. Why? Applying the addition property of equality to the last two equations we have $k_1(a_1 c + b_1 d + c_1) + k_2(a_2 c + b_2 d + c_2) = 0$. The two underlined statements demonstrate that (c, d) satisfies each component of the second system. Therefore $(c, d) \in T$. Since any member of S is a member of T, we know that $S \subseteq T$.

Proof of (2). If $(c, d) \in T$, then $a_1 c + b_1 d + c_1 = 0$ and $k_1(a_1 c + b_1 d + c_1) + k_2(a_2 c + b_2 d + c_2) = 0$. Why? $\overline{\text{It follows that } k_2(a_2 c + b_2 d + c_2) = 0}$. Why? Since $k_2 \neq 0$, we must have $a_2 c + b_2 d + c_2 = 0$. The two underlined statements demonstrate that (c, d) satisfies the first system. Since any member of T is a member of S, we know that $T \subseteq S$.

From the proofs of (1) and (2) we know that $S \subseteq T$ and $T \subseteq S$. This proves $S = T$. The statement $S = T$ in turn implies that the two systems are equivalent because two systems of polynomial equations are equivalent if they have the same solution set.

Returning to our solution of the original system $\begin{cases} 2x + 3y + 9 = 0 \\ 5x - 2y - 25 = 0 \end{cases}$, we observe that after we found $y = -5$, we might have substituted -5 for y in either of the equations $2x + 3y + 9 = 0$ or $5x - 2y - 25 = 0$ in order to find the corresponding value of x. Thus we would have had the following:

$$\begin{cases} 2x + 3y + 9 = 0 \\ 5x - 2y - 25 = 0 \end{cases} \leftrightarrow \begin{cases} 2x + 3y + 9 = 0 \\ y = -5 \end{cases} \nleftrightarrow$$

$$\mapsto \begin{cases} 2x + 3(-5) + 9 = 0 \\ y = -5 \end{cases} \leftrightarrow \begin{cases} x = 3 \\ y = -5 \end{cases}$$

This argument employs a special case of the following theorem. This theorem also justifies the substitution method of solution used in Chapter 5.

▶ **Theorem 3–12.** The systems

$$\begin{cases} y = ax + b \\ cx + dy + e = 0 \end{cases} \quad \text{and} \quad \begin{cases} y = ax + b \\ cx + d(ax + b) + e = 0 \end{cases} \quad \text{are equivalent}$$

provided each is a system of linear equations.

The proof of this theorem is left as an exercise.

Example 2. Using the method justified by Theorem 2–12 (multiplication and addition), find the solution set for $\begin{cases} 2\,x - y = -13 \\ 3\,x + 2\,y = 5 \end{cases}$.

Solution. $\begin{cases} 2\,x - y + 13 = 0 \\ 3\,x + 2\,y - 5 = 0 \end{cases} \longleftrightarrow \begin{cases} 2(2\,x - y + 13) + 1(3\,x + 2\,y - 5) = 0 \\ 3\,x + 2\,y - 5 = 0 \end{cases}$

$\longmapsto \begin{cases} 7\,x + 21 = 0 \\ 3\,x + 2\,y - 5 = 0 \end{cases} \longleftrightarrow \begin{cases} x = -3 \\ 3\,x + 2\,y - 5 = 0 \end{cases}$

$\longmapsto \begin{cases} x = -3 \\ -9 + 2\,y - 5 = 0 \end{cases} \longleftrightarrow \begin{cases} x = -3 \\ y = 7 \end{cases}$

$\therefore$ the solution set is $\{(-3, 7)\}$.

Example 3. Use the method justified by Theorem 3–12 (substitution method), to find the solution set for the system $\begin{cases} 8\,x - 4\,y = 36 \\ 2\,x + y = 1 \end{cases}$.

Solution. $\begin{cases} 8\,x - 4\,y = 36 \\ 2\,x + y = 1 \end{cases} \longleftrightarrow \begin{cases} 8\,x - 4\,y = 36 \\ y = -2\,x + 1 \end{cases} \longleftrightarrow \begin{cases} 8\,x - 4(-2\,x + 1) = 36 \\ y = -2\,x + 1 \end{cases}$

$\longmapsto \begin{cases} 16\,x = 40 \\ y = -2\,x + 1 \end{cases} \longleftrightarrow \begin{cases} x = 2.5 \\ y = -2\,x + 1 \end{cases}$

$\longmapsto \begin{cases} x = 2.5 \\ y = -2(2.5) + 1 \end{cases} \longleftrightarrow \begin{cases} x = 2.5 \\ y = -4 \end{cases}$

$\therefore$ the solution set is $\{(2.5, -4)\}$.

Example 4. Find the equation of a line which passes through $P_1(7, 5)$ and the intersection of the lines whose equations are $x + y = 1$ and $3\,x - 7\,y = -17$.

Solution. We can solve this problem without first finding the point of intersection of the lines whose equations are given by using **A** (page 650) as follows: $k_1(3\,x - 7\,y + 17) + k_2(x + y - 1) = 0$ is the equation of a line L which passes through the intersection of the lines whose equations are given. We want L to pass through $P_1(7, 5)$. Therefore $(7, 5)$ must satisfy the equation of L. Thus $k_1(3 \cdot 7 - 7 \cdot 5 + 17) + k_2(7 + 5 - 1) = 0$, or $3\,k_1 + 11\,k_2 = 0$, and for k_1 and k_2 we may choose any pair of numbers which satisfies this equation where $k_1{}^2 + k_2{}^2 \neq 0$. Let $k_1 = -11$ and $k_2 = 3$. Then the equation of L becomes $-11(3\,x - 7\,y + 17) + 3(x + y - 1) = 0$, or $3\,x - 8\,y + 19 = 0$.

We can verify this result by observing that both $P_1(7, 5)$ and $P_2(-1, 2)$, which is the point of intersection of the lines whose equations are given, lie in L.

A **EXERCISES**

1. Find a value of k_1 and a value of k_2 which will transform each of the following equations into the form $cx + 0\,y = a$.

   a. $k_1(5\,x - 2\,y - 16) + k_2(6\,x + y - 9) = 0$

   b. $k_1(2\,x + y + 3) + k_2(-3\,x - 5\,y + 13) = 0$

   c. $k_1(x + 3\,y + 2) + k_2(x - 2\,y - 13) = 0$

2. Find a value of k_1 and a value of k_2 which will transform each of the equations of Ex. 1 into the form $0\,x + dy = b$.

3. Using the results of Exercises 1 and 2 write the solution set of each of the following systems of equations.

   a. $\begin{cases} 5\,x - 2\,y - 16 = 0 \\ 6\,x + y - 9 = 0 \end{cases}$
   b. $\begin{cases} 2\,x + y + 3 = 0 \\ -3\,x - 5\,y + 13 = 0 \end{cases}$
   c. $\begin{cases} x + 3\,y + 2 = 0 \\ x - 2\,y - 13 = 0 \end{cases}$

4. Use the multiplication and addition method, which is justified by Theorem 2–12, to solve each of the following systems.

   a. $\begin{cases} 4\,x - 7\,y + 2 = 0 \\ 3\,x - 4\,y - 17 = 0 \end{cases}$
   c. $\begin{cases} 9\,x - 6\,y = 4 \\ 3\,x + 12\,y = 6 \end{cases}$
   e. $\begin{cases} 3\,x + 2\,y = 1 \\ 7\,x - 5\,y = 70 \end{cases}$

   b. $\begin{cases} 5\,x + 4\,y = -4 \\ 6\,x - 2\,y = 36 \end{cases}$
   d. $\begin{cases} -3\,x + 2\,y = -8 \\ -2\,x + 6\,y = 18 \end{cases}$
   f. $\begin{cases} \frac{1}{4}\,x + \frac{3}{5}\,y = 7 \\ \frac{5}{8}\,x + \frac{1}{10}\,y = \frac{7}{2} \end{cases}$

5. Use the method justified by Theorem 3–12 (the substitution method) to find the solution set of each of the following systems of equations.

   a. $\begin{cases} x + y = 3 \\ 9\,x + 6\,y = 25 \end{cases}$
   b. $\begin{cases} x + 2\,y = 2 \\ 25\,x - 15\,y = 29 \end{cases}$
   c. $\begin{cases} 3\,x - 5\,y = -12\,\sqrt{5} \\ 2\,x + 3\,y = 8\,\sqrt{5} \end{cases}$

B **EXERCISES**

6. Find the equation of each of the following:

   a. The line which passes through the point $P(1, 5)$ and the intersection of the lines which are the graphs of $-3\,x + 2\,y = 14$ and $x + y = 2$.

   b. The line which passes through the point $P(4, 6)$ and the intersection of the lines which are the graphs of $-3\,x + 5\,y = -5$ and $6\,x + 5\,y = 40$.

   c. The line which passes through the point $P(-4, 2)$ and the intersection of the lines which are the graphs of $y = 3\,x - 2$ and $x + y = 7$.

   d. The line which passes through the point $P(2, 7)$ and the intersection of the lines which are the graphs of $y = \frac{3}{2}\,x - 5$ and $2\,y = -7\,x + 8$.

7. Write the linear equation whose solution set contains the solutions of the two systems $\begin{cases} 2\,x + y = -4 \\ -2\,x + 3\,y = 4 \end{cases}$ and $\begin{cases} y = \frac{1}{5}\,x \\ y = -\frac{5}{4}\,x + 6. \end{cases}$

8. Write a proof for Theorem 3–12.

More about Solving Systems of Linear Equations in Two Variables

In this section we continue our study of systems having the form:

(i)
$$\begin{cases} a_1x + b_1y = c_1; \ a_1, b_1, c_1 \ \epsilon \ R \ \text{and} \ a_1{}^2 + b_1{}^2 \neq 0 \\ a_2x + b_2y = c_2; \ a_2, b_2, c_2 \ \epsilon \ R \ \text{and} \ a_2{}^2 + b_2{}^2 \neq 0 \end{cases}$$

We consider the conditions under which such systems are dependent, inconsistent, or independent and in the latter case we seek a general solution.

System (i) is dependent if and only if each of the expressions $a_1b_2 - a_2b_1$, $a_1c_2 - a_2c_1$, and $b_1c_2 - b_2c_1$ is equal to zero.

System (i) is inconsistent if and only if $a_1b_2 - a_2b_1 = 0$ and the expressions $c_1b_2 - c_2b_1$ and $c_1a_2 - c_2a_1$ are not both zero.

System (i) is independent if and only if $a_1b_2 - a_2b_1 \neq 0$.

We can prove the statement: (1) If $a_1b_2 - a_2b_1 \neq 0$, then (i) is an independent system as follows: Since $a_1b_2 - a_2b_1 \neq 0$, the numbers b_1 and b_2 cannot both be 0. Why? Since at least one of these numbers is not 0, let us suppose that $b_1 \neq 0$. We now apply Theorem 2–12 to (i) using $k_1 = b_2$ and $k_2 = -b_1$ to obtain a system equivalent to (i):

$$\begin{cases} b_2(a_1x + b_1y - c_1) - b_1(a_2x + b_2y - c_2) = 0 \\ a_1x + b_1y - c_1 = 0 \end{cases}.$$ By statement 4, page 646,

this system is equivalent to the system $\begin{cases} (a_1b_2 - a_2b_1)x = b_2c_1 - b_1c_2 \\ a_1x + b_1y - c_1 = 0 \end{cases}.$

Since $a_1b_2 - a_2b_1 \neq 0$, this system is equivalent to $\begin{cases} x = \dfrac{b_2c_1 - b_1c_2}{a_1b_2 - a_2b_1} \\ a_1x + b_1y - c_1 = 0 \end{cases}.$

By Theorem 3–12 this system is equivalent to

$$\begin{cases} x = \dfrac{b_2c_1 - b_1c_2}{a_1b_2 - a_2b_1} \\ a_1\dfrac{b_2c_1 - b_1c_2}{a_1b_2 - a_2b_1} + b_1y - c_1 = 0 \end{cases}$$

which, in turn, is equivalent to

$$\begin{cases} x = \dfrac{b_2c_1 - b_1c_2}{a_1b_2 - a_2b_1} \\ b_1(a_1b_2 - a_2b_1)y = b_1(a_1c_2 - a_2c_1). \end{cases}$$

Since $b_1 \neq 0$ and $a_1b_2 - a_2b_1 \neq 0$, we have the last and simplest of our sequence of equivalent systems, namely:
$$\begin{cases} x = \dfrac{b_2c_1 - b_1c_2}{a_1b_2 - a_2b_1} \\ y = \dfrac{a_1c_2 - a_2c_1}{a_1b_2 - a_2b_1} \end{cases}$$

By the transitive property of equivalence for systems, we see that:

B $\begin{cases} a_1x + b_1y = c_1; \ a_1{}^2 + b_1{}^2 \neq 0 \\ a_2x + b_2y = c_2; \ a_2{}^2 + b_2{}^2 \neq 0 \end{cases} \longleftrightarrow \begin{cases} x = \dfrac{c_1b_2 - c_2b_1}{a_1b_2 - a_2b_1} \\ y = \dfrac{a_1c_2 - a_2c_1}{a_1b_2 - a_2b_1} \end{cases}$

provided $a_1b_2 - a_2b_1 \neq 0.$

Now the system on the right has exactly one solution, namely:

$$\left(\frac{c_1b_2 - c_2b_1}{a_1b_2 - a_2b_1}, \ \frac{a_1c_2 - a_2c_1}{a_1b_2 - a_2b_1} \right)$$

Therefore, the equivalent system (i) has this solution and no other.

This, of course, implies that (i) is an independent system and completes the proof of (1). We can also prove the converse of (1): (2) If (i) is an independent system, then $a_1b_2 - a_2b_1 \neq 0$. Statements (1) and (2) combine to establish the following important theorem.

▶ **Theorem 4–12.** The system $\begin{cases} a_1x + b_1y = c_1; \ a_1{}^2 + b_1{}^2 \neq 0; \ a_1, b_1, c_1 \in R \\ a_2x + b_2y = c_2; \ a_2{}^2 + b_2{}^2 \neq 0; \ a_2, b_2, c_2 \in R \end{cases}$
is independent if and only if $a_1b_2 - a_2b_1 \neq 0.$

Ordinarily, when solving a system, we would not try to remember these complicated formulas for the values of x and y as stated in **B**. However, there is a method of expressing these formulas which makes them easy to recall and apply. This method involves the use of determinants.

Recalling that the determinant $\begin{vmatrix} a & b \\ c & d \end{vmatrix}$ has the expanded form $ad - bc$, we see that the right-hand system in **B** can be written in the form:

$$x = \frac{\begin{vmatrix} c_1 & b_1 \\ c_2 & b_2 \end{vmatrix}}{\begin{vmatrix} a_1 & b_1 \\ a_2 & b_2 \end{vmatrix}} \quad and \quad y = \frac{\begin{vmatrix} a_1 & c_1 \\ a_2 & c_2 \end{vmatrix}}{\begin{vmatrix} a_1 & b_1 \\ a_2 & b_2 \end{vmatrix}}$$

We also see that the determinant of the denominator in each case is the determinant formed using the coefficients of the variables in system (i), page 655. We use the Greek letter Δ (read "delta") to denote this determinant. Observe that when we are solving for x, we obtain the numerator determinant by replacing the coefficients of x in Δ with the constants c_1 and c_2. Since x is the first variable, that is, the one written on the left in each component equation of (i), we call this determinant Δ_1. When solving for y, we obtain the numerator determinant Δ_2 by replacing the coefficients of y in Δ with the constants c_1 and c_2.

C $\quad\begin{cases}a_1x+b_1y=c_1\\a_2x+b_2y=c_2\end{cases}\longleftrightarrow\begin{cases}x=\dfrac{\Delta_1}{\Delta}\\[2mm]y=\dfrac{\Delta_2}{\Delta}\end{cases}$, provided the components of the system are

linear equations and $a_1b_2-a_2b_1\neq 0$.

Example. Solve the following system for x and y: $\begin{cases}ax+3\,y=c\\x=-\,by+7\end{cases}$

Solution. We write the given system in the form $\begin{cases}ax+3\,y=c\\x+by=7\end{cases}$.

We have $\Delta=\begin{vmatrix}a&3\\1&b\end{vmatrix}$, $\Delta_1=\begin{vmatrix}c&3\\7&b\end{vmatrix}$, and $\Delta_2=\begin{vmatrix}a&c\\1&7\end{vmatrix}$.

Therefore $x=\dfrac{\begin{vmatrix}c&3\\7&b\end{vmatrix}}{\begin{vmatrix}a&3\\1&b\end{vmatrix}}$ and $y=\dfrac{\begin{vmatrix}a&c\\1&7\end{vmatrix}}{\begin{vmatrix}a&3\\1&b\end{vmatrix}}$, and the solution set of the

system is $\left\{\left(\dfrac{bc-21}{ab-3},\dfrac{7\,a-c}{ab-3}\right)\right\}$ provided $ab\neq 3$.

Thus $\{(x,\,y)\mid ax+3\,y=c\wedge x=-\,by+7\}=\left\{\left(\dfrac{bc-21}{ab-3},\dfrac{7\,a-c}{ab-3}\right)\right\}$.

The following properties of determinants are readily verified for determinants of order two and determinants of order three. These properties are also valid for determinants of any order.

1. If the rows of one determinant are respectively the columns of another, the two determinants are equal.
2. If two rows (or two columns) of a determinant are the same, then the determinant is 0.
3. If two rows (or two columns) of a determinant are interchanged, the sign of the determinant is changed.
4. If each of the elements in one row (or one column) of a determinant is multiplied by k, the determinant is multiplied by k.
5. If each element of a row (or column) of a determinant is increased by k times the corresponding element in another row (or column), the value of the determinant is not changed.

 EXERCISES

1. Which of the following systems are dependent, which are inconsistent, and which are independent?

a. $\begin{cases}2\,x-5\,y=-40\\5\,x-2\,y=26\end{cases}$
b. $\begin{cases}\frac13\,x+\frac23\,y=13\\\frac16\,x+\frac13\,y=6\frac12\end{cases}$
c. $\begin{cases}7=3\,x-7\,y\\\frac23\,x-\frac23\,y=2\end{cases}$

d. $\begin{cases} 2x - y = 7 \\ \frac{12}{5}x - \frac{6}{5}y = \frac{14}{5} \end{cases}$ **e.** $\begin{cases} \dfrac{2x}{3} + \dfrac{2y}{5} = 6 \\ \dfrac{3x}{2} + \dfrac{9y}{10} = 16 \end{cases}$ **f.** $\begin{cases} y = 14 - 3x \\ \frac{7}{2} = \frac{3}{4}x + \frac{1}{4}y \end{cases}$

2. Without drawing the graphs of the solution sets of the component equations of each of the following systems, determine in which cases the graphs would be the same straight line, in which they would be a pair of parallel lines, and in which they would be two intersecting lines.

   a. $\begin{cases} 4x + 3y = 10 \\ -3x - 7y = 2 \end{cases}$ **c.** $\begin{cases} x + 10y - 13 = 0 \\ 20y = 2x - 26 \end{cases}$ **e.** $\begin{cases} \frac{3}{4}x + y = 12 \\ x + \frac{4}{3}y = 16 \end{cases}$

   b. $\begin{cases} 3x - 2y = 11 \\ 6y = 9x - 33 \end{cases}$ **d.** $\begin{cases} y = 4x + 7 \\ y = 4x - 7 \end{cases}$ **f.** $\begin{cases} 0.2x = 0.3y + 2.0 \\ 0.1x + 0.2y = 6.8 \end{cases}$

3. Use determinants to find the solution set of each of the following systems of equations.

   a. $\begin{cases} \frac{3}{5}x + \frac{3}{4}y = 18 \\ \frac{2}{5}x - \frac{2}{3}y = -2 \end{cases}$ **b.** $\begin{cases} 3x + 5y = 5 \\ \dfrac{x}{2} - \dfrac{y}{3} = \dfrac{2}{15} \end{cases}$ **c.** $\begin{cases} y = \dfrac{8 - 4x}{-3} \\ 4x - 5y = 0 \end{cases}$

4. If Jim were 4 years older, he would be half as old as his father is now; and if he were 6 years younger, he would be one-fourth as old as his father is now. What are the ages of Jim and his father?

5. If Mr. Thomas were to invest a dollars at 4% per year and b dollars at $3\frac{1}{2}$% per year, his income from the investments would be $185 per year; but if he were to invest b dollars at 4% and a dollars at $3\frac{1}{2}$%, his income from the investment would be $190 per year. In this situation how many dollars are represented by a and how many by b?

6. The sum of the digits of a two-digit number is 11. If the tens digit is 2 more than twice the units digit, what is the number?

7. By means of the determinant $\begin{vmatrix} a_1 & b_1 & c_1 \\ a_1 & b_1 & c_1 \\ a_2 & b_2 & c_2 \end{vmatrix}$, verify that when two rows of a determinant are the same, the determinant represents 0.

8. Verify that $\begin{vmatrix} ka_1 & b_1 & c_1 \\ ka_2 & b_2 & c_2 \\ ka_3 & b_3 & c_3 \end{vmatrix} = k \begin{vmatrix} a_1 & b_1 & c_1 \\ a_2 & b_2 & c_2 \\ a_3 & b_3 & c_3 \end{vmatrix}$

 **B**   **EXERCISES**

9. Solve each of the following systems of equations for x and y.

   a. $\begin{cases} \sqrt{m-1}\,x - \sqrt{m}\,y = a \\ \sqrt{m}\,x + \sqrt{m-1}\,y = b \end{cases}$ **b.** $\begin{cases} ax + by = 4 \\ \dfrac{b}{3}x + ay = 0 \end{cases}$

c. $\begin{cases} \dfrac{x-y}{4} - \dfrac{x+2y-19}{6} = \dfrac{y-3}{4} - \dfrac{y+2x-17}{6} \\ 4x - 7y = 10 \end{cases}$

10. For what value or values of a does the solution of the system $\begin{cases} x + 4y = -5 \\ \frac{3}{4}x - y = a \end{cases}$ have its x and y values equal?

11. Prove property 5 for determinants of order 3. (You may use the first four properties in constructing your proof.)

12. Use the definition of determinants to prove statement **C**, page 657. *Hint.* Expand the determinant of the system on the right.

Three-Dimensional Coordinate System

In Chapter 5 we learned how to set up a one-to-one correspondence between the ordered pairs of real numbers (x, y) and the points in a plane. In this section, we shall consider ordered triples of real numbers (x, y, z) as representing solutions of an open sentence in three variables and as the coordinates of points in three-dimensional space. We begin by setting up a one-to-one correspondence between the ordered triples of real numbers (x, y, z) and the points in three-dimensional space. The method we use is similar to the one we used for two dimensions. We place three number lines having the same scale and a common origin so that they are mutually perpendicular as shown in the diagram at the right. We label the origin O and we identify $\overleftrightarrow{OY}$ and $\overleftrightarrow{OX}$ as hori- 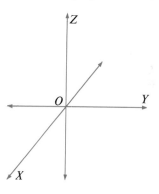 zontal lines that are perpendicular to each other just as the 30-yard line in a football field is perpendicular to the side boundary. The horizontal line $\overleftrightarrow{OY}$ which is parallel to the upper edge of the page is called the y-axis and its positive direction is the direction of $\overrightarrow{OY}$. The ray OX, which must be considered as extending toward the reader, represents the positive direction of the x-axis. We know that a linesman at a football game can place the pole that serves as yard marker so that it is perpendicular to both the 30-yard line and the sideline. Similarly, $\overrightarrow{OZ}$ which extends upward in our drawing and represents the positive half of the z-axis, is perpendicular to each of the lines OX and OY. There are three coordinate planes: the xy-plane which contains (is determined by) $\overleftrightarrow{OX}$ and $\overleftrightarrow{OY}$, the yz-plane which contains $\overleftrightarrow{OY}$ and $\overleftrightarrow{OZ}$, and the xz-plane which is determined by $\overleftrightarrow{OX}$ and $\overleftrightarrow{OZ}$. Observe that each axis is perpendicular to the coordinate plane which is determined by the other two axes. From geometry we know that a line is perpendicular to a plane if and only if it is perpendicular to every line in the plane which passes through its point of intersection with the plane.

Through P, any point in space, draw three planes which are respectively perpendicular to the three co- ordinate axes. The numbers which correspond to the points in which these planes intersect the x-axis, the y-axis, and the z-axis (points A, B, and C in figure) are called respectively the x-coordinate, the y-coordi- nate, and the z-coordinate of the point P. Portions of these planes and portions of the co- ordinate planes form a box-like 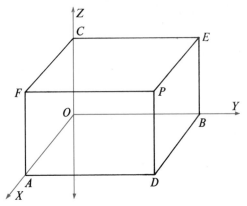 structure (called a rectangular parallelepiped) as shown in figure above.

Using this plan we can find the unique ordered triple of real numbers (coordinates) that corresponds to any point in space; and we can locate a unique point in space which corresponds to any given ordered triple of real numbers.

This one-to-one correspondence between ordered triples of real numbers and points in space is called a three-dimensional coordinate system.

Example. Locate the points $A(5, 0, 0)$, $B(0, 5, 0)$, $C(0, 0, -5)$, $D(-5, 0, 0)$, $E(5, 3, 0)$, $F(5, 3, -5)$.

Solution. The points are shown in the diagram below.

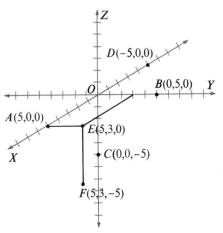

Observe that $P(a, 0, 0)$ is a point in the x-axis which is in the xy-plane and that $P(a, b, 0)$ is a point in the xy-plane. *Coplanar points* are points that lie in the same plane. From geometry we know that any three points are coplanar. The points A, B, E, and D in the figure for the previous example are coplanar. The three numbers in the ordered triple of numbers associated with a point in three-dimensional space are called the coordinates of the point, and the point is called the graph of the triple of numbers. Thus, in the figure, A is the graph of the ordered triple of numbers $(5, 0, 0)$ and $5, 0$, and 0 are respectively the x, y, and z coordinates of the point A.

Ⓐ EXERCISES

1. Draw a diagram which shows the location in three-dimensional space of each of the following ordered triples of real numbers.

   a. $(0, 4, 0)$ d. $(-1, 2, -4)$ g. $(0, -1, 0)$ j. $(-2, 4, 5)$

   b. $(0, 4, 3)$ e. $(0, 0, 5)$ h. $(4, 0, 4)$ k. $(3, 2, 5)$

   c. $(2, 0, 3)$ f. $(0, 2, 5)$ i. $(1, 2, 3)$ l. $(4, -2, 6)$

2. Show the graphs of each of the following ordered triples of real numbers.

   a. $(-1, -2, 4)$ c. $(5, -3, -2)$ e. $(0, 6, -3)$ g. $(3, 5, 2)$

   b. $(1, 2, 4)$ d. $(0, 0, 3)$ f. $(0, 1, 3)$ h. $(-7, -2, -5)$

3. Describe the location in three-dimensional space of all points for which

   a. $x = 0$ d. $y = -3$ g. $x = \pm 7$ j. $x = -5$

   b. $x = 1$ e. $z = 0$ h. $z \geq 4$ k. $y = 2$

   c. $y = 0$ f. $z = 5$ i. $z = -3$ l. $x \leq 3$

4. In the figure at the right, planes have been drawn through $P(x_1, y_1, z_1)$ perpendicular to the x-axis, the y-axis, and the z-axis, respectively. What are the coordinates of each of the following points?

   a. A c. B e. C

   b. D d. E f. F

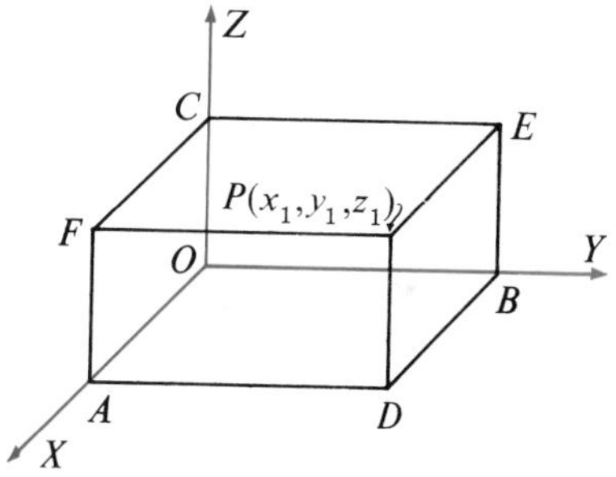

5. In the figure for Ex. 4 find the following:

   a. $|AD|$ d. $|PE|$ g. $|PD|$ j. $|BC|$

   b. $|DB|$ e. $|CF|$ h. $|OE|$ k. $|OD|$

   c. $|FP|$ f. $|AF|$ i. $|FO|$ l. $|AC|$

6. Let Q be a point in $\overrightarrow{FP}$ in the figure for Ex. 4 whose coordinates are (x_1, y_2, z_1). If through Q a plane is passed perpendicular to $\overrightarrow{FP}$, it will also be perpendicular to $\overrightarrow{AD}$, $\overrightarrow{OB}$, and $\overrightarrow{CE}$ as shown in the figure. Thus we obtain one rectangular parallelepiped whose vertices are A, G, H, O, F, Q, I, and C, and another whose vertices are D, G, H, B, P, Q, I, and E. With respect to the resulting figure find:

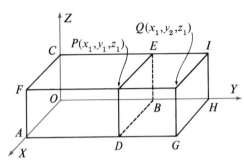

a. The coordinates of G, H, and I

b. $|PQ|, |DG|, |BH|, |EI|$

c. $|GH|, |QI|, |QG|, |HI|$

d. $|OI|, |BI|, |OF|, |OE|, |AB|$

7. We can name a plane by naming three noncollinear points in it. In the figure, planes UQR and VTS are perpendicular to the x-axis at points A and A', respectively; planes TSR and UVQ are perpendicular to the y-axis at points B and B', respectively; and planes UVT and QRS are perpendicular to the z-axis at points C and C', respectively. These six planes form a rectangular parallelepiped. One of the diagonals of this parallelepiped is the line segment joining

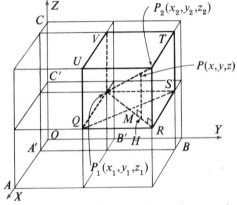

$P_1(x_1, y_1, z_1)$ and $P_2(x_2, y_2, z_2)$. We see that the coordinates of Q are (x_2, y_1, z_1).

a. What are the coordinates of R? S? T? U? V?

b. $VT = y_2 - y_1$, $UV = x_1 - x_2$, $|UV| = |x_1 - x_2|$. Find P_1Q, UP_2, SP_1, $|P_1Q|, |UP_2|, |SP_1|$, and $|RP_2|$.

c. $\overline{VS}$ is a diagonal of the rectangle $VTSP_1$. Therefore $|VS| = \sqrt{|TS|^2 + |P_1S|^2} = \sqrt{(z_2 - z_1)^2 + (y_2 - y_1)^2}$. Find $|VQ|, |QS|, |SV|$, $|UT|$, and $|P_1R|$.

d. Find the coordinates of M, the point where $\overline{QS}$ and $\overline{P_1R}$ intersect.

B **EXERCISES**

8. Use your knowledge of similar triangles and the figure in Exercise 7 to show that $(P(x, y, z) \in \overleftrightarrow{P_1P_2}) \longleftrightarrow [x = x_1 + k(x_2 - x_1) \wedge y = y_1 + k(y_2 - y_1) \wedge$

$z = z_1 + k(z_2 - z_1)$; $k \in R$]. Note that the three equations in the right-hand statement are the parametric equations of the line determined by points P_1 and P_2.

9. In Ex. 4 find the measure of AE.

10. In Ex. 6 find the measure of PH.

Distance Formula in Three Dimensions

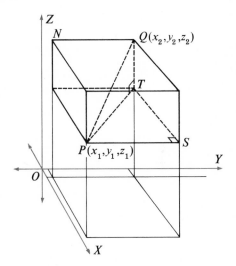

The figure at the right shows a rectangular parallelepiped formed by passing a set of three planes through each of the points $P(x_1, y_1, z_1)$ and $Q(x_2, y_2, z_2)$ so that the planes in each set are respectively perpendicular to the coordinate axes. Q, T, and N are in a plane parallel to the zy-plane, points P and Q are two opposite vertices of this parallelepiped, and $\overline{PQ}$ is one of its diagonals. The segment PT is a diagonal of its lower face. Since T is in the same horizontal plane with $P(x_1, y_1, z_1)$, we know that its z-coordinate is z_1; therefore, $|TQ| = |z_2 - z_1|$. Since T is in the same vertical line with Q, we know that its x-coordinate and y-coordinate are, respectively, x_2 and y_2. Since $\overline{QT}$ is perpendicular to the horizontal plane through P, it is perpendicular to $\overline{PT}$ and hence $\triangle PTQ$ is a right triangle. Applying the Pythagorean theorem to this right triangle, we have $|PQ|^2 = |PT|^2 + |TQ|^2$, or

(i) $|PQ|^2 = |PT|^2 + (z_2 - z_1)^2$.

Let S be a vertex in the same horizontal plane with P as shown in the diagram. Then we know that $\triangle PST$ is a right triangle and S has the coordinates (x_1, y_2, z_1). Why? Thus $|PS| = |y_2 - y_1|$ and $|ST| = |x_2 - x_1|$. Applying the Pythagorean theorem to right triangle PST, we obtain $|PT|^2 = |PS|^2 + |ST|^2$, or (ii) $|PT|^2 = (y_2 - y_1)^2 + (x_2 - x_1)^2$. Thus by (i) and (ii) we have:

$$|PQ|^2 = (x_2 - x_1)^2 + (y_2 - y_1)^2 + (z_2 - z_1)^2$$

If we let $d = |PQ|$ and note that $d \geq 0$, we have the three-dimensional form of the distance formula:

$$d = \sqrt{(x_2 - x_1)^2 + (y_2 - y_1)^2 + (z_2 - z_1)^2}.$$

Example 1.   Using the figure on the preceding page, find the measure of the distance d between $P(-3, -5, 4)$ and $Q(9, 11, 25)$; that is, find $|PQ|$.

Solution. $d = |PQ| = \sqrt{[9 - (-3)]^2 + [11 - (-5)]^2 + (25 - 4)^2} = \sqrt{12^2 + 16^2 + 21^2} = 29$.

Example 2.   Write an equation that is satisfied by (x, y, z) if the measure of the distance from the origin to point $P(x, y, z)$ is 10. Describe the location of these points.

Solution. $\sqrt{x^2 + y^2 + z^2} = 10$, or $x^2 + y^2 + z^2 = 100$. These points are located in a sphere whose center is at the origin and whose radius has the measure 10.

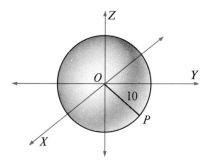

From plane geometry we know that $P(x, y)$ is equally distant (equidistant) from distinct points A and B if and only if P lies in the perpendicular bisector of $\overline{AB}$. Similarly, in space, $P(x, y, z)$ is equally distant (equidistant) from two distinct points A and B if and only if $P(x, y, z)$ is in plane M which is the perpendicular bisector of $\overline{AB}$. Points A and B are said to be *symmetric with respect to* M and are called *defining points for* M.

Example 3.   Determine the equation of a plane M which is the set of points equidistant from $A(4, 3, 2)$ and $B(8, 11, 12)$.

Solution.   If $P(x, y, z)$ is a point in the plane M, we know that: $P(x, y, z) \in M \longleftrightarrow |AP| = |PB| \longleftrightarrow \sqrt{(x - 4)^2 + (y - 3)^2 + (z - 2)^2} = \sqrt{(x - 8)^2 + (y - 11)^2 + (z - 12)^2} \longleftrightarrow (x - 4)^2 + (y - 3)^2 + (z - 2)^2 = (x - 8)^2 + (y - 11)^2 + (z - 12)^2 \longleftrightarrow x^2 - 8x + 16 + y^2 - 6y + 9 + z^2 - 4z + 4 = x^2 - 16x + 64 + y^2 - 22y + 121 + z^2 - 24z + 144 \longleftrightarrow 8x + 16y + 20z - 300 = 0 \longleftrightarrow 2x + 4y + 5z - 75 = 0$. Thus the equation of this plane is of the first degree in each of the three variables x, y, and z.

If we let $a = 2$, $b = 4$, $c = 5$, and $d = 75$, this equation has the general form $ax + by + cz = d$.

We can use this same method to prove that the equation of any plane is an equation of the first degree in three variables. Instead of using two specific points $A(4, 3, 2)$ and $B(8, 11, 12)$, we use $A(x_1, y_1, z_1)$ and $B(x_2, y_2, z_2)$ to represent any two distinct points in space. Then for each of the points $P(x, y, z)$ in plane M which is equidistant from points A and B, we have:

$$|AP| = |BP| \longleftrightarrow |AP|^2 = |BP|^2 \longleftrightarrow (x - x_1)^2 + (y - y_1)^2 + (z - z_1)^2 =$$
$$(x - x_2)^2 + (y - y_2)^2 + (z - z_2)^2 \longleftrightarrow 2(x_2 - x_1)x + 2(y_2 - y_1)y + 2(z_2 - z_1)z$$
$$= (x_2{}^2 - x_1{}^2) + (y_2{}^2 - y_1{}^2) + (z_2{}^2 - z_1{}^2).$$

The last equation has the form $ax + by + cz = d$ if we let $a = 2(x_2 - x_1)$, $b = 2(y_2 - y_1)$, $c = 2(z_2 - z_1)$, and $d = (x_2{}^2 - x_1{}^2) + (y_2{}^2 - y_1{}^2) + (z_2{}^2 - z_1{}^2)$. Moreover, this equation is of the first degree provided a, b, and c are not all zero. They can all be zero only if $x_1 = x_2$, $y_1 = y_2$, and $z_1 = z_2$, that is, if A and B are the same point. But points A and B are distinct. Therefore, we know that $a^2 + b^2 + c^2 \neq 0$ and hence the equation is a linear equation. Thus we have proved that:

(i) **Every plane has a linear equation of the form $ax + by + cz = d$ where the coefficients a, b, c, and d can be expressed, as shown above, in terms of the coordinates (x_1, y_1, z_1) and (x_2, y_2, z_2) of a pair of distinct defining points for the plane.**

We can also prove that the following statement is true:

(ii) **Every linear equation of the form $ax + by + cz = d$ is the equation of a plane provided $a^2 + b^2 + c^2 \neq 0$.**

In order to prove this, we must show that there exist two points, $A(x_1, y_1, z_1)$ and $B(x_2, y_2, z_2)$, such that the coordinates x, y, and z of a point P satisfy $ax + by + cz = d$ if and only if $|AP| = |BP|$. If $d \neq 0$, we can choose $A(0, 0, 0)$ and $B\left(\dfrac{2ad}{a^2 + b^2 + c^2}, \dfrac{2bd}{a^2 + b^2 + c^2}, \dfrac{2cd}{a^2 + b^2 + c^2}\right)$ as the two points and prove that $|AP| = |BP|$ if and only if $ax + by + cz = d$ as follows:

$$|AP| = |BP| \longleftrightarrow |AP|^2 = |BP|^2 \longleftrightarrow (x - 0)^2 + (y - 0)^2 + (z - 0)^2$$
$$= \left(x - \frac{2ad}{a^2 + b^2 + c^2}\right)^2 + \left(y - \frac{2bd}{a^2 + b^2 + c^2}\right)^2 + \left(z - \frac{2cd}{a^2 + b^2 + c^2}\right)^2 \longleftrightarrow$$
$$\longleftrightarrow x^2 + y^2 + z^2 = x^2 + y^2 + z^2 - \frac{4d}{a^2 + b^2 + c^2}(ax + by + cz) +$$
$$\frac{4d^2}{(a^2 + b^2 + c^2)^2}(a^2 + b^2 + c^2) \longleftrightarrow \frac{4d}{a^2 + b^2 + c^2}(ax + by + cz) =$$
$$\frac{4d^2}{a^2 + b^2 + c^2} \longleftrightarrow ax + by + cz = d.$$

If $d = 0$, we have $B(0, 0, 0)$ as well as $A(0, 0, 0)$. Therefore A and B are the same and no plane is determined. However, when $d = 0$, we can show that the points $A'(a, b, c)$ and $B'(-a, -b, -c)$ will serve as defining points for a plane whose equation is the linear equation $ax + by + cz = 0$ provided $a^2 + b^2 + c^2 \neq 0$. (See Exercise 4 below.)

Statements (*i*) and (*ii*) combine to establish:

(*iii*) **A set of points is a plane if and only if its equation has the form** $ax + by + cz = d$ **where** $a^2 + b^2 + c^2 \neq 0$.

A EXERCISES

1. Find the measure of the line segment between the points in each of the following pairs:

   a. $A(4, 7, 6)$, $B(1, 5, 3)$
   b. $M(3, 5, 7)$, $O(0, 0, 0)$
   c. $R(8, 5, 6)$, $S(3, 2, 1)$
   d. $D(1, 2, 5)$, $E(4, 7, 3)$
   e. $F(-2, 5, 3)$, $G(6, -5, 2)$
   f. $N(9, 4, -6)$, $Q(-3, -2, -8)$
   g. $B(3, -3, -3)$, $T(-7, 7, 7)$
   h. $N(10, 1, 11)$, $M(2, 8, -4)$

2. What equation must the coordinates (x, y, z) of the point P satisfy if the measure of the line segment from the origin to point P is 6?

3. For each of the following, determine the equation of the plane each of whose points is equidistant from the two given points.

   a. $A(2, 3, 5)$ and $B(9, 4, 1)$
   b. $M(8, -6, -3)$, and $N(4, 7, 3)$
   c. $R(0, 0, 6)$ and $S(-3, 4, 8)$
   d. $P(3, 9, 2)$ and $Q(3, 5, 2)$
   e. $C(6, 4, 2)$ and $D(-6, -4, -2)$
   f. $E(8, 0, 0)$ and $F(12, 0, 0)$
   g. $G(0, 0, -3)$ and $H(0, 0, 3)$
   h. $K(6, 0, 0)$ and $L(0, 6, 0)$

B EXERCISES

4. Prove that the points $A'(a, b, c)$ and $B'(-a, -b, -c)$ are defining points for a plane which has the linear equation $ax + by + cz = 0$ provided $a^2 + b^2 + c^2 \neq 0$.

5. In each of the following, describe the location of all points whose coordinates satisfy the equation.

   a. $y = x + 0\,z$
   b. $y = z + 0\,x$
   c. $x = z + 0\,y$
   d. $z = y + 0\,x$
   e. $y = a + 0\,x + 0\,z$
   f. $x = b + 0\,y + 0\,z$

Graphs of the Solution Sets of Linear Equations in Three Variables

The solution set of an open sentence in three variables is the set of ordered real number triples that satisfy the sentence.

Example 1. Find some of the elements in the solution set of the equation $2x + y + z = 6$.

Solution. We may obtain elements in the solution set of this equation by arbitrarily assigning any values to x and y and computing the corresponding values of z. In the first two lines of the table below, we give the values assigned to x and y and in the third line we give the computed value for z. We may, of course, choose values arbitrarily for any two of

x	0	1	5	-3	6	-5
y	0	-1	3	7	4	-2
z	6	5	-7	5	-10	18

these variables and then use the equation to compute the corresponding value of the remaining variable.

Example 2. By considering ordered triples of real numbers in the solution set of $2x + y = 8$, sketch the graph of the equation.

Solution. If we consider this equation as an equation in three variables, x, y, and z, it has the form $2x + y + 0 \cdot z = 8$. If $x = 1$, y has the value 6, and we are free to assign any value whatsoever to z. Thus $P(1, 6, c)$ is a point in the plane whose equation is given. Now we know from our definition of the coordinates of a point that all the points for which $x = 1$ and $y = 6$ lie in the line which is perpendicular to the xy-plane at $P_1(1, 6, 0)$. Since all of these points $P(1, 6, c)$ are the graphs of ordered real number triples in the solution set of $2x + y + 0 \cdot z = 8$ for all values of c, we see that this perpendicular line lies in the plane whose equation is $2x + y + 0 \cdot z = 8$. (See the drawing below.)

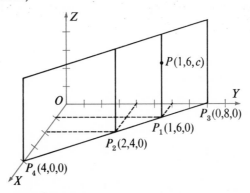

Similarly, perpendiculars to the xy-plane at $P_2(2, 4, 0)$, $P_3(0, 8, 0)$ and $P_4(4, 0, 0)$ lie in this plane. Since all of these perpendiculars to the xy-plane lie in a plane which is perpendicular to the xy-plane, we see that the equation $2x + y = 8$ is the equation of a plane which is perpendicular to the xy-plane. Its line of intersection with the xy-plane is a line whose equation in the xy-plane is $2x + y = 8$.

Example 3. By considering ordered triples of real numbers in the solution set of the equation $x = 5$, sketch the graph of the equation.

Solution. Viewed as an equation in the three variables x, y, and z, this equation has the form $x + 0 \cdot y +$ $0 \cdot z = 5$. Here we must assign x the value 5, but y and z can be chosen arbitrarily. Thus we see that the plane which is the graph of $x = 5$ is the set of points whose directed distance from the yz-plane is 5. It is, therefore, parallel to the yz-plane. See the figure at the right.

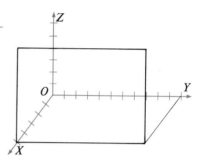

The two preceding examples give us a method for sketching the graph of the equation $ax + by + cz = d$ when one or two of the coefficients are 0. If all of the coefficients are different from zero, we can illustrate the appropriate procedure by sketching plane M, the graph of the equation given in Example 1: $2x + y + z = 6$.

We recall from Chapter 5 that an easy way to sketch the line which is the graph of a given linear equation is to find the intercepts of the line. Similarly, the graph of a plane is easy to sketch if we begin by finding the intersection of this plane with each of the coordinate planes. The intersections of plane M with the coordinate planes are called the *traces* of plane M.

If we want the equation of the intersection of plane M with the yz-plane, we must let $x = 0$ in the equation $2x + y + z = 6$. The resulting equation $y + z = 6$ is the equation of a line in the yz-plane and this line is called the trace of M in the yz-plane, or the yz-trace of M. Similarly, if we let $y = 0$ in the equation $2x + y + z = 6$, the resulting equation $2x + z = 6$ is the equation of a line in the xz-plane and this line is called the xz-trace of plane M. Also, if we let $z = 0$ in the equation $2x + y + z = 6$, the resulting equation $2x + y = 6$ is the equation of

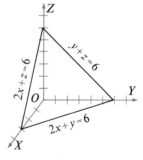

a line in the yz-plane and this line is called the yz-trace of plane M. The position of plane M is clearly indicated by the graphs of the three lines in the coordinate planes as shown in the figure.

1. Sketch the graph of the solution set of each of the following equations. Each equation is considered to be an equation in three variables.

a. $x + y + 0z = 4$

b. $x - y + 0z = 6$

c. $x + 3y + 0z = 9$

d. $2x + 3y = 6$

e. $x + 0y + z = 4$

f. $x + 0y - z = 6$

g. $2x + z = 8$

h. $3x + 4z = 12$

i. $0x + y + z = 4$

j. $y - z = 8$

k. $z - y = 6$

l. $2z + 5y = 10$

2. Sketch the graph of each of the following equations.

a. $x + 3y + 4z = 12$

b. $2x + 3y + z = 6$

c. $x - 2y + 5z = 10$

d. $4x + 2y - z = 8$

e. $3x - y - z = 6$

f. $\frac{1}{2}x + 2y - 3z = 0$

g. $\frac{x-y}{2} + z = 3$

h. $2x + y - z = 5$

i. $\frac{x}{3} + \frac{y}{4} - \frac{z}{2} = 1$

j. $\frac{x}{3} - \frac{y}{4} + \frac{z}{2} = 1$

k. $\frac{2}{3}x - \frac{3}{4}y = z$

l. $\frac{x}{2} + \frac{y}{3} = -\frac{z}{3}$

3. Sketch the graph of each of the following equations. Each equation is to be regarded as an equation in three variables.

a. $z = -2$ b. $y = 4$ c. $x = 6$ d. $z = 3$

4. For each of the following systems of equations, sketch the graphs of the solution sets of the component equations with respect to one set of axes. Indicate whether the planes you have sketched intersect in a line, are the same plane, or do not intersect.

a. $\begin{cases} x + y + 0z = 5 \\ x - y + 0z = 5 \end{cases}$

b. $\begin{cases} x + y + 0z = 5 \\ z = 3 \end{cases}$

c. $\begin{cases} x + y + 0z = 5 \\ z = 0 \end{cases}$

d. $\begin{cases} 2x + z = 4 \\ y = 0 \end{cases}$

e. $\begin{cases} 2x + z = 4 \\ y = -2 \end{cases}$

f. $\begin{cases} x + 3y + z = 6 \\ z = 2 \end{cases}$

g. $\begin{cases} 2x + 3y = 12 \\ z = 2 \end{cases}$

h. $\begin{cases} 2x + 3y = 12 \\ 4x + 6y = 24 \end{cases}$

i. $\begin{cases} 2x + 3y = 12 \\ 2x + 3y = -12 \end{cases}$

j. $\begin{cases} 3y - x = -18 \\ 3y + 4x = 12 \end{cases}$

Systems of Two Linear Equations in Three Variables

We know that every linear equation $ax + by + cz = d$ is the equation of a plane provided $a^2 + b^2 + c^2 \neq 0$. If we are given two such linear equations, the two planes which are their respective graphs may have one of three positions with respect to each other; they may intersect in a line, they may be parallel, or they may be the same plane. In this section we illustrate each of these possibilities.

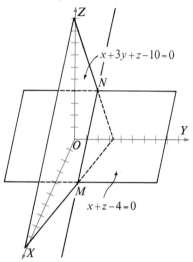

1. The two planes intersect in a line. The graph of the solution set of the system $\begin{cases} x + 3y + z - 10 = 0 \\ x + z - 4 = 0 \end{cases}$ is shown in the figure at the right.

It can be shown that an extension of Theorem 2–12 is valid for a system consisting of two linear equations in the three variables x, y, and z. In fact the proof of this extension of Theorem 2–12 is exactly the same as the proof of Theorem 2–12 if we substitute ordered triples for ordered pairs. Therefore the given system is equivalent to the system $\begin{cases} x + 3y + z - 10 = 0 \\ k_1(x + 3y + z - 10) + k_2(x + z - 4) = 0 \end{cases}$ provided $k_2 \neq 0$, or to the system $\begin{cases} x + z - 4 = 0 \\ k_1(x + 3y + z - 10) + k_2(x + z - 4) = 0 \end{cases}$ provided $k_1 \neq 0$.

If we choose 1 and -1 as k_1 and k_2, respectively, the second equation in each of these systems becomes $(x + 3y + z - 10) - (x + z - 4) = 0$, or $y = 2$. Thus the given system is equivalent to each of the systems:

$$\begin{cases} x + 3y + z = 10 \\ y = 2 \end{cases} \qquad \begin{cases} x + z = 4 \\ y = 2 \end{cases}$$

The graphs of these systems are shown on the left and right, respectively, at the top of the next page.

Our graphs verify the fact that each of the systems

$$\begin{cases} x + 3y + z - 10 = 0 \\ x + z - 4 = 0 \end{cases} \qquad \begin{cases} x + 3y + z = 10 \\ y = 2 \end{cases} \quad \text{and} \quad \begin{cases} x + z = 4 \\ y = 2 \end{cases}$$

has the same solution set, namely the set of ordered triples whose graph is $\overleftrightarrow{MN}$. Each of these systems is an independent system. Why? Note that in each drawing we show only a part of the graph of each plane.

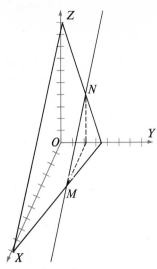

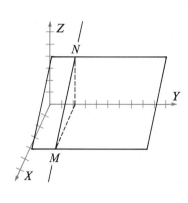

2. The two planes are parallel. The graphs of the component equations of the system

$$\begin{cases} x + 3\,y + z = 9 \\ x + 3\,y + z = 3 \end{cases}$$ are two parallel planes as

shown in the drawing at the right.

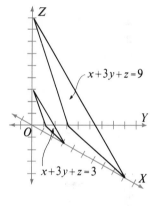

There is no ordered number triple that satisfies both of these equations because for each ordered triple the sum $x + 3\,y + z$ has a unique value and hence cannot be both 9 and 3. Thus the planes which are the graphs of these equations have no point in common; that is, they are parallel. The system is <u>inconsistent</u> because any ordered triple which satisfies one equation will not satisfy the other. Thus the solution set for the system is ∅.

3. The planes coincide (are the same). The graph

of the system $\begin{cases} x + 3\,y + z = 9 \\ 3\,x + 9\,y + 3\,z = 27 \end{cases}$ is shown

at the right.

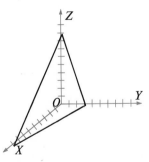

Any ordered triple of real numbers will satisfy either of these equations if and only if it satisfies the other. Thus the system is de-<u>pendent</u> and the graphs of its components are the same plane. We can use a procedure simi-lar to that employed in Theorem 1–12 to find the equation of a plane which contains the line of intersection of the graphs of two given linear equations in three variables. The process is shown in Examples 1 and 2.

Example 1.   Find the equation of a plane W which contains the point $P(1, 1, 1)$ and the line of intersection of the planes M and N whose equations are respectively (1) $x + 3y - 5z = 7$ and (2) $4x - y + 3z = -2$.

Solution.   The equation $k_1(x + 3y - 5z - 7) + k_2(4x - y + 3z + 2) = 0$ is a linear equation for all values of k_2 when $k_1 \neq 0$ and is therefore the equation of a plane. When $k_1 = 1$, we have: (3) $(x + 3y - 5z - 7) + k_2(4x - y + 3z + 2) = 0$. If $P(a, b, c)$ is a point in the line of intersection of M and N, then the triple (a, b, c) satisfies both (1) and (2) and therefore satisfies (3). Accordingly, (3) is the equation of a plane. We want a plane which contains every point common to planes M and N and which also contains $P(1, 1, 1)$. Therefore, we determine k_2 so that (3) is satisfied by this triple. Thus (3) becomes $-8 + 8k_2 = 0$, or $k_2 = 1$. Hence the equation of plane W is $(x + 3y - 5z - 7) + (4x - y + 3z + 2) = 0$, or $5x + 2y - 2z = 5$.

Example 2.   Determine k_2 in Example 1 so that (3) is the equation of plane Q which is perpendicular to the xz-plane and find the equation of the xz-trace of plane Q.

Solution.   We know that every plane which is perpendicular to the xz-plane has a linear equation of the form $ax + 0y + bz = d$. Accordingly, we determine k_2 in equation (3) so that the sum of the coefficients of y is 0. We see that $k_2 = 3$. Then the equation of plane Q is $(x + 3y - 5z - 7) + 3(4x - y + 3z + 2) = 0$, or $13x + 4z = 1$. In the xz-plane, the line L which is the graph of $13x + 4z = 1$ is the xz-trace of the plane Q. We should observe that a line in three-dimensional space is the graph of the truth set of a system of two linear equations in three variables. Thus the line L is the graph of the system $\begin{cases} y = 0 \\ 13x + 4z = 1. \end{cases}$

Example 3.   If line L is the graph of the solution set of the system $\begin{cases} 2x + y - z - 8 = 0 \\ x + y + z - 5 = 0 \end{cases}$, express x and y in terms of z and find the coordinates of the point A where L intersects the xy-plane.

Solution.   Write the equations of the system in the form $\begin{cases} 2x + y = z + 8 \\ x + y = -z + 5 \end{cases}$ and solve this system for x and y to obtain $\begin{cases} x = 2z + 3 \\ y = -3z + 2 \end{cases}$. Now for any assigned value of z we can easily find the corresponding values of x and y. For example, if we let

$z = 5$, then $x = 13$ and $y = -13$. Hence, $P(13, -13, 5) \in L$ and it is also in the plane whose equation is $z = 5$. In other words, $P(13, -13, 5)$ is the intersection of L and the plane whose equation is $z = 5$. Since we want the coordinates of the point A which is the intersection of L with the xy-plane, we let $z = 0$ and obtain $x = 3$ and $y = 2$. Thus $A(3, 2, 0)$ is the required point.

A EXERCISES

1. Show the graph of the solution set of each of the following systems of equations.

   a. $\begin{cases} x + 2y + z - 8 = 0 \\ x + z - 4 = 0 \end{cases}$

   b. $\begin{cases} x + 3y + z - 6 = 0 \\ x + z - 3 = 0 \end{cases}$

   c. $\begin{cases} 2x + y + 3z = 12 \\ y + 3z = 4 \end{cases}$

   d. $\begin{cases} 2x - 2y + z = 10 \\ x - y = 4 \end{cases}$

   e. $\begin{cases} 3x + 4y - z - 12 = 0 \\ 3x + 4y + 8 = 0 \end{cases}$

   f. $\begin{cases} x + 4y - z - 8 = 0 \\ -4y + z - 4 = 0 \end{cases}$

2. In which of the following are the graphs of the equations in the system a pair of parallel planes, in which are they a single plane, and in which are they a pair of planes intersecting in a single line?

   a. $\begin{cases} 2x + 3y - z = 12 \\ 4x + 6y - 2z = 16 \end{cases}$

   b. $\begin{cases} x + y + z = 4 \\ x + y + z = 8 \end{cases}$

   c. $\begin{cases} x - 2y + z = 10 \\ -x + 2y - z = -10 \end{cases}$

   d. $\begin{cases} x + y + z = 6 \\ x - y + z = 6 \end{cases}$

   e. $\begin{cases} x + 4y - z = 8 \\ x + 4y + z = -8 \end{cases}$

   f. $\begin{cases} 2x + 4y - z = 8 \\ x + 2y - \frac{1}{2}z = 4 \end{cases}$

3. Find the equation of the plane which contains the point $P(1, 2, 1)$ and L, the line of intersection of the two planes whose equations are $2x + 3y + z = 12$ and $2x - y - 2z = 4$.

4. Find the equation of the plane which contains the point $P(2, 1, -1)$ and the line of intersection of the two planes whose equations are $3x + y + 15 = 0$ and $x + 2y + z - 4 = 0$.

5. Find the equation of the plane which is perpendicular to the xz-plane and also contains the intersection of the planes which are the graphs of the equations $x + 2y + 3z - 6 = 0$ and $x - y + 4z - 8 = 0$.

6. If the line L is the graph of the solution set of the system $\begin{cases} x + 2y - z - 6 = 0 \\ x + y + z - 3 = 0 \end{cases}$, express x and y in terms of z and find the coordinates of the point where L intersects the xy-plane.

7. Find the equation of the plane which contains the origin and the line of intersection of the planes which are the graphs of the equations $3x + y + 10z + 15 = 0$ and $x - 2y + z - 4 = 0$.

8. Find the equation of the plane which is perpendicular to the yz-plane and also contains the intersection of the planes which are the graphs of the equations $x + 2y + 3z - 6 = 0$ and $x - y + 4z - 8 = 0$.

9. Find the coordinates of the point where the line L of Ex. 3 intersects the yz-plane.

10. Find the coordinates of the point where the line L of Ex. 3 intersects the plane whose equation is $2x + 5y - 3z = 25$.

Solution of a System of Three Linear Equations in Three Variables

In this section we will adapt the methods used in the solution of systems of two linear equations in two variables so that they can be applied to the solution of systems of three linear equations in three variables.

First we consider a system which has a unique solution.

$$\begin{cases} 3x + y + 3z = 12 \\ 3x + 6y + 4z = 24 \\ z = 2 \end{cases}$$
(plane ABC, or plane M)
(plane DEF, or plane N)
(plane GHI, or plane Q)

The figure at the right shows the graphs of the three equations. We see that point P is the only point common to the three planes.

In order to find the solution algebraically, we use the value of z given in the third equation and the substitution method to obtain two equations which can be solved for x and y. Thus, assuming that the numbers x, y, and z actually satisfy this system, we have:

$$\begin{cases} 3x + y + 3z = 12 \\ 3x + 6y + 4z = 24 \\ z = 2 \end{cases} \longrightarrow \begin{cases} 3x + y = 6 \\ 3x + 6y = 16 \end{cases} \longrightarrow 5y = 10 \longrightarrow y = 2$$

Also, $\begin{cases} 3x + y = 6 \\ y = 2 \end{cases} \longrightarrow 3x = 4 \longrightarrow x = \frac{4}{3}$.

If our system has a solution, it is $(\frac{4}{3}, 2, 2)$. Substituting these values in each of the component equations of the given system, we find that the ordered triple $(\frac{4}{3}, 2, 2)$ is a solution. Thus the solution set is $\{(\frac{4}{3}, 2, 2)\}$.

Ordinarily the graphical representation of the truth sets of three linear equations in three variables is very complicated to draw and when drawn, very difficult to read. Nevertheless, considerations based on the geometric meaning of the equations are very helpful when we think of the types of intersections that are possible for three planes in space.

In the following examples we consider a basic method for solving systems of three linear equations in three variables. Later we derive some general statements by considering the solution of a system of three linear equations in three variables by determinants.

Example 1. Solve the system: $\begin{cases} x - y + 11\,z = -50 \\ 4\,x - 3\,y + 2\,z = 7 \\ 3\,x + 7\,y - 5\,z = 10 \end{cases}$

Solution. Assuming that (x, y, z) is a solution of this system, we have:

$\begin{cases} x - y + 11\,z = -50 \\ 4\,x - 3\,y + 2\,z = 7 \\ 3\,x + 7\,y - 5\,z = 10 \end{cases} \longrightarrow \begin{cases} -4(x - y + 11\,z) = -4(-50) \\ 4\,x - 3\,y + 2\,z = 7 \\ -3(x - y + 11\,z) = -3(-50) \\ 3\,x + 7\,y - 5\,z = 10 \end{cases} \longrightarrow$

$\longmapsto \begin{cases} x - y + 11\,z = -50 \\ 0\,x + y - 42\,z = 207 \\ 0\,x + 10\,y - 38\,z = 160 \end{cases} \longrightarrow \begin{cases} x - y + 11\,z = -50 \\ -10(0\,x + y - 42\,z) = -10(207) \\ 0\,x + 10\,y - 382 = 160 \end{cases} \longrightarrow$

$\longmapsto \begin{cases} x - y + 11\,z = -50 \\ 0\,x + y - 42\,z = 207 \\ 0\,x + 0\,y + 382\,z = -1910 \end{cases} \longrightarrow \begin{cases} x - y + 11\,z = -50 \\ y = -3 \\ z = -5 \end{cases} \longrightarrow \begin{cases} x = 2 \\ y = -3 \\ z = -5 \end{cases}$

If the system has a solution, it is in $\{(2, -3, -5)\}$. Substituting these values in each of the component equations of the given system, we see that each is satisfied. This proves that the ordered triple $(2, -3, -5)$ is a solution. Thus the solution set is $\{(2, -3, -5)\}$.

The above procedure can be described as follows:

Step 1. Eliminate x from the second and third equations by adding multiples of the members of the first equation.

This gives the equivalent system: $\begin{cases} x - y + 11\,z = -50 \\ 0 + y - 42\,z = 207 \\ 0 + 10\,y - 38\,z = 160 \end{cases}$

Step 2. Working with the latter system, eliminate y from the third equation by adding an appropriate multiple of the numbers represented by the members of the second equation, and obtain the equivalent system:

$$\begin{cases} x - y + 11\,z = -50 \\ 0 + y - 42\,z = 207 \\ 0 + 0 + 382\,z = -1910 \end{cases}$$

From the last equation, we see that $z = -5$.

Step 3. Substitute -5 for z in the second equation to obtain $y = -3$.

Step 4. Substitute -5 for z and -3 for y in the first equation to obtain $x = 2$.

Step 5. Substitute the ordered triple $(2, -3, -5)$ in each of the component equations of the given system to see if $(2, -3, -5)$ is the solution of the system.

Since $(2, -3, -5)$ is the solution, we know that the three planes intersect in a point.

This method provides a systematic procedure for determining when the solution set of a system of three linear equations in three variables is empty; when it consists of a single ordered triple; when it contains infinitely many ordered triples whose graphs are the points in a line; or when it contains infinitely many ordered triples whose graphs are the points in a plane.

The method used in this example is called the *triangulation method* because, if there is a unique solution, the nonzero coefficients in the equations in step 2 are in a triangular arrangement.

$$\begin{matrix} 1 & -1 & 11 \\ 0 & 1 & -42 \\ 0 & 0 & 382 \end{matrix}$$

Example 2. Solve the system: $\begin{cases} 3x - 2y + z - 11 = 0 \\ x + 5y - 4z - 17 = 0 \\ 9x + 11y - 10z - 73 = 0 \end{cases}$

Solution. To simplify this computation, we interchange the first and second equations and then proceed as in Example 1.

Step 1. Eliminate x from two equations to obtain the equivalent system:

$$\begin{cases} x + 5y - 4z - 17 = 0 \\ 0x + 17y - 13z - 40 = 0 \\ 0x + 34y - 26z - 80 = 0 \end{cases}$$

Step. 2. Eliminate y from the third equation to obtain the equivalent system:

$$\begin{cases} x + 5y - 4z - 17 = 0 \\ 0 + 17y - 13z - 40 = 0 \\ 0 + 0 + 0 + 0 = 0 \end{cases}$$

We see that the third equation provides no information. If in step 2 one of the equations is the identity $0 = 0$, then the left member of any one of the given equations can be expressed as the sum of real number multiples of the left members of the other two equations. In this case, the left member of the third equation of the given system can be expressed as $2(3x - 2y + z - 11) + 3(x + 5y - 4z - 17)$. Thus $9x + 11y - 10z - 73 = 0$ can be written as $2(3x - 2y + z - 11) + 3(x + 5y - 4z - 17) = 0$.

Accordingly, we know by the reasoning used in Example 1 of the preceding section that the graph of the third equation contains the line of intersection of the planes M and N which are the graphs of $3x - 2y + z - 11 = 0$ and $x + 5y - 4z - 17 = 0$, respectively. Therefore, the solution of the given system is an infinite set of ordered triples each of which is the coordinates of a point in the line of intersection of planes M and N. If we wish to find some members of the solution set, we may use the method shown in Example 3 in the preceding section.

Note that if p_1, p_2, and p_3 are polynomials and $p_3 = k_1p_1 + k_2p_2$, then p_3 is said to be a linear combination of p_1 and p_2 provided k_1 and k_2 are not both zero. Thus the left member of the third equation of the given system in the preceeding example was expressed as a linear combination of the left members of the other two equations.

Example 3. Solve the system: $\begin{cases} x + 5y - 4z - 17 = 0 \\ 3x - 2y + z - 11 = 0 \\ 3x + 15y - 12z - 51 = 0 \end{cases}$

Solution. We see that the left-hand member of the third equation is three times the left-hand member of the first equation. We know that this means that the first and third planes coincide. Therefore, the solution set is the infinite set of ordered triples which are the coordinates of the points in the line of intersection of the planes which are the graphs of the first two equations. This is the same line we obtained in Example 2.

Example 4. Solve the system: $\begin{cases} x + 3y + 5z = 10 \\ 2x + 6y + 10z = 20 \\ -x - 3y - 5z = -10 \end{cases}$

Solution. Since any ordered triple which satisfies one of these equations will satisfy each of the other two, we see that the three graphs are coincident planes. Therefore the solution set is the infinite set of ordered triples which are the coordinates of points in the plane.

Example 5. Solve the system: $\begin{cases} x + 0\,y + z = -1 \\ x + 3\,y + 2\,z = 7 \\ 3\,x + 3\,y + 4\,z = -1 \end{cases}$

Solution. Step 1, eliminate x from two equations: $\begin{cases} x + 0\,y + z = -1 \\ 0 + 3\,y + z = 8 \\ 0 + 3\,y + z = 2 \end{cases}$

Since there are no ordered triples which satisfy the last two component equations of the system obtained in step 1, the system is inconsistent. In the original system, the plane which is the graph of the third equation is parallel to the intersection of the other two planes. Note that $3\,x + 3\,y + 4\,z + 1 = 2(x + z + 1) + 1(x + 3\,y + 2\,z - 7) + 6$. Therefore, any triple that satisfies the first two equations of the original system, and there are such ordered triples, will fail to satisfy the third equation. Thus the solution set is $\emptyset$.

Example 6. Solve the system: $\begin{cases} x + 2\,y + z = 1 \\ x + 2\,y + z = 3 \\ x + 2\,y + z = 7 \end{cases}$

Solution. Since there are no ordered triples which simultaneously satisfy any two of these three component equations, the system is inconsistent and the planes are parallel. Therefore the solution set is $\emptyset$.

Example 7. Solve the system: $\begin{cases} x + 2\,y + 3\,z = 7 \\ x + 2\,y + 3\,z = 15 \\ x - y - 2\,z = 14 \end{cases}$

Solution. The graphs of the first two equations are parallel planes, while each of the systems $\begin{cases} x + 2\,y + 3\,z = 7 \\ x - y - 2\,z = 14 \end{cases}$ and $\begin{cases} x + 2\,y + 3\,z = 15 \\ x - y - 2\,z = 14 \end{cases}$ do have solutions. Therefore the plane which is the graph of the third equation intersects the two parallel planes which are the graphs of the first two equations. Thus the solution set is $\emptyset$.

Example 8. Solve the system: $\begin{cases} x + 3\,y - z = 11 \\ 2\,x + 6\,y - 2\,z = 22 \\ x + 3\,y - z = -8 \end{cases}$

Solution. In this case the plane which is the graph of the third equation is parallel to the coincident planes which are the graphs of the first two equations. Therefore the solution set is $\emptyset$.

Example 9. Solve the system:
$$\begin{cases} \dfrac{1}{u} - \dfrac{1}{v} + \dfrac{11}{w} = -50 \\[2mm] \dfrac{4}{u} - \dfrac{3}{v} + \dfrac{2}{w} = 7 \\[2mm] \dfrac{3}{u} + \dfrac{7}{v} - \dfrac{5}{w} = 10 \end{cases}$$

Solution. The component equations of this system are not linear equations. However, if we substitute x for $\dfrac{1}{u}$, y for $\dfrac{1}{v}$, and z for $\dfrac{1}{w}$, we obtain the linear system that we solved in Example 1. Thus $\dfrac{1}{u} = 2$, $\dfrac{1}{v} = -3$, and $\dfrac{1}{w} = -5$. Accordingly, $u = \dfrac{1}{2}$, $v = -\dfrac{1}{3}$, and $w = -\dfrac{1}{5}$. Substitution shows that the system is satisfied. Therefore, the solution set of the given system is $\{(\frac{1}{2}, -\frac{1}{3}, -\frac{1}{5})\}$.

It is also instructive to consider the solution of a system of three linear equations in three variables by means of determinants. Consider the system:

$$\begin{cases} a_1 x + b_1 y + c_1 z = d_1 \\ a_2 x + b_2 y + c_2 z = d_2 \\ a_3 x + b_3 y + c_3 z = d_3 \end{cases}$$

Assuming that the ordered triple (x_1, y_1, z_1) is a solution of this system, we have:

$$(1)\ \Delta = \begin{vmatrix} a_1 & b_1 & c_1 \\ a_2 & b_2 & c_2 \\ a_3 & b_3 & c_3 \end{vmatrix} \ (2) \longrightarrow \Delta \cdot x_1 = \begin{vmatrix} a_1 x_1 & b_1 & c_1 \\ a_2 x_1 & b_2 & c_2 \\ a_3 x_1 & b_3 & c_3 \end{vmatrix} (3)$$

$$(3)\ \mapsto \Delta \cdot x_1 = \begin{vmatrix} a_1 x_1 + b_1 y_1 + c_1 z_1 & b_1 & c_1 \\ a_2 x_1 + b_2 y_1 + c_2 z_1 & b_2 & c_2 \\ a_3 x_1 + b_3 y_1 + c_3 z_1 & b_3 & c_3 \end{vmatrix} \ (4) \longrightarrow \Delta \cdot x_1 = \begin{vmatrix} d_1 & b_1 & c_1 \\ d_2 & b_2 & c_2 \\ d_3 & b_3 & c_3 \end{vmatrix}$$

We recognize the last determinant as Δ_1 because it can be obtained by replacing the first column in Δ with the column of constants d_1, d_2, and d_3. Thus our last equation has the form $\Delta \cdot x_1 = \Delta_1$. By similar procedures we can obtain $\Delta \cdot y_1 = \Delta_2$ and $\Delta \cdot z_1 = \Delta_3$. Therefore, if the given system has a solution (x_1, y_1, z_1), we have:

(A) $\Delta \cdot x_1 = \Delta_1$, $\Delta \cdot y_1 = \Delta_2$, and $\Delta \cdot z_1 = \Delta_3$

(B) If $\Delta \neq 0$, the system has the unique solution $\left(\dfrac{\Delta_1}{\Delta}, \dfrac{\Delta_2}{\Delta}, \dfrac{\Delta_3}{\Delta} \right)$.

If $\Delta = 0$ and at least one of the determinants Δ_1, Δ_2, or Δ_3 is <u>not</u> 0, the assumption that the system has a solution leads to a false statement and hence must be abandoned. Therefore,

(C) If $\Delta = 0$ and one or more of the determinants Δ_1, Δ_2, and Δ_3 is not zero, the system is inconsistent.

Ⓐ EXERCISES

1. Solve each of the following systems of equations by the triangulation method.

a. $\begin{cases} x+y+z=10 \\ 2x-3y-z=-10 \\ 3x+4y-2z=8 \end{cases}$ d. $\begin{cases} x+y+2z=0 \\ 3x-2y+z-5=0 \\ 2x-4y-z-6=0 \end{cases}$

b. $\begin{cases} 2x-3y-4z=-20 \\ 4x+5y+z=-8 \\ x-y+3z=19 \end{cases}$ e. $\begin{cases} 2x-3y-2z=-16 \\ 6x+y-3z=-6 \\ 4x+2y+z=12 \end{cases}$

c. $\begin{cases} x+2y+3z-4=0 \\ 3x+y-6z-7=0 \\ 5x+6y-4z-2=0 \end{cases}$ f. $\begin{cases} 2x+2y-z=9 \\ x+3y-3z=3 \\ 4x-y+2z=15 \end{cases}$

2. Describe the relationships existing between the graphs of the component equations in each of the following systems. If the graph of the solution set of the system is a line or a plane, state its equation; if it is a point, state its coordinates.

a. $\begin{cases} 2x+3y+z=1 \\ 4x+6y+2z=2 \\ 2x+3y+z=2 \end{cases}$ d. $\begin{cases} x+y+3z=6 \\ 2x+2y+6z=8 \\ z=5 \end{cases}$

b. $\begin{cases} 2x+4y+6z=10 \\ x+2y+3z=5 \\ 3x+6y+9z=15 \end{cases}$ e. $\begin{cases} x+2y+3z=5 \\ 4x-y-z=-20 \\ 2x+4y+6z=12 \end{cases}$

c. $\begin{cases} x+4y+z=6 \\ 2x+3y-z=7 \\ 5y+3z=10 \end{cases}$ f. $\begin{cases} x+4y+3z=1 \\ 3x-2y+z=23 \\ 5x+6y+7z=25 \end{cases}$

3. Solve the following systems of equations by use of determinants.

a. $\begin{cases} 3x+2y-z=-14 \\ x-y+z=-3 \\ 2x-y=1 \end{cases}$ b. $\begin{cases} 3x-2y=7 \\ 3y-4z=6 \\ 5x-2z=11 \end{cases}$

4. Solve: $\begin{cases} \dfrac{3}{u}+\dfrac{2}{v}-\dfrac{4}{w}+4=0 \\ \dfrac{1}{u}+\dfrac{1}{v}+\dfrac{1}{w}-9=0 \\ \dfrac{2}{u}-\dfrac{1}{v}+\dfrac{3}{w}-13=0 \end{cases}$

5. If the first and third digits of a three-digit number are interchanged, the number is increased by 99, and if the second and third digits are interchanged, the number is increased by 36. What is the number if the sum of its digits is 16?

6. The units digit of a three-digit number is twice the hundreds digit and four times the tens digit. If the sum of the digits is 14, what is the number?

7. A few years ago it required t hours for a train traveling r miles per hour to make the trip from city A to city B. Today, by traveling 8 miles per hour faster, a train can cover the distance between the cities in 1 hour less time. The railroad company hopes soon to have a train that can travel 20 miles per hour faster than the original train and cover the distance in 2 hours less time. What is the distance between the cities and what were the original rate and time required for the train to make the trip between them?

8. A and B working together can complete a particular job in $4\frac{4}{9}$ days, B and C working together can complete the job in $4\frac{4}{5}$ days, and A and C working together can complete the job in $5\frac{5}{11}$ days. How long would it take each man working alone to do the job?

9. In the figure at the left below, $\overline{AB}$ is tangent to the circle at D, $\overline{BC}$ is tangent to the circle at E, and $\overline{AC}$ is tangent to the circle at F. From geometry we know that $|AF|=|AD|$, $|DB|=|BE|$, and $|EC|=|FC|$. If $|AB|=28$, $|BC|=26$, and $|AC|=30$, what are the measures of $\overline{AD}$, $\overline{BE}$, and $\overline{CF}$?

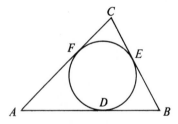
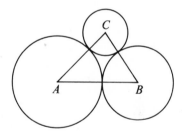

10. In the figure at the right above, circles are drawn with their centers at A, B, and C, the vertices of the triangle. If each circle is tangent to the other two circles, find the measures of the lengths of their radii if $|BC|=6$, $|AC|=8$, and $|AB|=10$.

ESSENTIALS

Before you leave this chapter, make sure that you

1. Know what we mean by a system of open sentences and the solution set of such a system. (Pages 642–644.)

2. Can find the solution set of a system of two open sentences in two variables by graphing. (Page 643.)

3. Know what we mean by dependent, independent, and inconsistent systems and can determine which of these words characterizes a particular system. (Pages 643, 644.)

4. Know what we mean by equivalent systems of open sentences and know the principles which govern such equivalencies. (Page 646.)

5. Understand the principles stated in Theorems 1–12, 2–12, and 3–12 and can apply these principles in finding the solution sets of systems of linear equations in two variables. (Pages 650–653.)

6. Can solve a system of two linear equations in two variables by use of determinants. (Pages 656, 657.)

7. Know the meaning of the three-dimensional coordinate system. (Page 659.)

8. Understand and can use the distance formula in three dimensions. (Page 663.)

9. Can draw the graph of the solution set of a linear equation in three variables and by graphing can find the solution set of a system of two linear equations in three variables or a system of three linear equations in three variables. (Pages 670–678.)

10. Can solve a system of two linear equations in three variables or a system of three linear equations in three variables by algebraic methods. (Pages 670–678.)

11. Can solve a system of three linear equations in three variables by use of determinants. (Pages 679, 680.)

CHAPTER REVIEW

1. Which of the following sentences are systems of open sentences?
   a. $3\,x = 15$ *or* $3\,x > 15$ c. $x - 1 = 15$ *or* $x = 3$
   b. $x + 2 = 8$ *and* $x - 6 = 0$ d. $x + 2 = 4$ *and* $x > 3$

2. By graphing indicate the solution set of each of the following systems:

   a. $\begin{cases} x + y > 16 \\ y < x \end{cases}$ d. $\begin{cases} x + y < 9 \\ y < x - 1 \end{cases}$ g. $\begin{cases} \dfrac{x}{9} + \dfrac{y}{4} = 1 \\ y = 2\,x + 4 \end{cases}$

   b. $\begin{cases} y > 3\,x + 2 \\ y < -2\,x - 3 \end{cases}$ e. $\begin{cases} y > |x| \\ y < 3 \end{cases}$

   c. $\begin{cases} y > x - 2 \\ y > 4 \end{cases}$ f. $\begin{cases} y < |x + 1| \\ y < 4 \end{cases}$ h. $\begin{cases} \dfrac{x}{4} + \dfrac{y}{2} = \dfrac{7}{4} \\ 2\,y - 5\,x = 1 \end{cases}$

3. Which of the following systems are inconsistent and which are consistent? Which of the consistent systems are dependent and which are independent?

a. $\begin{cases} x+y=3 \\ x \leq 3 \end{cases}$

c. $\begin{cases} y < -x+3 \\ y > 4 \end{cases}$

e. $\begin{cases} y=4\,x-2 \\ y=3\,x-2 \end{cases}$

b. $\begin{cases} y=3\,x+2 \\ 6\,x-y+4=0 \end{cases}$

d. $\begin{cases} x+y=1 \\ 3\,x+3\,y=3 \end{cases}$

f. $\begin{cases} y=x+1 \\ y=4 \end{cases}$

4. Which of the following statements are true and which are false?

a. $4\,x=20 \longleftrightarrow 2\,x=10$

b. $-3\,x < 12 \longleftrightarrow x < -4$

c. $x=-3 \longleftrightarrow x^2=(-3)^2$

d. $x=y \longleftrightarrow x-6=y-6$

e. $y=3\,x+5 \longleftrightarrow 3\,y=9\,x+15$

f. $y=|\,a\,|;\ a \in R \longleftrightarrow y^2=a^2;\ a \in R$

g. $ay > ax;\ a < 0 \longleftrightarrow y > x$

h. $3\,x+2=8 \longleftrightarrow (3\,x+2)x=8\,x$

5. Which of the following statements are true and which are false?

a. $\begin{cases} 3\,x+4\,y=7 \\ 5\,x-3\,y=2 \end{cases} \longleftrightarrow \begin{cases} 4\,x-11\,y=-7 \\ x-y=0 \end{cases}$

c. $\begin{cases} y=4\,x \\ x=2 \end{cases} \longleftrightarrow \begin{cases} y^2=16\,x^2 \\ x^2=4 \end{cases}$

b. $\begin{cases} 3\,x+y=2 \\ 2\,x-y=7 \end{cases} \longleftrightarrow \begin{cases} 6\,x+2\,y=4 \\ x=\dfrac{7+y}{2} \end{cases}$

d. $\begin{cases} y=\dfrac{5\,x-4}{2} \\ y=\frac{3}{4}\,x^2 \end{cases} \longleftrightarrow \begin{cases} x=2 \\ y=3 \end{cases}$

6. a. Show that the solution set of the equation $k_1(4\,x-y-1)+k_2(7\,x-3\,y-8)$ $=0$, $k_1 k_2 \neq 0$, contains the solution set of the system $\begin{cases} 4\,x-y-1=0 \\ 7\,x-3\,y-8=0. \end{cases}$

b. Let (a, b) represent the solution of the system in part **a**. Find a value of k_1 and of k_2 such that the equation $k_1(4\,x-y-1)+k_2(7\,x-3\,y-8)=0$ becomes the equation $x=a$. Find a value of k_1 and of k_2 such that the equation becomes $y=b$.

7. Use the multiplication and addition method to solve each of the following systems:

a. $\begin{cases} 4\,x-6\,y=22 \\ 2\,x-9\,y=5 \end{cases}$

b. $\begin{cases} \frac{1}{2}\,x+\frac{3}{4}\,y=-3 \\ 2\,x+\frac{1}{2}\,y=8 \end{cases}$

c. $\begin{cases} 2\,x=-3\,y \\ 4\,x+5\,y=-4 \end{cases}$

8. Use the substitution method to solve each of the following systems:

a. $\begin{cases} 4\,x+y=6 \\ 2\,x+3\,y=13 \end{cases}$

b. $\begin{cases} 4\,x+3\,y=-1 \\ y=\dfrac{1-3\,x}{2} \end{cases}$

c. $\begin{cases} 4\,x+5\,y+36=0 \\ 3\,x+2\,y+27=0 \end{cases}$

9. Use determinants to find the solution set of each of the following systems:

a. $\begin{cases} x+6\,y=-5 \\ 4\,x+5\,y=18 \end{cases}$

b. $\begin{cases} y=\dfrac{17-4\,x}{3} \\ x=\dfrac{5\,y-22}{6} \end{cases}$

c. $\begin{cases} \sqrt{2}\,x+\sqrt{3}\,y=5 \\ 3\sqrt{2}x-4\sqrt{3}y=-6 \end{cases}$

10. Draw a diagram which shows the location in three-dimensional space of each of the following ordered triples of real numbers.

    a. $(-4, 6, 2)$ **b.** $(5, 0, 7)$ **c.** $(6, -3, -4)$ **d.** $(-2, -4, -5)$

11. In the figure at the right, three planes have been drawn through the point $P(a, b, c)$ perpendicular to the x-axis, the y-axis, and the z-axis, respectively. Write the ordered triple of numbers corresponding to each of the points A, B, C, O, E, F, and G.

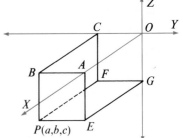

12. In the figure for Ex. 11 find the following:

    a. $|AB|$ **c.** $|FC|$ **e.** $|AC|$

    b. $|BC|$ **d.** $|EG|$ **f.** $|CE|$

13. Assuming that in the figure at the right $ABCD\text{–}EFGH$ is a rectangular parallelepiped four of whose vertices have the coordinates shown, write the coordinates of each of the following points:

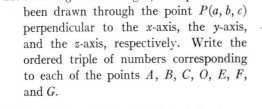

    a. I **c.** K **e.** A **g.** D

    b. J **d.** L **f.** B **h.** H

14. In the figure for Ex. 13, what measures are represented by each of the following?

    a. $|IL|$ **c.** $|DL|$ **e.** $|AC|$ **g.** $|IG|$

    b. $|LK|$ **d.** $|GK|$ **f.** $|AG|$ **h.** $|DJ|$

15. Sketch the graph of the solution set of each of the following equations:

    a. $x + y + 0z = 5$ **d.** $2x + y + 0z = 6$

    b. $x - y + 0z = 3$ **e.** $2x + 3y + 3z = 6$ **g.** $\dfrac{x}{5} - \dfrac{y}{4} + z = 1$

    c. $x + 0y + z = 4$ **f.** $6x + 4y - 5z = 12$ **h.** $\dfrac{x}{3} + \dfrac{y}{4} + z = 1$

16. Sketch the graphs of the solution sets of the components of each of the following systems. Indicate the graph of the solution set of each system.

    a. $\begin{cases} 2x + 5y = 10 \\ z = 3 \end{cases}$ **c.** $\begin{cases} 2x + 4y - z = 8 \\ x + y = 1 \end{cases}$ **e.** $\begin{cases} 3x + 4y - z = 10 \\ z = 0 \end{cases}$

    b. $\begin{cases} 3x + 4y + 2z = 12 \\ x + y = 2 \end{cases}$ **d.** $\begin{cases} x + 2y + z = 4 \\ 3x + 6y + 3z = 12 \end{cases}$ **f.** $\begin{cases} 2x - 6y - z = -12 \\ x + 2y = 2 \end{cases}$

17. Describe how the graphs of the component equations of each of the following systems are related to each other. Describe the graph of the solution set in each case.

a. $\begin{cases} x+2\,y+3\,z=4 \\ 2\,x+4\,y+6\,z=8 \\ 3\,x+6\,y+9\,z=6 \end{cases}$ b. $\begin{cases} 2\,x+3\,y-z=6 \\ 4\,x+6\,y-z=6 \\ x+2\,y=2 \end{cases}$ c. $\begin{cases} 2\,x+y+z=4 \\ 2\,x-y+z=4 \\ x=0 \end{cases}$

18. Find the solution set of each of the following systems of equations.

a. $\begin{cases} 4\,x+y+3\,z=1 \\ x-2\,y+2\,z=-1 \\ 3\,x-y+5\,z=-10 \end{cases}$ c. $\begin{cases} x+4\,y=2 \\ 2\,x-3\,y+z=2 \\ 5\,x-8\,y-z=15 \end{cases}$

b. $\begin{cases} 2\,x+5\,y+2\,z=5 \\ 3\,x-2\,y+8\,z=-9 \\ \frac{1}{2}\,x+y+3\,z=2 \end{cases}$ d. $\begin{cases} \dfrac{1}{x}+\dfrac{1}{y}+\dfrac{1}{z}=\dfrac{7}{4} \\ \dfrac{2}{x}-\dfrac{3}{y}+\dfrac{2}{z}=1 \\ \dfrac{3}{x}-\dfrac{2}{y}-\dfrac{1}{z}=-\dfrac{5}{4} \end{cases}$

19. We are given three alloys of the following composition: x, 5 parts (by weight) copper, 2 parts iron, and 1 part lead; y, 2 parts copper, 5 parts iron, and 1 part lead; z, 3 parts copper, 1 part iron, and 4 parts lead. To obtain 9 ounces of an alloy containing equal quantities (by weight) of copper, iron, and lead, how many ounces of x, y, and z must be melted and mixed together?

20. Find the solution set of each of the following systems by use of determinants.

a. $\begin{cases} 3\,x-2\,y-4\,z=15 \\ 4\,x+2\,y-5\,z=18 \\ x-3\,y-6\,z=5 \end{cases}$ c. $\begin{cases} x+2\,y-z=6 \\ 2\,x-y+3\,z=-13 \\ 3\,x-2\,y+3\,z=-16 \end{cases}$

b. $\begin{cases} x+y+z=6 \\ x+y-z=0 \\ x-y-z=2 \end{cases}$ d. $\begin{cases} 2\,x+3\,y+z=-1 \\ x-y+2\,z=6 \\ 3\,x+2\,y-z=1 \end{cases}$

21. Find the coordinates of the point where the line which is the graph of the truth set of the system $\begin{cases} 2\,x+y+z=6 \\ 3\,x+2\,y+6\,z=12 \end{cases}$ intersects the xy-plane.

CHAPTER TEST

1. Which of the following statements are true and which are false?

a. $6\,x+2=14 \longleftrightarrow x=2$ c. $3\,x^2=27 \longleftrightarrow x=|3|$

b. $\begin{cases} y=3\,x \\ x=4 \end{cases} \longleftrightarrow \begin{cases} y=3\,x \\ \frac{3}{2}\,x=-6 \end{cases}$ d. $\begin{cases} 4\,x+6\,y=36 \\ 3\,x-2\,y=14 \end{cases} \longleftrightarrow \begin{cases} x=6 \\ y=2 \end{cases}$

2. Which of the following systems are inconsistent, which are dependent, and which are independent?

a. $\begin{cases} 2x - 5y = 1 \\ 6x = 3 + 15y \end{cases}$

c. $\begin{cases} 3x + 7y = 10 \\ x + 4y = 0 \end{cases}$

b. $\begin{cases} 4x - 2y = 8 \\ x - \frac{1}{2}y = 4 \end{cases}$

d. $\begin{cases} 2x + 4y - 6z = 8 \\ x + 2y - 3z = 16 \\ 3x + 6y - 9z = 48 \end{cases}$

3. By means of a graph, show the solution set of $\begin{cases} y > x \\ y \le 3 \end{cases}$.

4. Write the simplest system equivalent to $\begin{cases} 2x - y = 4 \\ 3x - 4y = -9 \end{cases}$.

5. Use determinants to solve: $\begin{cases} 2x - 5y = 13 \\ 3x + 2y = 10 \end{cases}$

6. By means of a graph, show the solution set of $\begin{cases} 3x + y + 2z = 6 \\ x = 1 \end{cases}$.

7. Solve: $\begin{cases} 4x + 3y + z = 2 \\ 2x - y + 2z = 3 \\ 4x + 2y - z = -5 \end{cases}$

8. Find the measure of the line segment joining the points $A(2, 1, 5)$ and $B(-4, 3, 7)$.

9. Use determinants to solve: $\begin{cases} 3x - 2y + 5z = 15 \\ 4x + y - z = 9 \\ x - 5y + 2z = 18 \end{cases}$

10. Find the coordinates of the point where the line which is the graph of the truth set of the system $\begin{cases} 2x + 3y + 4z = 17 \\ x - y + 3z = 20 \end{cases}$ intersects the xy-plane.

11. Find the equation of a plane which contains the origin and the line of intersection of the planes whose equations are $x + 2y - z = 11$ and $3x - y + 2z = 31$.

Systems Involving Quadratic Sentences

Quadratic Sentences in Two Variables

Any sentence which is equivalent to a sentence having $ax^2 + bxy + cy^2 + dx + ey + f$ for one member and 0 for the other is called a quadratic sentence in two variables over the real numbers provided the coefficients a, b, c, d, e, $f \in R$ and $a^2 + b^2 + c^2 \neq 0$. The following are examples of quadratic sentences:

$$x^2 + y^2 > 25, \, 3xy + x - 7 = 0, \, y^2 \geq x, \, 3x^2 + xy - 3y^2 > 2x + 3y - 7$$

A *quadratic equation in two variables* is a quadratic sentence in two variables whose comparison symbol is a symbol of equality.

In this chapter we shall be concerned with systems whose components consist of either one quadratic sentence and one linear sentence or two quadratic sentences. Systems in which both of the components are quadratic sentences are called *systems of quadratic sentences* or *quadratic systems*. Sometimes we shall seek a solution of such a system in $R \times R$ and sometimes in $Z \times Z$. In many cases we shall find sketches of the graphs of the quadratic sentences involved helpful. For this reason we begin our study of systems involving quadratic sentences by considering the graphs of certain quadratic relations.

Graphs of Quadratic Equations in Two Variables

We have had some experience with the graphs of quadratic equations in two variables. Examples of such equations are $x^2 + y^2 = 25$, $y = x^2 - 2x - 9$, and $xy = 12$, whose graphs are respectively, a circle the measure of whose radius is 5, a parabola whose vertex is $P(1, -10)$ and whose axis is the vertical line which is the graph of $x = 1$, and an equilateral hyperbola in the first and third quadrants. The graphs of these equations are shown in the drawing at the top of the next page.

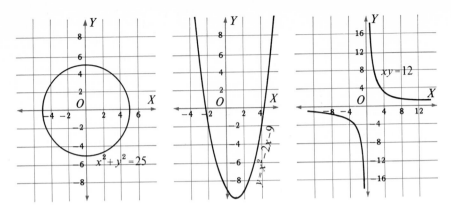

In the following examples, we shall consider the graphs of other quadratic equations in two variables.

Example 1. Sketch the graph of $\dfrac{x^2}{10^2} + \dfrac{y^2}{6^2} = 1$.

Solution. First, we observe that the graph of $\dfrac{x^2}{10^2} + \dfrac{y^2}{6^2} = 1$ is symmetric with respect to the x-axis, the y-axis, and the origin. Accordingly, the origin is called the *center* of this curve. We also see that when $y = \pm 6$, $x = 0$, and when $x = \pm 10$, $y = 0$. Therefore, $V(10, 0)$, $V'(-10, 0)$, $N(0, 6)$, and $N'(0, -6)$ are points in the graph.

Solving $\dfrac{x^2}{10^2} + \dfrac{y^2}{6^2} = 1$ for y, we obtain:

$\dfrac{x^2}{10^2} + \dfrac{y^2}{6^2} = 1 \longleftrightarrow 6^2 \cdot x^2 + 10^2 \cdot y^2 = 10^2 \cdot 6^2 \longleftrightarrow 10^2 \cdot y^2 =$
$10^2 \cdot 6^2 - 6^2 \cdot x^2 \longleftrightarrow 10^2 \cdot y^2 = 6^2(10^2 - x^2) \longleftrightarrow 10y =$
$6\sqrt{10^2 - x^2} \vee 10y = -6\sqrt{10^2 - x^2} \longleftrightarrow y = \tfrac{3}{5}\sqrt{10^2 - x^2} \vee y =$
$-\tfrac{3}{5}\sqrt{10^2 - x^2}$

We make a table of a few ordered pairs which satisfy the equation $y = \tfrac{3}{5}\sqrt{10^2 - x^2}$ by substituting each of the values 0, 2, 4, 6, 8, and 10 for the independent variable x and computing, in each case, the corresponding value of y.

x	0	2	4	6	8	10
y	6	$\tfrac{12}{5}\sqrt{6}$	$\tfrac{6}{5}\sqrt{21}$	4.8	3.6	0

Drawing a smooth curve through the points whose coordinates are shown in the table, we have the graph shown on the left in the figure. Recalling that the graph is symmetric with respect to the x-axis, the y-axis, and the origin, we complete the curve as shown on the right in the figure. The complete curve is called an *ellipse*.

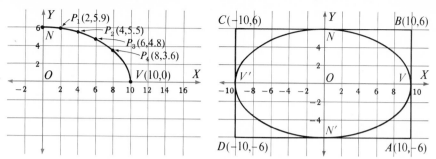

It was evident from the original equation that $|x| \le 10$ and $|y| \le 6$. Why? Thus the curve is contained in the rectangle *ABCD* whose sides are respectively parallel to the axes, whose center (intersection of diagonals) is at the origin, and whose vertices are $A(10, -6)$, $B(10, 6)$, $C(-10, 6)$, and $D(-10, -6)$. We shall call this rectangle the *reference rectangle* for the ellipse. Note that its center (the origin in this case) is the center of the ellipse. The x-intercepts of the ellipse are $V'(-10, 0)$ and $V(10, 0)$ and its y-intercepts are $N'(0, -6)$ and $N(0, 6)$. Observe that these points are the midpoints of the sides of the reference rectangle and that they are the only points common to the rectangle and the ellipse. The line segments VV' and NN' which join the midpoints of the opposite sides of the reference rectangle are called *axes* of the ellipse. The axis having the greater measure is called the *major axis* and the other axis is called the *minor axis*. In this case the major axis, $\overline{VV'}$, is a horizontal line segment whose measure is 20. The minor axis, $\overline{NN'}$, is a vertical line segment whose measure is 12. The end points of the major axis, V and V' in this case, are called the *vertices* of the ellipse. The measures of two adjacent sides of this reference rectangle are 20 and 12. What are the measures of two adjacent sides of the reference rectangle for the ellipse whose equation is $\dfrac{x^2}{a^2} + \dfrac{y^2}{b^2} = 1$? What is the measure of the major axis of this ellipse if $b > a$? What are the coordinates of its vertices?

Any equation which can be written in the form $cx^2 + dy^2 = e$, $c \ne d$, and c, d, and e are positive numbers is the equation of an ellipse because such an equation has the equivalent form $\dfrac{x^2}{\left(\sqrt{\frac{e}{c}}\right)^2} + \dfrac{y^2}{\left(\sqrt{\frac{e}{d}}\right)^2} = 1$. Since $cx^2 + dy^2 =$

$$e \longleftrightarrow \frac{c}{e}x^2 + \frac{d}{e}y^2 = 1 \longleftrightarrow \frac{x^2}{\dfrac{e}{c}} + \frac{y^2}{\dfrac{e}{d}} = 1 \longleftrightarrow \frac{x^2}{\left(\sqrt{\frac{e}{c}}\right)^2} + \frac{y^2}{\left(\sqrt{\frac{e}{d}}\right)^2} = \text{`1, the}$$

equation $cx^2 + dy^2 = e$ has the form $\dfrac{x^2}{a^2} + \dfrac{y^2}{b^2} = 1$, if we let $a = \sqrt{\dfrac{e}{c}}$ and $b = \sqrt{\dfrac{e}{d}}$. In sketching the graph of an equation having the form $cx^2 + dy^2 = e$, it is helpful to write the equation first in the form $\dfrac{x^2}{a^2} + \dfrac{y^2}{b^2} = 1$. For example, to draw the graph of the equation $4\,x^2 + 25\,y^2 = 100$, we would first write it in the equivalent form $\dfrac{x^2}{5^2} + \dfrac{y^2}{2^2} = 1$.

Ⓐ EXERCISES

1. By the procedure outlined in Example 1, draw the ellipse which is the graph of each of the following equations. In each case state the measure of the major axis, the measure of the minor axis, and the coordinates of the vertices.

a. $\dfrac{x^2}{2^2} + \dfrac{y^2}{3^2} = 1$ **d.** $\dfrac{x^2}{256} + \dfrac{y^2}{100} = 1$ **g.** $x^2 + 16\,y^2 = 16$

b. $\dfrac{x^2}{3^2} + y^2 = 1$ **e.** $\dfrac{x^2}{25} + \dfrac{y^2}{289} = 1$ **h.** $9\,x^2 + 25\,y^2 = 225$

c. $\dfrac{x^2}{49} + \dfrac{y^2}{81} = 1$ **f.** $\dfrac{x^2}{64} + \dfrac{y^2}{81} = 1$ **i.** $144\,x^2 + 169\,y^2 = 24336$

2. For each of the ellipses whose equations are given below, sketch the reference rectangle and then use the rectangle as a guide in sketching the ellipse.

a. $\dfrac{x^2}{4} + \dfrac{y^2}{25} = 1$ **b.** $25\,x^2 + 36\,y^2 = 900$ **c.** $\dfrac{x^2}{10} + \dfrac{y^2}{25} = 1$

Ⓑ EXERCISES

3. Write an equation of the ellipse whose center is at the origin of the xy-plane, whose major axis is a horizontal line segment having 10 as its measure, and whose minor axis is a vertical line segment having 6 as its measure.

4. Write an equation of the ellipse whose center is at the origin of the xy-plane, whose major axis is a vertical line segment having 16 as its measure, and whose minor axis is a horizontal line segment having 4 as its measure.

5. a. We have observed that the graph of the equation $\dfrac{x^2}{a^2} + \dfrac{y^2}{b^2} = 1$ is symmetric with respect to the x-axis and the y-axis. The graph of $\dfrac{(x - h)^2}{a^2} + \dfrac{(y - k)^2}{b^2} = 1$ is symmetric with respect to what lines?

b. The graph of $\dfrac{(x - h)^2}{a^2} + \dfrac{(y - k)^2}{b^2} = 1$ is an ellipse provided $a \ne b$. What are the coordinates of the center of this ellipse?

6. Consider the equation $\dfrac{(x-1)^2}{10^2} + \dfrac{(y-3)^2}{6^2} = 1.$

    a. The graph of the equation is symmetric with respect to what lines?

    b. What are the coordinates of the center of the graph of this equation?

    c. Draw the graph of this equation.

7. Draw the graph of each of the following equations:

    a. $\dfrac{(x+1)^2}{4} + \dfrac{y^2}{9} = 1$

    b. $\dfrac{(x+2)^2}{36} \div \dfrac{y^2}{16} = 1$

    c. $\dfrac{(x-2)^2}{36} + \dfrac{y^2}{16} = 1$

    d. $25(x+1)^2 + 4(y-2)^2 = 100$

    e. $36(x-1)^2 + 9(y+2)^2 = 324$

    f. $16(x+3)^2 + 4(y-1)^2 = 64$

    g. $16(x+3)^2 + 4(y-1)^2 = 128$

8. Write an equation whose graph is an ellipse having its center at the point $P(3, 2)$, its major axis parallel to the x-axis and 10 units long, and its minor axis parallel to the y-axis and 4 units long.

9. Write an equation whose graph is an ellipse having the points $P_1(-6, 3)$ and $P_2(4, 3)$ as its vertices and having its minor axis 4 units long.

10. Write an equation whose graph is an ellipse having the following points as the vertices of its reference rectangle: $A(4, -6)$, $B(4, -2)$, $C(-2, -2)$, $D(-2, -6)$.

Example 2. Sketch the graph of the equation $\dfrac{x^2}{10^2} - \dfrac{y^2}{6^2} = 1.$

Solution. As in Example 1, we observe that the curve will be symmetric with respect to the y-axis, the x-axis, and the origin. Accordingly, we regard the origin as the *center* of the curve. We note that there is no real number value of y when $x = 0$. Since we are graphing in the coordinate plane (the graph of $R \times R$), the curve does not cross the y-axis.

    Solving the given equation for y, we have:

$$\dfrac{x^2}{10^2} - \dfrac{y^2}{6^2} = 1 \longleftrightarrow 6^2 \cdot x^2 - 10^2 \cdot y^2 = 10^2 \cdot 6^2 \longleftrightarrow 10^2 \cdot y^2 =$$
$$6^2 \cdot x^2 - 10^2 \cdot 6^2 \longleftrightarrow 10^2 \cdot y^2 = 6^2(x^2 - 10^2) \longleftrightarrow 10\,y =$$
$$6\sqrt{x^2 - 10^2} \vee 10\,y = -6\sqrt{x^2 - 10^2} \longleftrightarrow y = \tfrac{3}{5}\sqrt{x^2 - 10^2} \vee y =$$
$$-\tfrac{3}{5}\sqrt{x^2 - 10^2}.$$

    From the last sentence we see that there is no real number value of y for any x in $\rangle -10, 10 \langle$. Why? We make a table of a few ordered pairs which satisfy the equation $y = \frac{3}{5}\sqrt{x^2 - 10^2}$ by assigning to x various numbers in $\langle\, 10,\ \infty\ \langle$ and finding the corresponding value of y.

x	10	15	20	25	30	40	80	90
y	0	6.7	10.4	13.7	17.0	23.2	47.6	53.7

We have used values of x far beyond those whose graphs are actually located in the portion of the graph we are drawing in order to suggest that as x becomes larger, the corresponding value of y becomes larger and approaches $\frac{3}{5}x$. Observe that $\frac{3}{5}(40) = 24$, $\frac{3}{5}(80) = 48$, $\frac{3}{5}(90) = 54$. Therefore, as x increases in $\langle\, 10,\ \infty\ \langle$, $P(x, y)$ in the graph gets closer and closer to the line whose equation is $y = \frac{6}{10}\, x$, yet always lies a little below it.

We can make good use of this fact in sketching the curve. First we draw the line L whose equation is $x = 10$. We understand that no portion of the graph of $y = \frac{3}{5}\sqrt{x^2 - 10^2}$, when $x \,\epsilon\, \langle\, 10,\ \infty\ \langle$, will lie to the left of this line. Now we draw the line G whose equation is $y = \frac{3}{5}\, x$. This line intersects line L at $P(10, 6)$. The curve will approach this line from below as x increases in $\langle\, 10,\ \infty\ \langle$. Thus for

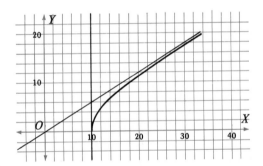

$x \geq 10$, the graph of $y = \frac{3}{5}\sqrt{x^2 - 10^2}$ has the appearance shown in the figure above. The line G is called an *asymptote* for this curve and the curve is said to approach G asymptotically as x increases in $\langle\, 10,\ \infty\ \langle$. We have had some previous experience with asymptotes in graphing such equations as $y = \dfrac{1}{x - 2}$ and $y = \tan x$.

In those cases, however, the asymptotes were vertical lines.

Since the curve we are drawing is symmetric with respect to both the x-axis and the y-axis, we reflect the portion we have drawn in each axis and the origin. We show as much of the graph as is possible within the limits of the space available for our drawing. The result is the curve shown in the following figure which is called a *hyperbola*.

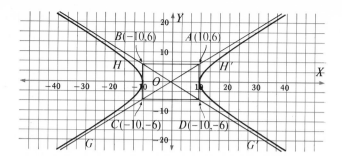

From this graph we see that the curve has a second asymptote G' whose equation is $y = -\frac{3}{5}x$. Moreover, the asymptotes G and G' contain the diagonals of the rectangle whose vertices are $A(10, 6)$, $B(-10, 6)$, $C(-10, -6)$, and $D(10, -6)$. This rectangle is called the *reference rectangle* of the hyperbola.

The x-intercepts of the hyperbola, namely $V(10, 0)$ and $V'(-10, 0)$, are called the vertices of the hyperbola and $\overline{VV'}$ is called the *transverse axis* of the hyperbola. We note that $|VV'| = 20$. We denote this hyperbola by the letter H_1.

Just as the equations of the asymptotes of the hyperbola H_1 whose equation is $\dfrac{x^2}{10^2} - \dfrac{y^2}{6^2} = 1$ are $y = \dfrac{6}{10}x$ and $y = -\dfrac{6}{10}x$, the equations of the asymptotes of a hyperbola H whose equation is $\dfrac{x^2}{a^2} - \dfrac{y^2}{b^2} = 1$ are $y = \dfrac{b}{a}x$ and $y = -\dfrac{b}{a}x$. The reference rectangle for H is the rectangle whose vertices are $P_1(a, b)$, $P_2(-a, b)$, $P_3(-a, -b)$, and $P_4(a, -b)$. Thus the diagonals of the reference rectangle for H lie in the asymptotes of H and the measures of two adjacent sides of the reference rectangle are $|2a|$ and $|2b|$.

Any equation which can be written in the form $cx^2 - dy^2 = e$ or $dy^2 - cx^2 = e$ where c, d, and e are positive numbers is the equation of a hyperbola because these equations have the equivalent forms $\dfrac{x^2}{\left(\sqrt{\frac{e}{c}}\right)^2} - \dfrac{y^2}{\left(\sqrt{\frac{e}{d}}\right)^2} = 1$

and $\dfrac{y^2}{\left(\sqrt{\frac{e}{d}}\right)^2} - \dfrac{x^2}{\left(\sqrt{\frac{e}{c}}\right)^2} = 1$, respectively. These equations have the forms

$\dfrac{x^2}{a^2} - \dfrac{y^2}{b^2} = 1$ and $\dfrac{y^2}{b^2} - \dfrac{x^2}{a^2} = 1$ if we let $a = \sqrt{\dfrac{e}{c}}$ and $b = \sqrt{\dfrac{e}{d}}$. In sketching the graph of an equation having either of the forms $cx^2 - dy^2 = e$ or $dy^2 - cx^2 = e$, it is helpful to write the equation first in either of the forms

$\dfrac{x^2}{a^2} - \dfrac{y^2}{b^2} = 1$ or $\dfrac{y^2}{b^2} - \dfrac{x^2}{a^2} = 1$. Thus to graph the equation $25\,y^2 - 4\,x^2 = 100$, we first write the equation in the equivalent form $\dfrac{y^2}{2^2} - \dfrac{x^2}{5^2} = 1$. Then

we see that the graph of this equation is a hyperbola having $T(0, 2)$ and $T_1(0, -2)$ for its vertices, $\overline{TT_1}$ for its transverse axis, and the lines A and A', whose equations are respectively $y = \frac{2}{5}\,x$ and $y = -\frac{2}{5}\,x$ for its asymptotes. (See figure at right.) Observe that the equation of $A \cup A'$ is $(y - \frac{2}{5}\,x)(y + \frac{2}{5}\,x) =$

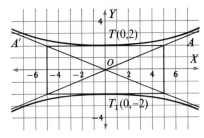

0, or $\left(\dfrac{y}{2} - \dfrac{x}{5}\right)\left(\dfrac{y}{2} + \dfrac{x}{5}\right) = 0$. Thus, it

appears that the equation of the asymp-

totes of a hyperbola whose equation is either $\dfrac{x^2}{a^2} - \dfrac{y^2}{b^2} = 1$ or $\dfrac{y^2}{b^2} - \dfrac{x^2}{a^2} = 1$

can be obtained by replacing the right member of either equation with 0.

Note that $\dfrac{y^2}{b^2} - \dfrac{x^2}{a^2} = 0 \longleftrightarrow \left(\dfrac{y}{b} + \dfrac{x}{a}\right)\left(\dfrac{y}{b} - \dfrac{x}{a}\right) = 0 \longleftrightarrow \left(y = -\dfrac{b}{a}\,x \;\vee\right.$

$\left. y = \dfrac{b}{a}\,x\right)$. Therefore, $\left\{(x, y) \mid \dfrac{y^2}{b^2} - \dfrac{x^2}{a^2} = 0\right\} = \left\{(x, y) \mid y = -\dfrac{b}{a}\,x\right\} \cup$

$\left\{(x, y) \mid y = \dfrac{b}{a}\,x\right\}$.

A EXERCISES

1. For each of the following equations, make a table of a few ordered pairs which satisfy the equation and which are the coordinates of points in a curve in the first quadrant. Then, using the idea of symmetry, draw the graph of each equation.

a. $\dfrac{x^2}{4^2} - \dfrac{y^2}{3^2} = 1$ **c.** $\dfrac{x^2}{25} - \dfrac{y^2}{36} = 1$ **e.** $16\,x^2 - 9\,y^2 = 1296$

b. $\dfrac{y^2}{3^2} - \dfrac{x^2}{4^2} = 1$ **d.** $\dfrac{y^2}{36} - \dfrac{x^2}{25} = 1$ **f.** $64\,x^2 - 36\,y^2 = 2304$

2. For each of the following, sketch the reference rectangle and the asymptotes, and locate the vertices of the hyperbola which is the graph of the equation. Then sketch the graph of the equation.

a. $\dfrac{x^2}{7^2} - \dfrac{y^2}{4^2} = 1$ **c.** $\dfrac{x^2}{25} - \dfrac{y^2}{64} = 1$ **e.** $4\,x^2 - 25\,y^2 = 100$

b. $\dfrac{y^2}{4^2} - \dfrac{x^2}{7^2} = 1$ **d.** $\dfrac{y^2}{64} - \dfrac{x^2}{36} = 1$ **f.** $25\,x^2 - 16\,y^2 = 400$

3. Write an equation whose graph is the hyperbola which has the points $P_1(8, 0)$ and $P_2(-8, 0)$ as its vertices and 6 as the measure of a vertical side of its reference rectangle.

4. Write an equation whose graph is the hyperbola which has the graphs of $y = \frac{3}{4} x$ and $y = -\frac{3}{4} x$ as its asymptotes and the points $P_1(-6, 0)$ and $P_2(6, 0)$ as its vertices.

5. a. We have observed that the graphs of the equations $\frac{x^2}{a^2} - \frac{y^2}{b^2} = 1$ and $\frac{y^2}{b^2} - \frac{x^2}{a^2} = 1$ are each symmetric with respect to the x-axis and the y-axis. The graph of $\frac{(x - h)^2}{a^2} - \frac{(y - k)^2}{b^2} = 1$ is symmetric with respect to what lines?

b. The graph of $\frac{(x - h)^2}{a^2} - \frac{(y - k)^2}{b^2} = 1$ is a hyperbola. What are the coordinates of the center of this hyperbola?

6. Consider the equation $\frac{(x - 1)^2}{4^2} - \frac{(y - 3)^2}{3^2} = 1$.

a. The graph of the equation is symmetric with respect to what lines?

b. What are the coordinates of the center of the hyperbola which is the graph of the equation?

c. Draw the hyperbola.

7. For each of the following, state the equations of the asymptotes and the coordinates of the vertices of the graph.

a. $\frac{(x - 2)^2}{5^2} - \frac{(y - 4)^2}{3^2} = 1$ **c.** $\frac{(x - 2)^2}{9} - \frac{(y + 4)^2}{16} = 1$

b. $\frac{(y - 4)^2}{5^2} - \frac{(x - 2)^2}{5^2} = 1$ **d.** $\frac{(y + 4)^2}{16} - \frac{(x + 2)^2}{9} = 1$

8. Draw the graph of each of the following equations.

a. $\frac{x^2}{7} - \frac{y^2}{5} = 1$ **c.** $\frac{(x + 3)^2}{4} - \frac{y^2}{25} = 1$

b. $\frac{x^2}{49} - \frac{y^2}{72} = 1$ **d.** $4(x - 2)^2 - 16(y + 1)^2 = 64$

9. Write an equation whose graph is a hyperbola which passes through the points $P_1(3, -7)$ and $P_2(6, 8)$, has its center at $P_3(2, -3)$, and has its transverse axis parallel to the y-axis.

10. Write an equation whose graph is a hyperbola which passes through $P(2, 1)$ and the union of whose asymptotes is the graph of $x^2 - y^2 = 0$.

Example 3. Draw the graph of each of the following equations.

$$(x + y - 5)(2x - y - 4) = 0 \qquad x^2 + 4y^2 = 0$$
$$(x - y - 7)(x - y - 3) = 0 \qquad x^2 + y^2 = 0$$
$$(2x - y - 4)^2 = 0$$

Solutions. $\{(x, y) \mid (x + y - 5)(2x - y - 4) = 0\} =$
$\{(x, y) \mid x + y - 5 = 0\} \cup \{(x, y) \mid 2x - y - 4 = 0\}$. The graph
of $\{(x, y) \mid x + y - 5 = 0\}$ is line L_1 and the graph of $\{(x, y) \mid 2x - y - 4 = 0\}$ is line L_2 in the figure on the left below. Therefore, the
graph of the equation $(x + y - 5)(2x - y - 4) = 0$ is $L_1 \cup L_2$.

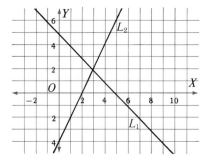
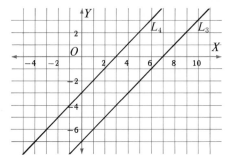

Similarly, the graph of equation $(x - y - 7)(x - y - 3) = 0$ is
the union of the parallel lines L_3 and L_4 shown in the figure on the
right above.

Do you see that L_2 in the figure on the left above is the graph of
$(2x - y - 4)^2 = 0$? The origin is the graph of $x^2 + 4y^2 = 0$ and
$x^2 + y^2 = 0$. Why?

A right circular cone is a set of points K which can be described as follows:
Let C be a circle having center Q and lying in plane N, and let O be a point not
in N such that $\overline{OQ}$ is perpendicu-
lar to plane N. Then $W \in K$ if and
only if $W \in \overleftrightarrow{OP}$ where P is any
point in C. (See figure at right.)
Any line $\overleftrightarrow{OT}$ is called an element
of this right circular cone pro-
vided $T \in C$. The point O is the
vertex of the cone and $\overleftrightarrow{OQ}$ is the
axis of the cone.

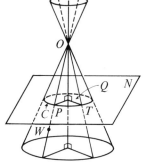

In the drawing of the parabola on page 697, the plane M
is parallel to an element of the
cone. Each of the graphs of the
equations considered in this section, with the exception of equation $(x - y -$

7) $(x - y - 3) = 0$, is readily identified as a set of points common to a plane M and a right circular cone, that is, as a plane section as shown in the figures below. If we hold C fixed and let $|OQ|$ increase without bound, the cone K becomes more and more like a right circular cylinder. If we regard a cylinder as a special (degenerate) type of cone, we can accept the graph of equation $(x - y - 7)(x - y - 3) = 0$, two parallel lines, as a plane section of the cone. Therefore, the graph of each equation considered in this section is called a *conic section*, or simply a *conic*, and it can be shown that the graph of every quadratic equation in two variables is a conic.

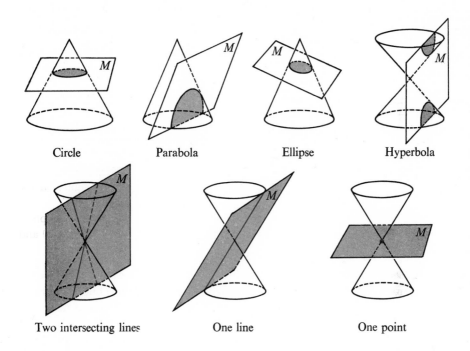

Circle	Parabola	Ellipse	Hyperbola

Two intersecting lines	One line	One point

1. Draw the graph of each of the following equations.

a. $(x + y - 4)(x + 2y - 3) = 0$ **g.** $(x + 3y - 5)^2 = 0$

b. $x^2 - 9y^2 = 0$ **h.** $3x^2 + 12y^2 = 48$

c. $x^2 + 9y^2 = 0$ **i.** $y - \frac{1}{2}(x - 4)^2 + 3 = 0$

d. $\dfrac{x^2}{9} + y^2 = 1$ **j.** $\dfrac{(x - 2)^2}{4} + (y + 3)^2 - 1 = 0$

e. $\dfrac{x^2}{9} - y^2 = 1$ **k.** $\dfrac{x^2}{7} + \dfrac{y^2}{7} = 1$

f. $(x - y - 7)(x + y + 1) = 0$ **l.** $4x^2 + 4y^2 = 144$

2. Without drawing the graph state whether the graph of each of the following equations would be a circle, a parabola, an ellipse, a hyperbola, a pair of parallel lines, a pair of intersecting lines, a single line, or a single point.

a. $2 x^2 - 6 y^2 = 12$

b. $x + 4 y^2 = 8$

c. $9(x - 1)^2 - 4(y + 2)^2 = 36$

d. $(x - 4)^2 + (y + 5)^2 = 25$

e. $(x + y - 3)^2 = 0$

f. $(4 x + y - 1) (x + y - 3) = 0$

g. $x^2 + 3 y^2 = 0$

h. $x^2 + 4 y^2 = 36$

3. Make a drawing to show the conic section formed when the cone shown at the right is intersected by the plane described in each of the following cases:

a. The graph of $x + y + 0 z = 2$

b. The graph of $z = 4$

c. The plane parallel to the z-axis and containing the points $B(4, 0, 0)$ and $C(0, 4, 0)$

d. The plane parallel to $\overleftrightarrow{AD}$ and containing the points $B(4, 0, 0)$ and $C(0, 4, 0)$

e. The graph of $y = 0$

f. The plane whose equation is $- y + z = 5$

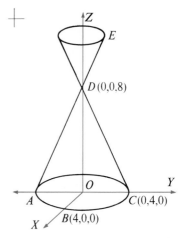

Linear-Quadratic Systems—Graphical Solutions

We can use graphical methods to obtain considerable information about the solution set of a system which consists of one linear equation $l_{(x, y)}$ and one quadratic equation $q_{(x, y)}$. From a rough sketch of the graph, we can usually determine how many solutions exist in $R \times R$, and from a carefully drawn graph, we can often find each solution as an ordered pair of real numbers with each number correct to the nearest unit. We know that the solution set of such a system of equations in two variables will be the coordinates of the points of intersection of the graphs of $l_{(x, y)}$ and $q_{(x, y)}$ if such points exist.

Example. Find the solution set of each of the following systems.

a. $\begin{cases} y = x^2 \\ y = -2x + 3 \end{cases}$ **b.** $\begin{cases} y = x^2 \\ y = -2x - 1 \end{cases}$ **c.** $\begin{cases} y = x^2 \\ y = -2x - 7 \end{cases}$

Solutions. We draw a graph of each equation in the three systems on the same set of axes and try to determine the coordinates of any points of intersection.

a. The graphs of the components of this system consist of the parabola and the line L_1. It appears that $(-3, 9)$ and $(1, 1)$ are the coordinates of the points of intersection of L_1 and the parabola. We find by substitution that these ordered pairs satisfy the given system. Thus this system has two solutions in $R \times R$.

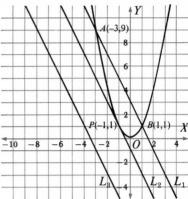

b. The graphs of the components of this system consist of the parabola and the line L_2. The graphs suggest that $P(-1, 1)$ may be a point of intersection for L_2 and the parabola. We find by substitution that $(-1, 1)$ is a solution of this system. The graphs show that L_2 and the parabola have no other point of intersection. Thus the system has one solution in $R \times R$.

c. The graphs of the component equations of this system consist of the parabola and the line L_3. The graphs clearly indicate that L_3, the graph of $y = -2x - 7$, does not intersect the parabola. Therefore, this system has no solution in $R \times R$ although, as we shall see later, it does have two solutions in $Z \times Z$.

Ⓐ EXERCISES

Make a carefully drawn graph of each component in each of the following systems of equations and from the graphs determine the set of approximate solutions for each system.

1. $\begin{cases} y = x^2 - x - 6 \\ y = 2x - 2 \end{cases}$

4. $\begin{cases} x + y = 1 \\ x^2 + \dfrac{y^2}{4} = 1 \end{cases}$

7. $\begin{cases} 5x + 3y = 16 \\ 16 = x^2 - y^2 \end{cases}$

2. $\begin{cases} 4x^2 + 4y^2 = 81 \\ y = -x + 2 \end{cases}$

5. $\begin{cases} 24 = 2x^2 - 3y^2 \\ 2x = 3y \end{cases}$

8. $\begin{cases} x^2 + y^2 = 25 \\ 3x - y + 5 = 0 \end{cases}$

3. $\begin{cases} xy = 3 \\ 2x = 3y + 3 \end{cases}$

6. $\begin{cases} y = \frac{1}{3}x^2 - \frac{2}{3}x - \frac{2}{3} \\ x + y = 0 \end{cases}$

9. $\begin{cases} 2x^2 + 2y^2 = 338 \\ 5x + 12y = 169 \end{cases}$

Linear-Quadratic Systems—Algebraic Solutions

Experience with the graphical solution of a system consisting of one linear equation and one quadratic equation is valuable because it serves to emphasize the fact that each solution in $R \times R$ of the system is an ordered pair of real numbers which are the coordinates of the point or points in the coordinate plane where the graphs of the two equations intersect. In this section we study the algebraic solution of such systems. Algebraic methods not only enable us to obtain more accurate results for solutions in $R \times R$, they also enable us to find solutions in $Z \times Z \smile R \times R$. The procedures for finding the solution set of a linear-quadratic system of equations in two variables by algebraic methods are illustrated by the following examples.

Example 1.　Find the solution set of the following system in $R \times R$:

$$\begin{cases} y = x^2 \\ y = -2x + 3 \end{cases}$$

Solution.　We begin by assuming that a solution (x, y) exists and we try to find a set S which contains the solution set. Then we eliminate from S those members that are not solutions by substituting each of its members in the given system and rejecting those that do not satisfy the system. If (x, y) is a solution of the given system, then each of the equations in the system is a true statement.

$$\left. \begin{array}{l} y = x^2 \\ y = -2x + 3 \end{array} \right\} \longrightarrow x^2 = -2x + 3 \longrightarrow x^2 + 2x - 3 = 0 \longrightarrow$$
$$\longmapsto (x + 3)(x - 1) = 0 \longrightarrow x = -3 \lor x = 1$$

Using the second equation of our system, we see that if $x = -3$, then $y = 9$ and if $x = 1$, $y = 1$. Thus $\{(-3, 9), (1, 1)\} \subseteq S$.

We find by substitution that each of these ordered pairs satisfies the given system. Therefore $\{(x, y) \mid y = x^2 \land y = -2x + 3\} = \{(-3, 9), (1, 1)\}$. This is the same solution set that we obtained from the use of graphs in the example in the preceding section.

　The above solution set was obtained by substituting in the quadratic equation the expression for y obtained from the linear equation. Each of the values of x obtained by solving the resulting quadratic equation was then substituted in the linear equation in order to find the corresponding value of y. This method of solving a system is called the *substitution method*.
　This method of solution is justified by the following extension of Theorem 3–12.

▶ **Theorem 1–13.** If $q_{(x, y)}$ is a quadratic sentence, then the systems
$$\begin{cases} y = ax + b \\ q_{(x, y)} \end{cases} \text{ and } \begin{cases} y = ax + b \\ q_{(x, ax + b)} \end{cases} \text{ are equivalent and the systems}$$
$$\begin{cases} x = cy + d \\ q_{(x, y)} \end{cases} \text{ and } \begin{cases} x = cy + d \\ q_{(cy + d, y)} \end{cases} \text{ are equivalent.}$$

It can be shown that any ordered pair (e, f) which satisfies either of the first pair of systems also satisfies the other. The same statement is true for the second pair of systems.

Example 2. Find the solution set in $Z \times Z$ for the following system:

$$\begin{cases} x^2 - y^2 = 75 \\ y = 2\,x \end{cases}$$

Solution. $\begin{cases} x^2 - y^2 = 75 \\ y = 2\,x \end{cases} \longrightarrow \begin{cases} x^2 - (2\,x)^2 = 75 \\ y = 2\,x \end{cases} \longrightarrow \begin{cases} x^2 = -\,25 \\ y = 2\,x \end{cases} \longrightarrow$

$\longmapsto \begin{cases} x = 5\,i \\ y = 2\,x \end{cases} \vee \begin{cases} x = -\,5\,i \\ y = 2\,x \end{cases} \longrightarrow \begin{cases} x = 5\,i \\ y = 10\,i \end{cases} \vee \begin{cases} x = -\,5\,i \\ y = -\,10\,i \end{cases}$

Thus we see that the set of possible solutions is $\{\,(5\,i, 10\,i),\ (-5i,\ -\,10\,i)\,\}$. Substituting these values in the equations of the given system, we find that each of these ordered pairs is a solution. Therefore, the solution set of our system is $\{\,(5\,i, 10\,i),\ (-\,5\,i,\ -\,10\,i)\,\}$.

Example 3. Find the solution set in $R \times R$ for the following system:

$$\begin{cases} x^2 + xy = 6\,y^2 \\ x = 2\,y \end{cases}$$

Solution. Substituting $2\,y$ for x in the first equation, we have $(2\,y)^2 + (2\,y)y = 6\,y^2$, or $6\,y^2 = 6\,y^2$. This equation is satisfied by any real number a. Thus we know that y may be any real number a and that x is always equal to $2\,y$. Our solution set is, therefore, the set of ordered pairs of the form $(2\,a, a)$ where a is any real number, or $\{(x, y) \mid y \in R \wedge x = 2\,y\}$. Thus we see that any solution of the linear equation is a solution of the quadratic equation. The truth of this statement can also be seen by writing the given system in the form $\begin{cases} (x - 2\,y)\,(x + 3\,y) = 0 \\ x - 2\,y = 0 \end{cases}$. Now we see that the graph of the linear equation, which is L_1 as shown in the figure below, is a subset of the graph of the quadratic equation which is $L_1 \cup L_2$ in the figure. It is also clear that there are solutions of the quadratic equation, such as $(-\,3, 1)$, which are not solutions of the linear equation. What is the solution set in $Z \times Z$ for this system?

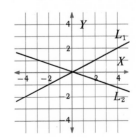

1. Use the substitution method to find the solution set in Z x Z for each of the
   following systems.

   a. $\begin{cases} xy = 24 \\ x - y = 5 \end{cases}$ c. $\begin{cases} x^2 + 2\,y^2 = 51 \\ y = -2\,x + 13 \end{cases}$ e. $\begin{cases} x^2 + 4\,y^2 - 4 = 0 \\ 3\,x + 6\,y = 1 \end{cases}$

   b. $\begin{cases} 40 = 4\,x^2 + y^2 \\ 2\,x + y = 8 \end{cases}$ d. $\begin{cases} (x-3)^2 + 4(y-1)^2 = 32 \\ x + 2\,y - 5 = 0 \end{cases}$ f. $\begin{cases} \dfrac{x^2}{4} - \dfrac{y^2}{9} = 1 \\ 3\,x + 5\,y - 6 = 0 \end{cases}$

   Use two variables to solve Exercises 2-9.

2. One of two real numbers is 6 greater than the other and the square of the
   greater is 528 more than the square of the lesser. What are the numbers?

3. The sum of the squares of two consecutive integers is 613. What are the
   integers?

4. One train traveling 2 miles per hour faster than a second train requires 15
   minutes less time to travel 300 miles. What is the rate of travel of each train?

5. It requires 144 rods of fencing to enclose a rectangular field. If the area of the
   field is 1280 square rods, how long and how wide is the field?

6. The ratio of the length, l, of a field to its width, w, is $\frac{3}{2}$. If $l^2 - w^2 = 405$,
   what are the measures of the length and the width?

7. An open-top box is made from a rectangular piece of metal by cutting 2 inch
   squares from the corners and folding up the edges. Find the dimensions of
   such a box if the perimeter of the rec-
   tangular piece of metal is 84 inches and the
   volume of the box is 560 cubic inches.

8. The measure of the hypotenuse of right triangle ABC, whose perimeter is 69 inches, is
   29 inches. Find the measures of $\overline{AC}$ and $\overline{BC}$.

9. If the sum of the smaller of two integers
   and twice the larger is 43 and the sum of
   the squares of the two integers is 370, find
   the integers.

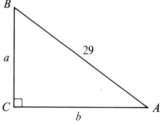

10. Find the solution set of each of the following systems by use of the substitution
    method.

    a. $\begin{cases} (x + 3)\,(y - 4) = 3 \\ 2\,x - 3\,y = 3 \end{cases}$ c. $\begin{cases} (x - 3)^2 + 4(y - 1)^2 = 32 \\ x + 2\,y = 8 \end{cases}$

    b. $\begin{cases} (x + 1)^2 + (y - 2)^2 = 19 \\ x + y = 2 \end{cases}$ d. $\begin{cases} 4(x - 2)^2 + 9(y - 3)^2 = 36 \\ 5\,x + 3\,y = 5 \end{cases}$

11. Solve for x and y: $\begin{cases} x + y = p + q \\ \dfrac{p}{x+q} + \dfrac{q}{y+p} = 1 \end{cases}$

12. The graph at the right indicates that the system $\begin{cases} x^2 + y^2 = 9 \\ y = -x + 5 \end{cases}$ has no solution in $R \times R$. What is the solution set in $Z \times Z$?

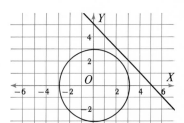

13. Find the solution set of each of the following as a subset of $Z \times Z$.

a. $\begin{cases} 9 x^2 - 4 y^2 = 36 \\ x = 1 \end{cases}$ **b.** $\begin{cases} 16 x^2 + 9 y^2 = 144 \\ y = -x + 6 \end{cases}$ **c.** $\begin{cases} y = x + 3 \\ y^2 = 4 x \end{cases}$

14. For what values of b does the graph of $y = ax + b$ intersect the graph of $x^2 + y^2 = r^2$ in exactly one point?

15. The product of the roots of a quadratic equation is $\frac{5}{2}$ and their sum is $\frac{59}{14}$. What are the roots of the equation? Write an equation that has these roots.

Quadratic Systems

Finding the solution set for a system of quadratic equations (quadratic system) in two variables can be very complicated. However, there are special methods that can be used to solve certain kinds of quadratic systems. Some of these methods are illustrated in the following examples.

Example 1. Find the solution set in $R \times R$ for the following system:
$$\begin{cases} 2 x^2 - y^2 = 34 \\ x^2 + 3 y^2 = 73 \end{cases}$$

Solution. Assuming that (x, y) is a solution, we have:

$2 x^2 - y^2 = 34 \longrightarrow 6 x^2 - 3 y^2 = 102 \Big| \longrightarrow 7 x^2 = 175 \longrightarrow$
$ x^2 + 3 y^2 = 73 \Big\}$

$\longrightarrow x^2 = 25 \longrightarrow x = 5 \lor x = -5.$

$\begin{rcases} x = 5 \\ x^2 + 3 y^2 = 73 \end{rcases} \longrightarrow 3 y^2 = 48 \longrightarrow y^2 = 16 \longrightarrow y = 4 \lor y = -4.$

$\begin{rcases} x = -5 \\ x^2 + 3 y^2 = 73 \end{rcases} \longrightarrow 3 y^2 = 48 \longrightarrow y^2 = 16 \longrightarrow y = 4 \lor y = -4.$

If (x, y) is a solution of the given system, then

$$(x, y) \in \{(5, 4), (5, -4), (-5, 4), (-5, -4)\}.$$

Substitution in the equations of the system reveals that each of these ordered pairs is a solution. Since the equation $x^2 = 25$ has exactly two solutions, there can be no solution where x has a value other than 5 or -5. Since $x = 5$ or $x = -5$ and the equation $y^2 = 16$ has exactly two solutions, there can be no solutions where y has a value other than 4 or -4. Thus $\{(x, y) \mid 2x^2 - y^2 = 34 \wedge x^2 + 3y^2 = 73\} = \{(5, 4), (5, -4), (-5, 4), (-5, -4)\}$.

Example 2. Solve the system: $\begin{cases} x^2 - 4y^2 = 0 \\ 3x^2 + 4xy + 40 = 0 \end{cases}$

Solution. $\begin{cases} x^2 - 4y^2 = 0 \\ 3x^2 + 4xy + 40 = 0 \end{cases} \longrightarrow \begin{cases} (x - 2y)(x + 2y) = 0 \\ 3x^2 + 4xy + 40 = 0 \end{cases} \dashrightarrow$

$\longmapsto \begin{cases} x = 2y \vee x = -2y \\ 3x^2 + 4xy + 40 = 0 \end{cases} \dashrightarrow$

$\longmapsto \begin{cases} x = 2y \\ 3x^2 + 4xy + 40 = 0 \end{cases} \vee \begin{cases} x = -2y \\ 3x^2 + 4xy + 40 = 0. \end{cases}$

Solving each of these linear-quadratic systems by the methods employed in the preceding section, we find the following set of possible solutions of the given system:

$\{(2i\sqrt{2}, i\sqrt{2}), (-2i\sqrt{2}, -i\sqrt{2}), (2i\sqrt{10}, -i\sqrt{10}), (-2i\sqrt{10}, i\sqrt{10})\}$

Substituting these values in the equations of the given system, we find that each of these ordered pairs is a solution.

Thus the solution set of the given system is:

$\{(2i\sqrt{2}, i\sqrt{2}), (-2i\sqrt{2}, -i\sqrt{2}), (2i\sqrt{10}, -i\sqrt{10}), (-2i\sqrt{10}, i\sqrt{10})\}$.

The above method can be applied when one of the component equations is written so that one of its members is 0 and we find that the other member can be factored in such a way that neither variable appears under a radical sign. The method is most easily applied when this member is factorable over the integers.

We state the following theorem which is suggested by Theorem 2–12.

▷ **Theorem 2–13.** If q_1 and q_2 are quadratic polynomials in the variables x and y, then the systems $\begin{cases} q_1 = 0 \\ q_2 = 0 \end{cases}$ and $\begin{cases} q_1 = 0 \\ k_1 q_1 + k_2 q_2 = 0 \end{cases}$ are equivalent provided $k_2 \neq 0$.

Sometimes we can obtain an equation which has one member that is 0 and the other member factorable over the integers by the method shown in the following example.

Example 3. Solve the system: $\begin{cases} 2\,y^2 + 3\,xy - 16 = 0 \\ 3\,x^2 + 4\,xy - 40 = 0 \end{cases}$

Solution. We choose appropriate multiples to eliminate the constant terms.

$$\begin{cases} 2\,y^2 + 3\,xy - 16 = 0 \\ 3\,x^2 + 4\,xy - 40 = 0 \end{cases} \longleftrightarrow \begin{cases} 2\,y^2 + 3\,xy - 16 = 0 \\ 5(2\,y^2 + 3\,xy - 16) - \\ \quad 2(3x^2 + 4\,xy - 40) = 0 \end{cases} \longleftrightarrow$$

$$\longmapsto \begin{cases} 2\,y^2 + 3\,xy - 16 = 0 \\ 10\,y^2 + 7\,xy - 6\,x^2 = 0 \end{cases} \longleftrightarrow \begin{cases} 2\,y^2 + 3\,xy - 16 = 0 \\ (5\,y + 6\,x)(2\,y - x) = 0 \end{cases} \longleftrightarrow$$

$$\longmapsto \begin{cases} 2\,y^2 + 3\,xy - 16 = 0 \\ y = -\tfrac{6}{5}\,x \ \vee \ x = 2\,y \end{cases} \longleftrightarrow \begin{cases} 2\,y^2 + 3\,xy = 16 \\ y = -\tfrac{6}{5}\,x \end{cases} \vee$$

$$\begin{cases} 2\,y^2 + 3\,xy = 16 \\ x = 2\,y \end{cases}$$

Solving each system of this disjunction of two systems, we find that the solution set of the given system is $\{(x,\ y)\,|\,2\,y^2 + 3\,xy = 16 \wedge y = -\tfrac{6}{5}\,x\} \cup \{(x,\ y)\,|\,2\,y^2 + 3\,xy = 16 \wedge x = 2\,y\}$, or $\{(2\sqrt{2},\ \sqrt{2}),\ (-2\sqrt{2},\ -\sqrt{2}),\ (\tfrac{10}{3}\,i\sqrt{2},\ -4\,i\sqrt{2}),\ (-\tfrac{10}{3}\,i\sqrt{2},\ 4\,i\sqrt{2})\}$. We leave the checking of these solutions to you.

While the methods described above were effective in the examples shown, we must not overlook the complexity of the problem of solving many quadratic systems. Very often, in an attempt to use the substitution method to eliminate one of the variables, we encounter a higher degree equation, such as a fourth-degree, in the other variable which we cannot solve. For example, if we attempt to solve the system $\begin{cases} x^2 - y = 1 \\ x^2 + 3\,y^2 - 2\,x - 5\,y = 12 \end{cases}$ by substituting $x^2 - 1$ for y in the second equation, we obtain the fourth degree equation $3\,x^4 - 10\,x^2 - 2\,x - 4 = 0$, and we do not have available methods for solving such equations.

Ⓐ EXERCISES

1. Find the solution set of each of the following systems by algebraic methods. It also will be helpful to sketch the graph of the system.

a. $\begin{cases} x^2 + y^2 = 25 \\ x^2 + y^2 - 20\,y + 75 = 0 \end{cases}$

b. $\begin{cases} 2\,x^2 + 8\,y = -22 \\ 3\,x^2 + 5\,y = 2 \end{cases}$

c. $\begin{cases} x^2 + y^2 = 25 \\ x^2 + y^2 = 75 \end{cases}$

d. $\begin{cases} x^2 + y^2 = 25 \\ 3\,x^2 - 4\,y^2 = 12 \end{cases}$

e. $\begin{cases} x^2 + 2\,y^2 = 54 \\ 2\,x^2 - 3\,y^2 = -67 \end{cases}$

f. $\begin{cases} x^2 + xy = 6 \\ x^2 - y^2 = 11 \end{cases}$

2. The volume of a box is 750 cubic inches and its surface area is 550 square inches. Find its length and width if its depth is 5 inches.

3. The perimeter of an isosceles triangle is 56 inches. If the length of the altitude from the intersection of the equal sides to the base is 24 inches, what is the length of each of the sides of the triangle?

B EXERCISES

4. Find the solution set of each of the following systems.

a. $\begin{cases} 4\,xy + y^2 = -11 \\ 3\,xy + 2\,y^2 = -7 \end{cases}$

d. $\begin{cases} x^2 + y^2 - 8\,x = 0 \\ x^2 + y^2 - 16\,y = 0 \end{cases}$

b. $\begin{cases} x^2 - xy - 6\,y^2 = 0 \\ y^2 + 4\,x - 2 = 15 \end{cases}$

e. $\begin{cases} 4\,x^2 + y^2 + 8\,x - 4\,y = 44 \\ 8y + 86 = 8\,x^2 + 2\,y^2 + 16\,x \end{cases}$

c. $\begin{cases} (x + y)^2 = 49 \\ x^2 - y^2 = -7 \end{cases}$

f. $\begin{cases} x^2 + y^2 - x - y = 20 \\ xy + 10 - 2(x + y) = 0 \end{cases}$

5. Planes A and B regularly make trips of 2400 miles and 1500 miles, respectively, plane A's trip requiring 2 hours more time than plane B's. If each plane were to make the trip of the other, but at its own regular rate of travel, plane B would require $4\frac{3}{5}$ more hours than plane A. At what rate does each plane regularly fly?

6. In $\triangle ABC$, $\angle ACB$ is a right angle, $|AC| = 5, |BC| = 12$, and $|AB| = 13$. What is the measure of the length of the altitude from C to $\overline{AB}$?

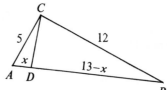

7. By means of a graph show the solution set of each of the following systems.

a. $\begin{cases} \dfrac{(x-4)^2}{9} + \dfrac{(y-3)^2}{4} = 1 \\ y = -(x-3)^2 + 5 \end{cases}$

b. $\begin{cases} \dfrac{(y-4)^2}{9} + \dfrac{(x-3)^2}{4} = 1 \\ \dfrac{(x-4)^2}{4} + \dfrac{(y-3)^2}{9} = 1 \end{cases}$

Graphs of Quadratic Sentences Involving Inequalities

The graph of a quadratic inequality in two variables is usually a region in the xy-plane.

Example 1.   Sketch the graph of the quadratic inequality $4\,x^2 + y^2 < 100$.

Solution.   The graph consists of all the points in the region enclosed by the ellipse whose equation is $4\,x^2 + y^2 = 100$. In order to prove this statement we must have an algebraic definition which enables us to say whether or not a given point is in the region enclosed by the ellipse. Draw the vertical line L whose equation is $x = c$ where $|c| < 5$. The line L intersects the ellipse which is the graph of $4x^2 + y^2 = 100$ in the points $A(c, 2\sqrt{25 - c^2})$ and $A'(c, -2\sqrt{25 - c^2})$. Any point in $\overline{AA'}$ except A and A' is in the region enclosed by the ellipse. We see that (*i*) $P(c, t)$ is in the region enclosed by the ellipse $\longleftrightarrow |c| < 5 \wedge |t| < 2\sqrt{25 - c^2}$. It can also be shown that (*ii*) $|c| < 5 \wedge |t| < 2\sqrt{25 - c^2}$ $\longleftrightarrow 4c^2 + t^2 < 100$. From (*i*) and (*ii*), we have: (*iii*) $P(c, t)$ is in the region enclosed by the ellipse $\longleftrightarrow 4c^2 + t^2 < 100$.

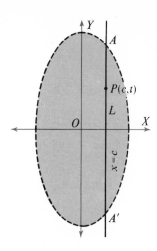

Statement (*iii*) establishes the fact that the set of points in the region enclosed by the ellipse is the graph of the sentence $4x^2 + y^2 < 100$.

In our next example we consider the graph of a system of quadratic inequalities.

Example 2. Draw the graph of the solution set of the system:

$$\begin{cases} y > x^2 - 8x \\ y < -x^2 + 12x - 32 \end{cases}$$

Solution. First we draw the graphs of the two parabolas whose equations are $y = x^2 - 8x$ and $y = -x^2 + 12x - 32$. Since $y = x^2 - 8x \longleftrightarrow y = (x - 4)^2 - 16$, we see that the graph of the first equation is a parabola P_1 which is concave upward and whose vertex is the point $V(4, -16)$. Since $y = -x^2 + 12x - 32 \longleftrightarrow y = -(x^2 - 12x + 32) \longleftrightarrow y = -[(x - 6)^2 - 4] \longleftrightarrow y = -(x - 6)^2 + 4$, we see that the graph of the second equation is a parabola P_2 which is concave downward and whose vertex is at the point $T(6, 4)$ as shown in the figure at the right. The graph of the solution set of the given system is the set of points above P_1 and below P_2, that is, the cross-hatched region in the figure.

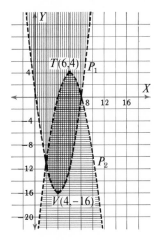

A EXERCISES

1. Draw the graph of each of the following:

  a. $x^2 + y^2 < 49$ **c.** $xy \geq 12$ **e.** $y^2 - 4(x+2)^2 \leq 16$

  b. $x^2 - y^2 < 25$ **d.** $xy < 8$ **f.** $(x - y + 4)(x - 3y + 1) > 0$

2. By means of a graph show the solution set of each of the following.

  a. $\begin{cases} x^2 + y^2 < 25 \\ x^2 - 3y > 21 \end{cases}$
  d. $\begin{cases} 9x^2 + y^2 < 36 \\ x^2 + y^2 > 16 \end{cases}$

  b. $\begin{cases} x^2 + y^2 < 16 \\ x^2 + 4y^2 < 32 \end{cases}$
  e. $\begin{cases} x^2 + 4y^2 \leq 100 \\ y \leq \frac{1}{4}x^2 \end{cases}$

  c. $\begin{cases} y \geq (x-2)^2 + 1 \\ y \geq (x+2)^2 + 1 \end{cases}$
  f. $\begin{cases} y > (x-3)^2 + 4 \\ (y-3)^2 + 4(x-3)^2 < 16 \end{cases}$

Geometric Definitions of the Conics

We have identified a parabola as the graph of an equation having the form $y = ax^2 + bx + c$ when $a \neq 0$, an ellipse with the graph of an equation having the form $\dfrac{x^2}{a^2} + \dfrac{y^2}{b^2} = 1$, and a hyperbola with the graph of an equation which has one of the forms $xy = k$, $\dfrac{x^2}{a^2} - \dfrac{y^2}{b^2} = 1$, or $-\dfrac{x^2}{a^2} + \dfrac{y^2}{b^2} = 1$.

We know from plane geometry that a circle, which we have identified with the graph of an equation of the form $x^2 + y^2 = r^2$, is the set of points in a plane at a given distance from a given point called the center. In this section, we give geometric definitions of the parabola, the ellipse, and the hyperbola and illustrate each with an example.

We state the following geometric definition of a parabola:

In a plane, the set of points equidistant from a line L and a point F not in the line, is called a *parabola*. The line is called the *directrix* of the parabola and the point is called the *focus* of the parabola. The point V where the line through the
focus perpendicular to the directrix intersects
the parabola is called the vertex of the pa-
rabola. $\overleftrightarrow{VF}$ is the axis of the parabola.

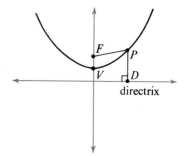

This definition is consistent with our concept of a parabola as the graph of an equation
having the form $y = ax^2 + bx + c$, $a \neq 0$,
because for every such graph it is possible to
find a point which serves as the focus and a
line which serves as the directrix.

Example 1. Show that the graph of the equation $y = \frac{1}{8} x^2$ is a parabola whose focus is $F(0, 2)$ and whose directrix is the line L which is the graph of $y = -2$.

Solution. According to our definition, $P(x, y)$ is a point in the parabola if and only if $|PF| = |PD|$ where $\overline{PD}$ is perpendicular to the directrix L as shown in the figure. Now $|PF| = \sqrt{x^2 + (y-2)^2}$ and

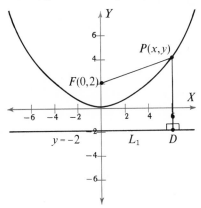

$|PD| = y + 2$. Therefore $|PF| = |PD| \longleftrightarrow |\sqrt{x^2 + (y-2)^2}| = |y + 2| \longleftrightarrow x^2 + y^2 - 4y + 4 = y^2 + 4y + 4 \longleftrightarrow y = \frac{1}{8}x^2$.

Considering Example 1, you might wonder how we find the focus and the directrix of the parabola whose equation is $y = \frac{1}{8}x^2$. Such questions are considered in analytic geometry and we are not primarily concerned with them in this course. However, the graph of $y = ax^2 + bx + c$, $a \neq 0$, can be shown by the above definition to be a parabola whose focus is $F\left(-\dfrac{b}{2a}, \dfrac{4ac - b^2 + 1}{4a}\right)$ and whose directrix has the equation $y = \dfrac{4ac - b^2 - 1}{4a}$.

There are two mutually consistent geometric definitions of an ellipse.

1. Given two points F_1 and F_2 in a plane and a positive number k greater than $|F_1F_2|$, the set consisting of every point P in the plane such that $|PF_1| + |PF_2| = k$ is an *ellipse*. Each of the points F_1 and F_2 is called a *focus* of the ellipse.

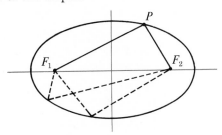

2. In a plane, given a line L and a point F_1 not in L and given a number e in $\rangle\, 0,\, 1\, \langle$, the set consisting of every point P in the plane such that the measure of the line segment from F_1 to P divided by the measure

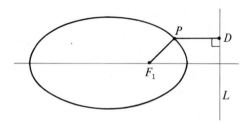

of the line segment from P perpendicular to L is equal to e is an *ellipse.* The point F_1 is called a *focus* of the ellipse, the line L is called a *directrix* of the ellipse, and the number e is called the *eccentricity* of the ellipse.

We use an example to indicate that these two definitions are consistent with each other and that the graph of an equation of the form $\dfrac{x^2}{a^2} + \dfrac{y^2}{b^2} = 1$ is an ellipse according to either definition.

Example 2. Show that G, the graph of the equation $\dfrac{x^2}{5^2} + \dfrac{y^2}{4^2} = 1$, is an ellipse according to each of the above definitions.

Solution.   We apply the first definition by identifying $F_2(-\,3,\,0)$ and $F_1(3,\,0)$ as the foci and letting $k = 10$. According to this definition, $P(x,\,y)$ is in the ellipse if and only if $|\,PF_2\,| + |\,PF_1\,| = 10$. Applying the distance formula, we have $\sqrt{(x + 3)^2 + y^2} +$

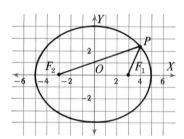

$\sqrt{(x - 3)^2 + y^2} = 10$. We need to show that this equation is equivalent to the equation $\dfrac{x^2}{5^2} + \dfrac{y^2}{4^2} = 1$. We write the equation in the form $\sqrt{(x + 3)^2 + y^2} = 10 - \sqrt{(x - 3)^2 + y^2}$ and square both members: $x^2 + 6\,x + 9 + y^2 = 100 - 20\sqrt{(x - 3)^2 + y^2} + x^2 - 6\,x + 9 + y^2$. Thus $5\sqrt{(x - 3)^2 + y^2} = 25 - 3\,x$. Squaring again, we have $25(x^2 - 6\,x + 9 + y^2) = 625 - 150\,x + 9\,x^2$.

This is equivalent to $16\,x^2 + 25\,y^2 = 400$, or $\dfrac{x^2}{5^2} + \dfrac{y^2}{4^2} = 1$. Since

$\dfrac{x^2}{5^2} + \dfrac{y^2}{4^2} = 1$ is equivalent to $\sqrt{(x+3)^2 + y^2} + \sqrt{(x-3)^2 + y^2}$

$= 10$, we see that G is an ellipse with foci F_1 and F_2 and with 10 as the given value of k.

We apply the second definition by identifying the given focus $F_1(3, 0)$, the directrix L as the line whose equation is $x = \frac{25}{3}$, and e as the number $\frac{3}{5}$. Therefore, $P(x, y)$ is in the ellipse if and only if $\dfrac{|\,PF_1\,|}{|\,PD\,|} = \dfrac{3}{5}$. As before, $|\,PF_1\,| = \sqrt{(x-3)^2 + y^2}$. From the

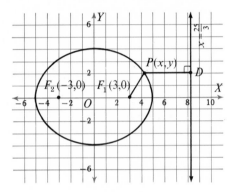

diagram, we see that $|\,PD\,| = \frac{25}{3} - x$. Thus we have:
$$\frac{\sqrt{(x-3)^2 + y^2}}{\frac{25}{3} - x} = \frac{3}{5}$$
and it is readily shown that this equation is equivalent to the

equation $\dfrac{x^2}{5^2} + \dfrac{y^2}{4^2} = 1$.

Considering Example 2, you might wonder how we located the foci (the plural for focus) and determined the distance k in applying the first definition and how we located the focus and directrix and determined e in applying the second definition. Again we observe that these questions are considered in analytic geometry and that we are not primarily concerned with them in this course. However, we state that G, the graph of the equation $\dfrac{x^2}{a^2} + \dfrac{y^2}{b^2} =$

1 where $a > b$, can be shown by the first definition to be an ellipse whose foci are $F_2(-\sqrt{a^2 - b^2},\, 0)$ and $F_1(\sqrt{a^2 - b^2},\, 0)$ and whose distance k is $2\,a$. It can also be shown by the second definition that G is an ellipse one of whose foci is $F_1(\sqrt{a^2 - b^2},\, 0)$, whose corresponding directrix is the line L, the graph of $x = \dfrac{a^2}{\sqrt{a^2 - b^2}}$, and whose eccentricity, e, is $\dfrac{\sqrt{a^2 - b^2}}{a}$.

There are two mutually consistent geometric definitions of a hyperbola.

1. Given two points F_1 and F_2 in a plane and a positive number k, the set consisting of every point P in the plane such that $\big|\,|PF_2| - |PF_1|\,\big| = k$ is a *hyperbola*. Each of the points F_1 and F_2 is called a *focus* of the hyperbola.

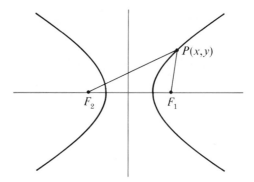

2. In a plane, given a line L and a point F_1 not in L and a given number e in $\rangle\,1,\ \infty\,\langle$, the set consisting of every point P in the plane, such that $|PF_2|$ divided by the measure of the line segment from P perpendicular to L is equal to e is a *hyperbola*. The point F_2 is called a *focus*

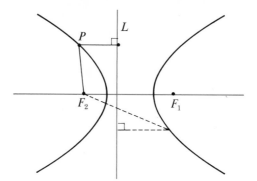

of the hyperbola, the line L is the corresponding *directrix* of the hyperbola, and the number e is the *eccentricity* of the hyperbola.

We use an example to indicate that these two definitions are consistent with each other and that the graph of an equation of the form $\dfrac{x^2}{a^2} - \dfrac{y^2}{b^2} = 1$ is a hyperbola according to either definition.

Example 3. Show that G the graph of the equation $\dfrac{x^2}{4^2} - \dfrac{y^2}{3^2} = 1$ is a hyperbola according to each of the above definitions.

Solution. We apply the first definition by identifying $F_2(-5, 0)$ and $F_1(5, 0)$ as the foci and letting $k = 8$.

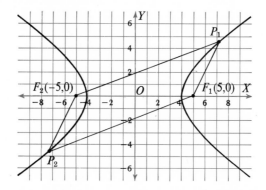

According to our definition $P(x, y)$ is in our hyperbola if and only if $(i)\,|PF_2| - |PF_1| = 8$ as is true when $P = P_1$ in the preceding drawing, or $(ii)\,|PF_1| - |PF_2| = 8$ as is true when $P = P_2$ in the preceding drawing. From (i) we have $|PF_2| = 8 + |PF_1|$. Applying the distance formula, we have $|PF_1| = \sqrt{(x-5)^2 + y^2}$ and $|PF_2| = \sqrt{(x+5)^2 + y^2}$. Therefore $\sqrt{(x+5)^2 + y^2} = 8 + \sqrt{(x-5)^2 + y^2}$. Proceeding as we did in Example 2, we find that this equation is equivalent to $\dfrac{x^2}{4^2} - \dfrac{y^2}{3^2} = 1 \wedge x \geq 4$. Also, by the same procedure, equation (ii) yields $\dfrac{x^2}{4^2} - \dfrac{y^2}{5} = 1 \wedge x \leq 4$.

We apply the second definition by identifying a focus as $F_1(5, 0)$, the directrix as the line L whose equation is $x = \frac{16}{5}$, and the eccentricity, e, as the number $\frac{5}{4}$. Therefore, $P(x, y)$ is in the hyperbola if and only if $\dfrac{|PF_1|}{|PD|} = \dfrac{5}{4}$. Since $|PD| = |x - \frac{16}{5}|$ and $|PF_1| = \sqrt{(x-5)^2 + y^2}$, we have $\dfrac{\sqrt{(x-5)^2 + y^2}}{|x - \frac{16}{5}|} = \dfrac{5}{4}$. Thus

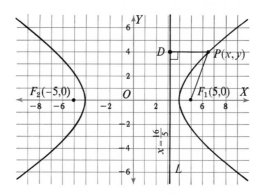

$4\sqrt{(x-5)^2+y^2} = |\,5\,x-16\,|,$ or $16(x^2 - 10\,x + 25 + y^2) = 25\,x^2 - 160\,x + 256.$ This equation is readily shown to be equivalent to the equation $\dfrac{x^2}{4^2} - \dfrac{y^2}{3^2} = 1,$ and we have shown that the graph of the equation $\dfrac{x^2}{4^2} - \dfrac{y^2}{3^2} = 1$ is a hyperbola by either of the definitions given.

Considering Example 3, you may ask how we located the foci and determined the distance k in applying the first definition and how we located the focus and directrix and determined the eccentricity e in applying the second definition. While we are not primarily concerned with these questions in this course, we state that G, the graph of the equation $\dfrac{x^2}{a^2} - \dfrac{y^2}{b^2} = 1,$ can be shown by the first definition to be a hyperbola whose foci are $F_2(-\sqrt{a^2+b^2},\ 0)$ and $F_1(\sqrt{a^2+b^2},\ 0)$ and whose distance k is $2\,a.$ By the second definition, G is a hyperbola, one of whose foci is $F_1(\sqrt{a^2+b^2},\ 0)$, whose corresponding directrix is the line L whose equation is $x = \dfrac{a^2}{\sqrt{a^2+b^2}},$ and whose eccentricity, e, is $\dfrac{\sqrt{a^2+b^2}}{a}.$

Ⓐ EXERCISES

1. Use the geometric definition of a parabola to show that the graph of each of the equations is a parabola having the indicated focus and directrix.

Equation	Focus	Directrix
$y = \frac{1}{12}x^2$	$(0, 3)$	$y = -3$
$y = -\frac{1}{16}x^2$	$(0, -4)$	$y = 4$
$y = \frac{1}{8}(x-3)^2$	$(3, 2)$	$y = -2$
$x = -\frac{1}{12}y^2$	$(-3, 0)$	$x = 3$

2. In each of the following cases, write an equation whose graph is a parabola having the given ordered pair as the coordinates of its focus and the given equation as the equation of its directrix.

a. $(0, 5),\ y = -5$ **c.** $(4, 2),\ y = 0$ **e.** $(0, 4),\ y = 2$

b. $(0, -4),\ y = 4$ **d.** $(-3, 2),\ x = 2$ **f.** $(4, 1),\ x = 2$

3. Show that the graph of each of the following equations is an ellipse according to the first geometric definition of an ellipse given in this section.

a. $\dfrac{x^2}{36} + \dfrac{y^2}{20} = 1$

c. $16\,x^2 + 7\,y^2 = 112$

b. $x^2 + 5\,y^2 = 5$

d. $\dfrac{x^2}{4} + \dfrac{y^2}{40} = 1$

4. In each of the following cases, write an equation of the ellipse which has the given ordered pairs as the coordinates of its foci and the given value of k as the sum of the measures of the distance from its foci to $P(x, y)$, any point in the ellipse.

a. $(4, 0), (-4, 0), k = 10$

b. $(0, 4), (0, -4), k = 10$

c. $(12, 0), (-12, 0), k = 26$

d. $(3\sqrt{3}, 0), (-3\sqrt{3}, 0), k = 12$

e. $(0, 5), (0, -5), k = 2\sqrt{29}$

f. $(0, \sqrt{7}), (0, -\sqrt{7}), k = 8$

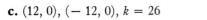 **B** **EXERCISES**

5. For each of the following equations, use the second geometric definition of a hyperbola given in this section to show that the graph is a hyperbola:

a. $\dfrac{x^2}{9} - \dfrac{y^2}{16} = 1$

c. $4\,x^2 - 9\,y^2 = 36$

e. $\dfrac{y^2}{144} - \dfrac{x^2}{81} = 1$

b. $\dfrac{y^2}{4} - \dfrac{x^2}{9} = 1$

d. $\dfrac{x^2}{64} - \dfrac{y^2}{36} = 1$

f. $x^2 - 9\,y^2 = 9$

6. In each of the following cases, write an equation whose graph is the hyperbola having the given ordered pairs as the coordinates of its foci and the given value of k as the difference of the measures of the distances from the foci to $P(x, y)$, any point in the hyperbola.

a. $(-3, 0)\ (3, 0), k = 2$

b. $(-6, 0), (6, 0), k = 8$

c. $(0, 5), (0, -5), k = 6$

d. $(0, 7), (0, -7), k = 7$

7. Use the geometric definition of an ellipse to show that the graph of $9(x + 2)^2 + 4(y - 1)^2 = 36$ is an ellipse. What are the coordinates of the vertices and the coordinates of the foci of the ellipse?

8. What are the coordinates of the focus and the equation of the directrix of the graph of each of the following equations?

a. $x = \frac{1}{8}y^2 + 2$

b. $y = x^2 + 4\,x + 4$

c. $y^2 = 4\,x + 5$

9. Show that according to either of the geometric definitions of an ellipse, the graph of the equation $\dfrac{(x-2)^2}{9} + \dfrac{(y-3)^2}{4} = 1$ is an ellipse. What are the coordinates of the foci and the equations of the directrices of the ellipse?

10. Write an equation whose graph is the path of a point which moves so that the sum of its distances from the points $F_1(3, 2)$ and $F_2(9, 2)$ is 8.

11. What are the coordinates of the vertices, the foci, and the center of the graph of $\dfrac{(x - 3)^2}{6} - \dfrac{(y + 2)^2}{9} = 1$? What are the equations of the directrices of the graph?

12. Identify the conic which is the graph of each of the following equations.

    a. $9\,x^2 - 4\,y^2 - 36\,x - 24\,y = 36$ **e.** $x^2 - y^2 - x + y = 0$

    b. $16\,x^2 + 9\,y^2 - 64\,x + 54\,y + 1 = 0$ **f.** $x^2 + y^2 - 4\,x - 6\,y - 13 = 0$

    c. $4\,x^2 - y^2 - 24\,x - 2\,y + 19 = 0$ **g.** $x^2 + y^2 - 3 = 0$

    d. $4\,x^2 + 9\,y^2 + 8\,x - 36\,y + 4 = 0$ **h.** $x^2 + 8\,x - 3\,y + 10 = 0$

13. In each of the following cases write an equation of the ellipse that has the given ordered pair as the coordinates of one of its foci, the given equation as the equation of one of its directrices, and the given number as its eccentricity, respectively.

    a. $(3, 0)$, $x = 6$, $\frac{1}{2}$ **b.** $(0, 4)$, $y = 8$, $\frac{1}{3}$ **c.** $(11, 0)$, $x = 16$, $\frac{2}{3}$

ESSENTIALS

Before you leave this chapter make sure that you

1. Know what we mean by a quadratic sentence in two variables and by a system of quadratic sentences. (Page 687.)

2. Can draw the graph of a quadratic equation in two variables. (Pages 687–690.)

3. Can find the solution set of a system consisting of one linear and one quadratic equation in two variables by graphing and by algebraic procedures. (Pages 698–701.)

4. Can use the special methods described in this chapter for solving a system of two quadratic equations in two variables. (Pages 703–705.)

5. Can draw the graphs of the quadratic inequalities described in this chapter and can use graphs to solve systems involving such inequalities. (Pages 706, 707.)

6. Understand and can use the geometric definitions of the circle, the parabola, the ellipse, and the hyperbola given in this chapter. (Pages 708–714.)

7. Know the meaning of, can spell, and can use correctly the following words and phrases.

asymptote (Page 692.)

center of an ellipse (Page 689.)

center of a hyperbola (Page 691.)

circle (Pages 687, 708.)

conic (Page 697.)

directrix (Page 708.)

eccentricity (Page 710.)

ellipse (Pages 688, 709.)

focus (Page 708.)

hyperbola (Pages 687, 693, 712.)

major axis of an ellipse (Page 689.)

minor axis of an ellipse (Page 689.)

parabola (Pages 687, 708.)

reference rectangle (Page 689.)

right circular cone (Page 696.)

right circular cylinder (Page 697.)

transverse axis (Page 693.)

vertex (Pages 689, 693.)

CHAPTER REVIEW

1. Without drawing the graph identify each of the following as an equation whose graph is a circle, an ellipse, a hyperbola, a parabola, a line, two lines, or a point in the xy-plane.

a. $2x^2 + 3y^2 = 12$

b. $x^2 + y^2 = 7$

c. $x^2 - y^2 = 9$

d. $3x^2 - 6y^2 = 11$

e. $(x - 2y + 3)^2 = 0$

f. $x^2 + 4y^2 = 0$

g. $x^2 - y^2 = 0$

h. $(x + 2y + 1)(x - y - 1) = 0$

i. $\dfrac{x^2}{4} + \dfrac{y^2}{5} = 1$

j. $\dfrac{x^2}{5} + \dfrac{y^2}{5} = 1$

2. For the graph of each of the following, considered as a subset of the graph of $R \times R$, state:

(1) The coordinates of the vertex or vertices, if vertices exist.

(2) The coordinates of the center, if there is a center.

(3) The equation(s) of the line containing the axis(es) if there are axes. Also state the measures of the axes of each ellipse and of the transverse axis of each hyperbola.

(4) In the case of the hyperbola, state the equations of the asymptotes.

a. $y = \frac{1}{9}x^2 - 3$

b. $x^2 + 3y^2 = 12$

c. $x^2 - 3y^2 = 12$

d. $x^2 + y^2 = 25$

e. $x^2 - y^2 = 25$

f. $y = -x^2 - 5$

g. $9(x + 2)^2 + 4(y + 3)^2 = 36$

h. $16x^2 + 9(y - 7)^2 = 144$

i. $16x^2 - 9(y - 7)^2 = 144$

j. $y = (x + 2)^2 + 4$

k. $(x - 4)^2 + (y + 5)^2 = 56$

l. $(x - 3)^2 + (y - 7)^2 = 16$

m. $(x - 3)^2 - (y - 7)^2 = 16$

n. $6(x - 3)^2 - 9(y - 7)^2 = 144$

o. $(x - 3)^2 + 9(y - 7)^2 = 144$

p. $9(x - 6)^2 + 16(y - 3)^2 = 144$

3. Write an equation whose graph fits each of the following descriptions.

a. A circle whose center is at the origin of the coordinate plane and whose radius has the measure 3.

b. A circle whose center is at the point $P(3, -6)$ and whose radius has the measure 4.

c. An ellipse whose center is at the origin, whose major axis has the measure 10 and is in the x-axis, and whose minor axis has the measure 6 and is in the y-axis.

d. An ellipse whose center is at the point $P(-4, 2)$, whose major axis is 24 units long and is parallel to the y-axis, and whose minor axis is 10 units long.

e. An ellipse whose foci have the coordinates $(2, 0)$ and $(18, 0)$ and one of whose vertices has the coordinates $(-2, 0)$.

f. An ellipse which is the path of a point moving so that the sum of its distances from the two points $F_1(-2, 4)$ and $F_2(2, 4)$ is always 8.

g. The hyperbola which is the path of a point moving so that the difference of its distances from the points $F_1(-5, 6)$ and $F_2(-5, -2)$ is always 4.

h. The hyperbola having the graphs of $y = \frac{5}{2}x$ and $y = -\frac{5}{2}x$ as its asymptotes and the point $P(1, 0)$ as one vertex.

i. The parabola whose focus is at the point $P(0, 4)$ and whose directrix is the graph of the equation $y = -4$.

j. The curve which is the path of a point which moves so that its distance from the point $P(3, 5)$ is always equal to its distance from the line which is the graph of $y = 9$.

4. For each of the following systems, draw the graphs of the sentences in the system and indicate the solution set of each system.

a. $\begin{cases} x^2 + y^2 = 36 \\ x + 2y = 1 \end{cases}$

e. $\begin{cases} x^2 - y^2 = 9 \\ 4x^2 + 25y^2 = 100 \end{cases}$

b. $\begin{cases} x^2 + 3y^2 = 9 \\ y = -\frac{1}{2}x^2 + 1 \end{cases}$

f. $\begin{cases} 9x^2 + 4y^2 \le 36 \\ y < -x^2 \end{cases}$

c. $\begin{cases} xy = 15 \\ x + 2y = 4 \end{cases}$

g. $\begin{cases} 9x^2 - 4y^2 \le 36 \\ x + y - 2 > 0 \end{cases}$

d. $\begin{cases} x^2 + y^2 = 9 \\ (x - y + 1)(x + y - 1) = 0 \end{cases}$

h. $\begin{cases} 9x^2 + 4y^2 \le 36 \\ x^2 + y^2 > 9 \end{cases}$

5. Use algebraic methods to find the solution set of each of the following systems.

a. $\begin{cases} xy = 1 \\ 2x - 3y = 2 \end{cases}$

b. $\begin{cases} x^2 + y^2 = 8 \\ (x - 1)^2 - (y - 1)^2 = 0 \end{cases}$

c. $\begin{cases} 2\,x^2 + 3\,y^2 = 2 \\ 3\,x^2 - 2\,y^2 = 3 \end{cases}$ f. $\begin{cases} x^2 + xy + y^2 = 7 \\ x^2 - xy + y^2 = 19 \end{cases}$

d. $\begin{cases} x^2 + y^2 - 5\,x = 0 \\ x^2 + y^2 - 10\,y = 0 \end{cases}$ g. $\begin{cases} x^2 + 2\,xy + y^2 = 25 \\ x^2 + 2\,xy + y^2 + 3\,x + 2\,y = 38 \end{cases}$

e. $\begin{cases} x^2 - y^2 = 8 \\ 3\,x^2 + 4\,y^2 = 31 \end{cases}$ h. $\begin{cases} x^2 + 2\,xy + y^2 + x = 53 \\ x + y = 7 \end{cases}$

CHAPTER TEST

1. Write an equation whose graph is a parabola which has (0, 2) as the coordinates of its focus and $y = -2$ as the equation of its directrix.

2. **a.** Sketch the graph of the equation $\dfrac{x^2}{36} + \dfrac{y^2}{16} = 1$.

   b. What is the name of the curve of part **a.**?

   c. State the measures of the axes.

   d. State the coordinates of the vertices.

3. Write the equation of the hyperbola whose vertices have the coordinates $(-8, 0)$ and $(8, 0)$ and whose asymptotes have the equations $y = \frac{1}{2}x$ and $y = -\frac{1}{2}x$.

4. Find the solution set of $\begin{cases} x^2 - y^2 = -9 \\ 2\,x + 3\,y = 7 \end{cases}$.

5. Find the solution set of $\begin{cases} 2\,x^2 + 5\,xy = -8 \\ 3\,x^2 - xy = 5 \end{cases}$.

6. By means of a graph show the solution set of $\begin{cases} 9\,x^2 + 25\,y^2 < 225 \\ x^2 + y^2 < 16 \end{cases}$ as a subset of the graph of $R \times R$.

Sequences, Series, and Binomial Theorem

Sequences and Series

We are often confronted with a set of numbers that are arranged in a specified order. Such a set of numbers forms a sequence of numbers, or more briefly, a *sequence*. We shall be concerned with both finite sequences and infinite sequences.

A *finite sequence* is a set of numbers arranged in order so that they are in one-to-one correspondence with a finite subset of counting numbers $\{1, 2, 3, \cdots, n\}$.

An *infinite sequence* is a set of numbers arranged in order so that they are in one-to-one correspondence with the set of counting numbers $\{1, 2, 3, \cdots, n, \cdots\}$.

Each number in a sequence is called a *term* of the sequence. The term corresponding to the counting number n is called the nth *term* of the sequence and is designated by a symbol such as t_n.

If we use the symbol $\{(n, t_n)\}$ to represent the set $\{(1, t_1), (2, t_2), (3, t_3), \cdots, (n, t_n)\}$, we see that $\{(n, t_n)\}$ is a function whose domain is the set of counting numbers in $\langle 1, n \rangle$. If our sequence is infinite, the domain of the function $\{(n, t_n)\}$ is C. Observe that in dealing with sequences, we use the symbol t_n instead of $t(n)$ to denote the value of the function which corresponds to the argument n. The function $\{(n, t_n)\}$ is called a *sequence function*.

A sequence is said to be defined or specified recursively if (1) the first term is known, and (2) we have a formula, called a *recursion* formula, which gives the relationship between any term and its successor.

Example 1. Write the first five terms t_1, t_2, t_3, t_4, t_5 of the sequence whose first term is -7 and whose recursion formula is $t_{n+1} = t_n + 3$.

Solution. Since $t_1 = -7$, we begin with -7 and obtain four other numbers, one after another by successive additions of 3. Thus $t_1 = -7$, $t_2 = t_1 + 3 = -7 + 3 = -4$, $t_3 = t_2 + 3 = -4 + 3 = -1$, $t_4 = t_3 + 3 = -1 + 3 = 2$, and $t_5 = t_4 + 3 = 2 + 3 = 5$. The numbers $-7, -4, -1, 2, 5$ in the order shown form a finite sequence whose terms are in one-to-one correspondence with $\{1, 2, 3, 4, 5\}$. Note that the recursion formula $t_{n+1} = t_n + 3$, together with the fact that $t_1 = -7$, specifies an infinite sequence, namely $-7, -4, -1, 2, 5, \cdots$, provided the domain of n is the set C.

Sometimes, instead of specifying a sequence recursively, we have a formula which gives t_n in terms of n.

Example 2. Write the first four terms and the 15th term of the sequence defined by the formula $t_n = n^2 + 7$. Also write the kth term and the $(k + 1)$th term.

Solution. Replacing n successively by 1, 2, 3, 4, 15, k, and $k + 1$, we have $t_1 = 1^2 + 7 = 8$, $t_2 = 2^2 + 7 = 11$, $t_3 = 3^2 + 7 = 16$, $t_4 = 4^2 + 7 = 23$, $t_{15} = 15^2 + 7 = 232$, $t_k = k^2 + 7$, and $t_{k+1} = (k + 1)^2 + 7$.

The indicated sum of the terms in a sequence is called a *series*. Thus if $t_1, t_2, t_3, \cdots, t_n$ is a finite sequence, the expression $t_1 + t_2 + t_3 + \cdots + t_n$ is the corresponding finite series and the numbers $t_1, t_2, \cdots, t_{n-1}$ and t_n are its terms. For example,

Finite sequence	Corresponding finite series
$-7, -4, -1, 2, 5$	$-7 + (-4) + (-1) + 2 + 5$

If $t_1, t_2, t_3, \cdots, t_n, \cdots$ is an infinite sequence, the expression $t_1 + t_2 + t_3 + \cdots + t_n + \cdots$ is the corresponding infinite series. For example,

Infinite sequence	Corresponding infinite series
$\dfrac{1}{2}, \dfrac{1}{2^2}, \dfrac{1}{2^3}, \cdots, \dfrac{1}{2^n}, \cdots$	$\dfrac{1}{2} + \dfrac{1}{2^2} + \dfrac{1}{2^3} + \cdots + \dfrac{1}{2^n} + \cdots$

We should remember that a series is an expression rather than a number. For example, it is not correct to say that the series $-7 + (-4) + (-1) + 2 + 5$ is -5. The number -5 is the sum of the terms of this series but the series itself is the expression $-7 + (-4) + (-1) + 2 + 5$.

The Greek letter Σ, pronounced sigma, is often used to represent series in the following ways:

If the series is finite, $t_1 + t_2 + t_3 + \cdots + t_n$, we use the following notation: $\sum_{i=1}^{n} t_i$

If the series is infinite, $t_1 + t_2 + t_3 + \cdots + t_n + \cdots$, we use the following notation: $\sum_{i=1}^{\infty} t_i$

This notation, called the *summation notation*, is particularly useful when we have a formula which enables us to express t_k in terms of k. The letter k is called the *index of summation*. We may use any other letter in place of k. If $t_k = 3k + 2$, then $\sum_{k=1}^{5} t_k = \sum_{k=1}^{5} (3k + 2) = (3 \cdot 1 + 2) + (3 \cdot 2 + 2) + (3 \cdot 3 + 2) + (3 \cdot 4 + 2) + (3 \cdot 5 + 2) = 5 + 8 + 11 + 14 + 17$. Also if $t_k = 3k + 2$, then $\sum_{k=3}^{n} t_k = (3 \cdot 3 + 2) + (3 \cdot 4 + 2) + (3 \cdot 5 + 2) + (3 \cdot 6 + 2) + (3 \cdot 7 + 2) + \cdots + (3n + 2)$.

If $1 \le k < n$, $\sum_{i=1}^{n} t_i = (t_1 + t_2 + \cdots + t_k) + (t_{k+1} + t_{k+2} + \cdots + t_n)$. The indicated sum in the first parentheses in the right member of this equation is represented by $\sum_{i=1}^{k} t_i$. We will represent the indicated sum in the second parentheses by $\sum_{i=k+1}^{n} t_i$. Thus $\sum_{i=1}^{n} t_i = \sum_{i=1}^{k} t_i + \sum_{i=k+1}^{n} t_i$.

Note also that when $t_k = f(k)$, the symbol $\sum_{k=1}^{n} f(k)$ denotes the series $f(1) + f(2) + f(3) + \cdots + f(n)$.

Example 3.   Write the series denoted by:

a. $\sum_{j=1}^{7} j^2$ **b.** $\sum_{j=1}^{\infty} \frac{1}{j}$

Solutions.   **a.** $\sum_{j=1}^{7} j^2 = 1^2 + 2^2 + 3^2 + 4^2 + 5^2 + 6^2 + 7^2$

b. $\sum_{j=1}^{\infty} \frac{1}{j} = 1 + \frac{1}{2} + \frac{1}{3} + \cdots + \frac{1}{n} + \cdots$

Example 4.   Prove the following:

a. $\sum_{i=1}^{6} cn_i = c \sum_{i=1}^{6} n_i$ **b.** $\sum_{i=1}^{6} (n_i + v_i) = \sum_{i=1}^{6} n_i + \sum_{i=1}^{6} v_i$

Solutions.   **a.** $\displaystyle\sum_{i=1}^{6} cn_i = cn_1 + cn_2 + cn_3 + \cdots + cn_6 = c(n_1 + n_2 + n_3 +$

$\cdots + n_6) = c\displaystyle\sum_{i=1}^{6} n_i.$

b. $\displaystyle\sum_{i=1}^{6} (n_i + v_i) = (n_1 + v_1) + (n_2 + v_2) + (n_3 + v_3) + \cdots +$

$(n_6 + v_6) = (n_1 + n_2 + n_3 + \cdots + n_6) + (v_1 + v_2 + v_3 +$

$\cdots + v_6) = \displaystyle\sum_{i=1}^{6} n_i + \displaystyle\sum_{i=1}^{6} v_i.$

While we have recognized the distinction between a series and the sum of its terms, we must also note that the symbol $\displaystyle\sum_{k=1}^{n} t_k$ is commonly used to denote either of these. Generally, as in Example 5, it will be clear from the context which meaning is intended.

Example 5.   Evaluate $\displaystyle\sum_{j=1}^{5} t_j$ where $t_j = j^3$.

Solution. $\displaystyle\sum_{j=1}^{5} t_j = \sum_{j=1}^{5} j^3 = 1^3 + 2^3 + 3^3 + 4^3 + 5^3 = 225.$

Ⓐ EXERCISES

Write the first four terms and the 12th term of the sequence whose nth term t_n is given by each of the following equations. In each case $n \,\epsilon\, C$.

1. $t_n = 2^n$ **4.** $t_n = i^n;\ i = \sqrt{-1}$ **7.** $t_n = 1 + i^n$

2. $t_n = 3n - 7$ **5.** $t_n = 2^{n-1}$ **8.** $t_n = \log 10^n$

3. $t_n = \dfrac{5}{n^2}$ **6.** $t_n = \dfrac{n(n-1)^2}{2}$ **9.** $t_n = 1 + (-1)^n$

In Exercises 10–17, a sequence is specified by giving its first term and a recursion formula for succeeding terms. Write the first five terms of each sequence.

10. $t_1 = 3,\ t_{n+1} = t_n + 3$ **14.** $t_1 = 1,\ t_{n+1} = (-1)^{n+1} 2 t_n$

11. $t_1 = 5,\ t_{n+1} = 2 t_n$ **15.** $t_1 = 4,\ t_{n+1} = \dfrac{n+1}{n} t_n$

12. $t_1 = 6,\ t_{n+1} = -3 t_n$ **16.** $t_1 = 2,\ t_{n+1} = t_n^2$

13. $t_1 = 16,\ t_{n+1} = \frac{1}{2} t_n$ **17.** $t_1 = 5,\ t_{n+1} = (t_n - 4)^2$

Specify each of the following sequences (1) recursively and (2) by finding an expression for t_n in terms of n.

18. 11, 13, 15, 17, 19, $\cdots$ **21.** $\frac{1}{3}, \frac{1}{9}, \frac{1}{27}, \frac{1}{81}, \frac{1}{243}, \cdots$

19. 1, -2, 4, -8, 16, $\cdots$ **22.** 3, 7, 15, 31, 63, $\cdots$

20. 1, $1 \cdot 2$, $1 \cdot 2 \cdot 3$, $1 \cdot 2 \cdot 3 \cdot 4$, $1 \cdot 2 \cdot 3 \cdot 4 \cdot 5$, $\cdots$

Write the series designated by each of the following. (Sometimes the series is called the expanded form of the symbol $\sum_{i=1}^{n} t_i$.)

23. $\sum_{k=1}^{7} k$ **25.** $\sum_{i=1}^{7} t_i$ **27.** $\sum_{k=1}^{8} (k^2 + 1)$

24. $\sum_{j=1}^{7} j$ **26.** $\sum_{k=4}^{7} (k + 1)^2$ **28.** $\sum_{k=1}^{\infty} \frac{1}{k^2}$

B **EXERCISE**

Represent each of the following series by means of the summation notation.

29. $3 + 6 + 9 + 12 + 15$ **31.** $z_1{}^3 + z_2{}^3 + z_3{}^3 + z_4{}^3 + z_5{}^3$

30. $16 - 8 + 4 - 2 + 1$ **32.** $2 + 8 + 26 + 80 + 242$

In Exercises 33–34 you are given t_1 and you are given t_{k+1} in terms of t_k. In each case find the formula for t_n in terms of n.

33. $t_1 = 5$, $t_{k+1} = t_k + 3$ **34.** $t_1 = 2$, $t_{k+1} = t_k + 2^k$

35. Find an expression for the sum of the terms in each of the following series. In each case k, $n \in C$.

a. $\sum_{k=1}^{n} t_k$ where $t_k = 1$ **c.** $\sum_{k=1}^{2n+1} (-1)^k$

b. $\sum_{k=1}^{4n} i^k$ where $i = \sqrt{-1}$ **d.** $\sum_{k=1}^{2n} |1 + (-1)^k|$

Show that the expressions in each of the Exercises 36–38 represent the same series.

36. $\sum_{k=1}^{7} k^2 + 1$ and $\sum_{k=6}^{12} (k - 5)^2 + 1$ **38.** $\sum_{i=1}^{n} t_i$ and $\sum_{i=1+k}^{n+k} t_{i-k}$

37. $\sum_{i=4}^{8} \frac{t + 3}{t}$ and $\sum_{i=1}^{5} \frac{t + 6}{t + 3}$

Arithmetic Progressions

Each of the following sequences is called an arithmetic progression (A.P.).

$3, 7, 11, 15, 19$ $-5, 0, 5, 10, 15$ $11, 4, -3, -10, -17$

An *arithmetic progression* is a sequence in which the difference obtained by subtracting any term from its successor is always the same. This difference is called the common difference of the arithmetic progression and it is denoted by the letter d. The common differences for the arithmetic progressions shown above are respectively 4, 5, and -7. In an arithmetic progression each term after the first is the sum of d and the preceding term. We can define an arithmetic progression recursively as follows:

If $t_1 = a$, $t_{k+1} = t_k + d$, $k \in C$, and a, $d \in Z$, then t_1, t_2, t_3, $\cdots$, t_n, $\cdots$ is an arithmetic progression.

Using this definition and a form of proof known as mathematical induction, which you will study in a future mathematics course, the following theorem can be proved.

▶ **Theorem 1–14.** If t_n is the nth term of an arithmetic progression whose first term is a and whose common difference is d, then $t_n = a + (n - 1)d$.

Example 1. Find the twentieth term of the arithmetic progression $- 17$, $- 13$, $- 9$, $\cdots$.

Solution. $a = - 17$, $d = 4$, $n = 20$, and $t_n = a + (n - 1)d$.
$t_{20} = - 17 + (20 - 1) \, 4 = 59$

Example 2. What term of the arithmetic progression 73, 61, 49, $\cdots$ is $- 47$?

Solution. $a = 73$, $d = - 12$, $t_k = - 47$, and $t_n = a + (n - 1)d$
$- 47 = 73 + (n - 1)(- 12)$
$- 132 = - 12 \, n$
$11 = n$
$\therefore - 47$ is the eleventh term.

Example 3. Find x if it is known that x^2, $2x + 5$, and x are the first three terms of an arithmetic progression.

Solution. The common difference d can be obtained by subtracting the first term from the second or by subtracting the second term from the third. Thus $d = 2x + 5 - x^2$ and $d = x - (2x + 5)$. $\therefore 2x + 5 - x^2 = x - (2x + 5)$. This equation is equivalent to $x^2 - 3x - 10 = 0$, whose solution set is $\{5, - 2\}$.
If we use 5 for x, the sequence x^2, $2x + 5$, x becomes 25, 15, 5, the first three terms of an arithmetic progression whose common difference is $- 10$.
If we use -2 for x, we obtain 4, 1, -2, the first three terms of an arithmetic progression whose common difference is $- 3$.

The terms between any two given terms of an arithmetic progression are called *arithmetic means*. For example, in the arithmetic progression 5, 11, 17, 23, 29, 35, the terms 11, 17, 23, and 29 are the arithmetic means between 5 and 35, and the terms 11 and 17 are the arithmetic means between 5 and

23. When we wish to find arithmetic means between two terms in an arithmetic progression, we use the formula $t_n = a + (n - 1)d$ to find the common difference as shown in the following example.

Example 4. Find four arithmetic means between 47 and -18.

Solution. $a = 47, n = 6, t_6 = -18$, and $t_n = a + (n - 1)d$.

$$-18 = 47 + 5d$$
$$-13 = d$$
$$\therefore 47, 34, 21, 8, -5, -18$$

If a, x, b is an arithmetic progression, then x is called the arithmetic mean of a and b. It can be shown that $x = \dfrac{a + b}{2}$.

An arithmetic series is the indicated sum of the terms in an arithmetic sequence. We seek a formula for S_n, the sum of the first n terms of an arithmetic progression whose first term is a and whose common difference is d. We have:

$(i) \ S_n = a + (a + d) + (a + 2 d) + \cdots + [a + (n - 1)d]$.

If we reverse the order of the terms in the right member and express each of the terms in terms of t_n and d, we obtain:

$(ii) \ S_n = t_n + (t_n - d) + (t_n - 2 d) + \cdots + [t_n - (n - 1) d]$.

By the addition property of equality, we have from (i) and (ii): $2 S_n = (a + t_n) + (a + t_n) + (a + t_n) + \cdots + (a + t_n)$ where the expression on the right indicates that $a + t_n$ appears n times. Thus $2 S_n = n(a + t_n)$, or $S_n = \dfrac{n}{2} (a + t_n)$. We know that $t_n = a + (n - 1) d$; therefore $S_n = \dfrac{n}{2} [a + a + (n - 1) d]$, or $S_n = \dfrac{n}{2} [2 a + (n - 1) d]$.

This discussion suggests the following theorem:

▷ **Theorem 2–14.** If S_n is the sum of the first n terms of an arithmetic progression whose first term is a and whose common difference is d, then

$$S_n = \frac{n}{2}[2 a + (n - 1) d].$$

The proof of Theorem 2–14 requires the use of mathematical induction.

Example 5. Find the sum of the first 15 terms of the arithmetic progression $-13, -7, -1, \cdots$.

Solution. $a = -13, d = 6, n = 15$, and $S_n = \dfrac{n}{2} [2 a + (n - 1) d]$.

$$S_{15} = \tfrac{15}{2} [2(-13) + (15 - 1) 6]$$
$$S_{15} = 435$$

Example 6. If S_n is the sum of the first n terms of the arithmetic progression 14, 12, 10, $\cdots$ and $S_n = 50$, find n.

Solution. $S_n = 50$, $a = 14$, $d = -2$, and $S_n = \dfrac{n}{2}[2a + (n-1)d]$.

$$50 = \frac{n}{2}[28 + (n-1)(-2)]$$
$$50 = n(14 + 1 - n)$$
$$50 = 15n - n^2$$
$n^2 - 15n + 50 = 0$. The solution set of this equation is $\{5, 10\}$. We see that each of the series $14 + 12 + 10 + 8 + 6$ and $14 + 12 + 10 + 8 + 6 + 4 + 2 + 0 + (-2) + (-4)$ has the sum 50.

Example 7. Find the sum of the series $\displaystyle\sum_{k=1}^{15} 5k + 3$.

Solution. Since a series is the sum of a sequence, we write the first three terms of the sequence of which we are to find the sum as follows: 8, 13, 18. From this we see that we have an arithmetic progression whose common difference, d, is 5, and whose first term, a, is 8. Using Theorem 2–14, we have:
$$S_{15} = \tfrac{15}{2}[2 \cdot 8 + 14 \cdot 5] = 645$$

Harmonic Progressions

If $t_1, t_2, t_3, \cdots, t_n, \cdots$ is an arithmetic progression and no t_n in the sequence is zero, then the sequence $\dfrac{1}{t_1}, \dfrac{1}{t_2}, \dfrac{1}{t_3}, \cdots, \dfrac{1}{t_n}, \cdots$ is called a *harmonic progression*. A *harmonic series* is the indicated sum of a harmonic progression.

Example 8. Write the harmonic series whose first term is $\frac{1}{2}$ and whose third term is $\frac{1}{6}$.

Solution. Since $\frac{1}{2}$ is the first term and $\frac{1}{6}$ is the third term of the harmonic progression, then 2 is the first term and 6 is the third term of the corresponding arithmetic progression. Using Theorem 1–14, we find the common difference of this arithmetic progression.
$$t_n = a + (n-1)d$$
$$6 = 2 + (3-1)d$$
$$\therefore d = 2.$$

It follows that the arithmetic progression is 2, 4, 6, 8, $\cdots$. Thus the required harmonic series is $\dfrac{1}{2} + \dfrac{1}{4} + \dfrac{1}{6} + \dfrac{1}{8} + \cdots$.

1. What is the sum of the first 500 terms of an arithmetic progression whose first term is 2 and whose common difference is 0?

In Ex. 2–9, $t_1, t_2, t_3, \cdots, t_n$ is an arithmetic progression whose common difference is d_1 and $n_1, n_2, n_3, \cdots, n_n$ is an arithmetic progression whose common difference is d_2. You are to determine whether or not each of the following sequences is an arithmetic progression. If it is, express its common difference d in terms of one or both of the numbers d_1 and d_2. It may be helpful to consider numerical examples.

2. $t_n, t_{n-1}, \cdots, t_2, t_1$

3. $t_1 + c, t_2 + c, t_3 + c, \cdots, t_n + c$

4. $cn_1, cn_2, cn_3, \cdots, cn_n$

5. $n_1{}^2, n_2{}^2, \cdots, n_n{}^2$

6. $t_1 + n_1, t_2 + n_2, \cdots, t_n + n_n$

7. $t_1 n_1, t_2 n_2, \cdots, t_n n_n$

8. $3 t_1 + 2 n_1, 3 t_2 + 2 n_2, \cdots, 3 t_n + 2 n_n$

9. $t_1, t_6, t_{11}, \cdots t_{5n-4}$

10. Give the next three terms for each of the following arithmetic progressions.

   a. $17, 11, \cdots$ **b.** $n, n + d, \cdots$ **c.** $a, 4 a, \cdots$

1. Find the required term of each of the following arithmetic progressions.
   a. Thirteenth term of $7, 11, 15, \cdots$
   b. Ninth term of $3\sqrt{5}, \sqrt{5}, -\sqrt{5}, \cdots$
   c. Eleventh term of $c + d, c, c - d, \cdots$
   d. Fifteenth term of $-3, -1\frac{1}{2}, 0, \cdots$

2. Insert two arithmetic means between 1 and 13.

3. Insert four arithmetic means between 3 and 5.

4. Insert seven arithmetic means between 1.751 and 1.775.

5. What is the arithmetic mean of 5 and 107?

6. What is the arithmetic mean of $\sqrt{5}$ and $\sqrt{45}$?

7. Replace each question mark with a number so that an arithmetic progression is formed.

   a. $7, ?, 13, ?, ?, ?, \cdots$ **d.** $2x - 5, ?, ?, ?, ?, 2x + 8, \cdots$
   b. $c, ?, d, ?, \cdots$ **e.** $x, ?, ?, x^2, \cdots$
   c. $-1, ?, ?, ?, ?, ?, 2, \cdots$ **f.** $2x + 5, ?, x - 5, ?, \cdots$

8. Which term of the arithmetic progression 7, 4, 1, $\cdots$ is -26?

9. Which term of the arithmetic progression $-8, -3, 2, \cdots$ is 92?

10. Find the sum of the first twenty-three terms of the arithmetic progression 9, 4, $-1, \cdots$.

11. Find the sum of the first thirty terms of the arithmetic progression $-5,$ $-2, 1, \cdots$.

12. If 2415 is the sum of the first n terms of the arithmetic progression 1, 5, 9, $\cdots$, what number is represented by n?

13. Find the sum of the odd counting numbers less than 100.

14. The third term of an arithmetic progression is -21 and the tenth term is 14. Find the common difference and the first term.

15. What is the tenth term of the harmonic progression $\frac{1}{3}, \frac{1}{8}, \frac{1}{13}, \cdots$?

B EXERCISES

16. Write the first five terms of the arithmetic progression whose third term is m and whose fourth term is n.

17. The fourth term of an arithmetic progression is -17 and the eighth term is -30. Find the sum of the first five terms of the progression.

18. The sum of the first three terms of an arithmetic progression is 27. If the third term is 13, what are the other terms?

19. How many multiples of 5 are there in $\langle 0, 489 \rangle$?

20. Find the sum of the positive multiples of 5 that are less than 490.

21. Find the sum of the terms in each of the following series:

a. $\displaystyle\sum_{k=1}^{20} k - 11$ **c.** $\displaystyle\sum_{k=1}^{n} a + (k-1)d$ **e.** $\displaystyle\sum_{k=2}^{15} 5k + \frac{2}{3}$

b. $\displaystyle\sum_{k=0}^{12} 4k + 5$ **d.** $\displaystyle\sum_{k=4}^{12} 3k - 4$ **f.** $\displaystyle\sum_{k=3}^{13} 7 - 2k$

22. The harmonic mean of two nonzero numbers a and b is a number x whose reciprocal is the arithmetic mean of the reciprocals of the numbers a and b. What is the harmonic mean of

a. $\frac{1}{5}$ and $\frac{1}{11}$?   **b.** 2 and $\frac{2}{5}$?   **c.** $\frac{1}{7}$ and $\frac{1}{10}$?   **d.** $\sqrt{3}$ and $\sqrt{12}$?

C EXERCISE

23. The measures of the sides of a right triangle form an arithmetic progression. Show that the triangle is similar to a triangle whose sides have the measures 3, 4, and 5.

Geometric Progressions

A sequence in which each term except the first term a is r times the preceding term is a *geometric progression* (G.P.) provided $a, r \in Z$ and $ar \neq 0$. The number r is called the *common ratio* of the geometric progression. The following are examples of geometric progressions:

$$1, 2, 4, 8, \cdots \qquad 16, -8, 4, -2, \cdots \qquad a, ar, ar^2, ar^3, \cdots$$

The common ratios for the above geometric progressions are respectively $2, -\frac{1}{2}$, and r.

We may define a geometric progression recursively as follows:

> If $t_1 = a$ and $t_{k+1} = rt_k$ where $k \in C$, $a, r \in Z$ and $ar \neq 0$, then $t_1, t_2, t_3, \cdots$, $t_n, \cdots$ is a geometric progression.

Considering $a, ar, ar^2, ar^3, \cdots$, we observe that the exponent for r is always one less than the number of the term. We state the following theorem:

▷ **Theorem 3–14.** If t_n is the nth term of a geometric progression whose first term is a and whose common ratio is r, then $t_n = ar^{n-1}$.

Example 1. Find the seventh term of the geometric progression $81, -27, 9, \cdots$.

Solution. $a = 81, r = -\frac{1}{3}, n = 7$, and $t_n = ar^{n-1}$.
$$t_7 = 81(-\tfrac{1}{3})^6 = \tfrac{1}{9}$$

Example 2. Which term of the geometric progression $8, 12, 18, \cdots$ is $\frac{729}{8}$?

Solution. $a = 8, r = \frac{3}{2}, t_n = \frac{729}{8}$, and $t_n = ar^{n-1}$.
$\frac{729}{8} = 8 \left(\frac{3}{2}\right)^{n-1}$. We solve this equation for n with the understanding that $n \in C$. We have $\frac{3^6}{2^3} = 2^3 \cdot \left(\frac{3}{2}\right)^{n-1}$, or $\left(\frac{3}{2}\right)^6 = \left(\frac{3}{2}\right)^{n-1}$.
Since $a^x = a^y \longrightarrow x = y$, we have $6 = n - 1$, or $n = 7$.
$\therefore \frac{729}{8}$ is the seventh term of the given geometric progression.

Example 3. The sixth term of a geometric progression is 481 and its first term is 5. Find r to the nearest hundredth.

Solution. $a = 5, t_6 = 481, n = 6$, and $t_n = ar^{n-1}$.
$$481 = 5 \cdot r^5$$
$$\log 481 = \log 5 + 5 \log r$$
$$\log r = \frac{\log 481 - \log 5}{5}$$
$$\log r = \frac{2.6821 - 0.6990}{5}$$

$$\log r = 0.3966$$
$$\therefore r = 2.49$$

The terms between any two given terms in a geometric progression are called *geometric means*. For example, in the geometric progression 1, 2, 4, 8, 16, 32, the terms 2, 4, 8, and 16 are geometric means between 1 and 32. When we want to insert geometric means between two numbers in a geometric progression, we use the formula $t_n = ar^{n-1}$ to find the common ratio.

Example 4. Insert three real geometric means between 2 and 162.

Solution. $a = 2, n = 5, t_5 = 162$ and $t_n = ar^{n-1}$.
$$162 = 2 \cdot r^4$$
$$3^4 = r^4 \longleftrightarrow r^4 - 81 = 0 \longleftrightarrow (r^2 + 9)(r + 3)(r - 3) = 0$$
The solution set of this equation in R is $\{3, -3\}$.
$$\therefore 2, 6, 18, 54, 162, \text{ or } 2, -6, 18, -54, 162.$$

If a, x, b are in geometric progression, x is called a geometric mean of the numbers a and b. It is readily shown that $|x| = \sqrt{ab}$ provided $a, b \in R$.

A geometric series is the indicated sum of the terms in a geometric progression. We seek a formula for S_n, the sum of the first n terms of a geometric progression whose first term is a and whose common ratio is r. The formula is obtained in the following manner:

$$S_n = a + ar + ar^2 + \cdots + ar^{n-1}$$
$$rS_n = \quad\quad ar + ar^2 + \cdots + ar^{n-1} + ar^n \quad \text{(Subtracting)}$$
$$\overline{S_n - rS_n = a - ar^n}$$
$$S_n(1 - r) = a - ar^n$$
$$\therefore S_n = \frac{a - ar^n}{1 - r} ; r \neq 1$$

This suggests the following theorem:

Theorem 4–14. If S_n is the sum of the first n terms of a geometric progression whose first term is a and whose common ratio is r and $r \neq 1$, then
$$S_n = \frac{a - ar^n}{1 - r}.$$

Since t_n, the nth or last term of this geometric progression, is equal to ar^{n-1}, we have the following:

Corollary to Theorem 4–14. If S_n is the sum of the first n terms of a geometric progression whose first term, nth term, and common ratio are respectively $a, t_n,$ and r, and $r \neq 1$, then $S_n = \frac{a - rt_n}{1 - r}.$

Example 5. Find the sum of the first eight terms of the geometric progression $-7, 14, -28, \cdots$.

Solution. $a = -7, r = -2, n = 8$, and $S_n = \dfrac{a - ar^n}{1 - r}$.

$$S_8 = \frac{-7 - (-7)(-2)^8}{1 - (-2)} = \frac{-7 + 1792}{3} = 595$$

ORAL EXERCISES

In Ex. 1–8, $t_1, t_2, \cdots, t_n$ is a geometric progression whose common ratio is r_1 and $n_1, n_2, \cdots, n_n$ is a geometric progression whose common ratio is r_2. You are to determine whether or not each of the following sequences is a geometric progression. If it is a geometric progression, express its common ratio in terms of one or both of the numbers r_1 and r_2.

It may be helpful to consider numerical examples.

1. $t_n, t_{n-1}, \cdots, t_2, t_1$

2. $t_1 + c, t_2 + c, \cdots, t_n + c$

3. $cn_1, cn_2, \cdots, cn_n$

4. $n_1^2, n_2^2, \cdots, n_n^2$

5. $t_1 + n_1, t_2 + n_2, \cdots, t_n + n_n$

6. $t_1 n_1, t_2 n_2, \cdots, t_n n_n$

7. $6 t_1 n_1, 6 t_2 n_2, \cdots, 6 t_n n_n$

8. $t_1, t_6, t_{11}, \cdots, t_{5n-4}$

9. Give the next three terms for each of the following geometric progressions.

    a. $5, 15, 45, \cdots$ **b.** $1, -1, 1, \cdots$ **c.** $a, b, \cdots$; $ab \neq 0$

10. Observe that the formula in Theorem 4–14 does not apply when $r = 1$. What is the sum of the first n terms of a geometric progression whose first term is a and whose common ratio is 1?

Ⓐ EXERCISES

1. Find the required term of each of the following geometric progressions.

    a. The seventh term of $5, -15, 45, \cdots$

    b. The ninth term of $16, 8, \cdots$

    c. The twelfth term of $(a - b), (a - b)^2, \cdots$

    d. The tenth term of $\dfrac{a}{256}, \dfrac{a^2}{128}, \dfrac{a^3}{64}, \cdots$

    e. The seventh term of $0.1, 0.01, 0.001, \cdots$

    f. The eighth term of $1, (r + s)^{\frac{1}{2}}, (r + s), \cdots$

2. Insert three positive geometric means between 1 and 256.

3. Insert three real geometric means between a and b. Show both possibilities.

4. Insert four geometric real means between $\sqrt{5}$ and 125.

5. What is the positive geometric mean of $4 a$ and $\frac{a}{16}$ when $a \in R$? What is the negative geometric mean?

6. State two numbers either of which is the geometric mean of a and b, $a, b \in R$.

7. Replace each question mark with a real number so that a geometric progression is formed. When more than one set of numbers meets the requirements, state both sets, $a, b, x, y \in R$.

a. $\dfrac{x}{y^2}, ?, \dfrac{y^2}{x}, ?, \cdots$ **c.** $9, ?, ?, \dfrac{8}{3}, ?, ?, \cdots$ **e.** $a\sqrt{b}, ?, ?, a^4 b^2, \cdots$

b. $2, ?, \dfrac{1}{2}, ?, \dfrac{1}{8}, ?, ?, \cdots$ **d.** $x, ?, ?, \dfrac{x^4}{64}, ?, \cdots$ **f.** $a^{\frac{1}{2}}, ?, a, ?, ?, \cdots$

8. Which term of the geometric progression $3, -9, 27, \cdots$ is -729?

9. Which term of the geometric progression $\dfrac{1}{a}, \dfrac{3}{a^3}, \cdots$ is $\dfrac{81}{a^9}$?

10. Find the sum of the first five terms of the geometric progression $-3, 12, -48, \cdots$.

11. Find the sum of the first ten terms of the geometric progression $\frac{5}{16}, \frac{1}{4}, \frac{1}{5}, \cdots$.

12. If -86 is the sum of the first n terms of the geometric progression $-2, 4, -8, \cdots$, what number is represented by n?

13. Find the sum of the positive integral powers of 7 less than 7^7.

14. Evaluate each of the following:

a. $\displaystyle\sum_{k=0}^{8} 2^{k+1}$ **b.** $\displaystyle\sum_{k=1}^{6} 4(-\tfrac{1}{3})^{k-1}$

 EXERCISES

15. What is the sum of the fifth through the fourteenth terms, inclusive, of the geometric progression whose first term is 12 and whose common ratio is $\sqrt{2}$?

16. The third term of a geometric progression is 528 and the sixth term is $7\sqrt{2}$. What is the seventh term?

17. For what value(s) of a will $3a + 1$, $a + 2$, and $4a + 8$ form a geometric progression?

18. The first three terms of a sequence of four numbers form an arithmetic progression and the last three terms form a geometric progression. If the sum of the first and third terms is 28 and the sum of the second and third terms is 10, what are the numbers?

19. A rubber ball dropped from a height of 15 feet rebounds $\frac{2}{3}$ of the distance through which it fell. If it continues to rebound $\frac{2}{3}$ of the distance of its last fall, how far will the ball have traveled when it strikes the ground on its seventh descent?

20. A jar containing 600 cubic inches of air is connected to an air pump. If 5 per cent of the air in the jar is removed with each stroke of the pump, how much of the air remains in the jar at the completion of the sixth stroke of the pump?

Limit of a Sequence

A thorough discussion of the limit of a sequence must be postponed until you study calculus. However, it is worthwhile to make some informal observations about such limits at this time.

The sequence (i) $\dfrac{1}{3}, \dfrac{2}{5}, \dfrac{3}{7}, \cdots, \dfrac{n}{2n+1}, \cdots$ contains the terms $t_1, t_2, t_3,$ $\cdots$ of the sequence function S defined by the equation $t_n = \dfrac{n}{2n+1}; n \in C.$ When we study this sequence, we see that S is an increasing function because each of the terms of this sequence is greater than the preceding term. In fact, we can show this as follows:

$$t_{n+1} - t_n = \frac{n+1}{2n+3} - \frac{n}{2n+1} = \frac{1}{(2n+1)(2n+3)}. \quad \text{Since } n \in C,$$

$\dfrac{1}{(2n+1)(2n+3)} > 0.$ Thus the values of S continue to increase as n increases. Nevertheless, the number named by $\dfrac{n}{2n+1}$ is less than $\dfrac{1}{2}$ no matter how large n may be. Thus $\dfrac{1}{2} - \dfrac{n}{2n+1} = \dfrac{2n+1-2n}{2(2n+1)} = \dfrac{1}{4n+2}.$ Since $n \in C,$ $\dfrac{1}{4n+2} > 0,$ and even though each term of the sequence is greater than the preceding term, every term is less than one half. Indeed any number $\dfrac{1}{2}$ or greater will serve as an upper bound of $\dfrac{1}{3}, \dfrac{2}{5}, \dfrac{3}{7}, \cdots, \dfrac{n}{2n+1}, \cdots.$ However, the important thing to observe is that the difference between $\dfrac{1}{2}$ and $\dfrac{n}{2n+1},$ namely $\dfrac{1}{4n+2},$ can be made as small as we please by taking n sufficiently large. For example, if we are challenged to make this difference, $d,$ less than 0.0001, we could easily meet this challenge by taking $n \geq 2500.$ We see that $d < 0.0001$ for every integer n in $\langle 2500, \infty \langle.$

When there exists a number l such that the nth term, $t_n,$ of a sequence differs from l by as little as we please for all n sufficiently large, we say that the sequence $t_1, t_2, \cdots, t_n, \cdots$ approaches l as a limit. We describe this situation by writing $\lim\limits_{n \to \infty} t_n = l.$ This is read "the limit of t_n as n increases without bound is $l.$" In such a situation we say that the sequence $t_1, t_2, \cdots, t_n, \cdots$ is a *convergent sequence* and that it converges to the number $l.$

Other examples of convergent sequences are:

(ii) $1, \frac{1}{2}, \frac{1}{3}, \frac{1}{4}, \cdots, \dfrac{1}{n}, \cdots,$ and (iii) $\frac{1}{2}, \frac{5}{4}, \frac{7}{8}, \frac{17}{16}, \cdots, 1 + (-\frac{1}{2})^n, \cdots$

Sequence (ii) is a decreasing sequence that converges to 0 and (iii) is a sequence that is neither increasing nor decreasing which converges to 1. We see that the difference $l - t_n$ is positive for sequence (i), negative for sequence (ii), and alternately positive and negative for sequence (iii). In all cases, however, the *absolute value of this difference*, $|l - t_n|$, approaches 0. We adopt the following definition:

A sequence $t_1, t_2, \cdots, t_n, \ldots$ converges to the number l if and only if the absolute value of the difference between the number l and the nth term of the sequence is as small as we please for all n sufficiently large. Thus $\lim\limits_{n \to \infty} t_n = l \longleftrightarrow \lim\limits_{n \to \infty} |l - t_n| = 0.$

There are, of course, sequences that do not converge. Examples of such sequences are:

$$1, 2, 3, \cdots, n, \cdots$$
$$1, -1, 1, -1, \cdots, (-1)^{n+1}, \cdots$$
$$2, -\frac{3}{2}, \frac{4}{3}, -\frac{5}{4}, \cdots, (-1)^{n+1} \frac{n+1}{n}, \cdots$$

In each of these three examples, it is impossible to find a number l such that $\lim\limits_{n \to \infty} |l - t_n| = 0$. Such sequences are said to *diverge*.

Example 1. Describe the behavior of each of the following as n increases without bound. **a.** $\dfrac{n}{3n+2}$ **b.** $4n$

Solutions. **a.** By writing $\dfrac{n}{3n+2}$ in the form $\dfrac{1}{3 + \dfrac{2}{n}}$, we see that

$$\lim_{n \to \infty} \frac{n}{3n+2} = \frac{1}{3}.$$

b. $4n$ does not approach any limit as n increases without bound, $4n$ simply increases without bound.

Example 2. Is the following sequence convergent?

$$4, \frac{7}{2}, \frac{10}{3}, \cdots, \frac{3n+1}{n}, \cdots$$

Solution. By writing the general term as $3 + \dfrac{1}{n}$, we see that

$$\lim_{n \to \infty} \frac{3n+1}{n} = 3. \text{ Therefore the sequence is convergent.}$$

Example 3. When a sequence approaches a limit l there is a counting number c such that $|l - t_n| < k$ for any preassigned positive k, however small, when $n \geq c$. Find c for the sequence $1, \dfrac{1}{2}$, $\dfrac{1}{3}, \cdots, \dfrac{1}{n}, \cdots$ if $k = 0.0003$.

Solution. The limit of this sequence is 0. Therefore we wish to solve the inequality $|0 - \dfrac{1}{n}| < 0.0003$.

Since $n > 0$, $|0 - \dfrac{1}{n}| = |-\dfrac{1}{n}| = \dfrac{1}{n}$.

Therefore, $\dfrac{1}{n} < 0.0003 \longleftrightarrow 1 < 0.0003\,n \longleftrightarrow \dfrac{1}{0.0003} < n \longleftrightarrow$

$\longleftrightarrow 3333.3 < n$.

The least integer which satisfies the last inequality is 3334. Therefore $c = 3334$.

Ⓐ EXERCISES

Describe the behavior of each of the following as n increases without bound.

1. $\dfrac{1}{n}$ 3. $\dfrac{n+4}{n}$ 5. $\dfrac{1}{n^3}$ 7. $\dfrac{1}{2^n}$ 9. $(\tfrac{3}{5})^n$

2. $3 + \dfrac{1}{n^2}$ 4. n^3 6. $(-1)^n$ 8. $\dfrac{n+7}{n^3}$ 10. r^n if $|r| < 1$

Which of the following sequences are convergent? If a sequence is convergent, find $\lim\limits_{n \to \infty} t_n$.

11. $1, -\tfrac{1}{3}, \tfrac{1}{9}, -\tfrac{1}{27}, \cdots, (-1)^{n+1} \cdot \dfrac{1}{3^n}, \cdots$ 15. $\tfrac{1}{2}, \tfrac{2}{3}, \tfrac{3}{4}, \cdots, \dfrac{n}{n+1}, \cdots$

12. $\tfrac{3}{2}, \tfrac{9}{4}, \tfrac{27}{8}, \cdots, (\tfrac{3}{2})^n, \cdots$

13. $2, \tfrac{5}{4}, \tfrac{10}{9}, \tfrac{17}{16}, \cdots, 1 + \dfrac{1}{n^2}, \cdots$ 16. $2, \tfrac{5}{2}, \tfrac{10}{3}, \cdots, \dfrac{n^2+1}{n}, \cdots$

14. $\tfrac{1}{3}, \tfrac{5}{9}, \tfrac{19}{27}, \tfrac{65}{81}, \cdots, 1 - (\tfrac{2}{3})^n, \cdots$

Each of the following sequences converges to a number l. Find the counting number c such that $|l - t_n| < k$ for all $n \geq c$ where k is the given small positive number.

17. $1, \dfrac{1}{2^3}, \dfrac{1}{3^3}, \dfrac{1}{4^3}, \cdots, \dfrac{1}{n^3}, \cdots$ $|0 - \dfrac{1}{n^3}| < k; k = 0.0001$

18. $2, \tfrac{3}{2}, \tfrac{4}{3}, \tfrac{5}{4}, \cdots, \dfrac{n+1}{n}, \cdots$ $|1 - \dfrac{n+1}{n}| < k; k = 0.01$

19. $\tfrac{1}{3}, \tfrac{5}{9}, \tfrac{19}{27}, \cdots, 1 - (\tfrac{2}{3})^n, \cdots$ $|1 - [1 - (\tfrac{2}{3})^n]| < k; k = 0.001$

Infinite Geometric Series

Corresponding to every infinite series $t_1 + t_2 + t_3 + t_4 + \cdots + t_n + \cdots$ there is a sequence of numbers known as the *sequence of partial sums*, namely, the sequence $t_1, t_1 + t_2, t_1 + t_2 + t_3, t_1 + t_2 + t_3 + t_4, \cdots$. This sequence of partial sums can be represented more compactly if we let $S_1 = t_1$, $S_2 = t_1 + t_2, \cdots, S_n = t_1 + t_2 + \cdots + t_n$.

The series $t_1 + t_2 + t_3 + \cdots + t_n + \cdots$ is said to have a sum if and only if the sequence of partial sums $S_1, S_2, S_3, \cdots, S_n, \cdots$ has a limit. If this limit is S, that is, if $\lim_{n \to \infty} S_n = S$, then S is said to be the sum of the series. In this case the series is called a *convergent series*. Any series which is not convergent is called a *divergent series*. In cases where we can find an expression for S_n in terms of n, it is sometimes easy to determine whether or not a series is convergent. For example, the infinite series $\dfrac{1}{1 \cdot 2}$
$+ \dfrac{1}{2 \cdot 3} + \cdots + \dfrac{1}{n(n + 1)} + \cdots$ is readily shown to be a convergent series.
If $S_n = \dfrac{1}{1 \cdot 2} + \dfrac{1}{2 \cdot 3} + \cdots + \dfrac{1}{n(n + 1)}$, then $S_n = \dfrac{n}{n + 1}$. This can be shown as follows:

$$\frac{1}{1 \cdot 2} = 1 - \frac{1}{2}$$

$$\frac{1}{2 \cdot 3} = \frac{1}{2} - \frac{1}{3}$$

$$\frac{1}{3 \cdot 4} = \frac{1}{3} - \frac{1}{4}$$

$$\cdot \quad \cdot \quad \cdot \quad \cdot$$
$$\cdot \quad \cdot \quad \cdot \quad \cdot$$
$$\cdot \quad \cdot \quad \cdot \quad \cdot$$

$$\frac{1}{n(n + 1)} = \frac{1}{n} - \frac{1}{n + 1}$$

$$S_n = 1 - \frac{1}{n + 1} \quad \text{(By the addition property of equality)}$$

Thus we have: $S_n = 1 - \dfrac{1}{n + 1}$, or $\lim_{n \to \infty} S_n = 1$. Hence this infinite series converges and the number 1 is assigned as its sum.

Consider the infinite geometric series $a + ar + ar^2 + \cdots + ar^{n-1} + \cdots$. We inquire if there are any circumstances under which this series is convergent. We know that the answer is yes if there are conditions under which the sequence of partial sums whose nth term is S_n approaches a limit as n increases without bound.

We know that $S_n = \dfrac{a - ar^n}{1 - r}$ when $r \neq 1$ and we observe that this equation can be written in the equivalent form: $S_n = \dfrac{a}{1 - r}(1 - r^n)$ when $r \neq 1$. Consider the factor $1 - r^n$ which appears in the right member of this equation. If $0 < |r| < 1$, then $|r^n|$ becomes smaller and smaller as n increases in C. Indeed $\lim\limits_{n\to\infty} |r^n| = 0$ and this implies that $\lim\limits_{n\to\infty} r^n = 0$. For example, if $r = \frac{2}{3}$, the sequence $\frac{2}{3}, \frac{4}{9}, \frac{8}{27}, \cdots$ converges to 0. Also if $r = -\frac{2}{3}$, the sequence $-\frac{2}{3}, +\frac{4}{9}, -\frac{8}{27}, \cdots$ converges to 0.

Since we can make r^n as near zero as we please for $0 < |r| < 1$, we can make the factor $1 - r^n$ as near one as we please by taking n sufficiently large. This means that we can make S_n as near as we please to $\dfrac{a}{1 - r}$ by taking n sufficiently large, or that $\lim\limits_{n\to\infty} S_n = \dfrac{a}{1 - r}$. Therefore, the infinite geometric series $a + ar + ar^2 + \cdots + ar^{n-1} + \cdots$ is convergent when $0 < |r| < 1$ and the number $\dfrac{a}{1 - r}$ is assigned as its sum. Thus we state the following theorem:

▷ **Theorem 5–14.** The sum of the infinite geometric series $a + ar + ar^2 + \cdots + ar^{n-1} + \cdots$ is $\dfrac{a}{1 - r}$ where $\lim\limits_{n\to\infty} S_n = \dfrac{a}{1 - r}$ provided $0 < |r| < 1$ and S_n represents the sum of its first n terms.

We also refer to the sum of an infinite geometric series as the sum of the corresponding *infinite geometric progression*.

Example 1.   Find the sum of the infinite geometric progression $8, 4, 2, \cdots$.

Solution. $a = 8$, $r = \frac{1}{2}$, and $\lim\limits_{n\to\infty} S_n = \dfrac{8}{1 - \frac{1}{2}} = 16$.

This means that for all n sufficiently large, the number $|16 - S_n|$ can be made less than any preassigned positive number k, however small.

Example 2.   Write $0.\dot{3}\dot{6}$ in the form $\dfrac{a}{b}$ where $a, b \in I$ and $b \neq 0$.

Solution. $0.\dot{3}\dot{6} = 0.36 + 0.0036 + 0.000036 + \cdots$

Thus $a = 0.36$ and $r = 0.01$. Hence,

$$\lim\limits_{n\to\infty} S_n = \dfrac{0.36}{1 - 0.01} = \dfrac{0.36}{0.99} = \dfrac{4}{11}.$$

1. Find the sum of each of the following geometric progressions.

a. $1, \frac{1}{2}, \frac{1}{4}, \cdots$ **e.** $9, -3, 1, \cdots$ **i.** $\sqrt{2}, \dfrac{\sqrt{2}}{\sqrt{3}}, \dfrac{\sqrt{2}}{3}, \cdots$

b. $1, -\frac{1}{2}, \frac{1}{4}, -\frac{1}{8}, \cdots$ **f.** $2, -1, \cdots$ **j.** $1, 0.1, 0.01, \cdots$

c. $\frac{5}{3}, \frac{1}{3}, \frac{1}{15}, \cdots$ **g.** $15, 3, \cdots$ **k.** $3, 0.6, 0.12, \cdots$

d. $18, -6, 2, \cdots$ **h.** $12, -4, \frac{4}{3}, \cdots$ **l.** $2, 2(10)^{-1}, 2(10)^{-2}, \cdots$

2. Evaluate each of the following:

a. $\displaystyle\sum_{k=0}^{\infty} 3(\tfrac{1}{3})^k$ **b.** $\displaystyle\sum_{k=1}^{\infty} (\sqrt{\tfrac{1}{2}})^k$ **c.** $\displaystyle\sum_{k=0}^{\infty} x^k;\ 0 < |x| < 1$

3. Find the sum of the terms in the infinite geometric progression which has $\sqrt{2}$ as its first term and $\dfrac{\sqrt{2}}{2}$ as its common ratio.

4. The sum of the terms of an infinite geometric progression is $\frac{3}{2}$. If the first term of the progression is $\frac{3}{4}$, what are the second and third terms?

5. Write each of the following in the form $\dfrac{a}{b}$ where $a, b \in I$ and $b \neq 0$.

a. $0.2\dot{2}\dot{2}$ **c.** $0.5\dot{5}$ **e.** $4.\dot{1}2\dot{3}$ **g.** $6.71\dot{8}\dot{2}$

b. $0.25\dot{2}\dot{5}$ **d.** $0.3\dot{6}$ **f.** $2.03\dot{1}$ **h.** $62.4\dot{3}07\dot{1}\dot{6}$

6. The sum of the terms of an infinite geometric progression is 12 and the sum of the first two terms of the progression is 6. Write the first three terms of the progression.

7. A rubber ball is thrown vertically upward to a height of 12 feet. After falling to the ground it rebounds $\frac{2}{3}$ of the distance through which it fell and then continues to rebound $\frac{2}{3}$ of the distance of its last fall. How far will the ball have traveled before coming to rest?

8. The rectangle $ABCD$ shown at the right has $|AB| = 8$ and $|BC| = 6$. The diagonals of the rectangle intersect in O and the successive midpoints of the half-diagonals $\overline{DO}, \overline{CO}, \overline{BO},$ and $\overline{AO}$ are joined to form a new rectangle which, in turn, has the midpoints of its half-diagonals joined to form a new rectangle, and the process is continued without end. What is the sum of the perimeters of the 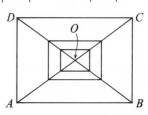 rectangles? (Recall that the diagonals of a rectangle bisect each other and that if a line segment joins the midpoints of two sides of a triangle, its measure is one half the measure of the third side of the triangle.)

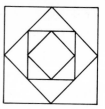

9. If the successive midpoints of the sides of a square are joined, a new square is formed. If the successive midpoints of the sides of this square are joined and the process continued to form more and more squares, what is the sum of the perimeters of these squares?

10. What is the sum of the areas of the squares in Ex. 9?

11. If a and b are two positive real numbers such that $b > a$, it can be shown that the arithmetic mean of a and b is greater than the positive geometric mean of a and b. Supply the reasons for the statements which are given in the following proof.

$$b > a > 0 \xrightarrow{\text{(1)}} b - a > 0 \xrightarrow{\text{(2)}} b^2 - 2\,ab + a^2 > 0 \xrightarrow{\text{(3)}} b^2 + 2\,ab + a^2 >$$

$$4\,ab \xrightarrow{\text{(4)}} (b+a)^2 > 4\,ab \xrightarrow{\text{(5)}} (b+a) > 2\sqrt{ab} \xrightarrow{\text{(6)}} \frac{b+a}{2} > \sqrt{ab}.$$

12. Find the sum of the terms of the infinite progression $\dfrac{1}{10}, \dfrac{2}{10^2}, \dfrac{3}{10^3}, \cdots,$

$\dfrac{n}{10^n}, \cdots.$ *Hint.* $\dfrac{1}{10} + \dfrac{2}{10^2} + \dfrac{3}{10^3} + \cdots + \dfrac{n}{10^n} + \cdots = \left(\dfrac{1}{10} + \dfrac{1}{10^2} + \dfrac{1}{10^3} + \right.$

$\left. \cdots + \dfrac{1}{10^n} + \cdots \right) + \left(\dfrac{1}{10^2} + \dfrac{1}{10^3} + \dfrac{1}{10^4} + \cdots + \dfrac{1}{10^n} + \cdots \right) + \left(\dfrac{1}{10^3} + \right.$

$\dfrac{1}{10^4} + \dfrac{1}{10^5} + \cdots + \dfrac{1}{10^n} + \cdots \Big) + \left(\dfrac{1}{10^4} + \dfrac{1}{10^5} + \dfrac{1}{10^6} + \cdots + \dfrac{1}{10^n} + \cdots \right)$

13. If $0 < x < 1$, find the sum of the terms of the infinite progression $1, 3\,x,$ $5\,x^2, 7\,x^3, \cdots, (2\,n - 1)\,x^{n-1}, \cdots.$

The Binomial Theorem

Consider the following array:

$(x + y)^0 = 1$
$(x + y)^1 = 1\,x + 1\,y$
$(x + y)^2 = 1\,x^2 + 2\,xy + 1\,y^2$
$(x + y)^3 = 1\,x^3 + 3\,x^2y + 3\,xy^2 + 1\,y^3$
$(x + y)^4 = 1\,x^4 + 4\,x^3y + 6\,x^2y^2 + 4\,xy^3 + 1\,y^4$
$(x + y)^5 = 1\,x^5 + 5\,x^4y + 10\,x^3y^2 + 10\,x^2y^3 + 5\,xy^4 + 1\,y^5$

$$\begin{array}{ccccccccc} \cdot & \cdot & \cdot & \cdot & \cdot & \cdot & \cdot & \cdot & \cdot \\ \cdot & \cdot & \cdot & \cdot & \cdot & \cdot & \cdot & \cdot & \cdot \\ \cdot & \cdot & \cdot & \cdot & \cdot & \cdot & \cdot & \cdot & \cdot \end{array}$$

We can continue using the procedure for multiplying polynomials to extend this sequence of equations as far as we choose. Thus:

$$(x + y)^6 = (x + y)(x + y)^5$$
$$= 1\,x^6 + 5\,x^5y + 10\,x^4y^2 + 10\,x^3y^3 + 5\,x^2y^4 + 1\,xy^5 +$$
$$1\,x^5y + 5\,x^4y^2 + 10\,x^3y^3 + 10\,x^2y^4 + 5\,xy^5 + 1\,y^6$$
$$= 1\,x^6 + 6\,x^5y + 15\,x^4y^2 + 20\,x^3y^3 + 15\,x^2y^4 + 6\,xy^5 + 1y^6$$

Proceeding in this way we can obtain an expression (expansion) for each higher power of the binomial $(x + y)$ in a step-by-step fashion. However, we would like a general formula for the expansion of $(x + y)^n$ when $n \, \epsilon \, C$ which would enable us to expand $(x + y)^7$, for example, without having to obtain all of the preceding expansions. Moreover, we would like a general formula for each term in this expansion. With this end in view, we study the preceding expansions and make the following observations:

1. The number of terms in the expansion of $(x + y)^n$ is $n + 1$.
2. The coefficient of the first term in the expansion is 1.
3. The exponent for x is n in the first term and decreases by one in each succeeding term; the exponent for y is 0 in the first term and increases by one in each succeeding term. (The sum of the exponents for x and y in any term is n.)
4. The coefficient of any term after the first is the product of the coefficient of the preceding term and the exponent of x in that term divided by the number of that term.

Using these observations we readily obtain: $(x + y)^7 = x^7 + 7\,x^6y + 21\,x^5y^2 + 35\,x^4y^3 + 35\,x^3y^4 + 21\,x^2y^5 + 7\,xy^6 + y^7$.

We generalize the preceding discussion with the following theorem, called the *binomial theorem*:

▶ **Theorem 6–14.** If $x, y \, \epsilon \, Z, n, r \, \epsilon \, C, xy \neq 0$, and $n \geq r$, then

$$(x + y)^n = x^n + nx^{n-1}y + \frac{n(n-1)}{1 \cdot 2}x^{n-2}y^2 + \frac{n(n-1)(n-2)}{1 \cdot 2 \cdot 3}x^{n-3}y^3 +$$

$$\cdots + \overbrace{\frac{n(n-1)(n-2) \cdots (n-r+1)}{\underbrace{1 \cdot 2 \cdot 3 \cdots r}_{r \text{ factors}}}}^{r \text{ factors}} x^{n-r}y^r + \cdots + y^n.$$

The conclusion of the binomial theorem is often called the *binomial formula*.

Example 1. Expand $(2a - b)^8$.

Solution. The required expansion may be obtained by substituting $2a$ for x and $-b$ for y in the binomial formula. We have:

$$(2\,a - b)^8 = [2\,a + (-\,b)]^8$$

$$= (2\,a)^8 + 8(2\,a)^7(-\,b) + \frac{8\cdot 7}{1\cdot 2}\,(2\,a)^6(-\,b)^2 +$$

$$\frac{8\cdot 7\cdot 6}{1\cdot 2\cdot 3}\,(2\,a)^5(-\,b)^3 + \frac{8\cdot 7\cdot 6\cdot 5}{1\cdot 2\cdot 3\cdot 4}\,(2\,a)^4(-\,b)^4 +$$

$$\frac{8\cdot 7\cdot 6\cdot 5\cdot 4}{1\cdot 2\cdot 3\cdot 4\cdot 5}\,(2\,a)^3(-\,b)^5 +$$

$$\frac{8\cdot 7\cdot 6\cdot 5\cdot 4\cdot 3}{1\cdot 2\cdot 3\cdot 4\cdot 5\cdot 6}\,(2\,a)^2(-\,b)^6 +$$

$$\frac{8\cdot 7\cdot 6\cdot 5\cdot 4\cdot 3\cdot 2}{1\cdot 2\cdot 3\cdot 4\cdot 5\cdot 6\cdot 7}\,(2\,a)(-\,b)^7 +$$

$$\frac{8\cdot 7\cdot 6\cdot 5\cdot 4\cdot 3\cdot 2\cdot 1}{1\cdot 2\cdot 3\cdot 4\cdot 5\cdot 6\cdot 7\cdot 8}\,(-\,b)^8$$

$$= 256\,a^8 - 1024\,a^7b + 1792\,a^6b^2 - 1792\,a^5b^3 +$$
$$1120\,a^4b^4 - 448\,a^3b^5 + 112\,a^2b^6 - 16\,ab^7 + b^8$$

In the preceding example, we observe the indicated product $8\cdot 7\cdot 6\cdot 5\cdot 4\cdot 3\cdot 2\cdot 1$ in the numerator of the term involving $(-\,b)^8$. Products such as this appear so frequently in mathematics that a special notation has been introduced for them, namely, "$n!$". Thus $8! = 8\cdot 7\cdot 6\cdot 5\cdot 4\cdot 3\cdot 2\cdot 1$. In general, if $n\,\epsilon\,C$, then $n! = n(n-1)\,(n-2)\cdots (3)\,(2)\,(1)$. The expression $n!$ is read "n factorial." The following are examples of the meaning of factorials:

$$3! = 3\cdot 2\cdot 1 = 6 \qquad 4! = 4\cdot 3\cdot 2\cdot 1 = 24 \qquad 5! = 5\cdot 4\cdot 3\cdot 2\cdot 1 = 120$$

We know that $n! = (n)\,(n-1)\,(n-2)\cdots (3)\,(2)\,(1)$. If we multiply both members of this equation by $(n+1)$, we have $(n+1)\,(n!) = (n+1)\cdot (n)\,(n-1)\,(n-2)\cdots (3)\,(2)\,(1)$. Therefore by the definition of factorial, we have $(n+1)\,(n!) = (n+1)!$.

This equation suggests a way to define $0!$. Let $n = 0$ and we have $1! = 1\cdot 0!$. Therefore, we accept the following definition: $0! = 1$.

Example 2. Evaluate the following expressions.

a. $\dfrac{800!}{798!}$ b. $\dfrac{7!}{3!\,4!}$ c. $\dfrac{3! + 5!}{(7-4)!}$ d. $\dfrac{(n+2)!}{n!}$ e. $\dfrac{(n-r+1)!}{(n-r-1)!}$

Solutions.   a. $\dfrac{800!}{798!} = \dfrac{800\cdot 799\,(798!)}{798!} = 800\times 799 = 639{,}200$

b. $\dfrac{7!}{3!\,4!} = \dfrac{7\cdot 6\cdot 5\,(4!)}{3\cdot 2\cdot 1\,(4!)} = \dfrac{7\cdot 6\cdot 5}{3\cdot 2\cdot 1} = 35$

c. $\dfrac{3! + 5!}{(7-4)!} = \dfrac{3!\,(1 + 5\cdot 4)}{3!} = 21$

d. $\dfrac{(n+2)!}{n!} = \dfrac{(n+2)\,(n+1)\,n!}{n!} = (n+2)\,(n+1)$

e. $\dfrac{(n-r+1)!}{(n-r-1)!} = \dfrac{(n-r+1)\,(n-r)[(n-r-1)!]}{(n-r-1)!}$

$$= (n-r+1)\,(n-r)$$

A **EXERCISES**

1. Using the binomial theorem, write the expansion of each of the following:

  a. $(a+b)^{10}$ **c.** $(x-5)^8$ **e.** $(b-c)^6$

  b. $(x+3)^7$ **d.** $(3\,a+2\,b)^5$ **f.** $(2\,a-3\,b)^5$

2. Evaluate each of the following:

  a. $\dfrac{19!}{16!}$ **c.** $\dfrac{1}{3!}+\dfrac{1}{5!}$ **e.** $\dfrac{15!-13!}{14!}$

  b. $\dfrac{52!}{49!\,3!}$ **d.** $\dfrac{(4+3)!}{4!\,3!}$ **f.** $\dfrac{3!\,4!}{4!-3!}$

3. Simplify:

  a. $\dfrac{(n+1)\,n\,(n-1)!}{(n+1)!}$ **e.** $\dfrac{(n!)^2}{(n+1)!\,(n-1)!}$

  b. $\dfrac{n!}{(n-2)!}$ **f.** $(n+1)\,[(n+1)!+n!]$

  c. $\dfrac{(n+3)!}{(n+2)!}$ **g.** $\dfrac{1}{(n-1)!}-\dfrac{1}{n!}$

  d. $\dfrac{(n-2)!}{(n+1)!}$ **h.** $\dfrac{(n+3)!+n!\,(n+2)}{n!\,(n+2)!}$

4. Solve for n.

  a. $n! = 720$ **c.** $n! = 930\,(n-2)!$

  b. $\dfrac{n!}{(n-2)!} = 72$ **d.** $\dfrac{(2\,n+1)!\,(2\,n-1)!}{[(2\,n)!]^2} = \dfrac{11}{10}$

B **EXERCISES**

5. Prove the identity $\dfrac{1}{(n-1)!}+\dfrac{1}{n!}=\dfrac{n+1}{n!}$.

6. For $m,\,k \,\epsilon\, C$ and $m \le k$, prove the identity:

$$\dfrac{k!}{(m-1)!\,(k-m+1)!}+\dfrac{k!}{m!\,(k-m)!}=\dfrac{(k+1)!}{m!\,(k-m+1)!}$$

7. Using Tables II and III, pages 759 and 761, find an approximation of each of the following correct to four significant digits.

  a. $10!$ **c.** $49!$ **e.** $\dfrac{98!}{43!}$ **f.** $(33!)^{\frac{1}{2}}$ **g.** $\dfrac{81!}{36!\,45!}$

  b. $32!$ **d.** $(22!)\,(41!)$

More about the Binomial Theorem

Referring to Theorem 6–14, we observe that the term involving y^r is the $(r + 1)$th term of the expansion of $(x + y)^n$.

A
If $x, y \in Z$, r, $n \in C$, $xy \neq 0$, and $n \geq r$, then the $(r + 1)$th term in the expansion of $(x + y)^n$ is $\dfrac{n(n - 1) \cdots (n - r + 1)}{r!} x^{n-r} y^r$.

The 5th term of the expansion of $(x + y)^8$ can be obtained by substituting 8 for n and 4 for r in statement **A**. Thus the 5th term in the expansion of $(x + y)^8$ is $\dfrac{8 \cdot 7 \cdot 6 \cdot 5}{4!} x^{8-4} y^4$, or $70 x^4 y^4$. The fraction $\dfrac{8 \cdot 7 \cdot 6 \cdot 5}{4!}$ can be expressed more compactly by multiplying both numerator and denominator by $4 \cdot 3 \cdot 2 \cdot 1$, or $4!$. We have:

$$\frac{8 \cdot 7 \cdot 6 \cdot 5}{4!} = \frac{8 \cdot 7 \cdot 6 \cdot 5 \cdot 4 \cdot 3 \cdot 2 \cdot 1}{4! \, 4!} = \frac{8!}{4! \, 4!}.$$

We can use the same procedure to write the coefficient $\dfrac{n(n - 1) \cdots (n - r + 1)}{r!}$ in statement **A** in a more compact form. This time we multiply both numerator and denominator by $(n - r)!$. We have:

$$\frac{n(n - 1) \cdots (n - r + 1)}{r!} =$$

$$\frac{n(n - 1) \cdots (n - r + 1) \, (n - r) \, (n - r - 1) \cdots 3 \cdot 2 \cdot 1}{r!(n - r)!} = \frac{n!}{r! \, (n - r)!}.$$

Accordingly, the coefficient of the term involving y^r in the expansion of $(x + y)^n$ is $\dfrac{n!}{r! \, (n - r)!}$. We will find it convenient to use the symbol ${}_nC_r$ to represent this coefficient. Thus ${}_8C_3 = \dfrac{8!}{3! \, 5!}$ is the coefficient of $x^5 y^3$ in the expansion of $(x + y)^8$; ${}_{11}C_8 = \dfrac{11!}{8! \, 3!}$ is the coefficient of $x^3 y^8$ in the expansion of $(x + y)^{11}$; and ${}_nC_r = \dfrac{n!}{r! \, (n - r)!}$ is the coefficient of $x^{n-r} y^r$ in the expansion of $(x + y)^n$. Using this notation, we can write the binomial formula in the following form:

B
$(x + y)^n = {}_nC_0 \, x^n y^0 + {}_nC_1 \, x^{n-1} y + {}_nC_2 \, x^{n-2} y^2 + \cdots + {}_nC_r \, x^{n-r} y^r + \cdots + {}_nC_n \, x^{n-n} y^n$ provided $n \in C$ and $xy \neq 0$.

Using the summation (sigma) notation, we may write the binomial theorem as follows:

C If $x, y \in Z, n, r \in C, xy \neq 0$, and $n \geq r$, then $(x + y)^n = \sum\limits_{r=0}^{n} {}_nC_r \, x^{n-r} \, y^r$.

We also observe that **A** can now be written somewhat more compactly as follows:

D If $x, y \in Z, n, r \in C, xy \neq 0$, and $n \geq r$, then the $(r + 1)$th term in the expansion of $(x + y)^n$ is ${}_nC_r \, x^{n-r} \, y^r$.

Example 3. Use statement **C** to expand $(2\,a - b)^8$.

Solution. Since **C** is merely another way of stating the binomial theorem, we again substitute $2\,a$ for x, $(-b)$ for y, and 8 for n. Thus

$$(2\,a - b)^8 = \sum\limits_{r=0}^{8} {}_8C_r \, (2\,a)^{8-r} (-b)^r.$$

When we expand the right member of this equation and simplify each term, we obtain the result shown in Example 1, page 741.

Example 4. **a.** Find the eleventh term in the expansion of $(2a - 1)^{13}$.
 b. Find the term involving b^3 in the expansion of $(a - 2\,b^{\frac{1}{2}})^9$.

Solutions. **a.** Let $n = 13, r = 10, x = 2\,a$, and $y = -1$ in statement **D**. The eleventh term of $(2\,a - 1)^{13} = {}_{13}C_{10} \, (2\,a)^3 (-1)^{10} = 2288\,a^3$.
 b. The required term involves $(-2\,b^{\frac{1}{2}})^6$. Therefore, let $r = 6$, $n = 9, x = a$, and $y = -2b^{\frac{1}{2}}$ in statement **D**. The required term is ${}_9C_6 \, a^3(-2\,b^{\frac{1}{2}})^6 = \dfrac{9 \cdot 8 \cdot 7}{3 \cdot 2 \cdot 1} \, a^3 \cdot 64\,b^3 = 5376\,a^3b^3.$

The coefficients in the expansions of $(x + y)^n$ shown on page 740 form the following array called Pascal's triangle.

n							
0	1						
1	1	1					
2	1	$(2 + 1) =$					
3	1	3	3	1			
4	1	4	$(6 + 4) =$	1			
5	1	5	10	10	5	1	

We see that if m_3 is the number in the array which has a number m_2 directly above it and a number m_1 directly above the number to its left, then $m_1 + m_2 = m_3$. Thus $2 + 1 = 3$ and $6 + 4 = 10$ as shown. When we express each of the numbers in Pascal's triangle in terms of "C symbols" for the coefficients in the expansion of $(x + y)^n$ and extend the table to include a line for n, we obtain the following array:

n							
0	$_0C_0$						
1	$_1C_0$	$_1C_1$					
2	$_2C_0$	$(_2C_1 + _2C_2) =$					
3	$_3C_0$	$_3C_1$	$_3C_2$	$_3C_3$			
4	$_4C_0$	$_4C_1$	$(_4C_2 + _4C_3) = _4C_4$				
5	$_5C_0$	$_5C_1$	$_5C_2$	$_5C_3$	$_5C_4$	$_5C_5$	
.	.	.	.	.	.	.	.
.	.	.	.	.	.	.	.
.	.	.	.	.	.	.	.
n	$_nC_0$	$_nC_1$	$_nC_2$			$_nC_r$	$_nC_{r+1}$

Now we see that the equations $2 + 1 = 3$ and $6 + 4 = 10$ can be written as $_2C_1 + _2C_2 = _3C_2$ and $_4C_2 + _4C_3 = _5C_3$, respectively, and in general,

E $\qquad _{n+1}C_r = {_nC_{r-1}} + {_nC_r}$

Since $_nC_r = \dfrac{n!}{r!\,(n-r)!}$, **E** can be written as:

F $\qquad \dfrac{(n+1)!}{r!\,(n-r+1)!} = \dfrac{n!}{(r-1)!\,(n-r+1)!} + \dfrac{n!}{r!\,(n-r)!}$

It can be readily shown that **F** is an identity and we have:

▷ **Theorem 7–14.** If $n, r \in C, r \leq n$, and $_nC_r = \dfrac{n!}{r!\,(n-r)!}$, then

$\qquad _{n+1}C_r = {_nC_r} + {_nC_{r-1}}.$

This theorem is known as Pascal's theorem for binomial coefficients because it was discovered by the great French mathematician Blaise Pascal.

If we expand the coefficients in formula **B**, we may write the binomial expansion in the following form:

$$(x + y)^n = x^n + nx^{n-1}y + \frac{n(n-1)}{2!}x^{n-2}y^2 + \frac{n(n-1)(n-2)}{3!}x^{n-3}y^3 + \cdots$$

If we let $x = 1$ in this formula, we obtain:

G $\qquad (1 + y)^n = 1 + ny + \dfrac{n(n-1)}{2!}y^2 + \dfrac{n(n-1)(n-2)}{3!}y^3 + \cdots$

In more advanced courses in mathematics it is proved that there are conditions under which formula **G** is valid even when n is not a counting number. For example, **G** is valid for any rational number n when $|y| < 1$. In fact, if $n \in Q \smallfrown W, y \in R$, and $|y| < 1$, the right member of **G** is a convergent infinite series whose "sum" is the left member of **G**.

Example 5. Expand $(1 - x)^{-1}$ by using statement **G**.

Solution. We substitute $-x$ for y and -1 for n.

$$(1 - x)^{-1} = [1 + (-x)]^{-1}$$

$$= 1 + (-1)(-x) + \frac{(-1)(-2)}{2!}(-x)^2 +$$

$$\frac{(-1)(-2)(-3)}{3!}(-x)^3 + \cdots$$

$$\therefore (1 - x)^{-1} = 1 + x + x^2 + x^3 + \cdots.$$

If $|x| < 1$, the right member of this equation is an infinite geometric series whose sum is $\dfrac{1}{1 - x}$ according to Theorem 5–14. It is also noteworthy that this expansion for $(1 - x)^{-1}$ can be obtained as follows: $1 \div (1 - x) = 1 + x + x^2 + \cdots$

Example 6. Use statement **G** to find $\sqrt{10}$ to the nearest thousandth.

Solution. $\sqrt{10} = (9 + 1)^{\frac{1}{2}} = [9(1 + \frac{1}{9})]^{\frac{1}{2}} = 9^{\frac{1}{2}}(1 + \frac{1}{9})^{\frac{1}{2}} = 3(1 + \frac{1}{9})^{\frac{1}{2}}$

$$(1 + \tfrac{1}{9})^{\frac{1}{2}} \approx 1^{\frac{1}{2}} + \tfrac{1}{2} \cdot 1^{-\frac{1}{2}} \cdot \tfrac{1}{9} + \frac{\frac{1}{2} \cdot (-\frac{1}{2})}{2!} \cdot 1^{-\frac{3}{2}} \frac{1}{9^2} +$$

$$\frac{\frac{1}{2}(-\frac{1}{2})(-\frac{3}{2})}{3!} 1^{-\frac{5}{2}} \cdot \frac{1}{9^3} + \cdots$$

$$(1 + \tfrac{1}{9})^{\frac{1}{2}} \approx 1 + \frac{1}{18} - \frac{1}{648} + \frac{1}{11664} - \cdots$$

$$(1 + \tfrac{1}{9})^{\frac{1}{2}} \approx 1 + 0.0555 - 0.0015 + 0.0001$$

$$(1 + \tfrac{1}{9})^{\frac{1}{2}} \approx 1.0541$$

$$\therefore \sqrt{10} = 3(1 + \tfrac{1}{9})^{\frac{1}{2}} \approx 3.162$$

Observe that in order to get the answer correct to three decimal places we retained four decimal places until the final step.

Example 7. Use DeMoivre's theorem, the corollary to Theorem 6–11, and the binomial theorem to obtain an expression for $\cos 5\,\theta$ in terms of $\sin \theta$ and $\cos \theta$.

Solution. By DeMoivre's theorem $(\cos \theta + i \sin \theta)^5 = \cos 5\,\theta + i \sin 5\,\theta$.
By the binomial theorem:

$$(\cos \theta + i \sin \theta)^5 = \cos^5 \theta + 5 \cos^4 \theta \cdot i \sin \theta +$$
$$10 \cos^3 \theta \, i^2 \sin^2 \theta + 10 \cos^2 \theta \, i^3 \sin^3 \theta +$$
$$5 \cos \theta \cdot i^4 \sin^4 \theta + i^5 \sin^5 \theta$$
$$= (\cos^5 \theta - 10 \cos^3 \theta \sin^2 \theta + 5 \cos \theta \sin^4 \theta) +$$
$$i(5 \cos^4 \theta \sin \theta - 10 \cos^2 \theta \sin^3 \theta + \sin^5\theta)$$
$$\therefore \cos 5\,\theta = \cos^5 \theta - 10 \cos^3 \theta \sin^2 \theta + 5 \cos \theta \sin^4 \theta$$

1. Using statement **B**, page 744, write the expansion of each of the following:

   a. $(a + b)^6$ **d.** $(2a + b)^5$ **g.** $(y + \frac{1}{2})^5$

   b. $(a - b)^5$ **e.** $(x - 6)^6$ **h.** $(a - bc)^4$

   c. $(x + 5)^7$ **f.** $(3u + v)^7$ **i.** $(2a + 3b)^4$

2. Expand $(a + b + c)^5$ by writing it as $[a + (b + c)]^5$ before expanding.

3. Expand each of the following:

   a. $(3x + y + z)^6$ **b.** $(r - s - t)^5$ **c.** $(a - 2x + 1)^4$

4. How many terms are there in the expansion of each of the following?

   a. $(a - 4b)^{75}$ **b.** $(x - 3)^{18}$ **c.** $(2a + \sqrt{b})^{25}$

5. If the expansion of $(a + b)^n$ has exactly one middle term, what must be true of n?

6. Find the required term without expanding the binomial expression. Simplify the expression you obtain.

   a. The fourth term of $(a + 8)^{12}$

   b. The sixth term of $\left(\dfrac{x}{3} - \dfrac{y}{4}\right)^{10}$

   c. The fifth term of $(\sqrt{a} - 3)^{11}$; $a > 0$

   d. The seventh term of $(i + 2)^{10}$; $i = \sqrt{-1}$

   e. The fifteenth term of $(a + b)^{25}$

   f. The eighth term of $(3 + \sqrt{5})^{10}$

7. Find the term in the expansion of $(a + b)^{10}$ which contains b^8.

8. Find the term in the expansion of $(x^2 - y)^8$ containing x^{12}.

9. Find the term in the expansion of $\left(\dfrac{1}{\sqrt{2}} + \sqrt{b}\right)^4$ which has b^2 as a factor.

10. Write the binomial expansion of each of the following.

   a. $\begin{vmatrix} a & 2 \\ 3 & b \end{vmatrix}^5$ **b.** $\begin{vmatrix} 4 & x \\ x & 2 \end{vmatrix}^6$ **c.** $\begin{vmatrix} \sqrt{3} & x \\ x & \sqrt{3} \end{vmatrix}^4$

11. Find the numerical value of each of the following to the nearest thousandth.

   a. 0.99^6 **b.** $(1.03)^{11}$ **c.** $(2.01)^8$ **d.** $\sqrt{5}$ **e.** $\sqrt{17}$ **f.** $\sqrt[3]{28}$

12. If $i = \sqrt{-1}$, evaluate:

   a. $(1 - i)^6$ **b.** $(2 + i)^7$ **c.** $(\frac{1}{2} + \frac{3}{2}i)^4$

13. Use DeMoivre's theorem and the binomial theorem to obtain an expression for $\sin 6\theta$ in terms of $\sin\theta$ and $\cos\theta$.

Before you leave this chapter make sure that you

1. Know what we mean by a sequence of numbers, can establish such sequences, and can determine particular terms in an established sequence. (Pages 720–721.)

2. Know what we mean by a series of numbers, by a finite series, by an infinite series, and can use $\sum\limits_{i=k}^{n} t_i$ (summation notation) to represent a finite series. (Pages 721–722.)

3. Know when a sequence of numbers is an arithmetic progression, know and can use the formula for finding any specific term of such a progression, and know and can use the formula for finding the sum of a finite number of terms of such a progression. (Pages 724–726.)

4. Know when a sequence of numbers is a geometric progression, know and can use the formula for finding any specific term of such a sequence, and know and can use the formula for finding the sum of a finite number of terms of such a progression. (Pages 730–732.)

5. Understand and can use the principles concerning limits of sequences given in this chapter. (Pages 734–736.)

6. Know what we mean by the sum of the terms of an infinite geometric series and can find such a sum. (Pages 737–738.)

7. Know how to expand $(x + y)^n$ using the binomial formula. (Pages 741–742.)

8. Understand the use of factorial and $_nC_r$ notation to represent the coefficients of the expansion of $(x + y)^n$. (Pages 744–747.)

9. Understand the meaning of, can spell, and can use correctly the following words and phrases.

arithmetic means (Page 725.)   index of summation (Page 722.)
binomial theorem (Page 741.)   Pascal's theorem (Page 746.)
convergent series (Page 737.)   Pascal's triangle (Page 745.)
divergent series (Page 737.)   recursion formula (Page 720.)
factorial (Page 742.)   sequence function (Page 720.)
geometric means (Page 731.)   series (Page 721.)
harmonic progression (Page 727.)   summation notation (Page 722.)

1. Write the first six terms of the sequence whose first term t_1 is -3 and whose recursion formula is $t_{n+1} = 2 t_n + 1$.

2. Write the first four terms of the sequence whose first term is 5 and whose recursion formula is $t_{n+1} = (t_n)^2 + 3$.

3. Express the following sequence by means of a formula: $1, \frac{1}{4}, \frac{1}{9}, \frac{1}{16}, \cdots$.

4. Write the first three terms and the thirteenth term of the sequence defined by the formula $t_n = (i + 1)^n$ where $i = \sqrt{-1}$ and t_n is the nth term.

5. Write the twentieth term of the sequence defined by the formula $t_n = 3 n^2 - 1$ and t_n is the nth term.

6. Write an expression for the nth term of the sequence $\frac{1}{9}, \frac{1}{16}, \frac{1}{25}, \cdots$ in terms of n.

7. Write the series designated by each of the following symbols.

a. $\displaystyle\sum_{k=2}^{10} k^3$

b. $\displaystyle\sum_{j=1}^{8} 2 j + 3$

c. $\displaystyle\sum_{k=1}^{10} k^2 - 1$

d. $\displaystyle\sum_{k=1}^{8} (-1)^k$

e. $\displaystyle\sum_{k=0}^{4} (-2)^k$

f. $\displaystyle\sum_{j=1}^{\infty} \frac{1}{j^3}$

g. $\displaystyle\sum_{j=1}^{5} j^2 + 3 j$

h. $\displaystyle\sum_{k=1}^{n} k(k + 1)$

i. $\displaystyle\sum_{k=1}^{n+1} \frac{2 k + 1}{k}$

8. Find the sum of the series indicated by $\displaystyle\sum_{k=1}^{6} 4 k$.

9. Which of the following sequences are arithmetic progressions, which are geometric progressions, and which are neither?

a. $5, 10, 15, 20, \cdots$

b. $5, 25, 125, \cdots$

c. $5, 30, 55, \cdots$

d. $3^2, 4^2, 5^2, \cdots$

e. $\frac{1}{3}, \frac{5}{6}, \frac{4}{3}, \cdots$

f. $1 \cdot 2, 2 \cdot 3, 3 \cdot 4, \cdots$

g. $\sqrt{3}, 3, 3\sqrt{3}, \cdots$

h. $\dfrac{1 + a}{2}, \dfrac{1 + 2 a}{2}, \dfrac{1 + 3 a}{2}, \cdots$

10. For what value(s) of b does each of the following form an arithmetic progression?

a. $-8, -11, b, \cdots$

b. $b, \dfrac{1}{m}, \dfrac{3}{m}, \cdots$

c. $x + 6, x^2, b, \cdots$

11. For what value(s) of b does each of the sequences of Ex. 10 form a geometric progression?

12. Find the required term for each of the given arithmetic progressions.

a. The 20th term of $-11, -8, -5, \cdots$

b. The 16th term of $4, 7, 10, \cdots$

c. The 10th term of $3.2, 3.8, 4.4, \cdots$

13. For what value of k do the terms $5 - 2k$, $k + 6$, and $5k + 8$ form an arithmetic progression?

14. Which term of the progression 28, 20, 12, $\cdots$ is $- 132$?

15. Find the sum of the first thirty terms of the arithmetic progression 10, 22, 34, $\cdots$.

16. Find the sum of the first 71 terms of the arithmetic progression 9, $8\frac{1}{2}$, 8, $\cdots$.

17. The sum of the first n terms of the arithmetic progression 15, 12, 9, $\cdots$ is $- 783$. What number is represented by n?

18. Find four arithmetic means between $- 2$ and 28.

19. Find three arithmetic means between $1\frac{1}{2}$ and $10\frac{1}{2}$.

20. Find the arithmetic mean of $\sqrt{2}$ and $(\sqrt{2} + 6)$.

21. The fourth term of an arithmetic progression is $- 3$ and the twelfth term is 37. Find the sum of the first twenty terms of the progression.

22. Find the required term of each of the following geometric progressions.
   a. The ninth term of 3, $- 6$, 12, $\cdots$
   b. The tenth term of $\sqrt{a + 1}$, $a + 1$, $(a + 1)\sqrt{a + 1}$, $\cdots$, if $a > 0$
   c. The eighth term of 2, 0.2, 0.02, $\cdots$

23. Insert six geometric means between 2 and 256.

24. Insert three geometric means between $\sqrt{3}$ and $3\sqrt{3}$.

25. Find the positive geometric mean and the negative geometric mean for each of the following:
   a. $\frac{1}{9}$ and 27   **b.** 100 and 200   **c.** m and $2n$; $mn > 0$

26. Find the sum of the first nine terms of the geometric progression $- 8$, 4, $- 2$, $\cdots$.

27. Find the sum of the first seven terms of the progression 3, $- 6$, 12, $\cdots$.

28. The sixth term of a geometric progression is $- \frac{1}{2}$ and the ninth term is $- \frac{1}{16}$. What is the sum of the first nine terms of the progression? What is the sum of all of the terms of the progression?

29. Describe the behavior of each of the following as n increases without bound.

   a. $9n$ **d.** $\dfrac{n}{4n + 1}$ **g.** $\dfrac{3n - 5}{2n + 1}$

   b. n^2 **e.** $\sqrt{n}$; $n > 0$ **h.** $\dfrac{n + 2}{n^2}$

   c. $\dfrac{1}{3^n}$ **f.** $\left(\dfrac{2}{3}\right)^n$

30. Which of the following sequences are convergent?

a. $1, 4, 16, \cdots$ **d.** $\frac{1}{2}, \frac{1}{4}, \frac{1}{8}, \cdots$ **g.** $\frac{5}{2}, \frac{5}{6}, \frac{5}{18}, \cdots$

b. $-12, -36, -72, \cdots$ **e.** $\frac{1}{8}, \frac{1}{4}, \frac{1}{2}, \cdots$ **h.** $1 \cdot 2, 2 \cdot 3, 3 \cdot 4, \cdots$

c. $-12, -6, -3, \cdots$ **f.** $1^2, 3^2, 5^2, \cdots$

31. Find each of the following limits if a limit exists.

a. $\displaystyle\lim_{n\to\infty} \frac{5n+3}{4n}$ **c.** $\displaystyle\lim_{n\to\infty} \frac{n^2+3n+2}{3n^2}$ **e.** $\displaystyle\lim_{n\to\infty} \frac{2n^2-5n}{3n+1}$

b. $\displaystyle\lim_{n\to\infty} \frac{n^2+3n+2}{n^2}$ **d.** $\displaystyle\lim_{n\to\infty} \left(\frac{2}{n}-\frac{1}{n^2}\right)$ **f.** $\displaystyle\lim_{n\to\infty} \frac{n^2-2n+1}{n^2+2n+1}$

32. Find the sum of the terms in each of the following infinite geometric series.

a. $9 + \frac{9}{2} + \frac{9}{4} + \cdots$ **d.** $1 + \frac{2}{3} + \frac{4}{9} + \cdots$

b. $18 + 6 + 2 + \cdots$ **e.** $-8 + (-4) + (-2) + \cdots$

c. $18 + (-6) + 2 + \cdots$ **f.** $1 + 0.1 + 0.01 + 0.001 + \cdots$

33. Write each of the following in the form $\frac{a}{b}$ when $a, b \in I$ and $b \neq 0$.

a. $0.\dot{8}$ **c.** $6.1\dot{4}\dot{2}$ **e.** $0.3\dot{4}\dot{2}$ **g.** $904.\dot{6}$

b. $0.\dot{3}\dot{1}$ **d.** $8.\dot{2}\dot{1}\dot{0}$ **f.** $2.64\dot{3}\dot{1}\dot{2}$ **h.** $726.5\dot{1}5\dot{4}6\dot{5}$

34. Evaluate each of the following:

a. $\dfrac{22!}{19!}$ **b.** $\dfrac{26! - 24!}{25!}$ **c.** $\dfrac{1}{6!} + \dfrac{1}{8!}$ **d.** $\dfrac{(4+6)!}{4! \, 6!}$

35. Simplify:

a. $\dfrac{n!}{(n+2)!}$ **b.** $\dfrac{[(n+1)!]^2}{n! \, (n-1)!}$ **c.** $\dfrac{(n+2)! \, (n-1)!}{n! \, (n+1)!}$

36. Write the expansion of each of the following:

a. $(a+b)^7$ **b.** $(x-4)^4$ **c.** $(2a+3b)^6$ **d.** $\left(\dfrac{x}{2}-\dfrac{y}{3}\right)^5$

37. Find the required term without expanding the binomial expression.

a. The sixth term of $\left(\dfrac{x}{2}-\dfrac{y}{5}\right)^{13}$

b. The seventh term of $(i+3)^{15}$; $i = \sqrt{-1}$

1. Write the first four terms of the sequence whose first term is 3 and whose recursion formula is $t_{n+1} = 2 t_n + 10$.

2. Write the series designated by $\displaystyle\sum_{k=1}^{8} \frac{k^2}{2}$.

3. What can be the value(s) of b if the sequence $-9, -3, b, \cdots$ is an arithmetic progression?

4. What can be the value(s) of b if the sequence $-9, -3, b, \cdots$ is a geometric progression?

5. What is the twentieth term of the arithmetic progression $-11, -5, 1, \cdots$?

6. What is the sum of the first twenty-four terms of the progression $-8, -6, -4, \cdots$?

7. What is the sixth term of the geometric progression $3, 9, 27, \cdots$?

8. What is the sum of the first eight terms of the progression in Ex. 7?

9. Which of the following sequences are convergent?

    a. $9, 3, 1, \cdots$ **b.** $1, 2, 4, \cdots$ **c.** $\frac{2}{3}, \frac{2}{6}, \frac{2}{9}, \cdots$ **d.** $1^2, 3^2, 5^2, \cdots$

10. Evaluate $\displaystyle\lim_{n\to\infty} \frac{n^2 + 5n + 6}{n^2}$.

11. What is the sum of all of the terms of $20, 5, \frac{5}{4}, \cdots$?

12. Express $0.41 2 \dot{5} \dot{6}$ as the indicated quotient of two nonzero integers.

13. A clock strikes each hour (once at one o'clock, twice at two o'clock, and so on). It also strikes once at a quarter after the hour, twice at the half hour, and three times at a quarter before the next hour. How many times does the clock strike in 24 hours?

14. Expand $(2a - b)^5$.

15. Expand $(a + x + y)^3$.

16. What is the middle term of the expansion of $(x + 4y)^{12}$?

1. Use graphs to show the solution set of each of the following systems of open sentences.

a. $\begin{cases} x + 3\,y > 4 \\ 2\,x - 5\,y > 10 \end{cases}$
b. $\begin{cases} y > 3\,x^2 + 4 \\ y < 6 \end{cases}$
c. $\begin{cases} x^2 + 3\,y^2 = 9 \\ x^2 + y^2 = 4 \end{cases}$

2. Which of the following statements are true?

a. $\begin{cases} x + 2\,y = 7 \\ 4\,x - 3\,y = 6 \end{cases} \longleftrightarrow \begin{cases} x = 3 \\ y = 2 \end{cases}$
c. $\begin{cases} \dfrac{y}{x-4} = 3 \\ x = 4 \end{cases} \longleftrightarrow \begin{cases} y = 3\,x - 12 \\ x = 4 \end{cases}$

b. $\begin{cases} x + 2\,y = 5 \\ 2\,x + 3\,y = 8 \end{cases} \longleftrightarrow \begin{cases} 2\,x + 4\,y = 10 \\ 2\,x + 3\,y = 8 \end{cases}$
d. $\begin{cases} -2\,x < 6\,y \\ y = 2 \end{cases} \longleftrightarrow \begin{cases} x < -3\,y \\ y = 2 \end{cases}$

3. Use the multiplication-addition method to solve each of the following systems.

a. $\begin{cases} 2\,x + 5\,y = -4 \\ 3\,x - 2\,y = 13 \end{cases}$
b. $\begin{cases} \frac{2}{3}\,x + \frac{1}{2}\,y = 6 \\ \frac{1}{6}\,x + \frac{1}{4}\,y = 2 \end{cases}$
c. $\begin{cases} x - 2\,y = 6 \\ 4\,x + 6\,y = 17 \end{cases}$

4. Use the substitution method to solve each of the following systems.

a. $\begin{cases} 3\,x - 2\,y = 13 \\ 2\,x + y = 18 \end{cases}$
b. $\begin{cases} \frac{1}{2}\,x + y = -5 \\ \frac{2}{3}\,x - y = 12 \end{cases}$
c. $\begin{cases} 4\,x + 3\,y = 3 \\ x + \frac{1}{2}\,y = \frac{5}{3} \end{cases}$

5. Solve by means of determinants.

a. $\begin{cases} x + 3\,y = -1 \\ 2\,x + 5\,y = 1 \end{cases}$
b. $\begin{cases} 0.5\,x + 0.3\,y = 7.4 \\ 0.2\,x - 0.5\,y = -2.0 \end{cases}$
c. $\begin{cases} 2\,x + y = 6 \\ 3\,x - 2\,y = 30 \end{cases}$

6. Classify each of the following systems as dependent, independent, or inconsistent.

a. $\begin{cases} 2\,x - 4\,y = 6 \\ x - y = 2 \end{cases}$
b. $\begin{cases} x + 3\,y = -1 \\ 2\,x + 6\,y = 2 \end{cases}$
c. $\begin{cases} 2\,x + 4\,y = 14 \\ 3\,x + 6\,y = 21 \end{cases}$

7. **a.** Draw a diagram which shows the location of the point $P\,(2, 4, 0)$, and the point $Q\,(0, 8, 3)$ in three-dimensional space.
   b. Find $|\,PQ\,|$.

8. Find the equation of the plane each of whose points is equidistant from the two points $P\,(1, 5, 3)$ and $Q\,(4, -3, -2)$.

9. Sketch the graph of the solution set of each of the following equations.

   a. $x + 4\,y + 2\,z = 8$
   b. $\dfrac{x+y}{2} + z = 3$
   c. $z = 4$

10. In each of the following cases state whether the two equations of the given system have graphs that are the same plane, planes that are parallel, or planes that intersect in a line.

a. $\begin{cases} 2x+4y+6z=14 \\ 3x+6y+9z=21 \end{cases}$ b. $\begin{cases} 2x+3y+4z=5 \\ 4x+6y+8z=12 \end{cases}$ c. $\begin{cases} x+4y+5z=-1 \\ 5x+y-3z=13 \end{cases}$

11. Find the equation of the plane W which contains the point P $(1,0,2)$ and the line of intersection of the planes M and N whose equations are respectively $3x+2y-z=10$ and $4x-y-3z=-2$.

12. Solve the system in part **a** by the triangulation method and the system in part **b** by determinants.

a. $\begin{cases} 3x+y+z=4 \\ 2x-y-4z=3 \\ x-5y-7z=10 \end{cases}$ b. $\begin{cases} 4x-y+z=3 \\ x-3y+2z=4 \\ 3x+2y-4z=11 \end{cases}$

13. Describe the relationships between the graphs of the component equations in each of the following systems.

a. $\begin{cases} x+2y-z=9 \\ 2x+4y-2z=27 \\ 4x-y+z=17 \end{cases}$ b. $\begin{cases} 2x+y-z=2 \\ 4x+2y-2z=4 \\ 6x+3y-3z=6 \end{cases}$ c. $\begin{cases} 2x+y-z=2 \\ 4x+2y-2z=4 \\ x+\frac{1}{2}y-\frac{1}{2}z=3 \end{cases}$

14. Without drawing the graph identify each of the following as an equation whose graph is a circle, a parabola, an ellipse, a hyperbola, a pair of straight lines, a line, or a point.

a. $3x^2+5y^2=15$ d. $(x-y+1)^2=0$ g. $x^2+y^2=0$

b. $x^2-2y^2=8$ e. $3x^2-3y^2=12$ h. $xy=8$

c. $x-2y^2=8$ f. $\dfrac{x^2}{3}+\dfrac{y^2}{3}=1$ i. $\dfrac{x^2}{4}-\dfrac{y}{4}=1$

15. Draw the graph of each of the following equations. In each case state the measures of the major and minor axes and the coordinates of the vertices.

a. $\dfrac{x^2}{3^2}+\dfrac{y^2}{6^2}=1$ b. $4x^2+9y^2=36$ c. $5(x-4)^2+2(y-1)^2=40$

16. Draw the graph of each of the following equations. In each case state the coordinates of the vertices and the equations of the asymptotes.

a. $9y^2-16x^2=144$ b. $16x^2-9y^2=144$ c. $\dfrac{(x-3)^2}{4}-\dfrac{y^2}{25}=1$

17. Solve each of the following systems.

a. $\begin{cases} x^2+4y^2=32 \\ y=-\frac{1}{2}x+4 \end{cases}$ d. $\begin{cases} 6x^2-3y^2=12 \\ 4x^2-2y^2=8 \end{cases}$

b. $\begin{cases} y=\frac{1}{4}x^2 \\ (x-y-1)(x-y+8)=0 \end{cases}$ e. $\begin{cases} xy=8 \\ \dfrac{1}{x}-\dfrac{1}{y}=\dfrac{1}{4} \end{cases}$

c. $\begin{cases} 4x^2-y^2=15 \\ 4x^2+y^2=65 \end{cases}$ f. $\begin{cases} xy-y^2=-24 \\ 2x^2+xy-y^2=-16 \end{cases}$

18. Which of the following are arithmetic progressions, which are geometric progressions and which are neither of these?

   a. $-7, -3, 1, 5, \cdots$

   b. $\frac{1}{4}, -\frac{1}{2}, 1, -2, \cdots$

   c. $1, 3, 5, 7, \cdots$

   d. $1, \frac{1}{3}, \frac{1}{5}, \frac{1}{7}, \cdots$

   e. $1, 4, 9, 16, \cdots$

   f. $2, 4, 8, 16, \cdots$

19. The third term of an arithmetic progression is 7 and the seventh term is 19. Find the first term, the fifth term, and the sum of the first nine terms.

20. Insert four arithmetic means between $\frac{1}{2}$ and $\frac{3}{4}$.

21. Evaluate each of the following:

   a. $\displaystyle\sum_{k=1}^{12} 2k - 1$

   b. $\displaystyle\sum_{k=0}^{20} 2(k+1) - 3$

22. **a.** Find the eighth term of the geometric progression $\frac{3}{4}, \frac{3}{2}, 3, \cdots$.

   b. Find the sum of the first eight terms of the progression in part **a**.

23. Which term of the progression $9, -2.7, 0.81, \cdots$ is .0729?

24. Insert three geometric means between $\sqrt{3}$ and $4\sqrt{3}$.

25. Describe the behavior of each of the following as n increases without bound.

   a. $\dfrac{1}{2n}$

   b. $4 + \dfrac{1}{n^2}$

   c. $\dfrac{n+1}{n}$

   d. $(\frac{1}{2})^n$

26. Which of the following sequences are convergent?

   a. $3, 6, 9, \cdots, 3n, \cdots$

   b. $\dfrac{1}{3}, \dfrac{1}{6}, \dfrac{1}{9}, \cdots, \dfrac{1}{3n}, \cdots$

   c. $\dfrac{1}{2}, \dfrac{2}{3}, \dfrac{3}{4}, \cdots, \dfrac{n}{n+1}, \cdots$

27. Find the sum of each of the following infinite geometric series.

   a. $9, 3, 1, \cdots$

   b. $12, 6, 3, \cdots$

   c. $1, .01, .0001, \cdots$

28. Express each of the following as the indicated quotient of two nonzero integers.

   a. $0.\dot{4}$

   b. $0.\dot{1}2\dot{5}$

   c. $3.04\dot{2}$

   d. $15.9\dot{5}\dot{2}$

29. Evaluate each of the following:

   a. $\dfrac{25!}{23!}$

   b. $\dfrac{1}{4!} + \dfrac{1}{5!}$

   c. $\dfrac{4! \, 5!}{4! + 3!}$

   d. $\dfrac{1}{100!} + \dfrac{1}{99!}$

30. Solve for n.

   a. $\dfrac{n!}{(n-2)!} = 600$

   b. $(n+3)! = 107[(n+2)!]$

   c. $n! + (n+1)! = 6(n!)$

31. Write the expansion of each of the following:

   a. $(x-5)^7$

   b. $(2a + 3b)^5$

   c. $\left(\dfrac{1}{x} + \dfrac{1}{2}\right)^6$

32. Find the required term of each of the following:

   a. The fourth term of $(a+9)^{11}$

   b. The eighth term of $(x^2 - 2y)^{10}$

1. Solve by determinants: $\begin{cases} 3x - 2y = 4 \\ 7x - 8y = 6 \end{cases}$

2. Find the distance between the points $P(3, -2, 5)$ and $Q(6, 4, -1)$.

3. Sketch the plane which is the graph of the solution set of $x + y + 2z = 4$.

4. Sketch the graph of $\dfrac{x^2}{25} + \dfrac{y^2}{36} = 1$.

5. Write the equations of the asymptotes of the graph of $\dfrac{x^2}{25} - \dfrac{y^2}{36} = 1$.

6. Solve $\begin{cases} x^2 + y^2 = 36 \\ x + y = 10 \end{cases}$ when $x, y \in Z$.

7. Solve $\begin{cases} x^2 - xy = 24 \\ y - x^2 + xy = -29 \end{cases}$ when $x, y \in Z$.

8. Use graphing to show the solution set of $\begin{cases} x^2 - y^2 = 6 \\ x^2 + y^2 = 25 \end{cases}$.

9. Find the eighteenth term of the arithmetic progression $-5, -3, -1, \cdots$.

10. What is the sum of the first eighteen terms of the arithmetic progression in Ex. 9?

11. Complete: The twelfth term of the geometric progression $4, \dfrac{4}{3}, \dfrac{4}{9}, \cdots$ is $\dfrac{4}{3^n}$ where $n = \_\_?\_\_$.

12. Insert two geometric means between $\sqrt{3}$ and 9.

13. Find the sum of the infinite geometric series $10, 5, \frac{5}{2}, \cdots$.

14. Write $6.7\overset{..}{1}\overset{..}{2}$ in the form $\dfrac{a}{b}$ where $a, b \in I$ and $b \neq 0$.

15. Expand $(a^2 - 3)^7$.

Rules for Rounding Numbers

1. If the first digit to the right of the last digit to be retained is greater than 5, increase the preceding digit by one.

2. If the first digit to the right of the last digit to be retained is less than 5, leave the preceding digit unchanged.

3. If the first digit to the right of the last digit to be retained is 5 and any digit to the right of this 5 is non-zero, increase by one the last digit to be retained. When the digits to the right of the 5 are zero, increase by one the last digit to be retained if it is an odd integer and leave it unchanged if it is an even integer.

Table I. Square Roots, Squares

n	$\sqrt{n}$	n^2	n	$\sqrt{n}$	n^2	n	$\sqrt{n}$	n^2
1	1.0000	1	34	5.8310	1 156	67	8.1854	4 489
2	1.4142	4	35	5.9161	1 225	68	8.2462	4 624
3	1.7320	9	36	6.0000	1 296	69	8.3066	4 761
4	2.0000	16	37	6.0828	1 369	70	8.3666	4 900
5	2.2361	25	38	6.1644	1 444	71	8.4261	5 041
6	2.4495	36	39	6.2450	1 521	72	8.4853	5 184
7	2.6458	49	40	6.3246	1 600	73	8.5440	5 329
8	2.8284	64	41	6.4031	1 681	74	8.6023	5 476
9	3.0000	81	42	6.4807	1 764	75	8.6602	5 625
10	3.1623	100	43	6.5574	1 849	76	8.7178	5 776
11	3.3166	121	44	6.6332	1 936	77	8.7750	5 929
12	3.4641	144	45	6.7082	2 025	78	8.8318	6 084
13	3.6056	169	46	6.7823	2 116	79	8.8882	6 241
14	3.7417	196	47	6.8556	2 209	80	8.9443	6 400
15	3.8730	225	48	6.9282	2 304	81	9.0000	6 561
16	4.0000	256	49	7.0000	2 401	82	9.0554	6 724
17	4.1231	289	50	7.0711	2 500	83	9.1104	6 889
18	4.2426	324	51	7.1414	2 601	84	9.1652	7 056
19	4.3589	361	52	7.2111	2 704	85	9.2195	7 225
20	4.4721	400	53	7.2801	2 809	86	9.2736	7 396
21	4.5826	441	54	7.3485	2 916	87	9.3274	7 569
22	4.6904	484	55	7.4162	3 025	88	9.3808	7 744
23	4.7958	529	56	7.4833	3 136	89	9.4340	7 921
24	4.8990	576	57	7.5498	3 249	90	9.4868	8 100
25	5.0000	625	58	7.6158	3 364	91	9.5394	8 281
26	5.0990	676	59	7.6811	3 481	92	9.5917	8 464
27	5.1962	729	60	7.7460	3 600	93	9.6436	8 649
28	5.2915	784	61	7.8102	3 721	94	9.6954	8 836
29	5.3852	841	62	7.8740	3 844	95	9.7468	9 025
30	5.4772	900	63	7.9373	3 969	96	9.7980	9 216
31	5.5678	961	64	8.0000	4 096	97	9.8489	9 409
32	5.6568	1 024	65	8.0623	4 225	98	9.8995	9 604
33	5.7446	1 089	66	8.1240	4 356	99	9.9499	9 801

Table II. Four-place Logarithms of Numbers

Each mantissa should be preceded by a decimal point, and the proper characteristic should be written.

On account of the great differences between the successive mantissas in the first ten rows interpolation is inaccurate in this part of the table and should be avoided.

N	0	1	2	3	4	5	6	7	8	9
10	0000	0043	0086	0128	0170	0212	0253	0294	0334	0374
11	0414	0453	0492	0531	0569	0607	0645	0682	0719	0755
12	0792	0828	0864	0899	0934	0969	1004	1038	1072	1106
13	1139	1173	1206	1239	1271	1303	1335	1367	1399	1430
14	1461	1492	1523	1553	1584	1614	1644	1673	1703	1732
15	1761	1790	1818	1847	1875	1903	1931	1959	1987	2014
16	2041	2068	2095	2122	2148	2175	2201	2227	2253	2279
17	2304	2330	2355	2380	2405	2430	2455	2480	2504	2529
18	2553	2577	2601	2625	2648	2672	2695	2718	2742	2765
19	2788	2810	2833	2856	2878	2900	2923	2945	2967	2989
20	3010	3032	3054	3075	3096	3118	3139	3160	3181	3201
21	3222	3243	3263	3284	3304	3324	3345	3365	3385	3404
22	3424	3444	3464	3483	3502	3522	3541	3560	3579	3598
23	3617	3636	3655	3674	3692	3711	3729	3747	3766	3784
24	3802	3820	3838	3856	3874	3892	3909	3927	3945	3962
25	3979	3997	4014	4031	4048	4065	4082	4099	4116	4133
26	4150	4166	4183	4200	4216	4232	4249	4265	4281	4298
27	4314	4330	4346	4362	4378	4393	4409	4425	4440	4456
28	4472	4487	4502	4518	4533	4548	4564	4579	4594	4609
29	4624	4639	4654	4669	4683	4698	4713	4728	4742	4757
30	4771	4786	4800	4814	4829	4843	4857	4871	4886	4900
31	4914	4928	4942	4955	4969	4983	4997	5011	5024	5038
32	5051	5065	5079	5092	5105	5119	5132	5145	5159	5172
33	5185	5198	5211	5224	5237	5250	5263	5276	5289	5302
34	5315	5328	5340	5353	5366	5378	5391	5403	5416	5428
35	5441	5453	5465	5478	5490	5502	5514	5527	5539	5551
36	5563	5575	5587	5599	5611	5623	5635	5647	5658	5670
37	5682	5694	5705	5717	5729	5740	5752	5763	5775	5786
38	5798	5809	5821	5832	5843	5855	5866	5877	5888	5899
39	5911	5922	5933	5944	5955	5966	5977	5988	5999	6010
40	6021	6031	6042	6053	6064	6075	6085	6096	6107	6117
41	6128	6138	6149	6160	6170	6180	6191	6201	6212	6222
42	6232	6243	6253	6263	6274	6284	6294	6304	6314	6325
43	6335	6345	6355	6365	6375	6385	6395	6405	6415	6425
44	6435	6444	6454	6464	6474	6484	6493	6503	6513	6522
45	6532	6542	6551	6561	6571	6580	6590	6599	6609	6618
46	6628	6637	6646	6656	6665	6675	6684	6693	6702	6712
47	6721	6730	6739	6749	6758	6767	6776	6785	6794	6803
48	6812	6821	6830	6839	6848	6857	6866	6875	6884	6893
49	6902	6911	6920	6928	6937	6946	6955	6964	6972	6981
50	6990	6998	7007	7016	7024	7033	7042	7050	7059	7067
N	0	1	2	3	4	5	6	7	8	9

II. Four-place Logarithms of Numbers

N	0	1	2	3	4	5	6	7	8	9
50	6990	6998	7007	7016	7024	7033	7042	7050	7059	7067
51	7076	7084	7093	7101	7110	7118	7126	7135	7143	7152
52	7160	7168	7177	7185	7193	7202	7210	7218	7226	7235
53	7243	7251	7259	7267	7275	7284	7292	7300	7308	7316
54	7324	7332	7340	7348	7356	7364	7372	7380	7388	7396
55	7404	7412	7419	7427	7435	7443	7451	7459	7466	7474
56	7482	7490	7497	7505	7513	7520	7528	7536	7543	7551
57	7559	7566	7574	7582	7589	7597	7604	7612	7619	7627
58	7634	7642	7649	7657	7664	7672	7679	7686	7694	7701
59	7709	7716	7723	7731	7738	7745	7752	7760	7767	7774
60	7782	7789	7796	7803	7810	7818	7825	7832	7839	7846
61	7853	7860	7868	7875	7882	7889	7896	7903	7910	7917
62	7924	7931	7938	7945	7952	7959	7966	7973	7980	7987
63	7993	8000	8007	8014	8021	8028	8035	8041	8048	8055
64	8062	8069	8075	8082	8089	8096	8102	8109	8116	8122
65	8129	8136	8142	8149	8156	8162	8169	8176	8182	8189
66	8195	8202	8209	8215	8222	8228	8235	8241	8248	8254
67	8261	8267	8274	8280	8287	8293	8299	8306	8312	8319
68	8325	8331	8338	8344	8351	8357	8363	8370	8376	8382
69	8388	8395	8401	8407	8414	8420	8426	8432	8439	8445
70	8451	8457	8463	8470	8476	8482	8488	8494	8500	8506
71	8513	8519	8525	8531	8537	8543	8549	8555	8561	8567
72	8573	8579	8585	8591	8597	8603	8609	8615	8621	8627
73	8633	8639	8645	8651	8657	8663	8669	8675	8681	8686
74	8692	8698	8704	8710	8716	8722	8727	8733	8739	8745
75	8751	8756	8762	8768	8774	8779	8785	8791	8797	8802
76	8808	8814	8820	8825	8831	8837	8842	8848	8854	8859
77	8865	8871	8876	8882	8887	8893	8899	8904	8910	8915
78	8921	8927	8932	8938	8943	8949	8954	8960	8965	8971
79	8976	8982	8987	8993	8998	9004	9009	9015	9020	9025
80	9031	9036	9042	9047	9053	9058	9063	9069	9074	9079
81	9085	9090	9096	9101	9106	9112	9117	9122	9128	9133
82	9138	9143	9149	9154	9159	9165	9170	9175	9180	9186
83	9191	9196	9201	9206	9212	9217	9222	9227	9232	9238
84	9243	9248	9253	9258	9263	9269	9274	9279	9284	9289
85	9294	9299	9304	9309	9315	9320	9325	9330	9335	9340
86	9345	9350	9355	9360	9365	9370	9375	9380	9385	9390
87	9395	9400	9405	9410	9415	9420	9425	9430	9435	9440
88	9445	9450	9455	9460	9465	9469	9474	9479	9484	9489
89	9494	9499	9504	9509	9513	9518	9523	9528	9533	9538
90	9542	9547	9552	9557	9562	9566	9571	9576	9581	9586
91	9590	9595	9600	9605	9609	9614	9619	9624	9628	9633
92	9638	9643	9647	9652	9657	9661	9666	9671	9675	9680
93	9685	9689	9694	9699	9703	9708	9713	9717	9722	9727
94	9731	9736	9741	9745	9750	9754	9759	9763	9768	9773
95	9777	9782	9786	9791	9795	9800	9805	9809	9814	9818
96	9823	9827	9832	9836	9841	9845	9850	9854	9859	9863
97	9868	9872	9877	9881	9886	9890	9894	9899	9903	9908
98	9912	9917	9921	9926	9930	9934	9939	9943	9948	9952
99	9956	9961	9965	9969	9974	9978	9983	9987	9991	9996
100	0000	0004	0009	0013	0017	0022	0026	0030	0035	0039
N	0	1	2	3	4	5	6	7	8	9

Table III. Factorials and Their Logarithms

n	$n!$	$\log n!$	n	$n!$	$\log n!$
			50	3.0414×10^{64}	64.4831
1	1.0000	0.0000	51	1.5511×10^{66}	66.1906
2	2.0000	0.3010	52	8.0658×10^{67}	67.9066
3	6.0000	0.7782	53	4.2749×10^{69}	69.6309
4	2.4000×10	1.3802	54	2.3084×10^{71}	71.3633
5	1.2000×10^2	2.0792	55	1.2696×10^{73}	73.1037
6	7.2000×10^2	2.8573	56	7.1100×10^{74}	74.8519
7	5.0400×10^3	3.7024	57	4.0527×10^{76}	76.6077
8	4.0320×10^4	4.6055	58	2.3506×10^{78}	78.3712
9	3.6288×10^5	5.5598	59	1.3868×10^{80}	80.1420
10	3.6288×10^6	6.5598	60	8.3210×10^{81}	81.9202
11	3.9917×10^7	7.6012	61	5.0758×10^{83}	83.7055
12	4.7900×10^8	8.6803	62	3.1470×10^{85}	85.4979
13	6.2270×10^9	9.7943	63	1.9826×10^{87}	87.2972
14	8.7178×10^{10}	10.9404	64	1.2689×10^{89}	89.1034
15	1.3077×10^{12}	12.1165	65	8.2477×10^{90}	90.9163
16	2.0923×10^{13}	13.3206	66	5.4435×10^{92}	92.7359
17	3.5569×10^{14}	14.5511	67	3.6471×10^{94}	94.5619
18	6.4024×10^{15}	15.8063	68	2.4800×10^{96}	96.3945
19	1.2165×10^{17}	17.0851	69	1.7112×10^{98}	98.2333
20	2.4329×10^{18}	18.3861	70	1.1979×10^{100}	100.0784
21	5.1091×10^{19}	19.7083	71	8.5048×10^{101}	101.9297
22	1.1240×10^{21}	21.0508	72	6.1234×10^{103}	103.7870
23	2.5852×10^{22}	22.4125	73	4.4701×10^{105}	105.6503
24	6.2045×10^{23}	23.7927	74	3.3079×10^{107}	107.5196
25	1.5511×10^{25}	25.1906	75	2.4809×10^{109}	109.3946
26	4.0329×10^{26}	26.6056	76	1.8855×10^{111}	111.2754
27	1.0889×10^{28}	28.0370	77	1.4518×10^{113}	113.1619
28	3.0489×10^{29}	29.4841	78	1.1324×10^{115}	115.0540
29	8.8418×10^{30}	30.9465	79	8.9462×10^{116}	116.9516
30	2.6525×10^{32}	32.4237	80	7.1569×10^{118}	118.8547
31	8.2228×10^{33}	33.9150	81	5.7971×10^{120}	120.7632
32	2.6313×10^{35}	35.4202	82	4.7536×10^{122}	122.6770
33	8.6833×10^{36}	36.9387	83	3.9455×10^{124}	124.5961
34	2.9523×10^{38}	38.4702	84	3.3142×10^{126}	126.5204
35	1.0333×10^{40}	40.0142	85	2.8171×10^{128}	128.4498
36	3.7199×10^{41}	41.5705	86	2.4227×10^{130}	130.3843
37	1.3764×10^{43}	43.1387	87	2.1078×10^{132}	132.3238
38	5.2302×10^{44}	44.7185	88	1.8548×10^{134}	134.2683
39	2.0398×10^{46}	46.3096	89	1.6508×10^{136}	136.2177
40	8.1592×10^{47}	47.9116	90	1.4857×10^{138}	138.1719
41	3.3453×10^{49}	49.5244	91	1.3520×10^{140}	140.1310
42	1.4050×10^{51}	51.1477	92	1.2438×10^{142}	142.0948
43	6.0415×10^{52}	52.7811	93	1.1568×10^{144}	144.0633
44	2.6583×10^{54}	54.4246	94	1.0874×10^{146}	146.0364
45	1.1962×10^{56}	56.0778	95	1.0330×10^{148}	148.0141
46	5.5026×10^{57}	57.7406	96	9.9168×10^{149}	149.9964
47	2.5862×10^{59}	59.4127	97	9.6193×10^{151}	151.9831
48	1.2414×10^{61}	61.0939	98	9.4269×10^{153}	153.9744
49	6.0828×10^{62}	62.7841	99	9.3326×10^{155}	155.9700
50	3.0414×10^{64}	64.4831	100	9.3326×10^{157}	157.9700

Table IV. Natural Trigonometric Functions

Measures in Degrees	Radians	Sin	Cos	Tan	Cot	Radians	Degrees
0.0	0.0000	0.0000	1.0000	0.0000		1.5708	90.0
.1	0.0017	0.0017	1.0000	0.0017	572.9572	1.5691	.9
.2	0.0035	0.0035	1.0000	0.0035	286.4777	1.5673	.8
.3	0.0052	0.0052	1.0000	0.0052	190.9842	1.5656	.7
.4	0.0070	0.0070	1.0000	0.0070	143.2371	1.5638	.6
.5	0.0087	0.0087	1.0000	0.0087	114.5887	1.5621	.5
.6	0.0105	0.0105	0.9999	0.0105	95.4895	1.5603	.4
.7	0.0122	0.0122	0.9999	0.0122	81.8470	1.5586	.3
.8	0.0140	0.0140	0.9999	0.0140	71.6151	1.5568	.2
.9	0.0157	0.0157	0.9999	0.0157	63.6567	1.5551	.1
1.0	0.0175	0.0175	0.9998	0.0175	57.2900	1.5533	89.0
.1	0.0192	0.0192	0.9998	0.0192	52.0807	1.5516	.9
.2	0.0209	0.0209	0.9998	0.0209	47.7395	1.5499	.8
.3	0.0227	0.0227	0.9997	0.0227	44.0661	1.5481	.7
.4	0.0244	0.0244	0.9997	0.0244	40.9174	1.5464	.6
.5	0.0262	0.0262	0.9997	0.0262	38.1885	1.5446	.5
.6	0.0279	0.0279	0.9996	0.0279	35.8006	1.5429	.4
.7	0.0297	0.0297	0.9996	0.0297	33.6935	1.5411	.3
.8	0.0314	0.0314	0.9995	0.0314	31.8205	1.5394	.2
.9	0.0332	0.0332	0.9995	0.0332	30.1446	1.5376	.1
2.0	0.0349	0.0349	0.9994	0.0349	28.6363	1.5359	88.0
.1	0.0367	0.0366	0.9993	0.0367	27.2715	1.5341	.9
.2	0.0384	0.0384	0.9993	0.0384	26.0307	1.5324	.8
.3	0.0401	0.0401	0.9992	0.0402	24.8978	1.5307	.7
.4	0.0419	0.0419	0.9991	0.0419	23.8593	1.5289	.6
.5	0.0436	0.0436	0.9990	0.0437	22.9038	1.5272	.5
.6	0.0454	0.0454	0.9990	0.0454	22.0217	1.5254	.4
.7	0.0471	0.0471	0.9989	0.0472	21.2049	1.5237	.3
.8	0.0489	0.0488	0.9988	0.0489	20.4465	1.5219	.2
.9	0.0506	0.0506	0.9987	0.0507	19.7403	1.5202	.1
3.0	0.0524	0.0523	0.9986	0.0524	19.0811	1.5184	87.0
.1	0.0541	0.0541	0.9985	0.0542	18.4645	1.5167	.9
.2	0.0559	0.0558	0.9984	0.0559	17.8863	1.5149	.8
.3	0.0576	0.0576	0.9983	0.0577	17.3432	1.5132	.7
.4	0.0593	0.0593	0.9982	0.0594	16.8319	1.5115	.6
.5	0.0611	0.0610	0.9981	0.0612	16.3499	1.5097	.5
.6	0.0628	0.0628	0.9980	0.0629	15.8945	1.5080	.4
.7	0.0646	0.0645	0.9979	0.0647	15.4638	1.5062	.3
.8	0.0663	0.0663	0.9978	0.0664	15.0557	1.5045	.2
.9	0.0681	0.0680	0.9977	0.0682	14.6685	1.5027	.1
4.0	0.0698	0.0698	0.9976	0.0699	14.3007	1.5010	86.0
.1	0.0716	0.0715	0.9974	0.0717	13.9507	1.4992	.9
.2	0.0733	0.0732	0.9973	0.0734	13.6174	1.4975	.8
.3	0.0750	0.0750	0.9972	0.0752	13.2995	1.4957	.7
.4	0.0768	0.0767	0.9971	0.0769	12.9962	1.4940	.6
.5	0.0785	0.0785	0.9969	0.0787	12.7062	1.4923	.5
.6	0.0803	0.0802	0.9968	0.0805	12.4288	1.4905	.4
.7	0.0820	0.0819	0.9966	0.0822	12.1632	1.4888	.3
.8	0.0838	0.0837	0.9965	0.0840	11.9087	1.4870	.2
.9	0.0855	0.0854	0.9963	0.0857	11.6645	1.4853	.1
5.0	0.0873	0.0872	0.9962	0.0875	11.4301	1.4835	85.0
Degrees	Radians	Cos	Sin	Cot	Tan	Radians	Degrees
							Measures in

IV. Natural Trigonometric Functions

Degrees	Radians	Sin	Cos	Tan	Cot	Radians	Degrees
5.0	0.0873	0.0872	0.9962	0.0875	11.4301	1.4835	**85.0**
.1	0.0890	0.0889	0.9960	0.0892	11.2048	1.4818	.9
.2	0.0908	0.0906	0.9959	0.0910	10.9882	1.4800	.8
.3	0.0925	0.0924	0.9957	0.0928	10.7797	1.4783	.7
.4	0.0942	0.0941	0.9956	0.0945	10.5789	1.4765	.6
.5	0.0960	0.0958	0.9954	0.0963	10.3854	1.4748	.5
.6	0.0977	0.0976	0.9952	0.0981	10.1988	1.4731	.4
.7	0.0995	0.0993	0.9951	0.0998	10.0187	1.4713	.3
.8	0.1012	0.1011	0.9949	0.1016	9.8448	1.4696	.2
.9	0.1030	0.1028	0.9947	0.1033	9.6768	1.4678	.1
6.0	0.1047	0.1045	0.9945	0.1051	9.5144	1.4661	**84.0**
.1	0.1065	0.1063	0.9943	0.1069	9.3572	1.4643	.9
.2	0.1082	0.1080	0.9942	0.1086	9.2052	1.4626	.8
.3	0.1100	0.1097	0.9940	0.1104	9.5079	1.4608	.7
.4	0.1117	0.1115	0.9938	0.1122	8.9152	1.4591	.6
.5	0.1134	0.1132	0.9936	0.1139	8.7769	1.4574	.5
.6	0.1152	0.1149	0.9934	0.1157	8.6427	1.4556	.4
.7	0.1169	0.1167	0.9932	0.1175	8.5126	1.4539	.3
.8	0.1187	0.1184	0.9930	0.1192	8.3863	1.4521	.2
.9	0.1204	0.1201	0.9928	0.1210	8.2636	1.4504	.1
7.0	0.1222	0.1219	0.9925	0.1228	8.1443	1.4486	**83.0**
.1	0.1239	0.1236	0.9923	0.1246	8.0285	1.4469	.9
.2	0.1257	0.1253	0.9921	0.1263	7.9158	1.4451	.8
.3	0.1274	0.1271	0.9919	0.1281	7.8062	1.4434	.7
.4	0.1292	0.1288	0.9917	0.1299	7.6996	1.4416	.6
.5	0.1309	0.1305	0.9914	0.1317	7.5958	1.4399	.5
.6	0.1326	0.1323	0.9912	0.1334	7.4947	1.4382	.4
.7	0.1344	0.1340	0.9910	0.1352	7.3962	1.4364	.3
.8	0.1361	0.1357	0.9907	0.1370	7.3002	1.4347	.2
.9	0.1379	0.1374	0.9905	0.1388	7.2066	1.4329	.1
8.0	0.1396	0.1392	0.9903	0.1405	7.1154	1.4312	**82.0**
.1	0.1414	0.1409	0.9900	0.1423	7.0264	1.4294	.9
.2	0.1431	0.1426	0.9898	0.1441	6.9395	1.4277	.8
.3	0.1449	0.1444	0.9895	0.1459	6.8548	1.4259	.7
.4	0.1466	0.1461	0.9893	0.1477	6.7720	1.4242	.6
.5	0.1484	0.1478	0.9890	0.1495	6.6912	1.4224	.5
.6	0.1501	0.1495	0.9888	0.1512	6.6122	1.4207	.4
.7	0.1518	0.1513	0.9885	0.1530	6.5350	1.4190	.3
.8	0.1536	0.1530	0.9882	0.1548	6.4596	1.4172	.2
.9	0.1553	0.1547	0.9880	0.1566	6.3859	1.4155	.1
9.0	0.1571	0.1564	0.9877	0.1584	6.3138	1.4137	**81.0**
.1	0.1588	0.1582	0.9874	0.1602	6.2432	1.4120	.9
.2	0.1606	0.1599	0.9871	0.1620	6.1742	1.4102	.8
.3	0.1623	0.1616	0.9869	0.1638	6.1066	1.4085	.7
.4	0.1641	0.1633	0.9866	0.1655	6.0405	1.4067	.6
.5	0.1658	0.1650	0.9863	0.1673	5.9758	1.4050	.5
.6	0.1676	0.1668	0.9860	0.1691	5.9124	1.4032	.4
.7	0.1693	0.1685	0.9857	0.1709	5.8502	1.4015	.3
.8	0.1710	0.1702	0.9854	0.1727	5.7894	1.3998	.2
.9	0.1728	0.1719	0.9851	0.1745	5.7297	1.3980	.1
10.0	0.1745	0.1736	0.9848	0.1763	5.6713	1.3963	**80.0**
.1	0.1763	0.1754	0.9845	0.1781	5.6140	1.3945	.9
.2	0.1780	0.1771	0.9842	0.1799	5.5578	1.3928	.8
.3	0.1798	0.1788	0.9839	0.1817	5.5026	1.3910	.7
.4	0.1815	0.1805	0.9836	0.1835	5.4486	1.3893	.6
.5	0.1833	0.1822	0.9833	0.1853	5.3955	1.3875	.5
.6	0.1850	0.1840	0.9829	0.1871	5.3435	1.3858	.4
.7	0.1868	0.1857	0.9826	0.1890	5.2924	1.3840	.3
.8	0.1885	0.1874	0.9823	0.1908	5.2422	1.3823	.2
.9	0.1902	0.1891	0.9820	0.1926	5.1929	1.3806	.1
11.0	0.1920	0.1908	0.9816	0.1944	5.1446	1.3788	**79.0**
Degrees	Radians	Cos	Sin	Cot	Tan	Radians	Degrees

IV. Natural Trigonometric Functions

Measures in Degrees	Radians	Sin	Cos	Tan	Cot	Radians	Degrees
11.0	0.1920	0.1908	0.9816	0.1944	5.1446	1.3788	79.0
.1	0.1937	0.1925	0.9813	0.1962	5.0970	1.3771	.9
.2	0.1955	0.1942	0.9810	0.1980	5.0504	1.3753	.8
.3	0.1972	0.1959	0.9806	0.1998	5.0045	1.3736	.7
.4	0.1990	0.1977	0.9803	0.2016	4.9594	1.3718	.6
.5	0.2007	0.1994	0.9799	0.2035	4.9152	1.3701	.5
.6	0.2025	0.2011	0.9796	0.2053	4.8716	1.3683	.4
.7	0.2042	0.2028	0.9792	0.2071	4.8288	1.3666	.3
.8	0.2059	0.2045	0.9789	0.2089	4.7867	1.3648	.2
.9	0.2077	0.2062	0.9785	0.2107	4.7453	1.3631	.1
12.0	0.2094	0.2079	0.9781	0.2126	4.7046	1.3614	78.0
.1	0.2112	0.2096	0.9778	0.2144	4.6646	1.3596	.9
.2	0.2129	0.2113	0.9774	0.2162	4.6252	1.3579	.8
.3	0.2147	0.2130	0.9770	0.2180	4.5864	1.3561	.7
.4	0.2164	0.2147	0.9767	0.2199	4.5483	1.3544	.6
.5	0.2182	0.2164	0.9763	0.2217	4.5107	1.3526	.5
.6	0.2199	0.2181	0.9759	0.2235	4.4737	1.3509	.4
.7	0.2217	0.2198	0.9755	0.2254	4.4373	1.3491	.3
.8	0.2234	0.2215	0.9751	0.2272	4.4015	1.3474	.2
.9	0.2251	0.2233	0.9748	0.2290	4.3662	1.3456	.1
13.0	0.2269	0.2250	0.9744	0.2309	4.3315	1.3439	77.0
.1	0.2286	0.2267	0.9740	0.2327	4.2972	1.3422	.9
.2	0.2304	0.2284	0.9736	0.2345	4.2635	1.3404	.8
.3	0.2321	0.2300	0.9732	0.2364	4.2303	1.3387	.7
.4	0.2339	0.2317	0.9728	0.2382	4.1976	1.3369	.6
.5	0.2356	0.2334	0.9724	0.2401	4.1653	1.3352	.5
.6	0.2374	0.2351	0.9720	0.2419	4.1335	1.3334	.4
.7	0.2391	0.2368	0.9715	0.2438	4.1022	1.3317	.3
.8	0.2409	0.2385	0.9711	0.2456	4.0713	1.3299	.2
.9	0.2426	0.2402	0.9707	0.2475	4.0408	1.3282	.1
14.0	0.2443	0.2419	0.9703	0.2493	4.0108	1.3265	76.0
.1	0.2461	0.2436	0.9699	0.2512	3.9812	1.3247	.9
.2	0.2478	0.2453	0.9694	0.2530	3.9520	1.3230	.8
.3	0.2496	0.2470	0.9690	0.2549	3.9232	1.3212	.7
.4	0.2513	0.2487	0.9686	0.2568	3.8947	1.3195	.6
.5	0.2531	0.2504	0.9681	0.2586	3.8667	1.3177	.5
.6	0.2548	0.2521	0.9677	0.2605	3.8391	1.3160	.4
.7	0.2566	0.2538	0.9673	0.2623	3.8118	1.3142	.3
.8	0.2583	0.2554	0.9668	0.2642	3.7848	1.3125	.2
.9	0.2601	0.2571	0.9664	0.2661	3.7583	1.3107	.1
15.0	0.2618	0.2588	0.9659	0.2679	3.7321	1.3090	75.0
.1	0.2635	0.2605	0.9655	0.2698	3.7062	1.3073	.9
.2	0.2653	0.2622	0.9650	0.2717	3.6806	1.3055	.8
.3	0.2670	0.2639	0.9646	0.2736	3.6554	1.3038	.7
.4	0.2688	0.2656	0.9641	0.2754	3.6305	1.3020	.6
.5	0.2705	0.2672	0.9636	0.2773	3.6059	1.3003	.5
.6	0.2723	0.2689	0.9632	0.2792	3.5816	1.2985	.4
.7	0.2740	0.2706	0.9627	0.2811	3.5576	1.2968	.3
.8	0.2758	0.2723	0.9622	0.2830	3.5339	1.2950	.2
.9	0.2775	0.2740	0.9617	0.2849	3.5105	1.2933	.1
16.0	0.2793	0.2756	0.9613	0.2867	3.4874	1.2915	74.0
.1	0.2810	0.2773	0.9608	0.2886	3.4646	1.2898	.9
.2	0.2827	0.2790	0.9603	0.2905	3.4420	1.2881	.8
.3	0.2845	0.2807	0.9598	0.2924	3.4197	1.2863	.7
.4	0.2862	0.2823	0.9593	0.2943	3.3977	1.2846	.6
.5	0.2880	0.2840	0.9588	0.2962	3.3759	1.2828	.5
.6	0.2897	0.2857	0.9583	0.2981	3.3544	1.2811	.4
.7	0.2915	0.2874	0.9578	0.3000	3.3332	1.2793	.3
.8	0.2932	0.2890	0.9573	0.3019	3.3122	1.2776	.2
.9	0.2950	0.2907	0.9568	0.3038	3.2914	1.2758	.1
17.0	0.2967	0.2924	0.9563	0.3057	3.2709	1.2741	73.0
Degrees	Radians	Cos	Sin	Cot	Tan	Radians	Degrees
							Measures in

IV. Natural Trigonometric Functions

Measures in Degrees	Radians	Sin	Cos	Tan	Cot	Radians	Degrees
17.0	0.2967	0.2924	0.9563	0.3057	3.2709	1.2741	73.0
.1	0.2985	0.2940	0.9558	0.3076	3.2506	1.2723	.9
.2	0.3002	0.2957	0.9553	0.3096	3.2305	1.2706	.8
.3	0.3019	0.2974	0.9548	0.3115	3.2106	1.2689	.7
.4	0.3037	0.2990	0.9542	0.3134	3.1910	1.2671	.6
.5	0.3054	0.3007	0.9537	0.3153	3.1716	1.2654	.5
.6	0.3072	0.3024	0.9532	0.3172	3.1524	1.2636	.4
.7	0.3089	0.3040	0.9527	0.3191	3.1334	1.2619	.3
.8	0.3107	0.3057	0.9521	0.3211	3.1146	1.2601	.2
.9	0.3124	0.3074	0.9516	0.3230	3.0961	1.2584	.1
18.0	0.3142	0.3090	0.9511	0.3249	3.0777	1.2566	72.0
.1	0.3159	0.3107	0.9505	0.3269	3.0595	1.2549	.9
.2	0.3176	0.3123	0.9500	0.3288	3.0415	1.2531	.8
.3	0.3194	0.3140	0.9494	0.3307	3.0237	1.2514	.7
.4	0.3211	0.3156	0.9489	0.3327	3.0061	1.2497	.6
.5	0.3229	0.3173	0.9483	0.3346	2.9887	1.2479	.5
.6	0.3246	0.3190	0.9478	0.3365	2.9714	1.2462	.4
.7	0.3264	0.3206	0.9472	0.3385	2.9544	1.2444	.3
.8	0.3281	0.3223	0.9466	0.3404	2.9375	1.2427	.2
.9	0.3299	0.3239	0.9461	0.3424	2.9208	1.2409	.1
19.0	0.3316	0.3256	0.9455	0.3443	2.9042	1.2392	71.0
.1	0.3334	0.3272	0.9449	0.3463	2.8878	1.2374	.9
.2	0.3351	0.3289	0.9444	0.3482	2.8716	1.2357	.8
.3	0.3368	0.3305	0.9438	0.3502	2.8556	1.2339	.7
.4	0.3386	0.3322	0.9432	0.3522	2.8397	1.2322	.6
.5	0.3403	0.3338	0.9426	0.3541	2.8239	1.2305	.5
.6	0.3421	0.3355	0.9421	0.3561	2.8083	1.2287	.4
.7	0.3438	0.3371	0.9415	0.3581	2.7929	1.2270	.3
.8	0.3456	0.3387	0.9409	0.3600	2.7776	1.2252	.2
.9	0.3473	0.3404	0.9403	0.3620	2.7625	1.2235	.1
20.0	0.3491	0.3420	0.9397	0.3640	2.7475	1.2217	70.0
.1	0.3508	0.3437	0.9391	0.3659	2.7326	1.2200	.9
.2	0.3526	0.3453	0.9385	0.3679	2.7179	1.2182	.8
.3	0.3543	0.3469	0.9379	0.3699	2.7034	1.2165	.7
.4	0.3560	0.3486	0.9373	0.3719	2.6889	1.2147	.6
.5	0.3578	0.3502	0.9367	0.3739	2.6746	1.2130	.5
.6	0.3595	0.3518	0.9361	0.3759	2.6605	1.2113	.4
.7	0.3613	0.3535	0.9354	0.3779	2.6464	1.2095	.3
.8	0.3630	0.3551	0.9348	0.3799	2.6325	1.2078	.2
.9	0.3648	0.3567	0.9342	0.3819	2.6187	1.2060	.1
21.0	0.3665	0.3584	0.9336	0.3839	2.6051	1.2043	69.0
.1	0.3683	0.3600	0.9330	0.3859	2.5916	1.2025	.9
.2	0.3700	0.3616	0.9323	0.3879	2.5782	1.2008	.8
.3	0.3718	0.3633	0.9317	0.3899	2.5649	1.1990	.7
.4	0.3735	0.3649	0.9311	0.3919	2.5517	1.1973	.6
.5	0.3752	0.3665	0.9304	0.3939	2.5386	1.1956	.5
.6	0.3770	0.3681	0.9298	0.3959	2.5257	1.1938	.4
.7	0.3787	0.3697	0.9291	0.3979	2.5129	1.1921	.3
.8	0.3805	0.3714	0.9285	0.4000	2.5002	1.1903	.2
.9	0.3822	0.3730	0.9278	0.4020	2.4876	1.1886	.1
22.0	0.3840	0.3746	0.9272	0.4040	2.4751	1.1868	68.0
.1	0.3857	0.3762	0.9265	0.4061	2.4627	1.1851	.9
.2	0.3875	0.3778	0.9259	0.4081	2.4504	1.1833	.8
.3	0.3892	0.3795	0.9252	0.4101	2.4383	1.1816	.7
.4	0.3910	0.3811	0.9245	0.4122	2.4262	1.1798	.6
.5	0.3927	0.3827	0.9239	0.4142	2.4142	1.1781	.5
.6	0.3944	0.3843	0.9232	0.4163	2.4023	1.1764	.4
.7	0.3962	0.3859	0.9225	0.4183	2.3906	1.1746	.3
.8	0.3979	0.3875	0.9219	0.4204	2.3789	1.1729	.2
.9	0.3997	0.3891	0.9212	0.4224	2.3673	1.1711	.1
23.0	0.4014	0.3907	0.9205	0.4245	2.3559	1.1694	67.0
Degrees	Radians	Cos	Sin	Cot	Tan	Radians	Degrees

Measures in

IV. Natural Trigonometric Functions

Measures in Degrees	Radians	Sin	Cos	Tan	Cot	Radians	Degrees
23.0	0.4014	0.3907	0.9205	0.4245	2.3559	1.1694	67.0
.1	0.4032	0.3923	0.9198	0.4265	2.3445	1.1676	.9
.2	0.4049	0.3939	0.9191	0.4286	2.3332	1.1659	.8
.3	0.4067	0.3955	0.9184	0.4307	2.3220	1.1641	.7
.4	0.4084	0.3971	0.9178	0.4327	2.3109	1.1624	.6
.5	0.4102	0.3987	0.9171	0.4348	2.2998	1.1606	.5
.6	0.4119	0.4003	0.9164	0.4369	2.2889	1.1589	.4
.7	0.4136	0.4019	0.9157	0.4390	2.2781	1.1572	.3
.8	0.4154	0.4035	0.9150	0.4411	2.2673	1.1554	.2
.9	0.4171	0.4051	0.9143	0.4431	2.2566	1.1537	.1
24.0	0.4189	0.4067	0.9135	0.4452	2.2460	1.1519	66.0
.1	0.4206	0.4083	0.9128	0.4473	2.2355	1.1502	.9
.2	0.4224	0.4099	0.9121	0.4494	2.2251	1.1484	.8
.3	0.4241	0.4115	0.9114	0.4515	2.2148	1.1467	.7
.4	0.4259	0.4131	0.9107	0.4536	2.2045	1.1449	.6
.5	0.4276	0.4147	0.9100	0.4557	2.1943	1.1432	.5
.6	0.4294	0.4163	0.9092	0.4578	2.1842	1.1414	.4
.7	0.4311	0.4179	0.9085	0.4599	2.1742	1.1397	.3
.8	0.4328	0.4195	0.9078	0.4621	2.1642	1.1380	.2
.9	0.4346	0.4210	0.9070	0.4642	2.1543	1.1362	.1
25.0	0.4363	0.4226	0.9063	0.4663	2.1445	1.1345	65.0
.1	0.4381	0.4242	0.9056	0.4684	2.1348	1.1327	.9
.2	0.4398	0.4258	0.9048	0.4706	2.1251	1.1310	.8
.3	0.4416	0.4274	0.9041	0.4727	2.1155	1.1292	.7
.4	0.4433	0.4289	0.9033	0.4748	2.1060	1.1275	.6
.5	0.4451	0.4305	0.9026	0.4770	2.0965	1.1257	.5
.6	0.4468	0.4321	0.9018	0.4791	2.0872	1.1240	.4
.7	0.4485	0.4337	0.9011	0.4813	2.0778	1.1222	.3
.8	0.4503	0.4352	0.9003	0.4834	2.0686	1.1205	.2
.9	0.4520	0.4368	0.8996	0.4856	2.0594	1.1188	.1
26.0	0.4538	0.4384	0.8988	0.4877	2.0503	1.1170	64.0
.1	0.4555	0.4399	0.8980	0.4899	2.0413	1.1153	.9
.2	0.4573	0.4415	0.8973	0.4921	2.0323	1.1135	.8
.3	0.4590	0.4431	0.8965	0.4942	2.0233	1.1118	.7
.4	0.4608	0.4446	0.8957	0.4964	2.0145	1.1100	.6
.5	0.4625	0.4462	0.8949	0.4986	2.0057	1.1083	.5
.6	0.4643	0.4478	0.8942	0.5008	1.9970	1.1065	.4
.7	0.4660	0.4493	0.8934	0.5029	1.9883	1.1048	.3
.8	0.4677	0.4509	0.8926	0.5051	1.9797	1.1030	.2
.9	0.4695	0.4524	0.8918	0.5073	1.9711	1.1013	.1
27.0	0.4712	0.4540	0.8910	0.5095	1.9626	1.0996	63.0
.1	0.4730	0.4555	0.8902	0.5117	1.9542	1.0978	.9
.2	0.4747	0.4571	0.8894	0.5139	1.9458	1.0961	.8
.3	0.4765	0.4586	0.8886	0.5161	1.9375	1.0943	.7
.4	0.4782	0.4602	0.8878	0.5184	1.9292	1.0926	.6
.5	0.4800	0.4617	0.8870	0.5206	1.9210	1.0908	.5
.6	0.4817	0.4633	0.8862	0.5228	1.9128	1.0891	.4
.7	0.4835	0.4648	0.8854	0.5250	1.9047	1.0873	.3
.8	0.4852	0.4664	0.8846	0.5272	1.8967	1.0856	.2
.9	0.4869	0.4679	0.8838	0.5295	1.8887	1.0838	.1
28.0	0.4887	0.4695	0.8829	0.5317	1.8807	1.0821	62.0
.1	0.4904	0.4710	0.8821	0.5340	1.8728	1.0804	.9
.2	0.4922	0.4726	0.8813	0.5362	1.8650	1.0786	.8
.3	0.4939	0.4741	0.8805	0.5384	1.8572	1.0769	.7
.4	0.4957	0.4756	0.8796	0.5407	1.8495	1.0751	.6
.5	0.4974	0.4772	0.8788	0.5430	1.8418	1.0734	.5
.6	0.4992	0.4787	0.8780	0.5452	1.8341	1.0716	.4
.7	0.5009	0.4802	0.8771	0.5475	1.8265	1.0699	.3
.8	0.5027	0.4818	0.8763	0.5498	1.8190	1.0681	.2
.9	0.5044	0.4833	0.8755	0.5520	1.8115	1.0664	.1
29.0	0.5061	0.4848	0.8746	0.5543	1.8040	1.0647	61.0
Degrees	Radians	Cos	Sin	Cot	Tan	Radians	Degrees
						Measures in	

IV. Natural Trigonometric Functions

Measures in Degrees	Radians	Sin	Cos	Tan	Cot	Radians	Degrees
29.0	0.5061	0.4848	0.8746	0.5543	1.8040	1.0647	61.0
.1	0.5079	0.4863	0.8738	0.5566	1.7966	1.0629	.9
.2	0.5096	0.4879	0.8729	0.5589	1.7893	1.0612	.8
.3	0.5114	0.4894	0.8721	0.5612	1.7820	1.0594	.7
.4	0.5131	0.4909	0.8712	0.5635	1.7747	1.0577	.6
.5	0.5149	0.4924	0.8704	0.5658	1.7675	1.0559	.5
.6	0.5166	0.4939	0.8695	0.5681	1.7603	1.0542	.4
.7	0.5184	0.4955	0.8686	0.5704	1.7532	1.0524	.3
.8	0.5201	0.4970	0.8678	0.5727	1.7461	1.0507	.2
.9	0.5219	0.4985	0.8669	0.5750	1.7391	1.0489	.1
30.0	0.5236	0.5000	0.8660	0.5774	1.7321	1.0472	60.0
.1	0.5253	0.5015	0.8652	0.5797	1.7251	1.0455	.9
.2	0.5271	0.5030	0.8643	0.5820	1.7182	1.0437	.8
.3	0.5288	0.5045	0.8634	0.5844	1.7113	1.0420	.7
.4	0.5306	0.5060	0.8625	0.5867	1.7045	1.0402	.6
.5	0.5323	0.5075	0.8616	0.5890	1.6977	1.0385	.5
.6	0.5341	0.5090	0.8607	0.5914	1.6909	1.0367	.4
.7	0.5358	0.5105	0.8599	0.5938	1.6842	1.0350	.3
.8	0.5376	0.5120	0.8590	0.5961	1.6775	1.0332	.2
.9	0.5393	0.5135	0.8581	0.5985	1.6709	1.0315	.1
31.0	0.5411	0.5150	0.8572	0.6009	1.6643	1.0297	59.0
.1	0.5428	0.5165	0.8563	0.6032	1.6577	1.0280	.9
.2	0.5445	0.5180	0.8554	0.6056	1.6512	1.0263	.8
.3	0.5463	0.5195	0.8545	0.6080	1.6447	1.0245	.7
.4	0.5480	0.5210	0.8536	0.6104	1.6383	1.0228	.6
.5	0.5498	0.5225	0.8526	0.6128	1.6319	1.0210	.5
.6	0.5515	0.5240	0.8517	0.6152	1.6255	1.0193	.4
.7	0.5533	0.5255	0.8508	0.6176	1.6191	1.0175	.3
.8	0.5550	0.5270	0.8499	0.6200	1.6128	1.0158	.2
.9	0.5568	0.5284	0.8490	0.6224	1.6066	1.0140	.1
32.0	0.5585	0.5299	0.8480	0.6249	1.6003	1.0123	58.0
.1	0.5603	0.5314	0.8471	0.6273	1.5941	1.0105	.9
.2	0.5620	0.5329	0.8462	0.6297	1.5880	1.0088	.8
.3	0.5637	0.5344	0.8453	0.6322	1.5818	1.0071	.7
.4	0.5655	0.5358	0.8443	0.6346	1.5757	1.0053	.6
.5	0.5672	0.5373	0.8434	0.6371	1.5697	1.0036	.5
.6	0.5690	0.5388	0.8425	0.6395	1.5637	1.0018	.4
.7	0.5707	0.5402	0.8415	0.6420	1.5577	1.0001	.3
.8	0.5725	0.5417	0.8406	0.6445	1.5517	0.9983	.2
.9	0.5742	0.5432	0.8396	0.6469	1.5458	0.9966	.1
33.0	0.5760	0.5446	0.8387	0.6494	1.5399	0.9948	57.0
.1	0.5777	0.5461	0.8377	0.6519	1.5340	0.9931	.9
.2	0.5794	0.5476	0.8368	0.6544	1.5282	0.9913	.8
.3	0.5812	0.5490	0.8358	0.6569	1.5224	0.9896	.7
.4	0.5829	0.5505	0.8348	0.6594	1.5166	0.9879	.6
.5	0.5847	0.5519	0.8339	0.6619	1.5108	0.9861	.5
.6	0.5864	0.5534	0.8329	0.6644	1.5051	0.9844	.4
.7	0.5882	0.5548	0.8320	0.6669	1.4994	0.9826	.3
.8	0.5899	0.5563	0.8310	0.6694	1.4938	0.9809	.2
.9	0.5917	0.5577	0.8300	0.6720	1.4882	0.9791	.1
34.0	0.5934	0.5592	0.8290	0.6745	1.4826	0.9774	56.0
.1	0.5952	0.5606	0.8281	0.6771	1.4770	0.9756	.9
.2	0.5969	0.5621	0.8271	0.6796	1.4715	0.9739	.8
.3	0.5986	0.5635	0.8261	0.6822	1.4659	0.9721	.7
.4	0.6004	0.5650	0.8251	0.6847	1.4605	0.9704	.6
.5	0.6021	0.5664	0.8241	0.6873	1.4550	0.9687	.5
.6	0.6039	0.5678	0.8231	0.6899	1.4496	0.9669	.4
.7	0.6056	0.5693	0.8221	0.6924	1.4442	0.9652	.3
.8	0.6074	0.5707	0.8211	0.6950	1.4388	0.9634	.2
.9	0.6091	0.5721	0.8202	0.6976	1.4335	0.9617	.1
35.0	0.6109	0.5736	0.8192	0.7002	1.4281	0.9599	55.0
Degrees	Radians	Cos	Sin	Cot	Tan	Radians	Degrees
						Measures in	

IV. Natural Trigonometric Functions

Measures in Degrees	Radians	Sin	Cos	Tan	Cot	Radians	Degrees
35.0	0.6109	0.5736	0.8192	0.7002	1.4281	0.9599	55.0
.1	0.6126	0.5750	0.8181	0.7028	1.4229	0.9582	.9
.2	0.6144	0.5764	0.8171	0.7054	1.4176	0.9564	.8
.3	0.6161	0.5779	0.8161	0.7080	1.4124	0.9547	.7
.4	0.6178	0.5793	0.8151	0.7107	1.4071	0.9530	.6
.5	0.6196	0.5807	0.8141	0.7133	1.4019	0.9512	.5
.6	0.6213	0.5821	0.8131	0.7159	1.3968	0.9495	.4
.7	0.6231	0.5835	0.8121	0.7186	1.3916	0.9477	.3
.8	0.6248	0.5850	0.8111	0.7212	1.3865	0.9460	.2
.9	0.6266	0.5864	0.8100	0.7239	1.3814	0.9442	.1
36.0	0.6283	0.5878	0.8090	0.7265	1.3764	0.9425	54.0
.1	0.6301	0.5892	0.8080	0.7292	1.3713	0.9407	.9
.2	0.6318	0.5906	0.8070	0.7319	1.3663	0.9390	.8
.3	0.6336	0.5920	0.8059	0.7346	1.3613	0.9372	.7
.4	0.6353	0.5934	0.8049	0.7373	1.3564	0.9355	.6
.5	0.6370	0.5948	0.8039	0.7400	1.3514	0.9338	.5
.6	0.6388	0.5962	0.8028	0.7427	1.3465	0.9320	.4
.7	0.6405	0.5976	0.8018	0.7454	1.3416	0.9303	.3
.8	0.6423	0.5990	0.8007	0.7481	1.3367	0.9285	.2
.9	0.6440	0.6004	0.7997	0.7508	1.3319	0.9268	.1
37.0	0.6458	0.6018	0.7986	0.7536	1.3270	0.9250	53.0
.1	0.6475	0.6032	0.7976	0.7563	1.3222	0.9233	.9
.2	0.6493	0.6046	0.7965	0.7590	1.3175	0.9215	.8
.3	0.6510	0.6060	0.7955	0.7618	1.3127	0.9198	.7
.4	0.6528	0.6074	0.7944	0.7646	1.3079	0.9180	.6
.5	0.6545	0.6088	0.7934	0.7673	1.3032	0.9163	.5
.6	0.6562	0.6101	0.7923	0.7701	1.2985	0.9146	.4
.7	0.6580	0.6115	0.7912	0.7729	1.2938	0.9128	.3
.8	0.6597	0.6129	0.7902	0.7757	1.2892	0.9111	.2
.9	0.6615	0.6143	0.7891	0.7785	1.2846	0.9093	.1
38.0	0.6632	0.6157	0.7880	0.7813	1.2799	0.9076	52.0
.1	0.6650	0.6170	0.7869	0.7841	1.2753	0.9058	.9
.2	0.6667	0.6184	0.7859	0.7869	1.2708	0.9041	.8
.3	0.6685	0.6198	0.7848	0.7898	1.2662	0.9023	.7
.4	0.6702	0.6211	0.7837	0.7926	1.2617	0.9006	.6
.5	0.6720	0.6225	0.7826	0.7954	1.2572	0.8988	.5
.6	0.6737	0.6239	0.7815	0.7983	1.2527	0.8971	.4
.7	0.6754	0.6252	0.7804	0.8012	1.2482	0.8954	.3
.8	0.6772	0.6266	0.7793	0.8040	1.2437	0.8936	.2
.9	0.6789	0.6280	0.7782	0.8069	1.2393	0.8919	.1
39.0	0.6807	0.6293	0.7771	0.8098	1.2349	0.8901	51.0
.1	0.6824	0.6307	0.7760	0.8127	1.2305	0.8884	.9
.2	0.6842	0.6320	0.7749	0.8156	1.2261	0.8866	.8
.3	0.6859	0.6334	0.7738	0.8185	1.2218	0.8849	.7
.4	0.6877	0.6347	0.7727	0.8214	1.2174	0.8831	.6
.5	0.6894	0.6361	0.7716	0.8243	1.2131	0.8814	.5
.6	0.6912	0.6374	0.7705	0.8273	1.2088	0.8796	.4
.7	0.6929	0.6388	0.7694	0.8302	1.2045	0.8779	.3
.8	0.6946	0.6401	0.7683	0.8332	1.2002	0.8762	.2
.9	0.6964	0.6414	0.7672	0.8361	1.1960	0.8744	.1
40.0	0.6981	0.6428	0.7660	0.8391	1.1918	0.8727	50.0
.1	0.6999	0.6441	0.7649	0.8421	1.1875	0.8709	.9
.2	0.7016	0.6455	0.7638	0.8451	1.1833	0.8692	.8
.3	0.7034	0.6468	0.7627	0.8481	1.1792	0.8674	.7
.4	0.7051	0.6481	0.7615	0.8511	1.1750	0.8657	.6
.5	0.7069	0.6494	0.7604	0.8541	1.1708	0.8639	.5
.6	0.7086	0.6508	0.7593	0.8571	1.1667	0.8622	.4
.7	0.7103	0.6521	0.7581	0.8601	1.1626	0.8604	.3
.8	0.7121	0.6534	0.7570	0.8632	1.1585	0.8587	.2
.9	0.7138	0.6547	0.7559	0.8662	1.1544	0.8570	.1
41.0	0.7156	0.6561	0.7547	0.8693	1.1504	0.8552	49.0
Degrees	Radians	Cos	Sin	Cot	Tan	Radians	Degrees
							Measures in

IV. Natural Trigonometric Functions

Measures in Degrees	Radians	Sin	Cos	Tan	Cot	Radians	Degrees
41.0	0.7156	0.6561	0.7547	0.8693	1.1504	0.8552	49.0
.1	0.7173	0.6574	0.7536	0.8724	1.1463	0.8535	.9
.2	0.7191	0.6587	0.7524	0.8754	1.1423	0.8517	.8
.3	0.7208	0.6600	0.7513	0.8785	1.1383	0.8500	.7
.4	0.7226	0.6613	0.7501	0.8816	1.1343	0.8482	.6
.5	0.7243	0.6626	0.7490	0.8847	1.1303	0.8465	.5
.6	0.7261	0.6639	0.7478	0.8878	1.1263	0.8447	.4
.7	0.7278	0.6652	0.7466	0.8910	1.1224	0.8430	.3
.8	0.7295	0.6665	0.7455	0.8941	1.1184	0.8412	.2
.9	0.7313	0.6678	0.7443	0.8972	1.1145	0.8395	.1
42.0	0.7330	0.6691	0.7431	0.9004	1.1106	0.8378	48.0
.1	0.7348	0.6704	0.7420	0.9036	1.1067	0.8360	.9
.2	0.7365	0.6717	0.7408	0.9067	1.1028	0.8343	.8
.3	0.7383	0.6730	0.7396	0.9099	1.0990	0.8325	.7
.4	0.7400	0.6743	0.7385	0.9131	1.0951	0.8308	.6
.5	0.7418	0.6756	0.7373	0.9163	1.0913	0.8290	.5
.6	0.7435	0.6769	0.7361	0.9195	1.0875	0.8273	.4
.7	0.7453	0.6782	0.7349	0.9228	1.0837	0.8255	.3
.8	0.7470	0.6794	0.7337	0.9260	1.0799	0.8238	.2
.9	0.7487	0.6807	0.7325	0.9293	1.0761	0.8220	.1
43.0	0.7505	0.6820	0.7314	0.9325	1.0724	0.8203	47.0
.1	0.7522	0.6833	0.7302	0.9358	1.0686	0.8186	.9
.2	0.7540	0.6845	0.7290	0.9391	1.0649	0.8168	.8
.3	0.7557	0.6858	0.7278	0.9424	1.0612	0.8151	.7
.4	0.7575	0.6871	0.7266	0.9457	1.0575	0.8133	.6
.5	0.7592	0.6884	0.7254	0.9490	1.0538	0.8116	.5
.6	0.7610	0.6896	0.7242	0.9523	1.0501	0.8098	.4
.7	0.7627	0.6909	0.7230	0.9556	1.0464	0.8081	.3
.8	0.7645	0.6921	0.7218	0.9590	1.0428	0.8063	.2
.9	0.7662	0.6934	0.7206	0.9623	1.0392	0.8046	.1
44.0	0.7679	0.6747	0.7193	0.9657	1.0355	0.8029	46.0
.1	0.7697	0.6959	0.7181	0.9691	1.0319	0.8011	.9
.2	0.7714	0.6972	0.7169	0.9725	1.0283	0.7994	.8
.3	0.7732	0.6984	0.7157	0.9759	1.0247	0.7976	.7
.4	0.7749	0.6997	0.7145	0.9793	1.0212	0.7959	.6
.5	0.7767	0.7009	0.7133	0.9827	1.0176	0.7941	.5
.6	0.7784	0.7022	0.7120	0.9861	1.0141	0.7924	.4
.7	0.7802	0.7034	0.7108	0.9896	1.0105	0.7906	.3
.8	0.7819	0.7046	0.7096	0.9930	1.0070	0.7889	.2
.9	0.7837	0.7059	0.7083	0.9965	1.0035	0.7871	.1
45.0	0.7854	0.7071	0.7071	1.0000	1.0000	0.7854	45.0
Degrees	Radians	Cos	Sin	Cot	Tan	Radians	Degrees
						Measures in	

769

V. Logarithms of Trigonometric Functions

Measures in Degrees	Radians	L.Sin	L.Cos	L.Tan	L.Cot	Radians	Degrees
0.0	0.0000		0.0000			1.5708	90.0
.1	0.0017	7.2419	0.0000	7.2419	2.7581	1.5691	.9
.2	0.0035	7.5429	0.0000	7.5429	2.4571	1.5673	.8
.3	0.0052	7.7190	0.0000	7.7190	2.2810	1.5656	.7
.4	0.0070	7.8439	0.0000	7.8439	2.1561	1.5638	.6
.5	0.0087	7.9408	0.0000	7.9409	2.0591	1.5621	.5
.6	0.0105	8.0200	0.0000	8.0200	1.9800	1.5603	.4
.7	0.0122	8.0870	0.0000	8.0870	1.9130	1.5586	.3
.8	0.0140	8.1450	0.0000	8.1450	1.8550	1.5568	.2
.9	0.0157	8.1961	9.9999	8.1962	1.8038	1.5551	.1
1.0	0.0175	8.2419	9.9999	8.2419	1.7581	1.5533	89.0
.1	0.0192	8.2832	9.9999	8.2833	1.7167	1.5516	.9
.2	0.0209	8.3210	9.9999	8.3211	1.6789	1.5499	.8
.3	0.0227	8.3558	9.9999	8.3559	1.6441	1.5481	.7
.4	0.0244	8.3880	9.9999	8.3881	1.6119	1.5464	.6
.5	0.0262	8.4179	9.9999	8.4181	1.5819	1.5446	.5
.6	0.0279	8.4459	9.9998	8.4461	1.5539	1.5429	.4
.7	0.0297	8.4723	9.9998	8.4725	1.5275	1.5411	.3
.8	0.0314	8.4971	9.9998	8.4973	1.5027	1.5394	.2
.9	0.0332	8.5206	9.9998	8.5208	1.4792	1.5376	.1
2.0	0.0349	8.5428	9.9997	8.5431	1.4569	1.5359	88.0
.1	0.0367	8.5640	9.9997	8.5643	1.4357	1.5341	.9
.2	0.0384	8.5842	9.9997	8.5845	1.4155	1.5324	.8
.3	0.0401	8.6035	9.9996	8.6038	1.3962	1.5307	.7
.4	0.0419	8.6220	9.9996	8.6223	1.3777	1.5289	.6
.5	0.0436	8.6397	9.9996	8.6401	1.3599	1.5272	.5
.6	0.0454	8.6567	9.9996	8.6571	1.3429	1.5254	.4
.7	0.0471	8.6731	9.9995	8.6736	1.3264	1.5237	.3
.8	0.0489	8.6889	9.9995	8.6894	1.3106	1.5219	.2
.9	0.0506	8.7041	9.9994	8.7046	1.2954	1.5202	.1
3.0	0.0524	8.7188	9.9994	8.7194	1.2806	1.5184	87.0
.1	0.0541	8.7330	9.9994	8.7337	1.2663	1.5167	.9
.2	0.0554	8.7468	9.9993	8.7475	1.2525	1.5149	.8
.3	0.0576	8.7602	9.9993	8.7609	1.2391	1.5132	.7
.4	0.0593	8.7731	9.9992	8.7739	1.2261	1.5115	.6
.5	0.0611	8.7857	9.9992	8.7865	1.2135	1.5097	.5
.6	0.0628	8.7979	9.9991	8.7988	1.2012	1.5080	.4
.7	0.0646	8.8098	9.9991	8.8107	1.1893	1.5062	.3
.8	0.0663	8.8213	9.9990	8.8223	1.1777	1.5045	.2
.9	0.0681	8.8326	9.9990	8.8336	1.1664	1.5027	.1
4.0	0.0698	8.8436	9.9989	8.8446	1.1554	1.5010	86.0
.1	0.0716	8.8543	9.9989	8.8554	1.1446	1.4992	.9
.2	0.0733	8.8647	9.9988	8.8659	1.1341	1.4975	.8
.3	0.0750	8.8749	9.9988	8.8762	1.1238	1.4957	.7
.4	0.0768	8.8849	9.9987	8.8862	1.1138	1.4940	.6
.5	0.0785	8.8946	9.9987	8.8960	1.1040	1.4923	.5
.6	0.0803	8.9042	9.9986	8.9056	1.0944	1.4905	.4
.7	0.0820	8.9135	9.9985	8.9150	1.0850	1.4888	.3
.8	0.0838	8.9226	9.9985	8.9241	1.0759	1.4870	.2
.9	0.0855	8.9315	9.9984	8.9331	1.0669	1.4853	.1
5.0	0.0873	8.9403	9.9983	8.9420	1.0580	1.4835	85.0
Degrees	Radians	L.Cos	L.Sin	L.Cot	L.Tan	Radians	Degrees
						Measures in	

Table V. Logarithms of Trigonometric Functions

Measures in Degrees	Radians	L.Sin	L.Cos	L.Tan	L.Cot	Radians	Degrees
5.0	0.0873	8.9403	9.9983	8.9420	1.0580	1.4835	85.0
.1	0.0890	8.9489	9.9983	8.9506	1.0494	1.4818	.9
.2	0.0908	8.9573	9.9982	8.9591	1.0409	1.4800	.8
.3	0.0925	8.9655	9.9981	8.9674	1.0326	1.4783	.7
.4	0.0942	8.9736	9.9981	8.9756	1.0244	1.4765	.6
.5	0.0960	8.9816	9.9980	8.9836	1.0164	1.4748	.5
.6	0.0977	8.9894	9.9979	8.9915	1.0085	1.4731	.4
.7	0.0995	8.9970	9.9978	8.9992	1.0008	1.4713	.3
.8	0.1012	9.0046	9.9978	9.0068	0.9932	1.4696	.2
.9	0.1030	9.0120	9.9977	9.0143	0.9857	1.4678	.1
6.0	0.1047	9.0192	9.9976	9.0216	0.9784	1.4661	84.0
.1	0.1065	9.0264	9.9975	9.0289	0.9711	1.4643	.9
.2	0.1082	9.0334	9.9975	9.0360	0.9640	1.4626	.8
.3	0.1100	9.0403	9.9974	9.0430	0.9570	1.4608	.7
.4	0.1117	9.0472	9.9973	9.0499	0.9501	1.4591	.6
.5	0.1134	9.0539	9.9972	9.0567	0.9433	1.4573	.5
.6	0.1152	9.0605	9.9971	9.0633	0.9367	1.4556	.4
.7	0.1169	9.0670	9.9970	9.0699	0.9301	1.4539	.3
.8	0.1187	9.0734	9.9969	9.0764	0.9236	1.4521	.2
.9	0.1204	9.0797	9.9968	9.0828	0.9172	1.4504	.1
7.0	0.1222	9.0859	9.9968	9.0891	0.9109	1.4486	83.0
.1	0.1239	9.0920	9.9967	9.0954	0.9046	1.4469	.9
.2	0.1257	9.0981	9.9966	9.1015	0.8985	1.4451	.8
.3	0.1274	9.1040	9.9965	9.1076	0.8924	1.4434	.7
.4	0.1292	9.1099	9.9964	9.1135	0.8865	1.4416	.6
.5	0.1309	9.1157	9.9963	9.1194	0.8806	1.4399	.5
.6	0.1326	9.1214	9.9962	9.1252	0.8748	1.4382	.4
.7	0.1344	9.1271	9.9961	9.1310	0.8690	1.4364	.3
.8	0.1361	9.1326	9.9960	9.1367	0.8633	1.4347	.2
.9	0.1379	9.1381	9.9959	9.1423	0.8577	1.4329	.1
8.0	0.1396	9.1436	9.9958	9.1478	0.8522	1.4312	82.0
.1	0.1414	9.1489	9.9956	9.1533	0.8467	1.4294	.9
.2	0.1431	9.1542	9.9955	9.1587	0.8413	1.4277	.8
.3	0.1449	9.1594	9.9954	9.1640	0.8360	1.4259	.7
.4	0.1466	9.1646	9.9953	9.1693	0.8307	1.4242	.6
.5	0.1484	9.1697	9.9952	9.1745	0.8255	1.4224	.5
.6	0.1501	9.1747	9.9951	9.1797	0.8203	1.4207	.4
.7	0.1518	9.1797	9.9950	9.1848	0.8152	1.4190	.3
.8	0.1536	9.1847	9.9949	9.1898	0.8102	1.4172	.2
.9	0.1553	9.1895	9.9947	9.1948	0.8052	1.4155	.1
9.0	0.1571	9.1943	9.9946	9.1997	0.8003	1.4137	81.0
.1	0.1588	9.1991	9.9945	9.2046	0.7954	1.4120	.9
.2	0.1606	9.2038	9.9944	9.2094	0.7906	1.4102	.8
.3	0.1623	9.2085	9.9943	9.2142	0.7858	1.4085	.7
.4	0.1641	9.2131	9.9941	9.2189	0.7811	1.4067	.6
.5	0.1658	9.2176	9.9940	9.2236	0.7764	1.4050	.5
.6	0.1676	9.2221	9.9939	9.2282	0.7718	1.4032	.4
.7	0.1693	9.2266	9.9937	9.2328	0.7672	1.4015	.3
.8	0.1710	9.2310	9.9936	9.2374	0.7626	1.3998	.2
.9	0.1728	9.2353	9.9935	9.2419	0.7581	1.3980	.1
10.0	0.1745	9.2397	9.9934	9.2463	0.7537	1.3963	80.0
.1	0.1763	9.2439	9.9932	9.2507	0.7493	1.3945	.9
.2	0.1780	9.2482	9.9931	9.2551	0.7449	1.3928	.8
.3	0.1798	9.2524	9.9929	9.2594	0.7406	1.3910	.7
.4	0.1815	9.2565	9.9928	9.2637	0.7363	1.3893	.6
.5	0.1833	9.2606	9.9927	9.2680	0.7320	1.3875	.5
.6	0.1850	9.2647	9.9925	9.2722	0.7278	1.3858	.4
.7	0.1868	9.2687	9.9924	9.2764	0.7236	1.3840	.3
.8	0.1885	9.2727	9.9922	9.2805	0.7195	1.3823	.2
.9	0.1902	9.2767	9.9921	9.2846	0.7154	1.3806	.1
11.0	0.1920	9.2806	9.9919	9.2887	0.7113	1.3788	79.0
Degrees	Radians	L.Cos	L.Sin	L.Cot	L.Tan	Radians	Degrees
							Measures in

V. Logarithms of Trigonometric Functions

Measures in Degrees	Radians	L.Sin	L.Cos	L.Tan	L.Cot	Radians	Degrees
11.0	0.1920	9.2806	9.9919	9.2887	0.7113	1.3788	79.0
.1	0.1937	9.2845	9.9918	9.2927	0.7073	1.3771	.9
.2	0.1955	9.2883	9.9916	9.2967	0.7033	1.3753	.8
.3	0.1972	9.2921	9.9915	9.3006	9.6994	1.3736	.7
.4	0.1990	9.2959	9.9913	9.3016	0.6954	1.3718	.6
.5	0.2007	9.2997	9.9912	9.3085	0.6915	1.3701	.5
.6	0.2025	9.3034	9.9910	9.3123	0.6877	1.3683	.4
.7	0.2042	9.3070	9.9909	9.3162	0.0838	1.3666	.3
.8	0.2059	9.3107	9.9907	9.3200	0.6800	1.3648	.2
.9	0.2077	9.3143	9.9906	9.3237	0.6763	1.3631	.1
12.0	0.2094	9.3179	9.9904	9.3275	0.6725	1.3614	78.0
.1	0.2112	9.3214	9.9902	9.3312	0.6688	1.3596	.9
.2	0.2129	0.3250	9.9901	9.3349	0.6651	1.3579	.8
.3	0.2147	9.3284	9.9899	9.3385	0.6615	1.3561	.7
.4	0.2164	9.3319	9.9897	9.3422	0.6578	1.3544	.6
.5	0.2182	9.3353	9.9896	9.3458	0.6542	1.3526	.5
.6	0.2199	9.3387	9.9894	9.3493	0.6507	1.3509	.4
.7	0.2217	9.3421	9.9892	9.3529	0.6471	1.3491	.3
.8	0.2234	9.3455	9.9891	9.3564	0.6436	1.3474	.2
.9	0.2251	9.3488	9.9889	9.3599	0.6401	1.3456	.1
13.0	0.2269	9.3521	9.9887	9.3634	0.6366	1.3439	77.0
.1	0.2286	9.3554	9.9885	9.3668	0.6332	1.3422	.9
.2	0.2304	9.3586	9.9884	9.3702	0.6298	1.3404	.8
.3	0.2321	9.3618	9.9882	9.3736	0.6264	1.3387	.7
.4	0.2339	9.3650	9.9880	9.3770	0.6230	1.3369	.6
.5	0.2356	9.3682	9.9878	9.3804	0.6196	1.3352	.5
.6	0.2374	9.3713	9.9876	9.3837	0.6163	1.3334	.4
.7	0.2391	9.3745	9.9875	9.3870	0.6130	1.3317	.3
.8	0.2409	9.3775	9.9873	9.3903	0.6097	1.3299	.2
.9	0.2426	9.3806	9.9871	9.3935	0.6065	1.3282	.1
14.0	0.2443	9.3837	9.9869	9.3968	0.6032	1.3265	76.0
.1	0.2461	9.3867	9.9867	9.4000	0.6000	1.3247	.9
.2	0.2478	9.3897	9.9865	9.4032	0.5968	1.3230	.8
.3	0.2496	9.3927	9.9863	9.4064	0.5936	1.3212	.7
.4	0.2513	9.3957	9.9861	9.4095	0.5905	1.3195	.6
.5	0.2531	9.3986	9.9859	9.4127	0.5873	1.3177	.5
.6	0.2548	9.4015	9.9857	9.4158	0.5842	1.3160	.4
.7	0.2566	9.4044	9.9855	9.4189	0.5811	1.3142	.3
.8	0.2583	9.4073	9.9853	9.4220	0.5780	1.3125	.2
.9	0.2601	9.4102	9.9851	9.4250	0.5750	1.3107	.1
15.0	0.2618	9.4130	9.9849	9.4281	0.5719	1.3090	75.0
.1	0.2635	9.4158	9.9847	9.4311	0.5689	1.3073	.9
.2	0.2653	9.4186	9.9845	9.4341	0.5659	1.3055	.8
.3	0.2670	9.4214	9.9843	9.4371	0.5629	1.3038	.7
.4	0.2688	9.4242	9.9841	9.4400	0.5600	1.3020	.6
.5	0.2705	9.4269	9.9839	9.4430	0.5570	1.3003	.5
.6	0.2723	9.4296	9.9837	9.4459	0.5541	1.2985	.4
.7	0.2740	9.4323	9.9835	9.4488	0.5512	1.2968	.3
.8	0.2758	9.4350	9.9833	9.4517	0.5483	1.2950	.2
.9	0.2775	9.4377	9.9831	9.4546	0.5454	1.2933	.1
16.0	0.2793	9.4403	9.9828	9.4575	0.5425	1.2915	74.0
.1	0.2810	9.4430	9.9826	9.4603	0.5397	1.2898	.9
.2	0.2827	9.4456	9.9824	9.4632	0.5368	1.2881	.8
.3	0.2845	9.4482	9.9822	9.4660	0.5340	1.2863	.7
.4	0.2862	9.4508	9.9820	9.4688	0.5312	1.2846	.6
.5	0.2880	9.4533	9.9817	9.4716	0.5284	1.2828	.5
.6	0.2897	9.4559	9.9815	9.4744	0.5256	1.2811	.4
.7	0.2915	9.4584	9.9813	9.4771	0.5229	1.2793	.3
.8	0.2932	9.4609	9.9811	9.4799	0.5201	1.2776	.2
.9	0.2950	9.4634	9.9808	9.4826	0.5174	1.2758	.1
17.0	0.2967	9.4659	9.9806	9.4853	0.5147	1.2741	73.0
Degrees	Radians	L.Cos	L.Sin	L.Cot	L.Tan	Radians	Degrees
						Measures in	

V. Logarithms of Trigonometric Functions

Measures in Degrees	Radians	L.Sin	L.Cos	L.Tan	L.Cot	Radians	Degrees
17.0	0.2967	9.4659	9.9806	9.4853	0.5147	1.2741	73.0
.1	0.2985	9.4684	9.9804	9.4880	0.5120	1.2723	.9
.2	0.3002	9.4709	9.9801	9.4907	0.5093	1.2706	.8
.3	0.3019	9.4733	9.9799	9.4934	0.5066	1.2689	.7
.4	0.3037	9.4757	9.9797	9.4961	0.5039	1.2671	.6
.5	0.3054	9.4781	9.9794	9.4987	0.5013	1.2654	.5
.6	0.3072	9.4805	9.9792	9.5014	0.4986	1.2636	.4
.7	0.3089	9.4829	9.9789	9.5040	0.4960	1.2619	.3
.8	0.3107	9.4853	9.9787	9.5066	0.4934	1.2601	.2
.9	0.3124	9.4876	9.9785	9.5092	0.4908	1.2584	.1
18.0	0.3142	9.4900	9.9782	9.5118	0.4882	1.2566	72.0
.1	0.3159	9.4923	9.9780	9.5143	0.4857	1.2549	.9
.2	0.3176	9.4946	9.9777	9.5169	0.4831	1.2531	.8
.3	0.3194	9.4969	9.9775	9.5195	0.4805	1.2514	.7
.4	0.3211	9.4992	9.9772	9.5220	0.4780	1.2497	.6
.5	0.3229	9.5015	9.9770	9.5245	0.4755	1.2479	.5
.6	0.3246	9.5037	9.9767	9.5270	0.4730	1.2462	.4
.7	0.3264	9.5060	9.9764	9.5295	0.4705	1.2444	.3
.8	0.3281	9.5082	9.9762	9.5320	0.4680	1.2427	.2
.9	0.3299	9.5104	9.9759	9.5345	0.4655	1.2409	.1
19.0	0.3316	9.5126	9.9757	9.5370	0.4630	1.2392	71.0
.1	0.3334	9.5148	9.9754	9.5394	0.4606	1.2374	.9
.2	0.3351	9.5170	9.9751	9.5419	0.4581	1.2357	.8
.3	0.3368	9.5192	9.9749	9.5443	0.4557	1.2339	.7
.4	0.3386	9.5213	9.9746	9.5467	0.4533	1.2322	.6
.5	0.3403	9.5235	9.9743	9.5491	0.4509	1.2305	.5
.6	0.3421	9.5256	9.9741	9.5516	0.4484	1.2287	.4
.7	0.3438	9.5278	9.9738	9.5539	0.4461	1.2270	.3
.8	0.3456	9.5299	9.9735	9.5563	0.4437	1.2252	.2
.9	0.3473	9.5320	9.9733	9.5587	0.4413	1.2235	.1
20.0	0.3491	9.5341	9.9730	9.5611	0.4389	1.2217	70.0
.1	0.3508	9.5361	9.9727	9.5634	0.4366	1.2200	.9
.2	0.3526	9.5382	9.9724	9.5658	0.4342	1.2182	.8
.3	0.3543	9.5402	9.9722	9.5681	0.4319	1.2165	.7
.4	0.3560	9.5423	9.9719	9.5704	0.4296	1.2147	.6
.5	0.3578	9.5443	9.9716	9.5727	0.4273	1.2130	.5
.6	0.3595	9.5463	9.9713	9.5750	0.4250	1.2113	.4
.7	0.3613	9.5484	9.9710	9.5773	0.4227	1.2095	.3
.8	0.3630	9.5504	9.9707	9.5796	0.4204	1.2078	.2
.9	0.3648	9.5523	9.9704	9.5819	0.4181	1.2060	.1
21.0	0.3665	9.5543	9.9702	9.5842	0.4158	1.2043	69.0
.1	0.3683	9.5563	9.9699	9.5864	0.4136	1.2025	.9
.2	0.3700	9.5583	9.9696	9.5887	0.4113	1.2008	.8
.3	0.3718	9.5602	9.9693	9.5909	0.4091	1.1990	.7
.4	0.3735	9.5621	9.9690	9.5932	0.4068	1.1973	.6
.5	0.3752	9.5641	9.9687	9.5954	0.4046	1.1956	.5
.6	0.3770	9.5660	9.9684	9.5976	0.4024	1.1938	.4
.7	0.3787	9.5679	9.9681	9.5998	0.4002	1.1921	.3
.8	0.3805	9.5698	9.9678	9.6020	0.3980	1.1903	.2
.9	0.3822	9.5717	9.9675	9.6042	0.3958	1.1886	.1
22.0	0.3840	9.5736	9.9672	9.6064	0.3936	1.1868	68.0
.1	0.3857	9.5754	9.9669	9.6086	0.3914	1.1851	.9
.2	0.3875	9.5773	9.9666	9.6108	0.3892	1.1833	.8
.3	0.3892	9.5792	9.9662	9.6129	0.3871	1.1816	.7
.4	0.3910	9.5810	9.9659	9.6151	0.3849	1.1798	.6
.5	0.3927	9.5828	9.9656	9.6172	0.3828	1.1781	.5
.6	0.3944	9.5847	9.9653	9.6194	0.3806	1.1764	.4
.7	0.3962	9.5865	9.9650	9.6215	0.3785	1.1746	.3
.8	0.3979	9.5883	9.9647	9.6236	0.3764	1.1729	.2
.9	0.3997	9.5901	9.9643	9.6257	0.3743	1.1711	.1
23.0	0.4014	9.5919	9.9640	9.6279	0.3721	1.1694	67.0
Degrees	Radians	L.Cos	L.Sin	L.Cot	L.Tan	Radians	Degrees
						Measures in	

V. Logarithms of Trigonometric Functions

Measures in Degrees	Radians	L.Sin	L.Cos	L.Tan	L.Cot	Radians	Degrees
23.0	0.4014	9.5919	9.9640	9.6279	0.3721	1.1694	67.0
.1	0.4032	9.5937	9.9637	9.6300	0.3700	1.1676	.9
.2	0.4049	9.5954	9.9634	9.6321	0.3679	1.1659	.8
.3	0.4067	9.5972	9.9631	9.6341	0.3659	1.1641	.7
.4	0.4084	9.5990	9.9627	9.6362	0.3638	1.1624	.6
.5	0.4102	9.6007	9.9624	9.6383	0.3617	1.1606	.5
.6	0.4119	9.6024	9.9621	9.6404	0.3596	1.1589	.4
.7	0.4136	9.6042	9.9617	9.6424	0.3576	1.1572	.3
.8	0.4154	9.6059	9.9614	9.6445	0.3555	1.1554	.2
.9	0.4171	9.6076	9.9611	9.6465	0.3535	1.1537	.1
24.0	0.4189	9.6093	9.9607	9.6486	0.3514	1.1519	66.0
.1	0.4206	9.6110	9.9604	9.6506	0.3494	1.1502	.9
.2	0.4224	9.6127	9.9601	9.6527	0.3473	1.1484	.8
.3	0.4241	9.6144	9.9597	9.6547	0.3453	1.1467	.7
.4	0.4259	9.6161	9.9594	9.6567	0.3433	1.1449	.6
.5	0.4276	9.6177	9.9590	9.6587	0.3413	1.1432	.5
.6	0.4294	9.6194	9.9587	9.6607	0.3393	1.1414	.4
.7	0.4311	9.6210	9.9583	9.6627	0.3373	1.1397	.3
.8	0.4328	9.6227	9.9580	9.6647	0.3353	1.1380	.2
.9	0.4346	9.6243	9.9576	9.6667	0.3333	1.1362	.1
25.0	0.4363	9.6259	9.9573	9.6687	0.3313	1.1345	65.0
.1	0.4381	9.6276	9.9569	9.6706	0.3294	1.1327	.9
.2	0.4398	9.6292	9.9566	9.6726	0.3274	1.1310	.8
.3	0.4416	9.6308	9.9562	9.6746	0.3254	1.1292	.7
.4	0.4433	9.6324	9.9558	9.6765	0.3235	1.1275	.6
.5	0.4451	9.6340	9.9555	9.6785	0.3215	1.1257	.5
.6	0.4468	9.6356	9.9551	9.6804	0.3196	1.1240	.4
.7	0.4485	9.6371	9.9548	9.6824	0.3176	1.1222	.3
.8	0.4503	9.6387	9.9544	9.6843	0.3157	1.1205	.2
.9	0.4520	9.6403	9.9540	9.6863	0.3137	1.1188	.1
26.0	0.4538	9.6418	9.9537	9.6882	0.3118	1.1170	64.0
.1	0.4555	9.6434	9.9533	9.6901	0.3099	1.1153	.9
.2	0.4573	9.6449	9.9529	9.6920	0.3080	1.1135	.8
.3	0.4590	9.6465	9.9525	9.6939	0.3061	1.1118	.7
.4	0.4608	9.6480	9.9522	9.6958	0.3042	1.1100	.6
.5	0.4625	9.6495	9.9518	9.6977	0.3023	1.1083	.5
.6	0.4643	9.6510	9.9514	9.6996	0.3004	1.1065	.4
.7	0.4660	9.6526	9.9510	9.7015	0.2985	1.1048	.3
.8	0.4677	9.6541	9.9506	9.7034	0.2966	1.1030	.2
.9	0.4695	9.6556	9.9503	9.7053	0.2947	1.1013	.1
27.0	0.4712	9.6570	9.9499	9.7072	0.2928	1.0996	63.0
.1	0.4730	9.6585	9.9495	9.7090	0.2910	1.0978	.9
.2	0.4747	9.6600	9.9491	9.7109	0.2891	1.0961	.8
.3	0.4765	9.6615	9.9487	9.7128	0.2872	1.0943	.7
.4	0.4782	9.6629	9.9483	9.7146	0.2854	1.0926	.6
.5	0.4800	9.6644	9.9479	9.7165	0.2835	1.0908	.5
.6	0.4817	9.6659	9.9475	9.7183	0.2817	1.0891	.4
.7	0.4835	9.6673	9.9471	9.7202	0.2798	1.0873	.3
.8	0.4852	9.6687	9.9467	9.7220	0.2780	1.0856	.2
.9	0.4869	9.6702	9.9463	9.7238	0.2762	1.0838	.1
28.0	0.4887	9.6716	9.9459	9.7257	0.2743	1.0821	62.0
.1	0.4904	9.6730	9.9455	9.7275	0.2725	1.0804	.9
.2	0.4922	9.6744	9.9451	9.7293	0.2707	1.0786	.8
.3	0.4939	9.6759	9.9447	9.7311	0.2689	1.0769	.7
.4	0.4957	9.6773	9.9443	9.7330	0.2670	1.0751	.6
.5	0.4974	9.6787	9.9439	9.7348	0.2652	1.0734	.5
.6	0.4992	9.6801	9.9435	9.7366	0.2634	1.0716	.4
.7	0.5009	9.6814	9.9431	9.7384	0.2616	1.0699	.3
.8	0.5027	9.6828	9.9427	9.7402	0.2598	1.0681	.2
.9	0.5044	9.6842	9.9422	9.7420	0.2580	1.0664	.1
29.0	0.5061	9.6856	9.9418	9.7438	0.2562	1.0647	61.0
Degrees	Radians	L.Cos	L.Sin	L.Cot	L.Tan	Radians	Degrees
						Measures in	

V. Logarithms of Trigonometric Functions

Measures in Degrees	Radians	L.Sin	L.Cos	L.Tan	L.Cot	Radians	Degrees
29.0	0.5061	9.6856	9.9418	9.7438	0.2562	1.0647	61.0
.1	0.5079	9.6869	9.9414	9.7455	0.2545	1.0629	.9
.2	0.5096	9.6883	9.9410	9.7473	0.2527	1.0612	.8
.3	0.5114	9.6896	9.9406	9.7491	0.2509	1.0594	.7
.4	0.5131	9.6910	9.9401	9.7509	0.2491	1.0577	.6
.5	0.5149	9.6923	9.9397	9.7526	0.2474	1.0559	.5
.6	0.5166	9.6937	9.9393	9.7544	0.2456	1.0542	.4
.7	0.5184	9.6950	9.9388	9.7562	0.2438	1.0524	.3
.8	0.5201	9.6963	9.9384	9.7579	0.2421	1.0507	.2
.9	0.5219	9.6977	9.9380	9.7597	0.2403	1.0489	.1
30.0	0.5236	9.6990	9.9375	9.7614	0.2386	1.0472	60.0
.1	0.5253	9.7003	9.9371	9.7632	0.2368	1.0455	.9
.2	0.5271	9.7016	9.9367	9.7649	0.2351	1.0437	.8
.3	0.5288	9.7029	9.9362	9.7667	0.2333	1.0420	.7
.4	0.5306	9.7042	9.9358	9.7684	0.2316	1.0402	.6
.5	0.5323	9.7055	9.9353	9.7701	0.2299	1.0385	.5
.6	0.5341	9.7068	9.9349	9.7719	0.2281	1.0367	.4
.7	0.5358	9.7080	9.9344	9.7736	0.2264	1.0350	.3
.8	0.5376	9.7093	9.9340	9.7753	0.2247	1.0332	.2
.9	0.5393	9.7106	9.9335	9.7771	0.2229	1.0315	.1
31.0	0.5411	9.7118	9.9331	9.7788	0.2212	1.0297	59.0
.1	0.5428	9.7131	9.9326	9.7805	0.2195	1.0280	.9
.2	0.5445	9.7144	9.9322	9.7822	0.2178	1.0263	.8
.3	0.5463	9.7156	9.9317	9.7839	0.2161	1.0245	.7
.4	0.5480	9.7168	9.9312	9.7856	0.2144	1.0228	.6
.5	0.5498	9.7181	9.9308	9.7873	0.2127	1.0210	.5
.6	0.5515	9.7193	9.9303	9.7890	0.2110	1.0193	.4
.7	0.5533	9.7205	9.9298	9.7907	0.2093	1.0175	.3
.8	0.5550	9.7218	9.9294	9.7924	0.2076	1.0158	.2
.9	0.5568	9.7230	9.9289	9.7941	0.2059	1.0140	.1
32.0	0.5585	9.7242	9.9284	9.7958	0.2042	1.0123	58.0
.1	0.5603	9.7254	9.9279	9.7975	0.2025	1.0105	.9
.2	0.5620	9.7266	9.9275	9.7992	0.2008	1.0088	.8
.3	0.5637	9.7278	9.9270	9.8008	0.1992	1.0071	.7
.4	0.5655	9.7290	9.9265	9.8025	0.1975	1.0053	.6
.5	0.5672	9.7302	9.9260	9.8042	0.1958	1.0036	.5
.6	0.5690	9.7314	9.9255	9.8059	0.1941	1.0018	.4
.7	0.5707	9.7326	9.9251	9.8075	0.1925	1.0001	.3
.8	0.5725	9.7338	9.9246	9.8092	0.1908	0.9983	.2
.9	0.5742	9.7349	9.9241	9.8109	0.1891	0.9966	.1
33.0	0.5760	9.7361	9.9236	9.8125	0.1875	0.9948	57.0
.1	0.5777	9.7373	9.9231	9.8142	0.1858	0.9931	.9
.2	0.5794	9.7384	9.9226	9.8158	0.1842	0.9913	.8
.3	0.5812	9.7396	9.9221	9.8175	0.1825	0.9896	.7
.4	0.5829	9.7407	9.9216	9.8191	0.1809	0.9879	.6
.5	0.5847	9.7419	9.9211	9.8208	0.1792	0.9861	.5
.6	0.5864	9.7430	9.9206	9.8224	0.1776	0.9844	.4
.7	0.5882	9.7442	9.9201	9.8241	0.1759	0.9826	.3
.8	0.5899	9.7453	9.9196	9.8257	0.1743	0.9809	.2
.9	0.5917	9.7464	9.9191	9.8274	0.1726	0.9791	.1
34.0	0.5934	9.7476	9.9186	9.8290	0.1710	0.9774	56.0
.1	0.5952	9.7487	9.9181	9.8306	0.1694	0.9756	.9
.2	0.5969	9.7498	9.9175	9.8323	0.1677	0.9739	.8
.3	0.5986	9.7509	9.9170	9.8339	0.1661	0.9721	.7
.4	0.6004	9.7520	9.9165	9.8355	0.1645	0.9704	.6
.5	0.6021	9.7531	9.9160	9.8371	0.1629	0.9687	.5
.6	0.6039	9.7542	9.9155	9.8388	0.1612	0.9669	.4
.7	0.6056	9.7553	9.9149	9.8404	0.1596	0.9652	.3
.8	0.6074	9.7564	9.9144	9.8420	0.1580	0.9634	.2
.9	0.6091	9.7575	9.9139	9.8436	0.1564	0.9617	.1
35.0	0.6109	9.7586	9.9134	9.8452	0.1548	0.9599	55.0
Degrees	Radians	L.Cos	L.Sin	L.Cot	L.Tan	Radians	Degrees
							Measures in

V. Logarithms of Trigonometric Functions

Measures in Degrees	Radians	L.Sin	L.Cos	L.Tan	L.Cot	Radians	Degrees
35.0	0.6109	9.7586	9.9134	9.8452	0.1548	0.9599	55.0
.1	0.6126	9.7597	9.9128	9.8468	0.1532	0.9582	.9
.2	0.6144	9.7607	9.9123	9.8484	0.1516	0.9564	.8
.3	0.6161	9.7618	9.9118	9.8501	0.1499	0.9547	.7
.4	0.6178	9.7629	9.9112	9.8517	0.1483	0.9530	.6
.5	0.6196	9.7640	9.9107	9.8533	0.1467	0.9512	.5
.6	0.6213	9.7650	9.9101	9.8549	0.1451	0.9495	.4
.7	0.6231	9.7661	9.9096	9.8565	0.1435	0.9477	.3
.8	0.6248	9.7671	9.9091	9.8581	0.1419	0.9460	.2
.9	0.6266	9.7682	9.9085	9.8597	0.1403	0.9442	.1
36.0	0.6283	9.7692	9.9080	9.8613	0.1387	0.9425	54.0
.1	0.6301	9.7703	9.9074	9.8629	0.1371	0.9407	.9
.2	0.6318	9.7713	9.9069	9.8644	0.1356	0.9390	.8
.3	0.6336	9.7723	9.9063	9.8660	0.1340	0.9372	.7
.4	0.6353	9.7734	9.9057	9.8676	0.1324	0.9355	.6
.5	0.6370	9.7744	9.9052	9.8692	0.1308	0.9338	.5
.6	0.6388	9.7754	9.9046	9.8708	0.1292	0.9320	.4
.7	0.6405	9.7764	9.9041	9.8724	0.1276	0.9303	.3
.8	0.6423	9.7774	9.9035	9.8740	0.1260	0.9285	.2
.9	0.6440	9.7785	9.9029	9.8755	0.1245	0.9268	.1
37.0	0.6458	9.7795	9.9023	9.8771	0.1229	0.9250	53.0
.1	0.6475	9.7805	9.9018	9.8787	0.1213	0.9233	.9
.2	0.6493	9.7815	9.9012	9.8803	0.1197	0.9215	.8
.3	0.6510	9.7825	9.9006	9.8818	0.1182	0.9198	.7
.4	0.6528	9.7835	9.9000	9.8834	0.1166	0.9180	.6
.5	0.6545	9.7844	9.8995	9.8850	0.1150	0.9163	.5
.6	0.6562	9.7854	9.8989	9.8865	0.1135	0.9146	.4
.7	0.6580	9.7864	9.8983	9.8881	0.1119	0.9128	.3
.8	0.6597	9.7874	9.8977	9.8897	0.1103	0.9111	.2
.9	0.6615	9.7884	9.8971	9.8912	0.1088	0.9093	.1
38.0	0.6632	9.7893	9.8965	9.8928	0.1072	0.9076	52.0
.1	0.6650	9.7903	9.8959	9.8944	0.1056	0.9058	.9
.2	0.6667	9.7913	9.8953	9.8959	0.1041	0.9041	.8
.3	0.6685	9.7922	9.8947	9.8975	0.1025	0.9023	.7
.4	0.6702	9.7932	9.8941	9.8990	0.1010	0.9006	.6
.5	0.6720	9.7941	9.8935	9.9006	0.0994	0.8988	.5
.6	0.6737	9.7951	9.8929	9.9022	0.0978	0.8971	.4
.7	0.6754	9.7960	9.8923	9.9037	0.0963	0.8954	.3
.8	0.6772	9.7970	9.8917	9.9053	0.0947	0.8936	.2
.9	0.6789	9.7979	9.8911	9.9068	0.0932	0.8919	.1
39.0	0.6807	9.7989	9.8905	9.9084	0.0916	0.8901	51.0
.1	0.6824	9.7998	9.8899	9.9099	0.0901	0.8884	.9
.2	0.6842	9.8007	9.8893	9.9115	0.0885	0.8866	.8
.3	0.6859	9.8017	9.8887	9.9130	0.0870	0.8849	.7
.4	0.6877	9.8026	9.8880	9.9146	0.0854	0.8831	.6
.5	0.6894	9.8035	9.8874	9.9161	0.0839	0.8814	.5
.6	0.6912	9.8044	9.8868	9.9176	0.0824	0.8796	.4
.7	0.6929	9.8053	9.8862	9.9192	0.0808	0.8779	.3
.8	0.6946	9.8063	9.8855	9.9207	0.0793	0.8762	.2
.9	0.6964	9.8072	9.8849	9.9223	0.0777	0.8744	.1
40.0	0.6981	9.8081	9.8843	9.9238	0.0762	0.8727	50.0
.1	0.6999	9.8090	9.8836	9.9254	0.0746	0.8709	.9
.2	0.7016	9.8099	9.8830	9.9269	0.0731	0.8692	.8
.3	0.7034	9.8108	9.8823	9.9284	9.0716	0.8674	.7
.4	0.7051	9.8117	9.8817	9.9300	0.0700	0.8657	.6
.5	0.7069	9.8125	9.8810	9.9315	0.0685	0.8639	.5
.6	0.7086	9.8134	9.8804	9.9330	0.0670	0.8622	.4
.7	0.7103	9.8143	9.8797	9.9346	0.0654	0.8604	.3
.8	0.7121	9.8152	9.8791	9.9361	0.0639	0.8587	.2
.9	0.7138	9.8161	9.8784	9.9376	0.0624	0.8570	.1
41.0	0.7156	9.8169	9.8778	9.9392	0.0608	0.8552	49.0
Degrees	Radians	L.Cos	L.Sin	L.Cot	L.Tan	Radians	Degrees

Measures in

V. Logarithms of Trigonometric Functions

Measures in Degrees	Radians	L.Sin	L.Cos	L.Tan	L.Cot	Radians	Degrees
41.0	0.7156	9.8169	9.8778	9.9392	0.0608	0.8552	49.0
.1	0.7173	9.8178	9.8771	9.9407	0.0593	0.8535	.9
.2	0.7191	9.8187	9.8765	9.9422	0.0578	0.8517	.8
.3	0.7208	9.8195	9.8758	9.9438	0.0562	0.8500	.7
.4	0.7226	9.8204	9.8751	9.9453	0.0547	0.8482	.6
.5	0.7243	9.8213	9.8745	9.9468	0.0532	0.8465	.5
.6	0.7261	9.8221	9.8738	9.9483	0.0517	0.8447	.4
.7	0.7278	9.8230	9.8731	9.9499	0.0501	0.8430	.3
.8	0.7295	9.8238	9.8724	9.9514	0.0486	0.8412	.2
.9	0.7313	9.8247	9.8718	9.9529	0.0471	0.8395	.1
42.0	0.7330	9.8255	9.8711	9.9544	0.0456	0.8378	48.0
.1	0.7348	9.8264	9.8704	9.9560	0.0440	0.8360	.9
.2	0.7365	9.8272	9.8697	9.9575	0.0425	0.8343	.8
.3	0.7383	9.8280	9.8690	9.9590	0.0410	0.8325	.7
.4	0.7400	9.8289	9.8683	9.9605	0.0395	0.8308	.6
.5	0.7418	9.8297	9.8676	9.9621	0.0379	0.8290	.5
.6	0.7435	9.8305	9.8669	9.9636	0.0364	0.8273	.4
.7	0.7453	9.8313	9.8662	9.9651	0.0349	0.8255	.3
.8	0.7470	9.8322	9.8655	9.9666	0.0334	0.8238	.2
.9	0.7487	9.8330	9.8648	9.9681	0.0319	0.8220	.1
43.0	0.7505	9.8338	9.8641	9.9697	0.0303	0.8203	47.0
.1	0.7522	9.8346	9.8634	9.9712	0.0288	0.8186	.9
.2	0.7540	9.8354	9.8627	9.9727	0.0273	0.8168	.8
.3	0.7557	9.8362	9.8620	9.9742	0.0258	0.8151	.7
.4	0.7575	9.8370	9.8613	9.9757	0.0243	0.8133	.6
.5	0.7592	9.8378	9.8606	9.9772	0.0228	0.8116	.5
.6	0.7610	9.8386	9.8598	9.9788	0.0212	0.8098	.4
.7	0.7627	9.8394	9.8591	9.9803	0.0197	0.8081	.3
.8	0.7645	9.8402	9.8584	9.9818	0.0182	0.8063	.2
.9	0.7662	9.8410	9.8577	9.9833	0.0167	0.8046	.1
44.0	0.7679	9.8418	9.8569	9.9848	0.0152	0.8029	46.0
.1	0.7697	9.8426	9.8562	9.9864	0.0136	0.8011	.9
.2	0.7714	9.8433	9.8555	9.9879	0.0121	0.7994	.8
.3	0.7732	9.8441	9.8547	9.9894	0.0106	0.7976	.7
.4	0.7749	9.8449	9.8540	9.9909	0.0091	0.7959	.6
.5	0.7767	9.8457	9.8532	9.9924	0.0076	0.7941	.5
.6	0.7784	9.8464	9.8525	9.9939	0.0061	0.7924	.4
.7	0.7802	9.8472	9.8517	9.9955	0.0045	0.7906	.3
.8	0.7819	9.8480	9.8510	9.9970	0.0030	0.7889	.2
.9	0.7837	9.8487	9.8502	9.9985	0.0015	0.7871	.1
45.0	0.7854	9.8495	9.8495	0.0000	0.0000	0.7854	45.0
Degrees	Radians	L.Cos	L.Sin	L.Cot	L.Tan	Radians	Degrees
						Measures in	

The Greek Alphabet

LETTERS		NAMES	LETTERS		NAMES	LETTERS		NAMES
Λ	α	Alpha	I	ι	Iota	P	ρ	Rho
B	β	Beta	K	κ	Kappa	Σ	σ	Sigma
Γ	γ	Gamma	Λ	λ	Lambda	T	τ	Tau
Δ	δ	Delta	M	μ	Mu	Υ	υ	Upsilon
E	ε	Epsilon	N	ν	Nu	Φ	φ	Phi
Z	ζ	Zeta	Ξ	ξ	Xi	X	χ	Chi
H	η	Eta	O	o	Omicron	Ψ	ψ	Psi
Θ	θ	Theta	Π	π	Pi	Ω	ω	Omega

Tables III, IV, and V, with minor changes, are used with the permission of The Chemical Rubber Company. These tables are based on tables in their publication *Mathematical Tables from Handbook of Chemistry and Physics*, Twelfth Edition, 1964.

Index

A B C D E F G H I J   0 6 9 8 7 6
PRINTED IN THE UNITED STATES OF AMERICA